McDougal Littell Math
Course 3

Larson   Boswell   Kanold   Stiff

Worked-Out Solution Key

The Solution Key provides step-by-step solutions for all exercises in the Student Edition.

McDougal Littell
A DIVISION OF HOUGHTON MIFFLIN COMPANY
Evanston, Illinois • Boston • Dallas

ISBN 13: 978-0-618-74116-8
ISBN 10: 0-618-74116-X

23456789-VEI-10 09 08 07

Contents

Chapter

Chapter 1

Chapter Get-Ready Games (p. 1)

1. Kim: 6 + 7 + 3 + 2 + 9 = 29
   Dave: 7 + 3 + 6 + 8 + 4 = 28
   Ann: 2.1 + 9.6 + 4.8 + 5.3 + 7.9 = 29.7
   Sam: 1.6 + 9.2 + 6.5 + 4.1 + 8.2 = 29.6
   Because 28 < 29 < 29.6 < 29.7, Dave gets to the top first.

2. Tens: 415.79 ≈ 420; U
   Ones: 19.45 ≈ 19; N
   Hundredths: 8.178 ≈ 8.18; H
   Tenths: 589.63 ≈ 589.6; C
   Hundreds: 627.4 ≈ 600; L

Hundreds	Tens	Ones	Tenths	Hundredths
L	U	N	C	H

The next stop is lunch.

Stop and Think (p. 1)

1. The names, in order from who gets to the top first to who gets there last, are Dave, Kim, Sam, and Ann. Dave's name is first.

2. *Sample answer:* Because 8 > 5, you cannot just drop it. You need to round up the digit in the hundredths place. So, the correct answer is 8.18.

Review Prerequisite Skills (p. 2)

1. When you add two numbers, the result is called the *sum*.

2. When you multiply two numbers, the result is called the *product*.

3. When you split up an amount into equal parts, the result is called the *quotient*.

4. The 6 is in the ones' place.

5. The 9 is in the tenths' place.

6. The 1 is in the hundreds' place.

7. The 4 is in the thousandths' place.

8.
$$\begin{array}{r} 12.7 \\ -\ 9.4 \\ \hline 3.3 \end{array}$$

9.
$$\begin{array}{r} \overset{1\ 1}{17.8} \\ +\ 26.3 \\ \hline 44.1 \end{array}$$

10.
$$\begin{array}{r} \overset{1\ \ 1}{9.64} \\ +\ 6.36 \\ \hline 16.00 \end{array}$$

11.
$$\begin{array}{r} \overset{1\ 9\ \ 12}{20.24} \\ -\ 16.50 \\ \hline 3.74 \end{array}$$

12.
$$\begin{array}{r} 1.3 \\ \times\ 3 \\ \hline 3.9 \end{array}$$

13.
$$6\overline{)9.6}$$
$$\begin{array}{r} 1.6 \\ 6\,)\,9.6 \\ \underline{6} \\ 3\,6 \\ \underline{3\,6} \\ 0 \end{array}$$

14.
$$\begin{array}{r} \overset{6\ 14\ \ 9\ 10}{75.00} \\ -\ 37.75 \\ \hline 37.25 \end{array}$$
You have $37.25 left.

Lesson 1.1

1.1 Guided Practice (pp. 3–4)

1. 110 − 30 = 80
   Chile has about 80 more active volcanoes than Mexico.

2. Canada has the least number of active volcanoes.

3. 15 + 30 + 170 = 215
   Canada, Mexico, and the U.S. have about 215 active volcanoes altogether.

4.

Height (m)	Tally	Frequency
60–71.9	ЖHТ ЖHТ ЖHТ	15
72–83.9	ll	2
84–95.9	l	1
96–107.9	l	1
108–119.9	l	1
120–131.9	l	1

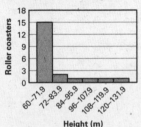

Roller Coaster Heights

1.1 Exercises (pp. 5–7)

Skill Practice

1. A histogram is a graph that shows data that are divided into equal *intervals*.

2. The lengths of bars are used to represent and compare data in categories in a *bar graph*.

3. Restaurants have the greatest number of businesses.

4. Department stores have the least number of businesses.

5. 19 − 10 = 9
   There are about 9 more shoe stores than jewelry stores.

6. No; The category with the most stores might not have the most floor space if each store is small, while the category with fewer stores might have the most floor space if each store is large.

Chapter 1, *continued*

7. a.

Hours spent on the Internet	Tally	Frequency
0–1.9	III	3
2–3.9	JHT II	7
4–5.9	JHT IIII	9
6–7.9	JHT	5
8–9.9	IIII	4
10–11.9	II	2

b.

Hours spent on the Internet	Tally	Frequency
0–2.9	JHT II	7
3–5.9	JHT JHT II	12
6–8.9	JHT II	7
9–11.9	IIII	4

c. The frequency table in part (a) gives a clearer representation of the data because the intervals are smaller.

8. The intervals Jack used are overlapping.

9.

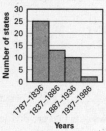

States Admitted to U.S. Statehood

10. The range of the data is too large for the data to be meaningful.

Problem Solving

11. a. The least data value is 357 and the greatest data value is 502. Appropriate intervals for the scale of a bar graph are 355, 385, 415, 445, 475, and 505.

b.

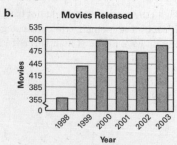

Movies Released

c. *Sample answer:* Overall, the number of movies released has increased, but not at a consistent rate.

12. Yearbook was offered the most in each of the 3 years.

13. Radio/TV saw the most growth from 1991 to 2002. The difference in the heights of the bars for 1991 and 2002 is greatest.

14. D; In 1998, about 80 high schools (per 100 schools) had newspapers and about 20 high schools (per 100 schools) had radio or TV stations. Because $4 \times 20 = 80$, about 4 times as many high schools had newspapers than high schools that had radio or TV stations.

15. The graph shows 50 years of data.

16. The number of hurricanes for 1965 cannot be determined because only the range of years from 1960–1969 is graphed.

17. The number of hurricanes for the years 2000–2009 cannot be predicted because there is no apparent pattern in the data.

18. *Sample answer:* The number of students who have visited particular states can be displayed on a bar graph but not on a histogram.

19. Frequency table; it would give exact numbers of high tides in certain intervals, while you would have to estimate the number from a histogram.

20. a.

Number of Meteors	Tally	Frequency
0–9	JHT JHT I	11
10–19	JHT JHT III	13
20–29	JHT III	8
30–39	II	2
40–49	I	1
50–59	I	1
60–69	III	3

b.

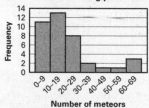

Meteors Falling per Hour

c. Exact tallies are given in the frequency table but may be difficult to determine from the histogram. In a histogram you can easily see where most of the data lies.

21. *Sample answer:* To collect pet data for a bar graph, choose a variety of animals such as dogs, cats, fish, etc. Then survey the class to find out how many students own each kind of pet. The same data cannot be used to make a histogram because the data is categorized, not grouped into intervals.

Chapter 1, *continued*

22. a.

Number of Medals Won by U.S.	Tally	Frequency
0–4	II	2
5–9	JHT III	8
10–14	JHT III	8
15–19		0
20–24		0
25–29		0
30–34	I	1

U.S. Medals at Winter Olympic Games

Number of Medals Won by U.S.	Tally	Frequency
0–9	JHT JHT	10
10–19	JHT III	8
20–29		0
30–39	I	1

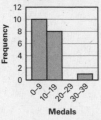

U.S. Medals at Winter Olympic Games

b. *Sample answer:* The first histogram gives a clearer picture of how many medals the U.S. can expect to win in the future. In 16 out of 19 Winter Olympics, the U.S. won between 5 and 14 medals. The 34 medals might be because some countries were not in attendance, or there was a particular athlete or team of athletes that excelled that year.

23. *Sample answer:* The number of DVD players sold in the U.S. greatly increased from 1997 to 2000. This is probably because the price of DVD players decreased and more DVDs were made available. The number of DVD players sold will go down once most people have one or if a new technology is released.

Mixed Review

24. $38 + 15 + 29 = 82$

25. $25 - 2 - 6 = 17$

26. $6.4 - 3.8 - 1.6 = 1$

27. $1.8 + 1.7 + 2.8 = 6.3$

28.
$$\overset{1}{3}4 \times 4 = 136$$

29.
$$\overset{3}{1}5 \times 6 = 90$$

30.
$$20)\overline{140} \quad \frac{140}{0} = 7$$

31.
$$7)\overline{84} \quad \frac{7}{14} \quad \frac{14}{0} = 12$$

32.
$$\overset{4}{3}6 \times 7 = 252$$

33.
$$\overset{7}{1}9 \times 8 = 152$$

34.
$$5)\overline{155} \quad \frac{15}{05} \quad \frac{5}{0} = 31$$

35.
$$4)\overline{92} \quad \frac{8}{12} \quad \frac{12}{0} = 23$$

36. B; The digit to the right of the 5 in the tenths' place is the 7 in the hundredths' place. Because 7 is 5 or greater round up to 453.6.

Lesson 1.2

1.2 Guided Practice (pp. 8–9)

1. $14 - 6 \div 2 + 12 = 14 - 3 + 12 = 11 + 12 = 23$

2. $20 - 7 \times 2 + 1 = 20 - 14 + 1 = 6 + 1 = 7$

3. $2 \cdot 13 - 2 \cdot 7 = 26 - 14 = 12$

4. $35 \div (9 - 4) = 35 \div 5 = 7$

5. $3 \cdot [(11 - 1) \div 5] = 3 \cdot [10 \div 5] = 3 \cdot 2 = 6$

6. $\dfrac{45 + 19}{2 \times 8} = \dfrac{64}{16} = 4$

7.
$$\begin{aligned}
\text{Total cost of visit} &= \text{Admission price} \times \text{Number of people} + \text{Movie price} \\
&\quad \times \text{Number of people} + \text{Cost for parking}
\end{aligned}$$

$$= 13.50 \times 50 + 8 \times 50 + 35$$
$$= 675 + 400 + 35$$
$$= 1075 + 35$$
$$= 1110$$

The total cost of their visit is $1110.

1.2 Exercises (pp. 10–11)

Skill Practice

1. Multiply 2 by 5. Add the result, 10, to 8. Subtract 4 from this sum, 18, to obtain the final result, 14.

2. A *numerical expression* consists of numbers and operations.

3. A; You should first multiply and divide from left to right, then subtract and add from left to right.

4. $12 - 10 + 4 = 2 + 4 = 6$

5. $7 + 3 - 2 + 4 = 10 - 2 + 4 = 8 + 4 = 12$

6. $18 + 6 \div 3 \times 2 = 18 + 2 \times 2 = 18 + 4 = 22$

7. $16 - 6 + 2 \times 4 = 16 - 6 + 8 = 10 + 8 = 18$

8. $26 - 15 + 8 \div 2 = 26 - 15 + 4 = 11 + 4 = 15$

9. $18 \div (8 + 4 - 9) = 18 \div (12 - 9) = 18 \div 3 = 6$

10. $\dfrac{8+2}{5-3} = \dfrac{10}{2} = 5$ **11.** $\dfrac{16}{7-3} = \dfrac{16}{4} = 4$

12. $8 \times [6 \div (5 - 3)] = 8 \times [6 \div 2] = 8 \times 3 = 24$

13. $120 \div [(6 + 2) \cdot 3] = 120 \div [8 \cdot 3] = 120 \div 24 = 5$

14. $9 \div \left[3 \cdot \left(\dfrac{5}{3} + \dfrac{4}{3}\right)\right] = 9 \div \left[3 \cdot \dfrac{9}{3}\right]$

$$= 9 \div [3 \cdot 3]$$
$$= 9 \div 9$$
$$= 1$$

15. $3 \cdot \left(\dfrac{7}{2} + \dfrac{1}{2}\right) = 3 \cdot \left(\dfrac{8}{2}\right) = 3 \cdot 4 = 12$

16. $(1.5 - 0.5) \times 2 = 1 \times 2 = 2$

17. $4 + 3.9 \div 1.3 = 4 + 3 = 7$

18. $9.4 + 4.2 \div 6 = 9.4 + 0.7 = 10.1$

19. $6 \times (2.4 - 0.4 + 3) = 6 \times (2 + 3) = 6 \times 5 = 30$

20. $7.8 \times (5 + 2) = 7.8 \times 7 = 54.6$

21. $8.4 \div (21 - 14) = 8.4 \div 7 = 1.2$

22. $3 \cdot (12 - 5) + \dfrac{23 - 9}{7} = 3 \cdot 7 + \dfrac{14}{7} = 21 + 2 = 23$

23. $\dfrac{41 - 2(3 + 4)}{(36 \div 4)} = \dfrac{41 - 2(7)}{9} = \dfrac{41 - 14}{9} = \dfrac{27}{9} = 3$

24. $\dfrac{62 - (3 + 4)}{3 + (4 \times 2)} = \dfrac{62 - 7}{3 + 8} = \dfrac{55}{11} = 5$

25. B; The quotient of eighteen and six is $18 \div 6$ and when you evaluate expressions, you perform any multiplications and divisions before you perform additions and subtractions.

26. The wrong order of operations was used in the second step of the solution. Divide before adding.

$3 \times 3 + 63 \div 9 = 9 + 63 \div 9 = 9 + 7 = 16$

27. $5 \cdot 2 + 3 - 8 \overset{?}{=} 17$

$5 \cdot (2 + 3) - 8 \overset{?}{=} 17$

$5 \cdot 5 - 8 \overset{?}{=} 17$

$25 - 8 \overset{?}{=} 17$

$17 = 17$

So, $5 \cdot (2 + 3) - 8 = 17$.

28. $12 \div 6 + 4 - 7 \overset{?}{=} 4$

$12 \div (6 + 4 - 7) \overset{?}{=} 4$

$12 \div (10 - 7) \overset{?}{=} 4$

$12 \div 3 \overset{?}{=} 4$

$4 = 4$

So, $12 \div (6 + 4 - 7) = 4$.

29. $13 - 5 \times 8 - 6 \overset{?}{=} 3$

$13 - 5 \times (8 - 6) \overset{?}{=} 3$

$13 - 5 \times 2 \overset{?}{=} 3$

$13 - 10 \overset{?}{=} 3$

$3 = 3$

So, $13 - 5 \times (8 - 6) = 3$.

30. $7 - 2 \times 3 + 12 \overset{?}{=} 27$

$(7 - 2) \times 3 + 12 \overset{?}{=} 27$

$5 \times 3 + 12 \overset{?}{=} 27$

$15 + 12 \overset{?}{=} 27$

$27 = 27$

So, $(7 - 2) \times 3 + 12 = 27$.

31. $12 \div 3 \times 4 + 1 \overset{?}{=} 20$

$(12 \div 3) \times (4 + 1) \overset{?}{=} 20$

$4 \times 5 \overset{?}{=} 20$

$20 = 20$

So, $(12 \div 3) \times (4 + 1) = 20$.

32. $24 \div 10 - 3 + 1 \overset{?}{=} 3$

$24 \div (10 - 3 + 1) \overset{?}{=} 3$

$24 \div (7 + 1) \overset{?}{=} 3$

$24 \div 8 \overset{?}{=} 3$

$3 = 3$

So, $24 \div (10 - 3 + 1) = 3$.

33. $(12 + 4) + 2 = 16 + 2 = 18$

$12 + (4 + 2) = 12 + 6 = 18$

$(12 - 4) + 2 = 8 + 2 = 10$

$12 - (4 + 2) = 12 - 6 = 6$

$(12 \times 4) + 2 = 48 + 2 = 50$

$12 \times (4 + 2) = 12 \times 6 = 72$

$(12 \div 4) + 2 = 3 + 2 = 5$

$12 \div (4 + 2) = 12 \div 6 = 2$

The expression $12 \times (4 + 2)$ gives the greatest possible value.

34. $(15 + 5) - 2 = 20 - 2 = 18$

$15 + (5 - 2) = 15 + 3 = 18$

$(15 - 5) - 2 = 10 - 2 = 8$

$15 - (5 - 2) = 15 - 3 = 12$

$(15 \times 5) - 2 = 75 - 2 = 73$

$15 \times (5 - 2) = 15 \times 3 = 45$

$(15 \div 5) - 2 = 3 - 2 = 1$

$15 \div (5 - 2) = 15 \div 3 = 5$

The expression $(15 \times 5) - 2$ gives the greatest possible value.

35. $(12 + 9) + 3 = 21 + 3 = 24$

$12 + (9 + 3) = 12 + 12 = 24$

$(12 + 9) - 3 = 21 - 3 = 18$

$12 + (9 - 3) = 12 + 6 = 18$

$(12 + 9) \times 3 = 21 \times 3 = 63$

$12 + (9 \times 3) = 12 + 27 = 39$

$(12 + 9) \div 3 = 21 \div 3 = 7$

$12 + (9 \div 3) = 12 + 3 = 15$

The expression $(12 + 9) \times 3$ gives the greatest possible value.

Problem Solving

36. A; $\begin{array}{c}\text{Your friend's}\\\text{contribution}\end{array} = \begin{array}{c}\text{Your friend's}\\\text{pledge}\end{array} + \begin{array}{c}\text{Pledge}\\\text{per mile}\end{array} \times \begin{array}{c}\text{Miles}\\\text{walked}\end{array}$

$= 10 + 0.25(6)$

37. Multiply 3 and 2 and multiply 4 and 1.5. Then add the two products to find the total cost to be $12.

38. $\begin{array}{c}\text{Money}\\\text{needed to}\\\text{be raised}\end{array} = \begin{array}{c}\text{Price}\\\text{of}\\\text{uniform}\end{array} \times \begin{array}{c}\text{Number}\\\text{of team}\\\text{members}\end{array} - \begin{array}{c}\text{School}\\\text{contribution}\end{array}$

$\times \begin{array}{c}\text{Number}\\\text{of team}\\\text{members}\end{array}$

$= 40 \times 25 - 30 \times 25$

$= 1000 - 750$

$= 250$

The team needs to raise $250 to buy uniforms for every member.

More than one verbal model is possible. You could subtract the school contribution from the cost of the uniforms and multiply the difference by the number of uniforms needed.

39. *Sample answer:*

$\begin{array}{c}\text{Balance in}\\\text{account}\end{array} = \begin{array}{c}\text{Original}\\\text{balance}\end{array} + \begin{array}{c}\text{Number of}\\\text{deposits}\end{array} \times \begin{array}{c}\text{Amount of}\\\text{deposits}\end{array}$

$- \begin{array}{c}\text{Amount of}\\\text{withdrawals}\end{array}$

$= 15 + 4 \times 25 - 90$

$= 15 + 100 - 90$

$= 115 - 90$

$= 25$

40. a. $\begin{array}{c}\text{Cookies}\\\text{baked}\end{array} = \begin{array}{c}\text{Batches}\\\text{Liz made}\end{array} \times \begin{array}{c}\text{Dozens}\\\text{made}\end{array} \times 12 + \begin{array}{c}\text{Batches}\\\text{Ty made}\end{array}$

$\times \begin{array}{c}\text{Dozens}\\\text{made}\end{array} \times 12$

b. $\begin{array}{c}\text{Cookies}\\\text{baked}\end{array} = 5 \times 3 \times 12 + 4 \times 4 \times 12$

$= 15 \times 12 + 16 \times 12$

$= 180 + 192$

$= 372$

There were 372 cookies baked.

c. $\begin{array}{c}\text{Number of}\\\text{packages}\end{array} = \begin{array}{c}\text{Number of}\\\text{cookies}\end{array} \div \begin{array}{c}\text{Number of cookies}\\\text{in a package}\end{array}$

$= 372 \div 3$

$= 124$

They can make 124 packages.

41. $8 + 6 - 3 - 7 + 1 \stackrel{?}{=} 5$

$14 - 3 - 7 + 1 \stackrel{?}{=} 5$

$11 - 7 + 1 \stackrel{?}{=} 5$

$4 + 1 \stackrel{?}{=} 5$

$5 = 5$

So, $8 + 6 - 3 - 7 + 1 = 5$.

42. $\begin{array}{c}\text{Cousin's}\\\text{age}\end{array} = \frac{1}{2} \times \begin{array}{c}\text{Your}\\\text{brother's age}\end{array}$

$= \frac{1}{2} \times \left[2\left(\begin{array}{c}\text{Your}\\\text{sister's age}\end{array}\right) - 10 \right]$

$= \frac{1}{2} \times [2(14) - 10]$

$= \frac{1}{2} \times [28 - 10]$

$= \frac{1}{2} \times 18$

$= 9$

Your cousin is 9 years old.

Mixed Review

43. $2 \times 2 = 4$

2 pounds of grapes cost $4.

44. $2 \times 3 = 6$

3 pounds of grapes cost $6.

45. $2 \times 0.5 = 1$

0.5 pound of grapes cost $1.

46. $2 \times 0.25 = 0.5$

0.25 pound of grapes cost $.50.

47. $8 \times \frac{5}{24} = \frac{8 \times 5}{24} = \frac{40}{24} = \frac{5}{3}$ or $1\frac{2}{3}$

48. $3 \times \frac{2}{7} = \frac{3 \times 2}{7} = \frac{6}{7}$

49. $4 \times \frac{5}{12} = \frac{4 \times 5}{12} = \frac{20}{12} = \frac{5}{3}$ or $1\frac{2}{3}$

50. $6 \times \frac{3}{8} = \frac{6 \times 3}{8} = \frac{18}{8} = \frac{9}{4}$ or $2\frac{1}{4}$

51. D;

$\begin{array}{r} \overset{9\ \ 9}{\overset{1\ \ 10\ 10\ 10}{2\,0\,0\,0}} \\ -\ 1\,3.4\,8 \\ \hline 6.5\,2 \end{array}$

You should receive $6.52 in change.

Technology Activity 1.2 (p. 12)

1. $62 + 7 \times 6.4 = 106.8$ **2.** $8.32 - 9 \div 2 = 3.82$

3. $6.8 \div 4 + 15.9 \div 3 = 7$

4. $36.2 - 4.3 \cdot 5 = 14.7$

5. $\dfrac{14 + 11}{4 + 1} = 5$

6. $\dfrac{20 - 3.5}{10.3 - 7} = 5$

7. $\dfrac{10}{3.8 + 1.2} = 2$

8. $\dfrac{17.7 - 13.7}{0.2 + 4.8} = 0.8$

9. $3 \cdot 1.49 + 2 \cdot 1.79 + 2.39 = 10.44$

The total cost is \$10.44.

10. $3 \cdot 9.99 + 44.89 + 10.59 + 8.60 \div 4 = 87.60$

The total cost for the clothing is \$87.60.

11. $2 \cdot 12.99 + 2 \cdot 9.49 + 15.97 + 9.49 \div 2 = 65.675$

The total cost for the CDs is \$65.68.

Lesson 1.3

1.3 Guided Practice (pp. 13–15)

1. $5 + 6(3) = 5 + 18 = 23$

The total distance if you travel at 6 miles per hour for 3 hours is 23 miles.

2. $5 + 6\left(\dfrac{1}{2}\right) = 5 + 3 = 8$

The total distance if you travel at 6 miles per hour for $\dfrac{1}{2}$ hour is 8 miles.

3. $5 + 3(2) = 5 + 6 = 11$

The total distance if you travel at 3 miles per hour for 2 hours is 11 miles.

4. $9a = 9(12) = 108$

5. $ab = 12(3) = 36$

6. $b(a - 6) = 3(12 - 6) = 3(6) = 18$

7. $\dfrac{6a}{a - b} = \dfrac{6(12)}{12 - 3} = \dfrac{72}{9} = 8$

8. $x + 15$

9. $8x$

10. $25 + 4n = 25 + 4(8) = 25 + 32 = 57$

Your total savings after 8 weeks is \$57.

1.3 Exercises (pp. 15–18)

Skill Practice

1. $3t - 4$ is a *variable* expression and $5 + 13$ is a *numerical* expression.

2. A *variable* is a symbol, usually a letter, that represents one or more numbers.

3. $4x - 5 = 4(7) - 5 = 28 - 5 = 23$

4. $10n + 115 = 10(9) + 115 = 90 + 115 = 205$

5. $3(c - d) = 3(12 - 7) = 3(5) = 15$

6. $4(f + g) = 4(10 + 6) = 4(16) = 64$

7. $7p + 6q = 7(3) + 6(1.5) = 21 + 9 = 30$

8. $8a - 3b = 8(3) - 3(8) = 24 - 24 = 0$

9. $3x + 4y = 3(6) + 4(2.5) = 18 + 10 = 28$

10. $6r + 4q = 6(5) + 4(6) = 30 + 24 = 54$

11. $\dfrac{d + 10}{c - d} = \dfrac{8 + 10}{14 - 8} = \dfrac{18}{6} = 3$

12. $\dfrac{50 - s}{p + 3} = \dfrac{50 - 5}{6 + 3} = \dfrac{45}{9} = 5$

13. You should multiply 4 by 7 before adding 5.

$5 + 4 \cdot x = 5 + 4 \cdot 7 = 5 + 28 = 33$

14. $\dfrac{2}{5}x$

15. $10 - x$

16. $12 + x$

17. $\dfrac{x}{7}$

18. $x + 11$

19. $x - 15$

20. $8x$

21. $22x$

22. D; $x \cdot [4 + (y \div 5)] = 3 \cdot [4 + (10 \div 5)]$

$\qquad\qquad\qquad\quad = 3 \cdot [4 + 2]$

$\qquad\qquad\qquad\quad = 3 \cdot 6$

$\qquad\qquad\qquad\quad = 18$

The value of the expression is 18 when $x = 3$ and $y = 10$.

23–30. Evaluate expressions when $x = 2.4$ and $y = 8$.

23. $7x + 2y = 7(2.4) + 2(8) = 16.8 + 16 = 32.8$

Swap values:

$7x + 2y = 7(8) + 2(2.4) = 56 + 4.8 = 60.8$

Swapping the values of x and y will increase the value of the expression because $60.8 > 32.8$.

24. $10(x + y) = 10(2.4 + 8) = 10(10.4) = 104$

Swap values:

$10(x + y) = 10(8 + 2.4) = 10(10.4) = 104$

Swapping the values of x and y will not change the value of the expression because $104 = 104$.

25. $5xy = 5(2.4)(8) = 12(8) = 96$

Swap values:

$5xy = 5(8)(2.4) = 40(2.4) = 96$

Swapping the values of x and y will not change the value of the expression because $96 = 96$.

26. $x(y - 2) = 2.4(8 - 2) = 2.4(6) = 14.4$

Swap values:

$x(y - 2) = 8(2.4 - 2) = 8(0.4) = 3.2$

Swapping the values of x and y will decrease the value of the expression because $3.2 < 14.4$.

27. $4x - y = 4 \cdot 2.4 - 8 = 9.6 - 8 = 1.6$

Swap values:

$4x - y = 4 \cdot 8 - 2.4 = 32 - 2.4 = 29.6$

Swapping the values of x and y will increase the value of the expression because $29.6 > 1.6$.

28. $7.2y \div x = 7.2(8) \div 2.4 = 57.6 \div 2.4 = 24$

Swap values:

$7.2y \div x = 7.2(2.4) \div 8 = 17.28 \div 8 = 2.16$

Swapping the values of x and y will decrease the value of the expression because $2.16 < 24$.

29. $\dfrac{3y}{x} = \dfrac{3(8)}{2.4} = \dfrac{24}{2.4} = 10$

Swap values:

$\dfrac{3y}{x} = \dfrac{3(2.4)}{8} = \dfrac{7.2}{8} = 0.9$

Swapping the values of x and y will decrease the value of the expression because $0.9 < 10$.

Chapter 1, *continued*

30. $x - \dfrac{y}{4} = 2.4 - \dfrac{8}{4} = 2.4 - 2 = 0.4$

Swap values:

$x - \dfrac{y}{4} = 8 - \dfrac{2.4}{4} = 8 - 0.6 = 7.4$

Swapping the values of x and y will increase the value of the expression because $7.4 > 0.4$.

31. $\dfrac{5(3x + 2z + 0.14)}{xy + z} = \dfrac{5[3(1.05) + 2(0.65) + 0.14]}{1.05(7) + 0.65}$

$= \dfrac{5(3.15 + 1.3 + 0.14)}{7.35 + 0.65}$

$= \dfrac{5(4.45 + 0.14)}{8}$

$= \dfrac{5(4.59)}{8}$

$= \dfrac{22.95}{8}$

≈ 2.87

32. $\dfrac{2x - 4y - 41.6 + 2z}{y - 5z} = \dfrac{2(1.05) - 4(7) - 41.6 + 2(0.65)}{7 - 5(0.65)}$

$= \dfrac{2.1 - 28 - 41.6 + 1.3}{7 - 3.25}$

$= \dfrac{-25.9 - 41.6 + 1.3}{3.75}$

$= \dfrac{-67.5 + 1.3}{3.75}$

$= \dfrac{-66.2}{3.75}$

≈ -17.65

33. $\dfrac{5y + 3z + x}{x + 2yz} = \dfrac{5(7) + 3(0.65) + 1.05}{1.05 + 2(7)(0.65)}$

$= \dfrac{35 + 1.95 + 1.05}{1.05 + 14(0.65)}$

$= \dfrac{36.95 + 1.05}{1.05 + 9.1}$

$= \dfrac{38}{10.15}$

≈ 3.74

34. $2x + 4 = 4$

$2(0) + 4 \stackrel{?}{=} 4$

$0 + 4 \stackrel{?}{=} 4$

$4 = 4$

Yes, 0 makes the statement true.

35. $x \div 9 = 9 \div x$

$9 \div 9 \stackrel{?}{=} 9 \div 9$

$1 = 1$

Yes, 9 makes the statement true.

36. $8 - 5x = 8 + 5x$

$8 - 5(0) \stackrel{?}{=} 8 + 5(0)$

$8 - 0 \stackrel{?}{=} 8 + 0$

$8 = 8$

Yes, 0 makes the statement true.

37. $4 + x = 3x$

$4 + 2 \stackrel{?}{=} 3(2)$

$6 = 6$

Yes, 2 makes the statement true.

Problem Solving

38. When $t = 2$: $9t = 9(2) = 18$

If you ride your bike for 2 hours, you will travel 18 miles.

39. When $t = 3\dfrac{1}{2}$: $9t = 9\left(3\dfrac{1}{2}\right) = 9\left(\dfrac{7}{2}\right) = \dfrac{63}{2} = 31\dfrac{1}{2}$

If you ride your bike for $3\dfrac{1}{2}$ hours you will travel $31\dfrac{1}{2}$ miles.

40. a. The expression for the cost to rent m videos is $3.8m$.

b. $3.8m + 8$

c. When $m = 5$: $3.8m + 8 = 3.8(5) + 8 = 19 + 8 = 27$

Altogether you spent $27.

41. The expression for the total number of minutes you spend watching television that week is $30x + 60y - 3z$.

42. The expression for the total grams of protein in x servings of rice, y servings of beans, and z oranges is $13x + 15y + 2z$.

43. The expression for the change you will receive from $20 if you buy p popcorns and d drinks is $20 - (2.75p + 2.5d)$.

When $p = 3$ and $d = 4$:

$20 - (2.75p + 2.5d) = 20 - (2.75 \cdot 3 + 2.5 \cdot 4)$

$= 20 - (8.25 + 10)$

$= 20 - 18.25$

$= 1.75$

Your change is $1.75.

44. The expression for the total cost of the CD player and n CDs is $35 + 15n$.

When $n = 4$: $35 + 15n = 35 + 15(4) = 35 + 60 = 95$

The total cost for the 4 CDs and the CD player is $95.

When $n = 8$:

$35 + 15n = 35 + 15(8) = 35 + 120 = 155$

You will spend $155 if you buy 8 CDs.

This is not twice the cost of 4 CDs. The total cost does not double when you buy twice as many CDs because the cost of the CD player, $35, remains the same.

45. B; $\dfrac{\text{Cost of bike}}{\text{Days in a week} \cdot \text{Number of weeks}} = \dfrac{152.88}{7n}$

46. The vine is currently about 6 centimeters long. The vine grows about 3 centimeters each week. An expression for the length of the vine w weeks from now is $6 + 3w$.

When $w = 19$: $6 + 3w = 6 + 3(19) = 6 + 57 = 63$

The vine's length 19 weeks from now will be about 63 centimeters.

Chapter 1, *continued*

47. *Sample answer:* You have $98 and you want to buy CDs. If each CD costs $8, how much money will you have left after buying *d* CDs?

You buy 10 CDs.

When $d = 10$: $98 - 8d = 98 - 8(10) = 98 - 80 = 18$

You will have $18 left after buying 10 CDs.

An unreasonable value for *d* is 1.5 because you cannot buy half of a CD.

48. The expression for the difference in cost between a 2 month subscription and the purchase of *n* downloaded songs is $14.85 \times 2 - 0.99n$.

When the expression has a value of zero, it means that both plans cost the same.

49. Amount melted = Melting rate × Time = $0.6t$

When $t = 3$: $0.6t = 0.6(3) = 1.8$

The sculpture melts 1.8 centimeters in 3 hours.

When $t = 6$: $0.6t = 0.6(6) = 3.6$

The sculpture melts 3.6 centimeters in 6 hours.

50. Time $= \dfrac{\text{Amount melted}}{\text{Melting rate}} = \dfrac{y}{0.6}$

When $y = 64$: $\dfrac{y}{0.6} = \dfrac{64}{0.6} = 106.\overline{6} \approx 107$

It would take about 107 hours for a sculpture 64 centimeters thick to melt.

51. *Sample answer:* The temperature of the room or the thickness of different parts of the sculpture could affect the melting rate.

52. a. Total gas used $= \dfrac{\text{Number of city miles}}{\text{City gas mileage}}$

$+ \dfrac{\text{Number of highway miles}}{\text{Highway gas mileage}}$

$= \dfrac{c}{18} + \dfrac{h}{26}$

b. Because 90 miles of the 480 mile trip is in city traffic, you know 390 miles of the trip is on the highway.

When $c = 90$ and $h = 390$:

$\dfrac{c}{18} + \dfrac{h}{26} = \dfrac{90}{18} + \dfrac{390}{26} = 5 + 15 = 20$

Jim uses 20 gallons of gasoline on his trip. Because he has 22 gallons in his tank, he does not need to buy more gasoline.

53. Amesville population: $6800 - 120x$

$6800 - 120(0) = 6800 - 0 = 6800$
$6800 - 120(1) = 6800 - 120 = 6680$
$6800 - 120(2) = 6800 - 240 = 6560$
$6800 - 120(3) = 6800 - 360 = 6440$
$6800 - 120(4) = 6800 - 480 = 6320$
$6800 - 120(5) = 6800 - 600 = 6200$
$6800 - 120(6) = 6800 - 720 = 6080$
$6800 - 120(7) = 6800 - 840 = 5960$
$6800 - 120(8) = 6800 - 960 = 5840$
$6800 - 120(9) = 6800 - 1080 = 5720$
$6800 - 120(10) = 6800 - 1200 = 5600$
$6800 - 120(11) = 6800 - 1320 = 5480$
$6800 - 120(12) = 6800 - 1440 = 5360$
$6800 - 120(13) = 6800 - 1560 = 5240$

Boomville population: $4200 + 80x$

$4200 + 80(0) = 4200 + 0 = 4200$
$4200 + 80(1) = 4200 + 80 = 4280$
$4200 + 80(2) = 4200 + 160 = 4360$
$4200 + 80(3) = 4200 + 240 = 4440$
$4200 + 80(4) = 4200 + 320 = 4520$
$4200 + 80(5) = 4200 + 400 = 4600$
$4200 + 80(6) = 4200 + 480 = 4680$
$4200 + 80(7) = 4200 + 560 = 4760$
$4200 + 80(8) = 4200 + 640 = 4840$
$4200 + 80(9) = 4200 + 720 = 4920$
$4200 + 80(10) = 4200 + 800 = 5000$
$4200 + 80(11) = 4200 + 880 = 5080$
$4200 + 80(12) = 4200 + 960 = 5160$
$4200 + 80(13) = 4200 + 1040 = 5240$

The two expressions have the same value when $x = 13$. In 13 years, the population of the two towns will be equal.

The year 2030 is 24 years after 2006.

Amesville: $6800 - 120x = 6800 - 120(24)$
$= 6800 - 2880$
$= 3920$

The population of Amesville will be 3920 in the year 2030.

Boomville: $4200 + 80x = 4200 + 80(24)$
$= 4200 + 1920$
$= 6120$

The population of Boomville will be 6120 in the year 2030.

Mixed Review

54. $12 \cdot 3 + 14 = 36 + 14 = 50$

55. $93 - 74 \div 2 = 93 - 37 = 56$

56. $16 + 6 \cdot 3 \div 2 - 7 = 16 + 18 \div 2 - 7$

$\qquad = 16 + 9 - 7$

$\qquad = 25 - 7$

$\qquad = 18$

57. $6 \times (6 - 4) \div 3 = 6 \times 2 \div 3 = 12 \div 3 = 4$

58. $38 - 56 \div 8 = 38 - 7 = 31$

59. $24 \cdot 5 + 18 = 120 + 18 = 138$

60. $12 + 9 \cdot 8 \div 4 - 2 = 12 + 72 \div 4 - 2$

$\qquad = 12 + 18 - 2$

$\qquad = 30 - 2$

$\qquad = 28$

61. $5 \times (7 + 3) \div 10 = 5 \times 10 \div 10 = 50 \div 10 = 5$

62. $45 + 20 \div 5 = 45 + 4 = 49$

63. D;

$$\begin{array}{r} \overset{3}{}\overset{2}{} \\ 1.65 \\ \times 5 \\ \hline 8.25 \end{array}$$

You pay \$8.25 for all 5 notebooks.

Lesson 1.4

1.4 Guided Practice (pp. 19–20)

1. 7^6 **2.** 10^4 **3.** w^2

4. 6 to the third power, or 6 cubed; $6^3 = 6 \times 6 \times 6 = 216$

5. 2 to the fifth power; $2^5 = 2 \times 2 \times 2 \times 2 \times 2 = 32$

6. 13 to the second power, or 13 squared; $13^2 = 13 \times 13 = 169$

7. 3 to the first power; $3^1 = 3$

8. $(5 - 2)^3 - 7 + 4^3 = 3^3 - 7 + 4^3$

$\qquad = 27 - 7 + 64$

$\qquad = 20 + 64$

$\qquad = 84$

9. $12.3 + (4 + 2)^2 - 2^4 = 12.3 + 6^2 - 2^4$

$\qquad = 12.3 + 36 - 16$

$\qquad = 48.3 - 16 = 32.3$

10. $7^3 + 24 \div (7 - 6)^4 = 7^3 + 24 \div 1^4$

$\qquad = 343 + 24 \div 1$

$\qquad = 343 + 24$

$\qquad = 367$

11. $16t^2 = 16(8)^2 = 16(64) = 1024$

The height of the cliff is 1024 feet.

1.4 Exercises (pp. 21–24)

Skill Practice

1. *Sample answer:* 6^3 ← exponent

        base ↗

2. Evaluate expressions inside grouping symbols before evaluating powers.

3. 9^5; 9 to the fifth power

4. 3^3; 3 to the third power, or 3 cubed

5. n^6; n to the sixth power

6. $3^2 = 3 \times 3 = 9$

7. $11^3 = 11 \times 11 \times 11 = 1331$

8. $1^9 = 1 \times 1 \times 1 \times 1 \times 1 \times 1 \times 1 \times 1 \times 1 = 1$

9. $2^6 = 2 \times 2 \times 2 \times 2 \times 2 \times 2 = 64$

10. $5^5 = 5 \times 5 \times 5 \times 5 \times 5 = 3125$

11. $0^7 = 0$ **12.** $6^1 = 6$

13. $11^2 = 11 \times 11 = 121$

14. $2^7 = 2 \times 2 \times 2 \times 2 \times 2 \times 2 \times 2 = 128$

15. $10^3 = 10 \times 10 \times 10 = 1000$

16. $1^8 = 1 \times 1 \times 1 \times 1 \times 1 \times 1 \times 1 \times 1 = 1$

17. $20^2 = 20 \times 20 = 400$

18. The error is that 7^2 means 7×7, not 7×2.

$\qquad 7^2 = 7 \times 7 = 49$

19. $g^4 \div 16 = 4^4 \div 16 = 256 \div 16 = 16$

20. $(3 + g)^3 = (3 + 4)^3 = 7^3 = 343$

21. $(3g)^2 - 25 = (3 \cdot 4)^2 - 25 = 12^2 - 25 = 144 - 25 = 119$

22. $(g - 1)^5 \div 9 = (4 - 1)^5 \div 9 = 3^5 \div 9 = 243 \div 9 = 27$

23. $2 \times (g + 2)^3 = 2 \times (4 + 2)^3 = 2 \times 6^3 = 2 \times 216 = 432$

24. $(2g + 3)^2 + 12 = (2 \cdot 4 + 3)^2 + 12$

$\qquad = (8 + 3)^2 + 12$

$\qquad = 11^2 + 12$

$\qquad = 121 + 12$

$\qquad = 133$

25. $(2 + 1)^4 \div 9 - 4 = 3^4 \div 9 - 4$

$\qquad = 81 \div 9 - 4$

$\qquad = 9 - 4$

$\qquad = 5$

26. $48 \div (9 - 7)^3 = 48 \div 2^3 = 48 \div 8 = 6$

27. $(5 \times 3)^2 - 4 = 15^2 - 4 = 225 - 4 = 221$

28. $(2 \times 5)^2 + 9 = 10^2 + 9 = 100 + 9 = 109$

29. $500 \div (12 - 7)^1 = 500 \div 5 = 100$

30. $6 \times 18 \div 3^2 = 6 \times 18 \div 9 = 108 \div 9 = 12$

31. $(9 - 7)^5 + 17 = 2^5 + 17 = 32 + 17 = 49$

32. $108 \div (5 + 1)^2 = 108 \div 6^2 = 108 \div 36 = 3$

33. $9^2 - 3^3 = 81 - 27 = 54$

34. $(8 - 5)^3 - 6.2 \times 3 = 3^3 - 6.2 \times 3$

$\qquad = 27 - 6.2 \times 3$

$\qquad = 27 - 18.6$

$\qquad = 8.4$

35. $\dfrac{3}{4} \times 4 + 6^2 \div 9 = \dfrac{3}{4} \times 4 + 36 \div 9$

$\qquad = \dfrac{3 \times 4}{4} + 36 \div 9$

$\qquad = \dfrac{12}{4} + 36 \div 9$

$\qquad = 3 + 4$

$\qquad = 7$

36. $10.7 - 0.8 + 4^4 \div 2^3 = 10.7 - 0.8 + 256 \div 8$

$$= 10.7 - 0.8 + 32$$
$$= 9.9 + 32$$
$$= 41.9$$

37. C; Addition and subtraction come last in the order of operations.

38. $3^2 = 9$ **39.** $5^4 = 625$ **40.** $10^1 = 10$

$2^3 = 8$ $4^5 = 1024$ $1^{10} = 1$

$3^2 > 2^3$ $5^4 < 4^5$ $10^1 > 1^{10}$

41. $\left(\frac{1}{4}\right)^4 = \frac{1^4}{4^4} = \frac{1}{256}$ **42.** $\left(\frac{5}{2}\right)^1 = \frac{5^1}{2^1} = \frac{5}{2}$

$\left(\frac{1}{3}\right)^4 = \frac{1^4}{3^4} = \frac{1}{81}$ $\left(\frac{2}{5}\right)^5 = \frac{2^5}{5^5} = \frac{32}{3125}$

$\left(\frac{1}{4}\right)^4 < \left(\frac{1}{3}\right)^4$ $\left(\frac{5}{2}\right)^1 > \left(\frac{2}{5}\right)^5$

43. $\left(\frac{1}{4}\right)^3 = \frac{1^3}{4^3} = \frac{1}{6^4}$

$\left(\frac{1}{2}\right)^6 = \frac{1^6}{2^6} = \frac{1}{6^4}$

$\left(\frac{1}{4}\right)^3 = \left(\frac{1}{2}\right)^6$

44. $a^3 b^2 + 4.2 = 2^3 \times 4^2 + 4.2$

$$= 8 \times 16 + 4.2$$
$$= 128 + 4.2$$
$$= 132.2$$

45. $5.9 \times (c - a)^3 = 5.9 \times (5 - 2)^3$

$$= 5.9 \times 3^3$$
$$= 5.9 \times 27$$
$$= 159.3$$

46. $2 \cdot (b + 2)^2 \div (3a) = 2 \cdot (4 + 2)^2 \div (3 \cdot 2)$

$$= 2 \cdot 6^2 \div 6$$
$$= 2 \cdot 36 \div 6$$
$$= 72 \div 6$$
$$= 12$$

47. The pattern with the ones' digit is 2, 4, 8, 6. The ones' digit in 2^{14} is 4.

48. $3^1 = 3$, $3^2 = 9$, $3^3 = 27$, $3^4 = 81$, $3^5 = 243$, $3^6 = 729$, $3^7 = 2187$, $3^8 = 6561$

The ones' digit in 3^{15} is 7 because the pattern with the ones' digit is 3, 9, 7, 1.

49. $4^1 = 4$, $4^2 = 16$, $4^3 = 64$, $4^4 = 256$, $4^5 = 1024$, $4^6 = 4096$

The ones' digit in 4^{24} is 6 and the ones' digit in 4^{87} is 4, because the pattern with the ones' digit is 6 and 4 alternating.

50. $3^x = 9^4$

$3^x = 9 \cdot 9 \cdot 9 \cdot 9$

$3^x = \overbrace{3 \cdot 3} \cdot \overbrace{3 \cdot 3} \cdot \overbrace{3 \cdot 3} \cdot \overbrace{3 \cdot 3}$

$3^x = 3^8$

$x = 8$

51. $6^{10} = 36^x$

$\overbrace{6 \cdot 6} \cdot \overbrace{6 \cdot 6} \cdot \overbrace{6 \cdot 6} \cdot \overbrace{6 \cdot 6} \cdot \overbrace{6 \cdot 6} = 36^x$

$36 \cdot 36 \cdot 36 \cdot 36 \cdot 36 = 36^x$

$36^5 = 36^x$

$5 = x$

52. $4^x = 64^3$

$4^x = \overbrace{64} \cdot \overbrace{64} \cdot \overbrace{64}$

$4^x = 4 \cdot 4 \cdot 4 \cdot 4 \cdot 4 \cdot 4 \cdot 4 \cdot 4 \cdot 4$

$4^x = 4^9$

$x = 9$

Problem Solving

53. $s^2 = 17^2 = 289$

The area of the square is 289 square inches.

54. D; $s^3 = 14^3 = 2744$

The volume of the cube is 2744 cubic centimeters.

55. a. To find how far the diver has fallen in 2 seconds, use $t = 2$ in the formula $16t^2$.

$16t^2 = 16 \cdot 2^2 = 16 \cdot 4 = 64$

The diver has fallen only 64 feet in 2 seconds, so the diver has not reached the water yet because the cliff is 82 feet high.

b. $16t^2 = 16 \cdot 3^2 = 16 \cdot 9 = 144$

After 3 seconds, the diver has fallen 144 feet. The difference of 144 and 64 is $144 - 64 = 80$. A diver would be 80 feet lower after 3 seconds than after 2 seconds.

56. To find the value of 3^9 when you know 3^8 is 6561, multiply 6561 by 3 because 3^9 is one more power of 3 than 3^8.

57. $1 = 1^2$, $4 = 2^2$, $9 = 3^2$, $16 = 4^2$, ...

So, an expression for the nth number of the sequence of numbers is n^2.

58. B; Because $3 \cdot 15 = 45$, the value of the account will double 3 times in 45 years. The expression 1275×2^3 represents the amount of money in the account after 45 years.

59. When evaluating $(4x)^2$, you are multiplying x^2 by 16, which will give a greater product than multiplying x^2 by 4.

60. The expression that shows the season attendance that doubles each year for the next three years is $1000 \cdot 2^3$.

61. Because $4 \cdot 6 = 24$, the speed of the skater will double 4 times.

$3 \cdot 2^4 = 3 \cdot 16 = 48$

The speed of the skater when the skater reaches the bottom of the hill is 48 miles per hour.

62. a.

Stage	1	2	3	4	5	6
Number of squares	1	4	16	64	256	1024

b. An expression for the number of squares in the dig at the 7th stage is 4^6.

c. The number of squares along each side is double the number in the previous stage. Because the 3rd stage has 4 squares along each side, the 4th stage has 8 squares along each side. Continuing this pattern, there are 16 squares along each side at the 5th stage and 32 squares along each side at the 6th stage. So, there are $2 \cdot 32$, or 64 squares along each side at the 7th stage. Because there are 64 squares along each side, the side length of each square at the 7th stage is 1 foot.

63. The existing breeding pair produces 15 breeding pairs. So, there are a total of 16 breeding pairs after 1 season. After 2 seasons, the original 16 breeding pairs produce 15 breeding pairs each. So, there are a total of $16 \cdot 16 = 256$ breeding pairs. It appears that breeding follows the pattern 16^n, so after n seasons there are 16^n breeding pairs.

64. $11^1 = 11$; $11^2 = 121$; $11^3 = 1331$; $11^4 = 14{,}641$; $11^5 = 161{,}051$

Because 161,051 does not read the same forward and backward, the smallest n such that 11^n does not read the same forward and backward is $n = 5$.

65. $7^4 = 2401$, $7^3 = 343$, $7^2 = 49$, $7^1 = 7$

To get the next number in the pattern, divide the previous number by 7. So, for 7^0 you have $7 \div 7 = 1$. The number before x^0 is $x^1 = x$. So, $x^0 = \frac{x}{x} = 1$.

66. 64 kilobytes $= 64(2^{10}) = (2 \cdot 2 \cdot 2 \cdot 2 \cdot 2 \cdot 2)(2^{10})$

$= (2 \cdot 2 \cdot 2 \cdot 2 \cdot 2 \cdot 2)$
$\quad (2 \cdot 2 \cdot 2 \cdot 2 \cdot 2 \cdot 2 \cdot 2 \cdot 2 \cdot 2 \cdot 2)$
$= 2^{16}$

The computers of the early 1980s had 2^{16} bytes of memory.

Mixed Review

67. Use the strategy Draw a Diagram to find the possible outfits from 3 shirts and 2 pairs of pants.

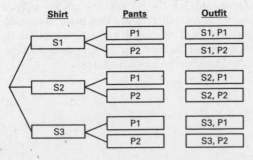

Draw a Diagram finds the possible combinations of 3 shirts and 2 pants in an organized way. There are 6 possible outfits.

68. $5x - 12 = 5(3) - 12 = 15 - 12 = 3$

69. $6x - y = 6 \cdot 3 - 9 = 18 - 9 = 9$

70. $\frac{y}{x} + 20 = \frac{9}{3} + 20 = 3 + 20 = 23$

71. $\frac{45}{x} - 2 = \frac{45}{3} - 2 = 15 - 2 = 13$

72. Between 7:00 and 7:59, 3 people arrived, between 8:00 and 8:59, 8 people arrived, between 9:00 and 9:59, 10 people arrived, and between 10:00 and 10:59, 4 people arrived. So, a total of $3 + 8 + 10 + 4 = 25$ people attended the party.

73. B; 10 people arrived between 9:00 and 9:59 and 4 people arrived between 10:00 and 10:59. So, a total of $10 + 4 = 14$ people arrived between 9:00 P.M. and 10:59 P.M.

Quiz 1.1–1.4 (p. 24)

1.

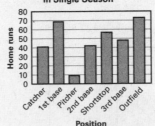

Record Home Runs in Single Season

2. $71 - 9 = 62$

The record for the outfield is 62 more home runs than the record for the pitcher.

3. $21 - 2 \cdot 7 = 21 - 14 = 7$

4. $8 \times 10 - 40 + 25 = 80 - 40 + 25 = 40 + 25 = 65$

5. $24 - (9 + 7) \div 4 = 24 - 16 \div 4 = 24 - 4 = 20$

6. $(3 + 1)^2 - 1^5 = 4^2 - 1^5 = 16 - 1 = 15$

7. $10^4 \div 5^3 = 10{,}000 \div 125 = 80$

8. $3^4 + 7 \cdot 5 = 81 + 7 \cdot 5 = 81 + 35 = 116$

9. The variable expression for the first plant is $14 + 4x$. The variable expression for the second plant is $8 + 6x$.

$14 + 4 \cdot 5 = 14 + 20 = 34$

The first plant will have a height of 34 inches in five years.

$8 + 6 \cdot 5 = 8 + 30 = 38$

The second plant will have a height of 38 inches in five years.

The 8 inch plant is taller after 5 years.

10. $5a - 3 + 7 = 5(4) - 3 + 7$
$\qquad = 20 - 3 + 7$
$\qquad = 17 + 7$
$\qquad = 24$

Chapter 1, *continued*

11. $8 + b + 4 \cdot 11 = 8 + 3 + 4 \cdot 11$
$\qquad\qquad\qquad\quad = 8 + 3 + 44$
$\qquad\qquad\qquad\quad = 11 + 44$
$\qquad\qquad\qquad\quad = 55$

12. $2 \cdot z^4 \div 8 = 2 \cdot 4^4 \div 8 = 2 \cdot 256 \div 8 = 512 \div 8 = 64$

13. $(9 - x)^5 \cdot 3 - 16 = (9 - 7)^5 \cdot 3 - 16$
$\qquad\qquad\qquad\qquad = 2^5 \cdot 3 - 16$
$\qquad\qquad\qquad\qquad = 32 \cdot 3 - 16$
$\qquad\qquad\qquad\qquad = 96 - 16$
$\qquad\qquad\qquad\qquad = 80$

Mixed Review of Problem Solving (p. 25)

1. a. The expression for the volume of zinc in the sample is $15 - x$.

b. The expression for the total mass of the sample is $80.1 + 7.1(15 - x)$.

c. $80.1 + 7.1(15 - x) = 80.1 + 7.1(15 - 9)$
$\qquad\qquad\qquad\qquad = 80.1 + 7.1(6)$
$\qquad\qquad\qquad\qquad = 80.1 + 42.6$
$\qquad\qquad\qquad\qquad = 122.7$

The total mass of the sample is 122.7 grams.

2. a.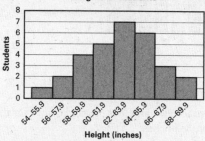

Heights of Students

b. The height interval that has the most students is 62–63.9 inches.

c. No, each individual data value is not shown. Although 60 inches is at the beginning of an interval, 65 inches is not at the end of an interval, so there is no way to determine the number of students who are between 60 and 65 inches tall.

3. $16t^2 = 16 \cdot 3^2 = 16 \cdot 9 = 144$

After 3 seconds, the rock has fallen 144 feet.

$16t^2 = 16 \cdot 4^2 = 16 \cdot 16 = 256$

After 4 seconds, the rock has fallen 256 feet.

The difference of 256 and 144 is $256 - 144 = 112$. The rock falls 112 more feet in 4 seconds than in 3 seconds.

4. a. The expression for the amount of money you raise if you walk the entire 20 miles is $150 + 15 \cdot 20$.

b. $150 + 15 \cdot 20 = 150 + 300 = 450$

You will raise $450 if you complete the walk.

c. 10 miles: $150 + 15 \cdot 10 \overset{?}{=} 300$
$\qquad\qquad\quad 150 + 150 \overset{?}{=} 300$
$\qquad\qquad\qquad\quad 300 = 300$

If you walk 10 miles, you will raise $300.

5. To keep at least two gallons in the tank, subtract 2 from 13, so you can use 11 gallons of gas. Eleven gallons times 22 miles per gallon will tell you how many miles you can travel before filling up.

$(13 - 2) \cdot 22 = 11 \cdot 22 = 242$

You should travel no more than 242 miles before filling up.

6. *Sample answers:*

$(3 + 18) \div 3 + 3 \times 5 + 3 = 21 \div 3 + 3 \times 5 + 3$
$\qquad\qquad\qquad\qquad\qquad = 7 + 15 + 3$
$\qquad\qquad\qquad\qquad\qquad = 22 + 3$
$\qquad\qquad\qquad\qquad\qquad = 25$

$3 + (18 \div 3) + 3 \times 5 + 3 = 3 + 6 + 3 \times 5 + 3$
$\qquad\qquad\qquad\qquad\qquad = 3 + 6 + 15 + 3$
$\qquad\qquad\qquad\qquad\qquad = 9 + 15 + 3$
$\qquad\qquad\qquad\qquad\qquad = 24 + 3$
$\qquad\qquad\qquad\qquad\qquad = 27$

$3 + 18 \div (3 + 3) \times 5 + 3 = 3 + 18 \div 6 \times 5 + 3$
$\qquad\qquad\qquad\qquad\qquad = 3 + 3 \times 5 + 3$
$\qquad\qquad\qquad\qquad\qquad = 3 + 15 + 3$
$\qquad\qquad\qquad\qquad\qquad = 18 + 3$
$\qquad\qquad\qquad\qquad\qquad = 21$

$3 + (18 \div 3 + 3) \times 5 + 3 = 3 + (6 + 3) \times 5 + 3$
$\qquad\qquad\qquad\qquad\qquad = 3 + 9 \times 5 + 3$
$\qquad\qquad\qquad\qquad\qquad = 3 + 45 + 3$
$\qquad\qquad\qquad\qquad\qquad = 48 + 3$
$\qquad\qquad\qquad\qquad\qquad = 51$

$3 + 18 \div 3 + 3 \times (5 + 3) = 3 + 18 \div 3 + 3 \times 8$
$\qquad\qquad\qquad\qquad\qquad = 3 + 6 + 24$
$\qquad\qquad\qquad\qquad\qquad = 9 + 24$
$\qquad\qquad\qquad\qquad\qquad = 33$

$(3 + 18 \div 3 + 3) \times 5 + 3 = (3 + 6 + 3) \times 5 + 3$
$\qquad\qquad\qquad\qquad\qquad = (9 + 3) \times 5 + 3$
$\qquad\qquad\qquad\qquad\qquad = 12 \times 5 + 3$
$\qquad\qquad\qquad\qquad\qquad = 60 + 3$
$\qquad\qquad\qquad\qquad\qquad = 63$

The following real-world problem can be modeled by the expression $(3 + 18) \div 3 + 3 \times 5 + 3$. You and two friends go to the mall. First you have lunch. You spend $3 on a pitcher of soda and $18 on a pizza, and you split the bill between the three of you. Then you buy 3 books that are $5 each and a poster for $3.

Chapter 1, *continued*

Lesson 1.5

Activity (p. 26)

Step 1. It will take four 1-tiles to replace the *x*-tile to make both sides of the equal sign have the same value because then there will be six tiles on each side of the equal sign.

Step 2. When the value of *x* is 4 then the equation $x + 2 = 6$ is a true statement.

1. $x + 3 = 8$

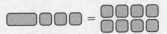

To make this statement true, *x* would be equal to 5.

2. $x + 4 = 5$

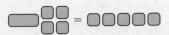

To make this statement true, *x* would be equal to 1.

3. $6 + x = 10$

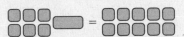

To make this statement true, *x* would be equal to 4.

1.5 Guided Practice (pp. 27–28)

1. 5 times what number equals 45?

$5 \times 9 = 45$, so $x = 9$.

2. 16 plus what number equals 21?

$16 + 5 = 21$, so $n = 5$.

3. What number divided by 6 equals 9?

$54 \div 6 = 9$, so $t = 54$.

4. $a + 9 = 16; a = 7$

$7 + 9 \overset{?}{=} 16$

$16 = 16$

Yes, $a = 7$ is a solution of the equation $a + 9 = 16$.

5. $88 \div y = 8; y = 8$

$88 \div 8 \overset{?}{=} 8$

$11 \neq 8$

No, $y = 8$ is not a solution of the equation $88 \div y = 8$.

6. $7n = 13; n = 2$

$7 \cdot 2 \overset{?}{=} 13$

$14 \neq 13$

No, $n = 2$ is not a solution of the equation $7n = 13$.

7. $\begin{pmatrix} \text{Money Julie} \\ \text{has} \end{pmatrix} = \begin{pmatrix} \text{Cost to} \\ \text{wash} \end{pmatrix} + \begin{pmatrix} \text{Cost to} \\ \text{dry} \end{pmatrix} \cdot \begin{pmatrix} \text{Number} \\ \text{of loads} \end{pmatrix}$

$9 = (1.75 + 1.25) \cdot n$

$9 = 3n$

$9 = 3 \cdot 3$

Because $n = 3$, Julie can do 3 loads.

8. Ceasar's height − Marco's height = 5

$50 - m = 5$

$50 - 45 = 5$

Marco is 45 inches tall. Use Marco's height to find Luis's height. Add: $45 + 3 = 48$.

Luis is 48 inches tall.

1.5 Exercises (pp. 28–30)

Skill Practice

1. The process of finding all possible values that make a mathematical sentence true is *solving an equation*.

2. An *equation* is a mathematical sentence formed by placing an equal sign between two expressions.

3. 9 plus what number equals 31?

$9 + 22 = 31$, so $p = 22$.

4. What number minus 10 equals 34?

$44 - 10 = 34$, so $y = 44$.

5. 7 times what number equals 77?

$7 \times 11 = 77$, so $x = 11$.

6. 56 divided by what number equals 8?

$56 \div 7 = 8$, so $k = 7$.

7. What number plus 8 equals 19?

$11 + 8 = 19$, so $z = 11$.

8. 6 times what number equals 48?

$6 \times 8 = 48$, so $m = 8$.

9. What number minus 16 equals 13?

$29 - 16 = 13$, so $c = 29$.

10. 51 divided by what number equals 3?

$51 \div 17 = 3$, so $k = 17$.

11. 32 divided by what number equals 16?

$\frac{32}{2} = 16$, so $n = 2$.

12. 26 minus what number equals 17?

$26 - 9 = 17$, so $r = 9$.

13. 10 times what number equals 150?

$10 \times 15 = 150$, so $y = 15$.

14. 7 plus what number equals 31?

$7 + 24 = 31$, so $x = 24$.

15. What number minus 5 equals 12?

$17 - 5 = 12$, so $z = 17$.

16. 6 times what number equals 42?

$6 \times 7 = 42$, so $x = 7$.

17. 22 divided by what number equals 11?

$22 \div 2 = 11$, so $c = 2$.

18. 3 plus what number equals 19?

$3 + 16 = 19$, so $a = 16$.

19. $35 - x = 21; x = 16$

$35 - 16 \stackrel{?}{=} 21$

$19 \neq 21$

No, $x = 16$ is not a solution of the equation $35 - x = 21$.

20. $75 \div x = 5; x = 15$

$75 \div 15 \stackrel{?}{=} 5$

$5 = 5$

Yes, $x = 15$ is a solution of the equation $75 \div x = 5$.

21. $7x = 84; x = 14$

$7 \cdot 14 \stackrel{?}{=} 84$

$98 \neq 84$

No, $x = 14$ is not a solution of the equation $7x = 84$.

22. $x + 29 = 42; x = 13$

$13 + 29 \stackrel{?}{=} 42$

$42 = 42$

Yes, $x = 13$ is a solution of the equation $x + 29 = 42$.

23. $15 + b = 28; b = 13$

$15 + 13 \stackrel{?}{=} 28$

$28 = 28$

Yes, $b = 13$ is a solution of the equation $15 + b = 28$.

24. $37 - d = 14; d = 21$

$37 - 21 \stackrel{?}{=} 14$

$16 \neq 14$

No, $d = 21$ is not a solution of the equation $37 - d = 14$.

25. B; 63 divided by what number equals 9?

$63 \div 7 = 9$, so $x = 7$.

26. 5 times 2 equals 10. The correct solution is $\frac{1}{2}$ because

$5 \div \frac{1}{2} = 10$.

27. 24 divided by what number equals 8?

$24 \div 3 = 8$, so $t = 3$.

28. What number plus 8 equals 24?

$16 + 8 = 24$, so $t = 16$.

29. 24 times what number equals 8?

$24 \times \frac{1}{3} = \frac{24 \times 1}{3} = \frac{24}{3} = 8$, so $t = \frac{1}{3}$.

30. What number divided by 24 equals 8?

$\frac{192}{24} = 8$, so $t = 192$.

31. $3x + 6 = x + 12; x = 1$

$3 \cdot 1 + 6 \stackrel{?}{=} 1 + 12$

$3 + 6 \stackrel{?}{=} 1 + 12$

$9 \neq 13$

$3x + 6 = x + 12; x = 2$

$3 \cdot 2 + 6 \stackrel{?}{=} 2 + 12$

$6 + 6 \stackrel{?}{=} 2 + 12$

$12 \neq 14$

$3x + 6 = x + 12; x = 3$

$3 \cdot 3 + 6 \stackrel{?}{=} 3 + 12$

$9 + 6 \stackrel{?}{=} 15$

$15 = 15$

The value $x = 3$ is a solution of the equation $3x + 6 = x + 12$.

32. $2x - 7 = x + 1; x = 8$

$2 \cdot 8 - 7 \stackrel{?}{=} 8 + 1$

$16 - 7 \stackrel{?}{=} 8 + 1$

$9 = 9$

$2x - 7 = x + 1; x = 9$

$2 \cdot 9 - 7 \stackrel{?}{=} 9 + 1$

$18 - 7 \stackrel{?}{=} 9 + 1$

$11 \neq 10$

$2x - 7 = x + 1; x = 10$

$2 \cdot 10 - 7 \stackrel{?}{=} 10 + 1$

$20 - 7 \stackrel{?}{=} 10 + 1$

$13 \neq 11$

The value $x = 8$ is a solution of the equation $2x - 7 = x + 1$.

33. $8 - 4x = 4x; x = 0$

$8 - 4 \cdot 0 \stackrel{?}{=} 4 \cdot 0$

$8 - 0 \stackrel{?}{=} 0$

$8 \neq 0$

$8 - 4x = 4x; x = 1$

$8 - 4 \cdot 1 \stackrel{?}{=} 4 \cdot 1$

$8 - 4 \stackrel{?}{=} 4$

$4 = 4$

$8 - 4x = 4x; x = 2$

$8 - 4 \cdot 2 \stackrel{?}{=} 4 \cdot 2$

$8 - 8 \stackrel{?}{=} 8$

$0 \neq 8$

The value $x = 1$ is a solution of the equation $8 - 4x = 4x$.

34. $2x - 4.5 = x \div 2; x = 3$

$2 \cdot 3 - 4.5 \overset{?}{=} 3 \div 2$

$6 - 4.5 \overset{?}{=} 1.5$

$1.5 = 1.5$

$2x - 4.5 = x \div 2; x = 4$

$2 \cdot 4 - 4.5 \overset{?}{=} 4 \div 2$

$8 - 4.5 \overset{?}{=} 2$

$3.5 \neq 2$

$2x - 4.5 = x \div 2; x = 5$

$2 \cdot 5 - 4.5 \overset{?}{=} 5 \div 2$

$10 - 4.5 \overset{?}{=} 2.5$

$5.5 \neq 2.5$

The value $x = 3$ is a solution of the equation $2x - 4.5 = x \div 2$.

35. $5x + 1 = x + 17; x = 3$

$5 \cdot 3 + 1 \overset{?}{=} 3 + 17$

$15 + 1 \overset{?}{=} 3 + 17$

$16 \neq 20$

$5x + 1 = x + 17; x = 4$

$5 \cdot 4 + 1 \overset{?}{=} 4 + 17$

$20 + 1 \overset{?}{=} 4 + 17$

$21 = 21$

$5x + 1 = x + 17; x = 5$

$5 \cdot 5 + 1 \overset{?}{=} 5 + 17$

$25 + 1 \overset{?}{=} 5 + 17$

$26 \neq 22$

The value $x = 4$ is a solution of the equation $5x + 1 = x + 17$.

36. $12 - 3x = 3x; x = 0$

$12 - 3 \cdot 0 \overset{?}{=} 3 \cdot 0$

$12 - 0 \overset{?}{=} 0$

$12 \neq 0$

$12 - 3x = 3x; x = 1$

$12 - 3 \cdot 1 \overset{?}{=} 3 \cdot 1$

$12 - 3 \overset{?}{=} 3$

$9 \neq 3$

$12 - 3x = 3x; x = 2$

$12 - 3 \cdot 2 \overset{?}{=} 3 \cdot 2$

$12 - 6 \overset{?}{=} 6$

$6 = 6$

The value $x = 2$ is a solution of the equation $12 - 3x = 3x$.

37. *Reasoning*   *Guess*   *Check*

Pick a number for x. $x = 3$ $[(x + 3) \cdot 4 - 7] \div 3 = 3$

$[(3 + 3) \cdot 4 - 7] \div 3 \overset{?}{=} 3$

$[6 \cdot 4 - 7] \div 3 \overset{?}{=} 3$

$[24 - 7] \div 3 \overset{?}{=} 3$

$17 \div 3 \overset{?}{=} 3$

$5.7 > 3$

Pick a number smaller than 3 for x. $x = 1$ $[(x + 3) \cdot 4 - 7] \div 3 \overset{?}{=} 3$

$[(1 + 3) \cdot 4 - 7] \div 3 \overset{?}{=} 3$

$[4 \cdot 4 - 7] \div 3 \overset{?}{=} 3$

$[16 - 7] \div 3 \overset{?}{=} 3$

$9 \div 3 \overset{?}{=} 3$

$3 = 3$

So, the value that makes the equation $[(x + 3) \cdot 4 - 7] \div 3 = 3$ true is $x = 1$.

38. *Reasoning*   *Guess*   *Check*

Pick a number for x. $x = 2$ $[(x + 3) \cdot 3 - 6] \div 5 = 3$

$[(2 + 3) \cdot 3 - 6] \div 5 \overset{?}{=} 3$

$[5 \cdot 3 - 6] \div 5 \overset{?}{=} 3$

$[15 - 6] \div 5 \overset{?}{=} 3$

$9 \div 5 \overset{?}{=} 3$

$1.8 < 3$

Pick a number larger than 2 for x. $x = 4$ $[(x + 3) \cdot 3 - 6] \div 5 = 3$

$[(4 + 3) \cdot 3 - 6] \div 5 \overset{?}{=} 3$

$[7 \cdot 3 - 6] \div 5 \overset{?}{=} 3$

$[21 - 6] \div 5 \overset{?}{=} 3$

$15 \div 5 \overset{?}{=} 3$

$3 = 3$

So, the value that makes the equation $[(x + 3) \cdot 3 - 6] \div 5 = 3$ true is $x = 4$.

39. *Reasoning*   *Guess*   *Check*

Pick a number for x. $x = 5$ $[(x - 2) \cdot 6 - 2] \div 5 = 2$

$[(5 - 2) \cdot 6 - 2] \div 5 \overset{?}{=} 2$

$[3 \cdot 6 - 2] \div 5 \overset{?}{=} 2$

$[18 - 2] \div 5 \overset{?}{=} 2$

$16 \div 5 \overset{?}{=} 2$

$3.2 > 2$

Pick a number smaller than 5 for x. $x = 4$ $[(x - 2) \cdot 6 - 2] \div 5 = 2$

$[(4 - 2) \cdot 6 - 2] \div 5 \overset{?}{=} 2$

$[2 \cdot 6 - 2] \div 5 \overset{?}{=} 2$

$[12 - 2] \div 5 \overset{?}{=} 2$

$10 \div 5 \overset{?}{=} 2$

$2 = 2$

So, the value that makes the equation $[(x - 2) \cdot 6 - 2] \div 5 = 2$ true is $x = 4$.

40. *Reasoning*

	Guess	Check
Pick a number for x.	$x = 3$	$[(x - 2) \cdot 5 + 8] \div 4 = 2$
		$[(3 - 2) \cdot 5 + 8] \div 4 \overset{?}{=} 2$
		$[1 \cdot 5 + 8] \div 4 \overset{?}{=} 2$
		$[5 + 8] \div 4 \overset{?}{=} 2$
		$13 \div 4 \overset{?}{=} 2$
		$3.25 > 2$
Pick a number smaller than 3 for x	$x = 2$	$[(x - 2) \cdot 5 + 8] \div 4 = 2$
		$[(2 - 2) \cdot 5 + 8] \div 4 \overset{?}{=} 2$
		$[0 \cdot 5 + 8] \div 4 \overset{?}{=} 2$
		$[0 + 8] \div 4 \overset{?}{=} 2$
		$8 \div 4 \overset{?}{=} 2$
		$2 = 2$

So, the value that makes the equation
$[(x - 2) \cdot 5 + 8] \div 4 = 2$ true is $x = 2$.

41. $\dfrac{x - 8}{6} = 12$

Break into parts:

Question 1: What number divided by 6 equals 12?

Solution: 72; so the numerator should equal 72.

Question 2: What number minus 8 equals 72?

Solution: 80; so, $x = 80$.

Check: $\dfrac{80 - 8}{6} = \dfrac{72}{6} = 12$

42. $\dfrac{71 - x}{7} = 8$

Break into parts:

Question 1: What number divided by 7 equals 8?

Solution: 56; so the numerator should equal 56.

Question 2: 71 minus what number equals 56?

Solution: 15; so, $x = 15$.

Check: $\dfrac{71 - 15}{7} = \dfrac{56}{7} = 8$

43. $\dfrac{x + 6}{9} = 5$

Break into parts:

Question 1: What number divided by 9 equals 5?

Solution: 45; so the numerator should equal 45.

Question 2: What number plus 6 equals 45?

Solution: 39; so, $x = 39$.

Check: $\dfrac{39 + 6}{9} = \dfrac{45}{9} = 5$

44. $\dfrac{64 - x}{4} = 10$

Break into parts:

Question 1: What number divided by 4 equals 10?

Solution: 40, so the numerator should equal 40.

Question 2: 64 minus what number equals 40?

Solution: 24; so, $x = 24$.

Check: $\dfrac{64 - 24}{4} = \dfrac{40}{4} = 10$

Problem Solving

45. An equation to find how much rainfall is needed to equal the record is $14 + r = 43$.

$$14 + r = 43$$
$$14 + 29 = 43$$

Twenty-nine more inches of rain is needed to equal the record.

46. There are 12 inches in 1 foot. So, an equation to find the number of feet f in 3600 inches is $12f = 3600$.

$$12f = 3600$$
$$12 \cdot 300 = 3600$$

There are 300 feet in 3600 inches.

47. The equation to find the weight of the baby elephant is $5033 + b = 5396$.

$$5033 + b = 5396$$
$$5033 + 363 = 5396$$

The weight of the baby elephant is 363 pounds.

48. To determine if 5 is a solution of the equation $4x = 20$, multiply 4 by 5 to see if the product is 20.

49. C; The equation to find out how many invitations can be written in an hour is $4x = 60$.

50.

Time show lasted	$\times$	Cost per minute	$=$	Total cost

$$20x = 25,000$$
$$20 \cdot 1250 = 25,000$$

The cost per minute is $1250.

If a show lasted twice as long as the 20 minute show, then the total cost is $50,000. If the rate stays the same and the time is doubled, then the total cost is also doubled.

51. *Sample answer:* Your mean deposit into your savings account over 9 weeks is $13. What is the total amount deposited?

$$\frac{x}{9} = 13$$

$$\frac{117}{9} = 13$$

A total of $117 is deposited into the account.

52. An equation to find out how much Maria has to improve her time by is $x + (3 \cdot 60 + 40) = 4 \cdot 60 + 5$.

$$x + (3 \cdot 60 + 40) = 4 \cdot 60 + 5$$
$$x + (180 + 40) = 240 + 5$$
$$x + 220 = 245$$
$$25 + 220 \overset{?}{=} 245$$
$$245 = 245$$

Maria needs to improve her time by 25 minutes.

53. An equation to find how many hours you will work per week over 8 weeks total is $8h = 200 - 80$.

$$8h = 200 - 80$$
$$8h = 120$$
$$8 \cdot 15 = 120$$

You will work 15 hours per week.

Chapter 1, *continued*

54. Let x be the first number and let $x + 1$ be the next consecutive number.

$$\frac{x + x + 1}{3} = 71$$

$$\frac{2x + 1}{3} = 71$$

Break into parts:

Question 1: What number divided by 3 equals 71?

Solution: 213; so the numerator should equal 213.

Question 2: 2 times what number plus 1 equals 213?

Solution: 106; so, $x = 106$.

Check: $\dfrac{2(106) + 1}{3} = \dfrac{212 + 1}{3} = \dfrac{213}{3} = 71$

The two numbers are 106 and 107.

55. Let x be the number of gumballs Joe has.

$$x - \left(\frac{1}{2}x + \frac{1}{6}x + \frac{1}{4}x\right) = 4$$

$$x - \left(\frac{6}{12}x + \frac{2}{12}x + \frac{3}{12}x\right) = 4$$

$$x - \frac{11}{12}x = 4$$

$$\frac{12}{12}x - \frac{11}{12}x = 4$$

$$\frac{x}{12} = 4$$

$$\frac{48}{12} = 4$$

Joe had 48 gumballs before he gave some away.

56. Let b be the amount of money that Bob has.

Rita has $150, which is $35 more than Bob. This can be represented by the equation $b + 35 = 150$.

$b + 35 = 150$

$115 + 35 = 150$

Bob has $115.

Jen has $\frac{4}{5}$ as much money as Bob. This can be represented by the equation $j = \frac{4}{5}b$, where j is the amount of money Jen has. Substitute 115 for b to find j.

$j = \frac{4}{5}b = \frac{4}{5} \times 115 = \frac{4 \times 115}{5} = \frac{460}{5} = 92$

Jen has $92.

Tim has $50 more than Jen.

Add: $92 + 50 = 142$

Tim has $142.

Mixed Review

57. $7y + 17 = 7 \cdot 8 + 17 = 56 + 17 = 73$

58. $(36 - 24) \cdot y = (36 - 24) \cdot 8 = 12 \cdot 8 = 96$

59. $y \cdot 4 + 20 \cdot y = 8 \cdot 4 + 20 \cdot 8 = 32 + 160 = 192$

60. $19 - 2y = 19 - 2 \cdot 8 = 19 - 16 = 3$

61. $8748 - 3109 \approx 9000 - 3000 = 6000$

62. $876 + 622 \approx 900 + 600 = 1500$

63. $111 + 89 + 791 \approx 100 + 100 + 800 = 1000$

64. $178 - 43 - 78 \approx 180 - 40 - 80 = 60$

65. B; $(20 + 4^3) \div 6 = (20 + 64) \div 6 = 84 \div 6 = 14$

Lesson 1.6

Investigation (p. 31)

Step 2. The area of the rectangle is 15 square units.

1.

Dimensions	Length	Width	Number of square tiles	Area of rectangle
3 by 4	3	4	12	12 square units
4 by 4	4	4	16	16 square units
5 by 6	5	6	30	30 square units
3 by 3	3	3	9	9 square units

2. A variable equation to find the area of a rectangle is $A = \ell w$, where A is the area, ℓ is the length, and w is the width.

3. A variable equation to find the area of a square is $A = s^2$, where A is the area, and s is the length of a side.

4. No, perimeter is not measured in square units because it is not a square measurement. It is a linear measurement.

1.6 Guided Practice (pp. 33–34)

1. $P = 2\ell + 2w;\ \ell = 25,\ w = 14$

$= 2(25) + 2(14)$

$= 50 + 28$

$= 78$

The perimeter of the rectangle is 78 inches.

$A = \ell w;\ \ell = 25,\ w = 14$

$= 25(14)$

$= 350$

The area of the rectangle is 350 square inches.

2. $P = 4s;\ s = 7$

$= 4(7)$

$= 28$

The perimeter of the square is 28 inches.

$A = s^2;\ s = 7$

$= 7^2$

$= 49$

The area of the square is 49 square inches.

3. $A = \ell w;\ A = 91,\ \ell = 13$

$91 = 13w$

$91 \overset{?}{=} 13 \cdot 7$

$91 = 91$

The width of the rectangle is 7 centimeters.

Chapter 1, *continued*

4. $A = s^2; A = 100$

$100 = s^2$

$100 = s \cdot s$

$100 \stackrel{?}{=} 10 \cdot 10$

$100 = 100$

The side length of the square is 10 yards.

5. $d = rt; r = 40, t = 2$

$d = 40 \cdot 2 = 80$

A car travels 80 miles in 2 hours.

6. $r = \frac{d}{t}; d = 192, t = 8$

$r = \frac{192}{8} = 24$

The rabbit is running at 24 feet per second.

1.6 Exercises (pp. 34–36)

Skill Practice

1. The difference between area and perimeter is that area measures the surface space a figure covers while perimeter is the distance around the figure.

2. The three forms of the distance formula are $d = rt$, $r = \frac{d}{t}$, and $t = \frac{d}{r}$.

3. $P = 2\ell + 2w; \ell = 9, w = 6$

$P = 2(9) + 2(6) = 18 + 12 = 30$

The perimeter of the rectangle is 30 yards.

$A = \ell w; \ell = 9, w = 6$

$= 9(6)$

$= 54$

The area of the rectangle is 54 square yards.

4. $P = 2\ell + 2w; \ell = 8, w = 3$

$P = 2(8) + 2(3) = 16 + 6 = 22$

The perimeter of the rectangle is 22 centimeters.

$A = \ell w; \ell = 8, w = 3$

$= 8(3)$

$= 24$

The area of the rectangle is 24 square centimeters.

5. $P = 4s; s = 5$

$P = 4(5) = 20$

The perimeter of the square is 20 meters.

$A = s^2; s = 5$

$A = 5^2 = 25$

The area of the square is 25 square meters.

6. $P = 4s; s = 12$

$P = 4(12) = 48$

The perimeter of the square is 48 feet.

$A = s^2; s = 12$

$A = 12^2 = 144$

The area of the square is 144 square feet.

7. The error is in the last step because, for area, units are always squared.

$A = s^2; s = 4$

$A = 4^2 = 16$

The area of the square is 16 square meters.

8. $A = s^2; A = 36$

$36 = s^2$

$36 = s \cdot s$

$36 \stackrel{?}{=} 6 \cdot 6$

$36 = 36$

The side length of the square is 6 yards.

9. $P = 4s; P = 24$

$24 = 4s$

$24 \stackrel{?}{=} 4 \cdot 6$

$24 = 24$

The side length of the square is 6 meters.

10. $A = s^2; A = 144$

$144 = s^2$

$144 = s \cdot s$

$144 \stackrel{?}{=} 12 \cdot 12$

$144 = 144$

The side length of the square is 12 feet.

11. $A = s^2; s = 18$

$A = 18^2 = 324$

The area of the square is 324 square inches.

12. $A = \ell w; \ell = 17, w = 9$

$A = 17(9) = 153$

The area of the rectangle is 153 square meters.

13. $A = \ell w; A = 88, w = 8$

$88 = \ell \cdot 8$

$88 \stackrel{?}{=} 11 \cdot 8$

$88 = 88$

The length of the rectangle is 11 inches.

14. $r = \frac{d}{t}; d = 36, t = 4$

$r = \frac{36}{4} = 9$

The rate of travel is 9 kilometers per hour.

15. $d = rt; r = 0.5, t = 10$

$d = 0.5(10) = 5$

The distance traveled is 5 miles.

16. $d = rt; r = 7, t = 1.5$

$d = 7(1.5) = 10.5$

The distance traveled is 10.5 miles.

17. $t = \frac{d}{r}; d = 40, r = 5$

$t = \frac{40}{5} = 8$

The time traveled is 8 seconds.

18. $t = \dfrac{d}{r}$; $d = 130$, $r = 65$

$t = \dfrac{130}{65} = 2$

The time traveled is 2 hours.

19. $r = \dfrac{d}{t}$; $d = 75$, $t = 5$

$r = \dfrac{75}{5} = 15$

The rate of travel is 15 feet per second.

20. B; $P = 2\ell + 2w$; $\ell = 2$, $w = 8$

$P = 2(2) + 2(8) = 4 + 16 = 20$

The perimeter of the rectangle does not equal 16 feet.

21.

$P = 6 + 3 + 6 + 9 + 12 + 12 = 48$

The perimeter of this figure is 48 inches.

The total area of this figure is the area of region I plus the area of region II.

$A_I = \ell w$; $\ell = 6$, $w = 3$

$A_I = 6(3) = 18$

$A_{II} = \ell w$; $\ell = 12$, $w = 9$

$A_{II} = 12(9) = 108$

$A_T = A_I + A_{II}$

$A_T = 18 + 108 = 126$

The total area is 126 square inches.

22.

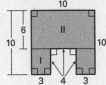

$P = 10 + 10 + 10 + 3 + 4 + 4 + 4 + 3 = 48$

The perimeter of this figure is 48 centimeters.

The total area of this figure is twice the area of region I plus the area of region II.

$A_I = \ell w$; $\ell = 4$; $w = 3$

$A_I = 4 \cdot 3 = 12$

$A_{II} = \ell w$; $\ell = 10$, $w = 6$

$A_{II} = 10 \cdot 6 = 60$

$A_T = 2 \cdot A_I + A_{II}$

$A_T = 2 \cdot 12 + 60 = 24 + 60 = 84$

The total area of this figure is 84 square centimeters.

23. Sample answer:

$P = 2\ell + 2w$; $\ell = 10$, $w = 2$

$P = 2(10) + 2(2) = 20 + 4 = 24$

$P = 2\ell + 2w$; $\ell = 8$, $w = 4$

$P = 2(8) + 2(4) = 16 + 8 = 24$

$P = 2\ell + 2w$; $\ell = 9$, $w = 3$

$P = 2(9) + 2(3) = 18 + 6 = 24$

The dimensions of three rectangles with a perimeter of 24 cm are 10 cm by 2 cm, 8 cm by 4 cm, and 9 cm by 3 cm.

$A = \ell w$; $\ell = 8$, $w = 3$

$A = 8(3) = 24$

$A = \ell w$; $\ell = 4$, $w = 6$

$A = 4(6) = 24$

$A = \ell w$, $\ell = 2$, $w = 12$

$A = 2(12) = 24$

The dimensions of three rectangles that have an area of 24 square centimeters are 8 cm by 3 cm, 4 cm by 6 cm, and 2 cm by 12 cm.

24. $A = \ell w$; $A = 60$

$60 = \ell w$

$P = 2\ell + 2w$; $P = 38$

$38 = 2\ell + 2w$

You can rewrite $60 = \ell w$ as $\dfrac{60}{w} = \ell$. Substitute the expression for ℓ into the equation $38 = 2\ell + 2w$ and solve for w.

$38 = 2\ell + 2w$

$38 = 2\left(\dfrac{60}{w}\right) + 2w$

$38 = \dfrac{120}{w} + 2w$

Use Guess, Check, and Revise.

Guess $w = 2$.

$\dfrac{120}{2} + 2(2) = 60 + 4 = 64 \neq 38$

Guess $w = 3$.

$\dfrac{120}{3} + 2(3) = 40 + 6 = 46 \neq 38$

Guess $w = 4$.

$\dfrac{120}{4} + 2(4) = 30 + 8 = 38$

So, $w = 4$ and $\ell = \dfrac{60}{4} = 15$.

The length of the rectangle is 15 inches and the width is 4 inches.

Chapter 1, *continued*

25. Area of base of box:

$A = \ell w; \ell = 10, w = 6$

$A = 10(6) = 60 \text{ cm}^2$

Area of top of box:

$A = \ell w; \ell = 10, w = 6$

$A = 10(6) = 60 \text{ cm}^2$

Area of 1st side:

$A = \ell h; \ell = 10, h = 5$

$A = 10(5) = 50 \text{ cm}^2$

Area of 2nd side:

$A = \ell h; \ell = 10, h = 5$

$A = 10(5) = 50 \text{ cm}^2$

Area of 3rd side:

$A = wh; w = 6, h = 5$

$A = 6(5) = 30 \text{ cm}^2$

Area of 4th side:

$A = wh; w = 6, h = 5$

$A = 6(5) = 30 \text{ cm}^2$

The areas of the six sides of the box are 60 cm², 60 cm², 50 cm², 50 cm², 30 cm², and 30 cm².

Problem Solving

26. $r = \frac{d}{t}; d = 210, t = 4$

$r = \frac{210}{4} = 52.5$

The beetle is running at 52.5 centimeters per second.

27. $F = \frac{9}{5}C + 32; C = 20$

$F = \frac{9}{5} \cdot 20 + 32$

$F = 36 + 32$

$F = 68$

When the Celsius temperature is 20°, the Fahrenheit temperature is 68°.

28. To find the width of a rectangle when you know its area and length, divide the area by the length.

29. $t = \frac{d}{r}; d = 240, r = 55$

$t = \frac{240}{55} \approx \frac{240}{60} \approx 4$

It takes about 4 hours to travel from Houston to Dallas.

30. The number of centimeters c is equal to 100 times the number of meters m. So, $c = 100 \, m$.

31. $d = rt; r = 13, t = 120$

$d = 13(120) = 1560$

Two minutes is the same as 120 seconds. The distance the parachutist falls in 2 minutes is 1560 feet.

32. C; $d = rt; r = 50, t = 1.5$

$d = 50 \times 1.5$

1 hour and 30 minutes is the same as 1.5 hours.

33. Total time = 1 h 13 min

$\underline{\quad + \text{ 1 h 44 min}}$

2 h 57 min

$2 \text{ h } 57 \text{ min} = \left(2 + \frac{57}{60}\right) \text{h} = 2.95 \text{ h}$

It took the train 2.95 hours to travel the 226 mile trip.

Use distance formula in the form $r = \frac{d}{t}$ to find the average speed of the train.

$r = \frac{d}{t}; d = 226, t = 2.95$

$r = \frac{226}{2.95} \approx 77$

The average speed of the train is about 77 miles per hour.

34.

	Length	Width	Area	Perimeter
Pool A	60 ft	22 ft	1320 ft²	164 ft
Pool B	120 ft	44 ft	5280 ft²	328 ft

Pool A:

$A = \ell w; \ell = 60, w = 22$

$A = 60(22) = 1320$

The area for pool A is 1320 square feet.

$P = 2\ell + 2w$

$P = 2(60) + 2(22) = 120 + 44 = 164$

The perimeter for pool A is 164 feet.

Pool B:

$A = \ell w; A = 5280, w = 44$

$5280 = \ell \cdot 44$

$5280 \overset{?}{=} 120 \cdot 44$

$5280 = 5280$

The length of pool B is 120 feet.

$P = 2\ell + 2w; \ell = 120 \, w = 44$

$P = 2(120) + 2(44) = 240 + 88 = 328$

The perimeter of pool B is 328 feet.

The length and width of pool B are double the length and width of pool A. The perimeter of pool B is double the perimeter of pool A. The area of pool B is 4 times the area of pool A.

35. $P = 2\ell + 2w; P = 240, \ell = 2w$

$240 = 2(2w) + 2w$

$240 = 4w + 2w$

$240 = 6w$

$240 \overset{?}{=} 6(40)$

$240 = 240$

$\ell = 2w = 2 \cdot 40 = 80$

$A = \ell w; \ell = 80, w = 40$

$A = 80(40) = 3200$

The length of the yard is 80 feet and the width is 40 feet, so the area is 3200 square feet. Each bag of fertilizer covers 2000 square feet, so you will need 2 bags to cover the whole yard.

Chapter 1, *continued*

Mixed Review

36. Multiply the number of dots in the previous stage by 2 to get the number of dots in the next stage.

37. Rotate the figure in the previous stage 90° clockwise to get the figure in the next stage.

38. 8 times what number equals 72?

$8 \times 9 = 72$, so $x = 9$.

39. What number minus 19 equals 37?

$56 - 19 = 37$, so $g = 56$.

40. What number divided by 3 equals 10?

$\frac{30}{3} = 10$, so $y = 30$.

41. What number plus 21 equals 52?

$31 + 21 = 52$, so $m = 31$.

42. C; $4\frac{3}{8} = \frac{32 + 3}{8} = \frac{35}{8}$

Lesson 1.7

1.7 Guided Practice (pp. 37–39)

1. B; You need to use the formula to find time.

2. $t = \frac{d}{r} = \frac{10}{0.44} \approx 22.73$ min

Your friend's total time: $2.42 + 22.73 = 25.15$ min

Because $25.15 < 25.86$, your friend had the better total time after two stages.

3. 50 ~~short blocks~~ $\times \frac{1 \text{ mile}}{20 \text{ ~~short blocks~~}} = 2.5$ miles

12 ~~long blocks~~ $\times \frac{1 \text{ mile}}{4 \text{ ~~long blocks~~}} = 3$ miles

You walk a total of $2.5 + 3 = 5.5$ miles.

1.7 Exercises (pp. 40–43)

Skill Practice

1. The four steps in the problem solving plan are Read and Understand, Make a Plan, Solve the Problem, and Look Back.

2. You can use *unit analysis* to evaluate expressions with units of measure and to check for the correct units.

3. You know the cost of lunch and the cost of the drink. You need to find out what the customer's change is.

4.

Quarters	Nickels	Dimes
2	1	2
2	3	1
1	2	4
1	4	3
1	6	2
1	8	1

5. Find the total spent on hot dogs and add it to the ticket cost. Then compare the total to $16.

6. The error is that Daniel must subtract the 45 pictures from the 96 before dividing by 3.

$\frac{96 - 45}{3} = \frac{51}{3} = 17$

Daniel will be able to take 17 pictures each day.

7. Dollars raised $= 2 \times 5 = 10$

The neighbor will give you $10.

8. C; The pattern alternates between blue, green, and red arrows, and rotations of the arrows 180°. So, the 15th arrow is red, pointing to the left.

9. Cost per pack $=$ Cost of packs $\div$ Number of packs

$= 12 \div 3$

$= 4$

Each pack of pens costs $4. "Each pack of pens contains 12 pens" is unnecessary information.

10. The next two expressions in the pattern are $31x^2$ and $39x^2$.

11. The next two expressions in the pattern are $69x^5$ and $66x^6$.

12. The rule is subtract 4, then double the difference.

The next three numbers are 32, 28, and 56.

13. The rule is double the number and add 6. The next three numbers are 826, 1658, and 3322.

14. The rule is add each number to the one before it.

The next three numbers are 19.5, 31.5, and 51.

Problem Solving

15. (1) $\dfrac{\text{Number of people who ride in one hour}}{5 \text{ cars} \cdot 4 \text{ passengers}}$

$=$ Number of trains

(2) $900 \div 20 = 45$

Forty-five trains will run each hour.

(3) $900 \overset{?}{=} 5 \cdot 4 \cdot 45$

$900 = 20 \cdot 45$

$900 = 900$ ✓

16. $5 \cdot 50 + 2 \cdot 40 = 250 + 80 = 330$

You practice for 330 minutes per week. Because there are 60 minutes in one hour, you can multiply the number of

minutes by $\dfrac{1 \text{ hour}}{60 \text{ minutes}}$ to convert to hours.

$330 \text{ minutes} \times \dfrac{1 \text{ hour}}{60 \text{ minutes}} = 5.5$

You practice for 5.5 hours per week.

17. To check that the price is correct write and check a number sentence.

$15 \cdot 4 + 2 \cdot 2 \overset{?}{=} 64$

$60 + 4 \overset{?}{=} 64$

$64 = 64$

Because the equation is true, the ticket price is correct.

18. B; $P + 1540 + 780 = 4000$

$P + 2320 = 4000$

$1680 + 2320 \overset{?}{=} 4000$

$4000 = 4000$

You need 1680 more points.

19. The length of the ride on the last day can be represented by the numerical expression $3462 - (3152 + 160)$.

$3462 - (3152 + 160) = 3462 - 3312 = 150$

On the last day, the Tour de France ride was 150 kilometers.

20. The numeric expression to find the dollar amount of sales needed for the fourth week is

$16{,}000 - (1240 + 3720 + 5980)$.

$16{,}000 - (1240 + 3720 + 5980) = 16{,}000 - 10{,}940$
$= 5060$

Week 4 sales need to be $5060.

21. C; Eight ounces of mozzarella would serve 10 people, so 4 ounces of cheese would serve 5 people. Twelve ounces of cheese would serve 15 people.

$30 \div 15 = 2$

$2 \times 12 = 24$

$24 - 12 = 12$

You would need 12 more ounces of cheese for 30 servings of lasagna.

22. With the information provided you can determine the amount of money she needs to still sell, but not the number of subscriptions because you do not know the cost of each subscription.

23. The number of pages you need to read each day to complete the assignment on time can be represented by the numerical expression $(60 + 20 - 16) \div 4$.

$(60 + 20 - 16) \div 4 = (80 - 16) \div 4 = 64 \div 4 = 16$

You need to read 16 pages each day to complete the assignment on time.

24. Fran will need $210 for the printer minus the $120 she will get from her mom. The rest she will earn at a rate of $6 per hour by baby-sitting. Divide the amount of money she needs by $6 to find out how many hours she will need to baby-sit.

$\dfrac{210 - 120}{6} = \dfrac{90}{6} = 15$

Fran will need to baby-sit at least 15 more hours.

25. The amount of coins you have can be represented by the expression $5 \times 0.05 + d \times 0.10 + q \times 0.25 = \$2.30$, where d is the number of dimes and q is the number of quarters. You also know that $5 + d + q = 15$.

Reasoning	Guess	Check
Choose 2 values for *d* and *q*.	$d = 5,$ $q = 5$	$5 \times 0.05 + 5$ $\times 0.10 + 5 \times 0.25 = 2$ $\neq 2.30$ ✗
Too low. Increase the number of quarters and decrease the number of dimes.	$d = 4,$ $q = 6$	$5 \times 0.05 + 4$ $+ 6 \times 0.25 = 2.15 \neq 2.30$ ✗
Too low. Increase the number of quarters and decrease the number of dimes.	$d = 3,$ $q = 7$	$5 \times 0.05 + 3$ $\times 0.10 + 7 \times 0.25 = 2.30$ ✓

You have 3 dimes and 7 quarters.

26.

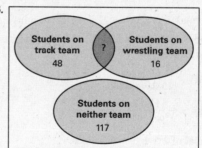

$117 + 48 + 16 - x = 171$

$181 - x = 171$

$181 - 10 \overset{?}{=} 171$

$171 = 171$

10 students are on both teams.

27. Make a table listing possible combinations. There will be a total of 14 one minute breaks so add 14 minutes to the total of each combination.

3 min acts	5 min acts	Total minutes
1	14	$3(1) + 5(14) + 14 = 87$
2	13	$3(2) + 5(13) + 14 = 85$
3	12	$3(3) + 5(12) + 14 = 83$
4	11	$3(4) + 5(11) + 14 = 81$
5	10	$3(5) + 5(10) + 14 = 79$

Chapter 1, *continued*

There are five 3 minute acts.

28.

Reasoning	*Guess*	*Check*
Pick a number close to what the perimeter divided by 4 sides is.	$28 \div 4 = 7$	$A = \ell w$ $= 7 \cdot 7$ $= 49$ ✓
Try more values to make sure the area is less than 49 square feet.	$28 = 2 \cdot 6 + 2 \cdot 8$	$A = \ell w$ $= 6 \cdot 8$ $= 48$ ✗
Try again.	$28 = 2 \cdot 9 + 2 \cdot 5$	$A = \ell w$ $= 9 \cdot 5$ $= 45$ ✗

The largest area for the garden is when the length and width are both 7 yards long. This is when the figure is a square. This results in an area of 49 square yards.

29.

Reasoning	*Guess*	*Check*
The product is too low. Try again.	$10 - 5 = 5s$	$10 \cdot 5 = 50$
The product is too high. Try again.	$15 - 10 = 5$	$15 \cdot 10 = 150$
The correct difference and product.	$13 - 8 = 5$	$13 \cdot 8 = 104$

The two numbers are 8 and 13.

30. Look for a pattern in the attendance from year to year. Then use the pattern to predict the 2005 attendance. The attendance increased from 2000 to 2002 and then started to decrease. The attendance decreased by about 200,000 from 2003 to 2004. So, the 2005 attendance will be 200,000 less than the 2004 attendance, which is about 1,698,077.

31. Distance from John's house to school: $1.2 + 0.6 = 1.8$ mi
Distance from school to post office: $2 \cdot 1.8 = 3.6$ mi
Distance from John's house to post office:
$1.8 + 3.6 = 5.4$ mi

John's house is 5.4 miles from the post office.

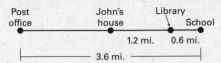

Distance from John's house to post office:
$3.6 - (1.2 + 0.6) = 3.6 - 1.8 = 1.8$ mi

If the post office is west of John's house, the post office is 1.8 miles from John's house.

32. Camper 1 shakes hands with campers 2, 3, 4, 5, 6, 7, 8, 9, 10, 11, and 12 for a total of 11 handshakes.

Camper 2 shakes hands with campers 3, 4, 5, 6, 7, 8, 9, 10, 11, and 12 for a total of 10 handshakes.

Camper 3 shakes hands with campers 4, 5, 6, 7, 8, 9, 10, 11, and 12 for a total of 9 handshakes.

Camper 4 shakes hands with campers 5, 6, 7, 8, 9, 10, 11, and 12 for a total of 8 handshakes.

Camper 5 shakes hands with campers 6, 7, 8, 9, 10, 11, and 12 for a total of 7 handshakes.

Camper 6 shakes hands with campers 7, 8, 9, 10, 11, and 12 for a total of 6 handshakes.

Camper 7 shakes hands with campers 8, 9, 10, 11, and 12 for a total of 5 handshakes.

Camper 8 shakes hands with campers 9, 10, 11, and 12 for a total of 4 handshakes.

Camper 9 shakes hands with campers 10, 11, and 12 for a total of 3 handshakes.

Camper 10 shakes hands with campers 11 and 12 for a total of 2 handshakes.

Camper 11 shakes hands with camper 12 for a total of 1 handshake.

$11 + 10 + 9 + 8 + 7 + 6 + 5 + 4 + 3 + 2 + 1 = 66$

There a total of 66 handshakes.

33. Solve this problem by drawing a diagram to show where each house is located.

House	1	2	3	4	5	6	7	8	9	10	11	12
Person	1		Bill			Chris						Audrey

There are 10 houses between Audrey's house and the first house. The diagram confirms where each house must be located.

Mixed Review

34. $23.2 > 23$

35. $0.5 < 5$

36. $0.1 > 0.01$

37. $1.4 < 4.1$

38. $7 + 4 \times 3 - 6 = 7 + 12 - 6 = 19 - 6 = 13$

39. $24 \div (2 \times 4) - 3 = 24 \div 8 - 3 = 3 - 3 = 0$

40. $P = 2\ell + 2w;\ \ell = 16,\ w = 3$

$P = 2(16) + 2(3) = 32 + 6 = 38$

The perimeter of the rectangle is 38 inches.

$A = \ell w;\ \ell = 16,\ w = 3$

$A = 16(3) = 48$

The area of the rectangle is 48 square inches.

41. $P = 4s;\ s = 237$

$P = 4(237) = 948$

The perimeter of the square is 948 feet.

$A = s^2;\ s = 237$

$A = 237^2 = 56,169$

The area of the square is 56,169 square feet.

42. C;

$4 \times 10,000 + 5 \times 1000 + 7 \times 10 = 40,000 +$
$\qquad\qquad\qquad\qquad\qquad\qquad\qquad 5000 + 70$
$\qquad\qquad\qquad\qquad = 45,000 + 70$
$\qquad\qquad\qquad\qquad = 45,070$

Chapter 1, continued

1. What number plus 12 equals 21?

   $9 + 12 = 21$, so $h = 9$.

2. 22 minus what number equals 8?

   $22 - 14 = 8$, so $y = 14$.

3. 54 equals 6 times what number?

   $54 = 6 \cdot 9$, so $x = 9$.

4. 108 divided by what number equals 9?

   $\frac{108}{12} = 9$, so $r = 9$.

5. An equation to find the number of video game rentals is $3x = 24$.

   $3x = 24$

   $3 \cdot 8 = 24$

   You can rent 8 $3 video games with $24.

6. $P = 2\ell + 2w$; $\ell = 14$, $w = 11$

   $P = 2(14) + 2(11) = 28 + 22 = 50$

   The perimeter of the rectangle is 50 feet.

   $A = \ell w$; $\ell = 14$, $w = 11$

   $A = 14(11) = 154$

   The area of the rectangle is 154 square feet.

7. $d = rt$; $r = 55$, $t = 3$

   $d = 55(3) = 165$

   Driving at 55 miles per hour for 3 hours, you will travel a total of 165 miles.

8. The expression to represent the number of minutes you need to exercise the fifth day is

   $200 - (45 + 30 + 20 + 60)$.

   $200 - (45 + 30 + 20 + 60) = 200 - 155 = 45$

   You still need 45 minutes of exercise the fifth day to reach your goal.

Brain Game (p. 43)

	Art club	Debate	Student council meeting	Tutoring
Scott	X	X	X	O
John	X	X	O	X
Annie	X	O	X	X
Rebecca	O	X	X	X

Scott is tutoring, John is at the student council meeting, Annie is at debate, and Rebecca is at art club.

Mixed Review of Problem Solving (p. 44)

1. a. Renee's total time:

   $48.5 + 22.4 = 70.9$ min

   Beth's total time:

   $47.6 + 22.8 = 70.4$ min

   Because $70.4 < 70.9$, Beth completed the two events in less time.

   b. Renee's running rate:

   $r = \frac{d}{t} = \frac{10}{48.5} \approx 0.206$ km/min

   Renee's swimming rate:

   $r = \frac{d}{t} = \frac{1000}{22.4} \approx 44.6$ m/min

   Beth's running rate:

   $r = \frac{d}{t} = \frac{10}{47.6} \approx 0.210$ km/min

   Beth's swimming rate:

   $r = \frac{d}{t} = \frac{1000}{22.8} \approx 43.9$ m/min

   Because $0.210 > 0.206$, Beth ran faster. Because $44.6 > 43.9$, Renee swam faster.

   c. Renee's biking time:

   $t = \frac{d}{r} = \frac{10}{0.46} \approx 21.7$ min

   Beth's biking time:

   $t = \frac{d}{r} = \frac{10}{0.44} \approx 22.7$ min

   Renee's total time:

   $48.5 + 22.4 + 21.7 = 92.6$ min

   Beth's total time:

   $47.6 + 22.8 + 22.7 = 93.1$ min

   Because $92.6 < 93.1$, Renee completed the three events in less time.

2. A numerical expression for the total number of pairs of sandals and shoes is $10 + 3 \cdot 10 + 10 + 10$.

   $$10 + 3 \cdot 10 + 10 + 10 = 10 + 30 + 10 + 10$$
   $$= 40 + 10 + 10$$
   $$= 50 + 10$$
   $$= 60$$

   The total number of pairs of sandals and shoes is 60.

Chapter 1, *continued*

3.

Weeks offered		
Free cake	Free pint of ice cream	Free ice cream cone
1	1	1
6	7	4
11	13	7
16	19	10
21	25	13
26	**31**	16
31	37	19
36	43	22
41	49	25
46		28
51		**31**
		34
		37
		40
		43
		46
		49
		52

By making a table that shows which weeks each deal will be offered, you can see that all three will be offered two times in one year, the first week and the 31st week.

4. Because there are 12 inches in 1 foot, use unit analysis to find how many feet are in 4 inches.

$$4 \text{ inches} \times \frac{1 \text{ foot}}{12 \text{ inches}} = \frac{4}{12} = \frac{1}{3} \text{ ft}$$

$$V = \ell wh; \ell = 60, w = 12, h = \frac{1}{3}$$

$$V = 60 \cdot 12 \cdot \frac{1}{3} = 720 \cdot \frac{1}{3} = 240 \text{ ft}^3$$

Because 1 ton of gravel covers 16 cubic feet, use unit analysis to find how many tons are in 240 cubic feet.

$$240 \text{ ft}^3 \times \frac{1 \text{ ton}}{16 \text{ ft}^3} = \frac{240}{16} = 15 \text{ tons}$$

Marcus should order 15 tons of gravel.

5. Divide the figure into three rectangles.

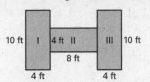

$$A_T = A_I + A_{II} + A_{III}$$
$$= \ell w + \ell w + \ell w$$
$$= 10(4) + 8(4) + 10(4)$$
$$= 40 + 32 + 40$$
$$= 72 + 40$$
$$= 112$$

The area of the figure is 112 square feet.

Another way to find the area of the figure is to divide the figure into five rectangles.

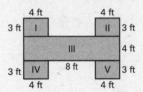

$$A_T = A_I + A_{II} + A_{III} + A_{IV} + A_V$$
$$= \ell w + \ell w + \ell w + \ell w + \ell w$$
$$= 4(3) + 4(3) + 16(4) + 4(3) + 4(3)$$
$$= 12 + 12 + 64 + 12 + 12$$
$$= 24 + 64 + 12 + 12$$
$$= 88 + 12 + 12$$
$$= 100 + 12$$
$$= 112$$

The area of the figure is 112 square feet.

6. *Sample answer:*

$$\frac{\text{Total}}{\text{cost}} = 3 \cdot \text{Cost of movie} + 3 \cdot \text{Cost of food and drinks}$$

7. $A = \ell w; A = 120, \ell = 15$

$$120 \overset{?}{=} 15 \cdot w$$

The equation to find the width is $120 = 15 \cdot w$.

$$120 = 15 \cdot w$$
$$120 \overset{?}{=} 15 \cdot 8$$
$$120 = 120$$

The width of the rectangle is 8 centimeters.

Chapter 1, continued

8. a. Possible dimensions of garden border:

15 ft by 1 ft, 14 ft by 2 ft, 13 ft by 3 ft, 12 ft by 4 ft, 11 ft by 5 ft, 10 ft by 6 ft, 9 ft by 7 ft, 8 ft by 8 ft

b. $A = \ell w; \ell = 15, w = 1$

$A = 15(1) = 15$ ft^2

$A = \ell w; \ell = 14, w = 2$

$A = 14(2) = 28$ ft^2

$A = \ell w; \ell = 13, w = 3$

$A = 13(3) = 39$ ft^2

$A = \ell w; \ell = 12, w = 4$

$A = 12(4) = 48$ ft^2

$A = \ell w; \ell = 11, w = 5$

$A = 11(5) = 55$ ft^2

$A = \ell w; \ell = 10, w = 6$

$A = 10(6) = 60$ ft^2

$A = \ell w; \ell = 9, w = 7$

$A = 9(7) = 63$ ft^2

$A = \ell w; \ell = 8, w = 8$

$A = 8(8) = 64$ ft^2

c. The 8 foot by 8 foot rectangle gives the largest area for the garden.

d. The 8 foot by 8 foot rectangle is a square. The 15 foot by 1 foot rectangle is long and narrow.

Chapter 1 Review (pp. 45–48)

1. You can graph data organized in a frequency table using a *histogram*.

2. *Area* is the amount of surface covered by a figure.

3. To evaluate an expression that has more than one operation, use the *order of operations*.

4. A power has an exponent and a *base*.

5. The 35 to 44 age group has the most volunteers and the 65 and older age group has the fewest volunteers.

6. No; the age group that includes teenagers also includes other ages.

7. $16 + 5 \times 3 + 8 = 16 + 15 + 8 = 39$

8. $40 \div [(14 + 6) \cdot 2] = 40 \div [20 \cdot 2] = 40 \div 40 = 1$

9. $10 + \dfrac{60}{31 - 26} = 10 + \dfrac{60}{5} = 10 + 12 = 22$

10. $50 + 40 \cdot 2 = 50 + 80 = 130$

The electrician charges $130 for 2 hours of work.

11–18. Evaluate expressions when $x = 4$ and $y = 9$.

11. $\dfrac{xy}{3x} = \dfrac{4(9)}{3(4)} = \dfrac{36}{12} = 3$

12. $\dfrac{y + 19}{x + 3} = \dfrac{9 + 19}{4 + 3} = \dfrac{28}{7} = 4$

13. $5y - 6x = 5(9) - 6(4) = 45 - 24 = 21$

14. $3xy - xy = 3(4)(9) - 4(9)$

$= 12(9) - 36$

$= 108 - 36$

$= 72$

15. $\dfrac{x + y}{y - x} = \dfrac{4 + 9}{9 - 4} = \dfrac{13}{5} = 2.6$

16. $\dfrac{x + y}{2xy} = \dfrac{4 + 9}{2(4)(9)} = \dfrac{13}{8(9)} = \dfrac{13}{72}$

17. $4x + 6y = 4(4) + 6(9) = 16 + 54 = 70$

18. $5xy + \dfrac{9x}{y} = 5(4)(9) + \dfrac{9(4)}{9}$

$= 20(9) + \dfrac{36}{9}$

$= 180 + 4$

$= 184$

19. $n + 12$

20. $\dfrac{1}{5}n$

21. The expression to find out how much more money you need to save is $2(28.50) - 20$.

$2(28.50) - 20 = 57 - 20 = 37$

You will still need to save $37 to be able to buy the 2 sweaters.

22. $15^2 = 15 \cdot 15 = 225$

23. $4^5 = 4 \cdot 4 \cdot 4 \cdot 4 \cdot 4 = 1024$

24. $10^4 = 10 \cdot 10 \cdot 10 \cdot 10 = 10,000$

25. $9^4 = 9 \cdot 9 \cdot 9 \cdot 9 = 6561$

26. $(5 + 4)^2 \div 3 = 9^2 \div 3 = 81 \div 3 = 27$

27. $5 \cdot (6 - 3)^5 + 45 = 5 \cdot (3)^5 + 45$

$= 5 \cdot 243 + 45$

$= 1215 + 45$

$= 1260$

28. $[10 + (4 \times 2)^3] \div 2 = [10 + 8^3] \div 2$

$= [10 + 512] \div 2$

$= 522 \div 2$

$= 261$

29. $16t^2 = 16 \cdot 3^2 = 16 \cdot 9 = 144$

The height of the building is 144 feet.

30. 7 times what number equals 56?

$7 \cdot 8 = 56$, so $b = 8$.

31. 84 divided by what number equals 12?

$\dfrac{84}{7} = 12$, so $x = 7$.

32. 98 minus what number equals 35?

$98 - 63 = 35$, so $t = 63$.

33. $t + 11 = 30; t = 29$

$29 + 11 \overset{?}{=} 30$

$40 \neq 30$

No, $t = 29$ is not a solution of the equation $t + 11 = 30$.

34. $48 \div k = 12; k = 4$

$48 \div 4 \overset{?}{=} 12$

$12 = 12$

Yes, $k = 4$ is a solution of the equation $48 \div k = 12$.

Chapter 1, *continued*

35. $8m = 68; m = 8$

$8 \cdot 8 \stackrel{?}{=} 68$

$64 \neq 68$

No, $m = 8$ is not a solution of the equation $8m = 68$.

36. Distance log has traveled $+$ Distance left to travel $=$ Total distance log travels

$40 + d = 50$

$40 + 10 \stackrel{?}{=} 50$

$50 = 50$

The log will travel 10 more feet in the remaining 5 seconds.

37. $P = 2\ell + 2w; P = 56, \ell = 12$

$56 = 2 \cdot 12 + 2w$

$56 = 24 + 2w$

$56 \stackrel{?}{=} 24 + 2 \cdot 16$

$56 \stackrel{?}{=} 24 + 32$

$56 = 56$

The width of the rectangle is 16 centimeters.

38. $A = s^2; A = 121$

$121 = s^2$

$121 = s \cdot s$

$121 \stackrel{?}{=} 11 \cdot 11$

$121 = 121$

The side length of the square is 11 feet.

39. $d = rt; r = 50, t = 3$

$d = 50(3) = 150$

A car traveling 50 miles per hour for 3 hours will go a distance of 150 miles.

40. Use unit analysis to convert ounces to teaspoons.

$36 \text{ ounces} \times \dfrac{2 \text{ teaspoons}}{8 \text{ ounces}} = \dfrac{36 \cdot 2}{8} = \dfrac{72}{8} = 9 \text{ teaspoons}$

You should add 9 teaspoons of sugar to a 36 ounce thermos of iced tea.

Chapter 1 Test (p. 49)

1. $20 + 12 \div 4 = 20 + 3 = 23$

2. $6 \times 5 - 20 \div 2 = 30 - 20 \div 2 = 30 - 10 = 20$

3. $(3 + 7) \div 5 + 10 = 10 \div 5 + 10 = 2 + 10 = 12$

4. $(2 + 3)^4 \div 5 = 5^4 \div 5 = 625 \div 5 = 125$

5. $10^2 - 3^4 + 22 = 100 - 81 + 22 = 19 + 22 = 41$

6. $(11 - 5)^4 - 300 \div 12 = 6^4 - 300 \div 12$

$= 1296 - 300 \div 12$

$= 1296 - 25$

$= 1271$

7. 17 minus what number equals 5?

$17 - 12 = 5$, so $t = 12$.

8. 9 times what number equals 72?

$9 \cdot 8 = 72$, so $n = 8$.

9. 49 divided by what number equals 7?

$49 \div 7 = 7$, so $b = 7$.

10. 21 plus what number equals 27?

$21 + 6 = 27$, so $a = 6$.

11. $z + 2 = 15; z = 13$

$13 + 2 \stackrel{?}{=} 15$

$15 = 15$

Yes, $z = 13$ is a solution of the equation $z + 2 = 15$.

12. $65 \div y = 16; y = 4$

$65 \div 4 \stackrel{?}{=} 16$

$16.25 \neq 16$

No, $y = 4$ is not a solution of the equation $65 \div y = 16$.

13. $11x = 45; x = 4$

$11 \cdot 4 \stackrel{?}{=} 45$

$44 \neq 45$

No, $x = 4$ is not a solution of the equation $11x = 45$.

14. $A = s^2; A = 64$

$64 = s^2$

$64 = s \cdot s$

$64 \stackrel{?}{=} 8 \cdot 8$

$64 = 64$

The side length of the square is 8 yards.

15. $P = 4s; P = 44$

$44 = 4s$

$44 \stackrel{?}{=} 4 \cdot 11$

$44 = 44$

The side length of the square is 11 meters.

16. $A = \ell w; \ell = 12, w = 9$

$A = 12(9) = 108$

The area of the rectangle is 108 square meters.

17. $A = \ell w; A = 128, w = 8$

$128 = \ell \cdot 8$

$128 \stackrel{?}{=} 16 \cdot 8$

$128 = 128$

The length of the rectangle is 16 inches.

18.

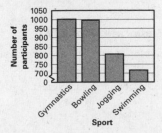

Participation in Sports in Japan

19. No, it is not possible to make a histogram because there are no intervals.

Chapter 1, *continued*

20. $25 + 55 \cdot 5 = 25 + 275 = 300$

The plumber will make $300.

21. A variable expression to represent the cost is $3x + 4y$.

$3x + 4y = 3(0.75) + 4(0.50) = 2.25 + 2.00 = 4.25$

Three apples and 4 oranges will cost $4.25.

22. $d = rt; r = 30, t = 4$

$d = 30(4) = 120$

The horse travels 120 feet in 4 seconds.

23. $A = \ell w; \ell = 32, w = 21$

$A = 32(21) = 672$

The area of the squash court is 672 square feet.

$A = \ell w; \ell = 78, w = 27$

$A = 78(27) = 2106$

The area of the tennis court is 2106 square feet.

$A = \ell w; \ell = 40, w = 20$

$A = 40(20) = 800$

The area of the racquetball court is 800 square feet. The tennis court has the largest area at 2106 square feet and the squash court has the smallest area with 672 square feet.

24. (1) Read and Understand

(2) Make a Plan: Draw a Diagram

(3) Solve the Problem:

60 ft
90 ft   90 ft
60 ft

Find the dimensions of the park in yards.

1 yard = 3 feet.

$90 \div 3 = 30$ yards

$60 \div 3 = 20$ yards

Find the area in square yards.

$A = \ell w; \ell = 30, w = 20$

$A = 30 \cdot 20 = 600$

The area of the park is 600 square yards so, 600 rolls of sod will be needed to cover the park.

(4) Look Back

Standardized Test Preparation (p. 51)

1. Partial credit; The reasoning and process are correct, but the substitution is incorrect so the answer is incorrect.

2. Full credit; The solution is complete and correct.

Standardized Test Practice (pp. 52–53)

1.

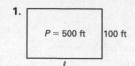

$P = 500$ ft   100 ft

ℓ

$P = 2\ell + 2w, P = 500, w = 100$

$500 = 2\ell + 2 \cdot 100$

$500 = 2\ell + 200$

You know that the two widths are 200 feet. So, subtract this amount from 500: $500 - 200 = 300$ ft. The two lengths total 300 feet. Because each length is the same, divide 300 by 2: $300 \div 2 = 150$ ft.

The field is 150 feet long.

2. Use the distance formula, $d = rt$, to find the distance Sita travels. In the formula, $r = 55$ and because 3 hours elapsed from 8:30 A.M. to 11:30 A.M., $t = 3$.

$d = rt; r = 55, t = 3$

$d = 55(3) = 165$

Sita travels 165 miles.

3. Work backwards; Because Angela used 15 tickets and has 30 tickets left, she originally had $30 + 15 = 45$ tickets. Angela took half of the tickets so there were originally $2 \cdot 45 = 90$ tickets.

4. You should collect the actual heights of the students in your class. You cannot use the same data to make a bar graph because bar graphs use data that are in categories.

5. $A = \ell w; \ell = 24, w = 15$

$A = 24(15) = 360$

The area of the floor is 360 square feet. Each box of tiles covers 20 square feet. So, divide 360 by 20 to find how many boxes are needed.

$360 \div 20 = 18$

Diego must buy 18 boxes.

6. The amount of coins you have can be represented by the expression

$n \times 0.05 + 3 \times 0.10 + q \times 0.25 = 1.15$, where n is the number of nickels and q is the number of quarters. You also know that $n + 3 + q = 12$.

Reasoning	Guess	Check
Choose 2 values for n and q.	$n = 6,$ $q = 3$	$6 \times 0.05 + 0.30 + 3$ $\times 0.25 = 1.35$
Too high. Increase the number of nickels and decrease the number of quarters.	$n = 7,$ $q = 2$	$7 \times 0.05 + 0.30 + 2$ $\times 0.25 = 1.15$

You have 7 nickels and 2 quarters.

Chapter 1, *continued*

7. Solve this problem by drawing a diagram to show how the heights compare.

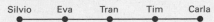

Silvio   Eva   Tran   Tim   Carla

The students in order, from tallest to shortest, are Silvio, Eva, Tran, Tim, and Carla.

8. Find how many minutes it takes to travel 1 mile. Then use unit analysis to find how long it takes to travel 4.5 miles.

$$\frac{56 \text{ min}}{7 \text{ mi}} = \frac{8 \text{ min}}{1 \text{ mi}}$$

$$4.5 \text{ mi} \times \frac{8 \text{ min}}{1 \text{ mi}} = 36 \text{ min}$$

It takes 36 minutes to travel 4.5 miles.

9. The total amount Jason is paid is the number of hours Jason worked times his pay rate.

Total pay = Hours worked $\cdot$ Pay rate

$$52 = h \cdot 8$$
$$52 \overset{?}{=} 6.5 \cdot 8$$
$$52 = 52$$

Jason worked 6.5 hours.

10. Convert 45 feet to yards by using the fact that there are 3 feet in 1 yard.

$$45 \text{ feet} \times \frac{1 \text{ yard}}{3 \text{ feet}} = \frac{45}{3} = 15 \text{ yards}$$

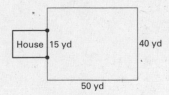

House | 15 yd   40 yd

50 yd

$$P = 2\ell + 2w; \ell = 50, w = 40$$
$$P = 2(50) + 2(40) = 100 + 80 = 180$$

Because 15 yards is taken up by the house, subtract 15 from 180.

$$180 - 15 = 165$$

You need 165 yards of fencing to fence in the yard.

11. (1) Read and Understand

(2) Make a Plan: Break into Parts

(3) Solve the Problem:

The amount of money you earn is $6 (2 \times 4) = 6(8)$
$$= \$48.$$

The amount of money you spend at the movies is

$$7 + 4 \times 2 = 7 + 8 = \$15.$$

The amount of money you have left is

$$48 - 15 = \$33.$$

(4) Look Back

12.

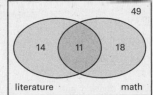

$$49 + 14 + 11 + 18 = 92$$

There are 92 students in Lezlie's grade.

13. Divide the area of the rectangle by the width to find the length of the rectangle.

$$A = \ell w \rightarrow \frac{A}{w} = \ell; A = 27, w = 3$$

$$\frac{A}{w} = \ell$$

$$\frac{27}{3} = \ell$$

$$9 = \ell$$

The length of the rectangle is 9 meters.

14. Time it takes to read = Number of pages ÷ Reading rate

Tomo's time: $420 \div 12 = 35$ hours

Umi's time: $420 \div 14 = 30$ hours

Subtract Umi's time from Tomo's time to find how much longer it takes Tomo to read a book.

$$35 - 30 = 5$$

It will take Tomo 5 hours longer to read a book that is 420 pages long.

15. $(8 + 5) \cdot 3 - 2 = 13 \cdot 3 - 2 = 39 - 2 = 37$

$(8 + 5) \cdot (3 - 2) = 13 \cdot 1 = 13$

16. B; $60 - 40 = 20$

There are 20 more mums than tulips in the garden.

17. A; $8x - 4y = 8(4) - 4(6) = 32 - 24 = 8$

18. $2 \cdot 6 - 10 \div 2 = 12 - 5 = 7$

19. $(6 - 2)^2 - 8 + 3^3 = 4^2 - 8 + 3^3$
$$= 16 - 8 + 27$$
$$= 8 + 27$$
$$= 35$$

20. $t = \frac{d}{r}; d = 275, r = 50$

$$t = \frac{275}{50} = 5.5$$

It will take Nikki 5.5 hours to travel 275 miles.

21. You will need to buy 8 of the packages of 8. This will cost $8 \cdot 10 = \$80$.

You will need to buy 4 of the packages of 15. This will cost $4 \cdot 16.50 = \$66$.

$$\$80 - \$66 = \$14$$

You will save $14 if you buy packages of 15 instead of packages of 8.

Chapter 1, continued

22. Amount saved each week:

    $40 - (25 + 8) = 40 - 33 = \$7$

    After 5 weeks, Sheila saved $5 \cdot 7 = \$35$.

23. Total gas used $= \dfrac{\text{Number of city miles}}{\text{City gas mileage}}$

    $+ \dfrac{\text{Number of highway miles}}{\text{Highway gas mileage}}$

    $= \dfrac{c}{15} + \dfrac{h}{24}$

    There is a total of $75 + 30 = 105$ miles driven in city traffic. Because 30 miles of the 350 mile trip is in city traffic, you know $350 - 30 = 320$ miles of the trip is on the highway.

    $\dfrac{c}{15} + \dfrac{h}{24} = \dfrac{105}{15} + \dfrac{320}{24} = 7 + 13\dfrac{1}{3} = 20\dfrac{1}{3}$

    Bud will need $20\dfrac{1}{3}$ gallons of gas. Because $20\dfrac{1}{3} > 20$, Bud should not expect to reach his uncle's house without buying gas.

24. a.

Interval	Tally	Frequency
0–1	IIII	4
2–3	IIII IIII I	11
4–5	IIII	4
6–7	IIII	4

    b. **Computer Use at Home**

    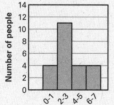

    c. $11 + 4 + 4 = 19$

    There are 19 people who use a computer more than once a week.

    The frequency table is more helpful because it gives exact numbers of people who use a computer, whereas you have to estimate the number from the histogram.

25. Solve the problem by using a table.

	White	Green	Yellow	Red
Ahmad	Yes	No	No	No
Betty	No	Yes	No	No
Cory	No	No	Yes	No
Deb	No	No	No	Yes

    Ahmad lives in the white house, Betty lives in the green house, Cory lives in the yellow house, and Deb lives in the red house.

Chapter 2

Chapter Get-Ready Games (pp. 54–55)

Answers will vary.

Stop and Think (p. 55)

1. You can get 4 answers in a row on your card 10 ways, as represented below with dotted lines.

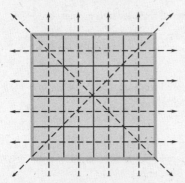

2. Each row and column must have at least one square that is not marked. So, up to 12 squares can be marked without winning.

Sample art:

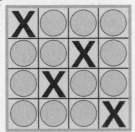

Unmarked squares are indicated with an "X".

Review Prerequisite Skills (p. 56)

1. A symbol that represents one or more numbers is called a *variable*.

2. The measure of the surface enclosed by a figure in a plane is its *area*.

3. The digit to the right of the 0 in the ones' place is the 6 in the tenths' place. Because 6 is greater than 5, round up. So, 10.61 rounded to the nearest whole number is 11.

4. The digit to the right of the 4 in the ones' place is the 7 in the tenths' place. Because 7 is greater than 5, round up. So, 134.7 rounded to the nearest whole number is 135.

5. The digit to the right of the 0 in the ones' place is the 2 in the tenths' place. Because 2 is less than 5, round down. So, 0.25 rounded to the nearest whole number is 0.

6. The digit to the right of the 2 in the ones' place is the 8 in the tenths' place. Because 8 is greater than 5, round up. So, 12.86 rounded to the nearest whole number is 13.

7. $32 - 27 + 14 = 5 + 14 = 19$

8. $4 \cdot 12 \div 6 = 48 \div 6 = 8$

9. $6 + 34 \div 2 = 6 + 17 = 23$

10. When $s = 4$ and $t = 16$:

$(t - 9) + s = (16 - 9) + 4 = 7 + 4 = 11$

11. When $s = 4$ and $t = 16$:

$s(t - 5) = 4(16 - 5) = 4(11) = 44$

12. When $t = 16$:

$\frac{1}{4}t - 4 = \frac{1}{4} \cdot 16 - 4 = 4 - 4 = 0$

13. $3x = 39$

3 times what number equals 39?

$3(13) = 39$, so $x = 13$.

14. $x - 6 = 12$

What number minus 6 equals 12?

$18 - 6 = 12$, so $x = 18$.

15. $x + 13 = 17$

What number plus 13 equals 17?

$4 + 13 = 17$, so $x = 4$.

Lesson 2.1

2.1 Guided Practice (pp. 57–58)

1.

The integers ordered from least to greatest are -7, -2, -1, 0, and 2.

2.

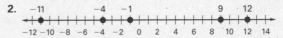

The integers ordered from least to greatest are -11, -4, -1, 9, and 12.

3.

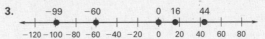

The integers ordered from least to greatest are -99, -60, 0, 16, and 44.

4. $|-16| = 16$

The opposite of -16 is 16.

5. $|140| = 140$

The opposite of 140 is -140.

6. $|-1| = 1$

The opposite of -1 is 1.

7. $|0| = 0$

The opposite of 0 is 0.

2.1 Exercises (pp. 59–61)

Skill Practice

1. The *absolute value* of a number is its distance from zero on a number line.

2. Two integers are *opposites* if their sum is 0.

3. $4 > -6$

4. $-12 < 1$

5. $-9 < -2$

6. $0 > -5$

7. $5 > -5$

8. $-17 < 2$

9. $34 > -29$

10. $-20 < -14$

Chapter 2, continued

11.

The integers ordered from least to greatest are -20, -10, 5, 13, 15, and 27.

12.

The integers ordered from least to greatest are -130, -56, 0, 62, 74, and 120.

13.

The integers ordered from least to greatest are -20, -12, 18, 44, 59, and 64.

14.

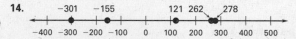

The integers ordered from least to greatest are -301, -155, 121, 262, and 278.

15. C;

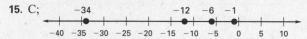

The integers ordered from least to greatest are -34, -12, -6, and -1.

16. Both -2 and -9 were ordered incorrectly because they are less than 0. The integers ordered from least to greatest are -9, -2, 0, 1, 3, and 5.

17. $|19| = 19$

The opposite of 19 is -19.

18. $|-8| = 8$

The opposite of -8 is 8.

19. $|-740| = 740$

The opposite of -740 is 740.

20. $|1327| = 1327$

The opposite of 1327 is -1327.

21. B   **22.** C   **23.** D   **24.** A

25. $|-32| = 32$ **26.** $-|9| = -9$

27. $-|29| = -29$ **28.** $-(-5) = 5$

29. $-(-81) = 81$ **30.** $-|-17| = -17$

31. $-|-3| = -3$ **32.** $-(-(-4)) = -(4) = -4$

33. $|4| = 4$ **34.** $|-6| = 6$
$|-4| = 4$ $-|6| = -6$
So, $|4| = |-4|$.   So, $|-6| > -|6|$.

35. $-|-9| = -9$ **36.** $|-2| = 2$
$-(-9) = 9$ $-(-2) = 2$
So, $-|-9| < -(-9)$.   So, $|-2| = -(-2)$.

37. $-(-73) = 73$ \hfill $|95| = 95$
$|-65| = 65$ \hfill $-|47| = -47$

The numbers ordered from least to greatest are $-|47|$, -28, $|-65|$, $-(-73)$, and $|95|$.

38. $|-19| = 19$ \hfill $-(-56) = 56$
$-|12| = -12$ \hfill $-|-58| = -58$

The numbers ordered from least to greatest are -74, $-|-58|$, $-|12|$, $|-19|$, and $-(-56)$.

39. $-|6| = -6$ \hfill $|-1| = 1$
$-(-5) = 5$

The numbers ordered from least to greatest are -14, -8, $-|6|$, $|-1|$, and $-(-5)$.

40. $|38| = 38$ \hfill $-(-29) = 29$
$-|-42| = -42$ \hfill $|-49| = 49$

The numbers ordered from least to greatest are $-|-42|$, -37, $-(-29)$, $|38|$, and $|-49|$.

41. The absolute value of a number x is *always* greater than or equal to x.

Sample answer:

When $x < 0$: $|x| > 0$, so $|x| > x$.

When $x \geq 0$: $|x| = x$

42. The opposite of a number y is *sometimes* greater than or equal to y.

Sample answer:

When $y < 0$: $-y > 0$, so $-y > y$.

When $y = 0$: $-y = y$

When $y > 0$: $-y < 0$, so $-y < y$.

43. The absolute value of a number z is *never* less than the opposite of z.

Sample answer:

When $z \leq 0$: $|z| = -z$

When $z > 0$: $|z| > -z$

Problem Solving

44.

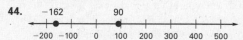

Because $-162 < 90$, Gieselmann Lake is at a lower elevation than Silver Lake.

45.

The lake elevations ordered from least to greatest are -162 (Gieselmann Lake), -30 (Jones Lake), 0 (Craigs Pond), 90 (Silver Lake), and 445 (Seneca Lake).

46. Negative numbers and zero have opposites that are the same as their absolute values. Positive numbers have opposites that are different from their absolute values.

Sample answer: Opposite of $-4 = 4$, $|-4| = 4$;

Opposite of $0 = 0$, $|0| = 0$;

Opposite of $2 = -2$, $|2| = 2$

Chapter 2, *continued*

47. A; Elevation below sea level is expressed as a negative number. So, the elevation is -7725 meters.

48.

T − 2 hours 55 minutes	Flight crew departs for launch pad.
T − 5 minutes	Pilot starts auxiliary power units.
T − 6 seconds	Main engine starts.
T − 0	Liftoff.
T + 7 seconds	Shuttle clears launch tower, and control switches to the Mission Control Center.

49. *A* is $\dfrac{|-11| + |5|}{2} = \dfrac{11 + 5}{2} = \dfrac{16}{2} = 8$ units from both -11 and 5.

So, *A* is $-11 + 8 = -3$ on the number line.

B is $\dfrac{|-3| + |3|}{2} = \dfrac{3 + 3}{2} = \dfrac{6}{2} = 3$ units from both -3 and 3.

So, *B* is $-3 + 3 = 0$ on the number line.

50. *Sample answer:* The absolute value of every number *x* is nonnegative. So, no value of *x* makes $|x| = -8$ true.

51. If $a \geq 0$ and $b > 0$, or $a \leq 0$ and $b > 0$, then $a < b$.
If $a \leq 0$ and $b < 0$, or $a \geq 0$ and $b < 0$, then $a > b$.

52. a. The 1st and 4th quarters showed gains.

1st quarter gains: $30,000

4th quarter gains: $50,000

b. The 2nd and 3rd quarters showed losses.

2nd quarter losses: $-$20,000

3rd quarter losses: $-$50,000

c. The gains and losses did not balance. The company made a profit for the year.

Sample answer: Gains: $30,000 + $50,000 = $80,000
Losses: $-$20,000 + ($-$50,000) = $-$70,000

The gains and losses do not balance because $|80,000| > |-70,000|$, so the company made a profit for the year.

53. $|-78| = 78$ $\qquad$ $|-65| = 65$
$-(-100) = 100$

The substances ordered from lowest boiling point to highest boiling point are $|-65|$ (Methanol), $|-78|$ (Ethanol), 97 (Propanol), and $-(-100)$ (Water).

You will expect water to be left at the end of the heating because it has the highest boiling point.

54.

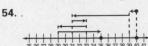

The price at the beginning of the 5 month period was $40.

55. When $a = 8$:
$a + 6 = 8 + 6 = 14$

56. When $b = 2$:
$b + 15 = 2 + 15 = 17$

57. When $a = 8$ and $b = 2$:
$5 + a + b = 5 + 8 + 2 = 13 + 2 = 15$

58. Pages to be read in 5 days $= 238 - 68 = 170$.
Pages to be read each day $= 170 \div 5 = 34$.
Patty needs to read 34 pages each day.

59. C; You need to add the amount you have to the amount you will earn.
$118 + 3(10) = 118 + 30 = 148

Lesson 2.2

Investigation (p. 62)

1. $4 + (-5)$;
$4 + (-5) = -1$

2. $-3 + (-6)$;
$-3 + (-6) = -9$

3.
$-7 + (-14) = -21$

4.
$20 + (-25) = -5$

5.
$-10 + 15 = 5$

6.
$-7 + (-33) = -40$

7.
$11 + (-13) = -2$

8.
$-23 + 5 = -18$

9.

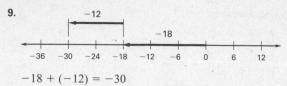

$-18 + (-12) = -30$

10.

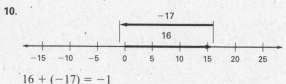

$16 + (-17) = -1$

11. The sign of the sum of two negative integers is negative.

Sample answer: You move to the left of 0 on the number line for both numbers, so the sum is negative.

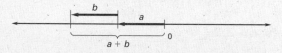

12. *Sample answer:* To predict the sign of the sum of a positive and a negative integer, compare the absolute values of the integers. If the absolute value of the positive integer is greater than the absolute value of the negative integer, then the sum is positive. If the absolute value of the negative integer is greater than the absolute value of the positive integer, then the sum is negative.

13. *Sample answer:* On a number line, move 25 units right, then 13 units left, then 5 units right, then 20 units left.

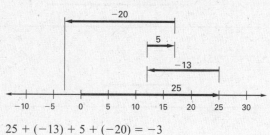

$25 + (-13) + 5 + (-20) = -3$

2.2 Guided Practice (pp. 63–65)

1.

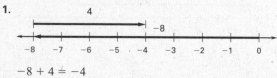

$-8 + 4 = -4$

2.

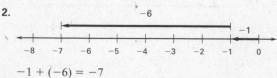

$-1 + (-6) = -7$

3. $-20 + (-15) = -35$

4. $18 + 0 + (-54) = 18 + (-54)$ Identity Property of Addition

$\qquad\qquad\qquad = -36$

5. $300 + 111 + (-44) + (-256)$

$= 411 + (-44) + (-256) = 367 + (-256) = 111$

6. $-230 + (-512) + 178 + 94$

$= -742 + 178 + 94 = -564 + 94 = -470$

7. First, add the positive integers. Then add the negative integers.

$825 + 625 + 36 + (-16) + (-100) + (-500)$

$= 1486 + (-616) = 870$

Your class raised $870.

2.2 Exercises (pp. 65–67)

Skill Practice

1. To add two integers with the same sign, add the *absolute values* and use the common sign.

2.

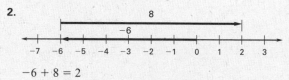

$-6 + 8 = 2$

3.

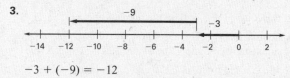

$-3 + (-9) = -12$

4.

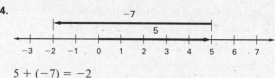

$5 + (-7) = -2$

5.

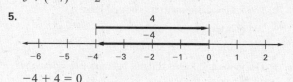

$-4 + 4 = 0$

6.

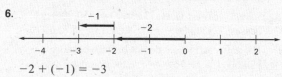

$-2 + (-1) = -3$

7.

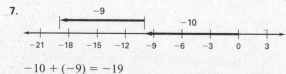

$-10 + (-9) = -19$

8.

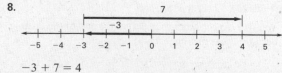

$-3 + 7 = 4$

9.

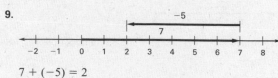

$7 + (-5) = 2$

Chapter 2, *continued*

10. The absolute value of 5 was added to the absolute value of −8 instead of being subtracted. The sign of the number with the greater absolute value is used.

    $-8 + 5 = -3$

11. B; $-8 + 3 = -5$

12. $42 + (-23) = 19$

13. $-63 + (-49) = -112$

14. $-93 + (-16) = -109$

15. $25 + (-25) = 0$ Inverse Property of Addition

16. $0 + (-82) = -82$ Identity Property of Addition

17. $98 + (-128) = -30$

18. $-9 + 9 + (-14) = 0 + (-14)$ Inverse Property
     of Addition

     $= -14$ Identity Property
     of Addition

19. $-12 + 9 + (-5) = -3 + (-5) = -8$

20. $20 + (-15) + (-22) = 5 + (-22) = -17$

21. $-12 + (-25) + 8 = -37 + 8 = -29$

22. $-21 + (-15) + (-25) = -36 + (-25) = -61$

23. $-17 + 8 + 16 = -9 + 16 = 7$

24. When $a = -13$ and $b = 24$:

    $a + b = -13 + 24 = 11$

25. When $b = 24$ and $c = -27$:

    $b + c = 24 + (-27) = -3$

26. When $b = 24$ and $c = -27$:

    $-b + c = -24 + (-27) = -51$

27. When $a = -13$ and $b = 24$:

    $a + (-b) = -13 + (-24) = -37$

28. When $a = -13$ and $c = -27$:

    $a + |c| = -13 + |-27| = -13 + 27 = 14$

29. When $a = -13$ and $b = 24$:

    $b + |a| = 24 + |-13| = 24 + 13 = 37$

30. When $a = -13$ and $c = -27$:

    $|a| + |c| = |-13| + |-27| = 13 + 27 = 40$

31. When $b = 24$ and $c = -27$:

    $|c| + |b| = |-27| + |24| = 27 + 24 = 51$

32. When $x = 806$:

    $x + (-478) = 806 + (-478) = 328$

33. When $x = -729$:

    $x + (-478) = -729 + (-478) = -1207$

34. When $x = |-349|$:

    $x + (-478) = |-349| + (-478)$

    $= 349 + (-478)$

    $= -129$

35. When $x = -|-521|$:

    $x + (-478) = -|-521| + (-478)$

    $= -521 + (-478)$

    $= -999$

36. *Sample answer:* The sum of -27 and -1 is -28.

    The sum of -30 and 2 is -28.

37. The sum of two negative integers is *always* negative because the sum will have the common sign, which is negative.

38. The sum of two positive integers is *never* negative because the sum will have the common sign, which is positive.

39. The sum of a positive integer and a negative integer is *sometimes* negative. It is negative when the integer with the greater absolute value is negative.

40. The sum of a negative integer and 0 is *always* negative because the sum is the negative integer by the Identity Property of Addition.

41. -92 plus what number equals 102?

    $-92 + 194 = 102$, so $k = 194$.

42. -6 equals what number plus -7?

    $-6 = 1 + (-7)$, so $x = 1$.

43. -9 equals 5 plus what number?

    $-9 = 5 + (-14)$, so $j = -14$.

44. -81 plus what number equals -90?

    $-81 + (-9) = -90$, so $b = -9$.

45. The absolute values of what numbers plus -13 equals 29?

    $|42| + (-13) = 29$ and $|-42| + (-13) = 29$, so $x = \pm 42$.

46. The absolute values of what numbers plus -45 equals -12?

    $|33| + (-45) = -12$ and $|-33| + (-45) = -12$, so $x = \pm 33$.

47. -123 plus the absolute values of what numbers equals -98?

    $-123 + |25| = -98$ and $-123 + |-25| = -98$, so $x = \pm 25$.

Problem Solving

48. $11 + (-10) = 1$

    The sum of the charges is $+1$.

49. $17 + (-17) = 0$

    The sum of the charges is 0.

50. $8 + (-10) = -2$

    The sum of the charges is -2.

51. $15 + (-12) = 3$

    The sum of the charges is $+3$.

52. $6 + 3 + (-5) = 9 + (-5) = 4$

    You exited on the 4th floor.

53. B; $25 + (-30) + 35 = -5 + 35 = 30$

    The sum of the transactions is $30.

54. *Sample answer:* You choose the sign of your answer to be the same as the sign of the number with the greater absolute value.

Chapter 2, *continued*

55. a. $-200 + 1100 = 900$

The classic Mexican period ended in about 900.

b. $-500 + 200 = -300$

The classic Greek period ended in about 300 B.C.

c. $-300 + x = 900$

-300 plus what number equals 900?

$-300 + 1200 = 900$, so $x = 1200$.

So, the classic Mexican period ended about 1200 years after the classic Greek period ended.

56. Yards gained after 3 plays: $7 + (-9) + 6 = -2 + 6 = 4$

The team gained 4 yards after 3 downs, but needs 10 yards after 4 downs. Because $4 + 6 = 10$, the team must gain 6 yards on the fourth play to get a first down.

57. First 8 holes:

$-2 + (-1) + 0 + 0 + 1 + 1 + 1 + 2 = -3 + 5 = 2$

So, Jill's score for the first 8 holes is *above par*. Because $2 + (-2) = 0$, Jill needs a score of -2 on the ninth hole to be at par for the first 9 holes.

58. If x and y are both positive, then $|x| = x$ and $|y| = y$.

$|x + y| = ||x| + |y|| = |x| + |y|$

If x and y are both negative, then $|x| = -x$ and $|y| = -y$.

$$|x + y| = |-(-x + (-y))|$$
$$= |-(|x| + |y|)|$$
$$= |x| + |y|$$

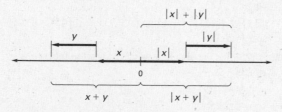

If x is positive and y is negative, then $|x + y| \neq |x| + |y|$.

Sample answer: Let $x = 2$ and $y = -3$.

Then $|2 + (-3)| = |-1| = 1$

and $|2| + |-3| = 2 + 3 = 5$.

Mixed Review

59. The opposite of 34 is -34.

60. The opposite of 187 is -187.

61. The opposite of -2321 is 2321.

62. The opposite of -4650 is 4650.

63.

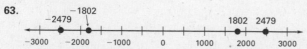

The integers ordered from least to greatest are -2479, -1802, 1802, and 2479.

64.

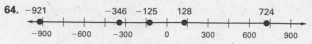

The integers ordered from least to greatest are -921, -346, -125, 128, and 724.

65. C; Multiply and divide first from left to right, then add and subtract from left to right. So, the order is $\times, \div, +, -$.

Lesson 2.3

Activity (p. 68)

1–2.

Subtraction Problem	Difference	Addition Problem
$3 - 3$	0	$3 + (-3)$
$3 - 2$	1	$3 + (-2)$
$3 - 1$	2	$3 + (-1)$
$3 - 0$	3	$3 + 0$
$3 - (-1)$	4	$3 + 1$
$3 - (-2)$	5	$3 + 2$
$3 - (-3)$	6	$3 + 3$

3. The second number in the addition problems is the opposite of the second number in the subtraction problems.

4. *Sample answer:* Two subtract two integers, add the opposite of the second integer to the first integer.

2.3 Guided Practice (p. 69)

1. $15 - 41 = 15 + (-41) = -26$

2. $-16 - 8 = -16 + (-8) = -24$

3. When $a = 8$ and $b = -15$:

$$a - b - (-6) = 8 - (-15) - (-6)$$
$$= 8 + 15 + 6$$
$$= 23 + 6$$
$$= 29$$

4. Difference in elevation $= 4 - (-30) = 4 + 30 = 34$

The difference in elevation is 34 feet.

2.3 Exercises (pp. 70–72)

Skill Practice

1. $-2 - 6$

2. $-5 - (-3)$

3. $5 - 12 = 5 + (-12) = -7$

4. $6 - (-16) = 6 + 16 = 22$

5. $-11 - (-7) = -11 + 7 = -4$

6. $-13 - 12 = -13 + (-12) = -25$

7. $-14 - (-14) = -14 + 14 = 0$

8. $11 - (-6) = 11 + 6 = 17$

9. $9 - 17 = 9 + (-17) = -8$

10. $-18 - (-12) = -18 + 12 = -6$

11. $-20 - 7 = -20 + (-7) = -27$

12. $32 - 40 = 32 + (-40) = -8$

13. $28 - (-16) = 28 + 16 = 44$

14. $-39 - (-13) = -39 + 13 = -26$

15. $-5 - (-5) - (-5) = -5 + 5 + 5 = 0 + 5 = 5$

16. $8 - 2 - 6 - 10 = 8 + (-2) + (-6) + (-10)$
$$= 6 + (-6) + (-10)$$
$$= 0 + (-10)$$
$$= -10$$

17. $-52 - (-18) - 37 = -52 + 18 + (-37)$
$$= -34 + (-37)$$
$$= -71$$

18. The calculation did not perform subtraction by adding the opposite.
$$-12 - 5 = -12 + (-5) = -17$$

19. When $a = -9$:
$$a - 6 = -9 - 6 = -9 + (-6) = -15$$

20. When $b = 18$ and $c = -4$:
$$b - c = 18 - (-4) = 18 + 4 = 22$$

21. When $a = -9$ and $c = -4$:
$$a - c = -9 - (-4) = -9 + 4 = -5$$

22. When $a = -9$ and $b = 18$:
$$14 - a - b = 14 - (-9) - 18$$
$$= 14 + 9 + (-18)$$
$$= 23 + (-18)$$
$$= 5$$

23. When $a = -9$, $b = 18$, and $c = -4$:
$$a - b - c = -9 - 18 - (-4)$$
$$= -9 + (-18) + 4$$
$$= -27 + 4$$
$$= -23$$

24. When $a = -9$, $b = 18$, and $c = -4$:
$$c - a - b = -4 - (-9) - 18$$
$$= -4 + 9 + (-18)$$
$$= 5 + (-18)$$
$$= -13$$

25. When $a = -9$, $b = 18$, and $c = -4$:
$$a + b - c = -9 + 18 - (-4)$$
$$= -9 + 18 + 4$$
$$= 9 + 4$$
$$= 13$$

26. When $a = -9$, $b = 18$, and $c = -4$:
$$c - a + b = -4 - (-9) + 18$$
$$= -4 + 9 + 18$$
$$= 5 + 18$$
$$= 23$$

27. C; When $a = 5$, $b = -9$, and $c = 3$.
$$-c + 2a - b = -3 + 2(5) - (-9)$$
$$= -3 + 10 + 9$$
$$= 7 + 9$$
$$= 16$$

28. 35 minus what number equals 45?
$$35 - (-10) = 35 + 10 = 45, \text{ so } x = -10.$$

29. -32 minus what number equals -37?
$$-32 - 5 = -32 + (-5) = -37, \text{ so } x = 5.$$

30. -49 equals 50 minus what number?
$$50 - 99 = 50 + (-99) = -49, \text{ so } x = 99.$$

31. What number minus 11 equals -3?
$$8 - 11 = 8 + (-11) = -3, \text{ so } x = 8.$$

32. -56 equals what number minus 52?
$$-4 - 52 = -4 + (-52) = -56, \text{ so } x = -4.$$

33. -36 equals what number minus 24?
$$-12 - 24 = -12 + (-24) = -36, \text{ so } x = -12.$$

34. 16 equals 12 minus what number?
$$12 - (-4) = 12 + 4 = 16, \text{ so } x = -4.$$

35. 64 minus what number equals -37?
$$64 - 101 = 64 + (-101) = -37, \text{ so } x = 101.$$

36. *Sample answer:* The difference of 1 and 10 is -9.
The difference of -8 and 1 is -9.

37. The expressions $x - y$ and $y - x$ are always opposites.
Sample answer: The distance between two numbers is the same regardless of the order in which you subtract them. However, the difference is positive if you start with the greater number and negative if you start with the lesser number. So, $x - y$ and $y - x$ are always opposites. The opposite of $(x - y)$ is $-(x - y) = -x + y = y - x$.

38. A positive number minus a negative number is *never* negative.
Sample answer: If x and y are positive, the expression $x - (-y)$ is a positive number minus a negative number. Because $x - (-y) = x + y$ is the sum of two positive numbers, the answer must be positive.

39. A negative number minus a negative number is *sometimes* positive.
Sample answer: $-5 - (-3) = -5 + 3 = -2$,
$-5 - (-7) = -5 + 7 = 2$

Problem Solving

40. **a.** The bird's elevation is greater than the boat's elevation.
The boat's elevation is greater than the reef's elevation.
The bird's elevation is greater than the reef's elevation.

b. $55 - 0 = 55$ feet
$0 - (-35) = 0 + 35 = 35$ feet
$55 - (-35) = 55 + 35 = 90$ feet

c. The bird is 55 feet above the boat. The boat is 35 feet above the reef. The bird is 90 feet above the reef.

Chapter 2, continued

41. Total score $= -400 - 600 = -400 + (-600) = -1000$

42. Total score $= -400 + 600 = 200$

43. D; $32 - (-660) = 32 + 660 = 692$

   The whale travels a vertical distance of 692 feet.

44. To find the distance between 123 and -137, subtract -137 from 123. This gives you $123 - (-137) = 123 + 137 = 260$, which is the distance between 123 and 0 added to the distance between -137 and 0.

45. Difference in temperatures

   $= -37 - (-80) = -37 + 80 = 43$

   Alaska's coldest temperature is 43°F colder than Kentucky's coldest temperature.

46. Difference in temperatures

   $= -19 - (-61) = -19 + 61 = 42$

   Colorado's coldest temperature is 42°F colder than Mississippi's coldest temperature.

47. Alaska and Mississippi have the greatest difference in coldest temperatures because Alaska is the coldest and Mississippi is the warmest. The difference between Alaska and Mississippi is $-80 - (-19) = -80 + 19 = -61$.

   Difference between Alaska and Colorado

   $= -61 - (-80) = -61 + 80 = 19$

   Difference between Colorado and Kentucky

   $= -37 - (-61) = -37 + 61 = 24$

   Difference between Kentucky and Mississippi

   $= -19 - (-37) = -19 + 37 = 18$

   Kentucky and Mississippi have the least difference in coldest temperatures.

48. *Sample answer:* You add an integer's opposite when you are subtracting integers, so you can use the established rules for adding integers.

49. Length of Jurassic Period:

   $-144 - (-208) = -144 + 208 = 64$

   The Jurassic Period lasted 64 million years.

   Length of all periods:

   $-65 - (-251) = -65 + 251 = 186$

   So, the Jurassic Period lasted $\frac{64}{186}$, or about $\frac{1}{3}$ of the three periods.

50. $265 - 136 = 265 + (-136) = 129$

   The difference between the high temperatures is 129°F.

51. $-129 - (-170) = -129 + 170 = 41$

   The difference between the low temperatures is 41°F.

52. Range of temperatures on Moon:

   $265 - (-170) = 265 + 170 = 435°F$

   Range of temperatures on Earth:

   $136 - (-129) = 136 + 129 = 265°F$

   The range of temperatures on the Moon is $435 - 265 = 435 + (-265) = 170°F$ greater than the range of temperatures on Earth.

Sample answer: Because there is no atmosphere on the moon, the high temperatures are higher and the low temperatures are lower, causing a greater range in temperatures.

53.
$$150 - 47 - 63 - x = -23$$
$$150 + (-47) + (-63) - x = -23$$
$$103 + (-63) - x = -23$$
$$40 - x = -23$$

Use mental math: 40 minus what number is -23?

$40 - 63 = 40 + (-63) = -23$, so $x = 63$.

The amount of the third check was $63.

Mixed Review

54. $5^3 + (21 \cdot 7) - 6 = 5^3 + 147 - 6$
$$= 125 + 147 - 6$$
$$= 272 - 6$$
$$= 266$$

55. $6^2 \cdot (4 - 2) \div 18 = 6^2 \cdot 2 \div 18$
$$= 36 \cdot 2 \div 18$$
$$= 72 \div 18$$
$$= 4$$

56. $(12 - 4) \cdot (9 - 1)^2 = 8 \cdot 8^2 = 8 \cdot 64 = 512$

57. What number plus 5 equals 13?

   $8 + 5 = 13$, so $v = 8$.

58. 7 times what number equals 42?

   $7(6) = 42$, so $w = 6$.

59. 12 minus what number equals 9?

   $12 - 3 = 9$, so $x = 3$.

60. C;

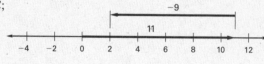

   $11 + (-9) = 2$

Lesson 2.4

2.4 Guided Practice (p. 74)

1. $d = rt$

   $d = -2(13)$

   $d = -26$

   The diver's position relative to sea level is -26 feet.

2. $-1(4) = -4$

3. $7(0) = 0$

4. $-6(-11) = 66$

5. $-1(-12)(-9) = 12(-9) = -108$

6. When $a = 3$, $b = -4$, and $c = -8$:

   $ac - b = 3(-8) - (-4)$
$$= -24 - (-4)$$
$$= -24 + 4$$
$$= -20$$

Chapter 2, *continued*

7. When $a = 3$, $b = -4$, and $c = -8$:

$ac + b = 3(-8) + (-4) = -24 + (-4) = -28$

8. When $a = 3$, $b = -4$, and $c = -8$:

$a^2 + bc = 3^2 + (-4)(-8)$

$= 9 + (-4)(-8)$

$= 9 + 32$

$= 41$

9. When $a = 3$, $b = -4$, and $c = -8$:

$ab - c^2 = 3(-4) - (-8)^2$

$= 3(-4) - 64$

$= -12 - 64$

$= -12 + (-64)$

$= -76$

2.4 Exercises (pp. 75–76)

Skill Practice

1. The product of a positive integer and a negative integer is a *negative* integer.

2. The product of two integers with the same sign is *positive*.

3. $-4(-7) = 28$

4. $0(-9) = 0$ Multiplication Property of Zero

5. $-3(6) = -18$ **6.** $8(-5) = -40$

7. $-6(7) = -42$ **8.** $-1(-17) = 17$

9. $0(-13) = 0$ Multiplication Property of Zero

10. $-4(-11) = 44$

11. $9(-2) = -18$ **12.** $3(-5) = -15$

13. $-15(-12) = 180$

14. $1(-32) = -32$ Identity Property of Multiplication

15. $-1(-2)(-3) = 2(-3) = -6$

16. $2(-4)(5) = -8(5) = -40$

17. $10(-9)(-3) = -90(-3) = 270$

18. $-7(-9)(-6) = 63(-6) = -378$

19. $-2(5)(-6) = -10(-6) = 60$

20. $6(-4)(12) = -24(12) = -288$

21. $-8(-7)(-5) = 56(-5) = -280$

22. $12(0)(-45) = 0(-45) = 0$ Multiplication Property of Zero

23. The sign of the product is incorrect.

$-8(-12) = 96$

24. When $x = -9$ and $y = -7$:

$xy = -9(-7) = 63$

25. When $y = -7$:

$y^2 = (-7)^2 = 49$

26. When $x = -9$, $y = -7$, and $z = -4$:

$2xyz = 2(-9)(-7)(-4)$

$= -18(-7)(-4)$

$= 126(-4)$

$= -504$

27. When $z = -4$:

$-3z^2 = -3(-4)^2 = -3(16) = -48$

28. When $x = -9$:

$-x(-x) = -(-9)[-(-9)] = -(-9)(9) = 9(9) = 81$

29. When $y = -7$ and $z = -4$:

$z(-y^2) = -4[-(-7)^2] = -4(-49) = 196$

30. When $x = -9$, $y = -7$, and $z = -4$:

$3xy - yz = 3(-9)(-7) - (-7)(-4)$

$= -27(-7) - 28$

$= 189 - 28$

$= 189 + (-28)$

$= 161$

31. When $x = -9$, $y = -7$, and $z = -4$:

$x + 2y^2 - z = -9 + 2(-7)^2 - (-4)$

$= -9 + 2(49) + 4$

$= -9 + 98 + 4$

$= 89 + 4$

$= 93$

32. When $x = -9$ and $y = -7$:

$x^2 + y = (-9)^2 + (-7) = 81 + (-7) = 74$

33. When $y = -7$ and $z = -4$:

$z - y^2 = -4 - (-7)^2 = -4 - 49 = -4 + (-49) = -53$

34. When $x = -9$ and $y = -7$:

$[x + (-x)y]^2 = [-9 + (-(-9))(-7)]^2$

$= [-9 + (9)(-7)]^2$

$= [-9 + (-63)]^2$

$= (-72)^2 = 5184$

35. When $x = -9$, $y = -7$, and $z = -4$:

$xz^2 - (-y)^2z = -9(-4)^2 - [-(-7)]^2(-4)$

$= -9(16) - (7)^2(-4)$

$= -144 - 49(-4)$

$= -144 + 196 = 52$

36. $-12 \cdot |11| = -12(11) = -132$

37. $-7(-8) \cdot |-4| = -7(-8)(4) = 56(4) = 224$

38. $10(-4) \cdot |13| = 10(-4)(13) = -40(13) = -520$

39. $|8| \cdot |-14| \cdot 3 = 8(14)(3) = 112(3) = 336$

40. D; $-4(-8) \cdot |-3| = -4(-8)(3) = 32(3) = 96$

41. 2 times what number equals -8?

$2(-4) = -8$, so $x = -4$.

42. -21 times what number equals 63?

$-21(-3) = 63$, so $y = -3$.

43. $-5(-4)z = -80$

$20z = -80$

20 times what number equals -80?

$20(-4) = -80$, so $z = -4$.

44. -4 times what number equals -20?

$-4(5) = -20$, so $a = 5$.

45. 130 equals -13 times what number?

$-13(-10) = 130$, so $b = -10$.

46. $6(-8)k = -96$

$-48k = -96$

-48 times what number equals -96?

$-48(2) = -96$, so $k = 2$.

47. -36 equals 9 times what number?

$9(-4) = -36$, so $a = -4$.

48. $7(-3)m = -21$

$-21m = -21$

-21 times what number equals -21?

$-21(1) = -21$, so $m = 1$.

49. $(-3)^2 \neq -3^2$ because $(-3)^2 = (-3)(-3) = 9$ and $-3^2 = (-1)(3)(3) = -9$.

50. The numbers alternate signs and are twice the value of n.

Next three numbers: -10, 12, and -14

Rule for sequence: $(-1)^n \cdot 2n$

51. Each number is 5 times n.

Next three numbers: 25, 30, and 35

Rule for sequence: $5n$

52. The numbers are powers of 3 and alternate signs.

Next three numbers: -243, 729, -2187

Rule for sequence: $(-3)^n$

Problem Solving

53. $d = rt$

$d = -8(12)$

$d = -96$

The depth of the coin 12 seconds after it hits the water is -96 inches.

54. New balance $= 500 + 9(-30) = 500 + (-270) = 230$

Your new balance is $230.

55. $400 + 5(-125) = 400 + (-625) = -225$

He now has -225 points.

56. When $t = 1$:

$h = -16(1)^2 + 64 = -16(1) + 64 = -16 + 64 = 48$

When $t = 2$:

$h = -16(2)^2 + 64 = -16(4) + 64 = -64 + 64 = 0$

When $t = 3$:

$h = -16(3)^2 + 64 = -16(9) + 64 = -144 + 64 = -80$

The height is 0 when $t = 2$, so the coconut hits the ground after 2 seconds.

57. $(-10)^1 = -10$

$(-10)^2 = (-10)(-10) = 100$

$(-10)^3 = (-10)(-10)(-10) = -1000$

$(-10)^4 = (-10)(-10)(-10)(-10) = 10,000$

$(-10)^5 = (-10)(-10)(-10)(-10)(-10) = -100,000$

An odd exponent gives a negative result and an even exponent gives a positive result.

58. *Sample answer:* Each pair of negative factors results in a positive product. So an odd number of negative factors results in pairs of negative factors that give a positive product and one leftover negative factor, which when multiplied with the positive product gives an overall negative product. An even number of negative factors results in pairs of negative factors that give an overall positive product.

59. D; The integers less than 1 are 0 and all negative integers. The integers less than -1 are all negative integers except -1. So the product of 0 and a negative integer is 0 and the product of two negative integers is positive.

60. Total change in value $= 25(0.56) + 45(-2) + 60(-0.56)$

$= 14 + (-90) + (-33.6)$

$= -76 + (-33.6)$

$= -109.60$

The total change in value of the stock was $-$109.60.

61. $\dfrac{8850 - 5400}{100} \cdot (-1) + (-3) = \dfrac{3450}{100} \cdot (-1) + (-3)$

$= 34.5 \cdot (-1) + (-3)$

$= -34.5 + (-3)$

$= -37.5$

The temperature at the top of the mountain is $-37.5°$C.

Mixed Review

62. $5.5\overline{)75} \longrightarrow$

```
        13.6363. . .
  55)750.0000
     55
     200
     165
     350
     330
     200
     165
     350
     330
     200
     165
      35
```

So, $75 \div 5.5 \approx 13.636$.

63.

```
      0.0708. . .
  12)0.8500
     84
     10
      0
    100
     96
      4
```

So, $0.85 \div 12 \approx 0.071$.

Chapter 2, *continued*

64.
$$17\overline{)3.4}$$
$$\underline{3\;4}$$
$$0$$
quotient 0.2

So, $3.4 \div 17 = 0.2$.

65.
$$7\overline{)6.3200}$$
quotient $0.9028\ldots$
$$\underline{6\;3}$$
$$02$$
$$\underline{0}$$
$$20$$
$$\underline{14}$$
$$60$$
$$\underline{56}$$
$$4$$

So, $6.32 \div 7 \approx 0.903$.

66. C; Let s be the side length of the square.

$P = 4s$

$64 = 4s$

Because $4(16) = 64$, the side length of the square is 16 feet.

Lesson 2.5

2.5 Guided Practice (pp. 77–78)

1. $\dfrac{-33}{11} = -3$

2. $\dfrac{-25}{-5} = 5$

3. $\dfrac{0}{-4} = 0$

4. $\dfrac{72}{-9} = -8$

5. $\dfrac{-36}{18} = -2$

6. $\dfrac{-28}{0}$ is undefined.

7. Sum of values $= -16 + 17 + 8 + (-23) + (-31)$
$$= -45$$

Mean $= \dfrac{-45}{5} = -9$

8. Sum of values
$$= 0 + (-4) + (-10) + 4 + 11 + (-9) + (-13)$$
$$= -21$$

Mean $= -\dfrac{21}{7} = -3$

9. When $a = -42$, $b = -3$, and $c = 7$:

$\dfrac{a}{bc} = \dfrac{-42}{-3 \cdot 7} = \dfrac{-42}{-21} = 2$

2.5 Exercises (pp. 79–81)

Skill Practice

1. To find the *mean* of three numbers, add them and divide the sum by three.

2. $\dfrac{-44}{4} = -11$

3. $\dfrac{0}{-7} = 0$

4. $\dfrac{-81}{-9} = 9$

5. $\dfrac{50}{-10} = -5$

6. $\dfrac{-49}{-7} = 7$

7. $\dfrac{-28}{2} = -14$

8. $\dfrac{36}{-4} = -9$

9. $\dfrac{-19}{-1} = 19$

10. $\dfrac{-66}{-11} = 6$

11. $\dfrac{-27}{0}$ is undefined.

12. $\dfrac{-9}{6} = \dfrac{-3}{2}$, or -1.5

13. $\dfrac{-6}{-30} = \dfrac{1}{5}$, or 0.2

14. Sum of values
$$= -12 + 5 + (-9) + 10 + 16 + (-8) + (-2) + 8$$
$$= 8$$

Mean $= \dfrac{8}{8} = 1$

15. Sum of values
$$= 4 + (-3) + (-8) + 7 + (-1) + 4 + (-2)$$
$$+ (-9) + (-1)$$
$$= -9$$

Mean $= \dfrac{-9}{9} = -1$

16. Sum of values
$$= -18 + 14 + 16 + (-24) + 31 + (-8) + (-19)$$
$$= -8$$

Mean $= -\dfrac{8}{7}$, or about -1.14

17. Sum of values
$$= -38 + 32 + 41 + (-45) + 39 + (-21) + (-24)$$
$$= -16$$

Mean $= -\dfrac{16}{7}$, or about -2.29

18. When $y = -12$ and $z = -6$:

$\dfrac{y}{z} = \dfrac{-12}{-6} = 2$

19. When $x = 18$ and $z = -6$:

$\dfrac{x}{z} = \dfrac{18}{-6} = -3$

20. When $x = 18$, $y = -12$, and $z = -6$:

$\dfrac{xz}{y} = \dfrac{18(-6)}{-12} = \dfrac{-108}{-12} = 9$

21. When $y = -12$ and $z = -6$:

$\dfrac{z^2}{y} = \dfrac{(-6)^2}{-12} = \dfrac{36}{-12} = -3$

22. When $x = 18$, $y = -12$, and $z = -6$:

$\dfrac{x}{y + z} = \dfrac{18}{-12 + (-6)} = \dfrac{18}{-18} = -1$

23. When $x = 18$, $y = -12$, and $z = -6$:

$\dfrac{x - yz}{x} = \dfrac{18 - (-12)(-6)}{18}$
$$= \dfrac{18 - 72}{18}$$
$$= \dfrac{18 + (-72)}{18}$$
$$= \dfrac{-54}{18}$$
$$= -3$$

24. When $x = 18$, $y = -12$, and $z = -6$:

$$\frac{x^2 + y}{z} = \frac{18^2 + (-12)}{-6} = \frac{324 + (-12)}{-6} = \frac{312}{-6} = -52$$

25. When $y = -12$ and $z = -6$:

$$\frac{y - z^2}{y} = \frac{-12 - (-6)^2}{-12}$$

$$= \frac{-12 - 36}{-12}$$

$$= \frac{-12 + (-36)}{-12}$$

$$= \frac{-48}{-12}$$

$$= 4$$

26. $2 + 3(-4) \div 6 = 2 + (-12) \div 6 = 2 + (-2) = 0$

27. $5 + 6 \cdot 8 \div 4 - 3 = 5 + 48 \div 4 - 3$

$$= 5 + 12 - 3$$
$$= 17 - 3$$
$$= 17 + (-3)$$
$$= 14$$

28. $12 \div 3 + 3 \cdot (-4) = 4 + 3 \cdot (-4) = 4 + (-12) = -8$

29. $16 + 8(-2) - 4 = 16 + (-16) - 4$

$$= 0 - 4$$
$$= 0 + (-4)$$
$$= -4$$

30. $7 - 10 \div 2 = 7 + (-10) \div 2 = 7 + (-5) = 2$

31. $5 \cdot 6 - 2(6) \div 4 = 30 - 2(6) \div 4$

$$= 30 + (-2)(6) \div 4$$
$$= 30 + (-12) \div 4$$
$$= 30 + (-3)$$
$$= 27$$

32. $-14 - 6 \div 2 + 7 = -14 + (-6) \div 2 + 7$

$$= -14 + (-3) + 7$$
$$= -17 + 7$$
$$= -10$$

33. $7 \cdot 3 - 12 \div 6 = 21 - 12 \div 6$

$$= 21 + (-12) \div 6$$
$$= 21 + (-2)$$
$$= 19$$

34. B; The quotient of a negative integer and a positive integer is negative. So, the product of the negative quotient and -1 is positive.

35. A; $-a$ and $-b$ are negative, so $-a \cdot (-b)$ is positive.

b is positive and $-a$ is negative, so $b \div (-a)$ is negative.

$-a$ is negative and b is positive, so $-ab$ is negative.

a is positive and $-b$ is negative, so $a \div (-b)$ is negative.

The expression $-a \cdot (-b)$ is the only positive expression, so A does not belong.

36. Only two depths were used in finding the mean, but there are three.

$$\frac{-(85 + 95 + 95)}{3} = \frac{-275}{3} = -91.\overline{6}$$

37. Using the number line shown, $\frac{a - b}{ab}$ is negative.

Sample answer: The number line shows that a is positive and b is negative. The numerator, $a - b$, is positive and the denominator, ab, is negative. The quotient of two numbers with different signs is negative, so $\frac{a - b}{ab}$ is negative.

Problem Solving

38. a. Sum of profits $= -172 + (-203) + 157$

$$= -375 + 157$$
$$= -218$$

b. There are 3 months given.

c. Mean $= \frac{-218}{3} \approx -\$72.67$

39. A; Sum of earnings

$$= 400 + (-76) + (-139) + 526 + 650 + (-17)$$
$$= 1344$$

Mean $= \frac{1344}{6} = 224$

The mean of the monthly earnings for the six months is $224.

40. Sum of temperatures $= -19 + (-14) + (-8) + 13 + 18$

$$= -10$$

Mean $= \frac{-10}{5} = -2$

The mean temperature for these 5 days was $-2°$F.

41. Sum of temperatures

$$= -8 + (-1) + (-6) + (-21) + (-31) = -67$$

Mean $= \frac{-67}{5} = -13.4$

The mean temperature for these 5 days was $-13.4°$F.

If the temperature on Tuesday was $5°$F lower, the calculation of the mean would change to $\frac{-72}{5} = -14.4°$F. So, the mean temperature would decrease.

42. The mean of a set of negative numbers is always negative because you're dividing a negative number by a positive number.

Sample answer:

Mean $= \frac{-7 + (-9) + (-3) + (-1)}{4} = \frac{-20}{4} = -5$

Mean $= \frac{-50 + (-50) + (-100) + (-1)}{4} = \frac{-201}{4} = -50.25$

43. Sum of points $= 18 + 26 + 19 = 63$

Mean $= \dfrac{63}{3} = 21$ points

Sum of assists $= 3 + 6 + 3 = 12$

Mean $= \dfrac{12}{3} = 4$ assists

Sum of rebounds $= 13 + 14 + 6 = 33$

Mean $= \dfrac{33}{3} = 11$ rebounds

Sample answer: Because the statistics are not all the same in a category, the mean cannot be the highest or lowest value.

So, there is at least one actual value above and below the mean for each category.

44. a.

Test	Score	Difference
1	81	$81 + (-85) = -4$
2	83	$83 + (-85) = -2$
3	92	$92 + (-85) = 7$
4	88	$88 + (-85) = 3$
5	79	$79 + (-85) = -6$

b. Sum of differences $= -4 + (-2) + 7 + 3 + (-6)$

$ = -2$

Mean $= \dfrac{-2}{5} = -0.4$

c. The mean difference is -0.4, so adjust the "close to mean" to $85 + (-0.4) = 84.6$.

The exact mean is

$\dfrac{81 + 83 + 92 + 88 + 79}{5} = \dfrac{423}{5} = 84.6$.

So, the adjusted mean is the exact mean.

45. When $C = -34$:

$F = \dfrac{9}{5}(-34) + 32 = -61.2 + 32 = -29.2$

The mean temperature is $-29.2°$F.

46. No. *Sample answer:* There is not enough information given about actual temperatures to find the high and low temperatures.

47. Let x be the fifth temperature.

Sum of temperatures $= -4 + (-6) + 3 + (-1) + x$

$ = -8 + x$

Because the mean is -2 and there are 5 temperatures, the sum of the temperatures must be $5(-2) = -10$.

So, $-8 + x = -10$.

Because $-8 + (-2) = -10$, $x = -2$.

The fifth temperature is $-2°$F.

Mixed Review

48. $2 + (-4) + 5 = -2 + 5 = 3$

49. $[2 + (-4)] + 5 = -2 + 5 = 3$

50. $2 + (-4 + 5) = 2 + 1 = 3$

51. $5 \cdot 5 \cdot 5 \cdot 5 \cdot 5 = 5^5$

52. $8 \cdot 8 \cdot 8 \cdot 8 \cdot 8 \cdot 8 = 8^6$

53. $b \cdot b \cdot b \cdot b = b^4$

54. D; $6(-8)(-2) = -48(-2) = 96$

Quiz 2.1–2.5 (p. 81)

1. $-8 < 8$

2. $0 > -14$

3. $|-30| = 30$
   So, $-20 < |-30|$.

4. $|-7| = 7$
   So, $|-7| > 5$.

5. $-6 + 1 = -5$

6. $-20 + (-10) = -30$

7. $-4 - (-3) = -4 + 3 = -1$

8. $\dfrac{36}{-9} = -4$

9. $-6(-8) = 48$

10. $-12(4) = -48$

11. $\dfrac{-48}{-8} = 6$

12. $-11 - 8 = -11 + (-8) = -19$

13. Sum of values
   $= -9 + (-15) + 16 + 4 + 2 + (-10) + 8 + 20$
   $= 16$

   Mean $= \dfrac{16}{8} = 2$

14. Sum of values
   $= -10 + 6 + (-11) + (-6) + (-7) + 3 + (-4) + 1 + 1$
   $= -27$

   Mean $= \dfrac{-27}{9} = -3$

15. When $t = 1$:
   $h = -16(1)^2 + 144 = -16 + 144 = 128$ ft

   When $t = 2$:
   $h = -16(2)^2 + 144 = -64 + 144 = 80$ ft

   When $t = 3$:
   $h = -16(3)^2 + 144 = -144 + 144 = 0$ ft

   The ball hits the ground after 3 seconds.

Mixed Review of Problem Solving (p. 82)

1. a. The club earned more than it spent for the winter play and the musical because the earnings were greater than the expenses.

b. Fall play: $500 + (-800) = -300$

   Winter play: $800 + (-600) = 200$

   Musical: $1500 + (-900) = 600$

   Spring play: $600 + (-700) = -100$

c. Profit $= -300 + 200 + 600 + (-100) = 400$

   The theater club's profit during the year was $400.

2. a. When $t = 3$:

$h = -16(3)^2 + 256$

$= -16(9) + 256$

$= -144 + 256$

$= 112$

When $t = 4$:

$h = -16(4)^2 + 256$

$= -16(16) + 256$

$= -256 + 256$

$= 0$

When $t = 5$:

$h = -16(5)^2 + 256$

$= -16(25) + 256$

$= -400 + 256$

$= -144$

b. When $t = 3$, the rock is $256 + (-112) = 144$ feet from its starting point and 112 feet from the ground.

When $t = 4$, the rock is on the ground, 256 feet from its starting point.

When $t = 5$, the rock is not falling because it is already on the ground, 256 feet from its starting point.

3. Yes, the advertisement is accurate.

Sample answer: The mean difference is

$\dfrac{-5 + 6 + 1 + (-2)}{4} = \dfrac{0}{4} = 0$, so the average is 16 shrimp

per pound.

4. *Sample answer:* Let $x = 2$ and $y = -10$.

$|x - y| = |2 - (-10)| = |2 + 10| = |12| = 12$

$|y - x| = |-10 - 2| = |-10 + (-2)| = |-12| = 12$

5. a.

Player	Score	Relation to par	Player	Score	Relation to par
Elliot	84	+12	Irma	72	0
Louisa	76	+4	Petra	65	-7
Chad	68	-4	Frank	70	-2
Mark	71	-1	Rosalinda	74	+2

b. Petra had the lowest score because 65 is less than all other scores.

c. Sum of values

$= 12 + 4 + (-4) + (-1) + 0 + (-7) + (-2) + 2$

$= 4$

Mean $= \dfrac{4}{8} = 0.5$

The mean is positive, so the mean score was *above* par.

6. a.

Race	1st Mile	2nd Mile
Race 1	6 min 45 sec	7 min 32 sec
Race 2	6 min 49 sec	7 min 27 sec
Difference	−4 sec	5 sec

b. The sum of the differences from race 1 to race 2 is $-4 + 5 = 1$, so race 1 took 1 second longer than race 2. The runner's overall time decreased from race 1 to race 2.

Lesson 2.6

2.6 Guided Practice (pp. 84–85)

1.

Total distance	=	Average speed	·	Hours per day	·	Number of days

$= 14 \cdot 6 \cdot 6$

$= 84 \cdot 6$

$= 504$

Because 400 is less than the 504 miles you can cycle in 6 days, you can complete the trip in 6 days.

2. $4 \cdot (-9) \cdot 25 = 4 \cdot 25 \cdot (-9) = 100 \cdot (-9) = -900$

3. $-13 + 34 - 7 = -13 + 34 + (-7)$

$= -13 + (-7) + 34$

$= -20 + 34$

$= 14$

4. $\dfrac{3}{7} + \left(8 + \dfrac{4}{7}\right) = \dfrac{3}{7} + \left(\dfrac{4}{7} + 8\right) = \dfrac{3}{7} + \dfrac{4}{7} + 8 = 1 + 8 = 9$

5. $18 + (-34 + 12) = 18 + [12 + (-34)]$

$= (18 + 12) + (-34)$

$= 30 + (-34)$

$= -4$

6. $\dfrac{4}{5} + \left(8 + \dfrac{1}{5}\right) = \dfrac{4}{5} + \left(\dfrac{1}{5} + 8\right) = \left(\dfrac{4}{5} + \dfrac{1}{5}\right) + 8 = 1 + 8 = 9$

7. $12\left(6 \cdot \dfrac{1}{12}\right) = 12\left(\dfrac{1}{12} \cdot 6\right) = \left(12 \cdot \dfrac{1}{12}\right) \cdot 6 = 1 \cdot 6 = 6$

8. $\dfrac{5}{6}\left(3 \cdot \dfrac{6}{5}\right) = \dfrac{5}{6}\left(\dfrac{6}{5} \cdot 3\right) = \left(\dfrac{5}{6} \cdot \dfrac{6}{5}\right) \cdot 3 = 1 \cdot 3 = 3$

9. $4\left(\dfrac{1}{4} \cdot 23\right) = \left(4 \cdot \dfrac{1}{4}\right) \cdot 23 = 1 \cdot 23 = 23$

10. $-2(46 \cdot 50) = -2(50 \cdot 46)$

$= (-2 \cdot 50) \cdot 46$

$= -100 \cdot 46$

$= -4600$

11. $[-21 \cdot (-29)] \cdot 0 = -21 \cdot [(-29) \cdot 0] = -21 \cdot 0 = 0$

12. $10(-6)\left(\dfrac{1}{10}\right) = 10\left(\dfrac{1}{10}\right)(-6) = 1(-6) = -6$

2.6 Exercises (pp. 85–87)

Skill Practice

1. E   **2.** F   **3.** B

4. A   **5.** D   **6.** C

Chapter 2, *continued*

7. $17 + 15 + 13 = 17 + 13 + 15 = 30 + 15 = 45$

The commutative property of addition was used.

8. $-27 + 43 - 13 = -27 + 43 + (-13)$

$\qquad\qquad\quad = -27 + (-13) + 43$

$\qquad\qquad\quad = -40 + 43$

$\qquad\qquad\quad = 3$

The commutative property of addition was used.

9. $5 \cdot (-29) \cdot 2 = 5 \cdot 2 \cdot (-29) = 10 \cdot (-29) = -290$

The commutative property of multiplication was used.

10. $-53 + (-27 + 44) = [-53 + (-27)] + 44$

$\qquad\qquad\qquad\quad = -80 + 44$

$\qquad\qquad\qquad\quad = -36$

The associative property of addition was used.

11. $(-39 + 48) + 12 = -39 + (48 + 12) = -39 + 60 = 21$

The associative property of addition was used.

12. $-2(-9 \cdot 50) = -2 \cdot [50 \cdot (-9)]$

$\qquad\qquad\quad = (-2 \cdot 50)(-9)$

$\qquad\qquad\quad = -100 \cdot (-9)$

$\qquad\qquad\quad = 900$

The commutative and associative properties of multiplication were used.

13. $[-4 \cdot (-7)] \cdot (-5) = (-5) \cdot [-4 \cdot (-7)]$

$\qquad\qquad\qquad\quad = [(-5) \cdot (-4)] \cdot (-7)$

$\qquad\qquad\qquad\quad = 20 \cdot (-7)$

$\qquad\qquad\qquad\quad = -140$

The commutative and associative properties of multiplication were used.

14. $[25 \cdot (-7)]4 = 4[25 \cdot (-7)]$

$\qquad\qquad\quad = (4 \cdot 25) \cdot (-7)$

$\qquad\qquad\quad = 100 \cdot (-7)$

$\qquad\qquad\quad = -700$

The commutative and associative properties of multiplication were used.

15. $(-20 \cdot 9) \cdot 5 = 5(-20 \cdot 9)$

$\qquad\qquad\quad = [5 \cdot (-20)] \cdot 9$

$\qquad\qquad\quad = -100 \cdot 9$

$\qquad\qquad\quad = -900$

The commutative and associative properties of multiplication were used.

16. $28 + 65 = 65 + 28$ — Commutative property of addition

17. $54 \cdot 16 = 16 \cdot 54$ — Commutative property of multiplication

18. $(7 \cdot 3)3 = 7(3 \cdot 3)$ — Associative property of multiplication

19. $4 + (9 + 2) = 4 + (2 + 9)$ or $4 + (9 + 2) = (9 + 2) + 4$ — Commutative property of addition

20. $5(11 \cdot 2) = 5(2 \cdot 11)$ or $5(11 \cdot 2) = (11 \cdot 2)5$ — Commutative property of multiplication

21. $(8 + 16) + 2 = (16 + 8) + 2$ or $(8 + 16) + 2 = 2 + (8 + 16)$ — Commutative property of addition

22. C; $7 + 5 - 17 = 7 + 5 + (-17)$

$\qquad\qquad\quad = 7 + (-17) + 5$

$\qquad\qquad\quad = 7 - 17 + 5$

23. $45 - (-68) - 44$

$= 45 + 68 + (-44)$ — Change subtraction to addition.

$= 45 + (-44) + 68$ — Commutative property of addition

$= 1 + 68$ — Add.

$= 69$ — Add.

24. $-57 - 38 - (-57)$

$= -57 + (-38) + 57$ — Change subtraction to addition.

$= -57 + 57 + (-38)$ — Commutative property of addition

$= 0 + (-38)$ — Inverse Property of addition

$= -38$ — Identity Property of addition

25. $(-26 + 33) + (-4)$

$= 7 + (-4)$ — Add.

$= 3$ — Add.

26. $(0.5)(45 \cdot 2) = (0.5)(2 \cdot 45)$ — Commutative property of multiplication

$\qquad\qquad\quad = (0.5 \cdot 2)(45)$ — Associative property of multiplication

$\qquad\qquad\quad = 1(45)$ — Multiply.

$\qquad\qquad\quad = 45$ — Identity property of multiplication

27. $\left(\frac{2}{7} + 5\right) + \frac{5}{7} = \left(5 + \frac{2}{7}\right) + \frac{5}{7}$ — Commutative property of addition

$\qquad\qquad\quad = 5 + \left(\frac{2}{7} + \frac{5}{7}\right)$ — Associative property of addition

$\qquad\qquad\quad = 5 + 1$ — Add.

$\qquad\qquad\quad = 6$ — Add.

28. $\left(\frac{2}{3} \cdot 7\right) \cdot 21 = \left(7 \cdot \frac{2}{3}\right) \cdot 21$ — Commutative property of multiplication

$\qquad\qquad\quad = 7 \cdot \left(\frac{2}{3} \cdot 21\right)$ — Associative property of multiplication

$\qquad\qquad\quad = 7 \cdot 14$ — Multiply.

$\qquad\qquad\quad = 98$ — Multiply.

Chapter 2, *continued*

29. $12 \cdot (7 \cdot 1 \cdot 5) = 12 \cdot (7 \cdot 5)$ Identity property of multiplication

           $= 12 \cdot (5 \cdot 7)$ Commutative property of multiplication

           $= (12 \cdot 5) \cdot 7$ Associative property of multiplication

           $= 60 \cdot 7$ Multiply.

           $= 420$ Multiply.

30. $-2 \cdot (19 \cdot 15) \cdot 1$

    $= -2 \cdot (15 \cdot 19) \cdot 1$ Commutative property of multiplication

    $= (-2 \cdot 15) \cdot 19 \cdot 1$ Associative property of multiplication

    $= -30 \cdot 19 \cdot 1$ Multiply.

    $= -570 \cdot 1$ Multiply.

    $= -570$ Identity property of multiplication

31. $36 + 57 + (-36)$

    $= 36 + (-36) + 57$ Commutative property of addition

    $= 0 + 57$ Inverse property of addition

    $= 57$ Identity property of addition

32. $17 + 0 + (-19) = 17 + (-19)$ Identity property of addition

           $= -2$ Add.

33. $24 + (-12 - 8) + 6$

    $= 24 + 6 + (-12 - 8)$ Commutative property of addition

    $= 24 + 6 + [-12 + (-8)]$ Change subtraction to addition.

    $= 24 + 6 + (-20)$ Add.

    $= 30 + (-20)$ Add.

    $= 10$ Add.

34. $5(7 \cdot 4)(0.25) = 5 \cdot 7 \cdot (4 \cdot 0.25)$ Associative property of multiplication

        $= 5 \cdot 7 \cdot 1$ Multiply.

        $= 35 \cdot 1$ Multiply.

        $= 35$ Identity property of multiplication

35. $7 \cdot x \cdot 10 = 7 \cdot 10 \cdot x = 70x$

36. $-67 + [x + (-13)] = -67 + [(-13) + x]$

               $= [-67 + (-13)] + x$

               $= -80 + x$

               $= x - 80$

37. $(52 + x) + 18 = (x + 52) + 18 = x + (52 + 18) = x + 70$

38. The associative property was applied incorrectly.

    $15 - (5 + 3) = 15 - 8 = 7$

39. $4 \cdot 8 + 5 = 8 \cdot 4 + 5$ Commutative property of multiplication

      $= 5 + 8 \cdot 4$ Commutative property of addition

      $= 5 + 4 \cdot 8$ Commutative property of multiplication

Problem Solving

40. Total number of rushing yards.

    $= 92 + 22 + 15 + 5 + 3 + (-4)$

    $= 114 + (15 + 5) + 3 + (-4)$

    $= 114 + 20 + 3 + (-4)$

    $= [114 + (-4)] + 20 + 3$

    $= 110 + 20 + 3$

    $= 133$

The total number of their rushing yards was 133.

41. $V = \ell wh = (2.5)(1.5)(4) = (2.5)(4)(1.5) = (10)(1.5) = 15$

The box could hold 15 cubic inches of juice.

Sample answer: You can verify that cubic units are appropriate by including units in the calculation, 2.5 in. $\cdot$ 1.5 in. $\cdot$ 4 in. So, the units are in. $\cdot$ in. $\cdot$ in., or in.^{3}

42. *Sample answer:*

$\dfrac{\text{hours}}{\text{per day}} \cdot \dfrac{\text{number}}{\text{of days}} \cdot \dfrac{\text{hourly}}{\text{wage}} = 2 \cdot 5 \cdot 8 = 10 \cdot 8 = 80$

You earned $80 for the week.

43. No. *Sample answer:* The expressions are not equivalent because

    $-15 + 34 - 44 - 19 + 51$

    $= 34 + (-15) - 44 - 19 + 51$

    $= 34 + (-15) - 19 - 44 + 51$

    $= 34 - 19 + (-15) - 44 + 51$

    $\neq 34 - 19 + 15 - 44 + 51$.

44. *Sample answer:* To find the sum $52 + 99 + 65 + 38 + 11$, use the commutative property to get 38 next to 52 and 11 next to 99. Then use the associative property to group the sum of 38 and 52 and group the sum of 11 and 99. Then mentally find $38 + 52$, which is 90, and $99 + 11$, which is 110. Add these two results to get 200. Finally, add 65 to 200 to get 265.

The properties help order the terms so that you can add mentally.

45. Using order of operations:

    $25 \cdot 6 \cdot 4 \cdot 7 = 150 \cdot 4 \cdot 7 = 600 \cdot 7 = 4200$

Sample answer: The properties help order the terms so that you can multiply mentally. To find the product $25 \cdot 6 \cdot 4 \cdot 7$ using properties of multiplication, use the commutative property to switch 6 and 4. Then use the associative property to group 25 and 4 and to group 6 and 7. Then find each product, 100 and 42. Finally, multiply 100 and 42 to get 4200.

46. Division is not commutative.

Sample answer:

    $4 \div 2 = 2$, but $2 \div 4 = 0.5$

Chapter 2, *continued*

47. Discount: $9 \cdot 5.25 \cdot \frac{1}{3} = 9 \cdot \frac{1}{3} \cdot 5.25 = 3 \cdot 5.25 = 15.75$

Purchase: $9 \cdot 5.25 - 15.75 = 47.25 - 15.75 = 31.50$

The discount is \$15.75 and the price after discount is \$31.50.

48. The student used the commutative property many times to write $1 + 2 + 3 + 4 + 5 + 6 + 7 + 8 + 9$ as $1 + 9 + 2 + 8 + 3 + 7 + 4 + 6 + 5$, then used the associative property many times to write $(1 + 9) + (2 + 8) + (3 + 7) + (4 + 6) + 5$
$= 10 + 10 + 10 + 10 + 5 = 45.$

Sum of numbers from 1 to 19:

$1 + 2 + 3 + 4 + 5 + 6 + 7 + 8 + 9 + 10 + 11 + 12$
$\quad + 13 + 14 + 15 + 16 + 17 + 18 + 19$

$= 1 + 19 + 2 + 18 + 3 + 17 + 4 + 16 + 5 + 15 + 6$
$\quad + 14 + 7 + 13 + 8 + 12 + 9 + 11 + 10$

$= (1 + 19) + (2 + 18) + (3 + 17) + (4 + 16)$
$\qquad + (5 + 15) + (6 + 14) + (7 + 13)$
$\qquad + (8 + 12) + (9 + 11) + 10$

$= 20 + 20 + 20 + 20 + 20 + 20 + 20 + 20 + 20 + 10$

$= 190$

Sample answer: To find the sum of the numbers from 1 to 99, use properties of addition to write $(1 + 99) + (2 + 98) + \cdots + (49 + 51) + 50.$ So, there are 49 pairs that add to 100, plus 50, or $49(100) + 50 = 4900 + 50 = 4950.$

49. Side lengths: $a, a + 4, a + 4 + 8 = a + 12,$
and $a + 12 - 6 = a + 6$

Perimeter: $P = a + a + 4 + a + 12 + a + 6$
$\qquad\qquad = a + a + a + a + 4 + 12 + 6$
$\qquad\qquad = 4a + 22$

When $a = 6$: $P = 4(6) + 22 = 24 + 22 = 46$ ft

Mixed Review

50. $3(12 - 5) = 3(7) = 21$

51. $7(2 + 4) = 7(6) = 42$

52. $2(18 - 14)(8) = 2(4)(8) = 8(8) = 64$

53. (1) Read and Understand

(2) Make a Plan: Guess, Check, and Revise

(3) Solve the Problem:

Let x and y be the heights of the bookcases.

Then $x + y = 60$ and $x - y = 8.$

Guess: $\quad x = 35$

$\qquad 35 + y = 60 \qquad 35 - 25 \overset{?}{=} 8$

$\qquad\qquad y = 25 \qquad\qquad 10 \neq 8$

Too high.

Guess: $\quad x = 32$

$\qquad 32 + y = 60 \qquad 32 - 28 \overset{?}{=} 8$

$\qquad\qquad y = 28 \qquad\qquad 4 \neq 8$

Too low.

Guess: $\quad x = 34$

$\qquad 34 + y = 60 \qquad 34 - 26 \overset{?}{=} 8$

$\qquad\qquad y = 26 \qquad\qquad 8 = 8$

One bookcase is 34 inches tall and the other bookcase is 26 inches tall.

(4) Look Back

Choose the Guess, Check, and Revise strategy because the approximate heights are close to 30 inches.

54. B; $18 + (-12) + (-8) = 6 + (-8) = -2$

Lesson 2.7

2.7 Guided Practice (pp. 89–90)

1. Area $= 10(12) + 10(22) = 10(12 + 22) = 10(34) = 340$

The total area is 340 square feet.

2. Area $= 14(3) + 14(9) = 14(3 + 9) = 14(12) = 168$

The total area is 168 square meters.

3. $-2(5 + 12) = -2(5) + (-2)(12) = -10 + (-24) = -34$

4. $-4(-7 - 10) = -4(-7) - (-4)(10) = 28 + 40 = 68$

5. $2(w - 8) = 2w - 2(8) = 2w - 16$

6. $-8(z + 25) = -8z + (-8)(25) = -8z - 200$

7. $2(x + 4) + 3x - 5 = 2x + 8 + 3x + (-5) = 5x + 3$

8. $5y + 9z - 7 - 3y = [5 + (-3)]y + 9z - 7$
$\qquad\qquad\qquad\qquad = 2y + 9z - 7$

9. $-3(6x + 2y) + 22x = -18x - 6y + 22x = 4x - 6y$

2.7 Exercises (pp. 90–92)

Skill Practice

1. -6 **2.** 1 **3.** $-6y$ **4.** 2

5. B; $3(x + 4) = 3x + 12$ **6.** D; $4(x + 3) = 4x + 12$

7. A; $2(2x - 6) = 4x - 12$ **8.** C; $x(4 + 9) = 13x$

9. $4(7 + 8) = 4(7) + 4(8) = 28 + 32 = 60$

10. $-7(3 + 2) = -7(3) + (-7)(2) = -21 + (-14) = -35$

11. $3(5 + 6) = 3(5) + 3(6) = 15 + 18 = 33$

12. $-13(-12 + 9) = -13(-12) + (-13)(9)$
$\qquad\qquad\qquad = 156 + (-117)$
$\qquad\qquad\qquad = 39$

13. $6(-5 + 10 + 2) = 6(-5) + 6(10) + 6(2)$
$\qquad\qquad\qquad\quad = -30 + 60 + 12$
$\qquad\qquad\qquad\quad = 42$

14. $-4[3 + 6 + (-8)] = -4(3) + (-4)(6) + (-4)(-8)$
$\qquad\qquad\qquad\qquad = -12 + (-24) + 32$
$\qquad\qquad\qquad\qquad = -4$

15. C; $-3(2x + 4) = -3(2x) + (-3)(4) = -6x - 12$

16. $9(x - 3) = 9x - 9(3) = 9x - 27$

17. $-8(5 - x) = -8(5) - (-8)(x)$
$\qquad\qquad\quad = -40 - (-8x)$
$\qquad\qquad\quad = -40 + 8x$

Chapter 2, *continued*

18. $-12(4 + 5 + y) = -12(4) + (-12)(5) + (-12)(y)$
$$= -48 + (-60) + (-12y)$$
$$= -108 - 12y$$

19. $19[7 + w + (-2)] = 19(7) + 19w + 19(-2)$
$$= 133 + 19w + (-38)$$
$$= 19w + 95$$

20. $-34(z - 21 - 5) = -34z - (-34)(21) - (-34)(5)$
$$= -34z + 714 + 170$$
$$= -34z + 884$$

21. $-2[4 - x + (-7)] = -2(4) - (-2)(x) + (-2)(-7)$
$$= -8 + 2x + 14$$
$$= 2x + 6$$

22. $r + 2s + 3r = (1 + 3)r + 2s = 4r + 2s$

23. $11w + 9z + 3z + 5w = (11 + 5)w + (9 + 3)z$
$$= 16w + 12z$$

24. $7a - 2a + 8b - 2b = [7 + (-2)]a + [8 + (-2)]b$
$$= 5a + 6b$$

25. $3x + 2x + y + 2y - 3 = (3 + 2)x + (1 + 2)y - 3$
$$= 5x + 3y - 3$$

26. $-3x + 2x - 9y - 2x = [-3 + 2 + (-2)]x - 9y$
$$= -3x - 9y$$

27. $r + 2s - (-3r) - s = r + 2s + 3r - s$
$$= (1 + 3)r + (2 - 1)s$$
$$= 4r + s$$

28. $2x$ and $-5y$ cannot be combined because they are not like terms.
$$4x + 2y - 7y - 2x = 4x - 2x + 2y - 7y = 2x - 5y$$

29. $5(z + 2z) - 4z = 5z + 10z - 4z = 11z$

30. $2(2x + 1) + 3x - 5x = 4x + 2 + 3x - 5x = 2x + 2$

31. $4(3c - 4) + 2 - 4c = 12c - 16 + 2 - 4c = 8c - 14$

32. $8d - 2(3d - 5d) = 8d - 6d + 10d = 12d$

33. $3(a + 4) + b - 5 - a + 7(b - 3)$
$$= 3a + 12 + b - 5 - a + 7b - 21$$
$$= 3a - a + b + 7b + 12 - 5 - 21$$
$$= 2a + 8b - 14$$

34. $7(y - 1.3) + 2.4 - 5.3y = 7y - 9.1 + 2.4 - 5.3y$
$$= 1.7y - 6.7$$

35. $3.2(2z - 3x) + 4(1.1y + x) - 2z$
$$= 6.4z - 9.6x + 4.4y + 4x - 2z$$
$$= -9.6x + 4x + 4.4y + 6.4z - 2z$$
$$= -5.6x + 4.4y + 4.4z$$

36. $5(x + 2) - 5(y + 3) - 2x + 5y$
$$= 5x + 10 - 5y - 15 - 2x + 5y$$
$$= 5x - 2x - 5y + 5y + 10 - 15$$
$$= 3x - 5$$

37. B; $5 - 4x + 2(2 - y) = 5 - 4x + 4 - 2y = 9 - 4x - 2y$

38. *Sample answer:*
$$4(34) = 4(30 + 4) = 4(30) + 4(4) = 120 + 16 = 136$$
It is easier to mentally find 4(30), 4(4), and their sum than it is to find 4(34).

39. *Sample answer:*
$$9(19) = 9(20 - 1) = 9(20) - 9(1) = 180 - 9 = 171$$
It is easier to mentally find 9(20), 9(1), and their difference than it is to find 9(19).

40. *Sample answer:*
$$24(12) = 24(10 + 2)$$
$$= 24(10) + 24(2)$$
$$= 240 + 48$$
$$= 288$$
It is easier to mentally find 24(10), 24(2), and their sum than it is to find 24(12).

41. *Sample answer:* $65(24) = 65(10 + 10 + 4)$
$$= 65(10) + 65(10) + 65(4)$$
$$= 650 + 650 + 260$$
$$= 1560$$
It is easier to mentally find 65(10), 65(4), and the sums than it is to find 65(24).

42. Yes. *Sample answer:* The terms $3xy$ and $4yx$ are like terms because they have the same variables, x and y, raised to the same power, 1.

43. *Sample answer:*
Using order of operations:
$7[6 - 2(x + 3)] = 7[6 - 2x + (-6)]$ Distributive property
$$= 7(-2x) \quad \text{Inverse property of addition}$$
$$= -14x \quad \text{Multiply.}$$
First distribute the 7:
$7[6 - 2(x + 3)] = 7(6) - 7[2(x + 3)]$
$$= 42 - 7(2x + 6)$$
$$= 42 - 14x + (-42)$$
$$= -14x$$
The second method works because it correctly uses the distributive property $a(b - c) = ab - ac$ to write an equivalent equation where $a = 7$, $b = 6$, and $c = 2(x + 3)$.

Problem Solving

44. a. $3(12.90) = 3(13 - 0.10)$
b. $3(13) = 39$
$3(0.10) = 0.30$
c. $39 - 0.30 = 39 + (-0.30) = 38.70$

45. *Sample answer:* You need 6 pounds of each, so find the total cost for 1 pound of bird seed, 1 pound of cat food, and 1 pound of dog bones: $0.30 + 0.70 + 0.90 = 1.90$, or \$1.90. So, 6 pounds of each is 6(1.90). Using mental math, $6(1.90) = 6(2 - 0.10) = 12 - 0.60 = 11.40$, or \$11.40.

Chapter 2, continued

46. *Sample answer:* Add the areas of walls individually, or multiply the total width of the walls by 8 feet.

Total area of murals
$$= 8(21.5) + 8(35) + 8(27.5) + 8(33.5) + 8(22.5)$$
$$= 8(21.5 + 35 + 27.5 + 33.5 + 22.5)$$
$$= 8(140)$$
$$= 1120$$

The total area of the murals is 1120 square feet.

47. Cost of carpeting $= 3.12(12 \cdot 12 + 12 \cdot 9)$
$$= 3.12(144 + 108)$$
$$= 3.12(252)$$
$$= 786.24$$

The carpeting will cost $786.24.

48. B; $23(35) = 23(30 + 5)$
$$= 23(30) + 23(5)$$
$$= (20 + 3)(30) + (20 + 3)(5)$$
$$= 30(20 + 3) + 5(20 + 3)$$

49. Perimeter $= 2 \cdot$ length $+ 2 \cdot$ width
$$200 = 2 \cdot 60 + 2 \cdot (5 + x + 10)$$
$$200 = 120 + 10 + 2x + 20$$
$$200 = 150 + 2x$$
$$50 = 2x$$
$$25 = x$$

To find the area, you could multiply the length, 60, by the width, $5 + 25 + 10$. You could also find the area by adding the area in front of the curtain, $60(5)$, the area of the stage, $60(25)$, and the area of the backstage, $60(10)$.

Area $= 60(5 + 25 + 10) = 60(40) = 2400$

The area of the entire stage is 2400 square feet.

50. You should determine whether you can mentally subtract then multiply or mentally multiply then subtract.

Sample answer: Problem that is easier to solve using the distributive property: $6(47) = 6(50 - 3)$. Problem that is more difficult to solve using the distributive property: $8(40) = 8(32 + 8)$.

51. Total cost for x shirts $= 7.25x + 25 + 1.85x = 9.1x + 25$

Total cost for 75 shirts $= 9.1(75) + 25$
$$= 9(75) + 0.1(75) + 25$$
$$= 675 + 7.5 + 25$$
$$= \$707.50$$

Total cost for 170 shirts $= 9.1(170) + 25$
$$= 9(170) + 0.1(170) + 25$$
$$= 1530 + 17 + 25$$
$$= \$1572$$

The distributive property applies when using the fact that $9.1x = x(9 + 0.1) = 9x + 0.1x$.

Mixed Review

52.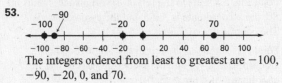

The integers ordered from least to greatest are -90, -35, 19, 35, and 80.

53.

The integers ordered from least to greatest are -100, -90, -20, 0, and 70.

54. $-5(4 \cdot 17) = (-5 \cdot 4)17 = -20(17) = -340$

55. $(-23 + 14) - 12 = [14 + (-23)] + (-12)$
$$= 14 + [(-23) + (-12)]$$
$$= 14 + (-35)$$
$$= -21$$

56. $17 + (3 - 12) + 24(0) = (17 + 3) + (-12) + 24(0)$
$$= 20 + (-12) + 0$$
$$= 8$$

57. $(-4 \cdot 7) \cdot 25 = [7 \cdot (-4)] \cdot 25$
$$= 7 \cdot [(-4) \cdot 25]$$
$$= 7 \cdot (-100)$$
$$= -700$$

58. A; Costs per disk: $\dfrac{\$10}{8 \text{ disks}} = \$1.25$ per disk

$\dfrac{\$16.50}{15 \text{ disks}} = \$1.10$ per disk

You save $1.25 - 1.10 = \$.15$ per disk if you buy a package of 15 instead of a package of 8.

Technology Activity 2.7 (p. 93)

1. $-28,546$ **2.** $-48,900$ **3.** 11,009

4. $-13,800$ **5.** $-2,105,804$ **6.** 1,336,660

7. $-262,890,144$ **8.** 478   **9.** -101

10. Diameter of Earth $= 4 \cdot$ Diameter of moon
$$= 4 \cdot 3476$$
$$= 13,904$$

The diameter of Earth is about 13,904 kilometers.

Difference between diameters $= 13,904 - 3476 = 10,428$

The difference between the diameters is about 10,428 kilometers.

11. *Sample answer:* Yes, the guarantee is accurate.
The numbers of blueberries in the 3 packages are $170 - 12 = 158$, $170 - 8 = 162$, and $170 + 16 = 186$. The average for the 3 packages is

$\dfrac{158 + 162 + 186}{3} = 168\frac{2}{3}$. This is less than the

manufacturer's guarantee, but it is very close and it is from a small sample, so the guarantee is accurate.

Chapter 2, *continued*

Lesson 2.8

2.8 Guided Practice (pp. 94–95)

1. Point D is 3 units to the right of the origin and 4 units down. So, the x-coordinate is 3 and the y-coordinate is -4. The coordinates of D are $(3, -4)$.

2. Point E is 2.5 units to the left of the origin and 2 units up. So, the x-coordinate is -2.5 and the y-coordinate is 2. The coordinates of E are $(-2.5, 2)$.

3. Point F is 3 units to the left of the origin. So, the x-coordinate is -3 and the y-coordinate is 0. The coordinates of F are $(-3, 0)$.

4–7. Graph:

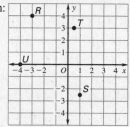

4. Begin at the origin, move 3 units to the left, then 4 units up. Point R lies in Quadrant II.

5. Begin at the origin, move 1 unit to the right, then 2.5 units down. Point S lies in Quadrant IV.

6. Begin at the origin, move 0.5 unit to the right, then 3 units up. Point T lies in Quadrant I.

7. Begin at the origin, move 4 units to the left. Point U lies on the x-axis.

8. *Sample answer:* Move A and B to $A(-30, 0)$ and $B(30, 0)$.

Horizontal distance from A to $B = \left| -30 - 30 \right|$

$$= \left| -60 \right|$$

$$= 60$$

Vertical distance from A to $D = \left| 0 - (-20) \right|$

$$= \left| 20 \right|$$

$$= 20$$

Perimeter: $2(60) + 2(20) = 160$ units

The region's perimeter is 160 feet.

2.8 Exercises (pp. 96–99)

Skill Practice

1.

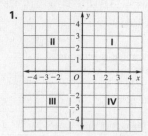

2. The y-coordinate in the ordered pair $(3, -4)$ is -4.

3. Point A is 3 units to the left of the origin and 3 units up. So, the x-coordinate is -3 and the y-coordinate is 3. The coordinates of A are $(-3, 3)$.

4. Point B is 1 unit to the right of the origin and 3 units up. So, the x-coordinate is 1 and the y-coordinate is 3. The coordinates of B are $(1, 3)$.

5. Point C is 5 units to the left of the origin. So, the x-coordinate is -5 and the y-coordinate is 0. The coordinates of C are $(-5, 0)$.

6. Point D is 4 units to the left of the origin and 3 units down. So, the x-coordinate is -4 and the y-coordinate is -3. The coordinates of D are $(-4, -3)$.

7. Point E is 2 units below the origin. So, the x-coordinate is 0 and the y-coordinate is -2. The coordinates of E are $(0, -2)$.

8. Point F is 4 units to the right of the origin and 1 unit down. So, the x-coordinate is 4 and the y-coordinate is -1. The coordinates of F are $(4, -1)$.

9. Point G is 2.5 units to the left of the origin and 2 units up. So, the x-coordinate is -2.5 and the y-coordinate is 2. The coordinates of G are $(-2.5, 2)$.

10. Point H is 3 units to the right of the origin and 1.5 units up. So, the x-coordinate is 3 and the y-coordinate is 1.5. The coordinates of H are $(3, 1.5)$.

11–22. Graph:

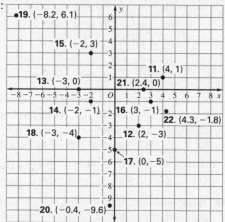

11. Begin at the origin, move 4 units to the right, then 1 unit up. The point lies in Quadrant I.

12. Begin at the origin, move 2 units to the right, then 3 units down. The point lies in Quadrant IV.

13. Begin at the origin, move 3 units to the left. The point lies on the x-axis.

14. Begin at the origin, move 2 units to the left, then 1 unit down. The point lies in Quadrant III.

15. Begin at the origin, move 2 units to the left, then 3 units up. The point lies in Quadrant II.

16. Begin at the origin, move 3 units to the right, then 1 unit down. The point lies in Quadrant IV.

17. Begin at the origin, move 5 units down. The point lies on the y-axis.

18. Begin at the origin, move 3 units to the left, then 4 units down. The point lies in Quadrant III.

Chapter 2, *continued*

19. Begin at the origin, move 8.2 units to the left, then 6.1 units up. The point lies in Quadrant II.

20. Begin at the origin, move 0.4 units to the left, then 9.6 units down. The point lies in Quadrant III.

21. Begin at the origin, move 2.4 units to the right. The point lies on the *x*-axis.

22. Begin at the origin, move 4.3 units to the right, then 1.8 units down. The point lies in Quadrant IV.

23. The *x*- and *y*-coordinates are reversed.

For $P(2, 3)$: Start at the origin, move 2 units to the right, then 3 units up.

For $Q(1, -1)$: Start at the origin, move 1 unit to the right, then 1 unit down.

24.

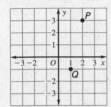

Points *A*, *B*, *C*, and *D* form a rectangle.

$\ell = |$x\text{-coordinate of } A - x\text{-coordinate of } B|$

$= |-2 - 2|$

$= |-4|$

$= 4$

$w = |$y\text{-coordinate of } A - y\text{-coordinate of } D|$

$= |6 - (-6)|$

$= |12|$

$= 12$

Perimeter $= 2\ell + 2w = 2(4) + 2(12) = 8 + 24 = 32$

The rectangle has a perimeter of 32 units.

25.

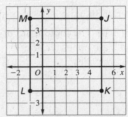

Points *E*, *F*, *G*, and *H* form a square.

$\ell = |$x\text{-coordinate of } G - x\text{-coordinate of } F|$

$= |-1 - 4|$

$= |5|$

$= 5$

$w = |$y\text{-coordinate of } G - y\text{-coordinate of } H|$

$= |3 - (-2)|$

$= |5|$

$= 5$

Perimeter $= 4s = 4(5) = 20$

The square has a perimeter of 20 units.

26.

Points *J*, *K*, *L*, and *M* form a square.

$\ell = |$x\text{-coordinate of } M - x\text{-coordinate of } J|$

$= |-1 - 5|$

$= |-6|$

$= 6$

$w = |$y\text{-coordinate of } M - y\text{-coordinate of } L|$

$= |4 - (-2)|$

$= |6|$

$= 6$

Perimeter $= 4s = 4(6) = 24$

The square has a perimeter of 24 units.

27.

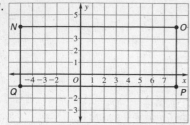

Points N, O, P, and Q form a rectangle.

$\ell = \left| x\text{-coordinate of } N - x\text{-coordinate of } O \right|$

$\quad = \left| -5 - 8 \right|$

$\quad = \left| -13 \right|$

$\quad = 13$

$w = \left| y\text{-coordinate of } N - y\text{-coordinate of } Q \right|$

$\quad = \left| 4 - (-1) \right|$

$\quad = \left| 5 \right|$

$\quad = 5$

Perimeter $= 2\ell + 2w = 2(13) + 2(5) = 26 + 10 = 36$

The rectangle has a perimeter of 36 units.

28. C; The coordinates of N are $(2, 0)$. The coordinates of R are $(-2, 0)$. Because -2 and 2 are opposites, the x-coordinates of N and R are opposites.

29.

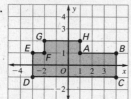

Horizontal or vertical distances between points:

A and B: $\left| 1 - 4 \right| = \left| -3 \right| = 3$

B and C: $\left| 1 - (-1) \right| = \left| 2 \right| = 2$

C and D: $\left| 4 - (-3) \right| = \left| 7 \right| = 7$

D and E: $\left| -1 - 1 \right| = \left| -2 \right| = 2$

E and F: $\left| -3 - (-2) \right| = \left| -1 \right| = 1$

F and G: $\left| 1 - 2 \right| = \left| -1 \right| = 1$

G and H: $\left| -2 - 1 \right| = \left| -3 \right| = 3$

H and A: $\left| 2 - 1 \right| = \left| 1 \right| = 1$

Perimeter $= 3 + 2 + 7 + 2 + 1 + 1 + 3 + 1 = 20$ units

Area $= 2(7) + 1(3) = 14 + 3 = 17$ square units

30.

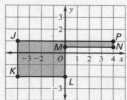

Horizontal or vertical distances between points:

J and K: $\left| 1 - (-2) \right| = \left| 3 \right| = 3$

K and L: $\left| -4 - 0 \right| = \left| -4 \right| = 4$

L and M: $\left| -2 - 0.5 \right| = \left| -2.5 \right| = 2.5$

M and N: $\left| 0 - 4 \right| = \left| -4 \right| = 4$

N and P: $\left| 0.5 - 1 \right| = \left| -0.5 \right| = 0.5$

P and J: $\left| 4 - (-4) \right| = \left| 8 \right| = 8$

Perimeter $= 3 + 4 + 2.5 + 4 + 0.5 + 8 = 22$ units

Area $= 3(4) + 0.5(4) = 12 + 2 = 14$ square units

31.

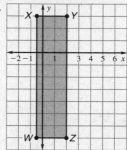

$\ell = \left| -\dfrac{1}{2} - 2 \right| = \left| -\dfrac{5}{2} \right| = \dfrac{5}{2}$

$w = \left| 3 - (-7) \right| = \left| 10 \right| = 10$

Perimeter $= 2\ell + 2w = 2\left(\dfrac{5}{2}\right) + 2(10) = 5 + 20 = 25$ units

Area $= \ell w = \dfrac{5}{2}(10) = 25$ square units

32. Horizontal distance between R and S:

$\left| 4 - (-1) \right| = \left| 5 \right| = 5$

Perimeter $= 2\ell + 2w$

$\qquad 22 = 2(5) + 2w$

$\qquad 22 = 10 + 2w$

Because $10 + 2(6) = 22$, $w = 6$.

The other side length is 6 units.

Other vertices:

$(4, -5 + 6) = (4, 1)$ and $(-1, -5 + 6) = (-1, 1)$, or

$(4, -5 - 6) = (4, -11)$ and $(-1, -5 - 6) = (-1, -11)$

33. Horizontal distance between R and S:

$\left| 2 - 9 \right| = \left| -7 \right| = 7$

Perimeter $= 2\ell + 2w$

$\qquad 36 = 2(7) + 2w$

$\qquad 36 = 14 + 2w$

Because $14 + 2(11) = 36$, $w = 11$.

The other side length is 11 units.

Other vertices:

$(2, 1 - 11) = (2, -10)$ and $(9, 1 - 11) = (9, -10)$ or

$(2, 1 + 11) = (2, 12)$ and $(9, 1 + 11) = (9, 12)$

Chapter 2, *continued*

34. Horizontal distance between R and S:

$$|-4 - 10| = |-14| = 14$$

$$
\begin{aligned}
\text{Perimeter} &= 2\ell + 2w \\
68 &= 2(14) + 2w \\
68 &= 28 + 2w
\end{aligned}
$$

Because $28 + 2(20) = 68$, $w = 20$.

The other side length is 20 units.

Other vertices: $(-4, -2 - 20) = (-4, -22)$ and $(10, -2 - 20) = (10, -22)$ or $(-4, -2 + 20) = (-4, 18)$ and $(10, -2 + 20) = (10, 18)$

35. *Sample answer:* The vertices $(4, 5)$ and $(-8, -5)$ form a rectangle.

$$\ell = |-8 - 4| = |-12| = 12$$
$$w = |5 - (-5)| = |10| = 10$$

$$
\begin{aligned}
\text{Perimeter} &= 2\ell + 2w \\
&= 2(12) + 2(10) \\
&= 24 + 20 \\
&= 44 \text{ units}
\end{aligned}
$$

Area $= \ell w = 12(10) = 120$ square units

Problem Solving

36. A; The intersection is 2 units to the right of the origin and 3 units up. So, the x-coordinate is 2 and the y-coordinate is 3. The coordinates are $(2, 3)$.

37.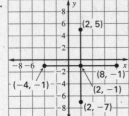

The endpoints of the four segments are $(2, 5)$, $(8, -1)$, $(2, -7)$, and $(-4, -1)$.

38. *Sample answer:* The coordinates of A are $(2 - 8, 5) = (-6, 5)$ in Quadrant II.

Let the width be 6 units.

So, C is $(2, -1)$ in Quadrant IV and D is $(-6, -1)$ in Quadrant III.

$$
\begin{aligned}
\text{Perimeter} &= 2\ell + 2w \\
&= 2(8) + 2(6) \\
&= 16 + 12 \\
&= 28 \text{ units}
\end{aligned}
$$

Area $= \ell w = 8(6) = 48$ square units

Let the width be 7 units.

So, C is $(2, -2)$ in Quadrant IV and D is $(-6, -2)$ in Quadrant III.

$$
\begin{aligned}
\text{Perimeter} &= 2\ell + 2w \\
&= 2(8) + 2(7) \\
&= 16 + 14 \\
&= 30 \text{ units}
\end{aligned}
$$

Area $= \ell w = 8(7) = 56$ square units

39. $\ell = |x\text{-coordinate of } A - x\text{-coordinate of } B|$
$$= |300 - (-300)|$$
$$= |600|$$
$$= 600$$

$w = |y\text{-coordinate of } A - y\text{-coordinate of } D|$
$$= |200 - (-200)|$$
$$= |400|$$
$$= 400$$

$$
\begin{aligned}
\text{Perimeter} &= 2\ell + 2w \\
&= 2(600) + 2(400) \\
&= 1200 + 800 \\
&= 2000
\end{aligned}
$$

The distance around the park is 2000 feet.

40. Length of Runway A: $|2000 - 0| = |2000| = 2000$ m

Length of Runway B: $|3000 - 0| = |3000| = 3000$ m

Plane 2 needs 2500 meters to take off, so it will use Runway B because Runway A is not long enough. Plane 1 will use Runway A.

Plane 1 take off point: $1500 = |2000 - x|$

Because $|2000 - 500| = 1500$, $x = 500$ and plane 1 takes off at $(500, 1500)$.

Plane 2 takeoff point: $2500 = |3000 - y|$

Because $|3000 - 500| = 2500$, $y = 500$ and plane 2 takes off at $(1000, 500)$.

41.

Cost of Pineapple

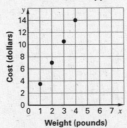

Sample answer: The points lie in a straight line. To estimate the cost of $2\frac{1}{2}$ pounds of pineapple, draw a line through the points and use it to approximate the value of y when $x = 2.5$. The y-value is 8.75.

42. Answers will vary.

43. a. Cost of 10-minute call $= 10(0.07) = \$.70$

Cost of 20-minute call $= 20(0.07) = \$1.40$

Cost of 30-minute call $= 30(0.07) = \$2.10$

Chapter 2, continued

b–c.

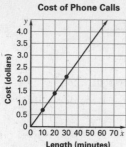

Cost of Phone Calls

The cost of an hour-long call is about $4.20.

44.

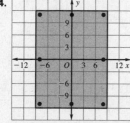

$\ell = \left| -9 - 9 \right| = \left| -18 \right| = 18$

$w = \left| 12 - (-12) \right| = \left| 24 \right| = 24$

Perimeter $= 2\ell + 2w = 2(18) + 2(24) = 36 + 48 = 84$

The perimeter of the desk top is 84 inches.

45.

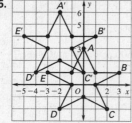

New coordinates:

$A'(-2, 6)$, $B'(1, 4)$, $C'(0, 1)$, $D'(-4, 1)$, $E'(-5, 4)$

46.

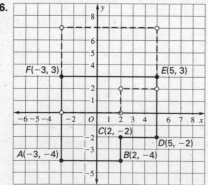

Horizontal or vertical distances between points:

A and B: $\left| -3 - 2 \right| = \left| -5 \right| = 5$

B and C: $\left| -4 - (-2) \right| = \left| -2 \right| = 2$

C and D: $\left| 2 - 5 \right| = \left| -3 \right| = 3$

D and E: $\left| -2 - 3 \right| = \left| -5 \right| = 5$

E and F: $\left| 5 - (-3) \right| = \left| 8 \right| = 8$

F and A: $\left| 3 - (-4) \right| = \left| 7 \right| = 7$

Perimeter of $ABCDEF = 5 + 2 + 3 + 5 + 8 + 7$

$= 30$ units

New coordinates: $A'(-3, 0)$, $B'(2, 0)$, $C'(2, 2)$, $D'(5, 2)$, $E'(5, 7)$, and $F'(-3, 7)$

Horizontal or vertical distances between points:

A' and B': $\left| -3 - 2 \right| = \left| -5 \right| = 5$

B' and C': $\left| 0 - 2 \right| = \left| -2 \right| = 2$

C' and D': $\left| 2 - 5 \right| = \left| -3 \right| = 3$

D' and E': $\left| 2 - 7 \right| = \left| -5 \right| = 5$

E' and F': $\left| 5 - (-3) \right| = \left| 8 \right| = 8$

F' and A': $\left| 7 - 0 \right| = \left| 7 \right| = 7$

Perimeter of $A'B'C'D'E'F' = 5 + 2 + 3 + 5 + 8 + 7$

$= 30$ units

The perimeters are the same.

47. *Sample answer:*

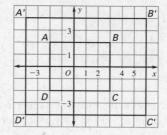

Perimeter of $ABCD = 2\ell + 2w$

$= 2(4) + 2(5)$

$= 8 + 10$

$= 18$

Perimeter of $A'B'C'D' = 2\ell + 2w$

$= 2(10) + 2(8)$

$= 20 + 16$

$= 36$

The new rectangle is larger than the original rectangle and the new perimeter is 2 times the original perimeter.

48.

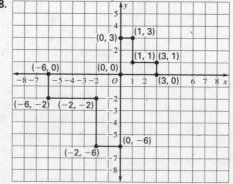

Perimeter of original figure $= 3 + 1 + 2 + 2 + 1 + 3$

$= 12$ units

Perimeter of new figure $= 6 + 2 + 4 + 4 + 2 + 6$

$= 24$ units

Sample answer: The new figure is rotated and larger than the original. The perimeter of the new figure is twice the perimeter of the original.

49.

Width x (cm)	1	2	3	4	5	6	7	8
Perimeter P (cm)	18	20	22	24	26	28	30	32

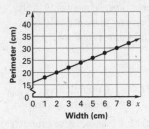

The data lie on a line.

Sample answer: The perimeter increases by 2 units for each additional unit of width.

50.

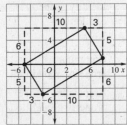

Area of dashed rectangle = 13(11) = 143

Total area of triangles

$= \frac{1}{2}(6)(10) + \frac{1}{2}(3)(5) + \frac{1}{2}(6)(10) + \frac{1}{2}(3)(5)$

$= 30 + 7.5 + 30 + 7.5$

$= 75$

The area of the rectangle is $143 - 75 = 68$ square units.

Sample answer: Draw a larger rectangle with horizontal and vertical side lengths passing through the original rectangle's vertices. Subtract the areas of the four triangles formed by the rectangles from the area of the larger rectangle.

Mixed Review

51. $23 - n = 12$ 23 minus what number equals 12? Because $23 - 11 = 12$, $n = 11$.

52. $x + 9 = 24$ What number plus 9 equals 24? Because $15 + 9 = 24$, $x = 15$.

53. $14 - y + 6 = 15$
$20 - y = 15$ 20 minus what number equals 15? Because $20 - 5 = 15$, $y = 5$.

54. $24 + (-9) + (-12) = 15 + (-12) = 3$

55. $-14 + 30 + (-17) = 16 + (-17) = -1$

56. $-40 + 8 + 12 = -32 + 12 = -20$

57. $4(x + 9) - 4 = 4x + 36 + (-4) = 4x + 32$

58. $6(y - 6) + 11 - 6y = 36 + 11 - 6y - 25$

59. $-9(z - 2) + z = -9z + 18 + z = -8z + 18$

60. B; Candles you still need to sell $= 35 - 18 = 17$
You need to sell 17 more candles.

Quiz 2.6–2.8 (p. 100)

1. $(19 + 33) + 11 = (33 + 19) + 11$ Commutative property of addition

$= 33 + (19 + 11)$ Associative property of addition

$= 33 + 30$ Add.

$= 63$ Add.

2. $(25 \cdot 16)(-4) = (16 \cdot 25)(-4)$ Commutative property of multiplication

$= 16[25 \cdot (-4)]$ Associative property of multiplication

$= 16(-100)$ Multiply.

$= -1600$ Multiply.

3. $5(-4 \cdot 9) = [5 \cdot (-4)]9$ Associative property of multiplication

$= -20(9)$ Multiply.

$= -180$ Multiply.

4. $9x + 22x = (9 + 22)x = 31x$

5. $3a - 2b + 6 - a = 3a - a - 2b + 6 = 2a - 2b + 6$

6. $8(y + 2) - 4y = 8y + 16 - 4y = 4y + 16$

7. Point A is 3 units to the left of the origin and 1 unit up. The coordinates of A are $(-3, 1)$.

Point B is 3 units above the origin. The coordinates of B are $(0, 3)$.

Point C is 3 units to the right of the origin and 4 units up. The coordinates of C are $(3, 4)$.

Point D is 2 units to the right of the origin and 3 units down. The coordinates of D are $(2, -3)$.

Point E is 2 units to the left of the origin and 1 unit down. The coordinates of E are $(-2, -1)$.

8. Point B lies on the y-axis.

9. Point A lies in Quadrant II.

10. Points scored $= 13 + 6 + 7 + 14$

$= 13 + 7 + 6 + 14$ Commutative property of addition

$= (13 + 7) + (6 + 14)$ Associative property of addition

$= 20 + 20$ Add.

$= 40$ Add.

Joe scored 40 points.

Sample answer: Use the commutative and associative properties of addition as shown to order the terms so that you can add mentally.

Chapter 2, continued

Brain Game (p. 100)

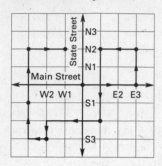

Stop	Number of blocks traveled
1	3
2	2
3	2
4	4
5	4
6	3
7	3
8	2

Total number of blocks traveled

$= 3 + 2 + 2 + 4 + 4 + 3 + 3 + 2 = 23$

Jack traveled 23 blocks.

Mixed Review of Problem Solving (p. 101)

1. a. $\ell = \left| x\text{-coordinate of } B - x\text{-coordinate of } C \right|$

$\quad = \left| -3 - 4 \right|$

$\quad = \left| -7 \right|$

$\quad = 7$

$w = \left| y\text{-coordinate of } B - y\text{-coordinate of } A \right|$

$\quad = \left| 4 - (-1) \right|$

$\quad = \left| 5 \right|$

$\quad = 5$

Area of $ABCD = \ell w = 7(5) = 35$ square units.

b.

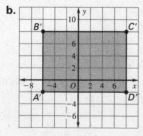

$\ell = \left| -6 - 8 \right| = \left| -14 \right| = 14$

$w = \left| 8 - (-2) \right| = \left| 10 \right| = 10$

Area of $A'B'C'D' = \ell w = 14(10) = 140$ square units

c. No, the new rectangle's area is four times the original rectangle's area because $4(35) = 140$.

2. Total spent $= 3(3.25) + 3(7.95) + 3(1)$

$\quad = 3(3.25 + 7.95 + 1)$

$\quad = 3(12.20)$

$\quad = 36.60$

You spent $36.60 on gifts for your friends.

3. She can calculate $6 \cdot 42 + 6 \cdot 87 + 6 \cdot 22 + 6 \cdot 29$ or $6(42 + 87 + 22 + 29)$. The expressions are related by the distributive property. *Sample answer:* I prefer $6(42 + 87 + 22 + 29)$ because there are only two operations, an addition (of 4 terms) and then a multiplication.

4. a. $(12 + 92) + (-12)$

$= (92 + 12) + (-12)$	Commutative property of addition
$= 92 + [12 + (-12)]$	Associative property of addition
$= 92 + 0$	Inverse property of addition
$= 92$	Identity property of addition

b. $-64 + (100 + 64)$

$= -64 + (64 + 100)$	Commutative property of addition
$= (-64 + 64) + 100$	Associative property of addition
$= 0 + 100$	Inverse property of addition
$= 100$	Identity property of addition

c. $[10 \times (-2)] \times 50$

$= 10 \times (-2 \times 50)$	Associative property of multiplication
$= 10 \times (-100)$	Multiply.
$= -1000$	Multiply.

d. $(20 \div 4) \div (-5)$

$= 5 \div (-5)$	Divide.
$= -1$	Divide.

e. $(16 - 5) - (-4)$

$= [16 + (-5)] + 4$	Change subtraction to addition.
$= 11 + 4$	Add.
$= 15$	Add.

5. Yes, Paulo can make his walk. *Sample answer:* One way is to follow the rectangular path given by the vertices $(-200, -400)$, $(300, -400)$, $(300, 200)$, and $(-200, 200)$. Notice that the distance walked is $\left| -200 - 300 \right| + \left| -400 - 200 \right| + \left| 300 - (-200) \right| + \left| 200 - (-400) \right| = 500 + 600 + 500 + 600$, or 2200 yards.

Chapter 2, continued

6. Total cost of trip for x students $= 250 + (8 + 5)x$
$$= 250 + 13x$$

When $x = 20$:

Total cost $= 250 + 13(20) = 250 + 260 = \$510$

When $x = 25$:

Total cost $= 250 + 13(25)$
$$= 250 + 13(20 + 5)$$
$$= 250 + 260 + 65$$
$$= \$575$$

Sample answer: The distributive property was used to find the total cost for 25 students because it allowed the use of mental math to easily calculate the answers.

7. *Sample answer:* Suppose it costs $5 to buy each sweatshirt, $200 plus $3 per sweatshirt to print them, and $100 for other expenses. Then the cost to buy and prepare x sweatshirts for sale is $5x + (200 + 3x) + 100$, or $8x + 300$. The revenue from selling x sweatshirts at $20 each is $20x$. So the profit is $20x - (8x + 300)$, or $12x - 300$.

Chapter 2 Review (pp. 102–106)

1. Two numbers, 15 and -15, have an absolute value of 15.

2. $-6y + 8 - 7x + 17x - 21y$

Terms: $-6y$, 8, $-7x$, $17x$, $-21y$

Coefficients: -6, -7, 17, -21

3. There are 4 quadrants in a coordinate plane.

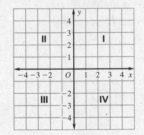

4. A point in a coordinate plane is represented by an *ordered pair*.

5. A *coordinate plane* is formed by the intersection of a horizontal number line and a vertical number line.

6. The *mean* is the sum of the values divided by the number of values.

7.

The integers ordered from least to greatest are -42, -31, -5, 8, 11, and 53.

8.

The integers ordered from least to greatest are -102, -58, -56, 98, and 114.

9. The opposite of 22 is -22.
$$|22| = 22$$

10. The opposite of -13 is 13.
$$|-13| = 13$$

11. The opposite of -512 is 512.
$$|-512| = 512$$

12. The opposite of 102 is -102.
$$|102| = 102$$

13. The opposite of -92 is 92.
$$|-92| = 92$$

14. The opposite of 76 is -76.
$$|76| = 76$$

15. The opposite of 147 is -147.
$$|147| = 147$$

16. The opposite of -250 is 250.
$$|-250| = 250$$

17. $-81 + (-91) = -172$ **18.** $32 + (-79) = -47$

19. $-324 + 500 = 176$ **20.** $-468 + (-196) = -664$

21. $752 + (-351) = 401$ **22.** $-96 + (-11) = -107$

23. $-246 + 198 = -48$ **24.** $-28 + (-59) = -87$

25. $-34 + 68 = 34$ **26.** $471 + (-504) = -33$

27. $-101 + (-235) = -336$

28. $97 + (-41) = 56$

29. $-29 - 57 = -29 + (-57) = -86$

30. $62 - (-58) = 62 + 58 = 120$

31. $-43 - (-122) = -43 + 122 = 79$

32. $31 - 108 = 31 + (-108) = -77$

33. $88 - (-49) = 88 + 49 = 137$

34. $-56 - (-32) = -56 + 32 = -24$

35. $-50 - 84 = -50 + (-84) = -134$

36. $61 - 28 = 61 + (-28) = 33$

37. $-6(9) = -54$ **38.** $31(-4) = -124$

39. $-9(-23)(0) = 207(0) = 0$

40. $-2(-3)(6)(-8) = 6(6)(-8) = 36(-8) = -288$

41. When $x = -6$, $y = -4$, and $z = -8$:

$xyz = -6(-4)(-8) = 24(-8) = -192$

42. When $x = -6$ and $z = -8$:

$9z - 2x = 9(-8) - 2(-6)$
$$= -72 - (-12)$$
$$= -72 + 12$$
$$= -60$$

43. When $x = -6$, $y = -4$, and $z = -8$:

$11y - 2xz = 11(-4) - 2(-6)(-8)$
$$= -44 - (-12)(-8)$$
$$= -44 - 96$$
$$= -44 + (-96)$$
$$= -140$$

Chapter 2, *continued*

44. When $x = -6$, $y = -4$, and $z = -8$:

$$
\begin{aligned}
2x + 3yz &= 2(-6) + 3(-4)(-8) \\
&= -12 + (-12)(-8) \\
&= -12 + 96 \\
&= 84
\end{aligned}
$$

45. When $x = -6$, $y = -4$, and $z = -8$:

$$
\begin{aligned}
2xy - z &= 2(-6)(-4) - (-8) \\
&= -12(-4) + 8 \\
&= 48 + 8 \\
&= 56
\end{aligned}
$$

46. When $x = -6$ and $y = -4$:

$$
3y + 4x = 3(-4) + 4(-6) = -12 + (-24) = -36
$$

47. When $y = -4$ and $z = -8$:

$$
\begin{aligned}
2yz + 3yz &= 2(-4)(-8) + 3(-4)(-8) \\
&= -8(-8) + (-12)(-8) \\
&= 64 + 96 \\
&= 160
\end{aligned}
$$

48. When $x = -6$, $y = -4$, and $z = -8$:

$$
\begin{aligned}
9z - 4xy &= 9(-8) - 4(-6)(-4) \\
&= -72 - (-24)(-4) \\
&= -72 - 96 \\
&= -72 + (-96) \\
&= -168
\end{aligned}
$$

49. Height of balloon $= 110 + 6(18) - 3(22)$

$$
\begin{aligned}
&= 110 + 108 - 66 \\
&= 218 - 66 \\
&= 218 + (-66) \\
&= 152
\end{aligned}
$$

The balloon is at a height of 152 feet.

50. $\dfrac{-26}{2} = -13$

51. $\dfrac{-98}{-7} = 14$

52. $\dfrac{-120}{-15} = 8$

53. $\dfrac{63}{-7} = -9$

54. $\dfrac{-56}{-14} = 4$

55. $\dfrac{-84}{12} = -7$

56. $\dfrac{45}{-9} = -5$

57. $\dfrac{-48}{-16} = 3$

58. Sum of data

$$
\begin{aligned}
&= 5 + 7 + (-9) + (-2) + (-6) + 8 + (-9) + 6 \\
&= 0
\end{aligned}
$$

Mean $= \dfrac{0}{8} = 0$

59. Sum of data $= 15 + (-9) + 6 + (-14) + (-18) + 12$
$$
\begin{aligned}
&\quad + 7 + 5 + (-2) + 8 \\
&= 10
\end{aligned}
$$

Mean $= \dfrac{10}{10} = 1$

60. Sum of data $= -11 + 15 + 26 + 12 + (-8) + 0 + 1$

$$
= 35
$$

Mean $= \dfrac{35}{7} = 5$

61. Sum of data $= 24 + (-23) + (-17) + (-13) + 27$
$$
\begin{aligned}
&\quad + 31 + (-44) + (-9) \\
&= -24
\end{aligned}
$$

Mean $= \dfrac{-24}{8} = -3$

62.
$$
\begin{aligned}
19 - (-58 - 81) &= 19 + (58 + 81) \\
&= 19 + (81 + 58) \\
&= (19 + 81) + 58 \\
&= 100 + 58 \\
&= 158
\end{aligned}
$$

The distributive property, the commutative property of addition, and the associative property of addition were used.

63. $(-28 - 95 + 85) + (-62)$

$$
\begin{aligned}
&= -28 + (-95) + 85 + (-62) \\
&= -28 + (-62) + (-95) + 85 \\
&= -90 + (-95) + 85 \\
&= -90 + (-10) \\
&= -100
\end{aligned}
$$

The commutative and associative properties of addition were used.

64.
$$
\begin{aligned}
(-45 + 97) - (-45) &= (97 + (-45)) + 45 \\
&= 97 + ((-45) + 45) \\
&= 97 + 0 \\
&= 97
\end{aligned}
$$

The commutative, associative, inverse, and identity properties of addition were used.

65. $4(19 \cdot 25) = 4(25 \cdot 19)$

$$
\begin{aligned}
&= (4 \cdot 25) \cdot 19 \\
&= 100 \cdot 19 \\
&= 1900
\end{aligned}
$$

The commutative and associative properties of multiplication were used.

66.
$$
\begin{aligned}
[-54 \cdot (-56)] \cdot 0 \cdot (-17) &= -54(-56 \cdot 0)(-17) \\
&= -54 \cdot 0 \cdot (-17) \\
&= 0(-17) \\
&= 0
\end{aligned}
$$

The multiplication property of zero and associative property of multiplication were used.

67. $(-15 \cdot 5) \cdot (-20) = -15[5 \cdot (-20)]$

$$
\begin{aligned}
&= -15(-100) \\
&= 1500
\end{aligned}
$$

The associative property of multiplication was used.

68. $(-19 - 56) + 19 = [-56 + (-19)] + 19$
$ = -56 + (-19 + 19)$
$ = -56 + 0$
$ = -56$

The commutative, associative, inverse, and identity properties of addition were used.

69. $12 \cdot 96 \cdot 0 + 3 = 12 \cdot 0 \cdot 96 + 3$
$ = 0 \cdot 96 + 3$
$ = 0 + 3$
$ = 3$

The commutative property of multiplication, multiplication property of zero, and identity property of addition were used.

70. $(-92 + 47) - (-92) = [47 + (-92)] + 92$
$ = 47 + (-92 + 92)$
$ = 47 + 0$
$ = 47$

The commutative, associative, inverse, and identity properties of addition were used.

71. $5(12x - 20) = 60x - 100$

72. $7(9 + 11y) = 63 + 77y$

73. $4(25z - 30) = 100z - 120$

74. $12(6y - 4) = 72y - 48$

75. $9(15 - 12t) = 135 - 108t$

76. $15(4r + 15) = 60r + 225$

77. $14x - 3y - 7x + y = 14x - 7x - 3y + y = 7x - 2y$

78. $4x - 11y + 2(1 - x) = 4x - 11y + 2 - 2x$
$ = 2x - 11y + 2$

79. $5x + 2y - 9x - 8y = 5x - 9x + 2y - 8y$
$ = -4x - 6y$

80. $6a + 2a - 5b - 11a = 6a + 2a - 11a - 5b$
$ = -3a - 5b$

81. $9(4a - 2b) + 13a + 19b = 36a - 18b + 13a + 19b$
$ = 36a + 13a - 18b + 19b$
$ = 49a + b$

82. $-2(5 - y) + 11y + 12 = -10 + 2y + 11y + 12$
$ = 2y + 11y + 12 - 10$
$ = 13y + 2$

83. $5(16.90) = 5(17 - 0.10)$
$ = 5(17) - 5(0.10)$
$ = 85 - 0.50$
$ = 84.50$

The total price is $84.50.

84. Point A is 3 units to the right of the origin and 1 unit down. The coordinates of A are $(3, -1)$.

85. Point B is 4 units to the left of the origin and 3 units up. The coordinates of B are $(-4, 3)$.

86. Point C is 4 units below the origin. The coordinates of C are $(0, -4)$.

87. Point D is 2 units to the left of the origin and 3 units down. The coordinates of D are $(-2, -3)$.

88.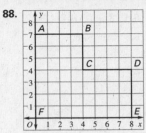

Length of $\overline{AB} = |x\text{-coordinate of } A - x\text{-coordinate of } B|$
$\phantom{\text{Length of } \overline{AB}} = |0 - 4|$
$\phantom{\text{Length of } \overline{AB}} = |-4|$
$\phantom{\text{Length of } \overline{AB}} = 4$

Length of $\overline{BC} = |y\text{-coordinate of } B - y\text{-coordinate of } C|$
$\phantom{\text{Length of } \overline{BC}} = |7 - 4|$
$\phantom{\text{Length of } \overline{BC}} = |3|$
$\phantom{\text{Length of } \overline{BC}} = 3$

Length of $\overline{CD} = |x\text{-coordinate of } C - x\text{-coordinate of } D|$
$\phantom{\text{Length of } \overline{CD}} = |4 - 8|$
$\phantom{\text{Length of } \overline{CD}} = |-4|$
$\phantom{\text{Length of } \overline{CD}} = 4$

Length of $\overline{DE} = |y\text{-coordinate of } D - y\text{-coordinate of } E|$
$\phantom{\text{Length of } \overline{DE}} = |4 - 0|$
$\phantom{\text{Length of } \overline{DE}} = |4|$
$\phantom{\text{Length of } \overline{DE}} = 4$

Length of $\overline{EF} = |x\text{-coordinate of } E - x\text{-coordinate of } F|$
$\phantom{\text{Length of } \overline{EF}} = |8 - 0|$
$\phantom{\text{Length of } \overline{EF}} = |8|$
$\phantom{\text{Length of } \overline{EF}} = 8$

Length of $\overline{FA} = |y\text{-coordinate of } F - y\text{-coordinate of } A|$
$\phantom{\text{Length of } \overline{FA}} = |0 - 7|$
$\phantom{\text{Length of } \overline{FA}} = |-7|$
$\phantom{\text{Length of } \overline{FA}} = 7$

Perimeter $= 4 + 3 + 4 + 4 + 8 + 7 = 30$

The perimeter is 30 units.

Chapter 2 Test (p. 107)

1.

The integers ordered from least to greatest are -11, -9, -1, 0, 8, and 14.

2.

The integers ordered from least to greatest are -111, -59, -12, 22, 87, and 123.

3. When $x = 2$: $|x| = |2| = 2$
When $x = -4$: $|x| = |-4| = 4$

Chapter 2, *continued*

4. When $x = -1$: $-(-x) = -[-(-1)] = -(1) = -1$

When $x = 7$: $-(-x) = -(-7) = 7$

5. $17 + (-9) = 8$

6. $-8 + (-14) = -22$

7. $-2 + (-21) = -23$

8. $-33 + 26 = -7$

9. $1 - 19 = 1 + (-19) = -18$

10. $-4 - 17 = -4 + (-17) = -21$

11. $10 - (-15) = 10 + 15 = 25$

12. $-7 - (-18) = -7 + 18 = 11$

13. $17 + 35 - 3 = 52 - 3 = 52 + (-3) = 49$

14. $-16 + 14 - 12 = -2 - 12 = -2 + (-12) = -14$

15. $11 + (-1 + 32) = 11 + 31 = 42$

16. $(-26 + 17) + 4 = -9 + 4 = -5$

17. $-5(14) = -70$

18. $-12(-20) = 240$

19. $\dfrac{-152}{-19} = 8$

20. $\dfrac{-132}{6} = -22$

21. When $a = 3$ and $c = 15$:

$\dfrac{c}{-a} = \dfrac{15}{-3} = -5$

22. When $b = -15$ and $c = 15$:

$\dfrac{6b}{2c} = \dfrac{6(-15)}{2(15)} = \dfrac{-90}{30} = -3$

23. When $a = 3$ and $c = 15$:

$\dfrac{c}{-5a} = \dfrac{15}{-5(3)} = \dfrac{15}{-15} = -1$

24. When $a = 3$ and $b = -15$:

$\dfrac{b^2}{a^2} = \dfrac{(-15)^2}{3^2} = \dfrac{225}{9} = 25$

25. $3x + 4 - x + 1 = 3x - x + 4 + 1 = 2x + 5$

26. $2x - 3y + 5x - (-9y) = 2x - 3y + 5x + 9y$

$= 2x + 5x - 3y + 9y$

$= 7x + 6y$

27. $2(9x - 22y) + 4x = 18x - 44y + 4x = 22x - 44y$

28–31. Graph: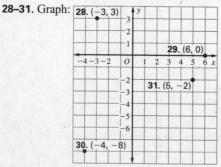

28. (−3, 3)   29. (6, 0)   31. (5, −2)   30. (−4, −8)

28. Begin at the origin, move 3 units to the left, then 3 units up. The point lies in Quadrant II.

29. Begin at the origin, move 6 units to the right. The point lies on the x-axis.

30. Begin at the origin, move 4 units to the left, then 8 units down. The point lies in Quadrant III.

31. Begin at the origin, move 5 units to the right, then 2 units down. The point lies in Quadrant IV.

32. Sum of temperatures

$= -5 + (-8) + (-13) + (-16) + (-8) + 11 + 0$

$= -39$

Mean $= \dfrac{-39}{7} \approx -6$

The mean temperature is about $-6°F$.

33. Total cost $= 2.16 + 3.25 + 2(0.42)$

$= 2.16 + 3.25 + 0.84$

$= 2.16 + 0.84 + 3.25$

$= 3.00 + 3.25$

$= 6.25$

The total cost is $6.25.

34.

x	−3	−2	−1	0	1	2	3
y	3	2	1	0	1	2	3

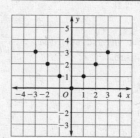

Standardized Test Preparation (pp. 108–109)

1. Full credit; The steps are clearly stated and reflect correct mathematical thinking. The calculations and answers are correct.

Standardized Test Practice (pp. 110–111)

1. Total cost for x students $= 150 + 8x + 3x = 150 + 11x$

When $x = 18$:

Total cost $= 150 + 11(18)$

$= 150 + 11(20 - 2)$

$= 150 + 220 - 22$

$= \$348$

When $x = 26$:

Total cost $= 150 + 11(26)$

$= 150 + 11(30 - 4)$

$= 150 + 330 - 44$

$= \$436$

Sample answer: The distributive property was used to find the total costs because it allowed the use of mental math to easily calculate the answers.

2. a. Monday: $30

Tuesday: −$10

Wednesday: $20

Thursday: $50

Friday: −$30

Saturday: $40

Sunday: −$20

b.

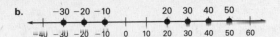

The integers ordered from least to greatest are -30, -20, -10, 20, 30, 40, and 50.

c. Total earnings
$$= 30 + (-10) + 20 + 50 + (-30) + 40 + (-20)$$
$$= \$80$$

The earnings are $80, so the store made a profit.

3. a. At 7 A.M.: $F = \frac{9}{5}(5) + 32 = 9 + 32 = 41°F$

At 6 P.M.: $F = \frac{9}{5}(15) + 32 = 27 + 32 = 59°F$

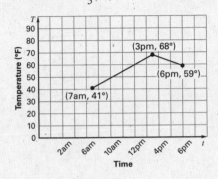

b. Change in temperature between 7 A.M. and 3 P.M.:
$68 - 41 = 27°F$

Change in temperature between 3 P.M. and 6 P.M.:
$59 - 68 = -9°F$

c. Next day temperature at 7 A.M.:

$F = \frac{9}{5}(10) + 32 = 18 + 32 = 50°F$

Temperature at 3 P.M.: $50 + 27 = 77°F$

Temperature at 6 P.M.: $77 - 9 = 68°F$

4. Vertices: $(-2, 3), (3, 3), (3, -1),$ and $(-2, -1)$
$\ell = \left| -2 - 3 \right| = \left| -5 \right| = 5$
$w = \left| 3 - (-1) \right| = \left| 4 \right| = 4$
Convert units to feet: $\ell = (5)(5 \text{ ft}) = 25 \text{ ft}$
$w = (4)(5 \text{ ft}) = 20 \text{ ft}$
Perimeter $= 2\ell + 2w$
$= 2(25) + 2(20)$
$= 50 + 40$
$= 90 \text{ ft}$
Area $= \ell w = 25(20) = 500 \text{ ft}^2$

5. A; $2(30) = 60$

Meg ascended 60 feet.

$n + 60 = -15$

Because $-75 + 60 = -15$, $n = -75$. Meg's position was at -75 feet.

6. B; $5 - 3x + 4 - 2y - x = 5 + 4 - 3x - x - 2y$
$$= 9 - 4x - 2y$$

7. B; When $a = 9$ and $b = -6$;
$$20 - a - (-b) = 20 - 9 - [-(-6)]$$
$$= 20 - 9 - 6$$
$$= 20 + (-9) + (-6)$$
$$= 5$$

8. Sum of numbers
$$= -6 + (-4) + (-1) + 3 + 6 + (-2) + 5 + 7$$
$$= 8$$

Mean $= \frac{8}{8} = 1$

9. Today's high temperature $= -3 + 8 = 5°F$

10. Height of bird $= 30 + 5(5) - 3(7)$
$$= 30 + 25 - 21$$
$$= 30 + 25 + (-21)$$
$$= 34$$

The bird is at a height of 34 feet.

11. $x + (-3) + 4 + 1 + (-2) + 4 = 26$
$$x + 4 = 26$$

Because $22 + 4 = 26$, $x = 22$.

The price of a share of the stock before the 5 week period started was $22.

12. *Sample answer:*

$(57 + 24) + (36 + 83)$

$= 57 + (24 + 36) + 83$	Associative property of addition
$= 57 + 83 + (24 + 36)$	Commutative property of addition
$= (57 + 83) + (24 + 36)$	Associative property of addition
$= 140 + 60$	Add.
$= 200$	Add.

You can use the commutative and associative properties of addition as shown above to make it easy to add mentally.

13.

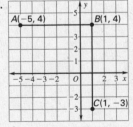

Point D must be $(-5, -3)$.
$\ell = \left| -5 - 1 \right| = \left| -6 \right| = 6$
$w = \left| 4 - (-3) \right| = \left| 7 \right| = 7$
Perimeter $= 2\ell + 2w = 2(6) + 2(7) = 12 + 14 = 26$ units

Chapter 2, *continued*

14. $-(x + y) = -x - y = -x + (-y)$

Yes, the opposite of the sum of two numbers equals the sum of the opposites of the numbers.

Sample examples: $-(5 + 6) = -11 = -5 + (-6)$

$-(1 + 2) = -3 = -1 + (-2)$

$-(2 + 7) = -9 = -2 + (-7)$

15. *Sample answer:*

$3(3.50) + 3(1.75) = 3(3) + 3(0.50) + 3(2) - 3(0.25)$

$= 9 + 1.50 + 6 - 0.75$

$= 16.50 + (-0.75)$

$= 15.75$

Your friend spends $15.75.

Chapter 3

1. $3 \times 16 = 48$;

   $12 \times 20 = 240$;

   $100 - 21 = 79$;

   $3.659 \times 10 = 36.59$;

   $\frac{250}{5} = 50$;

   $\frac{18}{3} = 6$;

   $9^2 = 81$

   $16 = P$; $20 = T$; $21 = U$; $10 = J$; $5 = E$; $18 = R$; $9 = I$

   The name of the planet is JUPITER.

2. Check student's work.

Stop and Think (p. 113)

1. $[[36 \times (-1)] - 8] \times (-4) = (-36 - 8) \times (-4)$

   $ = -44(-4)$

   $ = 176$

   Sample answer: I solved the paths and this was the highest score.

2. *Sample answer:*

   $5 \times$ _?_ $= 95$ $(19 \longrightarrow S)$

   $16 \times$ _?_ $= 16$ $(1 \longrightarrow A)$

   $\frac{180}{?} = 10$ $(18 \longrightarrow R)$

   $50 -$ _?_ $= 37$ $(13 \longrightarrow M)$

   Answer: MARS

Review Prerequisite Skills (p. 114)

1. 5 is the *opposite* of -5.

2. In the expression $6x$, 6 is the *coefficient*.

3. A statement with an equal sign between two expressions is an *equation*.

4. *Like terms* have identical variable parts raised to the same power.

5. Equation: $x - 1 = 5$

   Question: What number minus 1 equals 5?

   Solution: 6

6. Equation: $x - 2 = 9$

   Question: What number minus 2 equals 9?

   Solution: 11

7. Equation: $4 + x = 12$

   Question: 4 plus what number equals 12?

   Solution: 8

8. Equation: $10 = x + 3$

   Question: 10 equals what number plus 3?

   Solution: 7

9. Equation: $5x = 20$

   Question: 5 times what number equals 20?

   Solution: 4

10. Equation: $x \div 3 = 1$

    Question: What number divided by 3 equals 1?

    Solution: 3

11. Equation: $x \div 7 = 5$

    Question: What number divided by 7 equals 5?

    Solution: 35

12. Equation: $3x = 51$

    Question: Three times what number equals 51?

    Solution: 17

13. $-3 - 2 + 8 = -5 + 8 = 3$

14. $3 - 7 + 2 - 1 = -4 + 2 - 1 = -2 - 1 = -3$

15. $-2(3 + 1) + 2 = -2(4) + 2 = -8 + 2 = -6$

16. $8(1 - 4) - 9 = 8(-3) - 9 = -24 - 9 = -33$

17. $-5 \times 4 + 2 = -20 + 2 = -18$

18. $7(3 + 1) \div 2 = 7(4) \div 2 = 28 \div 2 = 14$

19. $-8 \div 2 + 4 \times 6 = -4 + 24 = 20$

20. $6(2 - 5) \times 3 = 6(-3) \times 3 = -18 \times 3 = -54$

21. $d = r \cdot t$

    $d = 540 \cdot \frac{1}{4}$

    $d = 135$

    The jet airplane travels 135 miles in 15 minutes.

Lesson 3.1

Investigation (pp. 115–116)

1. $x + 5 = 7$

   (1)

   (2)

   (3)

   The solution of the equation is 2.

2. $x + 4 = 9$

   (1)

   (2)

   (3)

   The solution of the equation is 5.

Chapter 3, *continued*

3. $5 + x = 7$

(1)

(2)

(3)

The solution of the equation is 2.

4. $6 = x + 2$

(1)

(2)

(3)

The solution of the equation is 4.

5. $7 + x = 9$

(1)

(2)

(3)

The solution of the equation is 2.

6. (1)

$x - 3 = 6$

(2)

$x - 3 + 3 = 6 + 3$

(3)

$x = 9$

The solution of the equation is 9.

7. (1)

$x - 5 = 5$

(2)

$x - 5 + 5 = 5 + 5$

(3)

$x = 10$

The solution of the equation is 10.

8. (1)

$x + 6 = 2$

(2)

$x + 6 - 6 = 2 - 6$

(3)

$x = -4$

The solution of the equation is -4.

9. (1)

$8 + x = 1$

(2)

$8 - 8 + x = 1 - 8$

(3)

$x = -7$

The solution of the equation is -7.

10. (1)

$x - 4 = -2$

(2)

$x - 4 + 4 = -2 + 4$

(3)

$x = 2$

The solution of the equation is 2.

11. (1)

$x - 7 = -3$

(2)

$x - 7 + 7 = -3 + 7$

(3)

$x = 4$

The solution of the equation is 4.

12. (1)

$x + 8 = 4$

(2)

$x + 8 - 8 = 4 - 8$

(3)

$x = -4$

The solution of the equation is -4.

13. (1)

$$x - 3 = -6$$

(2)

$$x - 3 + 3 = -6 + 3$$

(3)

$$x = -3$$

The solution of the equation is -3.

14. *Sample answer:* $x - 4 = -2$

Zero pairs are needed because there are not four -1 tiles on the right hand side, so you cannot simply remove four -1 tiles from each side.

3.1 Guided Practice (p. 118)

1.
$$x + 9 = 20$$
$$x + 9 - 9 = 20 - 9$$
$$x = 11$$
Check: $11 + 9 = 20$ ✓

2.
$$-10 = 3 + y$$
$$-10 - 3 = 3 + y - 3$$
$$-13 = y$$
Check: $-10 = 3 + (-13)$ ✓

3.
$$m - 14 = -15$$
$$m - 14 + 14 = -15 + 14$$
$$m = -1$$
Check: $-1 - 14 = -15$ ✓

4.
$$2 = z - 6.4$$
$$2 + 6.4 = z - 6.4 + 6.4$$
$$8.4 = z$$
Check: $2 = 8.4 - 6.4$ ✓

5.
$$s + 49 = 162$$
$$s + 49 - 49 = 162 - 49$$
$$s = 113$$
Jerry had 113 seashells.

3.1 Exercises (pp. 119–121)

Skill Practice

1. Addition and subtraction are *inverse* operations.

2. Equations that have the same solutions are called *equivalent*.

3.
$$x + 10 = 16$$
$$x + 10 - 10 = 16 - 10$$
$$x = 6$$
Check: $6 + 10 = 16$ ✓

4.
$$12 - x = 8$$
$$12 + 8 = x - 8 + 8$$
$$20 = x$$
Check: $12 = 20 - 8$ ✓

5.
$$43 - u = 21$$
$$43 + 21 = a - 21 + 21$$
$$64 = a$$
Check: $43 = 64 - 21$ ✓

6.
$$r + 2 = 7$$
$$r + 2 - 2 = 7 - 2$$
$$r = 5$$
Check: $5 + 2 = 7$ ✓

7.
$$t - 5 = 2$$
$$t - 5 + 5 = 2 + 5$$
$$t = 7$$
Check: $7 - 5 = 2$ ✓

8.
$$z + 9 = 11$$
$$z + 9 - 9 = 11 - 9$$
$$z = 2$$
Check: $2 + 9 = 11$ ✓

9.
$$23 = 6 + n$$
$$23 - 6 = 6 + n - 6$$
$$17 = n$$
Check: $23 = 6 + 17$ ✓

10.
$$y - 15 = 9$$
$$y - 15 + 15 = 9 + 15$$
$$y = 24$$
Check: $24 - 15 = 9$ ✓

11.
$$13 = d - 27$$
$$13 + 27 = d - 27 + 27$$
$$40 = d$$
Check: $13 = 40 - 27$ ✓

12.
$$24 = 52 + n$$
$$24 - 52 = 52 + n - 52$$
$$-28 = n$$
Check: $24 = 52 + (-28)$ ✓

13.
$$-204 = m - 41$$
$$-204 + 41 = m - 41 + 41$$
$$-163 = m$$
Check: $-204 = -163 - 41$ ✓

14.
$$11 = c + 48$$
$$11 - 48 = c + 48 - 48$$
$$-37 = c$$
Check: $11 = -37 + 48$ ✓

15.
$$p + 3.4 = 4.4$$
$$p + 3.4 - 3.4 = 4.4 - 3.4$$
$$p = 1$$
Check: $1 + 3.4 = 4.4$ ✓

16.
$$1.76 = a - 2.94$$
$$1.76 + 2.94 = a - 2.94 + 2.94$$
$$4.7 = a$$
Check: $1.76 = 4.7 - 2.94$ ✓

17.
$$3.777 + c = 3.977$$
$$3.777 + c - 3.777 = 3.977 - 3.777$$
$$c = 0.2$$
Check: $3.777 + 0.2 = 3.977$ ✓

18.
$$x + \frac{1}{2} = \frac{1}{2}$$
$$x + \frac{1}{2} - \frac{1}{2} = \frac{1}{2} - \frac{1}{2}$$
$$x = 0$$
Check: $0 + \frac{1}{2} = \frac{1}{2}$ ✓

19.
$$\frac{2}{3} = d + \frac{1}{3}$$
$$\frac{2}{3} - \frac{1}{3} = d + \frac{1}{3} - \frac{1}{3}$$
$$\frac{1}{3} = d$$
Check: $\frac{2}{3} = \frac{1}{3} + \frac{1}{3}$ ✓

20. $y - \frac{3}{4} = \frac{1}{4}$

$y - \frac{3}{4} + \frac{3}{4} = \frac{1}{4} + \frac{3}{4}$

$y = \frac{4}{4}$

$y = 1$

Check: $1 - \frac{3}{4} = \frac{1}{4}$ ✓

21. In line 2, adding 1000 to each side is the wrong method to undo adding 1000 to x. Also, line 3 incorrectly shows the sum $1000 + 1000$ to be 0.

A correct solution method is to subtract 1000 from each side.

$x + 1000 = 5000$

$x + 1000 - 1000 = 5000 - 1000$

$x = 4000$

22. D; $-4 + x = 8$

$-4 + x + 4 = 8 + 4$

$x = 12$

23. $m + (-20) = -12$

$m + (-20) - (-20) = -12 - (-20)$

$m = -12 + 20$

$m = 8$

Check: $8 + (-20) = -12$ ✓

24. $-2 = b + (-4)$

$-2 - (-4) = b + (-4) - (-4)$

$-2 + 4 = b$

$2 = b$

Check: $-2 = 2 + (-4)$ ✓

25. $r - (-36) = 5$

$r - (-36) + (-36) = 5 + (-36)$

$r = -31$

Check: $-31 - (-36) \overset{?}{=} 5$

$-31 + 36 = 5$ ✓

26. $2 + x - 4 = 12$

$x - 2 = 12$

$x - 2 + 2 = 12 + 2$

$x = 14$

Check: $2 + 14 - 4 = 12$ ✓

27. $m - 5 - 9 = 21$

$m - 14 = 21$

$m - 14 + 14 = 21 + 14$

$m = 35$

Check: $35 - 5 - 9 = 21$ ✓

28. $d + 6(3) = -11$

$d + 6(3) - 6(3) = -11 - 6(3)$

$d = -11 - 18$

$d = -29$

Check: $-29 + 6(3) \overset{?}{=} -11$

$-29 + 18 = -11$ ✓

29. $n + 12 = 25$

$n + 12 - 12 = 25 - 12$

$n = 13$

30. $35 = n + 8$

$35 - 8 = n + 8 - 8$

$27 = n$

31. $n - 3 = -16$

$n - 3 + 3 = -16 + 3$

$n = -13$

32. $16 = x + 2 + 3 + 6$

$16 = x + 11$

$16 - 11 = x + 11 - 11$

$5 = x$

The length of the fourth side is 5 feet.

33. $97 = k + 16 + 38 + 24$

$97 = k + 78$

$97 - 78 = k + 78 - 78$

$19 = k$

The length of the fourth side is 19 centimeters.

34. $40 = y + 7 + 11 + 8$

$40 = y + 26$

$40 - 26 = y + 26 - 26$

$14 = y$

The length of the fourth side is 14 meters.

35–37. *Sample answers given.*

35. The solution involves subtracting a 3 digit number so use paper and pencil.

$x + 367 = 426$

$x + 367 - 367 = 426 - 367$

$x = 59$

36. The solution involves subtracting a 1 digit number, so use mental math.

Equation: $y + 4 = 6$

Question: What number added to 4 equals 6?

Solution: 2

37. The solution requires more than one calculation, so use pencil and paper.

$m - \frac{8001}{21} = 792$

$m - 381 = 792$

$m - 381 + 381 = 792 + 381$

$m = 1173$

38. The solution will be negative, because it involves subtracting a larger number from a smaller number, $6 - 27$.

Chapter 3, *continued*

39. The solution will be negative, because it will be the result of $-50 + 12$.

40. The solution will be positive, because it will be the result of adding two positive numbers, $5 + 10$.

41. $3x - 2x + 8 - 10 = 7$

$$x - 2 = 7$$
$$x - 2 + 2 = 7 + 2$$
$$x = 9$$

42. $0.2x + 3.4 + 0.8x = 4$

$$x + 3.4 = 4$$
$$x + 3.4 - 3.4 = 4 - 3.4$$
$$x = 0.6$$

43. $7.3x + 9 - 6.3x = 12$

$$x + 9 = 12$$
$$x + 9 - 9 = 12 - 9$$
$$x = 3$$

44. $|x| - 3 = 14$

$$|x| - 3 + 3 = 14 + 3$$
$$|x| = 17$$
$$x = 17, \text{ or } x = -17$$

45. $|x| + 5 = 25$

$$|x| + 5 - 5 = 25 - 5$$
$$|x| = 20$$
$$x = 20, \text{ or } x = -20$$

46. $|x - 2| = 7$

$$x - 2 = 7 \qquad \text{or} \qquad x - 2 = -7$$
$$x - 2 + 2 = 7 + 2 \qquad x - 2 + 2 = -7 + 2$$
$$x = 9 \qquad\qquad x = -5$$

$x = 9$ or $x = -5$

Problem Solving

47. a. Price + Sales tax = Total cost

b. $54.99 + x = 58.29$

c. $54.99 + x - 54.99 = 58.29 - 54.99$

$$x = 3.30$$

Check: $54.99 + 3.30 = 58.29$ ✓

The sales tax is $3.30.

48. The equation $62 = h + 5$ correctly represents the situation.

$$62 = h + 5$$
$$62 - 5 = h + 5 - 5$$
$$57 = h$$

Your sister's height is 57 inches.

49. The equation $t - 3 = 29$ does not correctly represent the problem.

The correct equation is $t = 29 - 3$.

$t = 29 - 3 = 26$

The mean temperature for February is 26°F.

50. The equation $2.29 - c = 1.79$ correctly represents the problem.

$$2.29 - c = 1.79$$
$$2.29 - c + c = 1.79 + c$$
$$2.29 = 1.79 + c$$
$$2.29 - 1.79 = 1.79 + c - 1.79$$
$$0.50 = c$$

The coupon saves $.50 from the regular price.

51. D; "Five less than the total number of students x is twenty-four" is represented by $x - 5 = 24$.

52. Because addition and subtraction are inverse operations, use subtraction to "undo" addition and use addition to "undo" subtraction. For example,

(1) $x - 3 = 6$, add 3 to "undo" the subtraction:
$$x - 3 + 3 = 6 + 3$$
$$x = 9$$

(2) $x + 7 = 1$, subtract 7 to "undo" the addition:
$$x + 7 - 7 = 1 - 7$$
$$x = -6$$

53. An equation that models a female pup's growth from 45 inches at birth to 104 inches in adulthood is $45 + x = 104$.

$$45 + x = 104$$
$$45 + x - 45 = 104 - 45$$
$$x = 59$$

A female grows about 59 inches between birth and adulthood.

54. An equation that models on male pup's growth from 45 inches at birth to 128 inches in adulthood is $45 + x = 128$.

$$45 + x = 128$$
$$45 + x - 45 = 128 - 45$$
$$x = 83$$

A male grows about 83 inches between birth and adulthood.

55. Average growth of female: $\dfrac{59 \text{ inches}}{7 \text{ years}} \approx \dfrac{8 \text{ inches}}{1 \text{ year}}$

Average growth of male: $\dfrac{83 \text{ inches}}{12 \text{ years}} \approx \dfrac{7 \text{ inches}}{1 \text{ year}}$

At these rates, after 5 years you could expect a female to be $45 + 8 \times 5 = 85$ inches long and a male to be $45 + 7 \times 5 = 80$ inches long. So, a female would be longer.

56. *Sample answer:*

$s + 13 = 55$ could represent:

In thirteen years, Sheila will be 55 years old.

How old is Sheila now?

Chapter 3, continued

57. $24 = x + 21$ and $27 + x = 30$ are equivalent equations because they both have the same solution, 3.

$$24 = x + 21 \qquad\qquad 27 + x = 30$$
$$24 - 21 = x + 21 - 21 \qquad 27 + x - 27 = 30 - 27$$
$$3 = x \qquad\qquad x = 3$$

58. $2(1.29) + 3.50 + 1.49 + x = 11.09$
$$7.57 + x = 11.09$$
$$7.57 + x - 7.57 = 11.09 - 7.57$$
$$x = 3.52$$

The 10 markers cost \$3.52, so the cost per marker is about 35 cents.

59. Three equations that can be used to find b, c, and t:
$b = s + 3, s = c + 6, c = t - 8$

For $s = 18$,

$b = s + 3 \qquad s = c + 6 \qquad c = t - 8$
$b = 18 + 3 \qquad 18 = c + 6 \qquad 12 = t - 8$
$b = 21 \qquad 18 - 6 = c + 6 - 6 \qquad 12 + 8 = t - 8 + 8$
$\qquad\qquad 12 = c \qquad\qquad 20 = t$

The book bag costs \$21, the CD costs \$12, and the T-shirt costs \$20.

Mixed Review

60.
$$\begin{array}{r} 1.9 \\ \times\ 15 \\ \hline 95 \\ 19 \\ \hline 28.5 \end{array}$$

61.
$$\begin{array}{r} 13.2 \\ \times\ 11 \\ \hline 132 \\ 132 \\ \hline 145.2 \end{array}$$

62. $19.5\overline{)78.0} \longrightarrow$
$$\begin{array}{r} 4 \\ 195\overline{)780} \\ 780 \\ \hline 0 \end{array}$$

$78 \div 19.5 = 4$

63.
$$\begin{array}{r} 37.1 \\ 3\overline{)111.3} \\ 9 \\ \hline 21 \\ 21 \\ \hline 03 \\ 3 \\ \hline 0 \end{array}$$

64–67.

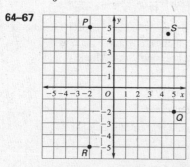

64. The point $P(-2, 5)$ is in Quadrant II.

65. The point $Q(5, -2)$ is in Quadrant IV.

66. The point $R(-2, -5)$ is in Quadrant III.

67. The point $S(4.5, 4.5)$ is in Quadrant I.

68. D; $3^5 = 3 \cdot 3 \cdot 3 \cdot 3 \cdot 3 = 243$
$$5^3 = 5 \cdot 5 \cdot 5 = 125$$
$$243 > 125, \text{ so } 3^5 > 5^3.$$

Lesson 3.2

Activity (p. 122)

1. $\dfrac{y}{5} = 4$

$\dfrac{y}{5} \cdot 5 = 4 \cdot 5$

$y = 20$

2. $\dfrac{h}{6} = 9$

$\dfrac{h}{6} \cdot 6 = 9 \cdot 6$

$h = 54$

3. $\dfrac{m}{6} = -3$

$\dfrac{m}{6} \cdot 6 = -3 \cdot 6$

$m = -18$

4. Multiplication was used to solve each division equation. You multiply each side of the equation by the denominator. Multiplying each side of an equation by the same nonzero number makes an equivalent equation.

3.2 Guided Practice (p. 123)

1. $21 = \dfrac{x}{9}$

$21 \cdot 9 = \dfrac{x}{9} \cdot 9$

$189 = x$

Check: $21 = \dfrac{189}{9}$ ✓

2. $\dfrac{x}{3.5} = 14$

$\dfrac{x}{3.5} \cdot 3.5 = 14 \cdot 3.5$

$x = 49$

Check: $\dfrac{49}{3.5} = 14$ ✓

3. $9x = 54$

$\dfrac{9x}{9} = \dfrac{54}{9}$

$x = 6$

Check: $9(6) = 54$ ✓

4. $48 = -3x$

$\dfrac{48}{-3} = \dfrac{-3x}{-3}$

$-16 = x$

Check: $48 = -3(-16)$ ✓

5. $\dfrac{x}{4} = 6$

$\dfrac{x}{4} \cdot 4 = 6 \cdot 4$

$x = 24$

There are 24 students in the class.

3.2 Exercises (pp. 124–126)

Skill Practice

1. To solve $6x = 36$, *divide* each side of the equation by 6.

2. Multiplying each side of an equation by *the same nonzero number* produces an equivalent equation.

3. Dividing by 5 will undo multiplying by 5.

4. Multiplying by -9 will undo dividing by -9.

5. Subtracting -6 will undo adding -6.

6. Adding 10 will undo subtracting 10.

7. Dividing by -3 will undo multiplying by -3.

8. Adding -4 will undo subtracting -4.

Chapter 3, *continued*

9. $\dfrac{p}{2} = 9$

$\dfrac{p}{2} \cdot 2 = 9 \cdot 2$

$p = 18$

Check: $\dfrac{18}{2} = 9$ ✓

10. $18 = 6g$

$\dfrac{18}{6} = \dfrac{6g}{6}$

$3 = g$

Check: $18 = 6(3)$ ✓

11. $3b = 39$

$\dfrac{3b}{3} = \dfrac{39}{3}$

$b = 13$

Check: $3(13) = 39$ ✓

12. $48 = 96z$

$\dfrac{48}{96} = \dfrac{96z}{96}$

$\dfrac{1}{2} = z$

Check: $48 = 96\left(\dfrac{1}{2}\right)$ ✓

13. $\dfrac{z}{1.8} = 5$

$\dfrac{z}{1.8} \cdot 1.8 = 5(1.8)$

$z = 9$

Check: $\dfrac{9}{1.8} = 5$ ✓

14. $14 = \dfrac{x}{5}$

$14 \cdot 5 = \dfrac{x}{5} \cdot 5$

$70 = x$

Check: $14 = \dfrac{70}{5}$ ✓

15. $44 = 4.4p$

$\dfrac{44}{4.4} = \dfrac{4.4p}{4.4}$

$10 = p$

Check: $44 = 4.4(10)$ ✓

16. $25 = \dfrac{h}{14}$

$25 \cdot 14 = \dfrac{h}{14} \cdot 14$

$350 = h$

Check: $25 = \dfrac{350}{14}$ ✓

17. $14h = 35$

$\dfrac{14h}{14} = \dfrac{35}{14}$

$h = 2.5$

Check: $14(2.5) = 35$ ✓

18. $\dfrac{r}{18} = 12$

$\dfrac{r}{18} \cdot 18 = 12 \cdot 18$

$r = 216$

Check: $\dfrac{216}{18} = 12$ ✓

19. $12m = 25.2$

$\dfrac{12m}{12} = \dfrac{-25.2}{12}$

$m = -2.1$

Check: $12(-2.1) = -25.2$ ✓

20. $7 = \dfrac{k}{15}$

$7 \cdot 15 = \dfrac{k}{15} \cdot 15$

$105 = k$

Check: $7 = \dfrac{105}{15}$ ✓

21. $1368 = 456x$

$\dfrac{1368}{456} = \dfrac{456x}{456}$

$3 = x$

Check: $1368 = 456(3)$ ✓

22. $\dfrac{h}{6} = -36$

$\dfrac{h}{6} \cdot 6 = -36 \cdot 6$

$h = -216$

Check: $\dfrac{-216}{6} = -36$ ✓

23. $12 = -2z$

$\dfrac{12}{-2} = \dfrac{-2z}{-2}$

$-6 = z$

Check: $12 = -2(-6)$ ✓

24. $-2.4k = 48$

$\dfrac{-2.4k}{-2.4} = \dfrac{48}{-2.4}$

$k = -20$

Check: $-2.4(-20) = 48$ ✓

25. $\dfrac{y}{-1.5} = 21$

$\dfrac{y}{-1.5} \cdot (-1.5) = 21(-1.5)$

$y = -31.5$

Check: $\dfrac{-31.5}{-1.5} = 21$ ✓

26. $-21 = -0.7p$

$\dfrac{-21}{-0.7} = \dfrac{-0.7p}{-0.7}$

$30 = p$

Check: $-21 = -0.7(30)$ ✓

27. C; $-3 = 0.3a$

$\dfrac{-3}{0.3} = \dfrac{0.3a}{0.3}$

$-10 = a$

28. To get the correct answer, you need to multiply each side by -7 instead of 7, because -7 is the number that divides x.

$\dfrac{x}{-7} = 56$

$\dfrac{x}{-7}(-7) = 56(-7)$

$x = -392$

29. B; To solve the equation represented by the verbal sentence, you should multiply each side by 4, because that undoes dividing by 4.

Chapter 3, *continued*

30. $-x = -8$ Original equation

$\dfrac{-x}{-1} = \dfrac{-8}{-1}$ Divide each side by -1.

$x = 8$ Simplify.

31. $-b = 12 - 4$ Original equation

$-b = 8$ Simplify.

$\dfrac{-b}{-1} = \dfrac{-8}{-1}$ Divide each side by -1.

$b = -8$ Simplify.

32. $15 - 21 = -n$ Original equation

$-6 = -n$ Simplify.

$\dfrac{-6}{-1} = \dfrac{-n}{-1}$ Divide each side by -1.

$6 = n$ Simplify.

33. $\dfrac{m}{6} = \dfrac{2}{3}$ Original equation

$\dfrac{m}{6} \cdot 6 = \dfrac{2}{3} \cdot 6$ Multiply each side by 6.

$m = 4$ Simplify.

34. $\dfrac{a}{3} = 5\dfrac{1}{3}$ Original equation

$\dfrac{a}{3} = \dfrac{16}{3}$ Write $5\dfrac{1}{3}$ as an improper fraction.

$\dfrac{a}{3} \cdot 3 = \dfrac{16}{3} \cdot 3$ Multiply each side by 3.

$a = 16$ Simplify.

35. $\dfrac{t}{4} = 3\dfrac{1}{6}$ Original equation

$\dfrac{t}{4} = \dfrac{19}{6}$ Write $3\dfrac{1}{6}$ as an improper fraction.

$\dfrac{t}{4} \cdot 4 = \dfrac{19}{6} \cdot 4$ Multiply each side by 4.

$t = 12\dfrac{2}{3}$ Simplify.

36-39 *Sample answers:*

36. $x = -7 \rightarrow 4x = -28$ Multiplication equation

$\dfrac{x}{7} = -1$ Division equation

37. $x = 2 \rightarrow 3x = 6$ Multiplication equation

$\dfrac{x}{2} = 1$ Division equation

38. $x = 9 \rightarrow 6x = 54$ Multiplication equation

$\dfrac{x}{3} = 3$ Division equation

39. $x = -2.5 \rightarrow -2x = 5$ Multiplication equation

$\dfrac{x}{-5} = 0.5$ Division equation

40. $A = \dfrac{1}{2}bh$

$2 \cdot A = 2 \cdot \dfrac{1}{2}bh$

$2A = bh$

$\dfrac{2A}{h} = \dfrac{bh}{h}$

$\dfrac{2A}{h} = b\pi$

41. $V = \dfrac{1}{3}Bh$

$3 \cdot V = 3 \cdot \dfrac{1}{3}Bh$

$3V = Bh$

$\dfrac{3V}{B} = \dfrac{Bh}{B}$

$\dfrac{3V}{B} = h$

42. $V = \pi r^2 h$

$\dfrac{V}{\pi r^2} = \dfrac{\pi r^2 h}{\pi r^2}$

$\dfrac{V}{\pi r^2} = h$

Problem Solving

43. People in theater = Seats per row • Number of rows

$1950 = 30x$

$\dfrac{1950}{30} = \dfrac{30x}{30}$

$65 = x$

There are 65 rows of seats.

44. C; One of eight slices costs $1.10, so 1.10 is the cost of the whole pizza divided by 8: $\dfrac{x}{8} = 1.10$

45. $7 \cdot$ Amount for mowing once $=$ Amount for mowing 7 times

$7a = 56$

$\dfrac{7a}{7} = \dfrac{56}{7}$

$a = 8$

Your friend charged $8 for mowing the lawn once.

46. a. $r \cdot t = d$

$r \cdot 3 = 174$

$3r = 174$

b. $3r = 174$

$\dfrac{3r}{3} = \dfrac{174}{3}$

$r = 58$

Joanne's speed was 58 miles per hour.

c. $r \cdot t = d$

$58 \cdot 2 = 116$

Yes, in two hours at the same speed Joanne can travel 116 miles.

47. To find how many five-person teams can be formed from ninety players, lay out 90 1-tiles and divide them into groups of 5. There will be a total of 18 groups.

Chapter 3, *continued*

48. Let n be the height of Niagara Falls.

$$20 \cdot \frac{\text{Height of}}{\text{Niagara Falls}} = \frac{\text{Height of}}{\text{Angel Falls}}$$

$$20n = 1000$$

$$\frac{20n}{20} = \frac{1000}{20}$$

$$n = 50$$

The height of Niagara Falls is 50 meters.

49. Let t be the height of Takkakaw Falls.

$$\frac{\text{Height of}}{\text{Comet Falls}} = \frac{1}{5} \cdot \frac{\text{Height of}}{\text{Takkakaw Falls}}$$

$$100 = \frac{1}{5}t$$

$$5 \cdot 100 = 5 \cdot \frac{1}{5}t$$

$$500 = t$$

The height of Takkakaw Falls is 500 meters.

50. Let f be the height of Feather Falls.

$$\frac{\text{Height of}}{\text{Skykje Falls}} = 1.25 \cdot \frac{\text{Height of}}{\text{Feather Falls}}$$

$$250 = 1.25f$$

$$\frac{250}{1.25} = \frac{1.25f}{1.25}$$

$$200 = f$$

The height of Feather Falls is 200 meters.

51. Let y be the number of eggs laid in a year by each hen.

$$\frac{\text{Number of}}{\text{hens}} \cdot \frac{\text{Number of}}{\text{eggs per hen}} = \frac{\text{Total number}}{\text{of eggs}}$$

$$285{,}000{,}000\,y = 76{,}000{,}000{,}000$$

$$\frac{285{,}000{,}000\,y}{285{,}000{,}000} = \frac{76{,}000{,}000{,}000}{285{,}000{,}000}$$

$$y = 266\frac{2}{3}$$

Let m be the number of eggs laid by each hen in 1 month.

$$\frac{\text{Yearly number}}{\text{of eggs per hen}} = \frac{\text{Monthly number}}{\text{of eggs per hen}} \cdot \frac{\text{The number of}}{\text{months in a year}}$$

$$266\frac{2}{3} = m \cdot 12$$

$$\frac{266\frac{2}{3}}{12} = \frac{12m}{12}$$

$$22\frac{2}{9} = m$$

Each hen lays about 22 eggs in a month.

Let w be the number of eggs laid by each hen in 1 week.

$$\frac{\text{Yearly number}}{\text{of eggs per hen}} = \frac{\text{Weekly number}}{\text{of eggs per hen}} \cdot \frac{\text{The number of}}{\text{weeks in a year}}$$

$$266\frac{2}{3} = w \cdot 52$$

$$\frac{266\frac{2}{3}}{52} = \frac{52w}{52}$$

$$5\frac{5}{39} = w$$

Each hen lays about 5 eggs in a week.

52. Let x be the total number of points for the season.

$$\frac{\text{Total number of}}{\text{points for season}} \div \frac{\text{Number}}{\text{of games}} = \frac{\text{Average points}}{\text{per game}}$$

$$x \div 20 = 65$$

$$x \div 20 \cdot 20 = 65 \cdot 20$$

$$x = 1300$$

The team scores 1300 points for the season.

The team wants to score 5 more points per game, so replace 65 by 70 in the model.

$$x \div 20 = 70$$

$$x \div 20 \cdot 20 = 70 \cdot 20$$

$$x = 1400$$

The team would score 1400 points next season.

53. Price of hardcover book: $19.50

Price of paperback book: $19.50t$

$$\frac{\text{Price of 26}}{\text{paperbacks}} = \frac{\text{Price of}}{\text{12 hardcovers}}$$

$$26(19.50t) = 12(19.50)$$

$$\frac{26(19.50t)}{26(19.50)} = \frac{12(19.50)}{26(19.50)}$$

$$t = \frac{6}{13}$$

Price of paperback: $19.50t = 19.50\left(\frac{6}{13}\right) = 9$

The price of one paperback is $9.

54. Width of rectangle: w

length of rectangle: $\ell = 3w$

$$P = 2\ell + 2w$$

$$36 = 2(3w) + 2w$$

$$36 = 6w + 2w$$

$$36 = 8w$$

$$\frac{36}{8} = \frac{8w}{8}$$

$$4.5 = w$$

$$\ell = 3w = 3(4.5) = 13.5$$

The rectangle is 4.5 inches wide and 13.5 inches long.

Mixed Review

55.
$$x + 3 = 12$$
$$x + 3 - 3 = 12 - 3$$
$$x = 9$$

56.
$$y - 8 = 4$$
$$y - 8 + 8 = 4 + 8$$
$$y = 12$$

57.
$$n - 14 = 325$$
$$n - 14 + 14 = 325 + 14$$
$$n = 339$$

58.
$$b + 38 = 9$$
$$b + 38 - 38 = 9 - 38$$
$$b = -29$$

59. $3 > -6$

60. $-21 < -17$

61. $-12 < -5$

62. $0 > -3$

63. 12,048

64. 5.017

65. B; When $t = 2$: $h = -16t^2 + 80$
$$= -16(2)^2 + 80$$
$$= -64 + 80$$
$$= 16$$

The height of the ball after 2 seconds is 16 feet.

Lesson 3.3

Investigation (pp. 127–128)

1. $3x + 1 = 10$

(1)

(2)

(3)

(4)

The solution is 3.

Check: $3(3) + 1 \stackrel{?}{=} 10$
$$9 + 1 = 10 ✓$$

2. $3x + 1 = 7$

(1)

(2)

(3)

(4)

The solution is 2.

Check: $3(2) + 1 \stackrel{?}{=} 7$
$$6 + 1 = 7 ✓$$

3. $2x + 4 = 10$

(1)

(2)

(3)

(4)

The solution is 3.

Check: $2(3) + 4 \stackrel{?}{=} 10$
$$6 + 4 = 10 ✓$$

4. $2x + 3 = 5$

(1)

(2)

(3)

(4)

The solution is 1.

Check: $2(1) + 3 \stackrel{?}{=} 5$
$$2 + 3 = 5 ✓$$

5. $4x + 1 = 9$

(1)

(2)

(3)

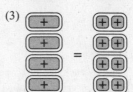

(4)

The solution is 2.

Check: $4(2) + 1 \stackrel{?}{=} 9$
$$8 + 1 = 9 ✓$$

Chapter 3, *continued*

6. Tile model   Algebra

(1)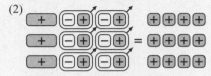

$$3x - 6 = 6$$

(2)

$$3x - 6 + 6 = 6 + 6$$

(3)

$$\frac{3x}{3} = \frac{12}{3}$$

(4)

$$x = 4$$

The solution is 4.

7. Tile Model   Algebra

(1)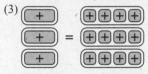

$$2x - 3 = 7$$

(2)

$$2x - 3 + 3 = 7 + 3$$

(3)

$$\frac{2x}{2} = \frac{10}{2}$$

(4)

$$x = 5$$

The solution is 5.

8. Tile Model   Algebra

(1)

$$4x + 2 = -10$$

(2)

$$4x + 2 - 2 = -10 - 2$$

(3)

$$\frac{4x}{4} = \frac{-12}{4}$$

(4)

$$x = -3$$

The solution is −3.

9. Tile Model   Algebra

(1)

$$2x - 5 = -9$$

(2)

$$2x - 5 + 5 = -9 + 5$$

(3)

$$\frac{2x}{2} = \frac{-4}{2}$$

(4)

$$x = -2$$

The solution is −2.

10. Equations with decimals or fractions as coefficients are difficult to solve with tiles. An example would be

$$\frac{2}{3}x + \frac{1}{2} = \frac{1}{4}.$$

11. *Sample answer:* $3x + 4 = 7$

3.3 Guided Practice (pp. 129–130)

1. Substitute the solution value for x in the algebraic model and verify that the left side equals the right side.

Check: $9.95 + 0.99(8) \stackrel{?}{=} 17.87$

$\qquad\qquad 9.95 + 7.92 \stackrel{?}{=} 17.87$

$\qquad\qquad\qquad 17.87 = 17.87$ ✓

2. The total cost at the right side of the algebraic model changes from 17.87 to 26.78.

$$
\begin{aligned}
9.95 + 0.99x &= 26.78 \\
-9.95 \qquad\qquad &\quad -9.95 \\
0.99x &= 16.83 \\
\frac{0.99x}{0.99} &= \frac{16.83}{0.99} \\
x &= 17
\end{aligned}
$$

You downloaded 17 songs.

Chapter 3, continued

3. $10x + 35 = 225$

$\underline{-35 \qquad -35}$

$10x = 190$

$x = 19$

You have developed 19 rolls of film.

4. $\qquad 13 = 11 + \dfrac{y}{3}$

$13 - 11 = 11 + \dfrac{y}{3} - 11$

$\qquad 2 = \dfrac{y}{3}$

$\qquad 2 \cdot 3 = \dfrac{y}{3} \cdot 3$

$\qquad 6 = y$

Check: $13 \overset{?}{=} 11 + \dfrac{6}{3}$

$\qquad 13 = 11 + 2 \checkmark$

5. $\qquad \dfrac{z}{5} - 3 = 4$

$\qquad \dfrac{z}{5} - 3 + 3 = 4 + 3$

$\qquad \dfrac{z}{5} = 7$

$\qquad \dfrac{z}{5} \cdot 5 = 7 \cdot 5$

$\qquad z = 35$

Check: $\dfrac{35}{5} - 3 \overset{?}{=} 4$

$\qquad 7 - 3 = 4 \checkmark$

6. $\qquad -6x + 5 = 23$

$-6x + 5 - 5 = 23 - 5$

$\qquad -6x = 18$

$\qquad \dfrac{-6x}{-6} = \dfrac{18}{-6}$

$\qquad x = -3$

Check: $-6(-3) + 5 \overset{?}{=} 23$

$\qquad 18 + 5 = 23 \checkmark$

7. $\qquad 6 = 16 - a$

$6 - 16 = 16 - a - 16$

$\qquad -10 = -a$

$\qquad \dfrac{-10}{-1} = \dfrac{-a}{-1}$

$\qquad 10 = a$

Check: $6 = 16 - 10 \checkmark$

8. $\qquad 10 - 4a = 34$

$10 - 4a - 10 = 34 - 10$

$\qquad -4a = 24$

$\qquad \dfrac{-4a}{-4} = \dfrac{24}{-4}$

$\qquad a = -6$

Check: $10 - 4(-6) \overset{?}{=} 34$

$\qquad 10 + 24 = 34 \checkmark$

9. $\qquad 8w - 3 = 21$

$8w - 3 + 3 = 21 + 3$

$\qquad 8w = 24$

$\qquad \dfrac{8w}{8} = \dfrac{24}{8}$

$\qquad w = 3$

Check: $8(3) - 3 \overset{?}{=} 21$

$\qquad 24 - 3 = 21 \checkmark$

10. $\qquad 7x + 3 = 17$

$7x + 3 - 3 = 17 - 3$

$\qquad 7x = 14$

$\qquad \dfrac{7x}{7} = \dfrac{14}{7}$

$\qquad x = 2$

Check: $7(2) + 3 \overset{?}{=} 17$

$\qquad 14 + 3 = 17 \checkmark$

11. $\qquad \dfrac{3}{4}m + 1 = 7$

$\qquad \dfrac{3}{4}m + 1 - 1 = 7 - 1$

$\qquad \dfrac{3}{4}m = 6$

$\qquad 4 \cdot \dfrac{3}{4}m = 4 \cdot 6$

$\qquad 3m = 24$

$\qquad \dfrac{3m}{3} = \dfrac{24}{3}$

$\qquad m = 8$

Check: $\dfrac{3}{4}(8) + 1 \overset{?}{=} 7$

$\qquad 6 + 1 = 7 \checkmark$

3.3 Exercises (pp. 131–133)

Skill Practice

1. A number that you can substitute for a variable to make an equation true is a *solution* of the equation.

2. A mathematical sentence formed by placing an equal sign ($=$) between two expressions is an *equation*.

3. $\qquad 2x + 1 = 7$

$2x + 1 - 1 = 7 - 1$

$\qquad 2x = 6$

$\qquad \dfrac{2x}{2} = \dfrac{6}{2}$

$\qquad x = 3$

Check: $2(3) + 1 \overset{?}{=} 7$

$\qquad 6 + 1 = 7 \checkmark$

4. $\qquad 3y - 4 = 2$

$3y - 4 + 4 = 2 + 4$

$\qquad 3y = 6$

$\qquad \dfrac{3y}{3} = \dfrac{6}{3}$

$\qquad y = 2$

Check: $3(2) - 4 \overset{?}{=} 2$

$\qquad 6 - 4 = 2 \checkmark$

5.
$$10 - 7z = 3$$
$$10 - 7z - 10 = 3 - 10$$
$$-7z = -7$$
$$\frac{-7z}{-7} = \frac{-7}{-7}$$
$$z = 1$$
Check: $10 - 7(1) \overset{?}{=} 3$
$$10 - 7 = 3 \checkmark$$

6.
$$15 = -4p + 7$$
$$15 - 7 = -4p + 7 - 7$$
$$8 = -4p$$
$$\frac{8}{-4} = \frac{-4p}{-4}$$
$$-2 = p$$
Check: $15 \overset{?}{=} -4(-2) + 7$
$$15 = 8 + 7 \checkmark$$

7.
$$9 - 2k = 25$$
$$9 - 2k - 9 = 25 - 9$$
$$-2k = 16$$
$$\frac{-2k}{-2} = \frac{16}{-2}$$
$$k = -8$$
Check: $9 - 2(-8) \overset{?}{=} 25$
$$9 + 16 = 25 \checkmark$$

8.
$$11 = \frac{h}{6} + 8$$
$$11 - 8 = \frac{h}{6} + 8 - 8$$
$$3 = \frac{h}{6}$$
$$3 \cdot 6 = \frac{h}{6} \cdot 6$$
$$18 = h$$
Check: $11 \overset{?}{=} \frac{18}{6} + 8$
$$11 = 3 + 8 \checkmark$$

9.
$$\frac{x}{9} - 4 = 5$$
$$\frac{x}{9} - 4 + 4 = 5 + 4$$
$$\frac{x}{9} = 9$$
$$\frac{x}{9} \cdot 9 = 9 \cdot 9$$
$$x = 81$$
Check: $\frac{81}{9} - 4 \overset{?}{=} 5$
$$9 - 4 = 5 \checkmark$$

10.
$$6 + 2c = 15$$
$$6 + 2c - 6 = 15 - 6$$
$$2c = 9$$
$$\frac{2c}{2} = \frac{9}{2}$$
$$c = 4\frac{1}{2}$$
Check: $6 + 2\left(4\frac{1}{2}\right) \overset{?}{=} 15$
$$6 + 9 = 15 \checkmark$$

11.
$$29 = -5a + 4$$
$$29 - 4 = -5a + 4 - 4$$
$$25 = -5a$$
$$\frac{25}{-5} = \frac{-5a}{-5}$$
$$-5 = a$$
Check: $29 \overset{?}{=} -5(-5) + 4$
$$29 = 25 + 4 \checkmark$$

12.
$$7 + 5b = -23$$
$$7 + 5b - 7 = -23 - 7$$
$$5b = -30$$
$$\frac{5b}{5} = \frac{-30}{5}$$
$$b = -6$$
Check: $7 + 5(-6) \overset{?}{=} -23$
$$7 - 30 = -23 \checkmark$$

13.
$$100 - 7r = 44$$
$$100 - 7r - 100 = 44 - 100$$
$$-7r = -56$$
$$\frac{-7r}{-7} = \frac{-56}{-7}$$
$$r = 8$$
Check: $100 - 7(8) \overset{?}{=} 44$
$$100 - 56 = 44 \checkmark$$

14.
$$20 - 6w = 14$$
$$20 - 6w - 20 = 14 - 20$$
$$-6w = -6$$
$$\frac{-6w}{-6} = \frac{-6}{-6}$$
$$w = 1$$
Check: $20 - 6(1) \overset{?}{=} 14$
$$20 - 6 = 14 \checkmark$$

15.
$$-32 = -17 - \frac{d}{2}$$
$$-32 + 17 = -17 - \frac{d}{2} + 17$$
$$-15 = -\frac{d}{2}$$
$$-15 \cdot -2 = -\frac{d}{2} \cdot -2$$
$$30 = d$$
Check: $-32 \overset{?}{=} -17 - \frac{30}{2}$
$$-32 = -17 - 15 \checkmark$$

16.
$$\frac{c}{3} - 7 = 5.3$$
$$\frac{c}{3} - 7 + 7 = 5.3 + 7$$
$$\frac{c}{3} = 12.3$$
$$\frac{c}{3} \cdot 3 = 12.3 \cdot 3$$
$$c = 36.9$$
Check: $\frac{36.9}{3} - 7 \overset{?}{=} 5.3$
$$12.3 - 7 = 5.3 \checkmark$$

17. $-7 + \dfrac{z}{4} = 5.2$

$$-7 + \dfrac{z}{4} + 7 = 5.2 + 7$$

$$\dfrac{z}{4} = 12.2$$

$$\dfrac{z}{4} \cdot 4 = 12.2 \cdot 4$$

$$z = 48.8$$

Check: $-7 + \dfrac{48.8}{4} \overset{?}{=} 5.2$

$$-7 + 12.2 = 5.2 \checkmark$$

18. $\dfrac{3x}{5} = 12$

$$\dfrac{3x}{5} \cdot 5 = 12 \cdot 5$$

$$3x = 60$$

$$\dfrac{3x}{3} = \dfrac{60}{3}$$

$$x = 20$$

Check: $\dfrac{3(20)}{5} \overset{?}{=} 12$

$$\dfrac{60}{5} = 12 \checkmark$$

19. $\dfrac{2x}{3} = -8$

$$\dfrac{2x}{3} \cdot 3 = -8 \cdot 3$$

$$2x = -24$$

$$\dfrac{2x}{2} = \dfrac{-24}{2}$$

$$x = -12$$

Check: $\dfrac{2(-12)}{3} \overset{?}{=} -8$

$$\dfrac{-24}{3} = -8 \checkmark$$

20. $-\dfrac{5m}{2} = 35$

$$-\left(\dfrac{5m}{2}\right) \cdot (-2) = 35 \cdot (-2)$$

$$5m = -70$$

$$\dfrac{5m}{5} = \dfrac{-70}{5}$$

$$m = -14$$

Check: $-\dfrac{5(-14)}{2} \overset{?}{=} 35$

$$-\dfrac{(-70)}{2} \overset{?}{=} 35$$

$$35 = 35 \checkmark$$

21. B; $21 = 3x + 9$

$$21 - 9 = 3x + 9 - 9$$

$$12 = 3x$$

$$\dfrac{12}{3} = \dfrac{3x}{3}$$

$$4 = x$$

22. The error occurred when 9 was subtracted from 18, instead of added.

$$3x - 9 = 18$$

$$3x - 9 + 9 = 18 + 9$$

$$3x = 27$$

$$\dfrac{3x}{3} = \dfrac{27}{7}$$

$$x = 9$$

23.

$2(m + 3) = 18$	Original equation
$2m + 6 = 18$	Apply the distributive property.
$2m + 6 - 6 = 18 - 6$	Subtract 6 from each side to undo addition.
$2m = 12$	Simplify.
$\dfrac{2m}{2} = \dfrac{12}{2}$	Divide each side by 2 to undo multiplication.
$m = 6$	Simplify.

24.

$2(m + 3) = 18$	Original equation
$\dfrac{2(m + 3)}{2} = \dfrac{18}{2}$	Divide each side by 2 to undo multiplication.
$m + 3 = 9$	Simplify.
$m + 3 - 3 = 9 - 3$	Subtract 3 from each side to undo addition.
$m = 6$	Simplify.

25. *Sample answer:* $3(r + 1) = 9$

$$\dfrac{3(r + 1)}{3} = \dfrac{9}{3}$$

$$r + 1 = 3$$

$$r + 1 - 1 = 3 - 1$$

$$r = 2$$

Use the method of Ex. 24 because it saves a step and because 9 is divisible by 3.

26. *Sample answer:*

$$4 = -1(z + 11)$$

$$\dfrac{4}{-1} = \dfrac{-1(z + 11)}{-1}$$

$$-4 = z + 11$$

$$-4 - 11 = z + 11 - 11$$

$$-15 = z$$

Use the method of Ex. 24, because it saves a step and because 4 can be divided by -1 easily.

27. *Sample answer:*

$$6\left(\dfrac{1}{3} + h\right) = 20$$

$$2 + 6h = 20$$

$$2 + 6h - 2 = 20 - 2$$

$$6h = 18$$

$$\dfrac{6h}{6} = \dfrac{18}{6}$$

$$h = 3$$

Use the method of Exercise 23 to eliminate the fraction on the left and to avoid forming a new fraction on the right side.

28. The figure is a square, so the sides have equal length.

$$3x - 8 = 10$$
$$3x - 8 + 8 = 10 + 8$$
$$3x = 18$$
$$\frac{3x}{3} = \frac{18}{3}$$
$$x = 6$$

29. The figure is a rectangle with a width of 2 and a length of 5.

$$3y - 10 = 2 \qquad\qquad 4x + 9 = 5$$
$$3y - 10 + 10 = 2 + 10 \qquad 4x + 9 - 9 = 5 - 9$$
$$3y = 12 \qquad\qquad 4x = -4$$
$$\frac{3y}{3} = \frac{12}{3} \qquad\qquad \frac{4x}{4} = -\frac{4}{4}$$
$$y = 4 \qquad\qquad x = -1$$

30. The figure is a rectangle with a width of 4 and a length of 8.

$$\frac{2x}{5} = 4 \qquad\qquad 7 - 5y = 8$$
$$\frac{2x}{5} \cdot 5 = 4 \cdot 5 \qquad 7 - 5y - 7 = 8 - 7$$
$$2x = 20 \qquad\qquad -5y = 1$$
$$\frac{2x}{2} = \frac{20}{2} \qquad\qquad \frac{-5y}{-5} = \frac{1}{-5}$$
$$x = 10 \qquad\qquad y = -\frac{1}{5}$$

31.

$\frac{4h - 6}{8} = -3$	Original equation
$\frac{4h - 6}{8} \cdot 8 = -3 \cdot 8$	Multiply each side by 8 to undo division.
$4h - 6 = -24$	Simplify.
$4h - 6 + 6 = -24 + 6$	Add 6 to each side to undo subtraction.
$4h = -18$	Simplify.
$\frac{4h}{4} = \frac{-18}{4}$	Divide each side by 4 to undo multiplication.
$h = -4.5$	Simplify.

32.

$\frac{3a + 4}{5} = 11$	Original equation
$\frac{3a + 4}{5} \cdot 5 = 11 \cdot 5$	Multiply each side by 5 to undo division.
$3a + 4 = 55$	Simplify.
$3a + 4 - 4 = 55 - 4$	Subtract 4 from each side to undo addition.
$3a = 51$	Simplify.
$\frac{3a}{3} = \frac{51}{3}$	Divide each side by 3 to undo division.
$a = 17$	Simplify.

33.

$\frac{2w - 3}{9} = 5$	Original equation
$\frac{2w - 3}{9} \cdot 9 = 5 \cdot 9$	Multiply each side by 9 to undo division.
$2w - 3 = 45$	Simplify.
$2w - 3 + 3 = 45 + 3$	Add 3 to each side to undo subtraction.
$2w = 48$	Simplify.
$\frac{2w}{2} = \frac{48}{2}$	Divide each side by 2 to undo multiplication.
$w = 24$	Simplify.

34.

$\frac{2(h + 12)}{5} = 10$	Original equation
$\frac{2(h + 12)}{5} \cdot 5 = 10 \cdot 5$	Multiply each side by 5 to undo division.
$2(h + 12) = 50$	Simplify.
$\frac{2(h + 12)}{2} = \frac{50}{2}$	Divide each side by 2 to undo multiplication.
$h + 12 = 25$	Simplify.
$h + 12 - 12 = 25 - 12$	Subtract 12 to undo addition.
$h = 13$	Simplify.

35.

$\frac{2(4t - 7)}{3} = -22$	Original equation
$\frac{2(4t - 7)}{3} \cdot 3 = -22 \cdot 3$	Multiply each side by 3 to undo division.
$2(4t - 7) = -66$	Simplify.
$\frac{2(4t - 7)}{2} = \frac{-66}{2}$	Divide each side by 2 to undo multiplication.
$4t - 7 = -33$	Simplify.
$4t - 7 + 7 = -33 + 7$	Add 7 to each side to undo subtraction.
$4t = -26$	Simplify.
$\frac{4t}{4} = \frac{-26}{4}$	Divide each side by 4 to undo multiplication.
$t = -6.5$	Simplify.

36. $\dfrac{6(4h + 5)}{7} = -6$ Original equation

$\dfrac{6(4h + 5)}{7} \cdot 7 = -6 \cdot 7$ Multiply each side by 7 to undo division.

$6(4h + 5) = -42$ Simplify.

$\dfrac{6(4h + 5)}{6} = \dfrac{-42}{6}$ Divide each side by 6 to undo multiplication.

$4h + 5 = -7$ Simplify.

$4h + 5 - 5 = -7 - 5$ Subtract 5 from each side to undo addition.

$4h = -12$ Simplify.

$\dfrac{4h}{4} = \dfrac{-12}{4}$ Divide each side by 4 to undo multiplication.

$h = -3$ Simplify.

37. a. $P = 2\ell + 2w$

$P - 2\ell = 2\ell + 2w - 2\ell$

$P - 2\ell = 2w$

$\dfrac{P - 2\ell}{2} = \dfrac{2w}{2}$

$\dfrac{P - 2\ell}{2} = w$

b. $P = 2\ell + 2w$

$P - 2w = 2\ell + 2w - 2w$

$P - 2w = 2\ell$

$\dfrac{P - 2w}{2} = \dfrac{2\ell}{2}$

$\dfrac{P - 2w}{2} = \ell$

Problem Solving

38. a. The main idea is that you get paid per illustration and per hour. You know you get paid $50 per illustration, and $12 per hour. Your paycheck is $198. You made three illustrations. You need to know how many hours you spent making changes.

b. The value of n is the number of hours you spent making changes because it is multiplied by 12. This is how much you make per hour while making changes.

c. $3(50) + 12n = 198$

$150 + 12n = 198$

$150 + 12n - 150 = 198 - 150$

$12n = 48$

$\dfrac{12n}{12} = \dfrac{48}{12}$

$n = 4$

Check: $3(50) + 12(4) \stackrel{?}{=} 198$

$150 + 48 = 198$ ✓

You spent 4 hours making changes to the illustrations.

39. $5w - 4 = 51$

$5w - 4 + 4 = 51 + 4$

$5w = 55$

$\dfrac{5w}{5} = \dfrac{55}{5}$

$w = 11$

You need to do 11 day walks to earn $51 per week.

40. $3h + 3 = 11$

$3h + 3 - 3 = 11 - 3$

$3h = 8$

$\dfrac{3h}{3} = \dfrac{8}{3}$

$h = 2\dfrac{2}{3}$

The value of h, or $2\dfrac{2}{3}$ hours, is an estimate of the number of hours it will take to finish cleaning based on the miles of trails cleaned in the first hour. The students may or may not clean the rest of the trails at the same rate.

41. *Sample answer*:

An airplane takes off and climbs at a rate of 1000 feet per minute for several minutes, then it drops 200 feet to a height of 11,800 feet. For how many minutes did the airplane climb?

Let m be the number of minutes the plane climbed.

Rate of climb	·	Number of minutes	−	Number of feet dropped	=	Height

$1000m - 200 = 11,800$

$1000m - 200 + 200 = 11,800 + 200$

$1000m = 12,000$

$\dfrac{1000m}{1000} = \dfrac{12,000}{1000}$

$m = 12$

The airplane climbed for 12 minutes.

42. B; Jamie's profit is the $15 per game that she earned, less the $35 she paid to take the course. So, the equation that subtracts the cost of the course, $15g - 35 = 280$, is the equation you can use to find the number of games that Jamie worked.

43. $0.75 + 0.07m = 2.10$

$0.75 + 0.07m - 0.75 = 2.10 - 0.75$

$0.07m = 1.35$

$\dfrac{0.07m}{0.07} = \dfrac{1.35}{0.07}$

$m = 19.29$

The maximum number of whole minutes that you can talk is 19.

44. Devon: D

Carla: $D + 8$

Ted: $(D + 8) + 12 = D + 20$

Equation:

$D + D + 8 + D + 20 = 73$

$3D + 28 = 73$

$3D + 28 - 28 = 73 - 28$

$3D = 45$

$\dfrac{3D}{3} = \dfrac{45}{3}$

$D = 15$

Devon has $15, Carla has $15 + 8 = 23, and Ted has $23 + 12 = 35.

45. a. $3(40) + 12 = 120 + 12 = 132$

The value of the expression represents the total cost ($132) of 40 visits to the pool using day passes.

b.
$$3x + 12 = 100$$
$$3x + 12 - 12 = 100 - 12$$
$$3x = 88$$
$$\frac{3x}{3} = \frac{88}{3}$$
$$x = 29\frac{1}{3}$$

The cost of the two plans would be the same for $29\frac{1}{3}$ visits. Because only whole numbers of visits are possible, this means that the total cost of using day passes is less expensive than a summer pass for 29 or fewer visits and more expensive than a summer pass for 30 or more visits.

c. *Sample answer:* Choose the summer pass if you go to the pool more than 29 times because it is cheaper. Choose the day pass if you go to the pool 29 times or less because it is cheaper.

46. Width $= w$
$$\ell = 2w - 5$$
$$P = 2\ell + 2w$$
$$38 = 2([2w - 5] - 6) + 2(w - 6)$$
$$38 = 2(2w - 11) + 2(w - 6)$$
$$38 = 4w - 22 + 2w - 12$$
$$38 = 6w - 34$$
$$38 + 34 = 6w - 34 + 34$$
$$72 = 6w$$
$$\frac{72}{6} = \frac{6w}{6}$$
$$12 = w$$

Using $w = 12$, the length is $2w - 5 = 2(12) - 5 = 19$. The original rectangle is 19 meters long and 12 meters wide.

Mixed Review

47.
$$p + 9 = 19$$
$$p + 9 - 9 = 19 - 9$$
$$p = 10$$
Check: $10 + 9 = 19$ ✓

48.
$$-20 = 4x$$
$$\frac{-20}{4} = \frac{4x}{4}$$
$$-5 = x$$
Check: $-20 = 4(-5)$ ✓

49.
$$\frac{1}{2}y = 24$$
$$2 \cdot \frac{1}{2}y = 2 \cdot 24$$
$$y = 48$$
Check: $\frac{1}{2} \cdot 48 = 24$ ✓

50. To find out how many races there will be altogether, we can *look for a pattern*. Let 1, 2, 3, 4, 5, and 6 stand for the 6 members.

1 must run against 2, 3, 4, 5, and 6, or 5 races.

2 must also run against 3, 4, 5, and 6, which is 4 races.

If we continue in this pattern, there will be $5 + 4 + 3 + 2 + 1$, or 15 races altogether.

Each member must race 5 times.

51. C; The digit to the right of 6 in the tenth's place is 5 in the hundredth's place. So round 4.6578 up to 4.7.

Lesson 3.4

3.4 Guided Practice (pp. 134–135)

1.

Budget available	=	Cost of each new tortoise	•	Number of new tortoises	+	Cost of existing tortoises

$$2875 = 575n + 1150$$
$$2875 - 1150 = 575n + 1150 - 1150$$
$$1725 = 575n$$
$$\frac{1725}{575} = \frac{575n}{575}$$
$$3 = n$$

The zoo can acquire 3 new tortoises.

2.
$$6n - 9 = -3$$
$$6n - 9 + 9 = -3 + 9$$
$$6n = 6$$
$$\frac{6n}{6} = \frac{6}{6}$$
$$n = 1$$
The number is 1.

3.
$$1244 = 5p + 714$$
$$1244 - 714 = 5p + 714 - 714$$
$$530 = 5p$$
$$\frac{530}{5} = \frac{5p}{5}$$
$$106 = p$$

You have to read 106 pages per week.

3.4 Exercises (pp. 136–139)

Skill Practice

1. You use two inverse operations to solve a *two-step equation*.

2. A *verbal* model uses symbols for operations and words to label information.

Chapter 3, *continued*

3. D   **4.** C   **5.** A   **6.** B

7. A

8. In the equation, 2 is subtracted from $3n$, but the verbal statement *the difference of 3 times a number and -2 is 4* indicates that -2 should be subtracted. The equation should be written

$3n - (-2) = 4$.

9.
$$5n + 4 = 9$$
$$5n + 4 - 4 = 9 - 4$$
$$5n = 5$$
$$\frac{5n}{5} = \frac{5}{5}$$
$$n = 1$$
The number is 1.

10.
$$\frac{n}{2} - 7 = -6$$
$$\frac{n}{2} - 7 + 7 = -6 + 7$$
$$\frac{n}{2} = 1$$
$$\frac{n}{2} \cdot 2 = 1 \cdot 2$$
$$n = 2$$
The number is 2.

11.
$$-2n + 3.5 = 7.5$$
$$-2n + 3.5 - 3.5 = 7.5 - 3.5$$
$$-2n = 4$$
$$\frac{-2n}{-2} = \frac{4}{-2}$$
$$n = -2$$
The number is -2.

12.
$$3n - \left(-\frac{1}{2}\right) = -\frac{5}{2}$$
$$3n - \left(-\frac{1}{2}\right) + \left(-\frac{1}{2}\right) = \frac{-5}{2} + \left(\frac{-1}{2}\right)$$
$$3n = -\frac{6}{2}$$
$$3n = -3$$
$$\frac{3n}{3} = -\frac{3}{3}$$
$$n = -1$$
The number is -1.

13.
$$\frac{|n|}{6} = 4$$
$$\frac{|n|}{6} \cdot 6 = 4 \cdot 6$$
$$|n| = 24$$
$$n = 24, \text{ or } n = -24$$
The number is 24 or -24.

14.
$$2|n| = 8$$
$$\frac{2|n|}{2} = \frac{8}{2}$$
$$|n| = 4$$
$$n = 4, \text{ or } n = -4$$
The number is 4 or -4.

15.
$$|n| + 6 = 12$$
$$|n| + 6 - 6 = 12 - 6$$
$$|n| = 6$$
$$n = 6, \text{ or } n = -6$$
The number is 6 or -6.

16.
$$2|n| - 5 = 3$$
$$2|n| - 5 + 5 = 3 + 5$$
$$2|n| = 8$$
$$\frac{2|n|}{2} = \frac{8}{2}$$
$$|n| = 4$$
$$n = 4, \text{ or } n = -4$$
The number is 4 or -4.

17.
$$\frac{n}{5} \cdot 2 = 1$$
$$\frac{n}{5} \cdot 2 \div 2 = 1 \div 2$$
$$\frac{n}{5} = \frac{1}{2}$$
$$\frac{n}{5} \cdot 5 = \frac{1}{2} \cdot 5$$
$$n = \frac{5}{2}$$
$$n = 2\frac{1}{2}$$
The number is $2\frac{1}{2}$.

18.
$$(2 + 3) + 3n = -4$$
$$5 + 3n = -4$$
$$5 + 3n - 5 = -4 - 5$$
$$3n = -9$$
$$\frac{3n}{3} = \frac{-9}{3}$$
$$n = -3$$
The number is -3.

19.
$$\frac{-36}{9} = 4n + 8$$
$$-4 = 4n + 8$$
$$-4 - 8 = 4n + 8 - 8$$
$$-12 = 4n$$
$$\frac{-12}{4} = \frac{4n}{4}$$
$$-3 = n$$
The number is -3.

20. $\dfrac{8^2}{16} \cdot n = 24$

$\dfrac{64}{16} \cdot n = 24$

$4n = 24$

$\dfrac{4n}{4} = \dfrac{24}{4}$

$n = 6$

The number is 6.

Problem Solving

21. a. $\dfrac{\text{Cost}}{\text{per car}} \cdot \dfrac{\text{Number}}{\text{of cars}} - \dfrac{\text{Amount spent}}{\text{on supplies}} = \text{Profit}$

b. $6n - 15 = 93$

c. $6n - 15 = 93$

$6n - 15 + 15 = 93 + 15$

$6n = 108$

$\dfrac{6n}{6} = \dfrac{108}{6}$

$n = 18$

d. You and your friends washed 18 cars. The answer is reasonable because if you estimate the profit based on 20 cars, you have $p = 6(20) - 15 = 105$, which is a little greater than $93, as you would expect.

22. Let x be your hourly earnings.

$\text{Profit} = \dfrac{\text{Number}}{\text{of hours}} \cdot \dfrac{\text{Hourly}}{\text{earnings}} - \dfrac{\text{Cost of}}{\text{gasoline}}$

$70 = 10x - 20$

$70 + 20 = 10x - 20 + 20$

$90 = 10x$

$\dfrac{90}{10} = \dfrac{10x}{10}$

$9 = x$

You earn $9 each hour.

23. Let c be the number of candles you sell.

$\text{Profit} = \dfrac{\text{Amount}}{\text{per candle}} \cdot \dfrac{\text{Number of}}{\text{candles}} - \dfrac{\text{Cost of}}{\text{materials}}$

$85 = 15c - 20$

$85 + 20 = 15c - 20 + 20$

$105 = 15c$

$\dfrac{105}{15} = \dfrac{15c}{15}$

$7 = c$

You need to sell 7 candles.

24. A; Let h be the number of hours.

$\dfrac{\text{Rate per}}{\text{hour}} \cdot \dfrac{\text{Number}}{\text{of hours}} + \text{Fee} = \dfrac{\text{Total}}{\text{cost}}$

$5h + 10 = 45$

25. Let x be the payment amount.

$\dfrac{\text{Number of}}{\text{payments}} \cdot \dfrac{\text{Payment}}{\text{amount}} + \dfrac{\text{Initial}}{\text{payment}} = \dfrac{\text{Yearly}}{\text{cost}}$

$3x + 5 = 26$

$3x + 5 - 5 = 26 - 5$

$3x = 21$

$\dfrac{3x}{3} = \dfrac{21}{3}$

$x = 7$

Each payment is $7.

26. $d = 35t + 0.1$

$0.7 = 35t + 0.1$

$0.7 - 0.1 = 35t + 0.1 - 0.1$

$0.6 = 35t$

$\dfrac{0.6}{35} = \dfrac{35t}{35}$

$t \approx 0.017$ hours, or $60(0.017) \approx 1.02$ minutes

It takes the dog about 1 minute to be 0.7 mile away from its owner.

27. *Sample answers:*

$3(8) + 5 = 29 \qquad 6(8) - 10 = 38$

Two different two-step equations with a solution of 8 are $3x + 5 = 29$ and $6x - 10 = 38$.

28. *Sample answer:* At a corner deli, you buy 5 pounds of lunch meat. The owner gives you a discount of $6, so you pay $9.

$5x - 6 = 9$

$5x - 6 + 6 = 9 + 6$

$5x = 15$

$\dfrac{5x}{5} = \dfrac{15}{5}$

$x = 3$

The lunch meat costs $3 per pound.

29. Let y be the number of rye bread sandwiches sold the day before.

$\dfrac{\text{Twice the rye}}{\substack{\text{bread sandwiches} \\ \text{as the day before}}} + \dfrac{\text{Number of}}{\substack{\text{white bread} \\ \text{sandwiches}}} = \dfrac{\text{Total}}{\substack{\text{number of} \\ \text{sandwiches}}}$

$2y + 28 = 60$

$2y + 28 - 28 = 60 - 28$

$2y = 32$

$\dfrac{2y}{2} = \dfrac{32}{2}$

$y = 16$

30. Let x be the number of boxes with 12 forks needed.

Number of boxes with 8 forks	•	Forks per box	+	Boxes with 12 forks	•	Forks per box	=	Total number of forks needed

$$5 \cdot 8 + 12x = 124$$
$$40 + 12x = 124$$
$$40 + 12x - 40 = 124 - 40$$
$$12x = 84$$
$$\frac{12x}{12} = \frac{84}{12}$$
$$x = 7$$

You need to buy 7 boxes that contain 12 forks each.

31. Let a be the number of adults. Then the total number of participants was $3a$.

Amount per participant	•	Total number of participants	−	Tank rental cost	=	Total profit

$$5(3a) - 135 = 300$$
$$15a - 135 = 300$$
$$15a - 135 + 135 = 300 + 135$$
$$15a = 435$$
$$\frac{15a}{15} = \frac{435}{15}$$
$$a = 29$$

The number of adults who participated was 29.

32. Let c be the measure of angle C.

Angle A: $c + 12$

Angle B: $4c$

Measure of angle A	+	Measure of angle B	+	Measure of angle C	=	Sum of angles of a Triangle

$$c + 12 + 4c + c = 180$$
$$6c + 12 = 180$$
$$6c + 12 - 12 = 180 - 12$$
$$6c = 168$$
$$\frac{6c}{6} = \frac{168}{6}$$
$$c = 28$$

Angle A: $c + 12 = 28 + 12 = 40$

Angle B: $4c = 4(28) = 112$

So, the measure of angle A is 40°, the measure of angle B is 112° and the measure of angle C is 28°.

33. Let m be the number of miles.

Cost per mile	•	Number of miles	+	Initial charge	=	Cost before tip

$$1.50m + 2 = 17$$
$$1.50m + 2 - 2 = 17 - 2$$
$$1.50m = 15$$
$$\frac{1.50m}{1.50} = \frac{15}{1.50}$$
$$m = 10$$

You traveled 10 miles.

It won't cost twice as much to go twice as far, because you won't have to pay the $2 charge again. The total cost to travel twice as far is $1.50(20) + 2 = \$32$ and twice the cost of the 10-mile ride is $2 \times 17 = \$34$.

34. To find out after how many weeks you will be training for a total of 85 minutes, you need to know by how much time you increase your running time each week.

35. To find out how much you made in tips, you need to know how many hours you worked.

36. Width: w

Length: $3w + 15$

Perimeter = $2 \cdot$ Length $+ 2 \cdot$ Width

$$94 = 2(3w + 15) + 2w$$
$$94 = 6w + 30 + 2w$$
$$94 - 30 = 8w + 30 - 30$$
$$64 = 8w$$
$$\frac{64}{8} = \frac{8w}{8}$$
$$8 = w$$

Length: $3(8) + 15 = 39$

Area: Length $\cdot$ Width $= 39 \cdot 8 = 312$

The area of the rectangle is 312 square feet.

37. Separate the prices of snacks and videos.

Number of videos	Total price		Price of videos		Price of snacks
1 video:	$P = 8$	=	3	+	5
2 videos:	$P = 11$	=	6	+	5
3 videos:	$P = 14$	=	9	+	5
4 videos:	$P = 17$	=	12	+	5

From the pattern, it costs $3 per video. So, an equation for the cost of renting x videos is $P = 3x + 5$.

12 videos: $P = 3(12) + 5 = 41$

It costs $41 to rent 12 videos including $5 for snacks.

Chapter 3, *continued*

38. Let h be the number of hours of labor.

$$\begin{array}{ccccc}\text{Cost of} & & \text{Labor} & \text{Hours} & \text{Total}\\\text{parts} & + & \text{rate} & \cdot\; \text{of labor} & = \text{cost}\end{array}$$

$$350 + 80h = 730$$
$$350 - 350 + 80h = 730 - 350$$
$$80h = 380$$
$$\frac{80h}{80} = \frac{380}{80}$$
$$h = \frac{19}{4} = 4\frac{3}{4}$$

Including the 45 minute lunch break, the mechanic finishes $4\frac{3}{4} + \frac{3}{4} = 5\frac{1}{2}$ hours after 10:30. So, the mechanic finishes at 4:00 P.M.

Mixed Review

39. $P = 2\ell + 2w = 2(12) + 2(3) = 24 + 6 = 30$

The perimeter is 30 feet.

$A = \ell w = 12(3) = 36$

The area is 36 square feet.

40. $P = 4s = 4(15) = 60$

The perimeter is 60 inches.

$A = s^2 = 15^2 = 225$

The area is 225 square inches.

41. $P = 2\ell + 2w = 2(24) + 2(18) = 48 + 36 = 84$

The perimeter is 84 meters.

$A = \ell w = 24(18) = 432$

The area is 432 square meters.

42. $3(7 + x) + x = 21 + 3x + x = 4x + 21$

43. $-2(8x - 3) + 2x = -16x + 6 + 2x = -14x + 6$

44. $4x + 9(2x - 5) = 4x + 18x - 45 = 22x - 45$

45.
$$6 + 4k = 14$$
$$6 + 4k - 6 = 14 - 6$$
$$4k = 8$$
$$\frac{4k}{4} = \frac{8}{4}$$
$$k = 2$$

46.
$$\frac{y}{2} + 7 = -10$$
$$\frac{y}{2} + 7 - 7 = -10 - 7$$
$$\frac{y}{2} = -17$$
$$\frac{y}{2} \cdot 2 = -17 \cdot 2$$
$$y = -34$$

17.
$$30 \quad\; 3u \quad\; 9$$
$$30 + 9 = -3a - 9 + 9$$
$$39 = -3a$$
$$\frac{39}{-3} = \frac{-3a}{-3}$$
$$-13 = a$$

48. C; $|-7| = 7, -|-7| = -7, -(-9) = 9, -|9| = -9$

So, $-(-9)$ has the greatest value.

Quiz 3.1–3.4 (p. 139)

1.
$$x - 16 = 8$$
$$x - 16 + 16 = 8 + 16$$
$$x = 24$$

2.
$$8 + x = 3$$
$$8 + x - 8 = 3 - 8$$
$$x = -5$$

3. $19r = 76$
$$\frac{19r}{19} = \frac{76}{19}$$
$$r = 4$$

4.
$$\frac{y}{-1.4} = -5$$
$$\frac{y}{-1.4} \cdot (-1.4) = -5 \cdot (-1.4)$$
$$y = 7$$

5.
$$3x - 8 = 7$$
$$3x - 8 + 8 = 7 + 8$$
$$3x = 15$$
$$\frac{3x}{3} = \frac{15}{3}$$
$$x = 5$$

6.
$$14 = 2 + \frac{x}{3}$$
$$14 - 2 = 2 + \frac{x}{3} - 2$$
$$12 = \frac{x}{3}$$
$$12 \cdot 3 = \frac{x}{3} \cdot 3$$
$$36 = x$$

7.
$$10n + 5 = -15$$
$$10n + 5 - 5 = -15 - 5$$
$$10n = -20$$
$$\frac{10n}{10} = \frac{-20}{10}$$
$$n = -2$$

The number is -2.

8.
$$4n - (-7) = 39$$
$$4n - (-7) + (-7) = 39 + (-7)$$
$$4n = 32$$
$$\frac{4n}{4} = \frac{32}{4}$$
$$n = 8$$

The number is 8.

McDougal Littell Math, Course 3
Worked-Out Solution Key **83**

9. Let w be the number of weeks.

$$\begin{array}{c}\text{Weekly}\\\text{amount}\end{array} \cdot \begin{array}{c}\text{Number of}\\\text{weeks}\end{array} + \begin{array}{c}\text{Amount}\\\text{paid by}\\\text{parents}\end{array} = \begin{array}{c}\text{Total}\\\text{cost}\end{array}$$

$$20w + 100 = 280$$
$$20w + 100 - 100 = 280 - 100$$
$$20w = 180$$
$$\frac{20w}{20} = \frac{180}{20}$$
$$w = 9$$

It will take 9 weeks to save enough money.

Brain Game (p. 139)

Sample answer: Choose 4.

$4 \times 2 = 8$

$8 + 14 = 22$

$22 \div 2 = 11$

$11 - 4 = 7$

$7 \times 3 = 21$

Let x be the number.

$2x$

$2x + 14$

$\dfrac{2x + 14}{2}$

$\dfrac{2x + 14}{2} - x$

$3\left(\dfrac{2x + 14}{2} - x\right)$

The algebraic expression is $3\left(\dfrac{2x + 14}{2} - x\right)$.

$$3\left(\frac{2x + 14}{2} - x\right) = 3\left(\frac{2(x + 7)}{2} - x\right)$$
$$= 3(x + 7 - x) = 3(7) = 21$$

When the expression is simplified, the answer is 21. So, 21 will be the result no matter what value is chosen for x.

Technology Activity 3.4 (p. 140)

1–2. Check work.

Mixed Review of Problem Solving (p. 141)

1. a. $\begin{array}{c}\text{Height of}\\\text{CN Tower}\end{array} - \begin{array}{c}\text{Height of}\\\text{Empire State}\end{array} = \text{Difference}$

b. Let C be the height of the CN Tower.

$$C - 1250 = 565$$
$$C - 1250 + 1250 = 565 + 1250$$
$$C = 1815$$

The height of the CN Tower is 1815 feet.

c. Let S be the height of the Sears Tower.

$$\begin{array}{c}\text{Height of}\\\text{Sears Tower}\end{array} + \begin{array}{c}\text{Difference of}\\\text{Sears and CN}\end{array} = \begin{array}{c}\text{Height of}\\\text{CN Tower}\end{array}$$

$$S + 365 = 1815$$
$$S + 365 - 365 = 1815 - 365$$
$$S = 1450$$

The height of the Sears Tower is 1450 feet.

2. Let x be the season rushing yards.

$$\frac{\text{Season rushing yards}}{\text{Number of games}} = \text{Rushing yards per game}$$

$$\frac{x}{16} = 93$$
$$\frac{x}{16} \cdot 16 = 93 \cdot 16$$
$$x = 1488$$

The team gained 1488 yards for the season.

To find the total yards next year, increase the rushing yards per game by 25 in the model.

$$\frac{x}{16} = 93 + 25$$
$$\frac{x}{16} = 118$$
$$\frac{x}{16} \cdot 16 = 118 \cdot 16$$
$$x = 1888$$

The goal for the total rushing yards next year is 1888 yards.

3. *Sample answer:*

Sam has four fewer than twice the number of CDs that Ralph has. Sam has 20 CDs. How many does Ralph have?

Let R be the number of CDs Ralph has.

$$2R - 4 = 20$$
$$2R - 4 + 4 = 20 + 4$$
$$2R = 24$$
$$\frac{2R}{2} = \frac{24}{2}$$
$$R = 12$$

So, Ralph has 12 CDs.

Chapter 3, continued

4. $d = rt$

$20 \text{ mi} = r \cdot 1 \text{ h}$

$\dfrac{20 \text{ mi}}{1 \text{ h}} = \dfrac{r \cdot 1 \text{ h}}{1 \text{ h}}$

$r = \dfrac{20 \text{ mi}}{1 \text{ h}}$

Jesse's average speed is 20 miles per hour.

Half again as fast: $\left(1 + \dfrac{1}{2}\right) \times 20 = \dfrac{3}{2} \times 20 = 30$ miles per hour

Let x be the time in hours.

$30x = 20$

$\dfrac{30x}{30} = \dfrac{20}{30}$

$x = \dfrac{2}{3}$

$\dfrac{2}{3} \text{ h} = \dfrac{2 \text{ h}}{3} \times \dfrac{60 \text{ min}}{1 \text{ h}} = \dfrac{2 \cancel{h} \times \overset{20}{\cancel{60}} \text{ min}}{\cancel{3} \times 1 \cancel{h}} = 40 \text{ min}$

It will take Jesse 40 minutes to return home.

5. 8; Let t be the number of tanks of fuel.

Miles per gallon	•	Gallons per fill-up	•	Number of fill-ups	=	Total number of Miles
5	•	80	•	t	=	3400

$400t = 3400$

$\dfrac{400t}{400} = \dfrac{3400}{400}$

$t = \dfrac{17}{2} = 8\dfrac{1}{2}$

Jen needs $8\dfrac{1}{2}$ tanks of fuel for the trip. She starts with a full tank, so she'll need to stop 8 times for the $7\dfrac{1}{2}$ additional tanks.

6. 20; Let d be the distance Lola travels on Bus 2.

Distance on Bus 1	+	Distance on Bus 2	=	Total Distance
3	+	d	=	18

$3 - 3 + d = 18 - 3$

$d = 15$

$r \cdot t = d$

$45 \cdot t = 15$

$\dfrac{45\,t}{45} = \dfrac{15}{45}$

$t = \dfrac{1}{3} \text{ h}$

$\dfrac{1}{3} \text{ h} = \dfrac{1 \text{ h}}{3} \times \dfrac{60 \text{ min}}{1 \text{ h}} = \dfrac{1 \cancel{h} \times \overset{20}{\cancel{60}} \text{ min}}{\cancel{3} \times 1 \cancel{h}} = 20 \text{ min}$

Lola spent 20 minutes on the second bus.

7. a.

$$\boxed{\begin{array}{c} P = 46 \text{ in.} \end{array}} \; x$$
$$x + 7$$

h. $P = 2\ell + 2w$

$46 = 2(x + 7) + 2x$

$46 = 2x + 14 + 2x$

$46 - 14 = 4x + 14 - 14$

$32 = 4x$

$\dfrac{32}{4} = \dfrac{4x}{4}$

$8 = x$

$x + 7 = 8 + 7 = 15$

The rectangle is 15 inches long and 8 inches wide.

c. $A = \ell \times w = 15 \times 8 = 120$

The area of the rectangle is 120 square inches.

d. Increasing the length and width by 4 times will make the perimeter 4 times greater.

This is true for any rectangle because the original perimeter is $2\ell + 2w$, and the perimeter of a rectangle with 4 times the dimensions is $2(4\ell) + 2(4w)$, which is equal to $4(2\ell + 2w)$, or 4 times the original perimeter.

The area will be increased by 16 times.

This is true because for any rectangle $A = \ell w$, but when the dimensions are increased by 4 times, the area becomes $(4\ell)(4w) = 16\,\ell w$, or 16 times the original area.

Lesson 3.5

Activity (p. 142)

1. Check work.

2. Check work.

3.

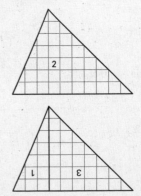

4. The height of triangle 2 is the same as the the height of the original rectangle. The area of the rectangle is 10×7, or 70 square units. Because the rectangle is divided as shown into two triangles of equal size, the area of triangle 2 must be half the area of the rectangle, or 35 square units.

5. Check work.

6. $A = \dfrac{b \times h}{2}$

Chapter 3, continued

3.5 Guided Practice (pp. 143–144)

1. $A = \frac{1}{2}bh = \frac{1}{2}(10)(9) = 45$

The area of the triangle is 45 square inches.

2. $P = a + b + c = 4 + 6 + 2.5 = 12.5$

The perimeter of the triangle is 12.5 feet.

3.
$$P = 2\ell + 2w$$
$$36 = 2\ell + 2(8)$$
$$36 = 2\ell + 16$$
$$36 - 16 = 2\ell + 16 - 16$$
$$20 = 2\ell$$
$$\frac{20}{2} = \frac{2\ell}{2}$$
$$10 = \ell$$

The length of the rectangle is 10 feet.

4. $A = \frac{1}{2}bh$

$$32 = \frac{1}{2}(8)h$$
$$32 = 4h$$
$$\frac{32}{4} = \frac{4h}{4}$$
$$8 = h$$

The height of the triangle is 8 millimeters.

5. $A = \frac{1}{2}bh$

$$6 = \frac{1}{2}b(4)$$
$$6 = 2b$$
$$\frac{6}{2} = \frac{2b}{2}$$
$$3 = b$$

The base of the triangle is 3 inches.

6. Total area $=$ $\begin{array}{c}\text{Area}\\\text{of pool}\end{array}$ $+$ $\begin{array}{c}\text{Area of}\\\text{rock region}\end{array}$

$$40 \cdot 64 = 20 \cdot 32 + r$$
$$2560 = 640 + r$$
$$2560 - 640 = 640 + r - 640$$
$$1920 = r$$

The area of the region with rocks is 1920 square feet.

3.5 Exercises (pp. 145–147)

Skill Practice

1. In order to find the area of a triangle, you need to know the length of a *base* and the *height*.

2. The *perimeter* of a triangle is the sum of the lengths of all three of its sides.

3. $A = \frac{1}{2}bh = \frac{1}{2}(6)(4) = 12$

The area of the triangle is 12 square centimeters.

$P = a + b + c = 5 + 6 + 5 = 16$

The perimeter of the triangle is 16 centimeters.

4. $A = \frac{1}{2}bh = \frac{1}{2}(4)(12) = 24$

The area of the triangle is 24 square inches.

$P = a + b + c = 15 + 4 + 13 = 32$

The perimeter of the triangle is 32 inches.

5. $A = \frac{1}{2}bh = \frac{1}{2}(5)(12) = 30$

The area of the triangle is 30 square feet.

$P = a + b + c = 12 + 5 + 13 = 30$

The perimeter of the triangle is 30 feet.

6. Because the units (in.) are included in the calculations, when $(5 \text{ in.})(4 \text{ in.})$ is multiplied, the result should have units in terms of square inches.

$$A = \frac{1}{2}(5 \text{ in.})(4 \text{ in.})$$
$$A = \frac{1}{2}(20 \text{ in.}^2)$$
$$A = 10 \text{ in.}^2$$

7. $A = lw$

$$18 = 6x$$
$$\frac{18}{6} = \frac{6x}{6}$$
$$3 = x$$

The width of the rectangle is 3 feet.

8. $A = s^2$

$$49 = s^2$$
$$\sqrt{49} = s$$
$$7 = s$$

The side length of the square is 7 inches.

9.
$$P = a + b + c$$
$$60 = 17 + 23 + c$$
$$60 = 40 + c$$
$$60 - 40 = 40 + c - 40$$
$$20 = c$$

The side length of the triangle is 20 meters.

10. B; $P = 2\ell + 2w$

$$24 = 2\ell + 2(4)$$
$$24 = 2\ell + 8$$
$$24 - 8 = 2\ell + 8 - 8$$
$$16 = 2\ell$$
$$\frac{16}{2} = \frac{2\ell}{2}$$
$$8 = \ell$$

The length of the rectangle is 8 feet.

11. Area of a square: $A = s^2 = 12^2 = 144$

Area of a triangle: $A = \frac{1}{2}bh = \frac{1}{2}(12)(18) = 108$

Total area: $A = 2(144) + 2(108) = 288 + 216 = 504$

The total area is 504 square inches.

12. Area of a triangle: $A = \frac{1}{2}bh = \frac{1}{2}(5)(3) = 7.5$

Total area: $A = 5(7.5) = 37.5$

The total area is 37.5 square meters.

13.

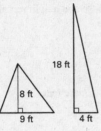

$A = \frac{1}{2}(9)(8) = 36 \text{ ft}^2$

$A = \frac{1}{2}(4)(18) = 36 \text{ ft}^2$

14.

$A = \frac{1}{2}(4)(10) = 20 \text{ in.}^2$

$A = \frac{1}{2}(5)(8) = 20 \text{ in.}^2$

15.

$A = \frac{1}{2}(3)(6) = 9 \text{ m}^2$

$A = \frac{1}{2}(2)(9) = 9 \text{ m}^2$

16.
$$P = 2\ell + 2w$$
$$146 = 2(49) + 2(2x)$$
$$146 = 98 + 4x$$
$$146 - 98 = 98 + 4x - 98$$
$$48 = 4x$$
$$\frac{48}{4} = \frac{4x}{4}$$
$$12 = x$$

The value of x is 12 inches.

17. $A = \frac{1}{2}bh$

$$36 = \frac{1}{2}(3y)(8)$$
$$36 = 12y$$
$$\frac{36}{12} = \frac{12y}{12}$$
$$3 = y$$

The value of y is 3 meters.

18. $A = \frac{1}{2}bh$

$$5 = \frac{1}{2}(2x)h$$
$$5 = xh$$
$$\frac{5}{x} = \frac{xh}{x}$$
$$\frac{5}{x} = h$$

The height if the triangle in terms of x is $\frac{5}{x}$ meters.

19.
$$A = \ell w$$
$$70 = \ell(3.5w)$$
$$70 = 3.5w\ell$$
$$\frac{70}{3.5w} = \frac{3.5w\ell}{3.5w}$$
$$\frac{20}{w} = \ell$$

The length of the rectangle in terms of w is $\frac{20}{w}$ inches.

20. $\text{Area of shaded region} = \text{Total area} - \text{Area of inside rectangle}$

$$16 = 3x(4) - 4x$$
$$16 = 12x - 4x$$
$$16 = 8x$$
$$\frac{16}{8} = \frac{8x}{8}$$
$$2 = x$$

The value of x is 2.

21. $\text{Area of shaded region} = \text{Area of square} - \text{Area of triangle}$

$$76 = 10^2 - \frac{1}{2}(8)(2x)$$
$$76 = 100 - 8x$$
$$76 - 100 = 100 - 8x - 100$$
$$-24 = -8x$$
$$\frac{-24}{-8} = \frac{-8x}{-8}$$
$$3 = x$$

The value of x is 3.

22. $\text{Area of shaded region} = \text{Area of rectangle} - \text{Area of unshaded triangle}$

$$180 = 8x(5x) - \frac{1}{2}(8x)(5x)$$
$$180 = 40x^2 - 20x^2$$
$$180 = 20x^2$$
$$\frac{180}{20} = \frac{20x^2}{20}$$
$$9 = x^2$$
$$\sqrt{9} = x$$
$$3 = x$$

The value of x is 3.

Chapter 3, continued

23. **a.** $A = lw = 7(6) = 42$ yd^2

The area of the rectangular portion of the patio is 42 square yards.

b. $A = s^2 = 3^2 = 9$ yd^2

The area of the square portion of the patio is 9 square yards.

c. $42 + 9 = 51$ yd^2

The area of the patio is 51 square yards.

24. D; $A = lw$

$64 = 16x$

25. D; $\quad P = 2l + 2w$

$114 = 2l + 2(22)$

$114 = 2l + 44$

$114 - 44 = 2l + 44 - 44$

$70 = 2l$

$\dfrac{70}{2} = \dfrac{2l}{2}$

$35 = l$

The length is 35 feet.

26. The bottom is not used as the base to find the area of the triangle, because the height is not given from the bottom, but the height from the 171 inch side is given.

27. Kate has less than half the room. The total area of the room is 18×14, or 252 square feet. Half of the total area is $252 \div 2$, or 126 square feet. Kate's square has an area of 11×11, or 121 square feet, which is less than 126 square feet.

28. Area of each triangle: $A = \frac{1}{2}bh = \frac{1}{2}(2)(1.732) = 1.732$

Area of the hexagon: $A = 6(1.732) = 10.392$

The area of the hexagon is 10.392 square millimeters.

29–32. *Sample answers:*

$A = \frac{1}{2}bh$

$\quad = \frac{1}{2}(6)(4)$

$\quad = 12$ units^2

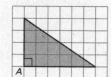

29. If the height is doubled, the area of the triangle is doubled.

$A = \frac{1}{2}(6)(2 \cdot 4) = 24$ units^2

30. If the base is doubled, the area of the triangle is doubled.

$A = \frac{1}{2}(2 \cdot 6)(4) = 24$ units^2

31. If the base and height are both doubled, the area is quadrupled.

$A = \frac{1}{2}(2 \cdot 6)(2 \cdot 4) = 48$ units^2

32. If the shape is changed, but the base and height remain the same, the area stays the same.

$A = \frac{1}{2}(6)(4) = 12$ units^2

33. **a.** $A = s^2 = 9(9) = 81$

The area of the tent floor is 81 square feet.

b. *Sample answer:*

$\ell = 6$ ft

$w = 3$ ft

$A = \ell w = 6(3) = 18$

The area of a sleeping bag is about 18 square feet.

c. *Sample answer:* Four 6 foot by 3 foot sleeping bags could fit inside the tent without overlapping as shown in the diagram. The bags will take up $4(18) = 72$ square feet of the tent's 81 square feet of area.

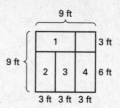

34.

Total perimeter of all windows	=	Perimeter of 3 square windows	+	Perimeter of rectangle windows

$P = 3(4s) + 2l + 2w$

$\quad = 3(4 \cdot 3) + 2(5) + 2(3)$

$\quad = 36 + 10 + 6$

$\quad = 52$ ft

$108 \text{ in.} \times \dfrac{1 \text{ ft}}{12 \text{ in.}} = \dfrac{\overset{9}{\cancel{108 \text{ in.}}} \times 1 \text{ ft}}{\underset{1}{\cancel{12 \text{ in.}}}} = 9 \text{ ft}$

Each roll has 9 feet of weather stripping.

$\dfrac{52}{9} = 5\dfrac{7}{9}$

So you need 6 rolls of weather stripping.

At \$4 per roll, you need $6 \times 4 = \$24$. So, \$25 is enough money.

35. In each of the triangles mentioned, the base is $\overline{YZ}$ and the height is the constant distance between lines a and b. Because, the height and base are the same for each triangle, the area of each triangle is the same.

Mixed Review

36. $-18 - 42 = -18 + (-42)$

$\quad = -60$

37. $-21 - (-14) = -21 + 14$

$\quad = -7$

Chapter 3, continued

38. $10 - 15 = 10 + (-15)$
$\qquad = -5$

39. $3 > -3$

40. $-5 > -6$

41. $-17 < -13$

42. $13 = \left|13\right|$

43. B; When $r = 5$ and $s = 2$, $6r + 7s = 6(5) + 7(2) = 44$

Lesson 3.6

3.6 Guided Practice (pp. 149–150)

1. $z \geq -1$

All numbers greater than or equal to -1

2. $4 > p$

All numbers less than 4

3. $k \leq -3.5$

All numbers less than or equal to -3.5

4. $m > \frac{1}{2}$

All numbers greater than $\frac{1}{2}$

5. $\quad x - 3 > -2$
$\quad x - 3 + 3 > -2 + 3$
$\qquad\qquad x > 1$

6. $\quad 6 > t - 1$
$\quad 6 + 1 > t - 1 + 1$
$\qquad 7 > t$
$\qquad t < 7$

7. $\qquad 12 \geq p + 14$
$\quad 12 - 14 \geq p + 14 - 14$
$\qquad -2 \geq p$
$\qquad p \leq -2$

8. $\quad x + 5 < 10$
$\quad x + 5 - 5 < 10 - 5$
$\qquad x < 5$

9. $\qquad t + 9 < 6$
$\quad t + 9 - 9 \leq 6 - 9$
$\qquad t \leq -3$

10. $\qquad -4 < k - 3$
$\quad -4 + 3 < k - 3 + 3$
$\qquad -1 < k$
$\qquad k > -1$

11. $\qquad d + 155 > 300$
$\quad d + 155 - 155 > 300 - 155$
$\qquad d > 145$

Your second throw needs to travel more than 145 feet.

3.6 Exercises (pp. 150–153)

Skill Practice

1. $-4 + x < -6$ and $x < -2$ are *equivalent inequalities*.

2. C; The circle at -1 is open, and the graph is shaded to the left.

3. A; The circle at 1 is closed, and the graph is shaded to the left.

4. B; The circle at 1 is closed, and the graph is shaded to the right.

5. D; The circle at -1 is open, and the graph is shaded to the right.

6. $x > -2$; All numbers greater than -2

7. $x \geq -5$; All numbers greater than or equal to -5

8. $x \leq 2$; All numbers less than or equal to 2

9. $x < 6$; All numbers less than 6

10. $x \geq 6$ represents all numbers greater than or equal to 6, so the circle at 6 needs to be filled in to show 6 as part of the solution.

11. $\qquad 12 + p < 7$
$\quad 12 + p - 12 < 7 - 12$
$\qquad\qquad p < -5$

12. $\qquad k + 4 \leq 11$
$\quad k + 4 - 4 \leq 11 - 4$
$\qquad\qquad k \leq 7$

13. $n - 6 > 3$

$n - 6 + 6 > 3 + 6$

$n > 9$

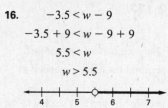

14. $17 + r \geq 25$

$17 + r - 17 \geq 25 - 17$

$r \geq 8$

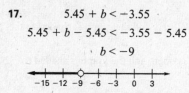

15. $-8 \geq m - 19$

$-8 + 19 \geq m - 19 + 19$

$11 \geq m$

$m \leq 11$

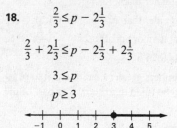

16. $-3.5 < w - 9$

$-3.5 + 9 < w - 9 + 9$

$5.5 < w$

$w > 5.5$

17. $5.45 + b < -3.55$

$5.45 + b - 5.45 < -3.55 - 5.45$

$b < -9$

18. $\frac{2}{3} \leq p - 2\frac{1}{3}$

$\frac{2}{3} + 2\frac{1}{3} \leq p - 2\frac{1}{3} + 2\frac{1}{3}$

$3 \leq p$

$p \geq 3$

19. $t + \frac{1}{4} > 5$

$t + \frac{1}{4} - \frac{1}{4} > 5 - \frac{1}{4}$

$t > 4\frac{3}{4}$

20. B; $x - 3 \geq 20$

$x - 3 + 3 \geq 20 + 3$

$x \geq 23$

The solution includes 23.

21. $-8 + x \leq 2$

$-8 + x + 8 \leq 2 + 8$

$x \leq 10$

The positive integers less than 10 that are solutions are 1 through 9.

22. $x - 20 > -15$

$x - 20 + 20 > -15 + 20$

$x > 5$

The positive integers less than 10 that are solutions are 6 through 9.

23. $-10 - x \leq -4$

$-10 - x + x \leq -4 + x$

$-10 \leq -4 + x$

$-10 + 4 \leq -4 + x + 4$

$-6 \leq x$

$x \geq -6$

The positive integers less than 10 that are solutions are 1 through 9.

24. $5 + x \leq 9$

$5 + x - 5 \leq 9 - 5$

$x \leq 4$

The positive integers less than 10 that are solutions are 1 through 4.

25. *Sample answer:*

$x < 4;$

$x + 2 < 4 + 2$

$x + 2 < 6;$

26. *Sample answer:*

$x > -10;$

$x + 3 > -10 + 3$

$x + 3 > -7;$

27. *Sample answer:*

$x > 19;$

$x + 6 > 19 + 6$

$x + 6 > 25;$

28. *Sample answer:*

$x < -7;$

$x - 3 < -7 - 3$

$x - 3 < -10;$

Chapter 3, *continued*

29. Yes, the inequalities $x < 2$ and $2 > x$ are equivalent, because the numbers that are less than 2 are the same as the numbers which 2 is greater than.

30. $|x| < 3$

By definition of absolute value, the distance between x and 0 is less than 3. Because you can move a distance of 3 on each side of 0, any value of x greater than -3 and less than 3 will make the statement true.

31. $|x| > 2$

By definition of absolute value, the distance between x and 0 is greater than 2. Because you can move a distance of 2 on each side of 0, any value of x less than -2 or greater than 2 will make the statement true.

32. $$|x| + 1 \le 5$$
$$|x| + 1 - 1 \le 5 - 1$$
$$|x| \le 4$$

By definition of absolute value, the distance between x and 0 is less than or equal to 4. Because you can move a distance of 4 on each side of 0, any value of x greater than or equal to -4 and less than or equal to 4 will make the statement true.

33. $$|x| + 1 \ge 7$$
$$|x| + 1 - 1 \ge 7 - 1$$
$$|x| \ge 6$$

By definition of absolute value, the distance between x and 0 is greater than or equal to 6. Because you can move a distance of 6 on each side of 0, any value of x less than or equal -6 or greater than or equal to 6 will make the statement true.

34. $-2 < y < 1$

Two inequalities: $-2 < y$ and $y < 1$

Two verbal sentences:

y is greater than -2 and y is less than 1.

y is between -2 and 1.

35. $7 \le t < 9$

Two inequalities: $7 \le t$ and $t < 9$

Two verbal sentences:

t is greater than or equal to 7 and t is less than 9.

t is between 7 and 9, including 7.

36. $4 \le m \le 11$

Two inequalities: $4 \le m$ and $m \le 11$

Two verbal sentences:

m is greater than or equal to 4 and m is less than or equal to 11.

m is between 4 and 11, including 4 and 11.

Problem Solving

37. a. $90 + 85 + 98 + 87 = 360$

b. $$360 + x \ge 425$$
$$360 + x - 360 \ge 425 - 360$$
$$x \ge 65$$

You must earn at least a 65 on your fifth test to earn a B in math class.

c.

$$\xleftarrow{\quad} \underset{55\quad 60\quad 65\quad 70\quad 75\quad 80}{+\!\!\!+\!\!\!+\!\!\!\bullet\!\!\!+\!\!\!+\!\!\!+} \xrightarrow{\quad}$$

38. Let x be the deposit amount.

$$\begin{array}{ccccc} \text{Deposit} \\ \text{amount} \end{array} + \begin{array}{c} \text{Amount} \\ \text{in account} \end{array} \ge \begin{array}{c} \text{Required} \\ \text{minimum balance} \end{array}$$

$$x + 33.96 \ge 50$$
$$x + 33.96 - 33.96 \ge 50 - 33.96$$
$$x \ge 16.04$$

You must deposit at least \$16.04 to equal or exceed the minimum balance.

39. Let x be the additional distance Cara needs to jump.

$$\begin{array}{c} \text{Additional} \\ \text{distance} \end{array} + \begin{array}{c} \text{Fourth place} \\ \text{distance} \end{array} > \begin{array}{c} \text{Longest current} \\ \text{distance} \end{array}$$

$$x + 57 > 93.5$$
$$x + 57 - 57 > 93.5 - 57$$
$$x > 36.5$$

Cara, the fourth place jumper, needs to jump more than 36.5 meters farther than her current jump to place first.

40. *Sample answer:*

You visit your cousin and it is 4 years since your last visit. Your cousin is under 10 years old now. How old was your cousin during your last visit?

$$p + 4 < 10$$
$$p + 4 - 4 < 10 - 4$$
$$p < 6$$

Your cousin was under 6 years old during your last visit.

41. $x - 3 \ge 10$ and $x \ge 13$ are equivalent inequalities because you can obtain $x \ge 13$ from $x - 3 \ge 10$ by adding 3 to each side, so both inequalities have the same solution. If you wanted to check whether the solution of $x - 3 \ge 10$ is the same as the solution of $x \ge 13$ by substituting values, then you could substitute 13 to check that the left side of $x - 3 \ge 10$ equals the right side as it does in $x \ge 13$. Then you could substitute 20 to check that the numbers greater than 13 satisfy the inequality $x - 3 \ge 10$ as they do in $x \ge 13$.

Chapter 3, *continued*

42. Let x be the time for scenic low-altitude flying.

$$\text{Scenic low-altitude time} + \text{Cork-screw roll time} + \text{Hammer-head time} + \text{Over-water time} \leq \text{Time limit}$$

$$x + 10 + 15 + 30 \leq 75$$
$$x + 55 \leq 75$$
$$x + 55 - 55 \leq 75 - 55$$
$$x \leq 20$$

She can use no more than 20 minutes for scenic low-altitude flying.

43. $2.5 \text{ hours} = \dfrac{2.5 \, \cancel{h} \times 60 \text{ min}}{1 \, \cancel{h}} = 150 \text{ min}$

$1.9 \text{ hours} = \dfrac{1.9 \text{ h} \times 60 \text{ min}}{1 \text{ h}} = 114 \text{ min}$

Let x be the number of minutes of improvement to break the record.

$$\text{Your race time} - \text{Minutes of improvement} < \text{Record time}$$

$$150 - x < 114$$
$$150 - x + x < 114 + x$$
$$150 - 114 < 114 + x - 114$$
$$36 < x$$

You need to take more than 36 minutes off your time to break the record.

44. D; Two inequalities that represent "f is between about 81 hertz and 1100 hertz" are $f \geq 81$ and $f \leq 1100$.

$f \geq 81$ is equivalent to $81 \leq f$.

$f \geq 1100$ is not true.

45. Let T be the number of tigers today.

$$\text{Current population} - \text{Increase since 1972} < \text{Number mentioned for 1972}$$

$$T - 2200 < 2000$$
$$T - 2200 + 2200 < 2000 + 2200$$
$$T < 4200$$

There are under 4200 tigers today.

Because each icon represents 4000 tigers there would be only 1 whole tiger icon on the map today.

46. Two inequalities that describe the cost of 30 seconds of commercial time during the Super Bowl from 1967 to 2005 are $\$42{,}000 \leq c$ and $c \leq \$2.4$ million.

47.
$$\text{Least amount for gifts} + \text{Greatest backpack amount} = \text{Total amount}$$

$$x + 35 = 75$$
$$x + 35 - 35 = 75 - 35$$
$$x = 40$$

The least amount Lauren will have for gifts is $40.

$$\text{Greatest amount for gifts} + \text{Least backpack amount} = \text{Total amount}$$

$$x + 25 = 75$$
$$x + 25 - 25 = 75 - 25$$
$$x = 50$$

The greatest amount Lauren will have for gifts is $50. The amount x that Lauren will have for gifts is given by the inequalities $40 \leq x$ and $x \leq 50$.

48. Because the sum of the lengths of any two sides is greater than the length of the third side, there are two cases to consider in determining the possible lengths x of the third side.

Case 1:

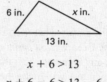

$$x + 6 > 13$$
$$x + 6 - 6 > 13 - 6$$
$$x > 7$$

Case 2:

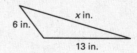

$$6 + 13 > x$$
$$19 > x$$
$$x < 19$$

The possible length x of the third side is given by $7 < x$ and $x < 19$.

Mixed Review

49. $\dfrac{x}{6} = -7$

$\dfrac{x}{6} \cdot 6 = -7 \cdot 6$

$x = -42$

50. $4m = 36$

$\dfrac{4m}{4} = \dfrac{36}{4}$

$m = 9$

Chapter 3, continued

51. $-9m = 126$

$$\frac{-9m}{-9} = \frac{126}{-9}$$

$$m = -14$$

52. $\frac{-22}{11} = -2$ **53.** $\frac{0}{3} = 0$

54. $\frac{45}{-5} = -9$ **55.** $\frac{-63}{-9} = 7$

56. $\frac{46}{2} = 23$ **57.** $\frac{35}{-7} = -5$

58. $\frac{-56}{-4} = 14$ **59.** $\frac{-72}{6} = -12$

60. B; nine and fifty-three thousandths = 9.053

Lesson 3.7

3.7 Guided Practice (p. 155)

1. $\frac{t}{6} > 4$ **2.** $-\frac{1}{2}x \le 10$

$$6 \cdot \frac{t}{6} > 6 \cdot 4 \qquad\qquad -2 \cdot \left(-\frac{1}{2}x\right) \ge -2 \cdot 10$$

$$t > 24 \qquad\qquad\qquad x \ge -20$$

3. $27 > -3t$ **4.** $9n < 63$

$$\frac{27}{-3} < \frac{-3t}{-3} \qquad\qquad \frac{9n}{9} < \frac{63}{9}$$

$$-9 < t \qquad\qquad\qquad n < 7$$

5. $\boxed{\text{Grams the bat can eat}} \le 2.5 \cdot \boxed{\text{The bat's mass}}$

$$g \le 2.5 \cdot 25$$

$$g \le 62.5$$

The bat can eat up to 62.5 grams of figs in one night.

3.7 Exercises (pp. 156–159)

Skill Practice

1. When you multiply both sides of an inequality by a negative number, you need to *reverse the direction of* the inequality symbol.

2. Dividing each side of an inequality by a *positive* number makes an equivalent inequality.

3. No; Multiplying each side by 3 will not require reversing the inequality symbol.

4. Yes; Dividing each side by -6 will require reversing the inequality symbol.

5. Yes; Multiplying each side by -8 will require reversing the inequality symbol.

6. No; Dividing each side by 2 will not require reversing the inequality symbol.

7. D; $\frac{1}{4}x \le 8$

$$4 \cdot \frac{1}{4}x \le 4 \cdot 8$$

$$x \le 32$$

8. C; $-4x \ge 8$ **9.** A; $4x \ge -8$

$$\frac{-4x}{-4} \le \frac{8}{-4} \qquad\qquad \frac{4x}{4} \ge \frac{-8}{4}$$

$$x \le -2 \qquad\qquad\qquad x \ge -2$$

10. B; $-\frac{1}{4}x \le 8$

$$-4 \cdot \left(-\frac{1}{4}x\right) \ge -4 \cdot 8$$

$$x \ge -32$$

11. $\frac{1}{2}x < 4$

$$2 \cdot \frac{1}{2}x < 2 \cdot 4$$

$$x < 8$$

12. $\frac{m}{-7} \ge 6$

$$-7 \cdot \left(\frac{m}{-7}\right) \le -7 \cdot 6$$

$$m \le -42$$

13. $9 \le 3z$

$$\frac{9}{3} \le \frac{3z}{3}$$

$$3 \le z$$

$$z \ge 3$$

14. $30 > -6p$

$$\frac{30}{-6} < \frac{-6p}{-6}$$

$$-5 < p$$

$$p > -5$$

15. $\frac{1}{4}x > 1$

$$4 \cdot \frac{1}{4}x > 4 \cdot 1$$

$$x > 4$$

16. $-\frac{1}{7}t \ge -3$

$$-7 \cdot \left(-\frac{1}{7}t\right) \le -7 \cdot (-3)$$

$$t \le 21$$

17. $-\frac{1}{5}b \geq 72$

$$-5 \cdot \left(-\frac{1}{5}b\right) \leq -5 \cdot 72$$

$$b \leq -360$$

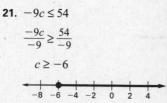

18. $\frac{1}{3}d < -33$

$$3 \cdot \left(\frac{1}{3}d\right) < 3 \cdot (-33)$$

$$d < -99$$

19. $4g < 24$

$$\frac{4g}{4} < \frac{24}{4}$$

$$g < 6$$

20. $12 \geq -3s$

$$\frac{12}{-3} \leq \frac{-3s}{-3}$$

$$-4 \leq s$$

$$s \geq -4$$

21. $-9c \leq 54$

$$\frac{-9c}{-9} \geq \frac{54}{-9}$$

$$c \geq -6$$

22. $5z < -15$

$$\frac{5z}{5} < \frac{-15}{5}$$

$$z < -3$$

23. $7 > -\frac{1}{8}r$

$$-8 \cdot 7 < -8 \cdot \left(-\frac{1}{8}r\right)$$

$$-56 < r$$

$$r > -56$$

24. $-6t \geq 36$

$$\frac{-6t}{-6} \leq \frac{36}{-6}$$

$$t \leq -6$$

25. $-39 \leq 13k$

$$\frac{-39}{13} \leq \frac{13k}{13}$$

$$-3 \leq k$$

$$k \geq -3$$

26. $-\frac{1}{6}a < -54$

$$-6 \cdot \left(2\frac{1}{6}a\right) > -6 \cdot (-54)$$

$$a > 324$$

27. The inequality symbol should not be reversed when each side is divided by 4.

$$-12 < 4x$$

$$-\frac{12}{4} < \frac{4x}{4}$$

$$-3 < x$$

28. The inequality symbol should be reversed when each side is divided by -7.

$$-7x \geq 35$$

$$\frac{-7x}{-7} \leq \frac{35}{-7}$$

$$x \leq -5$$

29. A; $2x \geq -8$

$$\frac{2x}{2} \geq \frac{-8}{2}$$

$$x \geq -4$$

30. $12 > 6 - 2x$

$$12 - 6 > 6 - 2x - 6$$

$$6 > -2x$$

$$\frac{6}{-2} < \frac{-2x}{-2}$$

$$-3 < x$$

$$x > -3$$

31. $4p - 9 \geq -1$

$$4p - 9 + 9 \geq -1 + 9$$

$$4p \geq 8$$

$$\frac{4p}{4} \geq \frac{8}{4}$$

$$p \geq 2$$

32.
$$5(5 - 2x) > 15$$
$$25 - 10x > 15$$
$$25 - 10x - 25 > 15 - 25$$
$$-10x > -10$$
$$\frac{-10x}{-10} < \frac{-10}{-10}$$
$$x < 1$$

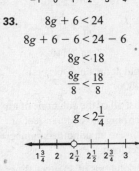

33.
$$8g + 6 < 24$$
$$8g + 6 - 6 < 24 - 6$$
$$8g < 18$$
$$\frac{8g}{8} < \frac{18}{8}$$
$$g < 2\frac{1}{4}$$

34.
$$\frac{8}{3}y + 3 \leq 51$$
$$\frac{8}{3}y + 3 - 3 \leq 51 - 3$$
$$\frac{8}{3}y \leq 48$$
$$3 \cdot \frac{8}{3}y \leq 3 \cdot 48$$
$$8y \leq 144$$
$$\frac{8y}{8} \leq \frac{144}{8}$$
$$y \leq 18$$

35.
$$\frac{5}{6}(a - 12) \leq 20$$
$$6 \cdot \frac{5}{6}(a - 12) \leq 6 \cdot 20$$
$$5(a - 12) \leq 120$$
$$\frac{5(a - 12)}{5} \leq \frac{120}{5}$$
$$a - 12 \leq 24$$
$$a - 12 + 12 \leq 24 + 12$$
$$a \leq 36$$

36. A; $-4 > 26 + 2x$
$$-4 - 26 > 26 + 2x - 26$$
$$-30 > 2x$$
$$\frac{-30}{2} > \frac{2x}{2}$$
$$-15 > x$$
$$x < -15$$

37. *Sample answer*:

You reverse the inequality symbol to solve $-4x > 8$.

You do *not* reverse the inequality symbol to solve $\frac{1}{2}x < 10$.

38.
$$\frac{n}{2} < 2 \qquad\qquad -6n \leq -6$$
$$2 \cdot \left(\frac{n}{2}\right) < 2 \cdot 2 \qquad \frac{-6n}{-6} \geq \frac{-6}{-6}$$
$$n < 4 \qquad\qquad n \geq 1$$

Both inequalities are satisfied by all real numbers greater than or equal to 1 and less than 4.

39.
$$3n + 4 < 52 \qquad\qquad 4n - 7 > 25$$
$$3n + 4 - 4 < 52 - 4 \qquad 4n - 7 + 7 > 25 + 7$$
$$3n < 48 \qquad\qquad 4n > 32$$
$$\frac{3n}{3} < \frac{48}{3} \qquad\qquad \frac{4n}{4} > \frac{32}{4}$$
$$n < 16 \qquad\qquad n > 8$$

Both inequalities are satisfied by all real numbers greater than 8 and less than 16.

40. $-6 < 2x < 10$
$$-6 < 2x \text{ and } 2x < 10$$
$$\frac{-6}{2} < \frac{2x}{2} \qquad \frac{2x}{2} < \frac{10}{2}$$
$$-3 < x \qquad x < 5$$
$$-3 < x < 5$$

41. $-35 \leq 7x \leq -14$
$$-35 \leq 7x \text{ and } 7x \leq -14$$
$$\frac{-35}{7} \leq \frac{7x}{7} \qquad \frac{7x}{7} \leq \frac{-14}{7}$$
$$-5 \leq x \qquad x \leq -2$$
$$-5 \leq x \leq -2$$

42. $10 < 5x < 100$
$$10 < 5x \text{ and } 5x < 100$$
$$\frac{10}{5} < \frac{5x}{5} \qquad \frac{5x}{5} < \frac{100}{5}$$
$$2 < x \qquad x < 20$$
$$2 < x < 20$$

Problem Solving

43. Let t be the number of tickets sold.

Price of a ticket	·	Number of tickets sold	≥	Amount paid disc jockey

$$5.50t \geq 275$$
$$\frac{5.50t}{5.50} \geq \frac{275}{5.50}$$
$$t \geq 50$$

At least 50 tickets must be sold to cover the cost of the disc jockey.

Chapter 3, *continued*

44. Let x be the number of cars washed.

$$\begin{array}{c}\text{Profit} \\ \text{per car}\end{array} \cdot \begin{array}{c}\text{Number} \\ \text{of cars}\end{array} \geq \begin{array}{c}\text{Minimum desired} \\ \text{amount raised}\end{array}$$

$$5 \cdot x \geq 300$$

$$\frac{5x}{5} \geq \frac{300}{5}$$

$$x \geq 60$$

They must wash at least 60 cars.

45. Solving an inequality is similar to solving an equation because the same steps are taken to isolate the variable.

The two processes are different in the case when each side is multiplied or divided by the same negative number. In an inequality, the direction of the inequality symbol must be reversed, whereas in an equality, no change is required for the equal sign.

46. Yes, the friend is correct. In solving by dividing each side by -1, the inequality symbol must be reversed. The solution is all numbers greater than 0.

$$-x < 0$$

$$\frac{-x}{-1} > \frac{0}{-1}$$

$$x > 0$$

47. a. $\begin{array}{c}\text{Average weight} \\ \text{of a person}\end{array} \cdot \begin{array}{c}\text{Number} \\ \text{of people}\end{array} \leq \begin{array}{c}\text{Maximum} \\ \text{elevator weight}\end{array}$

$$150p \leq 2000$$

b. $150p \leq 2000$

$$\frac{150p}{150} \leq \frac{2000}{150}$$

$$p \leq 13.\overline{3}$$

c. p represents the number of people the elevator can hold. No more than 13 people of average weight can ride in the elevator.

48. $\begin{array}{c}\text{Amount} \\ \text{borrowed}\end{array} - \begin{array}{c}\text{Amount} \\ \text{paid per} \\ \text{week}\end{array} \cdot \begin{array}{c}\text{Number} \\ \text{of} \\ \text{weeks}\end{array} < \begin{array}{c}\text{Target} \\ \text{debt} \\ \text{level}\end{array}$

$$200 - 12w < 60$$

$$200 - 12w - 200 < 60 - 200$$

$$-12w < -140$$

$$\frac{-12w}{-12} > \frac{-140}{-12}$$

$$w > 11\frac{2}{3}$$

You will owe her less than $60 in about 12 weeks.

49. $A > 228$

$$\ell \cdot w > 228$$

$$\ell \cdot 12 > 228$$

$$\frac{12\ell}{12} > \frac{228}{12}$$

$$\ell > 19$$

The length of the rectangle is greater than 19 meters.

50.

$$\begin{array}{c}\text{Price} \\ \text{of a} \\ \text{door} \\ \text{ticket}\end{array} \cdot \begin{array}{c}\text{Number} \\ \text{sold at} \\ \text{door}\end{array} + \begin{array}{c}\text{Price} \\ \text{of an} \\ \text{advanced} \\ \text{ticket}\end{array} \cdot \begin{array}{c}\text{Number} \\ \text{sold in} \\ \text{advance}\end{array} \geq \begin{array}{c}\text{Target} \\ \text{amount}\end{array}$$

$$20d + 15(120) \geq 4000$$

$$20d + 1800 \geq 4000$$

$$20d + 1800 - 1800 \geq 4000 - 1800$$

$$20d \geq 2200$$

$$\frac{20d}{20} \geq \frac{2200}{20}$$

$$d \geq 110$$

At least 110 tickets must be sold at the door for total ticket revenue to be at least $4000.

51. *Sample answers:* You cannot list all of the solutions of an inequality such as $w < 20$ describing the width in feet of a swimming pool, because there are an unlimited number of widths possible under 20 feet long.

You can list all of the possible solutions of an inequality such as $p \leq 50$ describing the number of people at a dance, because there is a countable number of possible solutions.

52. A; $\dfrac{75 + 84 + 88 + 77 + x}{5} \geq 80$

$$\frac{324 + x}{5} \geq 80$$

$$5 \cdot \left(\frac{324 + x}{5}\right) \geq 5 \cdot 80$$

$$324 + x \geq 400$$

$$324 + x - 324 \geq 400 - 324$$

$$x \geq 76$$

The lowest score John can get is 76.

53.
$$2x + 6 > 20 \qquad\qquad 3x - 10 < 17$$
$$2x + 6 - 6 > 20 - 6 \qquad 3x - 10 + 10 < 17 + 10$$
$$2x > 14 \qquad\qquad 3x < 27$$
$$\frac{2x}{2} > \frac{14}{2} \qquad\qquad \frac{3x}{3} < \frac{27}{3}$$
$$x > 7 \qquad\qquad x < 9$$

So, $7 < x$ and $x < 9$, which means that Joe has 8 baseball cards.

54.
$$13 \cdot 2 + 8h \geq 50$$
$$26 + 8h \geq 50$$
$$26 + 8h - 26 \geq 50 - 26$$
$$8h \geq 24$$
$$\frac{8h}{8} \geq \frac{24}{8}$$
$$h \geq 3$$

The racer bikes at 8 miles per hour for at least 3 hours.

Chapter 3, continued

Chapter 3, *continued*

55. We know that $h = 2w - 20$, $P = 2h + 2w$, and $53 \le P$.

$$53 \le P$$
$$53 \le 2h + 2w$$
$$53 \le 2(2w - 20) + 2w$$
$$53 \le 4w - 40 + 2w$$
$$53 \le 6w - 40$$
$$53 + 40 \le 6w - 40 + 40$$
$$93 \le 6w$$
$$\frac{93}{6} \le \frac{6w}{6}$$
$$15.5 \le w$$

Given that each dimension is an integer number of inches, the minimum width of the screen is 16 centimeters.

The minimum height of the screen is $2(16) - 20$, or 12 centimeters.

56. Let P be the total of the house sales. Then, the commission is $\frac{P}{1000} \cdot 50$.

$$\frac{P}{1000} \cdot 50 \ge 4000 \qquad \frac{P}{1000} \cdot 50 \le 5000$$
$$\frac{P}{20} \ge 4000 \qquad \frac{P}{20} \le 5000$$
$$20 \cdot \frac{P}{20} \ge 20 \cdot 4000 \qquad 20 \cdot \frac{P}{20} \le 20 \cdot 5000$$
$$P \ge 80{,}000 \qquad P \le 100{,}000$$

The range of prices that earn your neighbor $4000 to $5000 in commission is $80,000 to $100,000.

57. In the inequality $ad > bc$, use the Division Property of Inequality to divide each side by bd.

$$ad > bc$$
$$\frac{ad}{bd} > \frac{bc}{bd}$$
$$\frac{a}{b} > \frac{c}{d}$$

So, if $ad > bc$, then $\frac{a}{b} > \frac{c}{d}$.

For $\frac{3}{5}$ and $\frac{5}{8}$, $3 \cdot 8 = 24 < 25 = 5 \cdot 5$, so $\frac{3}{5} < \frac{5}{8}$.

You can see that $\frac{5}{8} < \frac{7}{8}$.

For $\frac{5}{8}$ and $\frac{9}{11}$, $5 \cdot 11 = 55 < 72 = 8 \cdot 9$, so $\frac{5}{8} < \frac{9}{11}$.

For $\frac{7}{8}$ and $\frac{9}{11}$, $7 \cdot 11 = 77 > 8 \cdot 9 = 72$, so $\frac{7}{8} > \frac{9}{11}$.

So, $\frac{3}{5} < \frac{5}{8} < \frac{9}{11} < \frac{7}{8}$.

If any of the integers are negative, the statement is not true because when you divide by a negative, you reverse the direction of the inequality symbol.

Mixed Review

58. 42: The last digit is 2, so it is divisible by 2, but not by 5 or 10.

The sum of digits is $4 + 2 = 6$, so it is divisible by 3, but not 9.

42 is not divisible by 4.

Because 42 is divisible by both 2 and 3, it is divisible by 6.

Because 42 is not divisible by 4, it is not divisible by 8.

So, 42 is divisible by 2, 3, and 6.

59. 26: The last digit is 6, so it is divisible by 2, but not by 5 or 10.

The sum of digits is $2 + 6 = 8$, so it is not divisible by 3, 6, or 9.

26 is not divisible by 4, so it is not divisible by 8 either.

So, 26 is divisible by 2.

60. 120: The last digit is 0, so it is divisible by 2, 5, and 10.

The sum of digits is $1 + 2 + 0 = 3$ so it is divisible by 3, but not 9.

120 is divisible by 4.

Because 120 is divisible by both 2 and 3, it is divisible by 6.

120 is divisible by 8.

So, 120 is divisible by 2, 3, 4, 5, 6, 8, and 10.

61. Equation: $-4x = 0$

Question: -4 times what number equals 0?

Solution: 0

Check: $-4(0) = 0$

62. Equation: $11a = 11$

Question: 11 times what number equals 11?

Solution: 1

Check: $11(1) = 11$

63. Equation: $z + (-12) = -12$

Question: What number plus -12 equals -12?

Solution: 0

Check: $0 + (-12) = -12$

64.
$$c + 7 \le 11$$
$$c + 7 - 7 \le 11 - 7$$
$$c \le 4$$

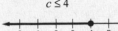

Chapter 3, continued

65.
$$3 < 12 + s$$
$$3 - 12 < 12 + s - 12$$
$$-9 < s$$
$$s > -9$$

66.
$$x - 12 > 17$$
$$x - 12 + 12 > 17 + 12$$
$$x > 29$$

67. C; $2\frac{3}{5} = \frac{10 + 3}{5}$

$$= \frac{13}{5}$$

Quiz 3.5–3.7 (p. 159)

1.
$$P = 2\ell + 2w$$
$$30 = 2\ell + 2(6)$$
$$30 = 2\ell + 12$$
$$30 - 12 = 2\ell + 12 - 12$$
$$18 = 2\ell$$
$$\frac{18}{2} = \frac{2\ell}{2}$$
$$9 = \ell$$

The length of the rectangle is 9 millimeters.

2. $A = \frac{1}{2}bh$

$$26 = \frac{1}{2}b(4)$$
$$26 = 2b$$
$$\frac{26}{2} = \frac{2b}{2}$$
$$13 = b$$

The base of the triangle is 13 yards.

3.
$$a + 9 \geq -1$$
$$a + 9 - 9 \geq -1 - 9$$
$$a \geq -10$$

4.
$$16 > y - 12$$
$$16 + 12 > y - 12 + 12$$
$$28 > y$$
$$y < 28$$

5.
$$\frac{x}{3} < -3$$
$$3 \cdot \frac{x}{3} < 3 \cdot (-3)$$
$$x < -9$$

6.
$$-7x > 42$$
$$\frac{-7x}{-7} < \frac{42}{-7}$$
$$x < -6$$

7.

Weight of apples	+	Weight of basket	>	Stated weight

$$a + 2 > 13$$
$$a + 2 - 2 > 13 - 2$$
$$a > 11$$

a represents the weight of the apples in the basket, in pounds. There are more than 11 pounds of apples in the basket when it is filled.

8.

Price per minute	$\cdot$	Number of minutes	$\leq$	Money available

$$0.10x \leq 9.50$$
$$\frac{0.10x}{0.10} \leq \frac{9.50}{0.10}$$
$$x \leq 95$$

You can add 95 minutes or less to your phone card.

Mixed Review of Problem Solving (p. 160)

1. a. $P = 12 + 15 + 9 = 36$

$$A = \frac{1}{2}bh = \frac{1}{2}(9)(12) = 54$$

The perimeter of the platform is 36 feet and the area is 54 square feet.

b. *Sample answers:*

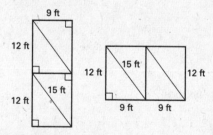

c. *Sample answers:*

First rectangle: $P = 12 + 12 + 9 + 12 + 12 + 9$
$$= 66 \text{ ft}$$
$$A = 9 \times 24 = 216 \text{ ft}^2$$

$$\frac{66 \text{ ft}}{36 \text{ ft}} = \frac{11}{6} \qquad \frac{216 \text{ ft}^2}{54 \text{ ft}^2} = 4$$

The first rectangle's perimeter is $\frac{11}{6}$ times that of the original triangle.

The first rectangle's area is 4 times that of the original triangle.

Second rectangle: $P = 12 + 9 + 9 + 12 + 9 + 9$

$$= 60 \text{ ft}$$

$$A = 18 \times 12 = 216 \text{ ft}^2$$

$$\frac{60 \text{ ft}}{36 \text{ ft}} = \frac{5}{3} \qquad \frac{216 \text{ ft}^2}{54 \text{ ft}^2} = 4$$

The second rectangle's perimeter is $\frac{5}{3}$ times that of the original triangle.

The second rectangle's area is 4 times that of the original triangle.

The perimeters are different, but the areas are both four times larger than the area of the triangle.

2. a. To easily find the rectangular dimensions, solve for w in terms of ℓ.

$$P = 2\ell + 2w$$

$$6000 = 2(\ell + w)$$

$$\frac{6000}{2} = \frac{2(\ell + w)}{2}$$

$$3000 = \ell + w$$

$$3000 - \ell = w$$

Then make a table and use Guess, Check, and Revise to find the dimensions of the rectangular pasture with the greatest area.

Length ℓ (ft)	Width $(3000 - \ell)$ ft	Area $\ell \cdot w$ ft^2
2700	300	810,000
2400	600	1,440,000
2100	900	1,890,000
1800	1200	2,160,000
1500	1500	2,250,000
1400	1600	2,240,000
1499	1501	2,249,999
1501	1499	2,249,999
1502	1498	2,249,996
1503	1497	2,249,991

A pasture that is 1500 feet by 1500 feet has the greatest area, 2,250,000 square feet.

b.

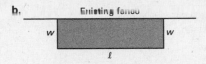

$$6000 = 2w + \ell$$
$$6000 - 2w = \ell$$

Width w (ft)	Length $(6000 - 2w)$ ft	Area $\ell \cdot w$ ft^2
500	5000	2,500,000
1000	4000	4,000,000
1500	3000	4,500,000
2000	2000	4,000,000
2500	1000	2,500,000
1499	3002	4,499,998
1501	2998	4,499,998

A 1500 foot by 3000 foot pasture has the greatest area, 4,500,000 square feet. The horse gets twice as much area as the enclosure in part (a).

3. *Sample answers:*

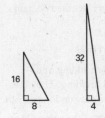

4. a. Figure A: $A = \frac{1}{2}bh = \frac{1}{2}(12)(8) = 48$

Figure B: $A = \frac{1}{2}bh = \frac{1}{2}(12)(8) = 48$

Figure C: $A = \frac{1}{2}bh = \frac{1}{2}(12)(8) = 48$

All three figures have an area of 48 square units.

b. The area of each figure is the same.

c. *Sample answers:*

$\ell \cdot w = 48$

If $\ell = 8$, $8w = 48$ If $\ell = 12$, $12w = 48$

$$\frac{8w}{8} = \frac{48}{8} \qquad\qquad\qquad \frac{12w}{12} = \frac{48}{12}$$

$$w = 6 \qquad\qquad\qquad\qquad w = 4$$

A 6 by 8 rectangle and a 4 by 12 rectangle have the same area as Figure A.

5. 27; Rebecca's contribution ≤ 9

Mike's contribution $\leq 2 \cdot 9$

Combined contribution $\leq 9 + 2 \cdot 9 = 27$

The most they can spend is $27.

Chapter 3, continued

6. $\dfrac{\text{Total}}{\text{area}} \geq \dfrac{\text{Area per}}{\text{person}} \cdot \dfrac{\text{Number}}{\text{of people}}$

$$28(18) \geq 20p$$
$$504 \geq 20p$$
$$\frac{504}{20} \geq \frac{20p}{20}$$
$$25.2 \geq p$$
$$p \leq 25.2$$

The solution $p \leq 25.2$ gives the allowable numbers of people. To find the maximum number allowed, find the largest integer solution.

25 or fewer people can legally be in the classroom.

7. a. Emma's score + Frank's score < Megan's score
$$E + F < M$$

  b.
$$E + F < M$$
$$E + 30 < 75$$
$$E + 30 - 30 < 75 - 30$$
$$E < 45$$

Emma has less than 45 points.

  c. Yes, if Emma doubles her score it is possible that she will have more points than Megan. Emma may have as many as 44 points. Doubling that would give her $2 \cdot 44 = 88$ points, which is greater than Megan's score of 75 points.

Chapter 3 Review (pp. 161–164)

1. Two pairs of inverse operations are adding and subtracting, and multiplying and dividing. They are called inverse operations because they undo each other.

2. Two inequalities can be equivalent if the same set of numbers is included in their solution. For example, $x \geq 2$, and $x + 2 \geq 4$ are equivalent inequalities because both have solutions of $x \geq 2$.

3. Two equations that have the same solution are *equivalent equations*.

4. An *inequality* is a statement formed by placing an inequality symbol between two expressions.

5.
$$c + 14 = 3$$
$$c + 14 - 14 = 3 - 14$$
$$c = -11$$

6.
$$y - 31 = 11$$
$$y - 31 + 31 = 11 + 31$$
$$y = 42$$

7.
$$7.7 = s - 4.3$$
$$7.7 + 4.3 = s - 4.3 + 4.3$$
$$12 = s$$

8.
$$29 = 40 + p$$
$$29 - 40 = 40 + p - 40$$
$$-11 = p$$

9.
$$b + 3.09 = -5.91$$
$$b + 3.09 - 3.09 = -5.91 - 3.09$$
$$b = 9$$

10.
$$v + 13 = 29$$
$$v + 13 - 13 = 29 - 13$$
$$v = 16$$

11.
$$t - \frac{3}{7} = \frac{1}{7}$$
$$t - \frac{3}{7} + \frac{3}{7} = \frac{1}{7} + \frac{3}{7}$$
$$t = \frac{4}{7}$$

12.
$$x + (-5) = -8$$
$$x + (-5) - (-5) = -8 - (-5)$$
$$x = -3$$

13.
$$y - 3.9 = 10.9$$
$$y - 3.9 + 3.9 = 10.9 + 3.9$$
$$y = 14.8$$

14. Let t be the number of trees planted this year.

$\dfrac{\text{Number of}}{\text{trees last year}} + \dfrac{\text{Trees planted}}{\text{this year}} = \dfrac{\text{Number of}}{\text{trees this year}}$

$$12 + t = 17$$
$$12 + t - 12 = 17 - 12$$
$$t = 5$$

Marguerite planted 5 elm trees this year.

15.
$$\frac{m}{3} = 9$$
$$\frac{m}{3} \cdot 3 = 9 \cdot 3$$
$$m = 27$$

16.
$$\frac{z}{-7} = 23$$
$$\frac{z}{-7} \cdot (-7) = 23 \cdot (-7)$$
$$z = -161$$

17.
$$-5 = \frac{w}{-11}$$
$$-5 \cdot (-11) = \frac{w}{-11} \cdot (-11)$$
$$55 = w$$

18.
$$-25x = 0$$
$$\frac{-25x}{-25} = \frac{0}{-25}$$
$$x = 0$$

19.
$$7 = 3.5t$$
$$\frac{7}{3.5} = \frac{3.5t}{3.5}$$
$$2 = t$$

20.
$$-9.5m = -22.8$$
$$\frac{-9.5m}{-9.5} = \frac{-22.8}{-9.5}$$
$$m = 2.4$$

21.
$$2p - 5 = 13$$
$$2p - 5 + 5 = 13 + 5$$
$$2p = 18$$
$$\frac{2p}{2} = \frac{18}{2}$$
$$p = 9$$

22.
$$19 + 8v = 43$$
$$19 + 8v - 19 = 43 - 19$$
$$8v = 24$$
$$\frac{8v}{8} = \frac{24}{8}$$
$$v = 3$$

23.
$$\frac{g}{9} + 6 = -2$$
$$\frac{g}{9} + 6 - 6 = -2 - 6$$
$$\frac{g}{9} = -8$$
$$\frac{g}{9} \cdot 9 = -8 \cdot 9$$
$$g = -72$$

24.
$$\frac{c}{-10} + 26 = 46$$
$$\frac{c}{-10} + 26 - 26 = 46 - 26$$
$$\frac{c}{-10} = 20$$
$$\frac{c}{-10} \cdot (-10) = 20 \cdot (-10)$$
$$c = -200$$

25.
$$-82 = 53 - 5t$$
$$-82 - 53 = 53 - 5t - 53$$
$$-135 = -5t$$
$$\frac{-135}{-5} = \frac{-5t}{-5}$$
$$27 = t$$

26.
$$-33 = -15t - 12$$
$$-33 + 12 = -15t - 12 + 12$$
$$-21 = -15t$$
$$\frac{-21}{-15} = \frac{-15t}{-15}$$
$$1.4 = t$$

27. Let p be the number of pages with four pictures.

$$\text{Pictures per page} \cdot \text{Number of pages} + \text{Number left over} = \text{Total number of pictures}$$
$$4p + 3 = 55$$
$$4p + 3 - 3 = 55 - 3$$
$$4p = 52$$
$$\frac{4p}{4} = \frac{52}{4}$$
$$p = 13$$

There are 13 pages with four pictures.

28.
$$3n + 6 = 12$$
$$3n + 6 - 6 = 12 - 6$$
$$3n = 6$$
$$\frac{3n}{3} = \frac{6}{3}$$
$$n = 2$$
The number is 2.

29.
$$2n - 4 = 20$$
$$2n - 4 + 4 = 20 + 4$$
$$2n = 24$$
$$\frac{2n}{2} = \frac{24}{2}$$
$$n = 12$$
The number is 12.

30. Let n be the number of fruit baskets.

$$\text{Price per basket} \cdot \text{Number of baskets} - \text{Cost of supplies} = \text{Profit}$$
$$7n - 26 = 100$$
$$7n - 26 + 26 = 100 + 26$$
$$7n = 126$$
$$\frac{7n}{7} = \frac{126}{7}$$
$$n = 18$$

Your class needs to sell 18 baskets.

31. Let w be the number of women that attend the college.

$$\text{Number of men} + \text{Number of women} = \text{Total number of students}$$
$$(w - 30) + w = 1250$$
$$2w - 30 + 30 = 1250 + 30$$
$$2w = 1280$$
$$\frac{2w}{2} = \frac{1280}{2}$$
$$w = 640$$

The number of women attending the college is 640.

32.
$$A = \frac{1}{2}bh$$
$$A = \frac{1}{2}(10)(5)$$
$$A = 25$$

The area of the triangle is 25 square centimeters.

33.
$$A = \frac{1}{2}bh$$
$$45 = \frac{1}{2}b(10)$$
$$45 = 5b$$
$$\frac{45}{5} = \frac{5b}{5}$$
$$9 = b$$

The base of the triangle is 9 feet.

34.
$$h - 12 > 12$$
$$h - 12 + 12 > 12 + 12$$
$$h > 24$$

35.
$$-4 + k \le 6$$
$$-4 + k + 4 \le 6 + 4$$
$$k \le 10$$

36.
$$7 < 15 + p$$
$$7 - 15 < 15 + p - 15$$
$$-8 < p$$
$$p > -8$$

37.
$$d + 11 \ge 5$$
$$d + 11 - 11 \ge 5 - 11$$
$$d \ge -6$$

38.
$$m - 10 > 21$$
$$m - 10 + 10 > 21 + 10$$
$$m > 31$$

39.
$$b + 13 \leq 11$$
$$b + 13 - 13 \leq 11 - 13$$
$$b \leq -2$$

40.
$$k - 8 \geq 2\tfrac{1}{2}$$
$$k - 8 + 8 \geq 2\tfrac{1}{2} + 8$$
$$k \geq 10\tfrac{1}{2}$$

41.
$$p - 2.5 < 7.7$$
$$p - 2.5 + 2.5 < 7.7 + 2.5$$
$$p < 10.2$$

42.

Total number of CDs	$\geq$	Number at home	$+$	Birthday CDs

$$m \geq 50 + 4$$

43.
$$\frac{d}{6} \leq 34$$
$$\frac{d}{6} \cdot 6 \leq 34 \cdot 6$$
$$d \leq 204$$

44.
$$-\tfrac{1}{5}x \geq 20$$
$$-\tfrac{1}{5}x \cdot (-5) \leq 20 \cdot (-5)$$
$$x \leq -100$$

45.
$$-15b < 60$$
$$\frac{-15b}{-15} > \frac{60}{-15}$$
$$b > -4$$

46.
$$5c > 25$$
$$\frac{5c}{5} > \frac{25}{5}$$
$$c > 5$$

47.
$$-4k \leq -36$$
$$\frac{-4k}{-4} \geq \frac{-36}{-4}$$
$$k \geq 9$$

48.
$$\tfrac{2}{3}y > -12$$
$$3 \cdot \tfrac{2}{3}y > 3 \cdot (-12)$$
$$2y > -36$$
$$\frac{2y}{2} > \frac{-36}{2}$$
$$y > -18$$

49.
$$16z < 32$$
$$\frac{16z}{16} < \frac{32}{16}$$
$$z < 2$$

50.
$$\frac{m}{5} \geq -11$$
$$\frac{m}{5} \cdot 5 \geq -11 \cdot 5$$
$$m \geq -55$$

Chapter 3 Test (p. 165)

1.
$$s - 6 = 39$$
$$s - 6 + 6 = 39 + 6$$
$$s = 45$$

2.
$$x + 12 = -2$$
$$x + 12 - 12 = -2 - 12$$
$$x = -14$$

3.
$$14.6 = \frac{k}{2.5}$$
$$14.6 \cdot 2.5 = \frac{k}{2.5} \cdot 2.5$$
$$36.5 = k$$

4. $24v = 288$
$$\frac{24v}{24} = \frac{288}{24}$$
$$v = 12$$

5.
$$\tfrac{1}{9} = t + \tfrac{1}{9}$$
$$\tfrac{1}{9} - \tfrac{1}{9} = t + \tfrac{1}{9} - \tfrac{1}{9}$$
$$0 = t$$

6.
$$-9.8 = \frac{y}{-4.7}$$
$$-9.8 \cdot (-4.7) = \frac{y}{-4.7} \cdot (-4.7)$$
$$46.06 = y$$

7.
$$5b - 7 = 120$$
$$5b - 7 + 7 = 120 + 7$$
$$5b = 127$$
$$\frac{5b}{5} = \frac{127}{5}$$
$$b = 25.4$$

8.
$$-236 = 29 - 5g$$
$$-236 - 29 = 29 - 5g - 29$$
$$-265 = -5g$$
$$\frac{-265}{-5} = \frac{-5g}{-5}$$
$$53 = g$$

9.
$$20 - 3n = -4$$
$$20 - 3n - 20 = -4 - 20$$
$$-3n = -24$$
$$\frac{-3n}{-3} = \frac{-24}{-3}$$
$$n = 8$$

10.
$$5n + 14 = 9$$
$$5n + 14 - 14 = 9 - 14$$
$$5n = -5$$
$$\frac{5n}{5} = \frac{-5}{5}$$
$$n = -1$$

11.
$$P = 2\ell + 2w$$
$$62 = 2\ell + 2(11)$$
$$62 = 2\ell + 22$$
$$62 - 22 = 2\ell + 22 - 22$$
$$40 = 2\ell$$
$$\frac{40}{2} = \frac{2\ell}{2}$$
$$20 = \ell$$

The length of the rectangle is 20 inches.

12. $A = \ell \cdot w$
$$72 = 9w$$
$$\frac{72}{9} = \frac{9w}{9}$$
$$8 = w$$

The width of the rectangle is 8 inches.

13. $A = \frac{1}{2}bh$
$$200 = \frac{1}{2}(25)h$$
$$200 = 12.5h$$
$$\frac{200}{12.5} = \frac{12.5h}{12.5}$$
$$16 = h$$

The height of the triangle is 16 centimeters.

14.
$$y + 78 < -124$$
$$y + 78 - 78 < -124 - 78$$
$$y < -202$$

15.
$$-8.56 + k \geq 5.32$$
$$-8.56 + k + 8.56 \geq 5.32 + 8.56$$
$$k \geq 13.88$$

16. $-8x < 64$
$$\frac{-8x}{-8} > \frac{64}{-8}$$
$$x > -8$$

17.
$$-\frac{1}{6}x > 5$$
$$-6 \cdot \left(-\frac{1}{6x}\right) < -6 \cdot 5$$
$$x < -30$$

18. $3x \leq 12$
$$\frac{3x}{3} \leq \frac{12}{3}$$
$$x \leq 4$$

19.
$$m - 9 \leq 19$$
$$m - 9 + 9 \leq 19 + 9$$
$$m \leq 28$$

20. Let m be the number of miles you have left to hike.

Morning miles	+	Additional miles by 2:00 P.M.	+	Miles left	=	Total miles

$$8.3 + 7.5 + m = 20$$
$$15.8 + m = 20$$
$$15.8 + m - 15.8 = 20 - 15.8$$
$$m = 4.2$$

You have 4.2 miles left to hike.

21. Let x be the cost of a book.

Number of books	•	Cost per book	=	Total cost

$$3x = 21.75$$
$$\frac{3x}{3} = \frac{21.75}{3}$$
$$x = 7.25$$

Each book costs $7.25.

22. Let m be the number of months.

Calf's present weight	+	Pounds per month	•	Number of months	=	Target weight

$$220 + 22m = 550$$
$$220 + 22m - 220 = 550 - 220$$
$$22m = 330$$
$$\frac{22m}{22} = \frac{330}{22}$$
$$m = 15$$

It will take the calf 15 months to reach 550 pounds.

23. Let m be the cost of your meal.

Your meal	+	Friend's meal	$\leq$	Limit for meals

$$m + 14.78 \leq 30$$
$$m + 14.78 - 14.78 \leq 30 - 14.78$$
$$m \leq 15.22$$

You can spend no more than $15.22 for your meal.

24. Let x be the number of lessons.

Price per lesson	•	Number of lessons	$>$	Cost to buy skates

$$5x > 75$$
$$\frac{5x}{5} > \frac{75}{5}$$
$$x > 15$$

It is cheaper to buy skates than to rent if you take 16 or more lessons.

Chapter 3, *continued*

Standardized Test Preparation (p. 167)

1. *Sample answer:*

   You still need to stuff $560 - 140 = 420$ envelopes in the four hours from 1:00 P.M. to 5:00 P.M., so 4 envelopes per hour will not be nearly fast enough. You can eliminate answer choice A.

2. Because $1.50 is raised per shirt, you can earn $500 by selling fewer than 500 T-shirts. You can eliminat answer choice D.

Standardized Test Practice (pp. 168–169)

1. C; $n - 34 = -17$

   $n - 34 + 34 = -17 + 34$

   $\qquad\qquad n = 17$

2. C; The graph has an open circle at 2 and is shaded to the left, so it represents $x < 2$.

3. C; $A = \frac{1}{2}bh = \frac{1}{2}(8)(4) = 16 \text{ ft}^2 \neq 8 \text{ ft}^2$

4. C; $A = 60 \times 90 - 45 \times (20 + 25) = 3375 \text{ ft}^2$

   The total rent is $35 \times 3375 = \$118{,}125$

5. B; $\frac{50 - 10}{20} = 2$

   Bob can spend 2 minutes on each multiple choice problem.

6. B; $A = \frac{1}{2}bh = \frac{1}{2}(7)(3) = 10.5 \text{ ft}^2$

7. A; $P = 2\ell + 2w$

   $54 = 2\ell + 2(8)$

   $54 = 2\ell + 16$

   $54 - 16 = 2\ell + 16 - 16$

   $38 = 2\ell$

   $\frac{38}{2} = \frac{2\ell}{2}$

   $19 = \ell$

   The length of the rectangle is 19 inches.

8. B; $\begin{array}{c}\text{Labor} \\ \text{rate}\end{array} \cdot \begin{array}{c}\text{Hours} \\ \text{of labor}\end{array} + \begin{array}{c}\text{Cost of} \\ \text{parts}\end{array} = \begin{array}{c}\text{Total bill} \\ \text{amount}\end{array}$

   $\qquad\qquad 40x + 440 = 560$

9. D; $x + 6.2 = 1.8$

   $x + 6.2 - 6.2 = 1.8 - 6.2$

   $\qquad\qquad x = -4.4$

10. C; $21 \leq -7x$

    $\frac{21}{-7} \geq \frac{-7x}{-7}$

    $-3 \geq x$

    $x \leq -3$

11. A; Area of bleachers open − Area of bleachers closed

    $= 2 \cdot 9 \cdot 100 - 2 \cdot 4 \cdot 100$

    $= 1800 - 800$

    $= 1000 \text{ ft}^2$

    The difference in the area of the floor when the bleachers are open and when they are closed is 1000 square feet.

12. 6; $20 = 3x + 2$

    $20 - 2 = 3x + 2 - 2$

    $\qquad 18 = 3x$

    $\qquad \frac{18}{3} = \frac{3x}{3}$

    $\qquad 6 = x$

    The value of x is 6.

13. 18; Let d be the number of weekdays Kate worked in July.

    $\begin{array}{c}\text{Number of} \\ \text{hours per} \\ \text{weekday}\end{array} \cdot \begin{array}{c}\text{Number of} \\ \text{weekdays}\end{array} + \begin{array}{c}\text{Additional} \\ \text{hours}\end{array} = \begin{array}{c}\text{Hours} \\ \text{in July}\end{array}$

    $\qquad\qquad 6d + 9 = 117$

    $\qquad 6d + 9 - 9 = 117 - 9$

    $\qquad\qquad 6d = 108$

    $\qquad\qquad \frac{6d}{6} = \frac{108}{6}$

    $\qquad\qquad d = 18$

    Kate worked 18 weekdays in July.

14. 8; Let w be the number of weeks.

    $\begin{array}{c}\text{Amount} \\ \text{in savings}\end{array} + \begin{array}{c}\text{Weekly} \\ \text{savings}\end{array} \cdot \begin{array}{c}\text{Number} \\ \text{of weeks}\end{array} = \begin{array}{c}\text{Target} \\ \text{savings} \\ \text{amount}\end{array}$

    $\qquad\qquad 60 + 5w = 100$

    $\qquad 60 + 5w - 60 = 100 - 60$

    $\qquad\qquad 5w = 40$

    $\qquad\qquad \frac{5w}{5} = \frac{40}{5}$

    $\qquad\qquad w = 8$

    It will take 8 weeks for Rachel to have $100 in savings.

15. 1.5; Let h be the number of hours they hiked after the break.

    $\begin{array}{c}\text{Total} \\ \text{distance}\end{array} \div \begin{array}{c}\text{Travel} \\ \text{speed}\end{array} = \begin{array}{c}\text{Hours hiked} \\ \text{before break}\end{array} + \begin{array}{c}\text{Hours} \\ \text{hiked after} \\ \text{break}\end{array}$

    $\qquad 10.5 \div 3 = 2 + h$

    $\qquad\qquad 3.5 = 2 + h$

    $\qquad 3.5 - 2 = 2 - 2 + h$

    $\qquad\qquad 1.5 = h$

    Caleb and Peter hiked for 1.5 hours after their break.

Chapter 3, *continued*

16. Find the time it takes the dog to reach the tree.

$$d = rt$$

$$46.2 + 25.2 = 17t$$

$$71.4 = 17t$$

$$\frac{71.4}{17} = \frac{17t}{17}$$

$$4.2 = t$$

It takes the dog 4.2 seconds to reach the tree. The squirrel must reach the tree in less than 4.2 seconds to escape.

$$t > d \div r$$

$$4.2 > 25.2 \div r$$

$$4.2r > 25.2 \div r \times r$$

$$4.2r > 25.2$$

$$\frac{4.2r}{4.2} > \frac{25.2}{4.2}$$

$$r > 6$$

The squirrel must run faster than 6 meters per second to escape the dog.

17. Let x be Tracy's age.

$$\begin{array}{ccc} \text{Tracy's} \\ \text{age} \end{array} - \begin{array}{ccc} \text{Number of years} \\ \text{she's had a license} \end{array} \geq \begin{array}{ccc} \text{Minimum} \\ \text{license age} \end{array}$$

$$x - 6 \geq 18$$

$$x - 6 + 6 \geq 18 + 6$$

$$x \geq 24$$

The inequality and graph show that because Tracy must have been at least 18 years old when she got her driver's license 6 years ago, she must be at least 24 years old now. So, Tracy cannot be 19 years old now, but she can be 30 years old.

18. a. Red carpet:

$$A = (3 + 1) \cdot 6 - 3 \cdot 2$$

$$A = 4 \cdot 6 - 3 \cdot 2$$

$$A = 18$$

The area of the room with the red carpet is 18 square yards.

Blue carpet:

$$A = [8 - (1 + 3 + 1)] \cdot 6 - 2 \cdot 1$$

$$A = (8 - 5) \cdot 6 - 2$$

$$A = 16$$

The area of the room with the blue carpet is 16 square yards.

b. Let b be the cost per square yard of blue carpet.

Total Cost	=	Square yards of blue carpet	$\cdot$	Cost per square yard	+	Square yards of red carpet	$\cdot$	Cost per square yard

$$444 = 18 \cdot 14 + 16b$$

$$444 = 252 + 16b$$

$$444 - 252 = 252 + 16b - 252$$

$$192 = 16b$$

$$\frac{192}{16} = \frac{16b}{16}$$

$$12 = b$$

The cost of the blue carpet is $12 per square yard.

c. The total area of red room and blue room is $16 + 18 = 34$ square feet.

Cost of blue carpet for both rooms: $12 \times 34 = \$408$

It would cost $408 to carpet both rooms in blue.

To find the answer, find the total area and multiply by the cost per square yard.

19. a. Let P be the money raised by Paul, D be the money raised by Don, and J be the money raised by Jeff.

Paul's amount is $\frac{1}{2}$ Don's amount plus 7.

$$P = \frac{1}{2}D + 7$$

Don's amount is twice Jeff's amount less 4.

$$D = 2J - 4$$

Jeff's amount is 85.

$$J = 85$$

b. $D = 2(85) - 4 = 166$

$$P = \frac{1}{2}(166) + 7 = 90$$

Jeff has raised $85.

Don has raised $166.

Paul has raised $90.

c. Let j, d, and p be the amounts Jeff, Don, and Paul still need to earn.

$$j + 85 \geq 200 \qquad\qquad d + 166 \geq 200$$

$$j + 85 - 85 \geq 200 - 85 \quad d + 166 - 166 \geq 200 - 166$$

$$j \geq 115 \qquad\qquad d \geq 34$$

$$p + 90 \geq 200$$

$$p + 90 - 90 \geq 200 - 90$$

$$p \geq 110$$

Jeff still has to earn at least $115 more, Don needs to earn at least $34 more, and Paul needs to earn at least $110 more.

d. If each person needed at least $250, each person's value would be $50 greater.

Chapter 3, *continued*

1. $8 + 6 \div 2 = 8 + 3$
$\qquad = 11$

2. $15 - 9 \div 3 = 15 - 3$
$\qquad = 12$

3. $3 \times (1.8 + 5 - 0.6) = 3 \times (6.8 - 0.6) = 3 \times 6.2$
$\qquad = 18.6$

4. $9 \times 2^3 - 15 = 9 \times 8 - 15 = 72 - 15 = 57$

5. $(2^5 + 8) \cdot 5^2 = (32 + 8) \cdot 25 = 40 \cdot 25 = 1000$

6. $(18 \div 6)^3 + (11 - 4)^3 = 3^3 + 7^3 = 27 + 343 = 370$

7. What number plus 3 equals 9?

$6 + 3 = 9$, so $x = 6$.

8. 3 times what number equals 33?

$3 \times 11 = 33$, so $w = 11$.

9. 24 divided by what number equals 6?

$24 \div 4 = 6$, so $r = 4$.

10. 34 minus what number equals 21?

$34 - 13 = 21$, so $z = 13$.

11. $P = 2\ell + 2w = 2(12) + 2(7) = 24 + 14 = 38$

$A = \ell w = 12(7) = 84$

The perimeter is 38 meters and the area is 84 square meters.

12. $P = 2\ell + 2w = 2(18) + 2(14) = 36 + 28 = 64$

$A = \ell w = 18(14) = 252$

The perimeter is 64 centimeters and the area is 252 square centimeters.

13. $P = 4s = 4(9) = 36$

$A = s^2 = 9^2 = 81$

The perimeter is 36 inches and the area is 81 square inches.

14. $P = 2\ell + 2w = 2(13) + 2(11) = 26 + 22 = 48$

$A = \ell w = 13(11) = 143$

The perimeter is 48 feet and the area is 143 square feet.

15.

The integers ordered from least to greatest are -15, -5, 1, 4, 8, and 16.

16.

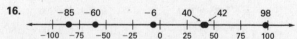

The integers ordered from least to greatest are -85, -60, -6, 40, 42, and 98.

17. $29 + (-18) = 11$

18. $-8 - 9 = -8 + (-9) = -17$

19. $44 - (-11) = 44 + 11 = 55$

20. $-5(4) = -20$

21. $-12(-8) = 96$

22. $\dfrac{42}{-3} = -14$

23. When $a = 4$ and $c = 12$: $\dfrac{-c}{a} = \dfrac{-12}{4} = -3$

24. When $b = -16$ and $c = 12$: $\dfrac{3b}{2c} = \dfrac{3(-16)}{2(12)} = \dfrac{-48}{24} = -2$

25. When $a = 4$ and $b = -16$: $\dfrac{b}{-4a} = \dfrac{-16}{-4(4)} = \dfrac{-16}{-16} = 1$

26. $9(3a + 11) - 4 = 27a + 99 - 4 = 27a + 95$

27. $-8b + 12(7b + 3) = -8b + 84b + 36 = 76b + 36$

28. $2c - 8(9c - 5) = 2c - 72c + 40 = -70c + 40$

29.

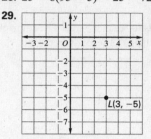

Point L is in quadrant IV.

30.

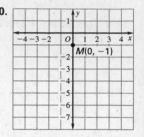

Point M is on the y-axis.

31.

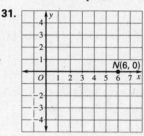

Point N is on the x-axis.

32. $\quad n + 8 = 15$
$\quad n + 8 - 8 = 15 - 8$
$\qquad\qquad n = 7$

33. $\quad z + 12 = 3$
$\quad z + 12 - 12 = 3 - 12$
$\qquad\qquad z = -9$

34. $4r = -32$
$\dfrac{4r}{4} = \dfrac{-32}{4}$
$r = -8$

35. $\dfrac{k}{7} = 5$
$\dfrac{k}{7} \cdot 7 = 5 \cdot 7$
$k = 35$

36. $\quad 8 = 7y - 13$
$\quad 8 + 13 = 7y - 13 + 13$
$\qquad 21 = 7y$
$\qquad \dfrac{21}{7} = \dfrac{7y}{7}$
$\qquad 3 = y$

37. $\qquad \dfrac{a}{6} + 4 = -8$
$\qquad \dfrac{a}{6} + 4 - 4 = -8 - 4$
$\qquad\qquad \dfrac{a}{6} \cdot 6 = -12 \cdot 6$
$\qquad\qquad\qquad a = -72$

Chapter 3, continued

38. $A = \frac{1}{2}bh$

$$48 = \frac{1}{2}b(6)$$

$$48 = 3b$$

$$\frac{48}{3} = \frac{3b}{3}$$

$$16 = b$$

The base of the triangle is 16 meters.

39.
$$96 \geq -12 + c$$
$$96 + 12 \geq -12 + c + 12$$
$$108 \geq c$$
$$c \leq 108$$

40.
$$-\frac{1}{3}x > 4$$
$$-3 \cdot \left(-\frac{1}{3}x\right) < -3 \cdot 4$$
$$x < -12$$

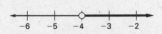

41. $-96 < 24h$

$$\frac{-96}{24} < \frac{24h}{24}$$

$$-4 < h$$

$$h > -4$$

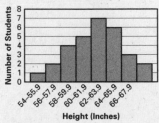

42.

Student Height

(bar graph: Number of Students vs. Height (Inches), intervals 54–55.9, 56–57.9, 58–59.9, 60–61.9, 62–63.9, 64–65.9, 66–67.9)

43. The greatest number of students, 7, have heights in the interval from 62 to 63.9 inches.

44. Yes; Because 60 is the lowest value of one interval and 69.9 is the greatest value of another interval, you can simply add the frequencies from 60 to 69.9 to find the number of students between 60 and 69.9 inches tall.

45. When $t = 2.4$:

$$22 + 18t = 22 + 18(2.4) = 22 + 43.2 = 65.2$$

So, the dolphin's total distance traveled is 65.2 miles.

46.

Reasoning	Guess	Check
Pick 3 songs A–E and determine if they, along with announcements will fill the 15 min. radio show.	3 minutes + Song A + Song B + Song C	3 + 6 + 4 + 3 = 16
Too long, adjust time	3 minutes + Song B, Song C and Song D	3 + 4 + 3 + 5 = 15

Three minutes for announcements plus songs B, C, and D will take up a total of 15 minutes of radio time.

47. $225 + 80 + 40 + (-100) + (-25) = 345 + (-125)$
$$= 220$$

The new balance of the check book is $220.

48. When $t = 2.5$:
$$h = -16t^2 + 144 = -16(2.5)^2 + 144$$
$$= -16(6.25) + 144$$
$$= -100 + 144$$
$$= 44$$

When $t = 3$:
$$h = -16(3)^2 + 144 = -16(9) + 144$$
$$= -144 + 144 = 0$$

When $t = 3.5$:
$$h = -16(3.5)^2 + 144$$
$$= -16(12.25) + 144$$
$$= -196 + 144$$
$$= -52$$

The rock hits the ground after 3 seconds. After 3.5 seconds, the rock is on the ground because it cannot pass through the ground to reach 52 feet below ground.

49. Let x be the fraction of a tank of fuel you used.

Fuel in tank − Fuel used = Fuel left

$$\frac{5}{8} - x = \frac{3}{8}$$

$$\frac{5}{8} - x - \frac{5}{8} = \frac{3}{8} - \frac{5}{8}$$

$$-x = -\frac{2}{8}$$

$$-x = -\frac{1}{4}$$

$$(-1)(-x) = (-1)\left(-\frac{1}{4}\right)$$

$$x = \frac{1}{4}$$

You used $\frac{1}{4}$ of a tank of fuel.

Chapter 3, *continued*

50. Let *s* be the total number of students that attend the college.

$$\begin{array}{c} \text{Students in} \\ \text{intramurals} \end{array} = \begin{array}{c} \text{one} \\ \text{third} \end{array} \cdot \begin{array}{c} \text{Total number} \\ \text{of students} \end{array}$$

$$215 = \frac{1}{3}s$$

$$3 \cdot 215 = 3 \cdot \left(\frac{1}{3}s\right)$$

$$645 = s$$

A total of 645 students attend the college.

51. Area of field = $300 \times 150 = 45,000$ ft^2

Bags needed: $\dfrac{45,000}{5,000} = 9$

You need 9 bags of grass seed to cover the field.

Chapter 4

Chapter Get-Ready Games (pp. 172–173)

1. A. $1884 \div 4 = 471$

B. $39{,}000{,}000 \div 13 = 3{,}000{,}000$

C. $189 \div 21 = 9$

2. $4(13 + 21) + 30.9 = 4(34) + 30.9$

$\qquad\qquad\qquad = 136 + 30.9$

$\qquad\qquad\qquad = 166.9$

The world record bicycle speed is 166.9 miles per hour.

Stop and Think (p. 173)

1. Rewrite 1884 as $1800 + 84$. While 42 divides evenly into 84, it does not divide evenly into 1800. So, 42 cannot divide evenly into 1884.

2. The number 2 divides evenly into any even number. You can think of the even numbers as multiples of 2. So, all even numbers are divisible by 2.

Review Prerequisite Skills (p. 174)

1. In the expression 2^6, 2 is called the *base*.

2. The expression 3^7 is a *power* of 3.

3. In the expression 5^4, 4 is called the *exponent*.

4. $3^2 \cdot 3 = 3 \cdot 3 \cdot 3 = 27$

5. $(2 + 3)^2 = 5^2 = 25$

6. $4^2 \div 4^2 = 16 \div 16 = 1$

7. $(6 - 5)^7 = 1^7 = 1$

8. $3^2 + 4 \cdot 5 = 9 + 20 = 29$

9. $12 - 8 \div 2^2 = 12 - 8 \div 4 = 12 - 2 = 10$

10. $7^2 - 3^3 = 49 - 27 = 22$ **11.** $6^2 \div 2^2 = 36 \div 4 = 9$

12. $7x + 4 - 3x = 4x + 4$

13. $-2x + 5x - x = 3x - x = 2x$

14. $x + 4 - 12x = -11x + 4$

15. $6x - 5 + x = 7x - 5$

16. $15y + 9x - 6x - y = 3x + 14y$

17. $-13y + 8x - 2x + 3y - 10 = 6x - 10y - 10$

18. $\qquad 2a + 6 = 14$

$2a + 6 - 6 = 14 - 6$

$\qquad\quad 2a = 8$

$\qquad\quad \dfrac{2a}{2} = \dfrac{8}{2}$

$\qquad\qquad a = 4$

19. $\qquad 8 - 4m = 20$

$8 - 4m - 8 = 20 - 8$

$\qquad\quad -4m = 12$

$\qquad\quad \dfrac{-4m}{-4} = \dfrac{12}{-4}$

$\qquad\qquad m = -3$

20. $\qquad -7 + 5c = -32$

$-7 + 5c + 7 = -32 + 7$

$\qquad\quad 5c = -25$

$\qquad\quad \dfrac{5c}{5} = \dfrac{-25}{5}$

$\qquad\qquad c = -5$

Investigation (p. 175)

1. Prime numbers are circled in the array.

```
 1   ②   ③   4̶   ⑤   6̶   ⑦   8̶   9̶   1̶0̶
⑪   1̶2̶   ⑬   1̶4̶   1̶5̶   1̶6̶   ⑰   1̶8̶   ⑲   2̶0̶
2̶1̶   2̶2̶   ㉓   2̶4̶   2̶5̶   2̶6̶   2̶7̶   2̶8̶   ㉙   3̶0̶
㉛   3̶2̶   3̶3̶   3̶4̶   3̶5̶   3̶6̶   ㊲   3̶8̶   3̶9̶   4̶0̶
㊶   4̶2̶   ㊳   4̶4̶   4̶5̶   4̶6̶   ㊼   4̶8̶   4̶9̶   5̶0̶
5̶1̶   5̶2̶   ㊿   5̶4̶   5̶5̶   5̶6̶   5̶7̶   5̶8̶   ㊾   6̶0̶
```

2. Composite numbers are crossed out because they are multiples of smaller numbers.

3. If you continued this process with the numbers 61 to 100, you would expect the prime numbers to be circled because they are not multiples of earlier numbers.

Lesson 4.1

4.1 Guided Practice (pp. 176–178)

1. Write 20 as a product of two numbers in all possible ways.

$1 \times 20 \qquad\qquad 2 \times 10 \qquad\qquad 4 \times 5$

The factors of 20 are 1, 2, 4, 5, 10, and 20.

2. Write 29 as a product of two numbers in all possible ways.

$1 \cdot 29$

The factors of 29 are 1 and 29.

3. Write 42 as a product of two numbers in all possible ways.

$1 \times 42 \qquad 2 \times 21 \qquad 3 \times 14 \qquad 6 \times 7$

The factors of 42 are 1, 2, 3, 6, 7, 14, 21, and 42.

4. Write 57 as a product of two numbers in all possible ways.

$1 \times 57 \qquad\qquad 3 \times 19$

The factors of 57 are 1, 3, 19, and 57.

5. Write 62 as a product of two numbers in all possible ways.

$1 \times 62 \qquad\qquad 2 \times 31$

Find all the possible rectangular arrangements of rows and columns.

$1 \times 62 \qquad\qquad 2 \times 31$

$62 \times 1 \qquad\qquad 31 \times 2$

There are four ways the 62 characters can be arranged in rows of equal length.

6. 24 is composite.

Using exponents, the prime factorization is $2^3 \cdot 3$.

Chapter 4, *continued*

7. 51 is composite.

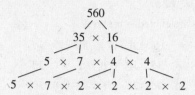

Using exponents, the prime factorization is $3 \cdot 17$.

8. 73 is a prime number.

9. 560 is composite.

$$
\begin{array}{c}
560 \\
35 \times 16 \\
5 \times 7 \times 4 \times 4 \\
5 \times 7 \times 2 \times 2 \times 2 \times 2
\end{array}
$$

Using exponents, the prime factorization is $2^4 \cdot 5 \cdot 7$.

10. $3mn = 3 \cdot m \cdot n$

11. $18t^2 = 2 \cdot 3 \cdot 3 \cdot t^2$

$ = 2 \cdot 3 \cdot 3 \cdot t \cdot t$

12. $14x^2y^3 = 2 \cdot 7 \cdot x^2 \cdot y^3$

$ = 2 \cdot 7 \cdot x \cdot x \cdot y \cdot y \cdot y$

13. $54w^3z^4 = 2 \cdot 3 \cdot 3 \cdot 3 \cdot w^3 \cdot z^4$

$ = 2 \cdot 3 \cdot 3 \cdot 3 \cdot w \cdot w \cdot w \cdot z \cdot z \cdot z \cdot z$

4.1 Exercises (pp. 178–180)

Skill Practice

1. The only positive factors of a *prime* number are the number itself and one.

2. The prime factorization of a number is the number written as the product of prime numbers.

3. Because 18 can be written 1×18, 2×9, and 3×6, the factors of 18 are 1, 2, 3, 6, 9, and 18.

4. Because 27 can be written 1×27 and 3×9, the factors of 27 are 1, 3, 9, and 27.

5. Because 34 can be written 1×34 and 2×17, the factors of 34 are 1, 2, 17, and 34.

6. Because 41 can be written 1×41, the factors of 41 are 1 and 41.

7. Because 29 can be written 1×29, the factors of 29 are 1 and 29.

8. Because 64 can be written 1×64, 2×32, 8×8, and 4×16, the factors of 64 are 1, 2, 4, 8, 16, 32, and 64.

9. Because 108 can be written 1×108, 2×54, 3×36, 4×27, 6×18, and 9×12, the factors of 108 are 1, 2, 3, 4, 6, 9, 12, 18, 27, 36, 54, and 108.

10. Because 175 can be written 1×175, 5×35, and 7×25, the factors of 175 are 1, 5, 7, 25, 35, and 175.

11. Because 299 can be written 1×299 and 13×23, the factors of 299 are 1, 13, 23, and 299.

12. Because 336 can be written 1×336, 2×168, 3×112, 4×84, 6×56, 7×48, 8×42, 12×28, 14×24, and 16×21, the factors of 336 are 1, 2, 3, 4, 6, 7, 8, 12, 14, 16, 21, 24, 28, 42, 48, 56, 84, 112, 168, and 336.

13. Because 400 can be written 1×400, 2×200, 4×100, 5×80, 8×50, 10×40, 16×25, and 20×20, the factors of 400 are 1, 2, 4, 5, 8, 10, 16, 20, 25, 40, 50, 80, 100, 200, and 400.

14. Because 512 can be written 1×512, 2×256, 4×128, 8×64, and 16×32, the factors of 512 are 1, 2, 4, 8, 16, 32, 64, 128, 256, and 512.

15. Factors of 21: 1, 3, 7, and 21

21 is composite because it has factors other than 1 and itself.

16. Factors of 45: 1, 3, 5, 9, 15, and 45

45 is composite because it has factors other than 1 and itself.

17. Factors of 59: 1 and 59

59 is prime because its only factors are 1 and itself.

18. Factors of 91: 1, 7, 13, and 91

91 is composite because it has factors other than 1 and itself.

19.

$$
\begin{array}{c}
88 \\
8 \times 11 \\
2 \times 4 \times 11 \\
2 \times 2 \times 2 \times 11
\end{array}
$$

Using exponents, the prime factorization of 88 is $2^3 \cdot 11$.

20.

$$
\begin{array}{c}
95 \\
5 \times 19
\end{array}
$$

The prime factorization of 95 is $5 \cdot 19$.

21.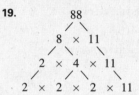

$$
\begin{array}{c}
210 \\
2 \times 105 \\
2 \times 5 \times 21 \\
2 \times 5 \times 3 \times 7
\end{array}
$$

The prime factorization of 210 is $2 \cdot 3 \cdot 5 \cdot 7$.

22.

$$
\begin{array}{c}
28 \\
4 \times 7 \\
2 \times 2 \times 7
\end{array}
$$

Using exponents, the prime factorization of 28 is $2^2 \cdot 7$.

23.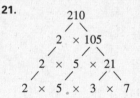

$$
\begin{array}{c}
55 \\
5 \times 11
\end{array}
$$

The prime factorization of 55 is $5 \cdot 11$.

24. 97 is a prime number.

25.

$$
\begin{array}{c}
96 \\
8 \times 12 \\
2 \times 4 \times 3 \times 4 \\
2 \times 2 \times 2 \times 3 \times 2 \times 2
\end{array}
$$

Using exponents, the prime factorization of 96 is $2^5 \cdot 3$.

Chapter 4, *continued*

26.

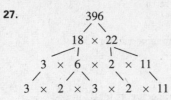

Using exponents, the prime factorization of 280 is $2^3 \cdot 5 \cdot 7$.

27.

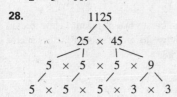

Using exponents, the prime factorization of 396 is $2^2 \cdot 3^2 \cdot 11$.

28.

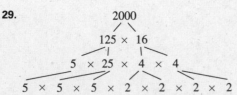

Using exponents, the prime factorization of 1125 is $3^2 \cdot 5^3$.

29.

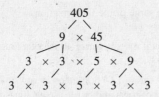

Using exponents, the prime factorization of 2000 is $2^4 \cdot 5^3$.

30. C;

```
          405
          / \
        9  ×  45
       /|     |\
      3 × 3 × 5 × 9
     /   /   /  / \
    3 × 3 × 5 × 3 × 3
```

Using exponents, the prime factorization of 405 is $3^4 \cdot 5$.

31. $15cd = 3 \cdot 5 \cdot c \cdot d$

32. $40pq = 2 \cdot 2 \cdot 2 \cdot 5 \cdot p \cdot q$

33. $9x^2y = 3 \cdot 3 \cdot x \cdot x \cdot y$

34. $24g^2h^3 = 2 \cdot 2 \cdot 2 \cdot 3 \cdot g^2 \cdot h^3$

$= 2 \cdot 2 \cdot 2 \cdot 3 \cdot g \cdot g \cdot h \cdot h \cdot h$

35. $48n^3m^3 = 2 \cdot 2 \cdot 2 \cdot 2 \cdot 3 \cdot n^3 \cdot m^3$

$= 2 \cdot 2 \cdot 2 \cdot 2 \cdot 3 \cdot n \cdot n \cdot n \cdot m \cdot m \cdot m$

36. $144n^2m^5 = 2 \cdot 2 \cdot 2 \cdot 2 \cdot 3 \cdot 3 \cdot n^2 \cdot m^5$

$= 2 \cdot 2 \cdot 2 \cdot 2 \cdot 3 \cdot 3 \cdot n \cdot n \cdot m \cdot m \cdot m \cdot m \cdot m$

37. $20ab^4c^2 = 2 \cdot 2 \cdot 5 \cdot a \cdot b^4 \cdot c^2$

$= 2 \cdot 2 \cdot 5 \cdot a \cdot b \cdot b \cdot b \cdot b \cdot c \cdot c$

38. $99r^3s^2t = 3 \cdot 3 \cdot 11 \cdot r^3 \cdot s^2 \cdot t$

$= 3 \cdot 3 \cdot 11 \cdot r \cdot r \cdot r \cdot s \cdot s \cdot t$

39. The errors are that 1 does not need to be included, 6 is not factored, and there are two factors of x.

$18x^2y = 2 \cdot 3 \cdot 3 \cdot x \cdot x \cdot y$

40.

```
          24
          / \
        3  ×  8
       /   / | \
      3 × 2 × 4
     /   /   / \
    3 × 2 × 2 × 2
```

Using exponents, the prime factorization of 24 is $2^3 \cdot 3$.

Find all other combinations of products of the prime factors.

2   3 $2 \cdot 2 = 4$ $2 \cdot 3 = 6$ $2 \cdot 2 \cdot 2 = 8$

$2 \cdot 2 \cdot 3 = 12$

All the factors of 24 besides 1 and itself are 2, 3, 4, 6, 8, and 12.

41.

```
          56
          / \
        7  ×  8
       /   / | \
      7 × 2 × 4
     /   /   / \
    7 × 2 × 2 × 2
```

Using exponents, the prime factorization of 56 is $2^3 \cdot 7$.

Find all other combinations of products of the prime factors.

2                   $2 \cdot 2 = 4$ 7

$2 \cdot 2 \cdot 2 = 8$ $2 \cdot 7 = 14$ $2 \cdot 2 \cdot 7 = 28$

All the factors of 56 besides 1 and itself are 2, 4, 7, 8, 14, and 28.

42.

```
          102
          / \
        2  ×  51
       /    / \
      2 × 3 × 17
```

Using exponents, the prime factorization of 102 is $2 \cdot 3 \cdot 17$.

Find all other combinations of products of the prime factors.

2   3 $2 \cdot 3 = 6$ 17 $2 \cdot 17 = 34$ $3 \times 17 = 51$

All of the factors of 102 besides 1 and itself are 2, 3, 6, 17, 34, and 51.

Chapter 4, continued

43.

$$
\begin{array}{c}
225 \\
\diagup\;\diagdown \\
9\;\times\;25 \\
\diagup\;|\qquad|\;\diagdown \\
3\;\times\;3\;\times\;5\;\times\;5
\end{array}
$$

Using exponents, the prime factorization of 225 is $3^2 \cdot 5^2$.

Find all other combinations of products of the prime factors.

$3 \qquad 5 \qquad 3 \cdot 3 = 9 \qquad 3 \cdot 5 = 15 \qquad 5 \cdot 5 = 25$

$3 \cdot 3 \cdot 5 = 45 \qquad 3 \cdot 5 \cdot 5 = 75$

All of the factors of 225 besides 1 and itself are 3, 5, 9, 15, 25, 45, and 75.

44. *Sample answer:* 10 can be expressed as the sum of two prime numbers, $3 + 7$.

45. *Sample answer:* 16 can be expressed as the sum of two prime numbers, $5 + 11$.

46. *Sample answer:* 28 can be expressed as the sum of two prime numbers, $5 + 23$.

47. *Sample answer:* 30 can be expressed as the sum of two prime numbers, $7 + 23$.

48. *Sample answer:* The factors of 9 are 1, 3, and 9. The factors of 16 are 1, 4, and 16. The factors of 25 are 1, 5, and 25. The numbers 4, 9, 16, and 25 are all perfect squares.

Problem Solving

49. a. The factors of 120 are 1, 2, 3, 4, 5, 6, 8, 10, 12, 15, 20, 24, 30, 40, 60, and 120.

    b.

1×120	2×60	3×40
120×1	60×2	40×3
4×30	5×24	6×20
30×4	24×5	20×6
8×15	10×12	
15×8	12×10	

    c. The two most reasonable arrangements for a quilt are 10×12 and 8×15. The other arrangements are not reasonable because the quilt would be too long and narrow to be practical.

50. The factors of 180 are 1, 2, 3, 4, 5, 6, 9, 10, 12, 15, 18, 20, 30, 36, 45, 60, 90, and 180.

List the possible combinations of number of teams and team sizes of 9 to 50.

4 teams of 45	5 teams of 36
6 teams of 30	9 teams of 20
10 teams of 18	12 teams of 15
15 teams of 12	18 teams of 10
20 teams of 9	

The two reasonable sizes are 15 or 18. *Sample answer:* Both of these sizes produce an even number of teams for the league, and allow for substitute players but are small enough that everyone can get a chance to play.

51. B;

23 is a prime number so its only factors are 1 and 23. It cannot be arranged in a rectangular arrangement with two or more rows all of equal length.

20, 25, and 27 desks can be arranged in a rectangular arrangement with two or more rows all of equal length.

Possible rectangular arrangements for 20 desks:

1×20	$\mathbf{2 \times 10}$	$\mathbf{4 \times 5}$
20×1	$\mathbf{10 \times 2}$	$\mathbf{5 \times 4}$

Possible rectangular arrangements for 25 desks:

1×25	$\mathbf{5 \times 5}$
25×1	

Possible rectangular arrangements for 27 desks:

1×27	$\mathbf{3 \times 9}$
27×1	

52. *Sample answer:* You can create two different factor trees for 540 by starting with two different sets of factors such as 10 and 54 or 5 and 108.

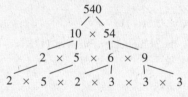

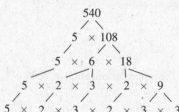

Both trees result in the same prime factorization, $2^2 \cdot 3^3 \cdot 5$.

53. You cannot have 40 equal rows because 40 is not a factor of 140.

You can have either 10 rows of 14 bottles or 14 rows of 10 bottles. The number of rows and bottles in each case is less than 15, so they will fit on the table.

54. Two prime numbers that have a difference of 1 are 3 and 2; $3 - 2 = 1$.

No other combination of two prime numbers have a difference of 1. *Sample answer:* If the difference of two numbers is 1, then the numbers must be consecutive. One of the consecutive numbers must be even, and the only prime even number is 2.

55. a. The area of a rectangle is found by multiplying the length by the width. If the area is 24 square inches, you need to find two numbers whose product is 24. Use the factors of 24. The possible dimensions and their corresponding perimeters are listed below.

1 in. by 24 in.	$P = 2(1) + 2(24) = 50$ in.
2 in. by 12 in.	$P = 2(2) + 2(12) = 28$ in.
3 in. by 8 in.	$P = 2(3) + 2(8) = 22$ in.
4 in. by 6 in.	$P = 2(4) + 2(6) = 20$ in.

The rectangle with the least perimeter has the dimensions 4 in. by 6 in.

b. The possible dimensions of a rectangle with an area of 36 square inches are listed below, along with their corresponding perimeters.

1 in. by 36 in.	$P = 2(1) + 2(36) = 74$ in.
2 in. by 18 in.	$P = 2(2) + 2(18) = 40$ in.
3 in. by 12 in.	$P = 2(3) + 2(12) = 30$ in.
4 in. by 9 in.	$P = 2(4) + 2(9) = 26$ in.
6 in. by 6 in.	$P = 2(6) + 2(6) = 24$ in.

The rectangle with the least perimeter has the dimensions 6 in. by 6 in.

The possible dimensions of a rectangle with an area of 40 square inches are listed below, along with their corresponding perimeters.

1 in. by 40 in.	$P = 2(1) + 2(40) = 82$ in.
2 in. by 20 in.	$P = 2(2) + 2(20) = 44$ in.
4 in. by 10 in.	$P = 2(4) + 2(10) = 28$ in.
5 in. by 8 in.	$P = 2(5) + 2(8) = 26$ in.

The rectangle with the least perimeter has the dimensions 5 in. by 8 in.

c. The rectangle with the least perimeter has the dimensions 10 in. by 10 in. *Sample answer:* The least perimeter occurs with the dimensions that are closest to a square.

56. If the volume of a box is 200 cubic inches, you need to find three numbers whose product is 200. The possible whole number dimensions are listed below.

1 in. by 1 in. by 200 in.	2 in. by 2 in. by 50 in.
1 in. by 2 in. by 100 in.	2 in. by 4 in. by 25 in.
1 in. by 4 in. by 50 in.	2 in. by 5 in. by 20 in.
1 in. by 5 in. by 40 in.	2 in. by 10 in. by 10 in.
1 in. by 8 in. by 25 in.	4 in. by 5 in. by 10 in.
1 in. by 10 in. by 20 in.	5 in. by 5 in. by 8 in.

57. *Sample answer:* Five pairs of twin primes are 11 and 13, 17 and 19, 29 and 31, 41 and 43, and 59 and 61.

58. The factors of 28 are 1, 2, 4, 7, 14, and 28.

$1 + 2 + 4 + 7 + 14 = 28$

Mixed Review

59. $n \cdot n \cdot n \cdot n = n^4$;

Words: n to the fourth power

60. $r \cdot r \cdot r = r^3$;

Words: r cubed

61. $m \cdot m \cdot m \cdot m \cdot m = m^5$;

Words: m to the fifth power

62. $i \cdot i \cdot i \cdot i \cdot i \cdot i \cdot i = i^7$;

Words: i to the seventh power

63. (1) Read and Understand

(2) Make a Plan: Draw a diagram

(3) Solve the Problem

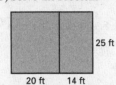

$P = 2(20 + 14) + 2(25) = 68 + 50 = 118$

The perimeter of the store with the additional space is 118 feet.

(4) Look Back

64. *Sample answer:* $x + 1 > 6$ and $2x > 10$

$$x + 1 > 6 \qquad 2x > 10$$
$$x + 1 - 1 > 6 - 1 \qquad \frac{2x}{2} > \frac{10}{2}$$
$$x > 5 \qquad x > 5$$

Lesson 4.2

Activity (p. 181)

Step 1: The numbers 1, 2, 3, and 6 are factors of both 18 and 24.

Step 2: The numbers 1, 2, and 4 are factors of both 20 and 24.

Step 3: The numbers 1 and 2 are factors of 18, 20, and 24.

Step 4: The greatest factor in all three lists is 2.

4.2 Guided Practice (pp. 181–183)

1. $12 = 2 \times 2 \times 3$

$32 = 2 \times 2 \times 2 \times 2 \times 2$

The GCF of 12 and 32 is 2×2, or 4.

2. $42 = 2 \times 3 \times 7$

$60 = 2 \times 2 \times 3 \times 5$

The GCF of 42 and 60 is 2×3, or 6.

3. $36 = 2 \times 2 \times 3 \times 3$

$90 = 2 \times 3 \times 3 \times 5$

The GCF of 36 and 90 is $2 \times 3 \times 3$, or 18.

4. $96 = 2 \times 2 \times 2 \times 2 \times 2 \times 3$

$120 = 2 \times 2 \times 2 \times 3 \times 5$

The GCF of 96 and 120 is $2 \times 2 \times 2 \times 3$, or 24.

5. $48 = 2 \times 2 \times 2 \times 2 \times 3$

$72 = 2 \times 2 \times 2 \times 3 \times 3$

48 and 72 are not relatively prime.

Their GCF is $2 \times 2 \times 2 \times 3$, or 24.

6. $124 = 2 \times 2 \times 31$

$128 = 2 \times 2 \times 2 \times 2 \times 2 \times 2 \times 2$

124 and 128 are not relatively prime.

Their GCF is 2×2, or 4.

7. $39 = 3 \times 13$

$44 = 2 \times 2 \times 11$

39 and 44 are relatively prime because they have no common prime factors.

8. $200 = 2 \times 2 \times 2 \times 5 \times 5$

$63 = 3 \times 3 \times 7$

200 and 63 are relatively prime because they have no common prime factors.

9. Find the greatest number of pep rally packs by finding the GCF.

$240 = 2^4 \cdot 3 \cdot 5$

$360 = 2^3 \cdot 3^2 \cdot 5$

$600 = 2^3 \cdot 3 \cdot 5^2$

The GCF is $2^3 \cdot 3 \cdot 5$, or 120. So, the greatest number of pep rally packs that can be made is 120.

Divide the number of items by the number of pep rally packs.

$240 \div 120 = 2$

$360 \div 120 = 3$

$600 \div 120 = 5$

Each pack will contain 2 bumper stickers, 3 pennants, and 5 pencils.

10. $6x = 2 \cdot 3 \cdot x$

$18x = 2 \cdot 3 \cdot 3 \cdot x$

The GCF of $6x$ and $18x$ is $2 \cdot 3 \cdot x$, or $6x$.

11. $6xy = 2 \cdot 3 \cdot x \cdot y$

$4xy^2 = 2 \cdot 2 \cdot x \cdot y \cdot y$

The GCF of $6xy$ and $4xy^2$ is $2 \cdot x \cdot y$, or $2xy$.

12. $15y = 3 \cdot 5 \cdot y$

$9x^2y^2 = 3 \cdot 3 \cdot x \cdot x \cdot y \cdot y$

The GCF of $15y$ and $4x^2y^2$ is $3 \cdot y$, or $3y$.

13. $5xy^3 = 5 \cdot x \cdot y \cdot y \cdot y$

$10x^2y^2 = 2 \cdot 5 \cdot x \cdot x \cdot y \cdot y$

The GCF of $5xy^3$ and $10x^2y^2$ is $5 \cdot x \cdot y \cdot y$, or $5xy^2$.

4.2 Exercises (pp. 183–185)

Skill Practice

1. Six is the *greatest common factor* of 12 and 18.

2. Two numbers are *relatively prime* if their GCF is 1.

3. $14 = 2 \times 7$

$70 = 2 \times 5 \times 7$

The GCF of 14 and 70 is 2×7, or 14.

4. $38 = 2 \times 19$

$51 = 3 \times 17$

38 and 51 are relatively prime because thay have no common prime factors.

5. $24 = 2 \times 2 \times 2 \times 3$

$196 = 2 \times 2 \times 7 \times 7$

The GCF of 24 and 196 is 2×2, or 4.

6. $42 = 2 \times 3 \times 7$

$184 = 2 \times 2 \times 2 \times 23$

The GCF of 42 and 184 is 2.

7. $3 = 3$

$9 = 3 \times 3$

$27 = 3 \times 3 \times 3$

The GCF of 3, 9, and 27 is 3.

8. $21 = 3 \times 7$

$28 = 2 \times 2 \times 7$

$56 = 2 \times 2 \times 2 \times 7$

The GCF of 21, 28, and 56 is 7.

9. $17 = 17$

$18 = 2 \times 3 \times 3$

$20 = 2 \times 2 \times 5$

17, 18, and 20 are relatively prime because they have no common prime factors.

10. $24 = 2 \times 2 \times 2 \times 3$

$36 = 2 \times 2 \times 3 \times 3$

$180 = 2 \times 2 \times 3 \times 3 \times 5$

The GCF of 24, 36, and 180 is $2 \times 2 \times 3$, or 12.

11. The error is that the student forgot to include 2 as a factor twice.

$140 = 2 \cdot 2 \cdot 5 \cdot 7$

$440 = 2 \cdot 2 \cdot 2 \cdot 5 \cdot 11$

The GCF is $2 \cdot 2 \cdot 5 = 20$.

12. $5 = 5$

$16 = 2 \times 2 \times 2 \times 2$

5 and 16 are relatively prime because they have no common prime factors.

13. $10 = 2 \times 5$

$25 = 5 \times 5$

10 and 25 are not relatively prime.

Their GCF is 5.

14. $28 = 2 \times 2 \times 7$

$42 = 2 \times 3 \times 7$

28 and 42 are not relatively prime.

Their GCF is 2×7, or 14.

15. $55 = 5 \times 11$

$72 = 2 \times 2 \times 2 \times 3 \times 3$

52 and 72 are relatively prime because they have no common prime factors.

16. $21 = 3 \times 7$

    $66 = 2 \times 3 \times 11$

    21 and 66 are not relatively prime.

    Their GCF is 3.

17. $18 = 2 \times 3 \times 3$

    $216 = 2 \times 2 \times 2 \times 3 \times 3 \times 3$

    18 and 216 are not relatively prime.

    Their GCF is $2 \times 3 \times 3$, or 18.

18. $212 = 2 \times 2 \times 53$

    $312 = 2 \times 2 \times 2 \times 3 \times 13$

    212 and 312 are not relatively prime.

    Their GCF is 2×2, or 4.

19. $268 = 2 \times 2 \times 67$

    $515 = 5 \times 103$

    268 and 515 are relatively prime because they have no common prime factors.

20. B; $4x^2 = 2 \cdot 2 \cdot x \cdot x$

    $6x = 2 \cdot 3 \cdot x$

    The GCF of $4x^2$ and $6x$ is $2 \cdot x$, or $2x$.

21. $3x^2 = 3 \cdot x \cdot x$

    $9x = 3 \cdot 3 \cdot x$

    The GCF of $3x^2$ and $9x$ is $3 \cdot x$, or $3x$.

22. $4z^3 = 2 \cdot 2 \cdot z \cdot z \cdot z$

    $2z^2 = 2 \cdot z \cdot z$

    The GCF of $4z^3$ and $2z^2$ is $2 \cdot z \cdot z$, or $2z^2$.

23. $5t^4 = 5 \cdot t \cdot t \cdot t \cdot t$

    $15t^5 = 3 \cdot 5 \cdot t \cdot t \cdot t \cdot t \cdot t$

    The GCF of $5t^4$ and $15t^5$ is $5 \cdot t \cdot t \cdot t \cdot t$, or $5t^4$.

24. $12x^2y^2 = 2 \cdot 2 \cdot 3 \cdot x \cdot x \cdot y \cdot y$

    $16xy^3 = 2 \cdot 2 \cdot 2 \cdot 2 \cdot x \cdot y \cdot y \cdot y$

    The GCF of $12x^2y^2$ and $16xy^3$ is $2 \cdot 2 \cdot x \cdot y \cdot y$, or $4xy^2$.

25. $18rs^2 = 2 \cdot 3 \cdot 3 \cdot r \cdot s \cdot s$

    $30st^2 = 2 \cdot 3 \cdot 5 \cdot s \cdot t \cdot t$

    The GCF of $18rs^2$ and $30st^2$ is $2 \cdot 3 \cdot s$, or $6s$.

26. $15bc^3 = 3 \cdot 5 \cdot b \cdot c \cdot c \cdot c$

    $75b^3c = 3 \cdot 5 \cdot 5 \cdot b \cdot b \cdot b \cdot c$

    The GCF of $15bc^3$ and $75b^3c$ is $3 \cdot 5 \cdot b \cdot c$, or $15bc$.

27. $9t^3 = 3 \cdot 3 \cdot t \cdot t \cdot t$

    $33t = 3 \cdot 11 \cdot t$

    $27t^4 = 3 \cdot 3 \cdot 3 \cdot t \cdot t \cdot t \cdot t$

    The GCF of $9t^3$, $33t$, and $27t^4$ is $3 \cdot t$, or $3t$.

28. $12x^2y^3 = 2 \cdot 2 \cdot 3 \cdot x \cdot x \cdot y \cdot y \cdot y$

    $42x^3y^2 = 2 \cdot 3 \cdot 7 \cdot x \cdot x \cdot x \cdot y \cdot y$

    $36x^2y^3 = 2 \cdot 2 \cdot 3 \cdot 3 \cdot x \cdot x \cdot y \cdot y \cdot y$

    The GCF of $12x^2y^3$, $42x^3y^2$, and $36x^2y^3$ is $2 \cdot 3 \cdot x \cdot x \cdot y \cdot y$, or $6x^2y^2$.

29. $63mn = 3 \cdot 3 \cdot 7 \cdot m \cdot n$

    $42m^3 = 2 \cdot 3 \cdot 7 \cdot m \cdot m \cdot m$

    $32n^2 = 2 \cdot 2 \cdot 2 \cdot 2 \cdot 2 \cdot n \cdot n$

    $63mn$, $42m^3$, and $32n^2$ are relatively prime because they have no common prime factors.

30. *Sample answer:*

    $16 = 2 \cdot 2 \cdot 2 \cdot 2$

    $32 = 2 \cdot 2 \cdot 2 \cdot 2 \cdot 2$

    The GCF of 16 and 32 is $2 \cdot 2 \cdot 2 \cdot 2$, or 16.

31. *Sample answer:*

    $21 = 3 \cdot 7$

    $42 = 2 \cdot 3 \cdot 7$

    The GCF of 21 and 42 is $3 \cdot 7$, or 21.

32. *Sample answer:*

    $18x^2 = 2 \cdot 3 \cdot 3 \cdot x \cdot x$

    $36x^3 = 2 \cdot 2 \cdot 3 \cdot 3 \cdot x \cdot x \cdot x$

    The GCF of $18x^2$ and $36x^3$ is $2 \cdot 3 \cdot 3 \cdot x \cdot x$, or $18x^2$.

33. *Sample answer:*

    $15sc^3 = 3 \cdot 5 \cdot s \cdot c \cdot c \cdot c$

    $15s^2c^4 = 3 \cdot 5 \cdot s \cdot s \cdot c \cdot c \cdot c \cdot c$

    The GCF of $15sc^3$ and $15s^2c^4$ is $3 \cdot 5 \cdot s \cdot c \cdot c \cdot c$, or $15sc^3$.

34. The greatest common factor of two numbers is *never* greater than both of the numbers. The largest a factor can be is equal to the lesser number.

35. The greatest common factor of two numbers is *sometimes* equal to one of the two numbers. For example, the GCF of 5 and 10 is 5.

36. The greatest common factor of two numbers is *sometimes* prime. For example, the GCF of 12 and 14 is 2, which is prime.

37. The greatest common factor of relatively prime numbers is *always* 1. 1 is the only factor two relatively prime numbers share.

38. $\times 2x \quad \times 2x$

    $5x, \ 10x^2, \ 20x^3, \ldots$

    To continue the pattern, multiply the previous monomial by $2x$.

    The next three monomials are listed below.

    $20x^3 \cdot 2x = 40x^4$

    $40x^4 \cdot 2x = 80x^5$

    $80x^5 \cdot 2x = 160x^6$

    Find the GCF of the list.

    $5x = 5 \cdot x$

    $10x^2 = 2 \cdot 5 \cdot x \cdot x$

    $20x^3 = 2 \cdot 2 \cdot 5 \cdot x \cdot x \cdot x$

    $40x^4 = 2 \cdot 2 \cdot 2 \cdot 5 \cdot x \cdot x \cdot x \cdot x$

    $\vdots$

    The GCF of the list is $5 \cdot x$, or $5x$.

39. $\times\, 4rs^2 \quad \times\, 4rs^2$

$4r^2s,\ 16r^3s^3,\ 64r^4s^5,\ \ldots$

To continue the pattern, multiply the previous monomial by $4rs^2$.

The next three monomials are listed below.

$64r^4s^5 \cdot 4rs^2 = 256r^5s^7$

$256r^5s^7 \cdot 4rs^2 = 1024r^6s^9$

$1024r^6s^9 \cdot 4rs^2 = 4096r^7s^{11}$

Find the GCF of the list.

$4r^2s = 2 \cdot 2 \cdot r \cdot r \cdot s$

$16r^3s^3 = 2 \cdot 2 \cdot 2 \cdot 2 \cdot r \cdot r \cdot r \cdot s \cdot s \cdot s$

$64r^4s^5 = 2 \cdot 2 \cdot 2 \cdot 2 \cdot 2 \cdot 2 \cdot r \cdot r \cdot r \cdot r \cdot s \cdot s \cdot s \cdot s \cdot s$

⋮

The GCF of the list is $2 \cdot 2 \cdot r \cdot r \cdot s$, or $4r^2s$.

Problem Solving

40. a.

The prime factorization of 60 is $2^2 \cdot 3 \cdot 5$.

The prime factorization of 66 is $2 \cdot 3 \cdot 11$.

b. The common prime factors of the two numbers are 2 and 3.

c. $2 \times 3 = 6$; The greatest number of teams that can be formed is 6, where each has $60 \div 6 = 10$ girls and $66 \div 6 = 11$ boys.

41. B;

$36 = 2 \times 2 \times 3 \times 3$

$45 = 3 \times 3 \times 5$

$81 = 3 \times 3 \times 3 \times 3$

$108 = 2 \times 2 \times 3 \times 3 \times 3$

The GCF of 36, 45, 81, and 108 is $3 \cdot 3$, or 9, so each piece should be 9 inches.

42. $360 = 2 \times 2 \times 2 \times 3 \times 3 \times 5$

$270 = 2 \times 3 \times 3 \times 3 \times 5$

$180 = 2 \times 2 \times 3 \times 3 \times 5$

The GCF of 360, 270, and 180 is $2 \times 3 \times 3 \times 5$, or 90.

Tulips: $360 \div 90 = 4$

Roses: $270 \div 90 = 3$

Lilies: $180 \div 90 = 2$

The florist can make 90 bouquets consisting of 4 tulips 3 roses, and 2 lilies.

43. Two even numbers cannot be relatively prime because

they will always have a prime factor of 2 in common.

44. *Sample answer:*

$26 = 2 \cdot 13$

$33 = 3 \cdot 11$

$35 = 5 \cdot 7$

26, 33, and 35 are three composite numbers that are relatively prime.

45. Two prime numbers are always relatively prime because prime numbers have two factors, one and the number itself. The only factor in common would be 1.

For example, 2 and 3 are both prime numbers, with factors of 2 and 1, and 3 and 1, respectively.

For example, 5 and 7 are both prime numbers, with factors of 5 and 1, and 7 and 1, respectively.

In each case, the only factor the numbers have in common is 1, so they are relatively prime.

46. Step 1 Determine the greatest length x by finding the GCF of the two areas.

$156 = 2 \cdot 2 \cdot 3 \cdot 13$

$204 = 2 \cdot 2 \cdot 3 \cdot 17$

The greatest length x the farmer can make the fence shared by the two pens is $2 \cdot 2 \cdot 3 = 12$ feet.

Step 2 Find the dimensions of each pen.

$156 \div 12 = 13$

$204 \div 12 = 17$

The dimensions are 12 feet by 13 feet and 12 feet by 17 feet.

Step 3 Find the number of feet of fence needed to build both pens.

$2(13) + 2(17) + 3(12) = 26 + 34 + 36 = 96$

The farmer needs 96 feet of fence to build both pens.

47. The GCF of cx, cy, and cz is the product of c and the GCF of x, y, and z.

48. *Sample answer:* First, find the GCF of the constants. Then for each variable that occurs in both monomials, take the factor with the lesser exponent. Multiply these factors by the GCF of the constants to find the GCF.

Mixed Review

49.

$$\begin{array}{c} 84 \\ \diagup \ \diagdown \\ 4 \ \times \ 21 \\ \mid \qquad \mid \\ 2 \times 2 \times 3 \times 7 \end{array}$$

The prime factorization of 84 is $2^2 \cdot 3 \cdot 7$.

50.

$$\begin{array}{c} 56 \\ \diagup \ \diagdown \\ 8 \ \times \ 7 \\ \diagup \diagdown \quad \diagdown \\ 2 \times 4 \times 7 \\ \diagup \diagdown \\ 2 \times 2 \times 2 \times 7 \end{array}$$

The prime factorization of 56 is $2^3 \cdot 7$.

Chapter 4, *continued*

51.

39
/ \
3 × 13

The prime factorization of 39 is 3 • 13.

52.

```
        1260
        /  \
      36 × 35
      /|    |
    4 × 9 × 5 × 7
   /|  |\      |
  2 × 2 × 3 × 3 × 5 × 7
```

The prime factorization of 1260 is $2^2 • 3^2 • 5 • 7$.

53.
$-6 + n = 4$
$-6 + n + 6 = 4 + 6$
$n = 10$

54.
$n + 13 = 5$
$n + 13 - 13 = 5 - 13$
$n = -8$

55.
$n + 2.7 = 5.7$
$n + 2.7 - 2.7 = 5.7 - 2.7$
$n = 3$

56.
$n - 4 = 20$
$n - 4 + 4 = 20 + 4$
$n = 24$

57. B;

$A = \frac{1}{2}bh = \frac{1}{2} • 12 • 9 = 54 \text{ m}^2$

Brain Game (p. 185)

$2 • 3 • 5 • 7 + 1 = 210 + 1 = 211$

There are 211 marbles in the bucket.

Lesson 4.3

Investigation (p. 186)

1–4. Sample answers are given.

1. $\frac{4}{6}$

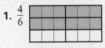

$\frac{2}{3}$ $\frac{6}{9}$

The fractions $\frac{2}{3}$ and $\frac{6}{9}$ are equivalent to $\frac{4}{6}$.

2. $\frac{10}{12}$

$\frac{5}{6}$ 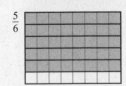 $\frac{20}{24}$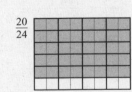

The fractions $\frac{5}{6}$ and $\frac{20}{24}$ are equivalent to $\frac{10}{12}$.

3. $\frac{4}{16}$

$\frac{2}{8}$  $\frac{1}{4}$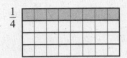

The fractions $\frac{2}{8}$ and $\frac{1}{4}$ are equivalent to $\frac{4}{16}$.

4. $\frac{10}{16}$

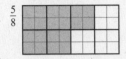

$\frac{5}{8}$ $\frac{20}{32}$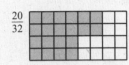

The fractions $\frac{5}{8}$ and $\frac{20}{32}$ are equivalent to $\frac{10}{16}$.

5. If you factor the numerator and denominator of a fraction, you can find the GCF. Divide the numerator and denominator by the GCF, or any common factor, to write an equivalent fraction.

4.3 Guided Practice (pp. 188–189)

1. $\frac{22}{116} = \frac{22 \div 2}{116 \div 2} = \frac{11}{58}$

The fraction of jewels that are pearls is $\frac{11}{58}$.

2. $\frac{19}{116}$ is in simplest form.

The fraction of jewels that are sapphires is $\frac{19}{116}$.

3. $\frac{44}{116} = \frac{44 \div 4}{116 \div 4} = \frac{11}{29}$

The fraction of jewels that are spinels is $\frac{11}{29}$.

4. $\frac{1}{6}$ is in simplest form.

$\frac{4}{24} = \frac{4 \div 4}{24 \div 4} = \frac{1}{6}$

The fractions $\frac{1}{6}$ and $\frac{4}{24}$ are equivalent.

5. $\frac{3}{7}$ is in simplest form.

$\frac{10}{21}$ is in simplest form.

The fractions $\frac{3}{7}$ and $\frac{10}{21}$ are not equivalent.

6. $\frac{24}{30} = \frac{24 \div 6}{30 \div 6} = \frac{4}{5}$

$\frac{4}{6} = \frac{4 \div 2}{6 \div 2} = \frac{2}{3}$

The fractions $\frac{24}{30}$ and $\frac{4}{6}$ are not equivalent.

7. $\frac{15}{35} = \frac{15 \div 5}{35 \div 5} = \frac{3}{7}$

$\frac{3}{7}$ is in simplest form.

The fractions $\frac{15}{35}$ and $\frac{3}{7}$ are equivalent.

8. *Sample answer:*

$\frac{8}{16} = \frac{8 \div 8}{16 \div 8} = \frac{1}{2}$

$\frac{8}{16} = \frac{8 \div 2}{16 \div 2} = \frac{4}{8}$

The fractions $\frac{1}{2}$ and $\frac{4}{8}$ are equivalent to $\frac{8}{16}$.

9. *Sample answer:*

$\frac{9}{15} = \frac{9 \div 3}{15 \div 3} = \frac{3}{5}$

$\frac{9}{15} = \frac{9 \times 2}{15 \times 2} = \frac{18}{30}$

The fractions $\frac{3}{5}$ and $\frac{18}{30}$ are equivalent to $\frac{9}{15}$.

10. *Sample answer:*

$\frac{10}{12} = \frac{10 \div 2}{12 \div 2} = \frac{5}{6}$

$\frac{10}{12} = \frac{10 \times 3}{12 \times 3} = \frac{30}{36}$

The fractions $\frac{5}{6}$ and $\frac{30}{36}$ are equivalent to $\frac{10}{12}$.

11. *Sample answer:*

$\frac{21}{24} = \frac{21 \div 3}{24 \div 3} = \frac{7}{8}$

$\frac{21}{24} = \frac{21 \times 2}{24 \times 2} = \frac{42}{48}$

The fractions $\frac{7}{8}$ and $\frac{42}{48}$ are equivalent to $\frac{21}{24}$.

12. $\frac{4xy}{6x} = \frac{\overset{1}{2} \cdot 2 \cdot \overset{1}{x} \cdot y}{\underset{1}{2} \cdot 3 \cdot \underset{1}{x}} = \frac{2y}{3}$

When $y = 3$: $\frac{2y}{3} = \frac{2(3)}{3} = 2$

13. $\frac{32x}{8xy} = \frac{\overset{1}{2} \cdot \overset{1}{2} \cdot \overset{1}{2} \cdot 2 \cdot 2 \cdot \overset{1}{x}}{\underset{1}{2} \cdot \underset{1}{2} \cdot \underset{1}{2} \cdot \underset{1}{x} \cdot y} = \frac{4}{y}$

When $y = 3$: $\frac{4}{y} = \frac{4}{3}$

14. $\frac{2x^3y}{6x} = \frac{\overset{1}{2} \cdot \overset{1}{x} \cdot x \cdot x \cdot y}{\underset{1}{2} \cdot 3 \cdot \underset{1}{x}} = \frac{x^2y}{3}$

When $x = -2$ and $y = 3$: $\frac{x^2y}{3} = \frac{(-2)^2(3)}{3} = 4$

15. $\frac{5x^2y}{10xy} = \frac{\overset{1}{5} \cdot \overset{1}{x} \cdot x \cdot \overset{1}{y}}{2 \cdot \underset{1}{5} \cdot \underset{1}{x} \cdot \underset{1}{y}} = \frac{x}{2}$

When $x = -2$: $\frac{x}{2} = \frac{-2}{2} = -1$

4.3 Exercises (pp. 189–191)

Skill Practice

1. The GCF of the numerator and denominator of a fraction in *simplest form* is 1.

2. Fractions with the same simplest form are *equivalent fractions*.

3. $\frac{21}{49} = \frac{21 \div 7}{49 \div 7} = \frac{3}{7}$

4. $\frac{-9}{72} = \frac{-9 \div 9}{72 \div 9} = -\frac{1}{8}$

5. $\frac{10}{15} = \frac{10 \div 5}{15 \div 5} = \frac{2}{3}$

6. $\frac{16}{20} = \frac{16 \div 4}{20 \div 4} = \frac{4}{5}$

7. $\frac{-25}{40} = \frac{-25 \div 5}{40 \div 5} = -\frac{5}{8}$

8. $\frac{-36}{72} = \frac{-36 \div 36}{72 \div 36} = -\frac{1}{2}$

9. $\frac{39}{52} = \frac{39 \div 13}{52 \div 13} = \frac{3}{4}$

10. $\frac{18}{27} = \frac{18 \div 9}{27 \div 9} = \frac{2}{3}$

11. $\frac{-49}{56} = \frac{-49 \div 7}{56 \div 7} = -\frac{7}{8}$

12. $\frac{33}{121} = \frac{33 \div 11}{121 \div 11} = \frac{3}{11}$

13. $\frac{4}{5}$ is in simplest form.

$\frac{20}{25} = \frac{20 \div 5}{25 \div 5} = \frac{4}{5}$

The fractions $\frac{4}{5}$ and $\frac{20}{25}$ are equivalent.

14. $\frac{1}{3}$ is in simplest form.

$\frac{21}{28} = \frac{21 \div 7}{28 \div 7} = \frac{3}{4}$

The fractions $\frac{21}{28}$ and $\frac{1}{3}$ are not equivalent.

15. $\frac{24}{40} = \frac{24 \div 8}{40 \div 8} = \frac{3}{5}$

$\frac{30}{50} = \frac{30 \div 10}{50 \div 10} = \frac{3}{5}$

The fractions $\frac{24}{40}$ and $\frac{30}{50}$ are equivalent.

16. $\frac{30}{60} = \frac{30 \div 30}{60 \div 30} = \frac{1}{2}$

$\frac{27}{54} = \frac{27 \div 27}{54 \div 27} = \frac{1}{2}$

The fractions $\frac{30}{60}$ and $\frac{27}{54}$ are equivalent.

17. $\frac{30}{75} = \frac{30 \div 15}{75 \div 15} = \frac{2}{5}$

$\frac{75}{105} = \frac{75 \div 15}{105 \div 15} = \frac{5}{7}$

The fractions $\frac{30}{75}$ and $\frac{75}{105}$ are not equivalent.

18. $\frac{45}{54} = \frac{45 \div 9}{54 \div 9} = \frac{5}{6}$

$\frac{90}{108} = \frac{90 \div 18}{108 \div 18} = \frac{5}{6}$

The fractions $\frac{45}{54}$ and $\frac{90}{108}$ are equivalent.

Chapter 4, *continued*

19. $\dfrac{54}{96} = \dfrac{54 \div 6}{96 \div 6} = \dfrac{9}{16}$

$\dfrac{144}{256} = \dfrac{144 \div 16}{256 \div 16} = \dfrac{9}{16}$

The fractions $\dfrac{54}{96}$ and $\dfrac{144}{256}$ are equivalent.

20. $\dfrac{84}{112} = \dfrac{84 \div 28}{112 \div 28} = \dfrac{3}{4}$

$\dfrac{168}{192} = \dfrac{168 \div 24}{192 \div 24} = \dfrac{7}{8}$

The fractions $\dfrac{84}{112}$ and $\dfrac{168}{192}$ are not equivalent.

21. C; $\dfrac{14}{21} = \dfrac{14 \div 7}{21 \div 7} = \dfrac{2}{3}$

$\dfrac{12}{18} = \dfrac{12 \div 6}{18 \div 6} = \dfrac{2}{3}$

22. *Sample answer:*

$\dfrac{45}{90} = \dfrac{45 \div 5}{90 \div 5} = \dfrac{9}{18}$

$\dfrac{45}{90} = \dfrac{45 \div 45}{90 \div 45} = \dfrac{1}{2}$

The fractions $\dfrac{9}{18}$ and $\dfrac{1}{2}$ are equivalent to $\dfrac{45}{90}$.

23. *Sample answer:*

$\dfrac{36}{81} = \dfrac{36 \div 9}{81 \div 9} = \dfrac{4}{9}$

$\dfrac{36}{81} = \dfrac{36 \div 3}{81 \div 3} = \dfrac{12}{27}$

The fractions $\dfrac{4}{9}$ and $\dfrac{12}{27}$ are equivalent to $\dfrac{36}{81}$.

24. *Sample answer:*

$\dfrac{24}{60} = \dfrac{24 \div 12}{60 \div 12} = \dfrac{2}{5}$

$\dfrac{24}{60} = \dfrac{24 \times 2}{60 \times 2} = \dfrac{48}{120}$

The fractions $\dfrac{2}{5}$ and $\dfrac{48}{120}$ are equivalent to $\dfrac{24}{60}$.

25. *Sample answer:*

$\dfrac{48}{140} = \dfrac{48 \div 4}{140 \div 4} = \dfrac{12}{35}$

$\dfrac{48}{140} = \dfrac{48 \div 2}{140 \div 2} = \dfrac{24}{70}$

The fractions $\dfrac{12}{35}$ and $\dfrac{24}{70}$ are equivalent to $\dfrac{48}{140}$.

26. $\dfrac{3x}{x^3} = \dfrac{3 \cdot x}{x \cdot x \cdot x}$

$= \dfrac{3 \cdot \cancel{x}^{\,1}}{\cancel{x}_{\,1} \cdot x \cdot x}$

$= \dfrac{3}{x^2}$

When $x = 3$:

$\dfrac{3}{x^2} = \dfrac{3}{3^2} = \dfrac{\cancel{3}^{\,1}}{3 \cdot \cancel{3}_{\,1}} = \dfrac{1}{3}$

27. $\dfrac{2y^2}{-5y} = \dfrac{2 \cdot y \cdot y}{-5 \cdot y}$

$= -\dfrac{2 \cdot \cancel{y}^{\,1} \cdot y}{-5 \cdot \cancel{y}_{\,1}}$

$= \dfrac{2y}{-5}$

When $y = 5$:

$\dfrac{2y}{-5} = \dfrac{2(\cancel{5})^{\,1}}{-\cancel{5}_{\,1}} = -2$

28. $\dfrac{5y}{y^2} = \dfrac{5 \cdot y}{y \cdot y} = \dfrac{5 \cdot \cancel{y}^{\,1}}{\cancel{y}_{\,1} \cdot y} = \dfrac{5}{y}$

When $y = 5$: $\dfrac{5}{y} = \dfrac{5}{5} = 1$

29. $\dfrac{4x^4}{24x^3} = \dfrac{2 \cdot 2 \cdot x \cdot x \cdot x \cdot x}{2 \cdot 2 \cdot 2 \cdot 3 \cdot x \cdot x \cdot x}$

$= \dfrac{\cancel{2}^{\,1} \cdot \cancel{2}^{\,1} \cdot \cancel{x}^{\,1} \cdot \cancel{x}^{\,1} \cdot \cancel{x}^{\,1} \cdot x}{\cancel{2}_{\,1} \cdot \cancel{2}_{\,1} \cdot 2 \cdot 3 \cdot \cancel{x}_{\,1} \cdot \cancel{x}_{\,1} \cdot \cancel{x}_{\,1}}$

$= \dfrac{x}{6}$

When $x = 3$: $\dfrac{x}{6} = \dfrac{\cancel{3}^{\,1}}{\cancel{6}_{\,2}} = \dfrac{1}{2}$

30. $\dfrac{-18x^2y}{24x} = \dfrac{-2 \cdot 3 \cdot 3 \cdot \cancel{x} \cdot x \cdot y}{2 \cdot 2 \cdot 2 \cdot 3 \cdot \cancel{x}} = \dfrac{-3xy}{4}$

When $x = 3$ and $y = 5$:

$\dfrac{-3xy}{4} = \dfrac{-3(3)(5)}{4} = \dfrac{-45}{4}$

31. $\dfrac{35xy^2}{7x^2y^4} = \dfrac{5 \cdot 7 \cdot x \cdot y \cdot y}{7 \cdot x \cdot x \cdot y \cdot y \cdot y \cdot y} = \dfrac{5}{xy^2}$

When $x = 3$ and $y = 5$:

$\dfrac{5}{xy^2} = \dfrac{5}{3(5)^2} = \dfrac{\cancel{5}}{3 \cdot 5 \cdot \cancel{5}} = \dfrac{1}{15}$

32. $\dfrac{6x^3y^2}{21xy^4} = \dfrac{2 \cdot 3 \cdot x \cdot x \cdot x \cdot y \cdot y}{3 \cdot 7 \cdot x \cdot y \cdot y \cdot y \cdot y} = \dfrac{2x^2}{7y^2}$

When $x = 3$ and $y = 5$: $\dfrac{2x^2}{7y^2} = \dfrac{2(3)^2}{7(5)^2} = \dfrac{18}{175}$

33. $\dfrac{-20x^2y}{8x^4y^3} = \dfrac{-2 \cdot 2 \cdot 5 \cdot x \cdot x \cdot y}{2 \cdot 2 \cdot 2 \cdot x \cdot x \cdot x \cdot x \cdot y \cdot y \cdot y} = \dfrac{-5}{2x^2y^2}$

When $x = 3$ and $y = 5$:

$\dfrac{-5}{2x^2y^2} = \dfrac{-5}{2(3)^2(5)^2} = \dfrac{-\cancel{5}}{2 \cdot 3 \cdot 3 \cdot 5 \cdot \cancel{5}} = -\dfrac{1}{90}$

34. D;

$\dfrac{180}{320} = \dfrac{180 \div 20}{320 \div 20} = \dfrac{9}{16}$

$\dfrac{9}{16}$ is in simplest form.

$\dfrac{81}{144} = \dfrac{81 \div 9}{144 \div 9} = \dfrac{9}{16}$

$\dfrac{14}{25}$ is in simplest form.

35. $x \div 14$

$\dfrac{x}{140} = \dfrac{1}{10}$ You divide 140 by 14 to get 10, so divide x by 14 to get 1.

$140 \div 14$

$\dfrac{x}{14} = 1$

$\dfrac{x}{14} \cdot 14 = 1 \cdot 14$

$x = 14$

36. $x \cdot 14$

$$\frac{x}{5} = \frac{42}{70}$$ You multiply 5 by 14 to get 70, so multiply x by 14 to get 42.

$5 \cdot 14$

$14x = 42$

$$\frac{14x}{14} = \frac{42}{14}$$

$x = 3$

37. $8 \cdot 3$

$$\frac{8}{18} = \frac{x}{54}$$ You multiply 18 by 3 to get 54, so multiply 8 by 3 to get x.

$18 \cdot 3$

$24 = x$

38. $36 \div 6$

$$\frac{36}{78} = \frac{x}{13}$$ You divide 78 by 6 to get 13, so divide 36 by 6 to get x.

$88 \div 6$

$36 \div 6 = x$

$6 = x$

39. $\frac{4c}{5a}$ is in simplest form.

$$\frac{4abc}{5ab} = \frac{4 \cdot a \cdot \overset{1}{\cancel{b}} \cdot c}{5 \cdot \cancel{a} \cdot \underset{1}{\cancel{b}}} = \frac{4c}{5}$$

The fractions $\frac{4abc}{5ab}$ and $\frac{4c}{5a}$ are not equivalent.

40. $\frac{3a}{5}$ is in simplest form.

$$\frac{6a^2}{10a} = \frac{2 \cdot 3 \cdot a \cdot a}{2 \cdot 5 \cdot a} = \frac{\overset{1}{\cancel{2}} \cdot 3 \cdot \overset{1}{\cancel{a}} \cdot a}{\underset{1}{\cancel{2}} \cdot 5 \cdot \underset{1}{\cancel{a}}} = \frac{3a}{5}$$

The fractions $\frac{3a}{5}$ and $\frac{6a^2}{10a}$ are equivalent.

41. $\frac{2a}{3b}$ is in simplest form.

$$\frac{10a^2b}{15ab^2} = \frac{2 \cdot 5 \cdot a \cdot a \cdot b}{3 \cdot 5 \cdot a \cdot b \cdot b} = \frac{2 \cdot \overset{1}{\cancel{5}} \cdot \overset{1}{\cancel{a}} \cdot a \cdot \overset{1}{\cancel{b}}}{3 \cdot \underset{1}{\cancel{5}} \cdot \underset{1}{\cancel{a}} \cdot \underset{1}{\cancel{b}} \cdot b} = \frac{2a}{3b}$$

The fractions $\frac{2a}{3b}$ and $\frac{10a^2b}{15a^2b}$ are equivalent.

42. $\frac{7a}{9b}$ is in simplest form.

$$\frac{21a^4b^3}{27a^5b^4} = \frac{\overset{1}{\cancel{3}} \cdot 7 \cdot \overset{1}{\cancel{a}} \cdot \overset{1}{\cancel{a}} \cdot \overset{1}{\cancel{a}} \cdot \overset{1}{\cancel{a}} \cdot \overset{1}{\cancel{b}} \cdot \overset{1}{\cancel{b}} \cdot \overset{1}{\cancel{b}}}{\underset{1}{\cancel{3}} \cdot 3 \cdot 3 \cdot \underset{1}{\cancel{a}} \cdot \underset{1}{\cancel{a}} \cdot \underset{1}{\cancel{a}} \cdot \underset{1}{\cancel{a}} \cdot a \cdot \underset{1}{\cancel{b}} \cdot \underset{1}{\cancel{b}} \cdot \underset{1}{\cancel{b}} \cdot b} = \frac{7}{9ab}$$

The fractions $\frac{7a}{9b}$ and $\frac{21a^4b^3}{27a^5b^4}$ are not equivalent.

43. $\frac{12!}{3! \cdot 4!} = \dfrac{\overset{2}{\cancel{12}} \cdot 11 \cdot 10 \cdot 9 \cdot 8 \cdot 7 \cdot 6 \cdot 5 \cdot \overset{1}{\cancel{4}} \cdot \overset{1}{\cancel{3}} \cdot \overset{1}{\cancel{2}} \cdot \overset{1}{\cancel{1}}}{\underset{1}{\cancel{3}} \cdot \underset{1}{\cancel{2}} \cdot 1 \cdot \underset{1}{\cancel{4}} \cdot \underset{1}{\cancel{3}} \cdot \underset{1}{\cancel{2}} \cdot \underset{1}{\cancel{1}}}$

$= 2 \cdot 11 \cdot 10 \cdot 9 \cdot 8 \cdot 7 \cdot 6 \cdot 5$

$= 3,326,400$

Problem Solving

44. $\frac{9}{50}$

The fraction of states in the Northeast is $\frac{9}{50}$.

45. $\frac{12}{50} = \frac{12 \div 2}{50 \div 2} = \frac{6}{25}$

The fraction of states in the Midwest is $\frac{6}{25}$.

46. $\frac{16}{50} = \frac{16 \div 2}{50 \div 2} = \frac{8}{25}$

The fraction of states in the South is $\frac{8}{25}$.

47. $\frac{13}{50}$

The fraction of states in the West is $\frac{13}{50}$.

48. A;

$$\frac{24 - 18}{24} = \frac{6}{24} = \frac{6 \div 6}{24 \div 6} = \frac{1}{4}$$

49. 3 out of 24 eggs are broken in both cartons.

$$\frac{3}{24} = \frac{3 \div 3}{24 \div 3} = \frac{1}{8}$$

$24 - 3 = 21$ out of the 24 eggs are unbroken in both cartons.

$$\frac{21}{24} = \frac{21 \div 3}{24 \div 3} = \frac{7}{8}$$

So, $\frac{1}{8}$ of the eggs are broken and $\frac{7}{8}$ of the eggs are unbroken.

50. a. $\frac{46}{460} = \frac{46 \div 46}{460 \div 46} = \frac{1}{10}$

The fraction of Peruvian mammals that are threatened is $\frac{1}{10}$.

$\frac{64}{1541}$ is in simplest form.

The fraction of Peruvian birds that are threatened is $\frac{64}{1541}$.

$\frac{9}{360} = \frac{9 \div 9}{360 \div 9} = \frac{1}{40}$

The fraction of Peruvian reptiles that are threatened is $\frac{1}{40}$.

b. Birds: $\frac{64}{1541} \approx \frac{60}{1500} = \frac{1}{25}$

c. Mammals: $\dfrac{46}{460} = \dfrac{1}{10}$

$\dfrac{1}{10} = \dfrac{1 \times 5}{10 \times 5} = \dfrac{5}{50}$ $\dfrac{1}{25} = \dfrac{1 \times 2}{25 \times 2} = \dfrac{2}{50}$

Because $\dfrac{2}{50} < \dfrac{5}{50}$, you know that $\dfrac{1}{25} < \dfrac{1}{10}$. So, the fraction of threatened birds is less than the fraction of threatened mammals.

Reptiles: $\dfrac{9}{360} = \dfrac{1}{40}$

$\dfrac{1}{40} = \dfrac{1 \times 5}{40 \times 5} = \dfrac{5}{200}$ $\dfrac{1}{25} = \dfrac{1 \times 8}{25 \times 8} = \dfrac{8}{200}$

Because $\dfrac{5}{200} < \dfrac{8}{200}$, you know that $\dfrac{1}{40} < \dfrac{1}{25}$. So, the fraction of threatened reptiles is less than the fraction of threatened birds.

The fractions of threatened animals, from least to greatest, are $\dfrac{1}{40}, \dfrac{64}{1541}$, and $\dfrac{1}{10}$.

51. *Sample answer:* 8 students chose to have a car wash and 12 students chose to have a fair. So that leaves 10 of the 30 students who chose to have a dance.

$\dfrac{10}{30} = \dfrac{10 \div 10}{30 \div 10} = \dfrac{1}{3}$

So, $\dfrac{1}{3}$ of the students chose to have a dance.

52. If you divide the numerator and the denominator of a fraction by a common factor, it might not be in simplest form. The fraction will be in simplest form when the common factor is the greatest common factor.

For example: $\dfrac{16}{32} = \dfrac{16 \div 4}{32 \div 4} = \dfrac{4}{8}$

$\dfrac{4}{8}$ is not in simplest form.

$\dfrac{16 \div 16}{32 \div 16} = \dfrac{1}{2}$

$\dfrac{1}{2}$ is in simplest form because the GCF of 16 and 32 is 16.

53. A fraction that has a prime numerator or denominator is not always in simplest form. If the composite number is a multiple of the prime number, the fraction can be simplified. For example, $\dfrac{5}{10}$ has a prime numerator, but 10 is a multiple of 5.

$\dfrac{5}{10} = \dfrac{5 \div 5}{10 \div 5} = \dfrac{1}{2}$

Mixed Review

54. $4a^5 = 2 \cdot 2 \cdot a \cdot a \cdot a \cdot a \cdot a$

$14a^2 = 2 \cdot 7 \cdot a \cdot a$

The GCF of $4a^5$ and $14a^2$ is $2 \cdot a \cdot a$, or $2a^2$.

55. $18s^2t^4 = 2 \cdot 3 \cdot 3 \cdot s \cdot s \cdot t \cdot t \cdot t \cdot t$

$12st = 2 \cdot 2 \cdot 3 \cdot s \cdot t$

The GCF of $18s^2t^4$ and $12st$ is $2 \cdot 3 \cdot s \cdot t$, or $6st$.

56. $3x^3y = 3 \cdot x \cdot x \cdot x \cdot y$

$6x^2y^2 = 2 \cdot 3 \cdot x \cdot x \cdot y \cdot y$

The GCF of $3x^3y$ and $6x^2y^2$ is $3 \cdot x \cdot x \cdot y$, or $3x^2y$.

57. $15a^2b^3 = 3 \cdot 5 \cdot a \cdot a \cdot b \cdot b \cdot b$

$40a^3b^2 = 2 \cdot 2 \cdot 2 \cdot 5 \cdot a \cdot a \cdot a \cdot b \cdot b$

The GCF of $15a^2b^3$ and $40a^3b^2$ is $5 \cdot a \cdot a \cdot b \cdot b$, or $5a^2b^2$.

58.   **59.**

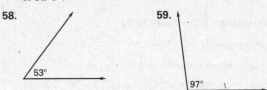

60.

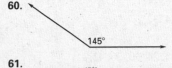

61.

62. B;

$-12 + 46 - 18 = -12 + (-18) + 46$
$= -30 + 46$
$= 16$

Lesson 4.4

4.4 Guided Practice (p. 193)

1. Use prime factorization.

3 and 7 are primes, so the LCM of 3 and 7 is the product of 3 and 7.

$3 \cdot 7 = 21$

In 21 days, the veterinarian will be on call on Saturday.

2. $6 = 2 \cdot 3$

$15 = 3 \cdot 5$

The LCM of 6 and 15 is $2 \cdot 3 \cdot 5$, or 30.

3. $4 = 2^2$

$20 = 2^2 \cdot 5$

The LCM of 4 and 20 is $2^2 \cdot 5$, or 20.

4. $12 = 2^2 \cdot 3$

$28 = 2^2 \cdot 7$

The LCM of 12 and 28 is $2^2 \cdot 3 \cdot 7$, or 84.

5. $24 = 2^3 \cdot 3$

$36 = 2^2 \cdot 3^2$

$72 = 2^3 \cdot 3^2$

The LCM or 24, 36, and 72 is $2^3 \cdot 3^2$, or 72.

6. $8x^3 = 2^3 \cdot x^3$

$20x^7 = 2^2 \cdot 5 \cdot x^7$

The LCM of $8x^3$ and $20x^7$ is $2^3 \cdot 5 \cdot x^7$, or $40x^7$.

7. $12y^4 = 2^2 \cdot 3 \cdot y^4$

$36y^8 = 2^2 \cdot 3^2 \cdot y^8$

The LCM of $12y^4$ and $36y^8$ is $2^2 \cdot 3^2 \cdot y^8$, or $36y^8$.

Chapter 4, *continued*

8. $4ab^2 = 2^2 \cdot a \cdot b^2$

$10a^2b = 2 \cdot 5 \cdot a^2 \cdot b$

The LCM of $4ab^2$ and $10a^2b$ is $2^2 \cdot 5 \cdot a^2 \cdot b^2$, or $20a^2b^2$.

9. $6m^3np^2 = 2 \cdot 3 \cdot m^3 \cdot n \cdot p^2$

$8mp^3 = 2^3 \cdot m \cdot p^3$

The LCM of $6m^3np^2$ and $8mp^3$ is $2^3 \cdot 3 \cdot m^3 \cdot n \cdot p^3$, or $24m^3np^3$.

4.4 Exercises (pp. 194–196)

Skill Practice

1. A *common multiple* of 6 and 9 is 54.

2. The *least common multiple* of 6 and 9 is 18.

3. Multiples of 6: 6, 12, 18, **24**, . . .

Multiples of 8: 8, 16, **24**, 32, . . .

The LCM of 6 and 8 is 24.

4. Multiples of 6: 6, 12, 18, 24, 30, 36, **42**, . . .

Multiples of 21: 21, **42**, . . .

The LCM of 6 and 21 is 42.

5. Multiples of 8: 8, 16, 24, 32, **40**, . . .

Multiples of 10: 10, 20, 30, **40**, . . .

The LCM of 8 and 10 is 40.

6. Multiples of 10: 10, 20, **30**, . . .

Multiples of 15: 15, **30**, . . .

The LCM of 10 and 15 is 30.

7. Multiples of 18: 18, **36**, . . .

Multiples of 36: **36**, 72, . . .

The LCM of 18 and 36 is 36.

8. Multiples of 45: 45, 90, 135, 180, **225**, . . .

Multiples of 75: 75, 150, **225**, . . .

The LCM of 45 and 75 is 225.

9. Multiples of 6: 6, 12, 18, **24**, . . .

Multiples of 8: 8, 16, **24**, . . .

Multiples of 12: 12, **24**, . . .

The LCM of 6, 8, and 12 is 24.

10. Multiples of 3: 3, 6, 9, 12, 15, 18, 21, 24, 27, **30**, . . .

Multiples of 6: 6, 12, 18, 24, **30**, . . .

Multiples of 15: 15, **30**, . . .

The LCM of 3, 6, and 15 is 30.

11. $14 = 2 \cdot 7$

$21 = 3 \cdot 7$

The LCM of 14 and 21 is $2 \cdot 3 \cdot 7$, or 42.

12. $7 = 7$

$56 = 2^3 \cdot 7$

The LCM of 7 and 56 is $2^3 \cdot 7$, or 56.

13. $15 = 3 \cdot 5$

$55 = 5 \cdot 11$

The LCM of 15 and 55 is $3 \cdot 5 \cdot 11$, or 165.

14. $36 = 2^2 \cdot 3^2$

$90 = 2 \cdot 3^2 \cdot 5$

The LCM of 36 and 90 is $2^2 \cdot 3^2 \cdot 5$, or 180.

15. $42 = 2 \cdot 3 \cdot 7$

$105 = 3 \cdot 5 \cdot 7$

The LCM of 42 and 105 is $2 \cdot 3 \cdot 5 \cdot 7$, or 210.

16. $90 = 2 \cdot 3^2 \cdot 5$

$108 = 2^2 \cdot 3^3$

The LCM of 90 and 108 is $2^2 \cdot 3^3 \cdot 5$, or 540.

17. $10 = 2 \cdot 5$

$12 = 2^2 \cdot 3$

$14 = 2 \cdot 7$

The LCM of 10, 12, and 14 is $2^2 \cdot 3 \cdot 5 \cdot 7$, or 420.

18. $16 = 2^4$

$20 = 2^2 \cdot 5$

$40 = 2^3 \cdot 5$

The LCM of 18, 20, and 40 is $2^4 \cdot 5$, or 80.

19. The error is that the LCM is found by multiplying the highest power of each prime number in the prime factorizations. The correct LCM is $2^3 \cdot 3$, or 24.

20–27. Methods and explanations will vary.

20. $17 = 17$

$57 = 3 \cdot 19$

The LCM of 17 and 57 is $3 \cdot 17 \cdot 19$, or 969.

21. $125 = 5^3$

$500 = 2^2 \cdot 5^3$

The LCM of 125 and 500 is $2^2 \cdot 5^3$, or 500.

22. $8 = 2^3$

$16 = 2^4$

$32 = 2^5$

The LCM of 8, 16, and 32 is 2^5, or 32.

23. $6 = 2 \cdot 3$

$15 = 3 \cdot 5$

$45 = 3^2 \cdot 5$

The LCM of 6, 15, and 45 is $2 \cdot 3^2 \cdot 5$, or 90.

24. $30 = 2 \cdot 3 \cdot 5$

$75 = 3 \cdot 5^2$

$100 = 2^2 \cdot 5^2$

The LCM of 30, 75, and 100 is $2^2 \cdot 3 \cdot 5^2$, or 300.

25. $36 = 2^2 \cdot 3^2$

$54 = 2 \cdot 3^3$

$72 = 2^3 \cdot 3^2$

The LCM of 36, 54, and 76 is $2^3 \cdot 3^3$, or 216.

26. $10 = 2 \cdot 5$

    $12 = 2^2 \cdot 3$

    $30 = 2 \cdot 3 \cdot 5$

    $60 = 2^2 \cdot 3 \cdot 5$

    The LCM of 10, 12, 30, and 60 is $2^2 \cdot 3 \cdot 5$, or 60.

27. $21 = 3 \cdot 7$

    $42 = 2 \cdot 3 \cdot 7$

    $63 = 3^2 \cdot 7$

    $105 = 3 \cdot 5 \cdot 7$

    The LCM of 21, 42, 63, and 105 is $2 \cdot 3^2 \cdot 5 \cdot 7$, or 630.

28. $4x = 2^2 \cdot x$

    $16x^3 = 2^4 \cdot x^3$

    The LCM of $4x$ and $16x^3$ is $2^4 \cdot x^3$, or $16x^3$.

29. $9y^4 = 3^2 \cdot y^4$

    $12y = 2^2 \cdot 3 \cdot y$

    The LCM of $9y^4$ and $12y$ is $2^2 \cdot 3^2 \cdot y^4$, or $36y^4$.

30. $24t = 2^3 \cdot 3 \cdot t$

    $60st = 2^2 \cdot 3 \cdot 5 \cdot s \cdot t$

    The LCM of $24t$ and $60st$ is $2^3 \cdot 3 \cdot 5 \cdot s \cdot t$, or $120st$.

31. $5ab = 5 \cdot a \cdot b$

    $7ab^2 = 7 \cdot a \cdot b^2$

    The LCM of $5ab$ and $7ab^2$ is $5 \cdot 7 \cdot a \cdot b^2$, or $35ab^2$.

32. $7s^3t = 7 \cdot s^3 \cdot t$

    $49st^2 = 7^2 \cdot s \cdot t^2$

    The LCM of $7s^3t$ and $49st^2$ is $7^2 \cdot s^3 \cdot t^2$, or $49s^3t^2$.

33. $4x^3y^3 = 2^2 \cdot x^3 \cdot y^3$

    $18xy^5 = 2 \cdot 3^2 \cdot x \cdot y^5$

    The LCM of $4x^3y^3$ and $18xy^5$ is $2^2 \cdot 3^2 \cdot x^3 \cdot y^5$, or $36x^3y^5$.

34. $18x^2y = 2 \cdot 3^2 \cdot x^2 \cdot y$

    $24x^4y = 2^3 \cdot 3 \cdot x^4 \cdot y$

    $30y^7 = 2 \cdot 3 \cdot 5 \cdot y^7$

    The LCM of $18x^2y$, $24x^4y$, and $30y^7$ is $2^3 \cdot 3^2 \cdot 5 \cdot x^4 \cdot y^7$, or $360x^4y^7$.

35. $24c^2d^3 = 2^3 \cdot 3 \cdot c^2 \cdot d^3$

    $30c^3d^2 = 2 \cdot 3 \cdot 5 \cdot c^3 \cdot d^2$

    $60c^2d^6 = 2^2 \cdot 3 \cdot 5 \cdot c^2 \cdot d^6$

    The LCM of $24c^2d^3$, $30c^3d^2$, and $60c^2d^6$ is $2^3 \cdot 3 \cdot 5 \cdot c^3 \cdot d^6$, or $120c^3d^6$.

36. $33g^4hk^3 = 3 \cdot 11 \cdot g^4 \cdot h \cdot k^3$

    $36g^3h^7k = 2^2 \cdot 3^2 \cdot g^3 \cdot h^7 \cdot k$

    $45gh^5k^3 = 3^2 \cdot 5 \cdot g \cdot h^5 \cdot k$

    The LCM of $33g^4hk^3$, $36g^3h^7k$, and $45gh^5k^3$ is $2^2 \cdot 3^2 \cdot 5 \cdot 11 \cdot g^4 \cdot h^7 \cdot k^3$, or $1980g^4h^7k^3$.

37. B;

    The LCM of two numbers is greater than or equal to both numbers.

38. *Sample answer:*

    15 and 30

    15 is a factor of 30.

    So their LCM is 30, the greater of the two numbers.

39. *Sample answer:*

    35 and 70

    35 is a factor of 70.

    So their LCM is 70, the greater of the two numbers.

40. *Sample answer:*

    5 and 105

    5 is a factor of 105.

    So their LCM is 105, the greater of the two numbers.

41. *Sample answer:*

    5 and 150

    5 is a factor of 150.

    So their LCM is 150, the greater of the two numbers.

42. $105 = 3 \cdot 5 \cdot 7$

    $15 = 3 \cdot 5$

    The other number must contain a factor of 7 and may or may not include the other factors 3 and 5.

    The least possible number for which the LCM of the number and 15 is 105 is 7.

    The greatest possible number for which the LCM of the number and 15 is 105 is $3 \cdot 5 \cdot 7 = 105$.

43. The GCF of two different numbers cannot be the same as the LCM of those numbers. The GCF is smaller than at least one of the numbers because it is a factor of both numbers. The LCM is bigger than at least one of the numbers because both numbers are factors of it.

Problem Solving

44. There are 5 days in a school week, and you have a three-day rotation. The LCM of 3 and 5 is 15, so in 15 school days, you will have math class the last period on Friday.

45. $45 = 3^2 \cdot 5$

    $60 = 2^2 \cdot 3 \cdot 5$

    The LCM of 45 and 60 is $2^2 \cdot 3^2 \cdot 5$, or 180. In 180 seconds, both traffic lights will turn red at the same time.

46. Multiples of 2: 2, 4, 6, 8, 10, 12, 14, 16, 18, 20, 22, 24, 26, 28, **30**, . . .

    Multiples of 5: 5, 10, 15, 20, 25, **30**, . . .

    Multiples of 6: 6, 12, 18, 24, **30**, . . .

    The LCM of 2, 5, and 6 is 30. So, the least number of students that a teacher can have in class is 30.

47. You cannot find the *greatest* common multiple of two numbers because there can always be a higher multiple found by multiplying the highest multiple you can think of by any other number. In other words, there are infinitely many multiples of each number.

Chapter 4, *continued*

48. $12 = 2^2 \cdot 3$

$14 = 2 \cdot 7$

The LCM of 12 and 14 is $2^2 \cdot 3 \cdot 7$, or 84. Zoe can make $84 \div 12$, or 7 batches of lasagna without having any noodles left over.

49. When finding the LCM of two numbers, and one number is a factor of the other number, there is a shortcut. The LCM will be the greater number because it is a multiple of both numbers.

50. $24 = 2^3 \cdot 3$

$36 = 2^2 \cdot 3^2$

$20 = 2^2 \cdot 5$

The LCM of 24, 36, and 20 is $2^3 \cdot 3^2 \cdot 5$, or 360. So, you can make 360 sets.

Spoons: $360 \div 24 = 15$

Forks: $360 \div 36 = 10$

Knives: $360 \div 20 = 18$

There are 15 packs of spoons, 10 packs of forks, and 18 packs of knives.

51. *Sample explanation:* The color repeats every fourth figure, and the orientation repeats every fifth figure.

$4 = 2^2$

$5 = 5$

The LCM of 4 and 5 is 20, and 20 figures after Figure 1 is Figure 21.

52. B;

Multiples of 4: 4, 8, **12**, 16, 20, **24**, 28, 32, **36**, 40; . . .

Multiples of 3: 3, 6, 9, **12**, 15, 18, 21, **24**, 27, 30, 33, **36**, 39, . . .

Becky and Tonya will both be at the starting point 12 minutes after 4:00 P.M., 24 minutes after 4:00 P.M., and 36 minutes after 4:00 P.M.

Becky and Tonya will not both be at the starting point 18 minutes after 4:00 P.M., at 4:18 P.M.

53. a. $45 = 3^2 \cdot 5$

$40 = 2^3 \cdot 5$

The LCM of 40 and 45 is $2^3 \cdot 3^2 \cdot 5$, or 360. Martin and Will will both be at the starting place in 360 seconds or 6 minutes.

b. In 1 hour or 3600 seconds, Kyle swims 75 lengths, so he can swim 1 length in $3600 \div 75 = 48$ seconds.

Kyle will end up at the starting place at the same time as Martin and Will if 360 is a multiple of 48.

$$
\begin{array}{r}
7.5 \\
48\overline{)360.0} \\
\underline{336} \\
240 \\
\underline{240} \\
0
\end{array}
\qquad 360 \text{ is not a multiple of } 48.
$$

So, Kyle will not end up at the starting place in 360 seconds.

c. The LCM of 45, 40, and 48 is 720. The three boys will all be at the start at intervals of 720 seconds. In 720 seconds, Kyle can swim $720 \div 48 = 15$ lengths. So, he will be at the start with the other boys after each of 3 sets of 15 lengths.

Mixed Review

54. $54 = 2 \cdot 3^3$

$81 = 3^4$

The GCF of 54 and 81 is 3^3, or 27.

55. $18 = 2 \cdot 3^2$

$125 = 5^3$

The GCF of 18 and 125 is 1.

56. $121 = 11 \cdot 11$

$187 = 11 \cdot 17$

The GCF of 121 and 187 is 11.

57. $64 = 2^6$

$144 = 2^4 \cdot 3^2$

The GCF of 64 and 144 is 2^4, or 16.

58. $7x + 9 + 12x + 11 + 2y = 19x + 2y + 20$

59. $18x - 2 + 5y + 2 + 3x = 21x + 5y$

60. $d = r \cdot t = 6 \cdot \frac{1}{2} = 3$

Rebecca ran 3 miles.

61. C;

Quiz 4.1–4.4 (p. 196)

1.

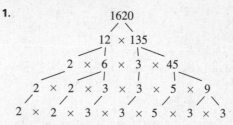

The prime factorization of 1620 is $2^2 \cdot 3^4 \cdot 5$.

2. $24 = 2^3 \cdot 3$

$90 = 2 \cdot 3^2 \cdot 5$

The GCF of 24 and 90 is $2 \cdot 3$, or 6.

3. $36 = 2^2 \cdot 3^2$

$72 = 2^3 \cdot 3^2$

$108 = 2^2 \cdot 3^3$

The GCF of 36, 72, and 108 is $2^2 \cdot 3^2$, or 36.

4. $20c^3 = 2^2 \cdot 5 \cdot c^3$

$48c^2 = 2^4 \cdot 3 \cdot c^2$

The GCF of $20c^3$ and $48c^2$ is $2^2 \cdot c^2$, or $4c^2$.

Chapter 4, *continued*

5. $64m^2 = 2^6 \cdot m^2$

$80m^5 = 2^4 \cdot 5 \cdot m^5$

The GCF of $64m^2$ and $80m^5$ is $2^4 \cdot m^2$, or $16m^2$.

6. $88 = 2^3 \cdot 11$

$99 = 3^2 \cdot 11$

The LCM of 88 and 99 is $2^3 \cdot 3^2 \cdot 11$, or 792.

7. $36 = 2^2 \cdot 3^2$

$96 = 2^5 \cdot 3$

The LCM of 36 and 96 is $2^5 \cdot 3^2$, or 288.

8. $7xy = 7 \cdot x \cdot y$

$21y^3 = 3 \cdot 7 \cdot y^3$

The LCM of $7xy$ and $21y^3$ is $3 \cdot 7 \cdot x \cdot y^3$, or $21xy^3$.

9. $6ab^2 = 2 \cdot 3 \cdot a \cdot b^2$

$30ab = 2 \cdot 3 \cdot 5 \cdot a \cdot b$

The LCM of $6ab^2$ and $30ab$ is $2 \cdot 3 \cdot 5 \cdot a \cdot b^2$, or $30ab^2$.

10. $\dfrac{9}{27} = \dfrac{9 \div 9}{27 \div 9} = \dfrac{1}{3}$

$\dfrac{60}{180} = \dfrac{60 \div 60}{180 \div 60} = \dfrac{1}{3}$

The fractions $\dfrac{9}{27}$ and $\dfrac{60}{180}$ are equivalent.

11. $\dfrac{39}{91} = \dfrac{39 \div 13}{91 \div 13} = \dfrac{3}{7}$

$\dfrac{42}{56} = \dfrac{42 \div 14}{56 \div 14} = \dfrac{3}{4}$

The fractions $\dfrac{39}{91}$ and $\dfrac{42}{56}$ are not equivalent.

12. $\dfrac{40}{48} = \dfrac{40 \div 8}{48 \div 8} = \dfrac{5}{6}$

$\dfrac{70}{84} = \dfrac{70 \div 14}{84 \div 14} = \dfrac{5}{6}$

The fractions $\dfrac{40}{48}$ and $\dfrac{70}{84}$ are equivalent.

13. $\dfrac{108}{120} = \dfrac{108 \div 12}{120 \div 12} = \dfrac{9}{10}$

$\dfrac{189}{210} = \dfrac{189 \div 21}{210 \div 21} = \dfrac{9}{10}$

The fractions $\dfrac{108}{120}$ and $\dfrac{189}{210}$ are equivalent.

14. $10 = 2 \cdot 5$

$25 = 5^2$

The LCM of 10 and 25 is $2 \cdot 5^2$, or 50. Every 50th customer will receive both a coupon and a gift, or customers numbered 50, 100, 150, and 200.

Mixed Review of Problem Solving (p. 197)

1. $\dfrac{2}{5} \cdot 500 = 200$ girls

The greatest number of girls at the assembly is 200.

$\dfrac{3}{5} \cdot 400 = 240$ boys

The least number of boys at the assembly is 240.

2. a. Factors of 35: 1, 5, 7, 35

Factors of 36: 1, 2, 3, 4, 6, 9, 12, 18, 36

Factors of 37: 1, 37

Factors of 38: 1, 2, 19, 38

Factors of 39: 1, 3, 13, 39

Factors of 40: 1, 2, 4, 5, 8, 10, 20, 40

b. The study could have 36 people, 9 groups of 4 or 40 people, 8 groups of 5 or 10 groups of 4.

There is more than 1 correct answer.

3. a. If she starts tennis on the 1st Saturday, they will conflict on the 4th Saturday. If she starts tennis on the 2nd Saturday, they will conflict on the 8th Saturday. If she starts tennis on the 3rd Saturday, they will conflict on the 12th Saturday.

She should start playing tennis on the third Saturday after her first visit to her aunt.

b. The LCM of 3 and 4 is 12. The first conflict will occur in 12 weeks.

c. The conflicts will occur 12 weeks after the other conflicts, because the LCM of 3 and 4 is 12.

4. Multiples of 8: 8, 16, 24, 32, 40, 48, 56, 64, **72**, . . .

Multiples of 6: 6, 12, 18, 24, 30, 36, 42, 48, 54, 60, 66, **72**, . . .

The least number of people who could have attended is 72.

5. a. $365 + 363 + 18 + 9 + 9 + 1 = 765$

The total number of jewels in the Orb of 1661 is 765.

b. $\dfrac{9}{765} = \dfrac{9 \div 9}{765 \div 9} = \dfrac{1}{85}$

$\dfrac{1}{85}$ of the jewels are emeralds.

c. No; *Sample answer:* $\dfrac{1}{85}$ of the jewels are emeralds, so $\dfrac{84}{85}$ of the jewels are not emeralds. $\dfrac{3}{4}$, which is 75%, is not a good estimate of $\dfrac{84}{85}$, which is about 99%.

6. Write 50 as a product of two numbers in all possible ways.

1×50 $\qquad\qquad$ 2×25 $\qquad\qquad$ 5×10

The rectangular pattern can be arranged in rows of 1, 2, 5, 10, 25, or 50.

Sample answer: They could be arranged in 4 rows of length 13, 12, 13, 12.

7. $56 = 2^3 \cdot 7$

$84 = 2^2 \cdot 3 \cdot 7$

The GCF is $2^2 \cdot 7$, or 28.

The wood width can be divided into $56 \div 28 = 2$ identical parts. The wood length can be divided into $84 \div 28 = 3$ identical parts. So, it can be divided into $2 \times 3 = 6$ identical squares.

Chapter 4, *continued*

4.5 Guided Practice (pp. 198–199)

1. $\frac{2}{3} = \frac{2 \cdot 8}{3 \cdot 8} = \frac{16}{24}$

   $\frac{5}{8} = \frac{5 \cdot 3}{8 \cdot 3} = \frac{15}{24}$

   Because $\frac{16}{24} > \frac{15}{24}$, you can write $\frac{2}{3} > \frac{5}{8}$.

2. $\frac{2}{4} = \frac{2 \cdot 5}{4 \cdot 5} = \frac{10}{20}$

   Because $\frac{10}{20} < \frac{15}{20}$, you can write $\frac{2}{4} < \frac{15}{20}$.

3. $\frac{3}{10} = \frac{3 \cdot 2}{10 \cdot 2} = \frac{6}{20}$

   $\frac{2}{4} = \frac{2 \cdot 5}{4 \cdot 5} = \frac{10}{20}$

   Because $\frac{6}{20} < \frac{10}{20}$, you can write $\frac{3}{10} < \frac{2}{4}$.

4. $\frac{9}{16} = \frac{9 \cdot 9}{16 \cdot 9} = \frac{81}{144}$

   $\frac{11}{18} = \frac{11 \cdot 8}{18 \cdot 8} = \frac{88}{144}$

   Because $\frac{81}{144} < \frac{88}{144}$, you can write $\frac{9}{16} < \frac{11}{18}$.

5. $\frac{16}{5} = \frac{16 \cdot 3}{5 \cdot 3} = \frac{48}{15}$

   $3\frac{1}{3} = \frac{3 \cdot 3 + 1}{3} = \frac{10}{3} = \frac{10 \cdot 5}{3 \cdot 5} = \frac{50}{15}$

   Because $\frac{48}{15} < \frac{50}{15}$, you can write $\frac{16}{5} < 3\frac{1}{3}$.

6. $1\frac{4}{5} = \frac{5 \cdot 1 + 4}{5} = \frac{9}{5} = \frac{9 \cdot 12}{5 \cdot 12} = \frac{108}{60}$

   $\frac{21 \cdot 5}{12 \cdot 5} = \frac{105}{60}$

   Because $\frac{108}{60} > \frac{105}{60}$, you can write $1\frac{4}{5} > \frac{21}{12}$.

7. $2\frac{2}{3} = \frac{2 \cdot 3 + 2}{3} = \frac{8}{3} = \frac{8 \cdot 2}{3 \cdot 2} = \frac{16}{6}$

   $4\frac{5}{6} = \frac{4 \cdot 6 + 5}{6} = \frac{29}{6}$

   Because $\frac{16}{6} < \frac{29}{6}$, you can write $2\frac{2}{3} < 4\frac{5}{6}$.

8. $2\frac{7}{9} = \frac{9 \cdot 2 + 7}{9} = \frac{25}{9} = \frac{25 \cdot 4}{9 \cdot 4} = \frac{100}{36}$

   $2\frac{5}{12} = \frac{12 \cdot 2 + 5}{12} = \frac{29}{12} = \frac{29 \cdot 3}{12 \cdot 3} = \frac{87}{36}$

   $\frac{11}{4} = \frac{11 \cdot 9}{4 \cdot 9} = \frac{99}{36}$

   $87 < 99$, and $99 < 100$, so $\frac{87}{36} < \frac{99}{36}$ and $\frac{99}{36} < \frac{100}{36}$.

   From least to greatest, the numbers are $2\frac{5}{12}$, $\frac{11}{4}$, and $2\frac{7}{9}$.

4.5 Exercises (pp. 200–201)

Skill Practice

1. The least common denominator of two fractions is the *least common multiple* of their denominators.

2. Rewrite each fraction using the LCD and then compare the numerators.

3. The least common denominator of $\frac{1}{2}$ and $\frac{2}{3}$ is $2 \cdot 3$, or 6.

4. The least common denominator of $\frac{3}{4}$ and $\frac{7}{20}$ is $2^2 \cdot 5$, or 20.

5. The least common denominator of $\frac{11}{24}$ and $\frac{5}{6}$ is $2^3 \cdot 3$, or 24.

6. The least common denominator of $\frac{5}{12}$ and $\frac{7}{18}$ is $2^2 \cdot 3^2$, or 36.

7. $\frac{5}{9} = \frac{5 \cdot 2}{9 \cdot 2} = \frac{10}{18}$

   Because $\frac{7}{18} < \frac{10}{18}$, you can write $\frac{7}{18} < \frac{5}{9}$.

8. $\frac{3}{4} = \frac{3 \cdot 8}{4 \cdot 8} = \frac{24}{32}$

   Because $\frac{24}{32} = \frac{24}{32}$, you can write $\frac{24}{32} = \frac{3}{4}$.

9. $\frac{5}{8} = \frac{5 \cdot 2}{8 \cdot 2} = \frac{10}{16}$

   Because $\frac{10}{16} > \frac{9}{16}$, you can write $\frac{5}{8} > \frac{9}{16}$.

10. $4\frac{5}{12} = \frac{12 \cdot 4 + 5}{12} = \frac{53}{12} = \frac{53 \cdot 3}{12 \cdot 3} = \frac{159}{36}$

    Because $\frac{165}{36} > \frac{159}{36}$, you can write $\frac{165}{36} > 4\frac{5}{12}$.

11. $2\frac{4}{5} = \frac{5 \cdot 2 + 4}{5} = \frac{14}{5} = \frac{14 \cdot 3}{5 \cdot 3} = \frac{42}{15}$

    $\frac{7}{3} = \frac{7 \cdot 5}{3 \cdot 5} = \frac{35}{15}$

    Because $\frac{42}{15} > \frac{35}{15}$, you can write $2\frac{4}{5} > \frac{7}{3}$.

12. $\frac{31}{6} = \frac{31 \cdot 2}{6 \cdot 2} = \frac{62}{12}$

    $5\frac{2}{12} = \frac{5 \cdot 12 + 2}{12} = \frac{62}{12}$

    Because $\frac{62}{12} = \frac{62}{12}$, you can write $\frac{31}{6} = 5\frac{2}{12}$.

13. $3\frac{1}{4} = \frac{3 \cdot 4 + 1}{4} = \frac{13}{4} = \frac{13 \cdot 7}{4 \cdot 7} = \frac{91}{28}$

    $\frac{13 \cdot 2}{14 \cdot 2} = \frac{26}{28}$

    Because $\frac{91}{28} > \frac{26}{28}$, you can write $3\frac{1}{4} > \frac{13}{14}$.

14. $\frac{5 \cdot 8}{9 \cdot 8} = \frac{40}{72}$

    $\frac{16 \cdot 3}{24 \cdot 3} = \frac{48}{72}$

    Because $\frac{40}{72} < \frac{48}{72}$, you can write $\frac{5}{9} < \frac{16}{24}$.

15. The error is that the student compared numerators before the fractions were rewritten using the LCD.

$$\frac{3 \cdot 7}{5 \cdot 7} = \frac{21}{35} \qquad \frac{4 \cdot 5}{7 \cdot 5} = \frac{20}{35}$$

Because $21 > 20$, $\frac{3}{5} > \frac{4}{7}$.

16. $\frac{1}{2} = \frac{1 \cdot 8}{2 \cdot 8} = \frac{8}{16}$

$\frac{1}{8} = \frac{1 \cdot 2}{8 \cdot 2} = \frac{2}{16}$

$\frac{3}{4} = \frac{3 \cdot 4}{4 \cdot 4} = \frac{12}{16}$

$2 < 5$, $5 < 8$, and $8 < 12$, so $\frac{2}{16} < \frac{5}{16}$, $\frac{5}{16} < \frac{8}{16}$, and $\frac{8}{16} < \frac{12}{16}$.

From least to greatest, the numbers are $\frac{1}{8}$, $\frac{5}{16}$, $\frac{1}{2}$, and $\frac{3}{4}$.

17. $1\frac{1}{2} = \frac{2 \cdot 1 + 1}{2} = \frac{3}{2} = \frac{3 \cdot 6}{2 \cdot 6} = \frac{18}{12}$

$\frac{5}{4} = \frac{5 \cdot 3}{4 \cdot 3} = \frac{15}{12}$

$\frac{11}{6} = \frac{11 \cdot 2}{6 \cdot 2} = \frac{22}{12}$

$15 < 18$ and $18 < 22$, so $\frac{15}{12} < \frac{18}{12}$ and $\frac{18}{12} < \frac{22}{12}$.

From least to greatest, the numbers are $\frac{5}{4}$, $1\frac{1}{2}$, and $\frac{11}{6}$.

18. $\frac{5}{3} = \frac{5 \cdot 80}{3 \cdot 80} = \frac{400}{240}$

$\frac{35}{15} = \frac{35 \cdot 16}{15 \cdot 16} = \frac{560}{240}$

$2\frac{2}{5} = \frac{5 \cdot 2 + 2}{5} = \frac{12}{5} = \frac{12 \cdot 48}{5 \cdot 48} = \frac{576}{240}$

$\frac{15}{16} = \frac{15 \cdot 15}{16 \cdot 15} = \frac{225}{240}$

$225 < 400$, $400 < 560$, and $560 < 576$,

so $\frac{225}{240} < \frac{400}{240}$, $\frac{400}{240} < \frac{560}{240}$, and $\frac{560}{240} < \frac{576}{240}$.

From least to greatest, the numbers are $\frac{15}{16}$, $\frac{5}{3}$, $\frac{35}{15}$, and $2\frac{2}{5}$.

19. $\frac{3}{4} = \frac{3 \cdot 9}{4 \cdot 9} = \frac{27}{36}$

$\frac{5}{9} = \frac{5 \cdot 4}{9 \cdot 4} = \frac{20}{36}$

$1\frac{1}{3} = \frac{1 \cdot 3 + 1}{3} = \frac{4}{3} = \frac{4 \cdot 12}{3 \cdot 12} = \frac{48}{36}$

$20 < 27$ and $27 < 48$, so $\frac{20}{36} < \frac{27}{36}$ and $\frac{27}{36} < \frac{48}{36}$.

From least to greatest, the numbers are $\frac{5}{9}$, $\frac{3}{4}$, and $1\frac{1}{3}$.

20. $\frac{19}{6} = \frac{19 \cdot 2}{6 \cdot 2} = \frac{38}{12}$

$3\frac{1}{2} = \frac{3 \cdot 2 + 1}{2} = \frac{7}{2} = \frac{7 \cdot 6}{2 \cdot 6} = \frac{42}{12}$

$\frac{11}{4} = \frac{11 \cdot 3}{4 \cdot 3} = \frac{33}{12}$

$33 < 38$ and $38 < 42$, so $\frac{33}{12} < \frac{38}{12}$ and $\frac{38}{12} < \frac{42}{12}$.

From least to greatest, the numbers are $\frac{11}{4}$, $\frac{19}{6}$, and $3\frac{1}{2}$.

21. $1\frac{3}{5} = \frac{1 \cdot 5 + 3}{5} = \frac{8}{5} = \frac{8 \cdot 12}{5 \cdot 12} = \frac{96}{60}$

$\frac{7}{3} = \frac{7 \cdot 20}{3 \cdot 20} = \frac{140}{60}$

$2\frac{1}{4} = \frac{2 \cdot 4 + 1}{4} = \frac{9}{4} = \frac{9 \cdot 15}{4 \cdot 15} = \frac{135}{60}$

$\frac{19}{12} = \frac{19 \cdot 5}{12 \cdot 5} = \frac{95}{60}$

$95 < 96$, $96 < 135$, and $135 < 140$, so $\frac{95}{60} < \frac{96}{60}$, $\frac{96}{60} < \frac{135}{60}$,

and $\frac{135}{60} < \frac{140}{60}$.

From least to greatest, the numbers are $\frac{19}{12}$, $1\frac{3}{5}$, $2\frac{1}{4}$, and $\frac{7}{3}$.

22. $\frac{15}{4} = \frac{15 \cdot 21}{4 \cdot 21} = \frac{315}{84}$

$3\frac{2}{3} = \frac{3 \cdot 3 + 2}{3} = \frac{11}{3} = \frac{11 \cdot 28}{3 \cdot 28} = \frac{308}{84}$

$\frac{25}{7} = \frac{25 \cdot 12}{7 \cdot 12} = \frac{300}{84}$

$300 < 308$ and $308 < 315$, so $\frac{300}{84} < \frac{308}{84}$ and $\frac{308}{84} < \frac{315}{84}$.

From least to greatest, the numbers are $\frac{25}{7}$, $3\frac{2}{3}$, and $\frac{15}{4}$.

23. $\frac{34}{3} = \frac{34 \cdot 4}{3 \cdot 4} = \frac{136}{12}$

$11\frac{7}{12} = \frac{11 \cdot 12 + 7}{12} = \frac{139}{12}$

$\frac{47}{4} = \frac{47 \cdot 3}{4 \cdot 3} = \frac{141}{12}$

$136 < 139$ and $139 < 141$, so $\frac{136}{12} < \frac{139}{12}$ and $\frac{139}{12} < \frac{141}{12}$.

From least to greatest, the numbers are $\frac{34}{3}$, $11\frac{7}{12}$, and $\frac{47}{4}$.

24. B;

$\frac{4}{18} = \frac{4 \cdot 15}{18 \cdot 15} = \frac{60}{270}$

$\frac{9}{15} = \frac{9 \cdot 18}{15 \cdot 18} = \frac{162}{270}$

$\frac{18}{27} = \frac{18 \cdot 10}{27 \cdot 10} = \frac{180}{270}$

25. $\frac{25}{50} = \frac{1}{2}$

$\frac{37}{74} = \frac{1}{2}$

Because both fractions are equivalent to $\frac{1}{2}$, $\frac{25}{50} = \frac{37}{74}$.

26. $\dfrac{17}{30} > \dfrac{1}{2}$

$\dfrac{10}{33} < \dfrac{1}{2}$

Because $\dfrac{17}{30} > \dfrac{1}{2}$ and $\dfrac{10}{33} < \dfrac{1}{2}, \dfrac{17}{30} > \dfrac{10}{33}$.

27. $\dfrac{23}{100} < \dfrac{1}{2}$

$\dfrac{19}{36} > \dfrac{1}{2}$

Because $\dfrac{23}{100} < \dfrac{1}{2}$ and $\dfrac{19}{36} > \dfrac{1}{2}, \dfrac{23}{100} < \dfrac{19}{36}$.

28. $\dfrac{105}{210} = \dfrac{1}{2}$

$\dfrac{13}{27} < \dfrac{1}{2}$

Because $\dfrac{105}{210} = \dfrac{1}{2}$ and $\dfrac{13}{27} < \dfrac{1}{2}, \dfrac{105}{210} > \dfrac{13}{27}$.

29. *Sample answer:* $\dfrac{5}{12}$

$\dfrac{1}{3} = \dfrac{1 \cdot 4}{3 \cdot 4} = \dfrac{4}{12}$

$\dfrac{1}{2} = \dfrac{1 \cdot 6}{2 \cdot 6} = \dfrac{6}{12}$

$\dfrac{1}{3} < \dfrac{5}{12} < \dfrac{1}{2}$

30. *Sample answer:* $\dfrac{31}{40}$

$\dfrac{3}{4} = \dfrac{3 \cdot 10}{4 \cdot 10} = \dfrac{30}{40}$

$\dfrac{4}{5} = \dfrac{4 \cdot 8}{5 \cdot 8} = \dfrac{32}{40}$

$\dfrac{3}{4} < \dfrac{31}{40} < \dfrac{4}{5}$

31. *Sample answer:* $\dfrac{31}{48}$

$\dfrac{5}{8} = \dfrac{5 \cdot 6}{8 \cdot 6} = \dfrac{30}{48}$

$\dfrac{2}{3} = \dfrac{2 \cdot 16}{3 \cdot 16} = \dfrac{32}{48}$

$\dfrac{5}{8} < \dfrac{31}{48} < \dfrac{2}{3}$

32. *Sample answer:* $\dfrac{11}{20}$

$\dfrac{3}{5} = \dfrac{3 \cdot 4}{5 \cdot 4} = \dfrac{12}{20}$

$\dfrac{1}{2} = \dfrac{1 \cdot 10}{2 \cdot 10} = \dfrac{10}{20}$

$\dfrac{1}{2} < \dfrac{11}{20} < \dfrac{3}{5}$

33–36. Explanations may vary.

33. $a > b$, so $\dfrac{a}{b}$ is greater than 1 and $\dfrac{b}{a}$ is less than 1. So, $\dfrac{a}{b} > \dfrac{b}{a}$.

34. $a > b$, so $\dfrac{1}{a} < \dfrac{1}{b}$. When two fractions have the same numerator, the fraction with the larger denominator is less than the other fraction. For example, $\dfrac{1}{3} < \dfrac{1}{2}$.

35. Consider the following example. Let $a = 5$ and $b = 4$. So $a > b$ and $b > 0$.

$\dfrac{a}{a + 1} = \dfrac{5}{5 + 1} = \dfrac{5}{6} = \dfrac{5 \cdot 5}{6 \cdot 5} = \dfrac{25}{30}$

$\dfrac{b}{b + 1} = \dfrac{4}{4 + 1} = \dfrac{4}{5} = \dfrac{4 \cdot 6}{5 \cdot 6} = \dfrac{24}{30}$

So, $\dfrac{a}{a + 1} > \dfrac{b}{b + 1}$.

36. $\dfrac{a + 1}{a} = \dfrac{a}{a} + \dfrac{1}{a} = 1 + \dfrac{1}{a}$

$\dfrac{b + 1}{b} = \dfrac{b}{b} + \dfrac{1}{b} = 1 + \dfrac{1}{b}$

Because the whole numbers are the same, you can compare the fractions. $a > b$, so $\dfrac{1}{a} < \dfrac{1}{b}$ as shown in Exercise 34. So, $1 + \dfrac{1}{a} < 1 + \dfrac{1}{b}$ and $\dfrac{a + 1}{a} < \dfrac{b + 1}{b}$.

Problem Solving

37. The least common denominator of $\dfrac{2}{3}$ and $\dfrac{5}{8}$ is $2^3 \cdot 3$, or 24.

$\dfrac{2}{3} = \dfrac{2 \cdot 8}{3 \cdot 8} = \dfrac{16}{24}$

$\dfrac{5}{8} = \dfrac{5 \cdot 3}{8 \cdot 3} = \dfrac{15}{24}$

Because $\dfrac{16}{24} > \dfrac{15}{24}, \dfrac{2}{3} > \dfrac{5}{8}$. So, Sarah's walk to school is longer.

38. $\dfrac{8 \text{ min}}{30 \text{ min}} = \dfrac{8 \cdot 4}{30 \cdot 4} = \dfrac{32}{120}$

$\dfrac{31 \text{ min}}{2 \text{ h}} = \dfrac{31}{120}$

Because $\dfrac{32}{120} > \dfrac{31}{120}$, the 30 minute TV show has a greater fraction of commercial time.

39. D;

$\dfrac{28}{32} = \dfrac{7}{8} = \dfrac{7 \cdot 315}{8 \cdot 315} = \dfrac{2205}{2520}$

$\dfrac{27}{30} = \dfrac{9}{10} = \dfrac{9 \cdot 252}{10 \cdot 252} = \dfrac{2268}{2520}$

$\dfrac{24}{27} = \dfrac{8}{9} = \dfrac{8 \cdot 280}{9 \cdot 280} = \dfrac{2240}{2520}$

$\dfrac{21}{24} = \dfrac{7}{8} = \dfrac{7 \cdot 315}{8 \cdot 315} = \dfrac{2205}{2520}$

$\dfrac{24}{28} = \dfrac{6}{7} = \dfrac{6 \cdot 360}{7 \cdot 360} = \dfrac{2160}{2520}$

$\dfrac{2160}{2520} < \dfrac{2205}{2520}$, so $\dfrac{24}{28} < \dfrac{28}{32}$.

40. *Sample answer:* When you compare fractions with like denominators, the fraction with the greater numerator is greater. When you compare fractions with like numerators, the fraction with the lesser denominator is greater, assuming all the fractions are positive.

41. $\dfrac{350 \div 350}{10{,}000 \div 350} \approx \dfrac{1}{29} > \dfrac{1}{30}$

$\dfrac{430 \div 430}{13{,}200 \div 430} \approx \dfrac{1}{31} < \dfrac{1}{30}$

$\dfrac{350}{10{,}000} > \dfrac{430}{13{,}200}$, so the 10,000 pound elephant's trunk represents the greater fraction of the elephant's weight.

42. *Sample answer:* It is easy to tell if a fraction is greater or less than $\dfrac{1}{2}$. This will only work if both fractions are not greater than $\dfrac{1}{2}$, or if both fractions are not less than $\dfrac{1}{2}$.

Chapter 4, *continued*

43. a. California: $\frac{5}{20} = \frac{5 \cdot 7}{20 \cdot 7} = \frac{35}{140}$

Texas: $\frac{2}{7} = \frac{2 \cdot 20}{7 \cdot 20} = \frac{40}{140}$

Because $\frac{40}{140} > \frac{35}{140}, \frac{2}{7} > \frac{5}{20}$.

So, Texas has won a greater fraction of world championships with $\frac{2}{7}$.

b. Explanations may vary.

California: $\frac{5 + x}{20 + x} = (5 + x) \cdot \frac{7}{(20 + x) \cdot 7}$

Texas: $\frac{2}{7} = \frac{2 \cdot (20 + x)}{7 \cdot (20 + x)}$

California will have a greater fraction of wins when $(5 + x) \cdot 7$ is greater than $2 \cdot (20 + x)$.

With 1 more win, $(5 + 1) \cdot 7 = 42$ and $2 \cdot (20 + 1) = 42$. Because $42 = 42$, the fraction for California equals the fraction for Texas.

With 2 more wins, $(5 + 2) \cdot 7 = 49$ and $2 \cdot (20 + 2) = 44$. Because $49 > 44$, the fraction for California is greater than the fraction for Texas. So, California must win two more games.

Mixed Review

44. $18^2 = 18 \cdot 18 = 324$

45. $10^4 = 10 \cdot 10 \cdot 10 \cdot 10 = 10,000$

46. $8^5 = 8 \cdot 8 \cdot 8 \cdot 8 \cdot 8 = 32,768$

47. $11^3 = 11 \cdot 11 \cdot 11 = 1331$

48.

The prime factorization of 336 is $2^4 \cdot 3 \cdot 7$.

49.

```
      258
      / \
     2  × 129
    / \  / \
   2 × 3 × 43
```

The prime factorization of 258 is $2 \cdot 3 \cdot 43$.

50.

```
       364
       / \
      4  × 91
    /─┤   ┤─\
   2 × 2 × 7 × 13
```

The prime factorization of 364 is $2^2 \cdot 7 \cdot 13$.

51.

```
      483
      / \
    21  × 23
   / \    \
  3 × 7 × 23
```

The prime factorization of 483 is $3 \cdot 7 \cdot 23$.

52. A;

Area of the rectangle:

$A = \ell \cdot w = 8 \cdot 4 = 32 \text{ ft}^2$

Area of the triangle:

$A = \frac{1}{2}bh = \frac{1}{2} \cdot 8 \cdot 4 = 16 \text{ ft}^2$

The total area of the figure is $32 + 16$, or 48 square feet.

Lesson 4.6

Activity (p. 202)

Step 1

Expression	Expanded Expression	Number of Factors	Product as a power
$2^2 \cdot 2^4$	$(2 \cdot 2) \cdot (2 \cdot 2 \cdot 2 \cdot 2)$	6	2^6
$3^3 \cdot 3^1$	$(3 \cdot 3 \cdot 3) \cdot 3$	4	3^4
$7^2 \cdot 7^3$	$(7 \cdot 7) \cdot (7 \cdot 7 \cdot 7)$	5	7^5

Step 2 Each exponent in the last column is the sum of the exponents in the first column.

1. $3^4 \cdot 3^3 = 3^{4 + 3} = 3^7$

2. $6^5 \cdot 6^{11} = 6^{5 + 11} = 6^{16}$

3. $10^7 \cdot 10^{13} = 10^{7 + 13} = 10^{20}$

4.6 Guided Practice (pp. 203–204)

1. $4^6 \cdot 4^4 = 4^{6 + 4} = 4^{10}$

2. $9^8 \cdot 9 = 9^{8 + 1} = 9^9$

3. $a^6 \cdot a^9 = a^{6 + 9} = a^{15}$

4. $c \cdot c^{12} \cdot c^3 = c^{1 + 12 + 3} = c^{16}$

5. $10^2 s^4 \cdot 10^4 s^2 = (10^2 \cdot 10^4) \cdot (s^4 \cdot s^2)$
$= 10^{2 + 4} \cdot s^{4 + 2}$
$= 10^6 \cdot s^6$
$= 1,000,000 s^6$

6. $6^3 t^5 \cdot 6^2 t^8 = (6^3 \cdot 6^2) \cdot (t^5 \cdot t^8)$
$= 6^{3 + 2} \cdot t^{5 + 8}$
$= 6^5 \cdot t^{13}$
$= 7776 t^{13}$

7. $7x^2 \cdot 7x^4 = (7 \cdot 7) \cdot (x^2 \cdot x^4)$
$= 7^{1 + 1} \cdot x^{2 + 4}$
$= 7^2 \cdot x^6$
$= 49x^6$

8. $5^2 z \cdot 5z^7 \cdot z^2 = (5^2 \cdot 5) \cdot (z \cdot z^7 \cdot z^2)$
$= 5^{2 + 1} \cdot z^{1 + 7 + 2}$
$= 5^3 \cdot z^{10}$
$= 125 z^{10}$

9. $\frac{a^6}{a^4} = a^{6 - 4} = a^2$

10. $\frac{10^9}{10^6} = 10^{9 - 6} = 10^3$

11. $\frac{q^3 \cdot q^5}{q^4} = \frac{q^8}{q^4} = q^{8 - 4} = q^4$

12. $\frac{a^2 b^8}{b^2} = a^2 b^{8 - 2} = a^2 b^6$

4.6 Exercises (pp. 204–207)

Skill Practice

1. Three is the *base* of the expression 3^4.

2. Seven is the *exponent* of the expression 4^7.

3. $4^2 \cdot 4^4 = 4^{2+4} = 4^6$

4. $8 \cdot 8^3 = 8^{1+3} = 8^4$

5. $a^5 \cdot a^7 = a^{5+7} = a^{12}$

6. $b^9 \cdot b^9 = b^{9+9} = b^{18}$

7. $u^7 \cdot u = u^{7+1} = u^8$

8. $v^2 \cdot v^{10} = v^{2+10} = v^{12}$

9. $b^9 \cdot b^6 = b^{9+6} = b^{15}$

10. $m^{11} \cdot m^8 = m^{11+8} = m^{19}$

11. $3^2 \cdot 3^5 = 3^{2+5} = 3^7$

12. $7^2 \cdot 7^2 = 7^{2+2} = 7^4$

13. $(-4)^2 \cdot (-4)^3 = (-4)^{2+3} = (-4)^5$

14. $(-5)^4 \cdot (-5) = (-5)^{4+1} = (-5)^5$

15. $3a^3 \cdot 3a^2 = (3 \cdot 3) \cdot (a^3 \cdot a^2)$
$$= 3^{1+1} \cdot a^{3+2}$$
$$= 3^2 a^5$$
$$= 9a^5$$

16. $2y^3 \cdot 2y^2 = (2 \cdot 2) \cdot (y^3 \cdot y^2)$
$$= 2^{1+1} \cdot y^{3+2}$$
$$= 2^2 y^5$$
$$= 4y^5$$

17. $3^2 x^5 \cdot 3^3 x^4 = (3^2 \cdot 3^3) \cdot (x^5 \cdot x^4)$
$$= 3^{2+3} \cdot x^{5+4}$$
$$= 3^5 x^9$$
$$= 243 x^9$$

18. $4a^3 b^4 \cdot 4^2 a^4 b^6 = (4 \cdot 4^2) \cdot (a^3 \cdot a^4) \cdot (b^4 \cdot b^6)$
$$= 4^{1+2} \cdot a^{3+4} \cdot b^{4+6}$$
$$= 4^3 a^7 b^{10}$$
$$= 64 a^7 b^{10}$$

19. $5x^7 \cdot 5x^9 = (5 \cdot 5) \cdot (x^7 \cdot x^9)$
$$= 5^{1+1} \cdot x^{7+9}$$
$$= 5^2 \cdot x^{16}$$
$$= 25 x^{16}$$

20. $7^2 b^3 \cdot 7^5 b^8 = (7^2 \cdot 7^5) \cdot (b^3 \cdot b^8)$
$$= 7^{2+5} \cdot b^{3+8}$$
$$= 7^7 \cdot b^{11}$$
$$= 823{,}543 b^{11}$$

21. $6^2 x^2 y \cdot 6x^4 y^3 = (6^2 \cdot 6) \cdot (x^2 \cdot x^4) \cdot (y \cdot y^3)$
$$= 6^{2+1} \cdot x^{2+4} \cdot y^{1+3}$$
$$= 6^3 \cdot x^6 \cdot y^4$$
$$= 216 x^6 y^4$$

22. $10c^4 \cdot 10c^2 = (10 \cdot 10) \cdot (c^4 \cdot c^2)$
$$= 10^{1+1} \cdot c^{4+2}$$
$$= 10^2 \cdot c^6$$
$$= 100 c^6$$

23. $\dfrac{5^8}{5^4} = 5^{8-4} = 5^4$

24. $\dfrac{8^7}{8^2} = 8^{7-2} = 8^5$

25. $\dfrac{d^8}{d} = d^{8-1} = d^7$

26. $\dfrac{a^4}{a} = a^{4-1} = a^3$

27. $\dfrac{w^{15}}{w^9} = w^{15-9} = w^6$

28. $\dfrac{y^{20}}{y^{18}} = y^{20-18} = y^2$

29. $\dfrac{(-7)^7}{(-7)^4} = (-7)^{7-4} = (-7)^3$

30. $\dfrac{(-2)^{13}}{(-2)^3} = (-2)^{13-3} = (-2)^{10}$

31. C;
$$\frac{a^9 \cdot a^6}{a^5} = \frac{a^{9+6}}{a^5} = \frac{a^{15}}{a^5} = a^{15-5} = a^{10}$$

32. $\dfrac{p^5 q^9}{pq^5} = p^{5-1} \cdot q^{9-5} = p^4 q^4$

33. $\dfrac{z^6 \cdot z^3}{z^4} = \dfrac{z^{6+3}}{z^4} = \dfrac{z^9}{z^4} = z^{9-4} = z^5$

34. $\dfrac{3^3 m^9}{3^2 m^5} = 3^{3-2} \cdot m^{9-5} = 3^1 m^4 = 3m^4$

35. $\dfrac{5^5 n^{15}}{5^3 n^{12}} = 5^{5-3} \cdot n^{15-12} = 5^2 \cdot n^3 = 25 n^3$

36. $\dfrac{6^4 k^5}{6k^3} = 6^{4-1} \cdot k^{5-3} = 6^3 k^2 = 216 k^2$

37. $\dfrac{7^9 r^{12}}{7^5 r^8} = 7^{9-5} \cdot r^{12-8} = 7^4 r^4 = 2401 r^4$

38. $\dfrac{a^{11} \cdot b^7}{a^{10} \cdot b} = a^{11-10} \cdot b^{7-1} = ab^6$

39. $\dfrac{y^6 \cdot y^{13}}{y^9} = \dfrac{y^{6+13}}{y^9} = \dfrac{y^{19}}{y^9} = y^{19-9} = y^{10}$

40. The error is that the bases should not be multiplied.
$$2^2 \cdot 2^4 = 2^{2+4} = 2^6$$

41. The error is that the exponents should not be divided.
$$\frac{x^{20} y^6}{x^5 y^3} = x^{20-5} \cdot y^{6-3} = x^{15} y^3$$

42–53. Let $x = 2$, $y = 3$, and $z = 4$.

42. $\dfrac{3^x \cdot 3^y}{3^z} = \dfrac{3^2 \cdot 3^3}{3^4} = \dfrac{3^5}{3^4} = 3$

43. $\dfrac{(-2)^{2z}}{(-2)^x} = \dfrac{(-2)^{2(4)}}{(-2)^2} = \dfrac{(-2)^8}{(-2)^2} = (-2)^6$

44. $\dfrac{(-6)^{2y}}{(-6)^z} = \dfrac{(-6)^{2(3)}}{(-6)^4} = \dfrac{(-6)^6}{(-6)^4} = (-6)^2$

45. $\dfrac{2^{2x}}{2^y} = \dfrac{2^{2(2)}}{2^3} = \dfrac{2^4}{2^3} = 2$

46. $\dfrac{5^x \cdot 5^z}{5^y} = \dfrac{5^2 \cdot 5^4}{5^3} = \dfrac{5^6}{5^3} = 5^3$

47. $\dfrac{(-3)^{3y}}{(-3)^z} = \dfrac{(-3)^{3(3)}}{(-3)^4} = \dfrac{(-3)^9}{(-3)^4} = (-3)^5$

48. $\dfrac{7^{3z}}{7^{2y}} = \dfrac{7^{3(4)}}{7^{2(3)}} = \dfrac{7^{12}}{7^6} = 7^6$

49. $\dfrac{w^{x+y+z}}{w^{3y}} = \dfrac{w^{2+3+4}}{w^{3(3)}} = \dfrac{w^9}{w^9} = 1$

50. $\dfrac{64 a^z}{4 a^y} = \dfrac{64 a^4}{4 a^3} = 16a$

51. $\dfrac{-20 b^{2y+z}}{5 b^{3x}} = \dfrac{-20 b^{2(3)+4}}{5 b^{3(2)}} = \dfrac{-20 b^{10}}{5 b^6} = -4 b^4$

52. $\dfrac{12 m^{x+y}}{6 m^{z-y}} = \dfrac{12 m^{2+3}}{6 m^{4-3}} = \dfrac{12 m^5}{6m} = 2m^4$

53. $\dfrac{27n^{x+y}}{3n^5} = \dfrac{27n^{2+3}}{3n^2} = \dfrac{27n^5}{3n^2} = 9n^3$

54. *Sample answer:*

$\dfrac{x^{20}y^6}{x^{16}y^2} = x^{20-16}y^{6-2} = x^4y^4$

$\dfrac{x^5y^5}{xy} = x^{5-1}y^{5-1} = x^4y^4$

$\dfrac{x^8y^4}{x^4} = x^{8-4}y^4 = x^4y^4$

$\dfrac{4b^3}{10a} = \dfrac{2b^3}{5a}$

$\dfrac{2b^5}{5ab^2} = \dfrac{2b^{5-2}}{5a} = \dfrac{2b^3}{5a}$

$\dfrac{20b^7}{50ab^4} = \dfrac{2b^{7-4}}{5a} = \dfrac{2b^3}{5a}$

55. $2^3 \cdot 2^8 = 2^{3+8} = 2^{11}; 8$

56. $5^4 \cdot 5^5 = 5^{4+5} = 5^9; 5$

57. $12^3 \cdot 12^{13} = 12^{3+13} = 12^{16}; 12$

58. $3^2 \cdot 3^5 = 3^{2+5} = 3^7; 5$

59. $\dfrac{8^7}{8^4} = 8^{7-4} = 8^3; 4$

60. $\dfrac{7^4}{7^3} = 7^{4-3} = 7; 3$

61. $\dfrac{13^{11}}{13^9} = 13^{11-9} = 13^2; 11$

62. $9^3 \cdot 9^{17} = 9^{3+17} = 9^{20}; 17$

63. $\dfrac{6^{14}}{6^8} = 6^{14-8} = 6^6; 8$

64. $\dfrac{12^9}{12^5} = 12^{9-5} = 12^4; 9$

65. $4^{12} \cdot 4^7 = 4^{12+7} = 4^{19}; 12$

66. $\dfrac{11^3}{11^1} = 11^{3-1} = 11^2; 1$

67. $4^{2x} \cdot 4^{x-3} = 4^{12}$

$2x + x - 3 = 12$

$3x - 3 = 12$

$3x = 15$

$x = 5$

68. $5^{x-3} \cdot 5^{3x} = 5^{13}$

$x - 3 + 3x = 13$

$4x - 3 = 13$

$4x = 16$

$x = 4$

69. $8^{3x+4} \cdot 8^x = 8^{12}$

$3x + 4 + x = 12$

$4x + 4 = 12$

$4x = 8$

$x = 2$

70. $2^{22} = 2^{2x-2} \cdot 2^{4x-6}$

$22 = 2x - 2 + 4x - 6$

$22 = 6x - 8$

$30 = 6x$

$5 = x$

71. $\dfrac{3^{2x-1}}{3^{x+4}} = 3^3$

$2x - 1 - (x + 4) = 3$

$2x - 1 - x - 4 = 3$

$x - 5 = 3$

$x = 8$

72. $7^8 = \dfrac{7^{3x-2}}{7^x}$

$8 = 3x - 2 - x$

$8 = 2x - 2$

$10 = 2x$

$5 = x$

73. $9^2 = \dfrac{9^{5x}}{9^{x+2}}$

$2 = 5x - (x + 2)$

$2 = 5x - x - 2$

$2 = 4x - 2$

$4 = 4x$

$1 = x$

74. $\dfrac{11^{6x+1}}{11^{3x-7}} = 11^{17}$

$6x + 1 - (3x - 7) = 17$

$6x + 1 - 3x + 7 = 17$

$3x + 8 = 17$

$3x = 9$

$x = 3$

75. $(3^2 \cdot 3)^2 = (3^{2+1})^2$

$= (3^3)^2$

$= 3^3 \cdot 3^3$

$= 3^{3+3}$

$= 3^6$

$= 729$

76. $(2^3 \cdot 2^2)^3 = (2^5)^3$

$= 2^5 \cdot 2^5 \cdot 2^5$

$= 2^{15}$

$= 32,768$

77. $\left(\dfrac{4^7}{4^5}\right)^2 = (4^2)^2 = 4^2 \cdot 4^2 = 4^4 = 256$

78. $\left(\dfrac{5^8}{5^7}\right)^4 = 5^4 = 625$

79. $4y^3 + \dfrac{6y^5}{2y^2} - 3y(y^2) = 4y^3 + 3y^{5-2} - 3y^{1+2}$

$= 4y^3 + 3y^3 - 3y^3$

$= 4y^3$

80. $\dfrac{9s^4t^2}{3st} + \dfrac{6s^2t^5}{2t^2} - \dfrac{s^5t^2}{s^2t}$

$= 3s^{4-1}t^{2-1} + 3s^2t^{5-2} - s^{5-2}t^{2-1}$

$= 3s^3t + 3s^2t^3 - s^3t$

$= 2s^3t + 3s^2t^3$

81. $\dfrac{x^{n+1}}{x^n} = x^{n+1-n} = x^1 = x$

Problem Solving

82. $\dfrac{10^{24}}{10^1} = 10^{24-1} = 10^{23}$

There are 10^{23} decameters in a yottameter.

83. $\dfrac{10^{15}}{10^3} = 10^{15-3} = 10^{12}$

There are 10^{12} kilometers in a petameter.

84. $\dfrac{10^{21}}{10^9} = 10^{21-9} = 10^{12}$

There are 10^{12} gigameters in a zettameter.

Chapter 4, continued

85. $\dfrac{10^{24}}{10^{12}} = 10^{24-12} = 10^{12}$

There are 10^{12} terameters in a yottameter.

86. $\dfrac{10^{18}}{10^6} = 10^{18-6} = 10^{12}$

There are 10^{12} megameters in an exameter.

87. $\dfrac{10^{21}}{10^{15}} = 10^{21-15} = 10^6$

There are 10^6 petameters in a zettameter.

88. C;

$10^3 \cdot 10^{15} = 10^{3+15} = 10^{18}$

89. a. $\dfrac{10^{18}}{10^{18}} = 1$

There is 1 exameter in 1 quintillion kilometers.

b. $\dfrac{21 \cdot 10^{18}}{10^{18}} = 21 \cdot 1 = 21$

There are 21 exameters in 21 quintillion kilometers.

c. $\dfrac{10^{18}}{10^9} = 10^{18-9} = 10^9$

There are 10^9 gigameters in 1 exameter.

d. $\dfrac{21 \cdot 10^{18}}{10^9} = 21 \cdot 10^{18-9}$

$= 21 \cdot 10^9$

$= 21 \cdot 1,000,000,000$

$= 21,000,000,000$

There are 21,000,000,000 gigameters in 21 quintillion kilometers.

90. *Sample answer:* You can simplify first and then substitute or substitute first and then simplify.

Simplify first, then substitute:

$\dfrac{6y^{10}}{3y^8} = \dfrac{6y^{10-8}}{3} = 2y^2$

When $y = 5$:

$2y^2 = 2(5)^2 = 50$

Substitute first, then simplify:

When $y = 5$:

$\dfrac{6y^{10}}{3y^8} = \dfrac{6 \cdot 5^{10}}{3 \cdot 5^8} = \dfrac{6 \cdot 5^{10-8}}{3} = 2 \cdot 5^2 = 50$

Preferences and explanations will vary.

91. *Sample answer:* The power is the number of zeros. For example, $10^5 = 100,000$.

92. $r = \dfrac{d}{t} = \dfrac{d}{5^2} = \dfrac{d \cdot 5}{5^2 \cdot 5} = \dfrac{5d}{5^3}$

Yes, if the distance is multiplied by 5, the time must also be multiplied by 5 in order for the rate to remain constant.

93. Area of small field $= 3^8 \cdot 3^8 = 3^{8+8} = 3^{16}$ mm^2

The area of the small field is 3^{16} square millimeters.

Area of large field $= (3^8 \cdot 9) \cdot (3^8 \cdot 9)$

$= (3^8 \cdot 3^8) \cdot (9 \cdot 9)$

$= 3^{8+8} \cdot 9^{1+1}$

$= 3^{16} \cdot 9^2$

$= 81 \cdot 3^{16}$ mm^2

Compare areas:

$\dfrac{\text{large area}}{\text{small area}} = \dfrac{3^{16} \cdot 81}{3^{16}} = 81$

The area of the larger field is 81 times greater than the area of the smaller field.

94. a. $2^3 \cdot 64 = 2^3 \cdot 2^6 = 2^9$

Your computer had 2^9 KB of available memory.

b. 2^9 MB $= (2^9)(2^{10})$ KB

$\dfrac{2^9 \cdot 2^{10}}{2^3} = \dfrac{2^{19}}{2^3} = 2^{16}$

A typical computer purchased in 2005 has 2^{16} times the memory of your friend's 1979 computer.

95. *Sample answer:* You can write x as $c \cdot 10^b$ and y as $d \cdot 10^b$. The number of times x is greater than y is $\dfrac{x}{y} = \dfrac{c \cdot 10^b}{d \cdot 10^b} = \dfrac{c}{d}$.

Mixed Review

96. $\dfrac{28xy}{7y} = \dfrac{2 \cdot 2 \cdot \overset{1}{\cancel{7}} \cdot x \cdot \overset{1}{\cancel{y}}}{\underset{1}{\cancel{7}} \cdot \underset{1}{\cancel{y}}} = 4x$

97. $\dfrac{24x}{18x} = \dfrac{2 \cdot 2 \cdot 2 \cdot \overset{1}{\cancel{3}} \cdot \overset{1}{\cancel{x}}}{\underset{1}{\cancel{2}} \cdot \underset{1}{\cancel{3}} \cdot 3 \cdot \underset{1}{\cancel{x}}} = \dfrac{4}{3}$

98. $\dfrac{46xyz}{82xy} = \dfrac{\overset{1}{\cancel{2}} \cdot 23 \cdot \overset{1}{\cancel{x}} \cdot \overset{1}{\cancel{y}} \cdot z}{\underset{1}{\cancel{2}} \cdot 41 \cdot \underset{1}{\cancel{x}} \cdot \underset{1}{\cancel{y}}} = \dfrac{23z}{41}$

99. $\dfrac{25y^2}{145y} = \dfrac{\overset{1}{\cancel{5}} \cdot 5 \cdot \overset{1}{\cancel{y}} \cdot y}{\underset{1}{\cancel{5}} \cdot 29 \cdot \underset{1}{\cancel{y}}} = \dfrac{5y}{29}$

100. $\dfrac{36yz}{45xy} = \dfrac{2 \cdot 2 \cdot \overset{1}{\cancel{3}} \cdot \overset{1}{\cancel{3}} \cdot \overset{1}{\cancel{y}} \cdot z}{\underset{1}{\cancel{3}} \cdot \underset{1}{\cancel{3}} \cdot 5 \cdot x \cdot \underset{1}{\cancel{y}}} = \dfrac{4z}{5x}$

101. $\dfrac{52x^2}{13x^4} = \dfrac{2 \cdot 2 \cdot \overset{1}{\cancel{13}} \cdot \overset{1}{\cancel{x}} \cdot \overset{1}{\cancel{x}}}{\underset{1}{\cancel{13}} \cdot \underset{1}{\cancel{x}} \cdot \underset{1}{\cancel{x}} \cdot x \cdot x} = \dfrac{4}{x^2}$

102. $\dfrac{30x^2y}{12xy^2} = \dfrac{\overset{1}{\cancel{2}} \cdot \overset{1}{\cancel{3}} \cdot 5 \cdot \overset{1}{\cancel{x}} \cdot x \cdot \overset{1}{\cancel{y}}}{\underset{1}{\cancel{2}} \cdot 2 \cdot \underset{1}{\cancel{3}} \cdot \underset{1}{\cancel{x}} \cdot \underset{1}{\cancel{y}} \cdot y} = \dfrac{5x}{2y}$

103. $\dfrac{6xy}{44xz} = \dfrac{\overset{1}{\cancel{2}} \cdot 3 \cdot \overset{1}{\cancel{x}} \cdot y}{\underset{1}{\cancel{2}} \cdot 2 \cdot 11 \cdot \underset{1}{\cancel{x}} \cdot z} = \dfrac{3y}{22z}$

104. 14 people completed the survey.

105. 4 of the surveyed people read 3 hours or less each week.

106. 6 of the surveyed people read more than 4 hours each week.

107. $4 - 1 = 3$

3 more people read 4 hours a week than 6 hours a week.

108. C;

$144 = 2^4 \cdot 3^2$

$300 = 2^2 \cdot 3 \cdot 5^2$

$240 = 2^4 \cdot 3 \cdot 5$

The GCF of 144, 300, and 240 is $2^2 \cdot 3$, or 12.

Lesson 4.7

4.7 Guided Practice (p. 209)

1. $\dfrac{1}{1000} = \dfrac{1}{10^3} = 10^{-3}$

One flash of the strobe light lasts 10^{-3} second.

2. $7^{-2} = \dfrac{1}{7^2} = \dfrac{1}{49}$

3. $(-2)^{-5} = \dfrac{1}{(-2)^5} = -\dfrac{1}{32}$

4. $6 \cdot 6^{-3} = 6^{1 + (-3)} = 6^{-2} = \dfrac{1}{6^2} = \dfrac{1}{36}$

5. $10^{-5} \cdot 10^5 = 10^{(-5) + 5} = 10^0 = 1$

6. $-6m^{-1} = -6 \cdot m^{-1} = \dfrac{-6}{m} = -\dfrac{6}{m}$

7. $b^2 \cdot b^{-2} = b^{2 + (-2)} = b^0 = 1$

8. $\dfrac{5x^4}{x^{-7}} = 5x^{4 - (-7)} = 5x^{11}$

9. $\dfrac{10a^{-3}}{a^4} = 10a^{(-3) - 4} = 10a^{-7} = \dfrac{10}{a^7}$

4.7 Exercises (pp. 210–211)

Skill Practice

1. The power x^0 is equal to 1.

2. The power x^{-h} is equal to $\dfrac{1}{x^h}$.

3. $3^{-4} = \dfrac{1}{3^4} = \dfrac{1}{81}$ **4.** $12^0 = 1$

5. $-2^{-4} = -\dfrac{1}{2^4} = -\dfrac{1}{16}$ **6.** $(-4)^{-3} = \dfrac{1}{(-4)^3} = -\dfrac{1}{64}$

7. $(-6)^{-2} \cdot (-6)^0 = \dfrac{1}{(-6)^2} \cdot 1 = \dfrac{1}{(-6)(-6)} = \dfrac{1}{36}$

8. $-2 \cdot 2^{-6} = -2^{1 + (-6)} = -2^{-5} = -\dfrac{1}{2^5} = -\dfrac{1}{32}$

9. $-5^4 \cdot 5^{-8} = -5^{4 + (-8)} = -5^{-4} = -\dfrac{1}{5^4} = -\dfrac{1}{625}$

10. $9^0 \cdot 9^{-2} = 1 \cdot \dfrac{1}{9^2} = \dfrac{1}{9^2} = \dfrac{1}{81}$

11. When an exponent is negative, the base and exponent must be moved to the denominator.

$5^{-3} = \dfrac{1}{5^3} = \dfrac{1}{125}$

12. $m^{-9} \cdot m^5 = m^{-9 + 5} = m^{-4} = \dfrac{1}{m^4}$

13. $x^5 \cdot x^{-5} = x^{5 + (-5)} = x^0 = 1$

14. $9n^{-3} = 9 \cdot n^{-3} = \dfrac{9}{n^3}$

15. $c^{-1} \cdot c^{-2} \cdot c^{-4} = c^{-1 + (-2) + (-4)} = c^{-7} = \dfrac{1}{c^7}$

16. $b^3 \cdot b^{-4} \cdot b^{-5} = b^{3 + (-4) + (-5)} = b^{-6} = \dfrac{1}{b^6}$

17. $\dfrac{4z^{-2}}{z^4} = 4z^{-2 - 4} = 4z^{-6} = \dfrac{4}{z^6}$

18. $\dfrac{a^{-5}}{a^8} = a^{-5 - 8} = a^{-13} = \dfrac{1}{a^{13}}$

19. $\dfrac{18r^{-6}}{3r^3} = 6r^{-6 - 3} = 6r^{-9} = \dfrac{6}{r^9}$

20. A; $\dfrac{-3x^{-4}}{x^2} = -3x^{-4 - 2} = -3x^{-6} = \dfrac{-3}{x^6} = -\dfrac{3}{x^6}$

21. $(4x^5)^0 = 1$; 0

22. $15a^{-8} = \dfrac{15}{a^8}$; -8

23. $y^{-5} \cdot y^4 = y^{-5 + 4} = y^{-1} = \dfrac{1}{y}$; -5

24. $\dfrac{x^{-3}}{x^{10}} = x^{-3 - 10} = x^{-13} = \dfrac{1}{x^{13}}$; 10

25. $\dfrac{5x^{-2}}{x^{-5}} = 5x^{-2 - (-5)} = 5x^3$; -2

26. $(2y^8)^0 = 1$; 0

27. $9b^{-7} = \dfrac{9}{b^7}$; -7

28. $a^6 \cdot a^{-8} = a^{6 + (-8)} = a^{-2} = \dfrac{1}{a^2}$; -8

29–32. Explanations may vary.

29. A power with an exponent of zero is *always* positive. A power with an exponent of zero is equal to 1, which is positive.

30. A power with a positive base and a negative exponent is *never* negative. A positive base raised to any power is always positive.

31. A power with a negative base and a positive exponent is *sometimes* positive. If the exponent is even it will be positive.

32. A power with an integer base and a negative exponent can *always* be written as a fraction.

$a^{-n} = \dfrac{1}{a^n}$

33. $c^{-1} \cdot (b^2c)^{-2} = \dfrac{1}{c} \cdot \dfrac{1}{(b^2c)^2}$

$= \dfrac{1}{c} \cdot \dfrac{1}{(b^2c)(b^2c)}$

$= \dfrac{1 \cdot 1}{b^{2 + 2} \cdot c^{1 + 1 + 1}}$

$= \dfrac{1}{b^4c^3}$

Chapter 4, continued

34. $\dfrac{x^6 y^4}{(x^3 y^{-4})^{-2}} = x^6 y^4 (x^3 y^{-4})^2$

$= x^6 y^4 (x^3 y^{-4})(x^3 y^{-4})$

$= x^{6+3+3} \cdot y^{4+(-4)+(-4)}$

$= x^{12} y^{-4}$

$= \dfrac{x^{12}}{y^4}$

35. $(2t)^{-3} \cdot 4t^3 \cdot (4t^{-3})^0 = \dfrac{4t^3}{(2t)^3} \cdot 1$

$= \dfrac{4t^3}{(2t)(2t)(2t)}$

$= \dfrac{4t^3}{8t^{1+1+1}}$

$= \dfrac{4t^3}{8t^3} = \dfrac{1}{2}$

Problem Solving

36. $0.2(10^{-6}) = \dfrac{0.2}{10^6} = \dfrac{2 \cdot 10^{-1}}{10^6} = \dfrac{2}{\cdot 10^7}$

The phytoplankton is $\dfrac{2}{10^7}$ of a meter.

37. When $t = 4$: $r = 2^{-t} = 2^{-4} = \dfrac{1}{2^4} = \dfrac{1}{16}$

$\dfrac{1}{16}$ remains after 4 half-lives.

$2^{-t} = \dfrac{1}{64} = \dfrac{1}{2^6} = 2^{-6}$

So, $t = 6$.

$\dfrac{1}{64}$ of the original amount remains after 6 half-lives.

38. $\text{kg} \cdot \text{m}^{-1} \cdot \text{s}^{-2} = \dfrac{\text{kg}}{\text{ms}^2}$

39. $\dfrac{10^{-1}}{10^{-12}} = 10^{-1-(-12)} = 10^{-1+12} = 10^{11}$

There are 10^{11} picometers in a decimeter.

40. $\dfrac{10^{-12}}{10^{-24}} = 10^{-12-(-24)} = 10^{-12+24} = 10^{12}$

There are 10^{12} yoctometers in a picometer.

41. $\dfrac{10^{-1}}{10^{-9}} = 10^{-1-(-9)} = 10^{-1+9} = 10^8$

There are 10^8 nanometers in a decimeter.

42. $\dfrac{10^{-2}}{10^{-18}} = 10^{-2-(-18)} = 10^{-2+18} = 10^{16}$

There are 10^{16} attometers in a centimeter.

43. A;

$A = \ell w = 2^3 \cdot 4^{-2} = 8 \cdot \dfrac{1}{4^2} = 8 \cdot \dfrac{1}{16} = \dfrac{1}{2}\ \text{m}^2$

44. Expanded form of 389.602:

$3 \times 100 + 8 \times 10 + 9 \times 1 + 6 \times 0.1 + 2 \times 0.001$

Using only positive and zero powers of 10:

$3 \times 10^2 + 8 \times 10^1 + 9 \times 10^0 + 6 \times \dfrac{1}{10^1} + 2 \times \dfrac{1}{10^3}$

Using positive, negative, and zero powers of 10:

$3 \times 10^2 + 8 \times 10^1 + 9 \times 10^0 + 6 \times 10^{-1} + 2 \times 10^{-3}$

45. *Sample answer:*

$a^0 = a^{-1+1} = a^{-1} \cdot a^1 = \dfrac{1}{a} \cdot a = \dfrac{a}{a} = 1$

Mixed Review

46. $32,501.5 = 3 \times 10,000 + 2 \times 1000 + 5 \times 100 + 1 \times 1 + 5 \times 0.1$

47. $8055.93 = 8 \times 1000 + 5 \times 10 + 5 \times 1 + 9 \times 0.1 + 3 \times 0.01$

48. $163.427 = 1 \times 100 + 6 \times 10 + 3 \times 1 + 4 \times 0.1 + 2 \times 0.01 + 7 \times 0.001$

49. $(4 \times 3)^2 + 13 = (12)^2 + 13 = 144 + 13 = 157$

50. $405 \div (14 - 11)^4 = 405 \div 3^4 = 405 \div 81 = 5$

51. $96 \div 2^5 \times 6 = 96 \div 32 \times 6 = 3 \times 6 = 18$

52. B; $b^3 \cdot b^2 = b^{3+2} = b^5$

Lesson 4.8

4.8 Guided Practice (pp. 212–214)

1. $4000 = 4 \times 10^3$

2. $7,300,000 = 7.3 \times 10^6$

3. $63,000,000,000 = 6.3 \times 10^{10}$

4. $230,000 = 2.3 \times 10^5$

5. $2,420,000 = 2.42 \times 10^6$

6. $105 = 1.05 \times 10^2$

7. $0.00475 = 4.75 \times 10^{-3}$

8. $0.00000526 = 5.26 \times 10^{-6}$

9. $0.0000000082 = 8.2 \times 10^{-9}$

10. $0.0237 = 2.37 \times 10^{-2}$

11. $0.000097 = 9.7 \times 10^{-5}$

12. $0.0003141 = 3.141 \times 10^{-4}$

13. $3.5 \times 10^3 = 3500$

14. $2.48 \times 10^6 = 2,480,000$

15. $5.1 \times 10^{-4} = 0.00051$

16. $9.16 \times 10^{-2} = 0.0916$

17. $(1.25 \times 10^6) \times (7.6 \times 10^{12}) = (1.25 \times 7.6) \times (10^6 \times 10^{12})$

$= 9.5 \times 10^{18}$

18. $(8 \times 10^5) \times (5.65 \times 10^4) = (8 \times 5.65) \times (10^5 \times 10^4)$

$= 45.2 \times 10^9$

$= 4.52 \times 10^1 \times 10^9$

$= 4.52 \times 10^{10}$

4.8 Exercises (pp. 214–217)

Skill Practice

1. 9.32×10^5 is expressed in scientific notation because 9.32 is between 1 and 10, and 5 is an integer.

2. 56.8×10^2 is not expressed in scientific notation because 56.8 is not less than 10.

3. 7×10^{-4} is expressed in scientific notation because 7 is between 1 and 10, and -4 is an integer.

4. $7900 = 7.9 \times 10^3$

5. $0.468 = 4.68 \times 10^{-1}$

6. $0.0000671 = 6.71 \times 10^{-5}$

7. $89,200,000,000 = 8.92 \times 10^{10}$

8. $8,100,000,000 = 8.1 \times 10^{9}$

9. $2,130,000 = 2.13 \times 10^{6}$

10. $0.0312 = 3.12 \times 10^{-2}$

11. $0.000000415 = 4.15 \times 10^{-7}$

12. $0.0000000342 = 3.42 \times 10^{-8}$

13. C; $0.000000765 = 7.65 \times 10^{-7}$

14. $5.72 \times 10^{-3} = 0.00572$

15. $4.35 \times 10^{6} = 4,350,000$

16. $9.62 \times 10^{7} = 96,200,000$

17. $8.71 \times 10^{-2} = 0.0871$

18. $6.35 \times 10^{-6} = 0.00000635$

19. $1.76 \times 10^{-9} = 0.00000000176$

20. $4.13 \times 10^{9} = 4,130,000,000$

21. $2.83 \times 10^{12} = 2,830,000,000,000$

22. $3.61 \times 10^{7} = 36,100,000$

23. $(3 \times 10^{3}) \times (2 \times 10^{5}) = (3 \times 2) \times (10^{3} \times 10^{5})$
$$= 6 \times 10^{8}$$

24. $(2 \times 10^{-6}) \times (4 \times 10^{-4}) = (2 \times 4) \times (10^{-6} \times 10^{-4})$
$$= 8 \times 10^{-10}$$

25. $(1.5 \times 10^{-2}) \times (3.9 \times 10^{-5}) = (1.5 \times 3.9) \times (10^{-2} \times 10^{-5})$
$$= 5.85 \times 10^{-7}$$

26. $(3.6 \times 10^{8}) \times (2.4 \times 10^{5}) = (3.6 \times 2.4) \times (10^{8} \times 10^{5})$
$$= 8.64 \times 10^{13}$$

27. $(7.8 \times 10^{6}) \times (8.4 \times 10^{7}) = (7.8 \times 8.4) \times (10^{6} \times 10^{7})$
$$= 65.52 \times 10^{13}$$
$$= 6.552 \times 10^{1} \times 10^{13}$$
$$= 6.552 \times 10^{14}$$

28. $(7.6 \times 10^{-8}) \times (4.8 \times 10^{-6})$
$$= (7.6 \times 4.8) \times (10^{-8} \times 10^{-6})$$
$$= 36.48 \times 10^{-14}$$
$$= 3.648 \times 10^{1} \times 10^{-14}$$
$$= 3.648 \times 10^{-13}$$

29. $(2.6 \times 10^{7}) \times (4.1 \times 10^{-3})$
$$= (2.6 \times 4.1) \times (10^{7} \times 10^{-3})$$
$$= 10.66 \times 10^{4}$$
$$= 1.066 \times 10^{1} \times 10^{4}$$
$$= 1.066 \times 10^{5}$$

30. $(5.4 \times 10^{5}) \times (3.6 \times 10^{-9})$
$$= (5.4 \times 3.6) \times (10^{5} \times 10^{-9})$$
$$= 19.44 \times 10^{-4}$$
$$= 1.944 \times 10^{1} \times 10^{-4}$$
$$= 1.944 \times 10^{-3}$$

31. The errors are that 18.6 is not between 1 and 10, and when multiplying powers with the same base, you must add the exponents, not multiply.
$$(3 \times 10^{2}) \times (6.2 \times 10^{3}) = (3 \times 6.2) \times (10^{2} \times 10^{3})$$
$$= 18.6 \times 10^{5}$$
$$= 1.86 \times 10^{1} \times 10^{5}$$
$$= 1.86 \times 10^{6}$$

32. $6.92 \times 10^{11} < 6.92 \times 10^{12}$ because $11 < 12$.

33. $1.06 \times 10^{6} > 9.98 \times 10^{5}$ because $6 > 5$.

34. $3.67 \times 10^{-3} > 3.76 \times 10^{-4}$ because $-3 > -4$.

35. $3.4 \times 10^{-20} > 4.1 \times 10^{-21}$ because $-20 > -21$.

36. $\dfrac{4.08 \times 10^{6}}{3.4 \times 10^{2}} = 1.2 \times 10^{6-2} = 1.2 \times 10^{4}$

37. $\dfrac{2.765 \times 10^{21}}{7.9 \times 10^{9}} = 0.35 \times 10^{21-9}$
$$= 0.35 \times 10^{12}$$
$$= 3.5 \times 10^{-1} \times 10^{12}$$
$$= 3.5 \times 10^{11}$$

38. $\dfrac{5.46 \times 10^{28}}{6.5 \times 10^{24}} = 0.84 \times 10^{28-24}$
$$= 0.84 \times 10^{4}$$
$$= 8.4 \times 10^{-1} \times 10^{4}$$
$$= 8.4 \times 10^{3}$$

39. $\dfrac{2.015 \times 10^{7}}{6.2 \times 10^{3}} = 0.325 \times 10^{7-3}$
$$= 0.325 \times 10^{4}$$
$$= 3.25 \times 10^{-1} \times 10^{4}$$
$$= 3.25 \times 10^{3}$$

40. $37,500,000 = 3.75 \times 10^{7}$

From least to greatest, the numbers are $37,500,000$, 5.37×10^{7}, 3.75×10^{8}, and 3.57×10^{9}.

41. $(3.2 \times 10^{5}) + (8.1 \times 10^{3}) = 320,000 + 8100$
$$= 328,100$$
$$= 3.281 \times 10^{5}$$

42. $(5 \times 10^{-1}) + (9.8 \times 10^{-3}) = 0.5 + 0.0098$
$$= 0.5098$$
$$= 5.098 \times 10^{-1}$$

43. $(4.1 \times 10^{8}) - (7.7 \times 10^{6}) = 410,000,000 - 7,700,000$
$$= 402,300,000$$
$$= 4.023 \times 10^{8}$$

44. $(6.4 \times 10^{4}) - (5.9 \times 10^{-2}) = 64,000 - 0.059$
$$= 63,999.941$$
$$= 6.3999941 \times 10^{4}$$

Problem Solving

45. a. $4.2 \div 1.3 \approx 3.2$

b. $\dfrac{10^{27}}{10^{25}} = 10^{27-25} = 10^{2}$

c. 3.2×10^{2}

Chapter 4, *continued*

46. A; 28.1 million is equal to 28,100,000.

47. $15,000,000 = 1.5 \times 10^7$

48. $1.2916 \times 10^7 = 12,916,000$

49. Oxygen: 0.000000000000000000000026561

    Hydrogen: 0.0000000000000000000000016735

    $2.6561 \times 10^{-23} > 1.6735 \times 10^{-24}$

    because $-23 > -24$. So an atom of oxygen has the greater mass.

    $\dfrac{2.6561 \times 10^{-23}}{1.6735 \times 10^{-24}} \approx 1.587 \times 10^1 = 15.87$

    The mass of an oxygen atom is about 15.87 times greater than the mass of a hydrogen atom.

50. The radius of a proton is 1.2×10^{-15} meters, or $1.2 \times 10^{-15} \times 10^2 = 1.2 \times 10^{-13}$ centimeters.

51.   21 million
      $\dfrac{-9 \text{ million}}{12 \text{ million}}$

    The space probe has 12 million miles left to travel.

    $12,000,000 = 1.2 \times 10^7$

    $\dfrac{1.2 \times 10^7}{1.5 \times 10^6} = 0.8 \times 10 = 8$

    The space probe has 8 days left of travel.

52. *Sample answer:* If the numbers are written in scientific notation, the number with the greater exponent is larger.

53. 11.4 million is equal to 11.4×10^6.

    $11.4 \times 10^6 \times 7 = 79.8 \times 10^6$
    $= 7.98 \times 10^1 \times 10^6$
    $= 7.98 \times 10^7$

    About 7.98×10^7 $1 bills were printed in one week.

    $11.4 \times 10^6 \times 365 = 4161 \times 10^6$
    $= 4.161 \times 10^3 \times 10^6$
    $= 4.161 \times 10^9$

    About 4.161×10^9 $1 bills were printed in one year.

54. 1.72 million is equal to 1.72×10^6.

    $1.72 \times 10^6 \times 7 = 12.04 \times 10^6$
    $= 1.204 \times 10^1 \times 10^6$
    $= 1.204 \times 10^7$

    About 1.204×10^7 $5 bills were printed in one week.

    $1.72 \times 10^6 \times 365 = 627.8 \times 10^6$
    $= 6.278 \times 10^2 \times 10^6$
    $= 6.278 \times 10^8$

    About 6.278×10^8 $5 bills were printed in one year.

55. Daily:
    $1.72 \times 10^6 \times 5 = 8.6 \times 10^6 = \$8,600,000$
    Weekly:
    $1.72 \times 10^6 \times 5 \times 7 = 60.2 \times 10^6$
    $= 6.02 \times 10^1 \times 10^6$
    $= 6.02 \times 10^7$
    $= \$60,200,000$
    Yearly:
    $1.72 \times 10^6 \times 5 \times 365 = 3139 \times 10^6$
    $= 3.139 \times 10^3 \times 10^6$
    $= 3.139 \times 10^9$
    $= \$3,139,000,000$

56. Value of $1 bills printed in 2004:
    $11.4 \times 10^6 \times 1 \times 365 = 4161 \times 10^6$
    $= 4.161 \times 10^3 \times 10^6$
    $= 4.161 \times 10^9$
    $= \$4,161,000,000$
    Value of $5 bills printed in 2004: $3,139,000,000
    $4,161,000,000 > $3,139,000,000,

    $\$4,161,000,000$
    $\dfrac{- \$3,139,000,000}{\$1,022,000,000}$

    The value of the $1 bills is greater than the value of $5 bills by $1,022,000,000.

57. One year is $60 \cdot 60 \cdot 24 \cdot 365$, or 31,536,000 seconds. In scientific notation, this is 3.1536×10^7.
    $1.86 \times 10^5 \times 3.1536 \times 10^7$
    $= (1.86 \times 3.1536) \times (10^5 \times 10^7)$
    $= 5.865696 \times 10^{12}$
    Light travels 5.865696×10^{12} miles in one year.

58. $1.86 \times 10^5 \times 60 = 111.6 \times 10^5$
    $= 1.116 \times 10^2 \times 10^5$
    $= 1.116 \times 10^7$
    Light travels about 1.116×10^7 miles in one minute.
    $1.116 \times 10^7 \times 8.3 = 9.2628 \times 10^7 = 92,628,000$
    Earth is about 92,628,000 miles from the sun.

Mixed Review

59. $\dfrac{3}{8} = \dfrac{3 \cdot 4}{8 \cdot 4} = \dfrac{12}{32}$
    Because $\dfrac{11}{32} < \dfrac{12}{32}, \dfrac{11}{32} < \dfrac{3}{8}$.

60. $5\dfrac{7}{24} = \dfrac{5 \cdot 24 + 7}{24} = \dfrac{127}{24} = \dfrac{127 \cdot 2}{24 \cdot 2} = \dfrac{254}{48}$
    Because $\dfrac{254}{48} = \dfrac{254}{48}, \dfrac{254}{48} = 5\dfrac{7}{24}$.

61. $\dfrac{5}{12} = \dfrac{5 \cdot 3}{12 \cdot 3} = \dfrac{15}{36}$
    Because $\dfrac{15}{36} > \dfrac{13}{36}, \dfrac{5}{12} > \dfrac{13}{36}$.

Chapter 4, continued

62. $2\frac{1}{6} = \frac{2 \cdot 6 + 1}{6} = \frac{13}{6} = \frac{13 \cdot 6}{6 \cdot 6} = \frac{78}{36}$

Because $\frac{78}{36} < \frac{79}{36}$, $2\frac{1}{6} < \frac{79}{36}$.

63. $\frac{-9a^4}{15a} = \frac{-\overset{3}{\cancel{3}} \cdot 3 \cdot \overset{1}{\cancel{a}} \cdot a \cdot a \cdot a}{\underset{1}{\cancel{3}} \cdot 5 \cdot \underset{1}{\cancel{a}}} = \frac{-3a^3}{5}$

64. $\frac{8x^2}{2x^5} = \frac{\overset{2}{\cancel{2}} \cdot 2 \cdot 2 \cdot \overset{1}{\cancel{x}} \cdot \overset{1}{\cancel{x}}}{\underset{1}{\cancel{2}} \cdot \underset{1}{\cancel{x}} \cdot \underset{1}{\cancel{x}} \cdot x \cdot x \cdot x} = \frac{4}{x^3}$

65. $\frac{6n}{9mn} = \frac{2 \cdot \overset{1}{\cancel{3}} \cdot \overset{1}{\cancel{n}}}{\underset{1}{\cancel{3}} \cdot 3 \cdot m \cdot \underset{1}{\cancel{n}}} = \frac{2}{3m}$

66. $\frac{10xy^5}{5x^2y^4} = \frac{2 \cdot \overset{1}{\cancel{5}} \cdot \overset{1}{\cancel{x}} \cdot \overset{1}{\cancel{y}} \cdot \overset{1}{\cancel{y}} \cdot \overset{1}{\cancel{y}} \cdot \overset{1}{\cancel{y}} \cdot y}{\underset{1}{\cancel{5}} \cdot \underset{1}{\cancel{x}} \cdot x \cdot \underset{1}{\cancel{y}} \cdot \underset{1}{\cancel{y}} \cdot \underset{1}{\cancel{y}} \cdot \underset{1}{\cancel{y}}} = \frac{2y}{x}$

67. $-8 + 12 + (-16) + 18 = 4 + (-16) + 18$
$$= -12 + 18$$
$$= 6$$

68. $34 - (-43) - (3 - 6) = 77 - (-3) = 80$

69. $6 + x = 15$
$6 - 6 + x = 15 - 6$
$x = 9$

70. $-4 + x = -7$
$-4 + 4 + x = -7 + 4$
$x = -3$

71. $x - \frac{1}{3} = 2$
$x - \frac{1}{3} + \frac{1}{3} = 2 + \frac{1}{3}$
$x = 2\frac{1}{3}$

72. $\frac{9}{10} = x + \frac{4}{5}$
$\frac{9}{10} - \frac{4}{5} = x + \frac{4}{5} - \frac{4}{5}$
$\frac{9}{10} - \frac{8}{10} = x$
$\frac{1}{10} = x$

73. A;

10:46 A.M. to 12:00 P.M.:

$$\begin{array}{r} 12 \text{ h} \quad 0 \text{ min} \\ - \ 10 \text{ h} \ 46 \text{ min} \end{array} \longrightarrow \begin{array}{r} 11 \text{ h} \ 60 \text{ min} \\ - \ 10 \text{ h} \ 46 \text{ min} \\ \hline 1 \text{ h} \ 14 \text{ min} \end{array}$$

From 10:46 A.M. to 12:00 P.M., 1 hour and 14 minutes have elapsed. From 12:00 P.M. to 3:13 P.M. 3 hours and 13 minutes have elapsed.

$$\begin{array}{r} 1 \text{ h} \ 14 \text{ min} \\ + \ 3 \text{ h} \ 13 \text{ min} \\ \hline 4 \text{ h} \ 27 \text{ min} \end{array}$$

From 10:46 A.M. to 3:13 P.M., 4 hours and 27 minutes have elapsed.

Quiz 4.5–4.8 (p. 217)

1. $\frac{2}{5} = \frac{2 \cdot 3}{5 \cdot 3} = \frac{6}{15}$

Because $\frac{6}{15} = \frac{6}{15}$, you can write $\frac{2}{5} = \frac{6}{15}$.

2. $\frac{5}{6} = \frac{5 \cdot 6}{6 \cdot 6} = \frac{30}{36}$

$\frac{4}{9} = \frac{4 \cdot 4}{9 \cdot 4} = \frac{16}{36}$

Because $\frac{30}{36} > \frac{16}{36}$, you can write $\frac{5}{6} > \frac{4}{9}$.

3. $\frac{99}{15} = \frac{99 \cdot 3}{15 \cdot 3} = \frac{297}{45}$

$6\frac{5}{9} = \frac{6 \cdot 9 + 5}{9} = \frac{59}{9} = \frac{59 \cdot 5}{9 \cdot 5} = \frac{295}{45}$

Because $\frac{297}{45} > \frac{295}{45}$, you can write $\frac{99}{15} > 6\frac{5}{9}$.

4. $4\frac{35}{40} = \frac{4 \cdot 40 + 35}{40} = \frac{195}{40} = \frac{195 \cdot 3}{40 \cdot 3} = \frac{585}{120}$

$4\frac{21}{24} = \frac{4 \cdot 24 + 21}{24} = \frac{117}{24} = \frac{117 \cdot 5}{24 \cdot 5} = \frac{585}{120}$

Because $\frac{585}{120} = \frac{585}{120}$, you can write $4\frac{35}{40} = 4\frac{21}{24}$.

5. $\frac{2}{3} = \frac{2 \cdot 4}{3 \cdot 4} = \frac{8}{12}$

$\frac{5}{6} = \frac{5 \cdot 2}{6 \cdot 2} = \frac{10}{12}$

$\frac{1}{2} = \frac{1 \cdot 6}{2 \cdot 6} = \frac{6}{12}$

$5 < 6$, $6 < 8$, and $8 < 10$, so $\frac{5}{12} < \frac{6}{12}$, $\frac{6}{12} < \frac{8}{12}$, and $\frac{8}{12} < \frac{10}{12}$.

From least to greatest, the numbers are $\frac{5}{12}, \frac{1}{2}, \frac{2}{3}$, and $\frac{5}{6}$.

6. $\frac{3}{5} = \frac{3 \cdot 8}{5 \cdot 8} = \frac{24}{40}$

$\frac{7}{10} = \frac{7 \cdot 4}{10 \cdot 4} = \frac{28}{40}$

$\frac{3}{4} = \frac{3 \cdot 10}{4 \cdot 10} = \frac{30}{40}$

$\frac{7}{8} = \frac{7 \cdot 5}{8 \cdot 5} = \frac{35}{40}$

$24 < 28$, $28 < 30$, and $30 < 35$, so $\frac{24}{40} < \frac{28}{40}$, $\frac{28}{40} < \frac{30}{40}$,

and $\frac{30}{40} < \frac{35}{40}$.

From least to greatest, the numbers are $\frac{3}{5}, \frac{7}{10}, \frac{3}{4}$, and $\frac{7}{8}$.

7. $1\frac{4}{7} = \frac{7 \cdot 1 + 4}{7} = \frac{11}{7} = \frac{11 \cdot 8}{7 \cdot 8} = \frac{88}{56}$

$1\frac{5}{14} = \frac{14 \cdot 1 + 5}{14} = \frac{19}{14} = \frac{19 \cdot 4}{14 \cdot 4} = \frac{76}{56}$

$\frac{5}{4} = \frac{5 \cdot 14}{4 \cdot 14} = \frac{70}{56}$

$1\frac{5}{8} = \frac{8 \cdot 1 + 5}{8} = \frac{13}{8} = \frac{13 \cdot 7}{8 \cdot 7} = \frac{91}{56}$

$70 < 76$, $76 < 88$, and $88 < 91$, so $\frac{70}{56} < \frac{76}{56}$, $\frac{76}{56} < \frac{88}{56}$,

and $\frac{88}{56} < \frac{91}{56}$.

From least to greatest, the numbers are $\frac{5}{4}$, $1\frac{5}{14}$, $1\frac{4}{7}$, and $1\frac{5}{8}$.

8. $4\frac{8}{9} = \frac{4 \cdot 9 + 8}{9} = \frac{44}{9} = \frac{44 \cdot 14}{9 \cdot 14} = \frac{616}{126}$

$4\frac{17}{18} = \frac{4 \cdot 18 + 17}{18} = \frac{89}{18} = \frac{89 \cdot 7}{18 \cdot 7} = \frac{623}{126}$

$\frac{65}{14} = \frac{65 \cdot 9}{14 \cdot 9} = \frac{585}{126}$

$4\frac{6}{7} = \frac{4 \cdot 7 + 6}{7} = \frac{34}{7} = \frac{34 \cdot 18}{7 \cdot 18} = \frac{612}{126}$

$585 < 612$, $612 < 616$, and $616 < 623$, so $\frac{585}{126} < \frac{612}{126}$,

$\frac{612}{126} < \frac{616}{126}$, and $\frac{616}{126} < \frac{623}{126}$.

From least to greatest, the numbers are $\frac{65}{14}$, $4\frac{6}{7}$, $4\frac{8}{9}$, and $4\frac{17}{18}$.

9. $b^2 \cdot b^4 = b^{2+4} = b^6$　　　**10.** $c^5 \cdot c^{-2} = c^{5+(-2)} = c^3$

11. $\frac{a^7}{a^2} = a^{7-2} = a^5$　　　**12.** $\frac{n^{-2}}{n^3} = n^{-2-3} = n^{-5} = \frac{1}{n^5}$

13. $1{,}120{,}000{,}000 = 1.12 \times 10^9$

Technology Activity 4.8 (p. 218)

1. $(3.19 \times 10^7) \times (8.5 \times 10^6) = 2.7115 \times 10^{14}$

2. $(6.7 \times 10^{-3}) \times (1.12 \times 10^{15}) = 7.504 \times 10^{12}$

3. $(3.3 \times 10^{-3}) \times (4.8 \times 10^{-9}) = 1.584 \times 10^{-11}$

4. $(7.1 \times 10^{-9}) \times (2.05 \times 10^6) = 1.4555 \times 10^{-2}$

5. $\frac{1.681 \times 10^{10}}{2.05 \times 10^2} = 8.2 \times 10^6$

6. $\frac{1.44 \times 10^{-15}}{1.2 \times 10} = 1.2 \times 10^{-16}$

7. $\frac{8.241 \times 10^{-11}}{2.05 \times 10^{-4}} = 4.02 \times 10^{-7}$

8. $\frac{6.25 \times 10^{-8}}{1.25 \times 10^{-12}} = 5 \times 10^4$

9. $\frac{1.26 \times 10^9}{2.8 \times 10^2} = 4.5 \times 10^6$

10. $\frac{2.64 \times 10^{-8}}{2.2 \times 10^{-13}} = 1.2 \times 10^5$

11. $\frac{2.59 \times 10^{-6}}{1.85 \times 10^3} = 1.4 \times 10^{-9}$

12. $\frac{3 \times 10^{16}}{3.75 \times 10^{-16}} = 8 \times 10^{31}$

13. 110 billion $= 1.1 \times 10^{11}$

Week: $7(1.1 \times 10^{11}) = 7.7 \times 10^{11}$

Year: $365(1.1 \times 10^{11}) = 4.015 \times 10^{13}$

In a week about 7.7×10^{11} gallons of water flow through Lake Erie. In a year about 4.015×10^{13} gallons of water flow through Lake Erie.

14. $\frac{7 \times 10^{-6}}{3 \times 10^{-8}} = 233\frac{1}{3}$

The nucleus is $233\frac{1}{3}$ times larger than a ribosome.

Mixed Review of Problem Solving (p. 219)

1. a. Antarctica: $14{,}000{,}000 = 1.4 \times 10^7$

Canada: $10 \times 10^6 = 1 \times 10^7$

Egypt: $1{,}000{,}000 = 1 \times 10^6$

India: $0.33 \times 10^7 = 3.3 \times 10^{-1} \times 10^7 = 3.3 \times 10^6$

Russia: 1.7×10^7

United States: $9{,}600{,}000 = 9.6 \times 10^6$

b. 1.7×10^7 is greater than 1×10^6,

3.3×10^6, or 9.6×10^6 because $7 > 6$.

1.7×10^7 is greater than 1.4×10^7 or 1×10^7 because $1.7 > 1.4$ and $1.7 > 1$.

So, Russia has the greatest land area.

c. 1×10^6 is less than 1.4×10^7, 1×10^7, or 1.7×10^7 because $6 < 7$.

1×10^6 is less than 3.3×10^6 and 9.6×10^6 because $1 < 3.3$ and $1 < 9.6$.

So, Egypt has the least land area.

d. To determine how many times greater the land area of Russia is than the land area of Egypt, divide the areas.

$\frac{1.7 \times 10^7}{1 \times 10^6} = 1.7 \times 10^1 = 17$

Russia is 17 times larger than Egypt.

2. a. Game 1: $\frac{10}{22} = \frac{\cancel{2} \cdot 5}{\cancel{2} \cdot 11} = \frac{5}{11}$

Game 2: $\frac{9}{12} = \frac{3 \cdot \cancel{3}}{2 \cdot 2 \cdot \cancel{3}} = \frac{3}{4}$

Game 3: $\frac{6}{18} = \frac{\cancel{2} \cdot \cancel{3}}{\cancel{2} \cdot \cancel{3} \cdot 3} = \frac{1}{3}$

Game 4: $\frac{15}{25} = \frac{3 \cdot \cancel{5}}{\cancel{5} \cdot 5} = \frac{3}{5}$

Game 5: $\frac{9}{18} = \frac{\cancel{3} \cdot \cancel{3}}{2 \cdot \cancel{3} \cdot \cancel{3}} = \frac{1}{2}$

b. $\frac{5}{11} = \frac{5 \cdot 60}{11 \cdot 60} = \frac{300}{660}$

$\frac{3}{4} = \frac{3 \cdot 165}{4 \cdot 165} = \frac{495}{660}$

$\frac{1}{3} = \frac{1 \cdot 220}{3 \cdot 220} = \frac{220}{660}$

$\frac{3}{5} = \frac{3 \cdot 132}{5 \cdot 132} = \frac{396}{660}$

$\frac{1}{2} = \frac{1 \cdot 330}{2 \cdot 330} = \frac{330}{660}$

In Game 2, you made the greatest fraction of your shots.

Chapter 4, *continued*

c. $\dfrac{5}{11} = \dfrac{5 \cdot 60}{11 \cdot 60} = \dfrac{300}{660}$

$\dfrac{3}{4} = \dfrac{3 \cdot 165}{4 \cdot 165} = \dfrac{495}{660}$

$\dfrac{1}{3} = \dfrac{1 \cdot 220}{3 \cdot 220} = \dfrac{220}{660}$

$\dfrac{3}{5} = \dfrac{3 \cdot 132}{5 \cdot 132} = \dfrac{396}{660}$

$\dfrac{1}{2} = \dfrac{1 \cdot 330}{2 \cdot 330} = \dfrac{330}{660}$

In Game 3, you made the least fraction of your shots.

d. No, you cannot conclude that your accuracy improved over time. *Sample answer:* Your accuracy went up and down from game to game.

3. *Sample answer:* The thickness of a piece of paper when measured in centimeters is best expressed in scientific notation using a negative power of 10.

4. A light year is equal to 9.5×10^{12} kilometers.

$9.5 \times 10^{12} \times 2.3 \times 10^6 = 21.85 \times 10^{18}$
$= 2.185 \times 10 \times 10^{18}$
$= 2.185 \times 10^{19}$

The Andromeda galaxy is 2.185×10^{19} kilometers away.

5. Because 1 nanometer equals 10^{-6} millimeter, 1 millimeter equals 10^6, or 1 million nanometers. To find the length of the teddy bear in nanometers, multiply 1 million nanometers per millimeter by 12 millimeters.

The teddy bear is $1 \times 12 = 12$ million nanometers long.

6. $6.3 \times 10^{-2} \times 10^2 = 6.3 \times 10^0 = 6.3$

Your wallet sized photo is about 6.3 cm wide.

7. a. Cube A: $V = 2^3$ m^3

Cube B: $V = (2^2)^3 = 2^6$ m^3

Cube C: $V = (2^3)^3 = 2^9$ m^3

b. $\dfrac{\text{Cube B}}{\text{Cube A}} = \dfrac{2^6}{2^3} = 2^3 = 8$

The volume of cube B is 8 times greater than the volume of cube A.

$\dfrac{\text{Cube C}}{\text{Cube A}} = \dfrac{2^9}{2^3} = 2^6 = 64$

The volume of cube C is 64 times greater than the volume of cube A.

c. *Sample answer:* Each comparison increases by a factor of 8, and $64(8) = 512$.

So, a cube with a side length of 2^4 has a volume that is 512 times greater than the volume of Cube A.

Chapter 4 Review (pp. 220–224)

1. The *greatest common factor* of two numbers is the highest number that divides into both numbers. The *least common denominator* is the smallest number into which both numbers divide.

2. *Sample answer:* Three examples of prime numbers greater than 20 are 23, 29, and 31.

3. *Sample answer:* Three examples of monomials are $2x$, $4a^2b$, and $5a^2d^3$.

4. Two numbers are relatively prime if their only common factor is 1.

5. A fraction is in *simplest form* if its numerator and denominator have 1 as their GCF.

6. A *composite number* is a whole number that has positive factors other than 1 and itself.

7. Two fractions are *equivalent* if they represent the same number.

8. Factors of 24: 1, 2, 3, 4, 6, 8, 12, 24

24 is composite because it has factors other than 1 and itself.

9. Factors of 91: 1, 7, 13, 91

91 is composite because it has factors other than 1 and itself.

10. Factors of 53: 1, 53

53 is prime because its only factors are 1 and itself.

11. Factors of 197: 1, 197

197 is prime because its only factors are 1 and itself.

12.

The prime factorization of 40 is $2^3 \cdot 5$.

13. The prime factorization of 7 is 7.

14.

85
5×17

The prime factorization of 85 is $5 \cdot 17$.

15.

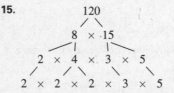

The prime factorization of 120 is $2^3 \cdot 3 \cdot 5$.

16. $19a^2b = 19 \cdot a \cdot a \cdot b$

17. $28xy^3 = 2 \cdot 2 \cdot 7 \cdot x \cdot y \cdot y \cdot y$

18. $56u^2v^2 = 2 \cdot 2 \cdot 2 \cdot 7 \cdot u \cdot u \cdot v \cdot v$

19. $80p^4q^3 = 2 \cdot 2 \cdot 2 \cdot 2 \cdot 5 \cdot p \cdot p \cdot p \cdot p \cdot q \cdot q \cdot q$

20. Write 48 as a product of two integers in all possible ways.

$1 \times 48 \qquad 2 \times 24 \qquad 3 \times 16$
$4 \times 12 \qquad 6 \times 8$

The factors of 48 are 1, 2, 3, 4, 6, 8, 12, 16, 24, and 48. So, each row can have 1, 2, 3, 4, 6, 8, 12, 16, 24, or 48 trees.

21. $48 = 2^4 \cdot 3$
$80 = 2^4 \cdot 5$

The GCF of 48 and 80 is 2^4, or 16.

Chapter 4, continued

22. $60 = 2^2 \cdot 3 \cdot 5$

$100 = 2^2 \cdot 5^2$

The GCF of 60 and 100 is $2^2 \cdot 5$, or 20.

23. $14a^3 = 2 \cdot 7 \cdot a^3$

$21a = 3 \cdot 7 \cdot a$

The GCF of $14a^3$ and $21a$ is $7 \cdot a$, or $7a$.

24. $20y^4 = 2^2 \cdot 5 \cdot y^4$

$60y^5 = 2^2 \cdot 3 \cdot 5 \cdot y^5$

The GCF of $20y^4$ and $60y^5$ is $2^2 \cdot 5 \cdot y^4$, or $20y^4$.

25. $20 = 2^2 \cdot 5$

$40 = 2^3 \cdot 5$

$90 = 2 \cdot 3^2 \cdot 5$

The GCF of 20, 40, and 90 is $2 \cdot 5$, or 10.

26. $48 = 2^4 \cdot 3$

$60 = 2^2 \cdot 3 \cdot 5$

$165 = 3 \cdot 5 \cdot 11$

The GCF of 48, 60, and 165 is 3.

27. $2x = 2 \cdot x$

$x^2 = x \cdot x$

$x^3 = x \cdot x \cdot x$

The GCF of $2x$, x^2, and x^3 is x.

28. $54s^4t^4 = 2 \cdot 3^3 \cdot s^4 \cdot t^4$

$164st^3 = 2^2 \cdot 41 \cdot s \cdot t^3$

The GCF of $54s^4t^4$ and $164st^3$ is $2 \cdot s \cdot t^3$, or $2st^3$.

29. 11 is a prime number.

$15 = 3 \cdot 5$

11 and 15 are relatively prime numbers because they have no common prime factors.

30. $92 = 2^2 \cdot 23$

$115 = 5 \cdot 23$

92 and 115 are not relatively prime because they share the factor 23.

31. $72 = 2^3 \cdot 3^2$

$176 = 2^4 \cdot 11$

72 and 176 are not relatively prime because they share the factors 2, 4, and 8.

32. $30 = 2 \cdot 3 \cdot 5$

$91 = 7 \cdot 13$

30 and 91 are relatively prime because they have no common prime factors.

33. $60 = 2^2 \cdot 3 \cdot 5$

$120 = 2^3 \cdot 3 \cdot 5$

$90 = 2 \cdot 3^2 \cdot 5$

The GCF of 60, 120, and 90 is $2 \cdot 3 \cdot 5$, or 30.

Cranberry sauce: $60 \div 30 = 2$

Fruit: $120 \div 30 = 4$

Corn: $90 \div 30 = 3$

Muffin mix: $60 \div 30 = 2$

Your class can make 30 baskets consisting of 2 cans of cranberry sauce, 4 cans of fruit, 3 cans of corn, and 2 boxes of muffin mix.

34. $\dfrac{15}{45} = \dfrac{15 \div 15}{45 \div 15} = \dfrac{1}{3}$

35. $\dfrac{12}{80} = \dfrac{12 \div 4}{80 \div 4} = \dfrac{3}{20}$

36. $\dfrac{9ab}{27a} = \dfrac{\overset{1}{\cancel{3}} \cdot \overset{1}{\cancel{3}} \cdot \overset{1}{\cancel{a}} \cdot b}{\cancel{3} \cdot \cancel{3} \cdot 3 \cdot \cancel{a}} = \dfrac{b}{3}$

37. $\dfrac{18n^3}{54n} = \dfrac{2 \cdot \overset{1}{\cancel{3}} \cdot \overset{1}{\cancel{3}} \cdot \overset{1}{\cancel{n}} \cdot n \cdot n}{2 \cdot \underset{1}{\cancel{3}} \cdot \underset{1}{\cancel{3}} \cdot 3 \cdot \underset{1}{\cancel{n}}} = \dfrac{n^2}{3}$

38. $28 = 2^2 \cdot 7$

$42 = 2 \cdot 3 \cdot 7$

The LCM of 28 and 42 is $2^2 \cdot 3 \cdot 7$, or 84.

39. $54 = 2 \cdot 3^3$

$90 = 2 \cdot 3^2 \cdot 5$

The LCM of 54 and 90 is $2 \cdot 3^3 \cdot 5$, or 270.

40. $10cd = 2 \cdot 5 \cdot c \cdot d$

$25c^2 = 5^2 \cdot c^2$

The LCM of $10cd$ and $25c^2$ is $2 \cdot 5^2 \cdot c^2 \cdot d$, or $50c^2d$.

41. $9n^3 = 3^2 \cdot n^3$

$12n^2 = 2^2 \cdot 3 \cdot n^2$

The LCM of $9n^3$ and $12n^2$ is $2^2 \cdot 3^2 \cdot n^3$, or $36n^3$.

42. $4 = 2^2$

$3 = 3$

The LCM of 4 and 3 is $2^2 \cdot 3$, or 12. So, Yolanda will have both classes on the same day again in 12 days.

43. $\dfrac{35}{8} = \dfrac{35 \cdot 2}{8 \cdot 2} = \dfrac{70}{16}$

Because $\dfrac{79}{16} > \dfrac{70}{16}$, you can write $\dfrac{79}{16} > \dfrac{35}{8}$.

44. $6\dfrac{2}{3} = \dfrac{3 \cdot 6 + 2}{3} = \dfrac{20}{3} = \dfrac{20 \cdot 4}{3 \cdot 4} = \dfrac{80}{12}$

Because $\dfrac{80}{12} < \dfrac{81}{12}$, you can write $6\dfrac{2}{3} < \dfrac{81}{12}$.

45. $17\dfrac{8}{9} = \dfrac{9 \cdot 17 + 8}{9} = \dfrac{161}{9}$

Because $\dfrac{161}{9} = \dfrac{161}{9}$, you can write $\dfrac{161}{9} = 17\dfrac{8}{9}$.

46. $14\dfrac{4}{5} = \dfrac{5 \cdot 14 + 4}{5} = \dfrac{74}{5} = \dfrac{74 \cdot 3}{5 \cdot 3} = \dfrac{222}{15}$

Because $\dfrac{223}{15} > \dfrac{222}{15}$, you can write $\dfrac{223}{15} > 14\dfrac{4}{5}$.

47. $\frac{7}{11} = \frac{7 \cdot 24}{11 \cdot 24} = \frac{168}{264}$

$\frac{2}{3} = \frac{2 \cdot 88}{3 \cdot 88} = \frac{176}{264}$

$\frac{5}{8} = \frac{5 \cdot 33}{8 \cdot 33} = \frac{165}{264}$

$165 < 168$ and $168 < 176$, so $\frac{165}{264} < \frac{168}{264}$ and $\frac{168}{264} < \frac{176}{264}$.

From least to greatest, the numbers are $\frac{5}{8}, \frac{7}{11}$, and $\frac{2}{3}$.

48. $9\frac{1}{2} = \frac{9 \cdot 2 + 1}{2} = \frac{19}{2} = \frac{19 \cdot 6}{2 \cdot 6} = \frac{114}{12}$

$\frac{29}{3} = \frac{29 \cdot 4}{3 \cdot 4} = \frac{116}{12}$

$\frac{37}{4} = \frac{37 \cdot 3}{4 \cdot 3} = \frac{111}{12}$

$111 < 114$ and $114 < 116$, so $\frac{111}{12} < \frac{114}{12}$ and $\frac{114}{12} < \frac{116}{12}$.

From least to greatest, the numbers are $\frac{37}{4}, 9\frac{1}{2}$, and $\frac{29}{3}$.

49. $5\frac{7}{8} = \frac{5 \cdot 8 + 7}{8} = \frac{47}{8} = \frac{47 \cdot 9}{8 \cdot 9} = \frac{423}{72}$

$\frac{53}{9} = \frac{53 \cdot 8}{9 \cdot 8} = \frac{424}{72}$

$\frac{17}{3} = \frac{17 \cdot 24}{3 \cdot 24} = \frac{408}{72}$

$408 < 423$ and $423 < 424$, so $\frac{408}{72} < \frac{423}{72}$ and $\frac{423}{72} < \frac{424}{72}$.

From least to greatest, the numbers are $\frac{17}{3}, 5\frac{7}{8}$, and $\frac{53}{9}$.

50. $\frac{25}{6} = \frac{25 \cdot 10}{6 \cdot 10} = \frac{250}{60}$

$\frac{49}{12} = \frac{49 \cdot 5}{12 \cdot 5} = \frac{245}{60}$

$4\frac{1}{10} = \frac{4 \cdot 10 + 1}{10} = \frac{41}{10} = \frac{41 \cdot 6}{10 \cdot 6} = \frac{246}{60}$

$245 < 246$ and $246 < 250$, so $\frac{245}{60} < \frac{246}{60}$ and $\frac{246}{60} < \frac{250}{60}$.

From least to greatest, the numbers are $\frac{49}{12}, 4\frac{1}{10}$, and $\frac{25}{6}$.

51. $4\frac{7}{8} = \frac{4 \cdot 8 + 7}{8} = \frac{39}{8} = \frac{39 \cdot 3}{8 \cdot 3} = \frac{117}{24}$

$\frac{29}{6} = \frac{29 \cdot 4}{6 \cdot 4} = \frac{116}{24}$

$\frac{117}{24} - \frac{116}{24} = \frac{1}{24}$

Because $\frac{117}{24} > \frac{116}{24}$, Joe picked more green beans than

Sarah. He picked $\frac{1}{24}$ cup more green beans.

52. $n^4 \cdot n^9 = n^{4+9} = n^{13}$ **53.** $9^6 \cdot 9^3 = 9^{6+3} = 9^9$

54. $5^4 \cdot 5^7 = 5^{4+7} = 5^{11}$ **55.** $a^{12} \cdot a^{11} = a^{12+11} = a^{23}$

56. $\frac{x^7}{x^5} = x^{7-5} = x^2$ **57.** $\frac{5^{10}}{5^7} = 5^{10-7} = 5^3$

58. $\frac{11^9}{11^3} = 11^{9-3} = 11^6$ **59.** $\frac{b^{15}}{b^8} = b^{15-8} = b^7$

00. $\frac{x^5 \cdot x^4}{x^8} = \frac{x^9}{x^8} = x^{0}$ $^{0} = x$

61. $\frac{y^{20}}{y^3 \cdot y^9} = \frac{y^{20}}{y^{12}}$ **62.** $\frac{2^5 \cdot x^7}{2^3 \cdot x} = 2^{5-3} \cdot x^{7-1}$

$\qquad = y^{20-12}$ $\qquad\qquad\qquad = 2^2 \cdot x^6$

$\qquad = y^8$ $\qquad\qquad\qquad\quad = 4x^6$

63. $\frac{y^6 \cdot x^{12}}{y^4 \cdot x^9} = y^{6-4} \cdot x^{12-9} = y^2 x^3$

64. $12a^{-5} \cdot a^0 = \frac{12}{a^5} \cdot 1 = \frac{12}{a^5}$

65. $n^7 \cdot n^{-10} = n^{7+(-10)} = n^{-3} = \frac{1}{n^3}$

66. $\frac{m^{-6}}{m^5} = m^{-6-5} = m^{-11} = \frac{1}{m^{11}}$

67. $\frac{18c^{-9}}{6c^4} = \frac{\overset{1}{\cancel{2}} \cdot \overset{1}{\cancel{3}} \cdot 3 \cdot c^{-9-4}}{\underset{1}{\cancel{2}} \cdot \underset{1}{\cancel{3}}} = 3c^{-13} = \frac{3}{c^{13}}$

68. $b^5 \cdot b^2 = b^{5+2} = b^7$

69. $\frac{9z^{-4}}{6z^{-2}} = \frac{\cancel{3} \cdot 3 \cdot z^{-4-(-2)}}{2 \cdot \cancel{3}} = \frac{3z^{-4+2}}{2} = \frac{3z^{-2}}{2} = \frac{3}{2z^2}$

70. $\frac{8y^5}{12y^{-11}} = \frac{\cancel{2} \cdot \cancel{2} \cdot 2 \cdot y^{5-(-11)}}{\cancel{2} \cdot \cancel{2} \cdot 3} = \frac{2y^{5+11}}{3} = \frac{2y^{16}}{3}$

71. $5x^3 \cdot 4x^{-3} = (5 \cdot 4) \cdot (x^{3+(-3)})$

$\qquad\qquad\qquad = 20 \cdot x^0$

$\qquad\qquad\qquad = 20 \cdot 1$

$\qquad\qquad\qquad = 20$

72. $34{,}600{,}000{,}000 = 3.46 \times 10^{10}$

73. $0.0000009 = 9 \times 10^{-7}$

74. $0.000000000502 = 5.02 \times 10^{-10}$

75. $2.36 \times 10^8 = 236{,}000{,}000$

76. $0.015 \times 10^5 = 1500$

77. $9.4 \times 10^{-3} = 0.0094$

78. $(3 \times 10^{16}) \times (5 \times 10^{-5}) = (3 \times 5) \times (10^{16} \times 10^{-5})$

$\qquad\qquad\qquad\qquad\qquad = 15 \times 10^{11}$

$\qquad\qquad\qquad\qquad\qquad = 1.5 \times 10 \times 10^{11}$

$\qquad\qquad\qquad\qquad\qquad = 1.5 \times 10^{12}$

79. $(6.2 \times 10^{-4}) \times (2.6 \times 10^{12})$

$\quad = (6.2 \times 2.6) \times (10^{-4} \times 10^{12})$

$\quad = 16.12 \times 10^8$

$\quad = 1.612 \times 10 \times 10^8$

$\quad = 1.612 \times 10^9$

80. $(1.08 \times 10^7) \times (2.09 \times 10^{-2})$

$\quad = (1.08 \times 2.09) \times (10^7 \times 10^{-2})$

$\quad = 2.2572 \times 10^5$

81. $(7.63 \times 10^{11}) \times (4.8 \times 10^{-3})$

$\quad = (7.63 \times 4.8) \times (10^{11} \times 10^{-3})$

$\quad = 36.624 \times 10^8$

$\quad = 3.6624 \times 10 \times 10^8$

$\quad = 3.6624 \times 10^9$

Chapter 4, continued

82. $100{,}000 = 1 \times 10^5$

$1 \times 10^5 \times 60 = 60 \times 10^5 = 6 \times 10^6$

$1 \times 10^5 \times 3600 = 3600 \times 10^5 = 3.6 \times 10^8$

Water flows at 6×10^6 cubic feet per minute, and 3.6×10^8 cubic feet per hour.

Chapter 4 Test (p. 225)

1.

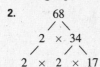

Using exponents, the prime factorization of 49 is 7^2.

2.

```
        68
       /  \
      2  × 34
     /    /  \
    2  ×  2  × 17
```

Using exponents, the prime factorization of 68 is $2^2 \cdot 17$.

3.

```
     95
    /  \
   5  × 19
```

The prime factorization of 95 is $5 \cdot 19$.

4.

```
              112
             /   \
           4   ×  28
          / |    |  \
        2 × 2 × 7 × 4
       /  /   /   /  \
      2 × 2 × 7 × 2 × 2
```

Using exponents, the prime factorization of 112 is $2^4 \cdot 7$.

5. $36 = 2^2 \cdot 3^2$

$84 = 2^2 \cdot 3 \cdot 7$

The GCF of 36 and 84 is $2^2 \cdot 3$, or 12.

6. $45 = 3^2 \cdot 5$

$117 = 3^2 \cdot 13$

The GCF of 45 and 117 is 3^2, or 9.

7. $2z^3 = 2 \cdot z^3$

$3z^2 = 3 \cdot z^2$

The GCF of $2z^3$ and $3z^2$ is z^2.

8. $14r^2 = 2 \cdot 7 \cdot r^2$

$42r = 2 \cdot 3 \cdot 7 \cdot r$

The GCF of $14r^2$ and $42r$ is $2 \cdot 7 \cdot r$, or $14r$.

9. $4 = 2^2$

$16 = 2^4$

$32 = 2^5$

The LCM of 4, 16, and 32 is 2^5, or 32.

10. $18 = 2 \cdot 3^2$

$24 = 2^3 \cdot 3$

$36 = 2^2 \cdot 3^2$

The LCM of 18, 24, and 36 is $2^3 \cdot 3^2$, or 72.

11. $5x^2y = 5 \cdot x^2 \cdot y$

$21xy^3 = 3 \cdot 7 \cdot x \cdot y^3$

The LCM of $5x^2y$ and $21xy^3$ is $3 \cdot 5 \cdot 7 \cdot x^2 \cdot y^3$, or $105x^2y^3$.

12. $54pq^2 = 2 \cdot 3^3 \cdot p \cdot q^2$

$63p^3q^3 = 3^2 \cdot 7 \cdot p^3 \cdot q^3$

The LCM of $54pq^2$ and $63p^3q^3$ is $2 \cdot 3^3 \cdot 7 \cdot p^3 \cdot q^3$, or $378p^3q^3$.

13. $\dfrac{11}{12} = \dfrac{11 \cdot 4}{12 \cdot 4} = \dfrac{44}{48}$

Because $\dfrac{44}{48} > \dfrac{41}{48}$, you can write $\dfrac{11}{12} > \dfrac{41}{48}$.

14. $4\dfrac{3}{6} = \dfrac{6 \cdot 4 + 3}{6} = \dfrac{27}{6}$

$\dfrac{9}{2} = \dfrac{9 \cdot 3}{2 \cdot 3} = \dfrac{27}{6}$

Because $\dfrac{27}{6} = \dfrac{27}{6}$, you can write $4\dfrac{3}{6} = \dfrac{9}{2}$.

15. $8\dfrac{7}{16} = \dfrac{16 \cdot 8 + 7}{16} = \dfrac{135}{16}$

$\dfrac{17}{2} = \dfrac{17 \cdot 8}{2 \cdot 8} = \dfrac{136}{16}$

Because $\dfrac{135}{16} < \dfrac{136}{16}$, you can write $8\dfrac{7}{16} < \dfrac{17}{2}$.

16. $5\dfrac{1}{7} = \dfrac{5 \cdot 7 + 1}{7} = \dfrac{36}{7}$

Because $\dfrac{35}{7} < \dfrac{36}{7}$, you can write $\dfrac{35}{7} < 5\dfrac{1}{7}$.

17. $m^8 \cdot m^3 = m^{8+3} = m^{11}$

18. $6^2 \cdot 6^6 \cdot 6^0 = 6^{2+6+0} = 6^8$

19. $\dfrac{n^{16}}{n^{10}} = n^{16-10} = n^6$

20. $\dfrac{p^4 \cdot p^6}{p^2 \cdot p^7} = \dfrac{p^{4+6}}{p^{2+7}} = \dfrac{p^{10}}{p^9} = p^{10-9} = p$

21. $5x^{-3} = 5 \cdot x^{-3} = \dfrac{5}{x^3}$

22. $c^{-1} \cdot c^{-7} = c^{-1+(-7)} = c^{-8} = \dfrac{1}{c^8}$

23. $\dfrac{-4u^{-9}}{u^3} = -4 \cdot u^{-9-3} = -4 \cdot u^{-12} = \dfrac{-4}{u^{12}}$

24. $\dfrac{16a^2b^5}{8a^4b} = 2 \cdot a^{2-4}b^{5-1} = 2 \cdot a^{-2}b^4 = \dfrac{2b^4}{a^2}$

25. $200{,}400 = 2.004 \times 10^5$

26. $0.000005126 = 5.126 \times 10^{-6}$

27. $42{,}000 = 4.2 \times 10^4$

28. $7.72 \times 10^6 = 7{,}720{,}000$

29. $1.46 \times 10^{-6} = 0.00000146$

30. $8.22 \times 10^{-4} = 0.000822$

31. $(6 \times 10^5) \times (5 \times 10^7) = (6 \times 5) \times (10^5 \times 10^7)$

$= 30 \times 10^{12}$

$= 3 \times 10^1 \times 10^{12}$

$= 3 \times 10^{13}$

32. $(8.1 \times 10^4) \times (9.2 \times 10^8) = (8.1 \times 9.2) \times (10^4 \times 10^8)$

$$= 74.52 \times 10^{12}$$
$$= 7.452 \times 10^1 \times 10^{12}$$
$$= 7.452 \times 10^{13}$$

33. $(4.2 \times 10^{-5}) \times (6 \times 10^{-2}) = (4.2 \times 6) \times (10^{-5} \times 10^{-2})$

$$= 25.2 \times 10^{-7}$$
$$= 2.52 \times 10^1 \times 10^{-7}$$
$$= 2.52 \times 10^{-6}$$

34. $(3.8 \times 10^{-4}) \times (2.9 \times 10^7) = (3.8 \times 2.9) \times (10^{-4} \times 10^7)$

$$= 11.02 \times 10^3$$
$$= 1.102 \times 10 \times 10^3$$
$$= 1.102 \times 10^4$$

35. $\dfrac{1}{8} = \dfrac{1 \cdot 6}{8 \cdot 6} = \dfrac{6}{48}$

$\dfrac{3}{16} = \dfrac{3 \cdot 3}{16 \cdot 3} = \dfrac{9}{48}$

$\dfrac{1}{6} = \dfrac{1 \cdot 8}{6 \cdot 8} = \dfrac{8}{48}$

The yellow cake had the least amount left over, while the chocolate cake had the most left over.

36. $\dfrac{1}{1,000,000} = \dfrac{1}{10^6} = 10^{-6}$

37. $120,000 = 1.2 \times 10^5$

38. $1.5 \times 10^{-3} = 0.0015$ kg

Standardized Test Preparation (pp. 226–227)

1. B;

$\dfrac{60}{210} = \dfrac{60 \div 30}{210 \div 30} = \dfrac{2}{7}$

$\dfrac{2}{7}$ of the total calories in bar B is from protein.

2. B;

$\dfrac{40}{170} = \dfrac{4}{17} = \dfrac{4 \cdot 4550}{17 \cdot 4550} = \dfrac{18,200}{77,350}$

$\dfrac{60}{210} = \dfrac{2}{7} = \dfrac{2 \cdot 11,050}{7 \cdot 11,050} = \dfrac{22,100}{77,350}$

$\dfrac{65}{250} = \dfrac{13}{50} = \dfrac{13 \cdot 1547}{50 \cdot 1547} = \dfrac{20,111}{77,350}$

$\dfrac{60}{260} = \dfrac{3}{13} = \dfrac{3 \cdot 5950}{13 \cdot 5950} = \dfrac{17,850}{77,350}$

Because 22,100 is greater than 18,200, 20,111, or 17,850, $\dfrac{22,111}{77,350}$ or $\dfrac{60}{210}$ is the greatest fraction.

So, bar B contains the greatest fraction of calories from protein.

Standardized Test Practice (pp. 228–229)

1. D;

List all possible arrangements by showing 80 as a product of two numbers in all possible ways. Then find the perimeter of each arrangement in terms of photo side lengths.

$1 \times 80 \quad P = 2(1) + 2(80) = 162$

$2 \times 40 \quad P = 2(2) + 2(40) = 84$

$4 \times 20 \quad P = 2(4) + 2(20) = 48$

$5 \times 16 \quad P = 2(5) + 2(16) = 42$

$8 \times 10 \quad P = 2(8) + 2(10) = 36$

The arrangement with the least possible perimeter is 8 photos by 10 photos or $8 \cdot 6 = 48$ inches by $10 \cdot 6 = 60$ inches.

The perimeter in terms of inches is $2(48) + 2(60) = 216$ inches.

2. B;

$36 \div 4 = 9$

$40 \div 4 = 10$

$60 \div 4 = 15$

Each number is divisible by 4, so 36, 40, and 60 could be the total number of scouts in each troop.

3. B;

$\dfrac{(3.6 \times 10^2) \times (1.95 \times 10^{-3})}{2 \times 10^{-3}} = \dfrac{(3.6 \times 1.95) \times (10^2 \times 10^{-3})}{2 \times 10^{-3}}$

$$= \dfrac{7.02 \times 10^{-1}}{2 \times 10^{-3}}$$
$$= 3.51 \times 10^2$$
$$= 351 \text{ coins}$$

4. C; $\dfrac{16}{30} = \dfrac{16 \div 2}{30 \div 2} = \dfrac{8}{15}$

5. A;

$w = x$

$P = 2\ell + 2w = 10x$

$2\ell + 2x = 10x$

$2\ell = 8x$

$\ell = 4x$

$A = \ell w = x \cdot 4x = 4x^2$

$\dfrac{\text{Perimeter of rectangle}}{\text{Area of rectangle}} = \dfrac{10x}{4x^2} = \dfrac{\overset{1}{2} \cdot 5x^{1-2}}{\underset{1}{2} \cdot 2} = \dfrac{5x^{-1}}{2} \text{ in.}^{-1}$

6. B;

$120 = 2^3 \cdot 3 \cdot 5$

$150 = 2 \cdot 3 \cdot 5^2$

The GCF of 120 and 150 is $2 \cdot 3 \cdot 5$, or 30.

There are $120 \div 30 = 4$ girls on each team.

Chapter 4, *continued*

7. B;

Alexis: $\dfrac{42}{150} = \dfrac{7}{25} = \dfrac{7 \cdot 8}{25 \cdot 8} = \dfrac{56}{200}$

Jim: $\dfrac{51}{170} = \dfrac{3}{10} = \dfrac{3 \cdot 20}{10 \cdot 20} = \dfrac{60}{200}$

Eric: $\dfrac{34}{136} = \dfrac{1}{4} = \dfrac{1 \cdot 50}{4 \cdot 50} = \dfrac{50}{200}$

Brad: $\dfrac{44}{160} = \dfrac{11}{40} = \dfrac{11 \cdot 5}{40 \cdot 5} = \dfrac{55}{200}$

Because 60 is greater than 56, 50, or 55, $\dfrac{60}{200}$ or $\dfrac{51}{170}$ is the

greatest fraction. So, Jim had the greatest fraction of hits.

8. C;

$45 = 3^2 \cdot 5$

$60 = 2^2 \cdot 3 \cdot 5$

The LCM of 45 and 60 is $2^2 \cdot 3^2 \cdot 5$, or 180.

$180 \div 45 = 4$

The least number of bottles he could have sold is 4.

9. C; $5^{-7} \cdot 625 = 5^{-7} \cdot 5^4 = 5^{-3}$ meters

10. $240 = 2^4 \cdot 3 \cdot 5$

$160 = 2^5 \cdot 5$

The GCF of 240 and 160 is $2^4 \cdot 5$, or 80. So, the florist can make at most 80 bouquets.

11. $20 = 2^2 \cdot 5$

$8 = 2^3$

The LCM of 20 and 8 is $2^3 \cdot 5$, or 40. So, the two cars will reach the starting line at the same time in 40 seconds.

12. $45 = 3^2 \cdot 5$

$75 = 3 \cdot 5^2$

The GCF of 45 and 75 is $3 \cdot 5$, or 15. So, the longest each strip can be is 15 feet.

13. $14 = 2 \cdot 7$

$8 = 2^3$

The LCM of 14 and 8 is $2^3 \cdot 7$, or 56. So, he will have both tests on the same day in 56 days.

$\dfrac{180}{56} \approx 3.2$

So, the greatest number of days both tests will fall on the same day is $1 + 3 = 4$. If the first test is within the first 12 school days, there will be 3 additional tests.

14. $12 = 2^2 \cdot 3$

$15 = 3 \cdot 5$

$8 = 2^3$

The LCM of 12, 15, and 8 is $2^3 \cdot 3 \cdot 5$, or 120. So, the two trains and bus will depart at the same time in 120 minutes.

15. The proton has the greater mass because $-27 > -31$.

$\dfrac{1.67 \times 10^{-27}}{9.11 \times 10^{-31}} \approx 0.183315 \times 10^4 = 1833.15$

The mass of a proton is about 1833.15 times greater than the mass of an electron.

16. a. The red door opens every 4 seconds, the blue door opens every $2 + 4 = 6$ seconds, and the yellow door opens every $6 + 2 + 1 = 9$ seconds.

  b. Blue and red:

  $6 = 2 \cdot 3$

  $4 = 2^2$

  The LCM of 6 and 4 is $2^2 \cdot 3$, or 12. So, the blue and red doors open in 12 seconds.

  Blue and yellow:

  $6 = 2 \cdot 3$

  $9 = 3^2$

  The LCM of 6 and 9 is $2 \cdot 3^2$, or 18. So, the blue and yellow doors open in 18 seconds.

  The blue and red doors will open first because $12 < 18$.

  c. $4 = 2^2$

  $6 = 2 \cdot 3$

  $9 = 3^2$

  The LCM of 4, 6, and 9 is $2^2 \cdot 3^2$, or 36. So, all three doors will open at the same time is 36 seconds.

17. a. $\dfrac{17}{24} = \dfrac{17 \cdot 60}{24 \cdot 60} = \dfrac{1020}{1440}$

  $\dfrac{41}{60} = \dfrac{41 \cdot 24}{60 \cdot 24} = \dfrac{984}{1440}$

  Because $1020 > 984$, $\dfrac{1020}{1440}$ is the greater fraction.

  b. *Sample answer:*

  You multiplied the numerators by the denominators of the other fraction, and then divided each new numerator by the product of the denominators.

  As a general rule, multiply each numerator by the other fractions denominator and compare products. So, to compare $\dfrac{a}{b}$ and $\dfrac{c}{d}$, compare ad and cb.

  For example, compare $\dfrac{4}{15}$ and $\dfrac{3}{10}$. Because $4 \cdot 10 = 40 < 15 \cdot 3 = 45$, $\dfrac{3}{10} > \dfrac{4}{15}$.

  c. *Sample answer:* An advantage is that you do not need to compute the LCD. A disadvantage is that the numbers being multiplied are often larger.

Chapter 5

Chapter Get-Ready Games (pp. 230–231)

1. $\frac{2}{3} \longrightarrow \frac{3}{5} \longrightarrow \frac{1}{2} \longrightarrow \frac{3}{8} \longrightarrow \frac{4}{15} \longrightarrow \frac{7}{32}$

2. $\frac{6}{8} = \frac{9}{12}$ S

$\frac{7}{21} = \frac{3}{9}$ H

$\frac{15}{18} = \frac{40}{48}$ O

$\frac{6}{42} = \frac{4}{28}$ E

$\frac{35}{40} = \frac{14}{16}$ S

Susan is missing her SHOES.

Stop and Think (p. 231)

1. *Sample answer:* Fractions are numbers that represent parts of a whole. You cannot compare different fractions by just looking at their denominators. You must rewrite the fractions as equivalent fractions with the same denominator first and then compare the numerators.

2. *Sample answer:* First you have to find a common denominator. Next, rewrite each fraction using the common denominator. Then, compare the numerators. If the numerators are equal, the fractions are equivalent.

Review Prerequisite Skills (p. 232)

1. If 1 is the greatest common factor of the numerator and the denominator, then the fraction is in *simplest form*.

2. A number like $3\frac{4}{7}$, whose value is the sum of a whole number part and a fraction part is called a *mixed number*.

3. A fraction whose numerator is greater than or equal to its denominator is an *improper fraction*.

4. $-125 \cdot 2 = -250$

5. $-4 \cdot (-23) = 92$

6. $20 \cdot (-6) = -120$

7. $-8 \cdot (-7) = 56$

8. $-39 \div 3 = -13$

9. $-136 \div (-17) = 8$

10. $64 \div (-16) = -4$

11. $-27 \div (-9) = 3$

12. $\frac{4}{12} = \frac{4 \div 4}{12 \div 4} = \frac{1}{3}$

13. $\frac{-35}{50} = \frac{-35 \div 5}{50 \div 5} = -\frac{7}{10}$

14. $\frac{24}{52} = \frac{24 \div 4}{52 \div 4} = \frac{6}{13}$

15. $\frac{14}{49} = \frac{14 \div 7}{49 \div 7} = \frac{2}{7}$

16. $\frac{-34}{51} = \frac{-34 \div 17}{51 \div 17} = -\frac{2}{3}$

17. $\frac{26}{65} = \frac{26 \div 13}{65 \div 13} = \frac{2}{5}$

18. $\frac{56}{72} = \frac{56 \div 8}{72 \div 8} = \frac{7}{9}$

19. $\frac{-16}{96} = \frac{-16 \div 16}{96 \div 16} = -\frac{1}{6}$

20. The total cost of your purchase is \$15.65 + \$23.95, or \$39.60.

Lesson 5.1

5.1 Guided Practice (pp. 234–235)

1. $\frac{1}{12} + \frac{5}{12} = \frac{1+5}{12} = \frac{6}{12} = \frac{1}{2}$

2. $\frac{3}{8} - 2\frac{1}{8} = \frac{3}{8} - \frac{8 \cdot 2 + 1}{8}$

$= \frac{3}{8} - \frac{17}{8}$

$= -\frac{14}{8}$

$= -\frac{7}{4}$

$= -1\frac{3}{4}$

3. $-\frac{t}{3} - \frac{2t}{3} = \frac{-t - 2t}{3} = -\frac{3t}{3} = -t$

4. $\frac{y}{8a} + \frac{-5y}{8a} = \frac{y + (-5y)}{8a} = \frac{-4y}{8a} = -\frac{y}{2a}$

5. $5\frac{7}{8} + x = 8\frac{3}{8}$

$5\frac{7}{8} + x - 5\frac{7}{8} = 8\frac{3}{8} - 5\frac{7}{8}$

$x = 7\frac{11}{8} - 5\frac{7}{8}$

$x = \left(7 + \frac{11}{8}\right) - \left(5 + \frac{7}{8}\right)$

$x = 7 + \frac{11}{8} - 5 - \frac{7}{8}$

$x = (7 - 5) + \left(\frac{11}{8} - \frac{7}{8}\right)$

$x = 2 + \frac{4}{8}$

$x = 2\frac{4}{8}$

$x = 2\frac{1}{2}$

The plant grew $2\frac{1}{2}$ inches.

6. $\frac{3}{4} + \frac{7}{4} + \frac{5}{4} = \frac{3 + 7 + 5}{4} = \frac{15}{4} = 3\frac{3}{4}$

7. $\frac{15}{8} - \frac{7}{8} + \frac{3}{8} = \frac{15 - 7 + 3}{8} = \frac{11}{8} = 1\frac{3}{8}$

8. $2\frac{1}{3} - \frac{2}{3} + 3\frac{2}{3} = (2 + 3) + \left(\frac{1}{3} - \frac{2}{3} + \frac{2}{3}\right) = 5\frac{1}{3}$

5.1 Exercises (pp. 235–237)

Skill Practice

1. In the fraction $\frac{4}{9}$, 9 is the *denominator* and 4 is the *numerator*.

2. $\frac{5}{18} + \frac{7}{18} = \frac{5 + 7}{18} = \frac{12}{18} = \frac{2}{3}$

3. $\frac{5}{21} + \frac{2}{21} = \frac{5 + 2}{21} = \frac{7}{21} = \frac{1}{3}$

4. $\frac{3}{10} - \frac{7}{10} = \frac{3 - 7}{10} = -\frac{4}{10} = -\frac{2}{5}$

5. $\frac{7}{18} - \frac{5}{18} = \frac{7 - 5}{18} = \frac{2}{18} = \frac{1}{9}$

6. $-4\frac{2}{7} - 4\frac{2}{7} = (-4 - 4) + \left(-\frac{2}{7} - \frac{2}{7}\right) = -8\frac{4}{7}$

7. $-4\frac{9}{14} + 3\frac{5}{14} = (-4 + 3) + \left(-\frac{9}{14} + \frac{5}{14}\right) = -1\frac{4}{14} = -1\frac{2}{7}$

8. $2\frac{7}{9} + \frac{8}{9} = 2 + \frac{7 + 8}{9} = 2 + \frac{15}{9} = 3 + \frac{6}{9} = 3\frac{2}{3}$

9. $-7\frac{3}{5} - \frac{4}{5} = -7 + \left(-\frac{3}{5} - \frac{4}{5}\right) = -7\frac{7}{5} = -8\frac{2}{5}$

10. $\frac{h}{13} + \frac{6h}{13} = \frac{h + 6h}{13} = \frac{7h}{13}$

11. $-\frac{8n}{21} + \frac{5n}{21} = \frac{-8n + 5n}{21} = -\frac{3n}{21} = -\frac{n}{7}$

12. $\frac{-8p}{9} - \frac{-p}{9} = \frac{-8p - (-p)}{9} = -\frac{7p}{9}$

13. $\frac{12}{a} + \frac{3}{a} = \frac{12 + 3}{a} = \frac{15}{a}$

14. $\frac{4x}{5y} - \frac{9x}{5y} = \frac{4x - 9x}{5y} = \frac{-5x}{5y} = -\frac{x}{y}$

15. $\frac{9a}{20b} - \frac{7a}{20b} = \frac{9a - 7a}{20b} = \frac{2a}{20b} = \frac{a}{10b}$

16. $-\frac{5q}{18p} - \frac{13q}{18p} = \frac{-5q - 13q}{18p} = -\frac{18q}{18p} = -\frac{q}{p}$

17. $\frac{5a}{2b} - \frac{a}{2b} = \frac{5a - a}{2b} = \frac{4a}{2b} = \frac{2a}{b}$

18. $7\frac{1}{3} - 3\frac{2}{3} = \frac{22}{3} - \frac{11}{3} = \frac{22 - 11}{3} = \frac{11}{3} = 3\frac{2}{3}$

19. $19\frac{1}{4} - 17\frac{3}{4} = \frac{77}{4} - \frac{71}{4} = \frac{6}{4} = 1\frac{2}{4} = 1\frac{1}{2}$

20. $1\frac{4}{15} + \left(-\frac{11}{15}\right) = \frac{19}{15} + \left(-\frac{11}{15}\right) = \frac{19 + (-11)}{15} = \frac{8}{15}$

21. $\frac{13}{18} + \frac{5}{18} + \frac{11}{18} = \frac{13 + 5 + 11}{18} = \frac{29}{18} = 1\frac{11}{18}$

22. $-\frac{4}{5} - \frac{1}{5} - \frac{2}{5} = \frac{-4 - 1 - 2}{5} = -\frac{7}{5} = -1\frac{2}{5}$

23. $4\frac{5}{12} - \left(1\frac{11}{12} - \frac{7}{12}\right) = 4\frac{5}{12} - \left(1 + \left(\frac{11}{12} - \frac{7}{12}\right)\right)$

$= 4\frac{5}{12} - 1\frac{4}{12}$

$= (4 - 1) + \left(\frac{5}{12} - \frac{4}{12}\right)$

$= 3\frac{1}{12}$

24. $-5\frac{4}{15} - \left(3\frac{7}{15} + \frac{8}{15}\right) = -5\frac{4}{15} - \left(3 + \left(\frac{7}{15} + \frac{8}{15}\right)\right)$

$= -4\frac{19}{15} - 3\frac{15}{15}$

$= (-4 - 3) + \left(-\frac{19}{15} - \frac{15}{15}\right)$

$= -7\frac{34}{15}$

$= -9\frac{4}{15}$

25. $-\frac{3}{16} - 2\frac{1}{16} - \frac{15}{16} = (-2) + \left(-\frac{3}{16} - \frac{1}{16} - \frac{15}{16}\right)$

$= -2 + \left(-1\frac{3}{16}\right)$

$= -3\frac{3}{16}$

26. $1\frac{3}{8} + \frac{5}{8} - 1\frac{7}{8} = (1 - 1) + \left(\frac{3}{8} + \frac{5}{8} - \frac{7}{8}\right) = \frac{1}{8}$

27. $2\frac{4}{9} - 1\frac{1}{9} = (2 - 1) + \left(\frac{4}{9} - \frac{1}{9}\right)$

$= 1 + \left(\frac{3}{9}\right)$

$= 1\frac{3}{9}$

$= 1\frac{1}{3}$

The $\frac{1}{9}$ must be subtracted, not added.

28. $x + \frac{5}{8} = 0$

$x + \frac{5}{8} - \frac{5}{8} = 0 - \frac{5}{8}$

$x = -\frac{5}{8}$

29. $\frac{7}{17} + k = \frac{9}{17}$

$\frac{7}{17} + k - \frac{7}{17} = \frac{9}{17} - \frac{7}{17}$

$k = \frac{2}{17}$

30. $z - \frac{9}{15} = \frac{11}{15}$

$z - \frac{9}{15} + \frac{9}{15} = \frac{11}{15} + \frac{9}{15}$

$z = \frac{20}{15}$

$z = \frac{4}{3}$

$z = 1\frac{1}{3}$

31. $m - \frac{6}{9} = \frac{2}{9}$

$m - \frac{6}{9} + \frac{6}{9} = \frac{2}{9} + \frac{6}{9}$

$m = \frac{8}{9}$

32. $j + \frac{2}{13} + \frac{5}{13} = \frac{8}{13}$

$j + \frac{2 + 5}{13} = \frac{8}{13}$

$j + \frac{7}{13} = \frac{8}{13}$

$j + \frac{7}{13} - \frac{7}{13} = \frac{8}{13} - \frac{7}{13}$

$j = \frac{1}{13}$

33. $\frac{1}{7} + a + \frac{3}{7} = \frac{4}{7}$

$a + \frac{1 + 3}{7} = \frac{4}{7}$

$a + \frac{4}{7} = \frac{4}{7}$

$a + \frac{4}{7} - \frac{4}{7} = \frac{4}{7} - \frac{4}{7}$

$a = 0$

34. $\frac{7}{16} + b - \frac{2}{16} = \frac{5}{16}$

$b + \frac{-2 + 7}{16} = \frac{5}{16}$

$b + \frac{5}{16} = \frac{5}{16}$

$b + \frac{5}{16} - \frac{5}{16} = \frac{5}{16} - \frac{5}{16}$

$b = 0$

35. $\frac{10}{11} - y = \frac{2}{11}$

$\frac{10}{11} - y - \frac{10}{11} = \frac{2}{11} - \frac{10}{11}$

$-y = -\frac{8}{11}$

$-1 \cdot -y = -1 \cdot \left(-\frac{8}{11}\right)$

$y = \frac{8}{11}$

36.
$$\frac{3}{19} - c = 0$$
$$\frac{3}{19} - c - \frac{3}{19} = 0 - \frac{3}{19}$$
$$-c = -\frac{3}{19}$$
$$-c \div (-1) = -\frac{3}{19} \div (-1)$$
$$c = \frac{3}{19}$$

37. *Sample answer:* $1\frac{1}{5} + 2\frac{3}{5} = 3\frac{4}{5}$ is an example of a pair of mixed numbers added to get a mixed number. $1\frac{1}{4} + \left(-1\frac{3}{4}\right) = -\frac{1}{2}$ is an example of a pair of mixed numbers added whose sum is not a mixed number.

38.
$$\frac{a}{10} + \frac{2a}{10} = -\frac{9}{10}$$
$$\frac{a + 2a}{10} = -\frac{9}{10}$$
$$\frac{3a}{10} = -\frac{9}{10}$$
$$\frac{3a}{10} \cdot 10 = -\frac{9}{10} \cdot 10$$
$$3a = -9$$
$$\frac{3a}{3} = -\frac{9}{3}$$
$$a = -3$$

39.
$$-\frac{3b}{15} + \frac{7b}{15} = \frac{8}{15}$$
$$\frac{-3b + 7b}{15} = \frac{8}{15}$$
$$\frac{4b}{15} = \frac{8}{15}$$
$$\frac{4b}{15} \cdot 15 = \frac{8}{15} \cdot 15$$
$$4b = 8$$
$$\frac{4b}{4} = \frac{8}{4}$$
$$b = 2$$

40.
$$\frac{5}{4c} - \frac{13}{4c} = -\frac{1}{3}$$
$$\frac{5 - 13}{4c} = -\frac{1}{3}$$
$$\frac{-8}{4c} = -\frac{1}{3}$$
$$\frac{-8}{4c} \cdot 4c = -\frac{1}{3} \cdot 4c$$
$$-8 = -\frac{4c}{3}$$
$$-8 \cdot 3 = -\frac{4c}{3} \cdot 3$$
$$-24 = -4c$$
$$\frac{-24}{-4} = \frac{-4c}{-4}$$
$$6 = c$$

Problem Solving

41. $21\frac{3}{8} - 2\frac{5}{8} = 20\frac{11}{8} - 2\frac{5}{8}$
$$= (20 - 2) + \left(\frac{11}{8} - \frac{5}{8}\right)$$
$$= 18 + \frac{6}{8}$$
$$= 18\frac{3}{4}$$

There are $18\frac{3}{4}$ inches of the scarf left.

42. D; $15\frac{5}{16} + 15\frac{5}{16} + 11\frac{7}{16} + 11\frac{7}{16}$
$$= (15 + 15 + 11 + 11) + \left(\frac{5}{16} + \frac{5}{16} + \frac{7}{16} + \frac{7}{16}\right)$$
$$= 52\frac{24}{16}$$
$$= 52\frac{3}{2}$$
$$= 53\frac{1}{2} \text{ feet}$$

43. $25\frac{3}{4} - 23\frac{1}{4} = (25 - 23) + \left(\frac{3}{4} - \frac{1}{4}\right) = 2 + \frac{2}{4} = 2\frac{1}{2}$

The 2-euro coin is $2\frac{1}{2}$ millimeters wider than the 1-euro coin.

44. Yes, your friend is correct because the circle graph is representing parts of 1 whole.
$$\frac{(60 + 25 + 15)}{100} \stackrel{?}{=} 1$$
$$\frac{100}{100} \stackrel{?}{=} 1$$
$$1 = 1$$

45.
$$17 \text{ ft } 8\frac{1}{4} \text{ in.} = 16 \text{ ft } 20\frac{1}{4} \text{ in.}$$
$$\underline{-15 \text{ ft } 11\frac{3}{4} \text{ in.}} \quad \underline{-15 \text{ ft } 11\frac{3}{4} \text{ in.}}$$
$$= 16 \text{ ft } 19\frac{5}{4} \text{ in.}$$
$$\underline{-15 \text{ ft } 11\frac{3}{4} \text{ in.}}$$
$$1 \text{ ft } 8\frac{2}{4} \text{ in.}$$
$$= 1 \text{ ft } 8\frac{1}{2} \text{ in.}$$

You need to jump 1 foot $8\frac{1}{2}$ inches farther.

46.
$$6\frac{1}{6} + 8\frac{5}{6} + 5\frac{1}{6} + x = 25$$
$$(6 + 8 + 5) + \left(\frac{1}{6} + \frac{5}{6} + \frac{1}{6}\right) + x = 25$$
$$19 + 1\frac{1}{6} + x = 25$$
$$20\frac{1}{6} + x = 25$$
$$20\frac{1}{6} + x - 20\frac{1}{6} = 25 - 20\frac{1}{6}$$
$$x = 4\frac{5}{6}$$

Sample answer: Set up an equation letting x be how much you need to work the last month and setting it equal to 25. Solve for x. You need to work $4\frac{5}{6}$ hours to earn the award.

47. a. $6\frac{1}{4} + \frac{1}{4} = 6\frac{2}{4} = 6\frac{1}{2}$

Add $\frac{1}{4}$ to the new height. The original height of the spoiler is $6\frac{1}{2}$ inches.

b. The height was reduced $\frac{1}{4}$. The original height was $6\frac{1}{2}$ or $6\frac{2}{4}$.

$\frac{1}{4} \div \frac{26}{4} = \frac{1}{4} \cdot \frac{4}{26} = \frac{1}{26}$

$\frac{1}{26}$ of the original height was removed.

48. Amanda: 4 ft $2\frac{1}{4}$ in. $= 50\frac{1}{4}$ in.

Chris: 4 ft $2\frac{1}{4}$ in. $+ 4\frac{7}{8}$ in. $= 50\frac{1}{4} + 4\frac{7}{8}$

$= (50 + 4) + \left(\frac{2}{8} + \frac{7}{8}\right)$

$= 54 + \frac{9}{8}$

$= 55\frac{1}{8}$

$= 4$ ft. $7\frac{1}{8}$ in.

Hollie: $55\frac{1}{8} + 6\frac{1}{8} = (55 + 6) + \left(\frac{1}{8} + \frac{1}{8}\right)$

$= 61 + \frac{2}{8}$

$= 61\frac{1}{4}$

$= 5$ ft $1\frac{1}{4}$ in.

Bill: $61\frac{1}{4} + 15\frac{1}{4} = (61 + 15) + \left(\frac{1}{4} + \frac{1}{4}\right)$

$= 76 + \left(\frac{2}{4}\right)$

$= 76\frac{1}{2}$

$= 6$ ft $4\frac{1}{2}$ in.

Chris is 4 feet $7\frac{1}{8}$ inches. Hollie is 5 feet $1\frac{1}{4}$ inches. Bill is 6 feet $4\frac{1}{2}$ inches.

Mixed Review

49. $15 = 3 \cdot 5$

$35 = 5 \cdot 7$

The LCM of 15 and 35 is $3 \cdot 5 \cdot 7$, or 105.

50. 19 is prime.

$76 = 2^2 \cdot 19$

The LCM of 19 and 76 is $2^2 \cdot 19$, or 76.

51. 37 is prime.

$50 = 2 \cdot 5^2$

The LCM of 37 and 50 is $2 \cdot 5^2 \cdot 37 = 1850$.

52. $27 = 3^3$

$81 = 3^4$

The LCM of 27 and 81 is 3^4, or 81.

53. The LCD of $\frac{2}{3}$ and $\frac{4}{9}$ is 3^2, or 9.

54. The LCD of $\frac{1}{5}$ and $\frac{9}{20}$ is $2^2 \cdot 5$, or 20.

55. The LCD of $\frac{3}{8}$ and $\frac{7}{12}$ is $2^3 \cdot 3$, or 24.

56. The LCD of $\frac{1}{6}$ and $\frac{4}{15}$ is $2 \cdot 3 \cdot 5$, or 30.

57. $2800 = 2.8 \times 10^3$ **58.** $0.0116 = 1.16 \times 10^{-2}$

59. $362{,}000{,}000 = 3.62 \times 10^8$ **60.** $0.0000099 = 9.9 \times 10^{-6}$

61. A; $-7 + (-35) = -42$

Lesson 5.2

5.2 Guided Practice (pp. 238–239)

1. $\frac{1}{3} + \frac{3}{8} = \frac{8}{24} + \frac{9}{24} = \frac{8 + 9}{24} = \frac{17}{24}$

2. $\frac{3}{4} - \frac{9}{10} = \frac{15}{20} - \frac{18}{20} = \frac{15 - 18}{20} = -\frac{3}{20}$

3. $\frac{5}{12} + \frac{-7}{9} = \frac{15}{36} + \frac{-28}{36} = \frac{15 + (-28)}{36} = -\frac{13}{36}$

4. $\frac{2}{8} + \frac{7}{16} = \frac{4}{16} + \frac{7}{16} = \frac{4 + 7}{16} = \frac{11}{16}$

5. $\frac{1}{6} - \frac{11}{15} = \frac{5}{30} - \frac{22}{30} = \frac{5 - 22}{30} = -\frac{17}{30}$

6. $-\frac{4}{33} - \frac{1}{11} = \frac{-4}{33} - \frac{3}{33} = \frac{-4 - 3}{33} = -\frac{7}{33}$

7. $\frac{2}{5} + \frac{2}{z} = \frac{2z}{5z} + \frac{10}{5z} = \frac{2z + 10}{5z}$

$\frac{2}{5} - \frac{2}{z} = \frac{2z}{5z} - \frac{10}{5z} = \frac{2z - 10}{5z}$

8. $L = 36\frac{5}{8} - \left(4\frac{5}{6} + \frac{1}{16}\right)$

$= 36\frac{5}{8} - \left(4\frac{40}{48} + \frac{3}{48}\right)$

$= 36\frac{5}{8} - 4\frac{43}{48}$

$= 36\frac{30}{48} - 4\frac{43}{48}$

$= 35\frac{78}{48} - 4\frac{43}{48}$

$= 31\frac{35}{48}$

The length of the remaining piece of wood is $31\frac{35}{48}$ inches.

5.2 Exercises (pp. 240–242)

Skill Practice

1. To add two fractions with different denominators, rewrite the fractions using the *least common denominator* of the fractions.

2. $\frac{1}{2} + \frac{1}{3} = \frac{3}{6} + \frac{2}{6} = \frac{3+2}{6} = \frac{5}{6}$

3. $\frac{7}{8} - \frac{1}{4} = \frac{7}{8} - \frac{2}{8} = \frac{7-2}{8} = \frac{5}{8}$

4. $\frac{1}{8} - \frac{5}{32} = \frac{4}{32} - \frac{5}{32} = \frac{4-5}{32} = -\frac{1}{32}$

5. $\frac{5}{9} + \frac{1}{6} = \frac{10}{18} + \frac{3}{18} = \frac{10+3}{18} = \frac{13}{18}$

6. $-\frac{7}{12} + \frac{4}{15} = -\frac{35}{60} + \frac{16}{60} = \frac{-35+16}{60} = -\frac{19}{60}$

7. $\frac{-3}{8} + \frac{-9}{20} = \frac{-15}{40} + \frac{-18}{40} = \frac{-15+(-18)}{40} = -\frac{33}{40}$

8. $4\frac{5}{8} - 2\frac{2}{3} = 4\frac{15}{24} - 2\frac{16}{24}$

$\qquad = 3\frac{39}{24} - 2\frac{16}{24}$

$\qquad = (3-2) + \left(\frac{39}{24} - \frac{16}{24}\right)$

$\qquad = 1\frac{23}{24}$

9. $5\frac{1}{2} - \frac{7}{10} = 5\frac{5}{10} - \frac{7}{10} = 4\frac{15}{10} - \frac{7}{10} = 4\frac{8}{10} = 4\frac{4}{5}$

10. $7\frac{4}{5} + 5\frac{3}{7} = 7\frac{28}{35} + 5\frac{15}{35}$

$\qquad = (7+5) + \left(\frac{28}{35} + \frac{15}{35}\right)$

$\qquad = 12\frac{43}{35}$

$\qquad = 13\frac{8}{35}$

11. $12\frac{5}{18} - \frac{3}{4} = 12\frac{10}{36} - \frac{27}{36} = 11\frac{46}{36} - \frac{27}{36} = 11\frac{19}{36}$

12. $12 - 16\frac{3}{7} = 11\frac{7}{7} - 16\frac{3}{7}$

$\qquad = (11-16) + \left(\frac{7}{7} - \frac{3}{7}\right)$

$\qquad = -5 + \frac{4}{7}$

$\qquad = -4\frac{3}{7}$

13. $-7\frac{3}{11} - (-8) = -7\frac{3}{11} + 8$

$\qquad = -7\frac{3}{11} + 7\frac{11}{11}$

$\qquad = (-7+7) + \left(-\frac{3}{11} + \frac{11}{11}\right)$

$\qquad = \frac{8}{11}$

14. $-\frac{7y}{12} + \frac{4y}{15} = \frac{-35y}{60} + \frac{16y}{60} = \frac{-19y}{60}$

15. $-\frac{3w}{8} + \frac{-9w}{20} = \frac{-15w}{40} + \frac{-18w}{40} = \frac{-33w}{40}$

16. $\frac{2x}{7} - \frac{x}{2} = \frac{4x}{14} - \frac{7x}{14} = \frac{4x-7x}{14} = \frac{-3x}{14}$

17. $\frac{9s}{4} - \frac{7s}{5} = \frac{45s}{20} - \frac{28s}{20} = \frac{45s-28s}{20} = \frac{17s}{20}$

18. $\frac{4}{x} + \frac{1}{9} = \frac{36}{9x} + \frac{x}{9x} = \frac{36+x}{9x}$

19. $\frac{16}{25n} - \frac{9}{10n} = \frac{32}{50n} - \frac{45}{50n} = \frac{32-45}{50n} = -\frac{13}{50n}$

20. $\frac{16}{25n} + \frac{9}{10n} = \frac{16}{25n} \cdot \left(\frac{2}{2}\right) + \frac{9}{10n} \cdot \left(\frac{5}{5}\right)$

$\qquad = \frac{32}{50n} + \frac{45}{50n}$

$\qquad = \frac{32+45}{50n}$

$\qquad = \frac{77}{50n}$

21. $\frac{18}{7a} + \frac{11}{21} = \frac{18}{7a} \cdot \left(\frac{3}{3}\right) + \frac{11}{21} \cdot \left(\frac{a}{a}\right)$

$\qquad = \frac{54}{21a} + \frac{11a}{21a}$

$\qquad = \frac{54+11a}{21a}$

22. C; $\frac{5}{6} + \frac{1}{9} - \frac{2}{3} = \frac{15}{18} + \frac{2}{18} - \frac{12}{18} = \frac{15+2-12}{18} = \frac{5}{18}$

23. $\frac{1}{4} - \frac{6}{7} + \frac{3}{14} = \frac{7}{28} - \frac{24}{28} + \frac{6}{28} = \frac{7-24+6}{28} = -\frac{11}{28}$

The statement is true.

Sample answer: paper and pencil

24. $\frac{3}{4} + 2\frac{1}{2} - \frac{1}{4} = \frac{3}{4} - \frac{1}{4} + 2\frac{1}{2} = \frac{1}{2} + 2\frac{1}{2} = 3$

The statement is true.

Sample answer: mental math

25. $\frac{4}{9} + \frac{7}{8} + \frac{1}{24} \approx \frac{1}{2} + 1 + 0 = 1\frac{1}{2}$

Because $1\frac{1}{2} \neq \frac{7}{8}$, the statement is false.

Sample answer: estimation

26. $3\frac{4}{9} - 1\frac{1}{2} - \frac{1}{3} \approx 3\frac{1}{2} - 1\frac{1}{2} - \frac{1}{3} = 1\frac{2}{3}$

Because $1\frac{2}{3} \neq 2\frac{5}{18}$, the statement is false.

Sample answer: estimation

27. $1\frac{1}{3} - \frac{2}{9} - \frac{5}{6} = 1\frac{6}{18} - \frac{4}{18} - \frac{15}{18}$

$\qquad = \frac{24}{18} - \frac{4}{18} - \frac{15}{18}$

$\qquad = \frac{24-4-15}{18}$

$\qquad = \frac{5}{18}$

Because $\frac{7}{18} \neq \frac{5}{18}$, the statement is false.

Sample answer: paper and pencil

28. $10\frac{7}{8} - 3\frac{1}{10} \approx 11 - 3 = 8$

Because $8 \neq 5\frac{31}{40}$, the statement is false.

Sample answer: estimation

29. $z + 3\frac{4}{7} - 5\frac{2}{5} = 1\frac{1}{2}$

$z + 3\frac{40}{70} - 5\frac{28}{70} = 1\frac{35}{70}$

$z + 3\frac{40}{70} - 4\frac{98}{70} = 1\frac{35}{70}$

$z - 1\frac{58}{70} = 1\frac{35}{70}$

$z - 1\frac{58}{70} + 1\frac{58}{70} = 1\frac{35}{70} + 1\frac{58}{70}$

$z = (1 + 1) + \left(\frac{35}{70} + \frac{58}{70}\right)$

$z = 2\frac{93}{70}$

$z = 3\frac{23}{70}$

30. $2\frac{3}{5} + w - 4\frac{1}{3} = 7\frac{8}{15}$

$2\frac{9}{15} + w - 4\frac{5}{15} = 7\frac{8}{15}$

$2\frac{9}{15} + w - 3\frac{20}{15} = 7\frac{8}{15}$

$w - 1\frac{11}{15} = 7\frac{8}{15}$

$w - 1\frac{11}{15} + 1\frac{11}{15} = 7\frac{8}{15} + 1\frac{11}{15}$

$w = (7 + 1) + \left(\frac{8}{15} + \frac{11}{15}\right)$

$w = 8\frac{19}{15}$

$w = 9\frac{4}{15}$

31. $6\frac{3}{8} + 2\frac{5}{12} - x = 4\frac{3}{4}$

$6\frac{9}{24} + 2\frac{10}{24} - x = 4\frac{18}{24}$

$8\frac{19}{24} - x = 4\frac{18}{24}$

$8\frac{19}{24} - x - 8\frac{19}{24} = 4\frac{18}{24} - 8\frac{19}{24}$

$-x = (4 - 8) + \left(\frac{18}{24} - \frac{19}{24}\right)$

$-x = -4\frac{1}{24}$

$-1 \cdot -x = -1 \cdot \left(-4\frac{1}{24}\right)$

$x = 4\frac{1}{24}$

32. $7\frac{7}{8} - 6\frac{5}{9} - y = \frac{1}{6}$

$7\frac{63}{72} - 6\frac{40}{72} - y = \frac{12}{72}$

$1\frac{23}{72} - y = \frac{12}{72}$

$1\frac{23}{72} - 1\frac{23}{72} - y = \frac{12}{72} - 1\frac{23}{72}$

$-y = \frac{12}{72} - \frac{95}{72}$

$-y = \frac{12 - 95}{72}$

$-y = -\frac{83}{72}$

$-y = -1\frac{11}{72}$

$-1 \cdot -y = -1 \cdot \left(-1\frac{11}{72}\right)$

$y = 1\frac{11}{72}$

33. $1\frac{7}{10}, 2, 2\frac{3}{10}, 2\frac{3}{5}, \ldots$

The pattern is add $\frac{3}{10}$ to the previous number.

$2\frac{3}{5} + \frac{3}{10} = 2\frac{6}{10} + \frac{3}{10} = 2\frac{9}{10}$;

$2\frac{9}{10} + \frac{3}{10} = 2\frac{12}{10} = 3\frac{2}{10} = 3\frac{1}{5}$;

$3\frac{1}{5} + \frac{3}{10} = 3\frac{2}{10} + \frac{3}{10} = 3\frac{5}{10} = 3\frac{1}{2}$

The next 3 fractions are $2\frac{9}{10}, 3\frac{1}{5}$, and $3\frac{1}{2}$.

34. $5\frac{3}{4}, 4\frac{5}{8}, 3\frac{1}{2}, 2\frac{3}{8}, \ldots$

The pattern is subtract $1\frac{1}{8}$ from the previous number.

$2\frac{3}{8} - 1\frac{1}{8} = 1\frac{2}{8} = 1\frac{1}{4}$; $1\frac{1}{4} - 1\frac{1}{8} = 1\frac{2}{8} - 1\frac{1}{8} = \frac{1}{8}$;

$\frac{1}{8} - 1\frac{1}{8} = -1$

The next 3 fractions are $1\frac{1}{4}, \frac{1}{8}$, and -1.

35. $\frac{11}{12}, \frac{19}{24}, \frac{2}{3}, \frac{13}{24}, \ldots$

The pattern is subtract $\frac{1}{8}$ from the previous number.

$\frac{13}{24} - \frac{1}{8} = \frac{13}{24} - \frac{3}{24} = \frac{10}{24} = \frac{5}{12}$; $\frac{5}{12} - \frac{1}{8} = \frac{10}{24} - \frac{3}{24} = \frac{7}{24}$;

$\frac{7}{24} - \frac{1}{8} = \frac{7}{24} - \frac{3}{24} = \frac{4}{24} = \frac{1}{6}$

The next 3 fractions are $\frac{5}{12}, \frac{7}{24}$, and $\frac{1}{6}$.

Chapter 5, *continued*

Problem Solving

36. a. $\dfrac{\text{Remaining}}{\text{length}} = \dfrac{\text{Original}}{\text{length}} - \left(\begin{array}{ccc}\text{Length} & & \text{Length}\\ \text{built} & + & \text{built}\\ \text{Monday} & & \text{Tuesday}\end{array}\right)$

b. $L = 13 - \left(4\frac{1}{3} + 5\frac{3}{4}\right)$

c. $L = 13 - \left(4\frac{4}{12} + 5\frac{9}{12}\right)$

$= 13 - 9\frac{13}{12}$

$= 13 - 10\frac{1}{12}$

$= 12\frac{12}{12} - 10\frac{1}{12}$

$= (12 - 10) + \left(\frac{12}{12} - \frac{1}{12}\right)$

$= 2\frac{11}{12}$

You have $2\frac{11}{12}$ feet left to build.

37. $47\frac{1}{4} - 31\frac{1}{2} = 47\frac{1}{4} - 31\frac{2}{4}$

$= 46\frac{5}{4} - 31\frac{2}{4}$

$= (46 - 31) + \left(\frac{5}{4} - \frac{2}{4}\right)$

$= 15\frac{3}{4}$

The difference in length is $15\frac{3}{4}$ inches.

38. D;

$2\frac{1}{4} + \frac{5}{6} = 2\frac{6}{24} + \frac{20}{24} = \frac{54}{24} + \frac{20}{24} = \frac{54 + 20}{24} = \frac{74}{24} = 3\frac{1}{12}$

The combined thickness is $3\frac{1}{12}$ inches.

39. Round $1\frac{5}{8}$ to $1\frac{1}{2}$. Add $\frac{1}{2}$ to get 2 and then add $2\frac{3}{4}$ to get $4\frac{3}{4}$. It is less than 5 miles.

40. $6\frac{7}{50} - 5\frac{19}{20} = 5\frac{114}{100} - 5\frac{95}{100} = (5 - 5) + \left(\frac{114}{100} - \frac{95}{100}\right)$

$= \frac{19}{100}$

The world record is $\frac{19}{100}$ meter higher.

41. $\dfrac{\text{Remaining}}{\text{tree}} = \dfrac{\text{Height}}{\text{of tree}} - \left(\begin{array}{ccc}\text{Amount} & & \text{Amount}\\ \text{cut down} & + & \text{cut down}\\ \text{1st cut} & & \text{2nd cut}\end{array}\right)$

$x = 25\frac{1}{2} - \left(9\frac{1}{3} + 7\frac{5}{6}\right)$

$= 25\frac{1}{2} - \left(9\frac{2}{6} + 7\frac{5}{6}\right)$

$= 25\frac{1}{2} - 16\frac{7}{6}$

$= 25\frac{1}{2} - 17\frac{1}{6}$

$= 25\frac{3}{6} - 17\frac{1}{6}$

$= (25 - 17) + \left(\frac{3}{6} - \frac{1}{6}\right)$

$= 8\frac{2}{6}$

$= 8\frac{1}{3}$

There are $8\frac{1}{3}$ feet of the tree remaining to be cut down.

42. *Sample answer:*

Strategy 1: Add the whole parts and then the fraction parts.

Strategy 2: Convert the mixed number to improper fractions, add, and convert back to mixed numbers.

If the fraction parts of the mixed numbers have sums greater than 1, it may be better to convert to improper fractions first. If the sums of the fractions is less than 1, add the whole and fraction parts separately.

43. *Sample answer:* $\frac{1}{2} + \frac{1}{4} + \frac{1}{8}$ can easily be changed to $\frac{4}{8} + \frac{2}{8} + \frac{1}{8} = \frac{7}{8}$.

44. a. Curtis:

$51\frac{1}{3} + 85\frac{1}{2} + 80\frac{1}{4} = 51\frac{4}{12} + 85\frac{6}{12} + 80\frac{3}{12}$

$= (51 + 85 + 80) + \left(\frac{4}{12} + \frac{6}{12} + \frac{3}{12}\right)$

$= 216 + 1\frac{1}{12}$

$= 217\frac{1}{12}$

Shanee:

$102\frac{1}{2} + 54\frac{2}{3} + 57\frac{3}{4} = 102\frac{6}{12} + 54\frac{8}{12} + 57\frac{9}{12}$

$= (102 + 54 + 57) + \left(\frac{6}{12} + \frac{8}{12} + \frac{9}{12}\right)$

$= 213 + 1\frac{11}{12}$

$= 214\frac{11}{12}$

Chapter 5, continued

Dave:

$$71\frac{1}{3} + 72\frac{3}{4} + 67\frac{1}{6} = 71\frac{4}{12} + 72\frac{9}{12} + 67\frac{2}{12}$$

$$= (71 + 72 + 67) + \left(\frac{4}{12} + \frac{9}{12} + \frac{2}{12}\right)$$

$$= 210 + 1\frac{1}{4}$$

$$= 211\frac{1}{4}$$

Curtis won the contest with a combined distance of $217\frac{1}{12}$ feet.

b. $217\frac{1}{12} - 211\frac{1}{4} = 217\frac{1}{12} - 211\frac{3}{12}$

$$= 216\frac{13}{12} - 211\frac{3}{12}$$

$$= (216 - 211) + \left(\frac{13}{12} - \frac{3}{12}\right)$$

$$= 5 + \frac{10}{12}$$

$$= 5\frac{5}{6}$$

The difference between the winner's combined distance and the 3rd place player's combined distance is $5\frac{5}{6}$ feet.

c. $217\frac{1}{12} - 214\frac{11}{12} = 216\frac{13}{12} - 214\frac{11}{12} = 2\frac{2}{12} = 2\frac{1}{6}$

$57\frac{3}{4} + 2\frac{1}{6} = 57\frac{9}{12} + 2\frac{2}{12} = 59\frac{11}{12}$

Shanee would need a distance of $59\frac{11}{12}$ feet on her 3rd throw to tie the winner's combined distance.

Find the difference of the combined distance of the winner's throws (Curtis) and the 2nd place player's throws (Shanee). Then add this distance to Shanee's 3rd throw.

45. a. $\frac{9}{25} + \frac{9}{50} = \frac{18}{50} + \frac{9}{50} = \frac{18+9}{50} = \frac{27}{50}$

You cover $\frac{27}{50}$ of the equator.

b. If you travel east, you cover $\frac{27}{50}$ of the equator.

If you travel west, you cover $1 - \frac{27}{50}$, or $\frac{50}{50} - \frac{27}{50} = \frac{23}{50}$

of the equator. It is shorter to travel west.

46. $\frac{5}{8} + \frac{13}{24} = \frac{15}{24} + \frac{13}{24} = \frac{28}{24} = 1\frac{1}{6}$

This is one complete revolution, 60 min, plus $\frac{1}{6} \cdot 60 = $ 10 min or a total of 1 h and 10 min.

3:17 + 1 h 10 min = 4:27

The cake is done at 4:27 P.M.

47. $\frac{a}{b} + \frac{c}{d} = \frac{ad}{bd} + \frac{cb}{bd} = \frac{ad + cb}{bd}$

48. $-9(7) = -63$

49. $0(-5) = 0$

50. $7(-3)(13) = -273$

51. $-9(-7)(-2) = -126$

52. $\frac{3}{5} + \frac{3}{5} = \frac{6}{5} = 1\frac{1}{5}$

53. $\frac{1}{4} + \frac{1}{4} + \frac{1}{4} = \frac{3}{4}$

54. $2\frac{1}{3} + 2\frac{1}{3} = (2 + 2) + \left(\frac{1}{3} + \frac{1}{3}\right) = 4\frac{2}{3}$

55. $\frac{3}{8} + \frac{3}{8} + \frac{3}{8} = \frac{9}{8} = 1\frac{1}{8}$

56. $\frac{1}{7} = \frac{1 \cdot 8}{7 \cdot 8} = \frac{8}{56}$

$\frac{1}{8} = \frac{1 \cdot 7}{8 \cdot 7} = \frac{7}{56}$

Because $\frac{8}{56} > \frac{7}{56}$, you can write $\frac{1}{7} > \frac{1}{8}$.

57. $\frac{3}{8} = \frac{3 \cdot 9}{8 \cdot 9} = \frac{27}{72}$

$\frac{4}{9} = \frac{4 \cdot 8}{9 \cdot 8} = \frac{32}{72}$

Because $\frac{27}{72} < \frac{32}{72}$, you can write $\frac{3}{8} < \frac{4}{9}$.

58. $\frac{5}{12} = \frac{5 \cdot 12}{12 \cdot 12} = \frac{60}{144}$

$\frac{7}{16} = \frac{7 \cdot 9}{16 \cdot 9} = \frac{63}{144}$

Because $\frac{60}{144} < \frac{63}{144}$, you can write $\frac{5}{12} < \frac{7}{16}$.

59. $\frac{7}{10} = \frac{7 \cdot 5}{10 \cdot 5} = \frac{35}{50}$

$\frac{18}{25} = \frac{18 \cdot 2}{25 \cdot 2} = \frac{36}{50}$

Because $\frac{35}{50} < \frac{36}{50}$, you can write $\frac{7}{10} < \frac{18}{25}$.

60. C;

$284 = 2 \times 2 \times 71$

$426 = 2 \times 3 \times 71$

The GCF of 284 and 426 is $2 \cdot 71$, or 142.

Lesson 5.3

5.3 Guided Practice (pp. 243–244)

1. $-\frac{5}{12} \cdot \frac{9}{10} = \frac{(\overset{-1}{\cancel{-5}}) \cdot \overset{3}{\cancel{9}}}{\underset{4}{\cancel{12}} \cdot \underset{2}{\cancel{10}}} = -\frac{3}{8}$

2. $-\frac{5}{6} \cdot -\frac{7}{9} = \frac{(-5) \cdot (-7)}{6 \cdot 9} = \frac{35}{54}$

3. $\frac{1}{6} \cdot \frac{12}{17} = \frac{1 \cdot \overset{2}{\cancel{12}}}{\underset{1}{\cancel{6}} \cdot 17} = \frac{2}{17}$

4. $\frac{7}{12} \cdot (-15) = \frac{7 \cdot (\overset{-5}{\cancel{-15}})}{\underset{4}{\cancel{12}} \cdot 1} = \frac{-35}{4} = -8\frac{3}{4}$

5. $1\frac{2}{5} \cdot 3\frac{1}{2} = \frac{7}{5} \cdot \frac{7}{2} = \frac{7 \cdot 7}{5 \cdot 2} = \frac{49}{10} = 4\frac{9}{10}$

6. $5\frac{1}{2} \cdot \left(-1\frac{5}{6}\right) = \frac{11}{2} \cdot \left(-\frac{11}{6}\right) = \frac{11 \cdot (-11)}{2 \cdot 6} = \frac{-121}{12} = -10\frac{1}{12}$

7. $-5\frac{3}{4} \cdot 2\frac{3}{3} = \frac{-23}{4} \cdot \frac{13}{3} = \frac{(-23) \cdot 13}{4 \cdot 3} = -\frac{299}{20} = -14\frac{19}{20}$

8. $-2\frac{1}{3} \cdot \left(-\frac{3}{4}\right) = -\frac{7}{3} \cdot \left(-\frac{3}{4}\right)$

$= \frac{-7 \cdot -3}{3 \cdot 4}$

$= \frac{-7 \cdot \overset{-1}{\cancel{-3}}}{\underset{1}{\cancel{3}} \cdot 4}$

$= \frac{7}{4}$

$= 1\frac{3}{4}$

9. $\frac{2}{3}x = \frac{2}{3} \cdot \left(-\frac{3}{4}\right) = \frac{\overset{1}{2} \cdot (\overset{-1}{\cancel{-3}})}{\underset{1}{\cancel{3}} \cdot \underset{2}{\cancel{4}}} = -\frac{1}{2}$

10. $2y = 2 \cdot \frac{5}{6} = \frac{2}{1} \cdot \frac{5}{6} = \frac{2 \cdot 5}{1 \cdot 6} = \frac{\overset{1}{2} \cdot 5}{1 \cdot \underset{3}{\cancel{6}}} = \frac{5}{3} = 1\frac{2}{3}$

11. $xy = -\frac{3}{4} \cdot \frac{5}{6} = \frac{-3 \cdot 5}{4 \cdot 6} = \frac{\overset{-1}{\cancel{-3}} \cdot 5}{4 \cdot \underset{2}{\cancel{6}}} = -\frac{5}{8}$

12. $xy^2 = -\frac{3}{4} \cdot \left(\frac{5}{6}\right)^2$

$= -\frac{3}{4} \cdot \frac{5}{6} \cdot \frac{5}{6}$

$= \frac{-3 \cdot 5 \cdot 5}{4 \cdot 6 \cdot 6}$

$= \frac{\overset{-1}{\cancel{-3}} \cdot 5 \cdot 5}{4 \cdot \underset{2}{\cancel{6}} \cdot 6}$

$= -\frac{25}{48}$

5.3 Exercises (pp. 245–246)

Skill Practice

1. The product of two or more fractions is equal to the product of the fractions' *numerators* divided by the product of the fractions' *denominators*.

2. $\frac{5}{8} \cdot \frac{7}{16} = \frac{5 \cdot 7}{8 \cdot 16} = \frac{35}{128}$

3. $-\frac{9}{4} \cdot \frac{5}{6} = \frac{-9 \cdot 5}{4 \cdot 6} = \frac{\overset{-3}{\cancel{-9}} \cdot 5}{4 \cdot \underset{2}{\cancel{6}}} = -\frac{15}{8} = -1\frac{7}{8}$

4. $\frac{7}{11} \cdot \frac{1}{6} = \frac{7 \cdot 1}{11 \cdot 6} = \frac{7}{66}$

5. $\frac{4}{5} \cdot \frac{3}{10} = \frac{4 \cdot 3}{5 \cdot 10} = \frac{\overset{2}{\cancel{4}} \cdot 3}{5 \cdot \underset{5}{\cancel{10}}} = \frac{6}{25}$

6. $-\frac{3}{4} \cdot \left(-\frac{2}{9}\right) = \frac{-3 \cdot (-2)}{4 \cdot 9} = \frac{\overset{-1}{\cancel{-3}} \cdot (\overset{-1}{\cancel{-2}})}{\underset{2}{\cancel{4}} \cdot \underset{3}{\cancel{9}}} = \frac{1}{6}$

7. $-\frac{5}{6} \cdot \frac{5}{12} = \frac{-5 \cdot 5}{6 \cdot 12} = -\frac{25}{72}$

8. $-4 \cdot \frac{3}{5} = -\frac{4}{1} \cdot \frac{3}{5} = \frac{-4 \cdot 3}{1 \cdot 5} = -\frac{12}{5} = -2\frac{2}{5}$

9. $12 \cdot \frac{3}{8} = \frac{12}{1} \cdot \frac{3}{8} = \frac{12 \cdot 3}{1 \cdot 8} = \frac{\overset{3}{\cancel{12}} \cdot 3}{1 \cdot \underset{2}{\cancel{8}}} = \frac{9}{2} = 4\frac{1}{2}$

10. $-4 \cdot 2\frac{9}{16} = \frac{4}{1} \cdot \frac{41}{16}$

$= \frac{-4 \cdot 41}{1 \cdot 16}$

$= \frac{\overset{-1}{\cancel{-4}} \cdot 41}{1 \cdot \underset{4}{\cancel{16}}}$

$= -\frac{41}{4}$

$= -10\frac{1}{4}$

11. $6\frac{3}{16} \cdot \left(-3\frac{1}{5}\right) = \frac{99}{16} \cdot \left(-\frac{16}{5}\right)$

$= \frac{99 \cdot (-16)}{16 \cdot 5}$

$= \frac{99 \cdot (\overset{-1}{\cancel{-16}})}{\underset{1}{\cancel{16}} \cdot 5}$

$= -\frac{99}{5}$

$= -19\frac{4}{5}$

12. $-9\frac{2}{7} \cdot 1\frac{2}{5} = -\frac{65}{7} \cdot \frac{7}{5}$

$= \frac{(-\overset{13}{\cancel{65}}) \cdot \overset{1}{\cancel{7}}}{\underset{1}{\cancel{7}} \cdot \underset{1}{\cancel{5}}}$

$= -13$

13. $5\frac{2}{3} \cdot (-6) = \frac{17}{3} \cdot \frac{-6}{1}$

$= \frac{17 \cdot (\overset{-2}{\cancel{-6}})}{\underset{1}{\cancel{3}} \cdot 1}$

$= -34$

14. *Sample answer:* Mixed numbers should be converted into improper fractions before you can multiply.

$2\frac{2}{3} \cdot 3\frac{3}{4} = \frac{8}{3} \cdot \frac{15}{4}$

$= \frac{\overset{2}{\cancel{8}} \cdot \overset{5}{\cancel{15}}}{\underset{1}{\cancel{3}} \cdot \underset{1}{\cancel{4}}}$

$= 10$

15. $\frac{5}{8} \cdot \left(-1\frac{1}{2}\right) = \frac{5}{8} \cdot \left(-\frac{3}{2}\right)$

$= \frac{5 \cdot (-3)}{8 \cdot 2}$

$= \frac{-15}{16}$, or $-\frac{15}{16}$

16. $-\frac{7}{6} \cdot \left(-1\frac{1}{2}\right) = -\frac{7}{6} \cdot \left(\frac{-3}{2}\right)$

$= \frac{(-7) \cdot (\overset{-1}{\cancel{-3}})}{\underset{2}{\cancel{6}} \cdot 2}$

$= \frac{7}{4} = 1\frac{3}{4}$

17. $\frac{5}{8} \cdot \left(-\frac{7}{6}\right)^2 = \frac{5}{8} \cdot \frac{49}{36}$

$= \frac{5 \cdot 49}{8 \cdot 36}$

$= \frac{245}{288}$

18. $16\left(-1\frac{1}{2}\right)^3 = 16 \cdot \left(-3\frac{3}{8}\right)$

$= 16 \cdot \left(-\frac{27}{8}\right)$

$= \frac{\overset{2}{\cancel{16}} \cdot (-27)}{1 \cdot \underset{1}{\cancel{8}}}$

$= -54$

Chapter 5, continued

19. $A = \ell w$

$\quad = 2 \cdot \dfrac{15}{16}$

$\quad = \dfrac{2}{1} \cdot \dfrac{15}{16}$

$\quad = \dfrac{2 \cdot 15}{1 \cdot 16}$

$\quad = \dfrac{\overset{1}{2} \cdot 15}{1 \cdot \underset{8}{16}}$

$\quad = \dfrac{15}{8}$

$\quad = 1\dfrac{7}{8}$

The area of the rectangle is $1\dfrac{7}{8}$ square inches.

20. $A = \dfrac{1}{2}bh$

$\quad = \dfrac{1}{2} \cdot 1\dfrac{2}{3} \cdot \dfrac{4}{5}$

$\quad = \dfrac{1}{2} \cdot \dfrac{5}{3} \cdot \dfrac{4}{5}$

$\quad = \dfrac{1 \cdot 5 \cdot 4}{2 \cdot 3 \cdot 5}$

$\quad = \dfrac{1 \cdot \overset{1}{5} \cdot \overset{2}{4}}{\underset{1}{2} \cdot 3 \cdot \underset{1}{5}}$

$\quad = \dfrac{2}{3}$

The area of the triangle is $\dfrac{2}{3}$ square foot.

21. $A = s^2$

$\quad = \left(3\dfrac{5}{11}\right)^2$

$\quad = 3\dfrac{5}{11} \cdot 3\dfrac{5}{11}$

$\quad = \dfrac{38}{11} \cdot \dfrac{38}{11}$

$\quad = \dfrac{38 \cdot 38}{11 \cdot 11}$

$\quad = \dfrac{1444}{121}$

$\quad = 11\dfrac{113}{121}$

The area of the square is $11\dfrac{113}{121}$ square meters.

22. A; $\dfrac{1}{3} \cdot 1 = \dfrac{1}{3}$

$\quad \dfrac{1}{3} \cdot 2 = \dfrac{2}{3}$

$\quad \dfrac{1}{3} \cdot 3 = 1$

$\quad \dfrac{1}{3} \cdot n = \dfrac{1}{3}n$

23. $\dfrac{2}{5} \cdot 1\dfrac{1}{5} \cdot \left(-4\dfrac{7}{12}\right) = \dfrac{2}{5} \cdot \dfrac{6}{5} \cdot \left(-\dfrac{55}{12}\right)$

$\quad = \dfrac{2 \cdot 6 \cdot (-55)}{5 \cdot 5 \cdot 12}$

$\quad = \dfrac{2 \cdot \overset{}{6} \cdot (\overset{-11}{-55})}{5 \cdot \underset{1}{5} \cdot \underset{}{12}}$

$\quad = -\dfrac{11}{5}$

$\quad = -2\dfrac{1}{5}$

24. $-\dfrac{7}{8} + 5\dfrac{1}{2} \cdot \dfrac{11}{15} = -\dfrac{7}{8} + \dfrac{11}{2} \cdot \dfrac{11}{15}$

$\quad = -\dfrac{7}{8} + \dfrac{11 \cdot 11}{2 \cdot 15}$

$\quad = -\dfrac{7}{8} + \dfrac{121}{30}$

$\quad = -\dfrac{7}{8} + 4\dfrac{1}{30}$

$\quad = -\dfrac{105}{120} + 4\dfrac{4}{120}$

$\quad = -\dfrac{105}{120} + \dfrac{484}{120}$

$\quad = \dfrac{-105 + 484}{120}$

$\quad = \dfrac{379}{120}$

$\quad = 3\dfrac{19}{120}$

25. $\dfrac{5}{2} \cdot \left(\dfrac{8}{9} - \dfrac{5}{12}\right) = \dfrac{5}{2} \cdot \left(\dfrac{32}{36} - \dfrac{15}{36}\right) = \dfrac{5}{2} \cdot \dfrac{17}{36} = \dfrac{85}{72} = 1\dfrac{13}{72}$

26. $5 - \left(\dfrac{1}{3} + \dfrac{1}{6}\right)^2 = 5 - \left(\dfrac{2}{6} + \dfrac{1}{6}\right)^2$

$\quad = 5 - \left(\dfrac{3}{6}\right)^2$

$\quad = 5 - \left(\dfrac{1}{2}\right)^2$

$\quad = 5 - \dfrac{1}{2} \cdot \dfrac{1}{2}$

$\quad = 5 - \dfrac{1}{4}$

$\quad = 4\dfrac{4}{4} - \dfrac{1}{4}$

$\quad = 4\dfrac{3}{4}$

27. $4 - \left(\dfrac{3}{4} + \dfrac{7}{8}\right) = 4 - \left(\dfrac{6}{8} + \dfrac{7}{8}\right)$

$\quad = 4 - \left(\dfrac{13}{8}\right)$

$\quad = 4 - 1\dfrac{5}{8}$

$\quad = 2\dfrac{3}{8}$

Chapter 5, continued

28. $\frac{2}{3}\left(\frac{3}{5} - \frac{7}{12}\right) = \frac{2}{3}\left(\frac{36}{60} - \frac{35}{60}\right)$

$\qquad = \frac{2}{3}\left(\frac{1}{60}\right)$

$\qquad = \frac{2 \cdot 1}{3 \cdot \overset{30}{\cancel{60}}}$

$\qquad = \frac{1}{90}$

29. $-\frac{7}{16} + 8\frac{1}{3} \cdot \frac{3}{5} = -\frac{7}{16} + \frac{25}{3} \cdot \frac{3}{5}$

$\qquad = -\frac{7}{16} + \frac{\overset{5}{\cancel{25}} \cdot \overset{1}{\cancel{3}}}{\underset{1}{\cancel{3}} \cdot \underset{1}{\cancel{5}}}$

$\qquad = -\frac{7}{16} + \frac{5}{1}$

$\qquad = -\frac{7}{16} + \frac{80}{16}$

$\qquad = \frac{73}{16}$

$\qquad = 4\frac{9}{16}$

30. $\frac{2}{9}\left(-2\frac{1}{5}\right)\left(3\frac{3}{10}\right) = \frac{2}{9}\left(-\frac{11}{5}\right)\left(\frac{33}{10}\right)$

$\qquad = \frac{\overset{1}{\cancel{2}} \cdot (-11) \cdot \overset{11}{\cancel{33}}}{\underset{3}{\cancel{9}} \cdot 5 \cdot \underset{5}{\cancel{10}}}$

$\qquad = \frac{-121}{75}$

$\qquad = -1\frac{46}{75}$

31. $2\left(\frac{2}{3}\right)(3) = \frac{2 \cdot 2 \cdot \cancel{3}}{\cancel{3}} = 4$

$\left(\frac{2}{3}\right)(3)^2 = \frac{2}{3} \cdot 9 = \frac{2 \cdot \overset{3}{\cancel{9}}}{\underset{1}{\cancel{3}}} = 6$

$\left(2\frac{3}{4}\right)^2\left(\frac{2}{3}\right) = \left(\frac{11}{4}\right)^2\left(\frac{2}{3}\right) = \frac{121}{16} \cdot \frac{2}{3} = \frac{121 \cdot \overset{1}{\cancel{2}}}{\underset{8}{\cancel{16}} \cdot 3} = \frac{121}{24} = 5\frac{1}{24}$

$2\frac{3}{4} + \left(\frac{2}{3}\right)(3) = 2\frac{3}{4} + \frac{2 \cdot \overset{1}{\cancel{3}}}{\underset{1}{\cancel{3}} \cdot 1} = 2\frac{3}{4} + 2 = 4\frac{3}{4}$

The expressions from least to greatest value are
$2bc$, $a + bc$, a^2b, and bc^2.

32. $-\left(\frac{2}{3}\right)^2 + 2\left(2\frac{3}{4}\right)(3) = -\frac{4}{9} + 2\left(\frac{11}{4}\right)(3)$

$\qquad = -\frac{4}{9} + \frac{\overset{1}{\cancel{2}} \cdot 11 \cdot 3}{\underset{2}{\cancel{4}}}$

$\qquad = -\frac{4}{9} + \frac{33}{2}$

$\qquad = -\frac{8}{18} + \frac{297}{18}$

$\qquad = \frac{289}{18}$

$\qquad = 16\frac{1}{18}$

$-\left(2\frac{3}{4}\right) + 5(3) = -2\frac{3}{4} + 15 = 12\frac{1}{4}$

$\left(2\frac{3}{4}\right)^2\left(\frac{2}{3}\right)(3) = \left(\frac{121}{16}\right)\left(\frac{2}{3}\right)(3) = \frac{121 \cdot \overset{1}{\cancel{2}} \cdot \overset{1}{\cancel{3}}}{\underset{8}{\cancel{16}} \cdot \underset{1}{\cancel{3}}} = \frac{121}{8} = 15\frac{1}{8}$

The expressions from least to greatest value are
$-a + 5c$, a^2bc, and $-b^2 + 2ac$.

Problem Solving

33. $\frac{1}{5} \cdot 7 = \frac{1}{5} \cdot \frac{7}{1} = \frac{1 \cdot 7}{5 \cdot 1} = \frac{7}{5} = 1\frac{2}{5}$

The Moltke Crater is about $1\frac{2}{5}$ kilometers deep.

34. $\frac{7}{8} \cdot 15 = \frac{7}{8} \cdot \frac{15}{1} = \frac{7 \cdot 15}{8} = \frac{105}{8} = 13\frac{1}{8}$

You need to take $13\frac{1}{8}$ cups of snack mix. If you estimate
$\frac{7}{8}$ cup to be about 1 cup, you would need about 15 cups
of snack mix, so your answer is reasonable.

35. $\frac{1}{5000} \cdot 11{,}000 = \frac{1}{5000} \cdot \frac{11{,}000}{1}$

$\qquad = \frac{1 \cdot 11{,}000}{5000 \cdot 1}$

$\qquad = \frac{11}{5}$

$\qquad = 2\frac{1}{5}$

It would take $2\frac{1}{5}$ seconds.

36. If you run 1 mile in 8 minutes, you run $\frac{1}{8}$ mile in 1 minute.

miles $= \frac{1}{8} \cdot$ minutes, m

miles $= \frac{1}{8} \cdot m$

When $m = 11$: $\frac{1}{8} \cdot m = \frac{1}{8} \cdot 11$

$\qquad\qquad\qquad = \frac{1}{8} \cdot \frac{11}{1}$

$\qquad\qquad\qquad = \frac{1 \cdot 11}{8 \cdot 1}$

$\qquad\qquad\qquad = \frac{11}{8}$

$\qquad\qquad\qquad = 1\frac{3}{8}$

You run $1\frac{3}{8}$ miles in 11 minutes.

37. $1\frac{2}{5} \times 1\frac{2}{5} = \frac{7}{5} \cdot \frac{7}{5} = \frac{49}{25} = 1\frac{24}{25}$

$1\frac{24}{25} \cdot 1000 = 1960$

Divide 1960 by 144 (12×12 ft^2), or $13\frac{11}{18}$.

1000 mosaic tiles cover $13\frac{11}{18}$ square feet.

38. C; $8\frac{1}{2} \cdot 1\frac{1}{2} = \frac{17}{2} \cdot \frac{3}{2} = \frac{17 \cdot 3}{2 \cdot 2} = \frac{51}{4} = 12\frac{3}{4}$ in.

$11 \cdot 1\frac{1}{2} = 11 \cdot \frac{3}{2} = \frac{11}{1} \cdot \frac{3}{2} = \frac{11 \cdot 3}{1 \cdot 2} = \frac{33}{2} = 16\frac{1}{2}$ in.

The new dimensions are $12\frac{3}{4}$ inches by $16\frac{1}{2}$ inches.

$A = \ell w$

$\quad = 12\frac{3}{4} \cdot 16\frac{1}{2}$

$\quad = \frac{51}{4} \cdot \frac{33}{2}$

$\quad = \frac{51 \cdot 33}{4 \cdot 2}$

$\quad = \frac{1683}{8}$

$\quad = 210\frac{3}{8}$ in.^{2}

39. $\frac{1}{8} \cdot 1200 = 150$

150 students/teachers have signed the petition.

$\frac{1}{25} \cdot 150 = 6$

6 teachers need to sign the petition.

$\frac{73}{75} \cdot 150 = 146$

146 students have signed the petition, which means 4 teachers have signed it $(146 + 4 = 150)$. The petition cannot be presented.

Mixed Review

40. $\frac{48}{-4} = -12$

41. $\frac{-24}{8} = -3$

42. $\frac{0}{-6} = 0$

43. $\frac{-32}{-2} = 16$

44. $5^3 \cdot 5^2 = 5^5 = 3125$

$\frac{5^3}{5^2} = 5^1 = 5$

45. A; $-2\frac{4}{9} + \frac{5}{21} = -2\frac{28}{63} + \frac{15}{63}$

$\quad = -2 + \left(\frac{-28}{63} + \frac{15}{63}\right)$

$\quad = -2\frac{13}{63}$

Lesson 5.4

Activity (p. 247)

2. $6 \cdot \frac{4}{3} = \frac{6}{1} \cdot \frac{4}{3} = \frac{6 \cdot 4}{1 \cdot 3} = \frac{\overset{2}{\cancel{6}} \cdot 4}{1 \cdot \underset{1}{\cancel{3}}} = \frac{8}{1} = 8$

The values of $6 \div \frac{3}{4}$ and $6 \cdot \frac{4}{3}$ are both 8.

3.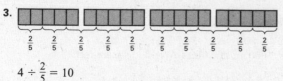

$4 \div \frac{2}{5} = 10$

4. $4 \cdot \frac{5}{2} = \frac{4}{1} \cdot \frac{5}{2} = \frac{4 \cdot 5}{1 \cdot 2} = \frac{\overset{2}{\cancel{4}} \cdot 5}{1 \cdot \underset{1}{\cancel{2}}} = 10$

The values of $4 \div \frac{2}{5}$ and $4 \cdot \frac{5}{2}$ are both 10.

5. You can multiply 5 by $\frac{3}{2}$ to find the value of $5 \div \frac{2}{3}$.

5.4 Guided Practice (pp. 248–249)

1. $\frac{5}{8} \div \left(-\frac{7}{10}\right) = \frac{5}{8} \cdot -\frac{10}{7}$

$\quad = \frac{5 \cdot (-10)}{8 \cdot 7}$

$\quad = \frac{5 \cdot (-\overset{5}{\cancel{10}})}{\underset{4}{\cancel{8}} \cdot 7}$

$\quad = -\frac{25}{28}$

2. $\frac{2}{15} \div 8 = \frac{2}{15} \cdot \frac{1}{8} = \frac{2 \cdot 1}{15 \cdot 8} = \frac{\overset{1}{\cancel{2}} \cdot 1}{15 \cdot \underset{4}{\cancel{8}}} = \frac{1}{60}$

3. $-\frac{3}{4} \div \left(-\frac{7}{12}\right) = -\frac{3}{4} \cdot \left(-\frac{12}{7}\right)$

$\quad = \frac{-3 \cdot (-12)}{4 \cdot 7}$

$\quad = \frac{-3 \cdot (-\overset{-3}{\cancel{12}})}{\underset{1}{\cancel{4}} \cdot 7}$

$\quad = \frac{9}{7}$

$\quad = 1\frac{2}{7}$

4. $\frac{6}{7} \div 2 = \frac{6}{7} \cdot \frac{1}{2} = \frac{6 \cdot 1}{7 \cdot 2} = \frac{\overset{3}{\cancel{6}} \cdot 1}{7 \cdot \underset{1}{\cancel{2}}} = \frac{3}{7}$

5. $6\frac{2}{7} \div 4 = \frac{44}{7} \div \frac{4}{1}$

$\quad = \frac{44}{7} \cdot \frac{1}{4}$

$\quad = \frac{44 \cdot 1}{7 \cdot 4}$

$\quad = \frac{\overset{11}{\cancel{44}} \cdot 1}{7 \cdot \underset{1}{\cancel{4}}}$

$\quad = \frac{11}{7}$

$\quad = 1\frac{4}{7}$

6. $-12\frac{1}{4} \div 7 = -\frac{49}{4} \div \frac{7}{1}$

$\quad = -\frac{49}{4} \cdot \frac{1}{7}$

$\quad = \frac{-49 \cdot 1}{4 \cdot 7}$

$\quad = \frac{-\overset{-7}{\cancel{49}} \cdot 1}{4 \cdot \underset{1}{\cancel{7}}}$

$\quad = -\frac{7}{4}$

$\quad = -1\frac{3}{4}$

7. $10 \div 3\frac{1}{3} = 10 \div \frac{10}{3}$

$\quad = \frac{10}{1} \cdot \frac{3}{10}$

$\quad = \frac{10 \cdot 3}{1 \cdot 10}$

$\quad = \frac{\overset{1}{\cancel{10}} \cdot 3}{1 \cdot \underset{1}{\cancel{10}}}$

$\quad = \frac{3}{1} = 3$

Chapter 5, *continued*

8. $-15\frac{3}{4} \div \left(-2\frac{5}{8}\right) = -\frac{63}{4} \div \left(-\frac{21}{8}\right)$

$$= \frac{-63}{4} \cdot \left(\frac{-8}{21}\right)$$

$$= \frac{-63 \cdot (-8)}{4 \cdot 21}$$

$$= \frac{\overset{-3}{\cancel{-63}} \cdot (\overset{-2}{\cancel{-8}})}{\underset{1}{\cancel{4}} \cdot \underset{1}{\cancel{21}}}$$

$$= \frac{6}{1} = 6$$

9. $\quad 5 = \frac{20}{24}d$

$$5 \cdot \frac{24}{20} = \frac{24}{20} \cdot \frac{20}{24}d$$

$$\frac{\overset{1}{\cancel{5}}}{1} \cdot \frac{24}{\underset{4}{\cancel{20}}} = 1 \cdot d$$

$$6 = d$$

It will take 6 days.

5.4 Exercises (pp. 249–252)

Skill Practice

1. The multiplicative inverse, or reciprocal, of a number is the number that when multiplied by the original number equals 1.

2.

Number	Reciprocal
$\frac{1}{2}$	2
$\frac{4}{7}$	$\frac{7}{4}$
-8	$-\frac{1}{8}$
$1\frac{1}{2} = \frac{3}{2}$	$\frac{2}{3}$

3. $\frac{3}{4} \div \frac{1}{8} = \frac{3}{4} \cdot \frac{8}{1} = \frac{3 \cdot 8}{4 \cdot 1} = \frac{3 \cdot \overset{2}{\cancel{8}}}{\underset{1}{\cancel{4}} \cdot 1} = 6$

4. $\frac{11}{12} \div \frac{11}{16} = \frac{11}{12} \cdot \frac{16}{11} = \frac{\overset{1}{\cancel{11}} \cdot \overset{4}{\cancel{16}}}{\underset{3}{\cancel{12}} \cdot \underset{1}{\cancel{11}}} = \frac{4}{3} = 1\frac{1}{3}$

5. $\frac{5}{6} \div \left(-\frac{1}{3}\right) = \frac{5}{6} \cdot -\frac{3}{1}$

$$= \frac{5 \cdot (-3)}{6 \cdot 1}$$

$$= \frac{5 \cdot (\overset{-1}{\cancel{-3}})}{\underset{2}{\cancel{6}} \cdot 1}$$

$$= -\frac{5}{2}$$

$$= -2\frac{1}{2}$$

6. $-\frac{7}{10} \div \frac{4}{5} = -\frac{7}{10} \cdot \frac{5}{4} = \frac{-7 \cdot \overset{1}{\cancel{5}}}{\underset{2}{\cancel{10}} \cdot 4} = -\frac{7}{8}$

7. $\frac{4}{9} \div \frac{4}{7} = \frac{4}{9} \cdot \frac{7}{4} = \frac{4 \cdot 7}{9 \cdot 4} = \frac{\overset{1}{\cancel{4}} \cdot 7}{9 \cdot \underset{1}{\cancel{4}}} = \frac{7}{9}$

8. $-\frac{3}{8} \div \frac{7}{12} = -\frac{3}{0} \cdot \frac{12}{7} = \frac{-3 \cdot 12}{8 \cdot 7} = \frac{-3 \cdot \overset{3}{\cancel{12}}}{\underset{2}{\cancel{8}} \cdot 7} = -\frac{9}{14}$

9. $\frac{9}{14} \div \left(-\frac{3}{26}\right) = \frac{9}{14} \cdot \left(-\frac{26}{3}\right)$

$$= \frac{9 \cdot (-26)}{14 \cdot 3}$$

$$= \frac{\overset{3}{\cancel{9}} \cdot (\overset{-13}{\cancel{-26}})}{\underset{7}{\cancel{14}} \cdot \underset{1}{\cancel{3}}}$$

$$= -\frac{39}{7}$$

$$= -5\frac{4}{7}$$

10. $-\frac{21}{22} \div \frac{-7}{11} = -\frac{21}{22} \cdot \frac{-11}{7} = \frac{\overset{-3}{\cancel{-21}} \cdot (\overset{-1}{\cancel{-11}})}{\underset{2}{\cancel{22}} \cdot \underset{1}{\cancel{7}}} = \frac{3}{2} = 1\frac{1}{2}$

11. $-\frac{5}{6} \div (-2) = -\frac{5}{6} \cdot \left(-\frac{1}{2}\right) = \frac{-5 \cdot (-1)}{6 \cdot 2} = \frac{5}{12}$

12. $\frac{2}{3} \div 3 = \frac{2}{3} \cdot \frac{1}{3} = \frac{2 \cdot 1}{3 \cdot 3} = \frac{2}{9}$

13. $\frac{3}{5} \div (-4) = \frac{3}{5} \cdot \left(-\frac{1}{4}\right) = \frac{3 \cdot (-1)}{5 \cdot 4} = -\frac{3}{20}$

14. $\frac{-8}{5} \div 12 = \frac{-8}{5} \cdot \frac{1}{12} = \frac{(\overset{-2}{\cancel{-8}}) \cdot 1}{5 \cdot \underset{3}{\cancel{12}}} = -\frac{2}{15}$

15. The wrong fraction was inverted.

$$\frac{-3}{10} \div \left(-\frac{4}{5}\right) = \frac{-3}{10} \cdot \left(-\frac{5}{4}\right)$$

$$= \frac{-3 \cdot (-5)}{10 \cdot 4}$$

$$= \frac{-3 \cdot (\overset{-1}{\cancel{-5}})}{\underset{2}{\cancel{10}} \cdot 4}$$

$$= \frac{3}{8}$$

16. $\frac{1}{2} \div 3 = \frac{1}{6}$

17. $4 \div \frac{1}{2} = 8$

18. $1 \div \frac{4}{7} = \frac{7}{4} = 1\frac{3}{4}$

19. $\frac{2}{3} \div \frac{3}{2} = \frac{4}{9}$

20. $9 \div \frac{1}{3} = 27$

21. $\frac{5}{6} \div \frac{6}{5} = \frac{25}{36}$

22. $6 \div \frac{2}{3} = 9$

23. $10 \div \frac{1}{10} = 100$

24. $5\frac{1}{4} \div 2\frac{1}{3} = \frac{21}{4} \div \frac{7}{3}$

$$= \frac{21}{4} \cdot \frac{3}{7}$$

$$= \frac{21 \cdot 3}{4 \cdot 7}$$

$$= \frac{\overset{3}{\cancel{21}} \cdot 3}{4 \cdot \underset{1}{\cancel{7}}}$$

$$= \frac{9}{4}$$

$$= 2\frac{1}{4}$$

25. $12\frac{1}{7} \div 5\frac{5}{6} = \frac{85}{7} \div \frac{35}{6}$

$$= \frac{85}{7} \cdot \frac{6}{35}$$

$$= \frac{85 \cdot 6}{7 \cdot 35}$$

$$= \frac{\overset{17}{\cancel{85}} \cdot 6}{7 \cdot \underset{7}{\cancel{35}}}$$

$$= \frac{102}{49}$$

$$= 2\frac{4}{49}$$

26. $7\frac{7}{8} \div \left(-2\frac{1}{4}\right) = \frac{63}{8} \div \left(-\frac{9}{4}\right)$

$\qquad = \frac{63}{8} \cdot \left(-\frac{4}{9}\right)$

$\qquad = \frac{\overset{7}{\cancel{63}} \cdot (\overset{-1}{\cancel{-4}})}{\underset{2}{\cancel{8}} \cdot \underset{1}{\cancel{9}}}$

$\qquad = -\frac{7}{2}$

$\qquad = -3\frac{1}{2}$

27. $-22\frac{2}{3} \div 3\frac{1}{5} = -\frac{68}{3} \div \frac{16}{5}$

$\qquad = -\frac{68}{3} \cdot \frac{5}{16}$

$\qquad = \frac{-68 \cdot 5}{3 \cdot 16}$

$\qquad = \frac{\overset{-17}{\cancel{-68}} \cdot 5}{3 \cdot \underset{4}{\cancel{16}}}$

$\qquad = -\frac{85}{12}$

$\qquad = -7\frac{1}{12}$

28. $(-8) \div -9\frac{3}{5} = -8 \div \left(-\frac{48}{5}\right)$

$\qquad = -\frac{8}{1} \cdot \left(-\frac{5}{48}\right)$

$\qquad = \frac{-8 \cdot (-5)}{1 \cdot 48}$

$\qquad = \frac{\overset{-1}{\cancel{-8}} \cdot (-5)}{1 \cdot \underset{6}{\cancel{48}}}$

$\qquad = \frac{5}{6}$

29. $8\frac{4}{13} \div 6\frac{3}{4} = \frac{108}{13} \div \frac{27}{4}$

$\qquad = \frac{108}{13} \cdot \frac{4}{27}$

$\qquad = \frac{108 \cdot 4}{13 \cdot 27}$

$\qquad = \frac{\overset{4}{\cancel{108}} \cdot 4}{13 \cdot \underset{1}{\cancel{27}}}$

$\qquad = \frac{16}{13}$

$\qquad = 1\frac{3}{13}$

30. $1\frac{5}{7} \div (-6) = \frac{12}{7} \div \left(\frac{-6}{1}\right)$

$\qquad = \frac{12}{7} \cdot \left(\frac{-1}{6}\right)$

$\qquad = \frac{12 \cdot (-1)}{7 \cdot 6}$

$\qquad = \frac{\overset{2}{\cancel{12}} \cdot (-1)}{7 \cdot \underset{1}{\cancel{6}}}$

$\qquad = \frac{-2}{7}, \text{ or } -\frac{2}{7}$

31. $15 \div 4\frac{1}{6} = 15 \div \frac{25}{6}$

$\qquad = \frac{15}{1} \cdot \frac{6}{25}$

$\qquad = \frac{15 \cdot 6}{1 \cdot 25}$

$\qquad = \frac{\overset{3}{\cancel{15}} \cdot 6}{1 \cdot \underset{5}{\cancel{25}}}$

$\qquad = \frac{18}{5}$

$\qquad = 3\frac{3}{5}$

32. $2 \div 1\frac{1}{3} = 2 \div \frac{4}{3}$

$\qquad = \frac{2}{1} \cdot \frac{3}{4}$

$\qquad = \frac{2 \cdot 3}{1 \cdot 4}$

$\qquad = \frac{\overset{1}{\cancel{2}} \cdot 3}{1 \cdot \underset{2}{\cancel{4}}}$

$\qquad = \frac{3}{2} = 1\frac{1}{2}$

33. $6\frac{4}{7} \div (-4) = \frac{46}{7} \div \frac{-4}{1}$

$\qquad = \frac{46}{7} \cdot \left(-\frac{1}{4}\right)$

$\qquad = \frac{\overset{23}{\cancel{46}} \cdot (-1)}{7 \cdot \underset{2}{\cancel{4}}}$

$\qquad = -\frac{23}{14}$

$\qquad = -1\frac{9}{14}$

34. $13\frac{1}{6} \div \frac{2}{5} = \frac{79}{6} \div \frac{2}{5}$

$\qquad = \frac{79}{6} \cdot \frac{5}{2}$

$\qquad = \frac{79 \cdot 5}{6 \cdot 2}$

$\qquad = \frac{395}{12}$

$\qquad = 32\frac{11}{12}$

35. $-9\frac{5}{6} \div 1\frac{2}{3} = -\frac{59}{6} \div \frac{5}{3}$

$\qquad = -\frac{59}{6} \cdot \frac{3}{5}$

$\qquad = \frac{-59 \cdot 3}{6 \cdot 5}$

$\qquad = \frac{-59 \cdot \overset{1}{\cancel{3}}}{\underset{2}{\cancel{6}} \cdot 5}$

$\qquad = \frac{-59}{10}$

$\qquad = -5\frac{9}{10}$

36. B; $\frac{5}{6}a = -15$

$$\frac{6}{5} \cdot \frac{5}{6}a = -15 \cdot \frac{6}{5}$$

Multiply both sides by the reciprocal of $\frac{5}{6}$, which is $\frac{6}{5}$.

37. $2 \div \frac{4}{5} = \frac{2}{1} \cdot \frac{5}{4} = \frac{2 \cdot 5}{1 \cdot 4} = \frac{\overset{1}{2} \cdot 5}{1 \cdot \underset{2}{4}} = \frac{5}{2} = 2\frac{1}{2}$

38. $3 \div \frac{2}{3} = \frac{3}{1} \cdot \frac{3}{2} = \frac{3 \cdot 3}{1 \cdot 2} = \frac{9}{2} = 4\frac{1}{2}$

39.  **40.**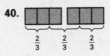

$\frac{1}{2}$ $\frac{1}{2}$ $\frac{1}{2}$ $\frac{1}{2}$ $\frac{1}{2}$ $\frac{1}{2}$ $\frac{2}{3}$ $\frac{2}{3}$ $\frac{2}{3}$

41.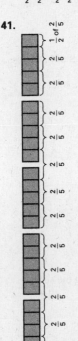

42.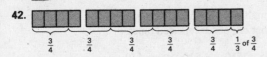

$\frac{3}{4}$ $\frac{3}{4}$ $\frac{3}{4}$ $\frac{3}{4}$ $\frac{3}{4}$ $\frac{1}{3}$ of $\frac{3}{4}$

43. $\frac{3}{4}a = 15$

$$\frac{3}{4}a \div \frac{3}{4} = 15 \div \frac{3}{4}$$

$$a = \frac{15}{1} \cdot \frac{4}{3}$$

$$a = \frac{\overset{5}{15} \cdot 4}{1 \cdot \underset{1}{3}}$$

$$a = 20$$

44. $\frac{7}{10}b = 28$

$$\frac{7}{10}b \div \frac{7}{10} = 28 \div \frac{7}{10}$$

$$b = \frac{28}{1} \cdot \frac{10}{7}$$

$$b = \frac{\overset{4}{28} \cdot 10}{1 \cdot \underset{1}{7}}$$

$$b = 40$$

45. $-\frac{9}{17}r = 3$

$$-\frac{9}{17}r \div \left(-\frac{9}{17}\right) = 3 \div \left(-\frac{9}{17}\right)$$

$$r = \frac{3}{1} \cdot \left(-\frac{17}{9}\right)$$

$$r = \frac{\overset{1}{3} \cdot (-17)}{1 \cdot \underset{3}{9}}$$

$$r = -\frac{17}{3}$$

$$r = -5\frac{2}{3}$$

46. $-11 = -9\frac{1}{6}h$

$$-11 \div -9\frac{1}{6} = -9\frac{1}{6}h \div \left(-9\frac{1}{6}\right)$$

$$-\frac{11}{1} \div \left(-\frac{55}{6}\right) = h$$

$$-\frac{11}{1} \cdot \left(-\frac{6}{55}\right) = h$$

$$\frac{-\overset{1}{11} \cdot (-6)}{1 \cdot \underset{5}{55}} = h$$

$$\frac{6}{5} = h$$

$$1\frac{1}{5} = h$$

47. $-\frac{8}{11}k = -48$

$$-\frac{8}{11}k \div \left(-\frac{8}{11}\right) = -48 \div \left(-\frac{8}{11}\right)$$

$$k = \frac{-48}{1} \cdot \left(-\frac{11}{8}\right)$$

$$k = \frac{\overset{-6}{-48} \cdot (-11)}{1 \cdot \underset{1}{8}}$$

$$k = 66$$

48. $\frac{2}{5}m = -18$

$$\frac{2}{5}m \div \frac{2}{5} = -18 \div \frac{2}{5}$$

$$m = \frac{-18}{1} \cdot \frac{5}{2}$$

$$m = \frac{\overset{-9}{-18} \cdot 5}{1 \cdot \underset{1}{2}}$$

$$m = -45$$

49.
$$42 = -5\tfrac{1}{4}p$$
$$42 = -\tfrac{21}{4}p$$
$$42 \div \left(-\tfrac{21}{4}\right) = -\tfrac{21}{4}p \div \left(-\tfrac{21}{4}\right)$$
$$\tfrac{42}{1} \cdot \left(-\tfrac{4}{21}\right) = p$$
$$\frac{\overset{2}{\cancel{42}} \cdot (-4)}{1 \cdot \underset{1}{\cancel{21}}} = p$$
$$-8 = p$$

50.
$$9 = \tfrac{-9}{10}t$$
$$9 \div \left(-\tfrac{9}{10}\right) = -\tfrac{9}{10}t \div \left(-\tfrac{9}{10}\right)$$
$$\tfrac{9}{1} \cdot \left(-\tfrac{10}{9}\right) = t$$
$$\frac{\overset{1}{\cancel{9}} \cdot (-10)}{1 \cdot \underset{1}{\cancel{9}}} = t$$
$$-10 = t$$

51. Juan's method works because

$$\frac{a}{c} \div \frac{b}{c} = \frac{a}{c} \cdot \frac{c}{b} = \frac{a \cdot c}{c \cdot b} = \frac{a}{b}.$$

It is unnecessary to find a common denominator when dividing fractions, but this method will work.

52. a. $\dfrac{10}{21} \div \dfrac{2}{3} = \dfrac{\overset{5}{\cancel{10}}}{\underset{7}{\cancel{21}}} \cdot \dfrac{\overset{1}{\cancel{3}}}{\underset{1}{\cancel{2}}} = \dfrac{5}{7}$

b. $\dfrac{9}{20} \div \dfrac{3}{4} = \dfrac{\overset{3}{\cancel{9}}}{\underset{5}{\cancel{20}}} \cdot \dfrac{\overset{1}{\cancel{4}}}{\underset{1}{\cancel{3}}} = \dfrac{3}{5}$

c. $\dfrac{15}{16} \div \dfrac{5}{8} = \dfrac{\overset{3}{\cancel{15}}}{\underset{2}{\cancel{16}}} \cdot \dfrac{\overset{1}{\cancel{8}}}{\underset{1}{\cancel{5}}} = \dfrac{3}{2} = 1\tfrac{1}{2}$

d. $\dfrac{24}{25} \div \dfrac{4}{5} = \dfrac{\overset{6}{\cancel{24}}}{\underset{5}{\cancel{25}}} \cdot \dfrac{\overset{1}{\cancel{5}}}{\underset{1}{\cancel{4}}} = \dfrac{6}{5} = 1\tfrac{1}{5}$

Sample answer: You can divide numerators and

denominators to find a quotient $\dfrac{\frac{a}{b}}{\frac{c}{d}} = \dfrac{a}{b} \times \dfrac{d}{c} = \dfrac{ad}{bc} = \dfrac{\frac{a}{c}}{\frac{b}{d}}$.

Problem Solving

53. Use division because you are splitting 5 pounds into $\tfrac{1}{4}$ pound sections.

$$5 \div \tfrac{1}{4} = n$$
$$5 \cdot 4 = n$$
$$20 = n$$

You can make 20 hamburgers.

54. Use division because you are splitting $6\tfrac{1}{2}$ hours into $\tfrac{5}{6}$ hour intervals.

$$6\tfrac{1}{2} \div \tfrac{5}{6} = \tfrac{13}{2} \div \tfrac{5}{6}$$
$$= \tfrac{13}{2} \cdot \tfrac{6}{5}$$
$$= \tfrac{13 \cdot 6}{2 \cdot 5}$$
$$= \frac{13 \cdot \overset{3}{\cancel{6}}}{\underset{1}{\cancel{2}} \cdot 5}$$
$$= \tfrac{39}{5}$$
$$= 7\tfrac{4}{5}$$

You can listen to $7\tfrac{4}{5}$ CDs using one new set of batteries.

55. Use addition because you are looking for a total of 3 different distances.

$$9\tfrac{1}{3} + 6\tfrac{3}{4} + 9\tfrac{1}{2} = 9\tfrac{4}{12} + 6\tfrac{9}{12} + 9\tfrac{6}{12}$$
$$= (9 + 6 + 9) + \left(\tfrac{4}{12} + \tfrac{9}{12} + \tfrac{6}{12}\right)$$
$$= 24 + 1\tfrac{7}{12}$$
$$= 25\tfrac{7}{12}$$

Jasmine's total distance was $25\tfrac{7}{12}$ feet.

56. Use multiplication because you are adding the same width repeated times.

$$4 \cdot 2\tfrac{1}{3} = 4 \cdot \tfrac{7}{3} = \tfrac{4 \cdot 7}{1 \cdot 3} = \tfrac{28}{3} = 9\tfrac{1}{3}$$

4 bookshelves will take up $9\tfrac{1}{3}$ feet of wall space.

57. Use multiplication because you are adding the same number of pounds repeated times.

$$6 \cdot 85 = 510 \qquad 510 \cdot 1\tfrac{1}{2} = 510 \cdot \tfrac{3}{2}$$
$$= \frac{\overset{255}{\cancel{510}} \cdot 3}{1 \cdot \underset{1}{\cancel{2}}} = 765$$

The chickens will eat 765 pounds in $1\tfrac{1}{2}$ years.

58. a. Haley earns $180 in 3 days, or $60 per day. She works $7\tfrac{1}{2}$ hours each day.

$$60 \div 7\tfrac{1}{2} = 60 \div \tfrac{15}{2} = \tfrac{60}{1} \cdot \tfrac{2}{15} = \frac{\overset{4}{\cancel{60}} \cdot 2}{1 \cdot \underset{1}{\cancel{15}}} = 8$$

Haley earns $8 per hour.

b. Haley earns $8 per hour and if she works 3 extra hours $(8 \cdot 3)$, she will earn $24 more.

$$180 + 24 = 204$$

Haley will earn $204.

Chapter 5, continued

c. *Sample answer:*

Multiply the number of weeks Haley is working, 7, by how much she makes in a normal week, 180.

$180 \cdot 7 = \$1260$

Haley wants to make $1356

$1356 - 1260 = \$96$

To find the number of extra shifts divide 96 by 24.

$96 \div 24 = 4$

Haley needs to work 4 extra 3 hour shifts.

59. *Sample answer:* Exchange the numerator and denominator for a positive or a negative fraction. Positive fractions stay positive and negative fractions stay negative.

60. B; $C = (F - 32) \div \frac{9}{5}$

$= (77 - 32) \div \frac{9}{5}$

$= 45 \div \frac{9}{5}$

$= \frac{\overset{5}{\cancel{45}}}{1} \cdot \frac{5}{\cancel{9}}$

$= 25$

61. $8\frac{1}{2} \div 1\frac{1}{4} = \frac{17}{2} \div \frac{5}{4} = \frac{17}{2} \cdot \frac{4}{5} = \frac{17 \cdot \overset{2}{\cancel{4}}}{\underset{1}{\cancel{2}} \cdot 5} = \frac{34}{5} = 6\frac{4}{5}$

So, 6 game pieces will fit across the $8\frac{1}{2}$ inch side.

$11 \div 1\frac{1}{4} = \frac{11}{1} \div \frac{5}{4} = \frac{11}{1} \cdot \frac{4}{5} = \frac{11 \cdot 4}{1 \cdot 5} = \frac{44}{5} = 8\frac{4}{5}$

So, 8 game pieces will fit across the 11 inch side. The total number of game pieces that can be cut is $6 \cdot 8 = 48$.

Find the area of the sheet of paper and then subtract the area of one game piece times 48.

$\left(8\frac{1}{2} \times 11\right) - (48)\left(1\frac{1}{4}\right)^2 = 93.5 - (48)\left(\frac{5}{4}\right)^2$

$= 93.5 - \left(\frac{48}{1}\right)\left(\frac{25}{16}\right)$

$= 93.5 - \left(\frac{\overset{3}{\cancel{48}} \cdot 25}{1 \cdot \underset{1}{\cancel{16}}}\right)$

$= 93.5 - 75$

$= 18.5$

There are 18.5 square inches of paper left over.

62. Divide 270 by $\frac{2}{5}$ to determine the number of students in the school.

$270 \div \frac{2}{5} = \frac{270}{1} \cdot \frac{5}{2} = \frac{\overset{135}{\cancel{270}} \cdot 5}{1 \cdot \underset{1}{\cancel{2}}} = 675$

There are 675 students in your school.

63. *Sample answer:* I gave $\frac{4}{9}$ of my button collection to Tina. I gave $\frac{1}{2}$ of that number to Jenna. If I gave 28 buttons to Jenna, how many did I start with?

$\frac{1}{2}\left(\frac{4}{9}x\right) = 28$

$\frac{1 \cdot \overset{2}{\cancel{4}}}{2 \cdot 9}x = 28$
$\underset{1}{}$

$\frac{2}{9}x = 28$

$\frac{2}{9}x \div \frac{2}{9} = 28 \div \frac{2}{9}$

$x = \frac{28}{1} \cdot \frac{9}{2}$

$x = \frac{\overset{14}{\cancel{28}} \cdot 9}{1 \cdot \underset{1}{\cancel{2}}}$

$x = 126$

I started with 126 buttons.

64. Students who chose fall sports, soccer: $\frac{1}{3} \cdot \frac{2}{7} = \frac{2}{21}$

Students who chose spring sports, baseball: $\frac{1}{2} \cdot \frac{3}{5} = \frac{3}{10}$

Baseball $\div$ soccer $= \frac{3}{10} \div \frac{2}{21}$

$= \frac{3}{10} \cdot \frac{21}{2}$

$= \frac{3 \cdot 21}{10 \cdot 2}$

$= \frac{63}{20} = 3\frac{3}{20}$

The number of students who chose baseball was $3\frac{3}{20}$ times the number who chose soccer.

Mixed Review

65. $3\frac{1}{2} = \frac{7}{2} = \frac{14}{4}$; $14 > 11$, so $3\frac{1}{2} > \frac{11}{4}$

66. $5\frac{1}{4} = \frac{21}{4}$; $21 = 21$, so $\frac{21}{4} = 5\frac{1}{4}$

67. $2\frac{2}{5} = \frac{12}{5} = \frac{36}{15}$

$\frac{8}{3} = \frac{40}{15}$; $36 < 40$, so $2\frac{2}{5} < \frac{8}{3}$

68. $\frac{44}{3} = \frac{176}{12}$

$14\frac{5}{12} = \frac{173}{12}$; $176 > 173$, so $\frac{44}{3} > 14\frac{5}{12}$

69. $\frac{9x^2}{27x} = \frac{3 \cdot 3 \cdot x \cdot x}{3 \cdot 3 \cdot 3 \cdot x} = \frac{\overset{1}{\cancel{3}} \cdot \overset{1}{\cancel{3}} \cdot \overset{1}{\cancel{x}} \cdot x}{\underset{1}{\cancel{3}} \cdot \underset{1}{\cancel{3}} \cdot 3 \cdot \underset{1}{\cancel{x}}} = \frac{x}{3}$

70. $\dfrac{24y^4}{15y^2} = \dfrac{2 \cdot 2 \cdot 2 \cdot 3 \cdot y \cdot y \cdot y \cdot y}{3 \cdot 5 \cdot y \cdot y}$

$= \dfrac{2 \cdot 2 \cdot 2 \cdot \overset{1}{\cancel{3}} \cdot \overset{1}{\cancel{y}} \cdot \overset{1}{\cancel{y}} \cdot y \cdot y}{\underset{1}{\cancel{3}} \cdot 5 \cdot \underset{1}{\cancel{y}} \cdot \underset{1}{\cancel{y}}}$

$= \dfrac{8y^2}{5}$

71. $\dfrac{14x^3y}{18xy^3} = \dfrac{2 \cdot 7 \cdot x \cdot x \cdot x \cdot y}{2 \cdot 3 \cdot 3 \cdot x \cdot y \cdot y \cdot y}$

$= \dfrac{\overset{1}{\cancel{2}} \cdot 7 \cdot \overset{1}{\cancel{x}} \cdot x \cdot x \cdot \overset{1}{\cancel{y}}}{\underset{1}{\cancel{2}} \cdot 3 \cdot 3 \cdot \underset{1}{\cancel{x}} \cdot \underset{1}{\cancel{y}} \cdot y \cdot y}$

$= \dfrac{7x^2}{9y^2}$

72. $\dfrac{54yz^2}{81xz^2} = \dfrac{2 \cdot 3 \cdot 3 \cdot 3 \cdot y \cdot z \cdot z}{3 \cdot 3 \cdot 3 \cdot 3 \cdot x \cdot z \cdot z}$

$= \dfrac{2 \cdot \overset{1}{\cancel{3}} \cdot \overset{1}{\cancel{3}} \cdot \overset{1}{\cancel{3}} \cdot y \cdot \overset{1}{\cancel{z}} \cdot \overset{1}{\cancel{z}}}{3 \cdot \underset{1}{\cancel{3}} \cdot \underset{1}{\cancel{3}} \cdot \underset{1}{\cancel{3}} \cdot x \cdot \underset{1}{\cancel{z}} \cdot \underset{1}{\cancel{z}}}$

$= \dfrac{2y}{3x}$

73. D; $6\dfrac{1}{2} \cdot 3\dfrac{3}{4} = \dfrac{13}{2} \cdot \dfrac{15}{4} = \dfrac{195}{8} = 24\dfrac{3}{8}$

Quiz 5.1–5.4 (p. 252)

1. $1\dfrac{5}{8} - \dfrac{7}{8} = \dfrac{13}{8} - \dfrac{7}{8} = \dfrac{13 - 7}{8} = \dfrac{6}{8} = \dfrac{3}{4}$

2. $-\dfrac{4}{9} + 3\dfrac{5}{9} = -\dfrac{4}{9} + \dfrac{32}{9} = \dfrac{-4 + 32}{9} = \dfrac{28}{9} = 3\dfrac{1}{9}$

3. $\dfrac{x}{12} + \dfrac{5x}{12} = \dfrac{x + 5x}{12} = \dfrac{6x}{12} = \dfrac{x}{2}$

4. $\dfrac{4}{9} - \dfrac{8}{9} + \dfrac{5}{9} = \dfrac{4 - 8 + 5}{9} = \dfrac{1}{9}$

5. $\dfrac{2}{3} + \dfrac{9}{6} = \dfrac{4}{6} + \dfrac{9}{6} = \dfrac{13}{6} = 2\dfrac{1}{6}$

6. $\dfrac{6y}{21} - \dfrac{2y}{7} = \dfrac{6y}{21} - \dfrac{6y}{21} = 0$

7. $-5\dfrac{3}{4} - 2\dfrac{1}{3} = -\dfrac{23}{4} - \dfrac{7}{3}$

$= -\dfrac{69}{12} - \dfrac{28}{12}$

$= \dfrac{-69 - 28}{12}$

$= -\dfrac{97}{12}$

$= -8\dfrac{1}{12}$

8. $\dfrac{3}{10} + 4\dfrac{2}{5} - 1\dfrac{1}{2} = \dfrac{3}{10} + 4\dfrac{4}{10} - 1\dfrac{5}{10}$

$= (4 - 1) + \left(\dfrac{3}{10} + \dfrac{4}{10} - \dfrac{5}{10}\right)$

$= 3\dfrac{2}{10}$

$= 3\dfrac{1}{5}$

9. $4\dfrac{2}{3} + 4\dfrac{1}{4} = 4\dfrac{8}{12} + 4\dfrac{3}{12} = (4 + 4) + \left(\dfrac{8}{12} + \dfrac{3}{12}\right) = 8\dfrac{11}{12}$

The two recipes call for $8\dfrac{11}{12}$ cups of flour. Because you have 9 cups of flour, you can make both recipes.

10. $\dfrac{7}{12} \cdot \dfrac{8}{21} = \dfrac{7 \cdot 8}{12 \cdot 21} = \dfrac{\overset{1}{\cancel{7}} \cdot \overset{2}{\cancel{8}}}{\underset{3}{\cancel{12}} \cdot \underset{3}{\cancel{21}}} = \dfrac{2}{9}$

11. $-\dfrac{11}{12} \cdot \left(-\dfrac{3}{10}\right) = \dfrac{-11 \cdot (-3)}{12 \cdot 10} = \dfrac{-11 \cdot (\overset{-1}{\cancel{-3}})}{\underset{4}{\cancel{12}} \cdot 10} = \dfrac{11}{40}$

12. $-\dfrac{14}{5} \cdot 2\dfrac{6}{7} = -\dfrac{14}{5} \cdot \dfrac{20}{7} = \dfrac{-14 \cdot 20}{5 \cdot 7} = \dfrac{\overset{-2}{\cancel{-14}} \cdot \overset{4}{\cancel{20}}}{\underset{1}{\cancel{5}} \cdot \underset{1}{\cancel{7}}} = -8$

13. $1\dfrac{1}{8} \cdot (-3) = \dfrac{9}{8} \cdot \dfrac{-3}{1} = \dfrac{9 \cdot (-3)}{8 \cdot 1} = -\dfrac{27}{8} = -3\dfrac{3}{8}$

14. $\dfrac{1}{2} \div \dfrac{5}{6} = \dfrac{1}{2} \cdot \dfrac{6}{5} = \dfrac{1 \cdot 6}{2 \cdot 5} = \dfrac{1 \cdot \overset{3}{\cancel{6}}}{\underset{1}{\cancel{2}} \cdot 5} = \dfrac{3}{5}$

15. $\dfrac{4}{9} \div 8 = \dfrac{4}{9} \cdot \dfrac{1}{8} = \dfrac{4 \cdot 1}{9 \cdot 8} = \dfrac{\overset{1}{\cancel{4}} \cdot 1}{9 \cdot \underset{2}{\cancel{8}}} = \dfrac{1}{18}$

16. $-\dfrac{4}{5} \div \dfrac{3}{2} = -\dfrac{4}{5} \cdot \dfrac{2}{3} = \dfrac{-4 \cdot 2}{5 \cdot 3} = -\dfrac{8}{15}$

17. $-1\dfrac{3}{4} \div \left(-\dfrac{7}{12}\right) = -\dfrac{7}{4} \div \left(-\dfrac{7}{12}\right)$

$= -\dfrac{7}{4} \cdot \left(-\dfrac{12}{7}\right)$

$= \dfrac{\overset{-1}{\cancel{-7}} \cdot (\overset{-3}{\cancel{-12}})}{\underset{1}{\cancel{4}} \cdot \underset{1}{\cancel{7}}}$

$= 3$

18. $3\dfrac{1}{2} \cdot \dfrac{1}{2} = \dfrac{7}{2} \cdot \dfrac{1}{2} = \dfrac{7}{4} = 1\dfrac{3}{4}$

A human hair grows about $1\dfrac{3}{4}$ inches in $3\dfrac{1}{2}$ months.

Technology Activity 5.4 (p. 253)

1. $\dfrac{5}{11} + \dfrac{2}{5} = \dfrac{47}{55}$ **2.** $3\dfrac{1}{4} + \left(-\dfrac{6}{7}\right) = 2\dfrac{11}{28}$

3. $7\dfrac{1}{2} - 6\dfrac{5}{6} = \dfrac{2}{3}$ **4.** $\dfrac{2}{5} - \dfrac{2}{3} = -\dfrac{4}{15}$

5. $\dfrac{7}{9} \cdot 1\dfrac{1}{3} = 1\dfrac{1}{27}$ **6.** $\dfrac{2}{5} \cdot \left(-\dfrac{3}{4}\right) = -\dfrac{3}{10}$

7. $\dfrac{4}{7} \cdot \dfrac{1}{2} = \dfrac{2}{7}$ **8.** $2\dfrac{2}{3} \cdot \left(-\dfrac{1}{4}\right) = -\dfrac{2}{3}$

9. $9\dfrac{4}{5} \div \dfrac{7}{8} = 11\dfrac{1}{5}$ **10.** $-10\dfrac{2}{13} \div \left(-3\dfrac{1}{3}\right) = 3\dfrac{3}{65}$

11. $1\dfrac{7}{9} \div \dfrac{1}{3} = 5\dfrac{1}{3}$ **12.** $\dfrac{5}{8} \div \left(-\dfrac{1}{7}\right) = -4\dfrac{3}{8}$

13. $1000 - 625\dfrac{3}{8} = 374\dfrac{5}{8}$

They need $374\dfrac{5}{8}$ pounds to reach their goal.

Chapter 5, continued

14. $4\frac{1}{4} \cdot \frac{3}{4} = 3\frac{3}{16}$

Rosa has $3\frac{3}{16}$ quarts of oil.

$4\frac{1}{4} - 3\frac{3}{16} = 1\frac{1}{16}$

She should add $1\frac{1}{16}$ quarts of oil for her car to run properly.

Mixed Review of Problem Solving (p. 254)

1. a. $100 \cdot \frac{1}{5} = 20$

Bill's pack should not weigh more than 20 pounds.

b. $8\frac{1}{2} + 13\frac{1}{2} + 2\frac{1}{4} = 8\frac{2}{4} + 13\frac{2}{4} + 2\frac{1}{4}$

$$= (8 + 13 + 2) + \left(\frac{2}{4} + \frac{2}{4} + \frac{1}{4}\right)$$

$$= 23 + 1\frac{1}{4}$$

$$= 24\frac{1}{4}$$

$24\frac{1}{4} - 20 = 4\frac{1}{4}$

Bill's pack weighs $4\frac{1}{4}$ pounds more than what is recommended.

c. $130 \cdot \frac{1}{5} = 26$

T. J.'s pack should not weigh more than 26 pounds. If T. J. takes Bill's extra weight $\left(23 + 4\frac{1}{4} = 27\frac{1}{4}\right)$, T. J. will carry more weight than he should $\left(27\frac{1}{4} - 26 = 1\frac{1}{4}\right)$ by $1\frac{1}{4}$ pounds. T. J. should not carry Bill's extra weight.

2. First, multiply how many yards of ribbon per bow by the number of bows you make to see how many yards you will need:

$1\frac{1}{2} \times 5 = 7\frac{1}{2}$

Second, subtract what you will need from how much you have total:

$20 - 7\frac{1}{2} = 12\frac{1}{2}$

Third, divide $12\frac{1}{2}$ by how much ribbon you need to make each ribbon, $1\frac{1}{2}$:

$12\frac{1}{2} \div 1\frac{1}{2} = \frac{25}{2} \div \frac{3}{2} = \frac{25}{2} \cdot \frac{2}{3} = \frac{25 \cdot \overset{1}{\cancel{2}}}{\cancel{2} \cdot 3} = \frac{25}{3} = 8\frac{1}{3}$

You can make 8 more ribbons.

3. First, divide the total number of cups of flour, 17, by the number of cups the recipe calls for, $5\frac{2}{3}$:

$17 \div 5\frac{2}{3} = 17 \div \frac{17}{3} = \frac{17}{1} \cdot \frac{3}{17} = \frac{\overset{1}{\cancel{17}} \cdot 3}{1 \cdot \cancel{17}} = 3$

Second, multiply 3 by the number of dozens each batch makes:

$3 \cdot 3\frac{1}{2} = 3 \cdot \frac{7}{2} = \frac{3 \cdot 7}{1 \cdot 2} = \frac{21}{2} = 10\frac{1}{2}$

You can make $10\frac{1}{2}$ dozen rolls with 17 cups of flour.

4. The result will be greater than the original number of hours because the reciprocal will be greater than 1, making the product of the reciprocal and the original number of hours larger.

5. a. Anna: $\frac{1}{6} \cdot 24 = 4$

John: 2

Lena: $4 + 2 = 6$; $24 - 6 = 18$; $\frac{1}{9} \cdot 18 = 2$

Dawn: $18 - 2 = 16$; $\frac{1}{4} \cdot 16 = 4$

Jamal: 5

Anna takes 4 beads, John takes 2 beads, Lena takes 2 beads, Dawn takes 4 beads, and Jamal takes 5 beads.

b. $24 - 4 - 2 - 2 - 4 - 5 = 7$

There are 7 beads left or $\frac{7}{24}$ of the 24 beads.

6. *Sample answer:* $\frac{4}{5}$ and $1\frac{1}{6}$

$\frac{4}{5} + 1\frac{1}{6} = \frac{24}{30} + 1\frac{5}{30} = 1 + \left(\frac{24}{30} + \frac{5}{30}\right) = 1\frac{29}{30}$

$\frac{4}{5} \cdot 1\frac{1}{6} = \frac{4}{5} \cdot \frac{7}{6} = \frac{\overset{2}{\cancel{4}} \cdot 7}{5 \cdot \underset{3}{\cancel{6}}} = \frac{14}{15}$

$1\frac{1}{6} - \frac{4}{5} = 1\frac{5}{30} - \frac{24}{30} = \frac{35}{30} - \frac{24}{30} = \frac{11}{30} \left(\frac{1}{2} = \frac{15}{30}\right)$

7. Divide number of students who have a part-time job by the fraction. This will tell how many students there are at the school.

$400 \div \frac{2}{7} = \frac{400}{1} \cdot \frac{7}{2} = \frac{\overset{200}{\cancel{400}} \cdot 7}{1 \cdot \underset{1}{\cancel{2}}} = 1400$

Subtract the number of students that have a part-time job from the total number of students.

$1400 - 400 = 1000$

There are 1000 students who do not have part-time jobs.

8 a. $1\frac{1}{2} + 1\frac{1}{4} + \frac{4}{3} + \frac{5}{4} + 1\frac{1}{6}$

$= 1\frac{6}{12} + 1\frac{3}{12} + \frac{16}{12} + \frac{15}{12} + 1\frac{2}{12}$

$= (1 + 1 + 1) + \left(\frac{6}{12} + \frac{3}{12} + \frac{16}{12} + \frac{15}{12} + \frac{2}{12}\right)$

$= 3 + 3\frac{1}{2}$

$= 6\frac{1}{2}$

The fitness trail is $6\frac{1}{2}$ miles long.

Chapter 5, *continued*

b. $1\frac{1}{2} + \frac{4}{3} + 1\frac{1}{6} = 1\frac{6}{12} + \frac{16}{12} + 1\frac{2}{12}$

$$= (1 + 1) + \left(\frac{6}{12} + \frac{16}{12} + \frac{2}{12}\right)$$

$$= 2 + 2$$

$$= 4$$

$4 \div 6\frac{1}{2} = 4 \div \frac{13}{2} = \frac{4}{1} \cdot \frac{2}{13} = \frac{8}{13}$

You run $\frac{8}{13}$ of the trail.

c. First, find out how many miles you walked.

$6\frac{1}{2} - 4 = 2\frac{1}{2}$

Second, divide distance by rate for both walking and running:

$\left(2\frac{1}{2} \div 4\right) + (4 \div 8) \overset{?}{<} 1$

$\frac{5}{2} \div 4 + 4 \div 8 \overset{?}{<} 1$

$\frac{5}{2} \cdot \frac{1}{4} + \frac{\overset{1}{\cancel{4}}}{1} \cdot \frac{1}{\underset{2}{\cancel{8}}} \overset{?}{<} 1$

$\frac{5}{8} + \frac{1}{2} \overset{?}{<} 1$

$\frac{5}{8} + \frac{4}{8} \overset{?}{<} 1$

$\frac{9}{8} \not< 1$

No, you cannot complete the fitness trail in less than 1 hour.

Lesson 5.5

5.5 Guided Practice (pp. 255–257)

1. $\frac{8}{25}$ $\quad$
$$\begin{array}{r} 0.32 \\ 25\overline{)8.00} \\ 7\,5 \\ \hline 50 \\ 50 \\ \hline 0 \end{array}$$

$\frac{8}{25} = 0.32$

2. $\frac{1}{6}$ $\quad$
$$\begin{array}{r} 0.166 \\ 6\overline{)1.000} \\ 6 \\ \hline 40 \\ 36 \\ \hline 40 \\ 36 \\ \hline 4 \end{array}$$

$\frac{1}{6} = 0.1\overline{6}$

3. $\frac{3}{5} = 0.6$ $\quad$ $\frac{11}{20} = 0.55$ $\quad$ $\frac{2}{3} = 0.\overline{6}$

From least to greatest, the numbers are $0.5\overline{1}$, $\frac{11}{20}$, $\frac{3}{5}$, $0.6\overline{2}$, and $\frac{2}{3}$.

4. $-1\frac{1}{8} = -1.125$ $\quad$ $-1\frac{3}{7} = -1.\overline{428571}$ $\quad$ $-1\frac{4}{15} = 1.2\overline{6}$

From least to greatest, the numbers are $-1.4\overline{3}$, $-1\frac{3}{7}$, $-1\frac{4}{15}$, $-1\frac{1}{8}$, and -1.1.

5. $0.62 = \frac{62}{100} = \frac{31}{50}$ $\qquad$ **6.** $-2.45 = -2\frac{45}{100} = -2\frac{9}{20}$

---

7. Let $x = -0.\overline{7}$.

$$\begin{array}{r} 10x = -7.7777\ldots \\ -\quad x = -0.7777\ldots \\ \hline 9x = -7 \\ x = -\frac{7}{9} \end{array}$$

8. Let $x = 0.\overline{36}$.

$$\begin{array}{r} 100x = 36.36\ldots \\ -\quad x = 0.36\ldots \\ \hline 99x = 36 \\ x = \frac{36}{99} = \frac{4}{11} \end{array}$$

5.5 Exercises (pp. 257–259)

Skill Practice

1. The number 0 is a rational number, integer, and whole number.

2. The number 0.55 is a rational number because its decimal terminates.

3. The number -14 is a rational number and an integer.

4. $0.\overline{3}$ is a rational number because it can be written as a fraction, $\frac{1}{3}$.

5.
$$\begin{array}{r} 0.75 \\ 4\overline{)3.00} \\ 2\,8 \\ \hline 20 \\ 20 \\ \hline 0 \end{array}$$

$\frac{3}{4} = 0.75$

6.
$$\begin{array}{r} -0.11\ldots \\ -9\overline{)1.00} \\ 9 \\ \hline 10 \\ 9 \\ \hline 1 \end{array}$$

$-\frac{1}{9} = -0.\overline{1}$

7.
$$\begin{array}{r} -0.48 \\ -25\overline{)12.00} \\ 10\,0 \\ \hline 2\,00 \\ 2\,00 \\ \hline 0 \end{array}$$

$-\frac{12}{25} = -0.48$

8.
$$\begin{array}{r} 0.5833\ldots \\ 12\overline{)7.0000} \\ 6\,0 \\ \hline 1\,00 \\ 96 \\ \hline 40 \\ 36 \\ \hline 40 \\ 36 \\ \hline 4 \end{array}$$

$\frac{7}{12} = 0.58\overline{3}$

9.
$$\begin{array}{r} -0.16 \\ -25\overline{)4.00} \\ 2\,5 \\ \hline 1\,50 \\ 1\,50 \\ \hline 0 \end{array}$$

$-\frac{4}{25} = -0.16$

10.
$$\begin{array}{r} 0.54 \\ 50\overline{)27.00} \\ 25\,0 \\ \hline 2\,00 \\ 2\,00 \\ \hline 0 \end{array}$$

$\frac{27}{50} = 0.54$

11. $3\frac{11}{16} = \frac{59}{16}$

$$16\overline{)59.0000}$$ $\quad 3\frac{11}{16} = 3.6875$

3.6875

48

$\overline{11\,0}$

$\;9\,6$

$\overline{1\,40}$

$\;1\,28$

$\overline{120}$

$\;112$

$\overline{\;80}$

$\;80$

$\overline{\;\;0}$

12. $-4\frac{33}{80} = \frac{-353}{80}$

$$80\overline{)-353.0000}$$ $\quad -4\frac{33}{80} = -4.4125$

-4.4125

320

$\overline{33\,0}$

$32\,0$

$\overline{1\,00}$

$\;80$

$\overline{200}$

160

$\overline{400}$

400

$\overline{\;\;0}$

13. $-33\overline{)14.0000}$ $\quad -\frac{14}{33} = -0.\overline{42}$

$-0.4242\ldots$

$13\,2$

$\overline{\;80}$

66

$\overline{140}$

132

$\overline{\;80}$

66

$\overline{14}$

14. $44\overline{)27.000000}$ $\quad \frac{27}{44} = 0.61\overline{36}$

$0.613636\ldots$

$26\,4$

$\overline{\;60}$

44

$\overline{160}$

132

$\overline{280}$

264

$\overline{160}$

132

$\overline{280}$

264

$\overline{16}$

15. $6\frac{8}{15} = \frac{98}{15}$

$$15\overline{)98.000}$$ $\quad 6\frac{8}{15} = 6.5\overline{3}$

$6.533\ldots$

90

$\overline{8\,0}$

$7\,5$

$\overline{50}$

45

$\overline{50}$

45

$\overline{5}$

16. $-14\frac{7}{11} = -\frac{161}{11}$

$$-11\overline{)161.0000}$$ $\quad -14\frac{7}{11} = -14.\overline{63}$

$14.6363\ldots$

11

$\overline{51}$

44

$\overline{7\,0}$

$6\,6$

$\overline{40}$

33

$\overline{70}$

66

$\overline{40}$

33

$\overline{7}$

17. $\frac{3}{10}$ has a decimal value of 0.3, not 0.03.

$2\frac{3}{10} = 2.3$

18. $1.1 > 1.09$

19. $-4.29 > -4.3$

20. $-\frac{7}{15} = -0.4\overline{6}$

$-\frac{3}{8} = -0.375$

$-0.4\overline{6} < -0.375$

$-\frac{7}{15} < -\frac{3}{8}$

21. $-\frac{11}{20} = -0.55$

$-\frac{5}{9} = -0.\overline{5}$

$-0.55 > -0.\overline{5}$

$-\frac{11}{20} > -\frac{5}{9}$

22. $\frac{11}{18} = 0.6\overline{1}$

$0.6\overline{1} = 0.6\overline{1}$

$\frac{11}{18} = 0.6\overline{1}$

23. $\frac{6}{7} = 0.\overline{857142}$

$0.857 < 0.\overline{857142}$

$0.857 < \frac{6}{7}$

24. $-\frac{17}{24} = -0.708\overline{3}$

$-0.71 < -0.708\overline{3}$

$-0.71 < -\frac{17}{24}$

25. $-\frac{23}{30} = -0.7\overline{6}$

$-0.7\overline{6} = -0.7\overline{6}$

$-\frac{23}{30} = -0.7\overline{6}$

26. $7\frac{4}{5} = 7.8;\; 7\frac{2}{3} = 7.\overline{6};\; 7.6;\; 7.71;\; 7\frac{8}{21} = 7.380952$

Numbers in order from least to greatest are $7\frac{8}{21}$, 7.6, $7\frac{2}{3}$, 7.71, and $7\frac{4}{5}$.

27. $0.1;\; \frac{5}{6} = 0.8\overline{3};\; \frac{3}{10} = 0.3;\; -\frac{2}{7} = -0.\overline{285714};\; -0.4$

Numbers in order from least to greatest are -0.4, $-\frac{2}{7}$, 0.1, $\frac{3}{10}$, and $\frac{5}{6}$.

28. $9\frac{3}{4} = 9.75;\; 9.74;\; 9\frac{5}{7} = 9.\overline{714285};\; 9.72;\; 9\frac{9}{13} = 9.\overline{692307}$

Numbers in order from least to greatest are $9\frac{9}{13}$, $9\frac{5}{7}$, 9.72, 9.74, and $9\frac{3}{4}$.

29. $0.6 = \frac{6}{10} = \frac{3}{5}$

30. $-6.4 = -6\frac{4}{10} = -6\frac{2}{5}$

Chapter 5, *continued*

31. $0.48 = \dfrac{48}{100} = \dfrac{12}{25}$ **32.** $-2.79 = -2\dfrac{79}{100}$

33. $0.365 = \dfrac{365}{1000} = \dfrac{73}{200}$ **34.** $7.253 = 7\dfrac{253}{1000}$

35. $-5.0032 = -5\dfrac{32}{10,000} = -5\dfrac{2}{625}$

36. $-0.0012 = -\dfrac{12}{10,000} = -\dfrac{3}{2500}$

37. Let $x = 0.\overline{8}$.

$10x = 8.88\ldots$
$\underline{-\quad x = 0.88\ldots}$
$9x = 8$

$x = \dfrac{8}{9}$

38. Let $x = 0.\overline{53}$.

$100x = 53.53\ldots$
$\underline{-\quad x = 0.53\ldots}$
$99x = 53$

$x = \dfrac{53}{99}$

39. Let $x = 0.\overline{21}$.

$100x = 21.21\ldots$
$\underline{-\quad x = 0.21\ldots}$
$99x = 21$

$x = \dfrac{7}{33}$

40. Let $x = 0.\overline{6}$.

$10x = 6.6\ldots$
$\underline{-\quad x = 0.6\ldots}$
$9x = 6$

$x = \dfrac{2}{3}$

41. Let $x = 0.\overline{635}$.

$1000x = 635.635\ldots$
$\underline{-\quad x = 0.635\ldots}$
$999x = 635$

$x = \dfrac{635}{999}$

42. Let $x = -0.\overline{187}$.

$1000x = -187.187\ldots$
$\underline{-\quad x = -0.187\ldots}$
$999x = -187$

$x = -\dfrac{187}{999}$

43. Let $x = -0.1\overline{5}$.

$10x = -1.555\ldots$
$\underline{-\quad x = -0.155\ldots}$
$9x = -1.4$

$90x = -14$

$x = -\dfrac{14}{90}$

$x = -\dfrac{7}{45}$

44. Let $x = 4.0\overline{25}$.

$100x = 402.525\ldots$
$\underline{-\quad x = 4.025\ldots}$
$99x = 398.5$

$990x = 3985$

$x = \dfrac{3985}{990}$

$x = 4\dfrac{25}{990}$

$x = 4\dfrac{5}{198}$

45. $\left(\dfrac{1}{3}\right)^3 = \dfrac{1}{27} = 0.\overline{037}$ $3^{-2} = \dfrac{1}{3^2} = \dfrac{1}{9} = 0.\overline{1}$

Numbers in order from least to greatest are $1.\overline{21}$, 1.21, 3^{-2}, and $\left(\dfrac{1}{3}\right)^3$.

46. $\dfrac{13}{5} = 2.6$ $2\dfrac{2}{5} = 2.4$

Numbers in order from least to greatest are $\dfrac{13}{5}$, $2.4\overline{1}$, 2.411, and $2\dfrac{2}{5}$.

47. $\left(\dfrac{1}{5}\right)^2 = \dfrac{1}{25} = 0.04$ $\dfrac{3}{7} = 0.\overline{428571}$ $4^{-2} = \dfrac{1}{4^2} = \dfrac{1}{16} = 0.0625$

Numbers in order from least to greatest are $0.\overline{4}$, $\dfrac{3}{7}$, 4^{-2}, and $\left(\dfrac{1}{5}\right)^2$.

48. $\left(\dfrac{1}{3}\right)^{-1} = 3$ $-3\dfrac{2}{5} = -3.4$

Numbers in order from least to greatest are $\left(\dfrac{1}{3}\right)^{-1}$, $-3\dfrac{2}{5}$, $-3.4\overline{2}$, and $-3.\overline{4}$.

49. $2^{-4} = \dfrac{1}{2^4} = \dfrac{1}{16} = 0.0625$ $-\dfrac{1}{15} = -0.0\overline{6}$

Numbers in order from least to greatest are 0.66, 2^{-4}, $-\dfrac{1}{15}$, and $-0.\overline{6}$.

50. $\left(\dfrac{2}{3}\right)^{-2} = 2\dfrac{1}{4} = 2.25$ $-\dfrac{9}{4} = -2.25$

Numbers in order from least to greatest are $\left(\dfrac{2}{3}\right)^{-2}$, -2.2, $\dfrac{(-9)}{4}$, and $-2.2\overline{5}$.

51. From least to greatest, the expressions are $\dfrac{x}{8}, \dfrac{x}{7}, \dfrac{x}{6}, \dfrac{x}{5}, \dfrac{x}{4}, \dfrac{x}{3}, \dfrac{x}{2}$, and x.

x continues to be divided by smaller and smaller numbers, resulting in greater values.

52.

$\dfrac{y}{15} = 2.\overline{45}$

$\dfrac{y}{15} = 2\dfrac{5}{11}$

$\dfrac{y}{15} \cdot 15 = 2\dfrac{5}{11} \cdot 15$

$y = 36\dfrac{9}{11}$

$y = 36.\overline{81}$

Let $x = 2.\overline{45}$.

$100x = 245.45\ldots$
$\underline{-\quad x = 2.45\ldots}$
$99x = 243$

$x = \dfrac{243}{99}$

$x = 2\dfrac{5}{11}$

53.

$\dfrac{x}{12} = 0.41\overline{6}$

$\dfrac{x}{12} = \dfrac{5}{12}$

$\dfrac{x}{12} \cdot 12 = \dfrac{5}{12} \cdot 12$

$x = 5$

Let $y = 0.41\overline{6}$.

$100y = 41.666$
$\underline{-\quad y = 0.416}$
$99y = 41.25$

$y = \dfrac{41.25}{99}$

$y = \dfrac{5}{12}$

54.

$\dfrac{z}{20} = 0.\overline{27}$

$\dfrac{z}{20} = \dfrac{3}{11}$

$\dfrac{z}{20} \cdot 20 = \dfrac{3}{11} \cdot 20$

$z = \dfrac{60}{11}$

$z = 5\dfrac{5}{11}$

$z = 5.\overline{45}$

Let $y = 0.\overline{27}$.

$100y = 27.27\ldots$
$\underline{-\quad y = 0.27\ldots}$
$99y = 27$

$y = \dfrac{27}{99}$

$y = \dfrac{3}{11}$

Problem Solving

55. D;

$$\begin{array}{r} 0.88 \\ 25\overline{)22.00} \\ \underline{20\ 0} \\ 2\ 00 \\ \underline{2\ 00} \\ 0 \end{array}$$

Chapter 5, *continued*

56.

$5\frac{1}{4} = \frac{21}{4}$ $4\overline{)21.00}$ → 5.25 $\$5\frac{1}{4} = \$5.25$

$$
\begin{array}{r}
5.25 \\
4\overline{)21.00} \\
\underline{20} \\
1\,0 \\
\underline{8} \\
20 \\
\underline{20} \\
0
\end{array}
$$

$44\frac{1}{2} = \frac{89}{2}$ $2\overline{)89.0}$ → 44.5 $\$44\frac{1}{2} = \$44.50$

$$
\begin{array}{r}
44.5 \\
2\overline{)89.0} \\
\underline{88} \\
1\,0 \\
\underline{1\,0} \\
0
\end{array}
$$

$53\frac{3}{8} = \frac{427}{8}$ $8\overline{)427.000}$ → 53.375 $\$53\frac{3}{8} \approx \$53.38$

$$
\begin{array}{r}
53.375 \\
8\overline{)427.000} \\
\underline{40} \\
27 \\
\underline{24} \\
3\,0 \\
\underline{2\,4} \\
60 \\
\underline{56} \\
40 \\
\underline{40} \\
0
\end{array}
$$

$17\frac{7}{16} = \frac{279}{16}$ $16\overline{)279.0000}$ → 17.4375 $\$17\frac{7}{16} \approx \$17.44$

$$
\begin{array}{r}
17.4375 \\
16\overline{)279.0000} \\
\underline{16} \\
119 \\
\underline{112} \\
7\,0 \\
\underline{6\,4} \\
60 \\
\underline{48} \\
120 \\
\underline{112} \\
80 \\
\underline{80} \\
0
\end{array}
$$

57. $1\frac{7}{8}$ in. $= 1.875$ in., $\frac{3}{20}$ ft $= 1\frac{4}{5}$ in. $= 1.8$ in., $2\frac{1}{9}$ in. $= 2.\overline{1}$,

$\frac{7}{40}$ ft $= 2\frac{1}{10} = 2.1$ in.

From least to greatest, the lengths of the caterpillars are 1.8 inches, 1.875 inches, 2.1 inches, and $2.\overline{1}$ inches.

58. $\frac{32{,}000}{182{,}000} = \frac{32}{182} = \frac{16}{91} = 0.\overline{175824}$

To use estimation, round 32 to 30 and 182 to 180. Then simplify this fraction. $\frac{30}{180} = \frac{1}{6} = 0.1\overline{6}$

59. No; 0.1010010001 . . . is not a rational number because there are no digits or groups of digits that repeat. So, the number cannot be expressed as a fraction $\frac{a}{b}$.

60.

$$
\begin{array}{r}
0.0909\ldots \\
11\overline{)1.0000} \\
\underline{99} \\
10 \\
\underline{0} \\
100 \\
\underline{99} \\
1
\end{array}
\qquad
\begin{array}{r}
0.1818\ldots \\
11\overline{)2.0000} \\
\underline{1\,1} \\
90 \\
\underline{88} \\
20 \\
\underline{11} \\
90 \\
\underline{88} \\
2
\end{array}
$$

$$
\begin{array}{r}
0.2727\ldots \\
11\overline{)3.0000} \\
\underline{2\,2} \\
80 \\
\underline{77} \\
30 \\
\underline{22} \\
80 \\
\underline{77} \\
3
\end{array}
$$

$\frac{1}{11} = 0.\overline{09}$, $\frac{2}{11} = 0.\overline{18}$, $\frac{3}{11} = 0.\overline{27}$

The repeating decimal is 9 hundredths times the numerator.

$\frac{4}{11} = 0.\overline{36}$ and $\frac{5}{11} = 0.\overline{45}$.

61. a.

$$
\text{Bagels: }
\begin{array}{r}
0.125 \\
8\overline{)1.000} \\
\underline{8} \\
20 \\
\underline{16} \\
40 \\
\underline{40} \\
0
\end{array}
\qquad
\text{Bacon: }
\begin{array}{r}
0.0833\ldots \\
12\overline{)1.0000} \\
\underline{96} \\
40 \\
\underline{36} \\
40 \\
\underline{36} \\
3
\end{array}
$$

$$
\text{Eggs: }
\begin{array}{r}
0.1875 \\
16\overline{)3.000} \\
\underline{1\,6} \\
1\,40 \\
\underline{1\,28} \\
120 \\
\underline{112} \\
80 \\
\underline{80} \\
0
\end{array}
\qquad
\text{Cereal: }
\begin{array}{r}
0.25 \\
4\overline{)1.00} \\
\underline{8} \\
20 \\
\underline{20} \\
0
\end{array}
$$

$$
\text{Pancakes: }
\begin{array}{r}
0.12 \\
25\overline{)3.00} \\
\underline{2\,5} \\
50 \\
\underline{50} \\
0
\end{array}
$$

The foods in order from most popular to least popular are cereal, eggs, bagels, pancakes, and bacon.

Chapter 5, *continued*

b. If 1200 students responded to the survey, you can multiply 1200 by a fraction to find out how many students picked that food.

Most popular (cereal): $1200 \cdot \dfrac{1}{4} = \dfrac{1200 \cdot 1}{1 \cdot 4}$

$= 300$ students

Least popular (bacon): $1200 \cdot \dfrac{1}{12} = \dfrac{1200 \cdot 1}{12 \cdot 1}$

$= 100$ students

$300 - 100$, or 200 more students picked the most popular food than the least popular food.

c. To find out how many of the 1200 students did not choose any of the foods shown, you need to find out how many chose bagels, eggs, and pancakes.

Bagels: $1200 \cdot \dfrac{1}{8} = \dfrac{1200}{1} \cdot \dfrac{1}{8} = \dfrac{1200 \cdot 1}{1 \cdot 8} = 150$ students

Eggs: $1200 \cdot \dfrac{3}{16} = \dfrac{1200}{1} \cdot \dfrac{3}{16} = \dfrac{1200 \cdot 3}{1 \cdot 16} = 225$ students

Pancakes: $1200 \cdot \dfrac{3}{25} = \dfrac{1200}{1} \cdot \dfrac{3}{25}$

$= \dfrac{1200 \cdot 3}{1 \cdot 25}$

$= 144$ students

So, altogether, $150 + 100 + 225 + 300 + 144$, or 919 students chose from the foods listed. $1200 - 919$, or 281 students did not choose any of the foods shown.

62. *Sample answer:* $-\dfrac{1}{64} = -0.015625$

$-\dfrac{1}{63} = -0.0\overline{15873}$

A decimal that falls between $-\dfrac{1}{64}$ and $-\dfrac{1}{63}$ is -0.01584786. An example of a fraction is $-\dfrac{10}{631}$.

63. To find out what Kim's posted time was, change the 34 seconds to minutes $\left(\dfrac{34}{60} = 0.5667\right)$, then change 22.5667 minutes to hours $\left(\dfrac{22.5667}{60} = 0.3761\right)$.

1 hour $+ 0.3761$ hour $= 1.3761$ hours ≈ 1.376 hours.

Kim's posted time is 1.376 hours.

1.3755 h $= 1$ h $+ 22.53$ min ≈ 1 h $+ 22$ min $+ 32$ sec

1.3764 h $= 1$ h $+ 22.584$ min ≈ 1 h $+ 22$ min $+ 35$ sec

$1.3755 \approx 1.376$, $1.3764 \approx 1.376$

The times from 1 hour 22 minutes 32 seconds through 1 hour 22 minutes 35 seconds all round to 1.376 hours.

Mixed Review

64. $129 + 42 \approx 130 + 40 = 170$

65. $457 + 304 \approx 460 + 300 = 760$

66. $91 - 28 \approx 90 - 30 = 60$

67. $217 - 188 \approx 220 - 190 = 30$

68. (1) Read and Understand

(2) Make a Plan: Make a List

(3) Solve the Problem.

You and your friends can finish the race in the following ways:

You, Al, Sue, Kim

You, Al, Kim, Sue

You, Sue, Al, Kim

You, Sue, Kim, Al

You, Kim, Al, Sue

You, Kim, Sue, Al

If you win, there are 6 orders. If any of your 3 friends win, there would be 6 orders as well. In all, there are $4(6)$, or 24 ways you and your friends can finish the race.

(4) Look Back

69. A; $4x = 24$

$x = 6$

Lesson 5.6

5.6 Guided Practice (pp. 260–262)

1.
$$\begin{array}{r} 12.50 \\ + 4.55 \\ \hline 17.05 \end{array}$$

2.
$$\begin{array}{r} 8.930 \\ + 0.367 \\ \hline 9.297 \end{array}$$

$-12.5 + (-4.55) = -17.05$

3.
$$\begin{array}{r} 7.624 \\ - 0.050 \\ \hline 7.574 \end{array}$$

4.
$$\begin{array}{r} 8.910 \\ - 2.745 \\ \hline 6.165 \end{array}$$

5.
$$\begin{array}{r} 5.30 \\ + 11.49 \\ \hline 16.79 \end{array}$$

6.
$$\begin{array}{r} 5.376 \\ + 0.800 \\ \hline 6.176 \end{array}$$

$-5.3 - 11.49 = -16.79$

7. $\quad x + 1.38 = 2.55$

$x + 1.38 - 1.38 = 2.55 - 1.38$

$x = 1.17$

8. $\quad z - 5.3 = 16.29$

$z - 5.3 + 5.3 = 16.29 + 5.3$

$z = 21.59$

9. $\quad y - (-0.83) = 0.48$

$y - (-0.83) - 0.83 = 0.48 - 0.83$

$y = -0.35$

10. $1.95 + 7.49 + 3.50$

Front end:

$\begin{array}{r} \$1.95 \\ \$7.49 \\ + \$3.50 \\ \hline \$11 \end{array}$

Remaining digits:

$\begin{array}{r} \$1.95 - \$1 \\ \$7.49 \\ \$3.50 \end{array} \Big\rangle \$1$ $\dfrac{}{\$2}$

$\$11 + \$2 = \$13$

Chapter 5, *continued*

11. $K = C + 273.15$

$K = 29 + 273.15$

$K = 302.15$

The temperature is 302.15 K.

12.
$$K = C + 273.15$$
$$324.15 = C + 273.15$$
$$324.15 - 273.15 = C + 273.15 - 273.15$$
$$51 = C$$

The temperature is 51°C.

5.6 Exercises (pp. 262–264)

Skill Practice

1. You can get a low estimate of $13.56 + 11.42 + 25.94$ by adding the front-end digits *13*, *11*, and *25*.

2.
$$\begin{array}{r} 30.193 \\ + 7.910 \\ \hline 38.103 \end{array}$$

3.
$$\begin{array}{r} 2.507 \\ + 0.586 \\ \hline 3.093 \end{array}$$

4.
$$\begin{array}{r} 6.080 \\ - 2.661 \\ \hline 3.419 \end{array}$$
$-6.08 + 2.661 = -3.419$

5.
$$\begin{array}{r} 0.37 \\ + 1.80 \\ \hline 2.17 \end{array}$$
$-0.37 + (-1.8) = -2.17$

6.
$$\begin{array}{r} 6.800 \\ - 1.812 \\ \hline 4.988 \end{array}$$

7.
$$\begin{array}{r} 12.09 \\ - 1.20 \\ \hline 10.89 \end{array}$$
$-12.09 + 1.20 = -10.89$

8. $3.28 + (-4.91) = -4.91 + 3.28 = -1.63$
$$\begin{array}{r} 4.91 \\ - 3.28 \\ \hline 1.63 \end{array}$$

9. $1.46 + (-1.564) = -1.564 + 1.46 = -0.104$
$$\begin{array}{r} 1.564 \\ - 1.460 \\ \hline 0.104 \end{array}$$

10. $1.57 - 9.28 = -9.28 + 1.57 = -7.71$
$$\begin{array}{r} 9.28 \\ - 1.57 \\ \hline 7.71 \end{array}$$

11.
$$\begin{array}{r} 68.79 \\ - 9.18 \\ \hline 59.61 \end{array}$$

12. $15.7 - (-6.4) = 15.7 + 6.4$
$$\begin{array}{r} 15.7 \\ + 6.4 \\ \hline 22.1 \end{array}$$

13.
$$\begin{array}{r} 0.990 \\ + 0.304 \\ \hline 1.294 \end{array}$$
$-0.99 - 0.304 = -1.294$

14.
$$\begin{array}{r} 25.885 \\ - 6.900 \\ \hline 18.985 \end{array}$$

15. $29.1 - (-3.05) = 29.1 + 3.05$
$$\begin{array}{r} 29.10 \\ + 3.05 \\ \hline 32.15 \end{array}$$

16.
$$\begin{array}{r} 4.220 \\ + 0.807 \\ \hline 5.027 \end{array}$$
$-4.22 - 0.807 = -5.027$

17. The error occurred when the decimal points were not aligned.
$$\begin{array}{r} 10.430 \\ + 7.521 \\ \hline 17.951 \end{array}$$

18. D;
$$\begin{array}{r} 9.87 \\ + 0.49 \\ \hline 10.36 \end{array}$$
You pay a total of $10.36.

19.
$$x + 2.9 = 5.3$$
$$x + 2.9 - 2.9 = 5.3 - 2.9$$
$$x = 2.4$$

20.
$$y - 4.15 = -4.26$$
$$y - 4.15 + 4.15 = -4.26 + 4.15$$
$$y = -0.11$$

21.
$$z - (-7.7) = 13.31$$
$$z - (-7.7) - 7.7 = 13.31 - 7.7$$
$$z = 5.61$$

22.
$$y + 1.5 = 37$$
$$y + 1.5 - 1.5 = 37 - 1.5$$
$$y = 35.5$$

23.
$$-2.8 + x = 4.51$$
$$-2.8 + x + 2.8 = 4.51 + 2.8$$
$$x = 7.31$$

24.
$$10.4 = 12.46 + z$$
$$10.4 - 12.46 = 12.46 + z - 12.46$$
$$-2.06 = z$$

25.
$$7.81 = 7.98 + y$$
$$7.81 - 7.98 = 7.98 + y - 7.98$$
$$-0.17 = y$$

26.
$$z + (-3.19) = 5.83$$
$$z + (-3.19) + 3.19 = 5.83 + 3.19$$
$$z = 9.02$$

27.
$$x - 0.013 = -6.36$$
$$x - 0.013 + 0.013 = -6.36 + 0.013$$
$$x = -6.347$$

28. $2.32 + 6.69 + 8.50 + 4.46$

Front end:

$$\begin{array}{r} 2.32 \\ 6.69 \\ 8.50 \\ + \ 4.46 \\ \hline 20 \end{array}$$

Remaining digits:

$$\begin{array}{r} 2.32 \\ 6.69 \end{array} \Big\rangle 1$$
$$\begin{array}{r} 8.50 \\ 4.46 \end{array} \Big\rangle 1 \\ \hline \qquad 2$$

$20 + 2 = 22$

29. $10.23 + 6.98 + 9.05 + 5.80$

Front end:

$$\begin{array}{r} 10.23 \\ 6.98 \\ 9.05 \\ + \ 5.80 \\ \hline 30 \end{array}$$

Remaining digits:

$$\begin{array}{r} 10.23 \\ 6.98 \\ 9.05 \\ 5.80 \end{array} \quad 1 \ \Big\rangle 1 \\ \hline \qquad 2$$

$30 + 2 = 32$

30. $5.62 + 4.89 + 3.44 + 9.98$

Front-end

$$\begin{array}{r} 5.62 \\ 4.89 \\ 3.44 \\ + \ 9.98 \\ \hline 21 \end{array}$$

Remaining digits:

$$\begin{array}{r} 5.62 \\ 4.89 - 1 \\ 3.44 \\ 9.98 - 1 \end{array} \Big\rangle 1 \\ \hline \qquad 3$$

$21 + 3 = 24$

31. $23.70 + 16.12 + 5.96 + 14.18$

Front-end

$$\begin{array}{r} 23.70 \\ 16.12 \\ 5.96 \\ 14.18 \\ \hline 58 \end{array}$$

Remaining digits:

$$\begin{array}{r} 23.70 \\ 16.12 \\ 5.96 - 1 \\ 14.18 \end{array} \Big\rangle 1 \\ \hline \qquad 2$$

$58 + 2 = 60$

32. $a - \dfrac{5}{2} = 6.28 - 2.5 = 3.78$

33. $\dfrac{3}{8} + a = \dfrac{3}{8} + 6.28 = 0.375 + 6.28 = 6.655$

34. $b - \dfrac{3}{4} = -0.35 - 0.75 = -1.1$

35. $\dfrac{9}{20} + b = 0.45 + (-0.35) = 0.1$

36. $P = a + b + c = 28.4 + 20.35 + 19 = 67.75$

The perimeter of the triangle is 67.75 feet.

37. $P = a + b + c + d = 5.8 + 6.25 + 5.8 + 3.05 = 20.9$

The perimeter of the trapezoid is 20.9 centimeters.

38. $P = a + b + c + d + e$

$\qquad = 3.2 + 3.2 + 9.41 + 3.2 + 7.41$

$\qquad = 26.42$

The perimeter of the pentagon is 26.42 meters.

39.

$\ell = AB = 4.25 - 1.25 = 3$ units

$w = AD = 6.75 - 3.5 = 3.25$ units

$P = 2\ell + 2w$

$\quad = 2(3) + 2(3.25)$

$\quad = 6 + 3.25 + 3.25$

$\quad = 6 + 6.5$

$\quad = 12.5$

The perimeter of the rectangle is 12.5 units.

40.

$$\begin{array}{r} 100x = 67.\overline{67} \\ - \quad x = \ \ 0.\overline{67} \\ \hline 99x = 67 \end{array}$$

$$x = \frac{67}{99}$$

$$\begin{array}{r} 10x = 6.\overline{6} \\ - \quad x = 0.\overline{6} \\ \hline 9x = 6 \end{array}$$

$$x = \frac{6}{9} = \frac{2}{3}$$

$$\frac{67}{99} + \frac{2}{3} = \frac{67}{99} + \frac{66}{99} = \frac{133}{99} = 1\frac{34}{99}$$

The sum in decimal form is $1.\overline{34}$.

41.

$$\begin{array}{r} 1000x = 5345.\overline{345} \\ - \quad x = \quad \ \ 5.\overline{345} \\ \hline 999x = 5340 \end{array}$$

$$x = \frac{5340}{999}$$

$$x = 5\frac{115}{333}$$

$$\begin{array}{r} 100x = 87.\overline{87} \\ - \quad x = \ \ 0.\overline{87} \\ \hline 99x = 87 \end{array}$$

$$x = \frac{87}{99}$$

$$x = \frac{29}{33}$$

$$5\frac{115}{333} + \frac{29}{33} = 5\frac{3795}{10,989} + \frac{9657}{10,989}$$

$$= 5 + \left(\frac{3795}{10,989} + \frac{9657}{10,989} \right)$$

$$= 5 + \frac{13,452}{10,989}$$

$$= 5 + 1.\overline{224133}$$

$$= 6.\overline{224133}$$

Chapter 5, continued

42.
$$10x = 17.\overline{7}$$
$$\underline{-\quad x = 1.\overline{7}}$$
$$9x = 16$$

$$x = \frac{16}{9} = 1\frac{7}{9}$$

$$1{,}000{,}000\,x = 1{,}876{,}621.\overline{876621}$$
$$\underline{-\qquad\quad x = \phantom{1{,}876{,}621.}1.\overline{876621}}$$
$$999{,}999x = 1{,}876{,}620$$

$$x = \frac{1{,}876{,}620}{999{,}999}$$

$$x = 1\frac{876621}{999{,}999} = 1\frac{292{,}207}{333{,}333}$$

$$1\frac{7}{9} + 1\frac{292{,}207}{333{,}333} = (1+1) + \left(\frac{2{,}333{,}331}{2{,}999{,}997} + \frac{2{,}629{,}863}{2{,}999{,}997}\right)$$

$$= 2 + \frac{4{,}963{,}194}{2{,}999{,}997}$$

$$= 3.\overline{654399}$$

43.
$$100x = 319.\overline{19}$$
$$\underline{-\quad x = 3.\overline{19}}$$
$$99x = 316$$

$$x = \frac{316}{99}$$

$$x = 3\frac{19}{99}$$

$$100x = 791.\overline{91}$$
$$\underline{-\quad x = 7.\overline{91}}$$
$$99x = 784$$

$$x = \frac{784}{99}$$

$$x = 7\frac{91}{99}$$

$$3\frac{19}{99} + 7\frac{91}{99} = (3+7) + \left(\frac{19}{99} + \frac{91}{99}\right)$$

$$= 10 + \frac{110}{99}$$

$$= 11.\overline{1}$$

Problem Solving

44.
$$58.01$$
$$\underline{-\,55.49}$$
$$2.52$$

Your time is 2.52 seconds more than the school record.

45. a.
$$23.12$$
$$\underline{-\,21.16}$$
$$1.96$$

The world record throw was 1.96 meters longer.

b.
$$22.47$$
$$\underline{-\,21.16}$$
$$1.31$$

The Olympic record throw was 1.31 meters longer.

46. B; $K = (F - 32)\frac{5}{9} + 273.15$

$$K = (212 - 32)\frac{5}{9} + 273.15$$

$$K = 100 + 273.15$$

$$K = 373.15$$

The temperature is 373.15 K.

47.
$$4.52$$
$$5.23$$
$$\underline{+\,3.41}$$
$$13.16$$

Yes, the city did have more than 12 inches of rain. *Sample answer:* An estimation is sufficient to answer this question because all you need to know if it rained more than 12 inches, not the exact amount. Since the sum of whole parts is 12, you can conclude that the city had more than 12 inches of rain.

48. When adding two positive decimals that are less than one, the sum is always positive; you do not know if the sum is less than, equal to, or greater than 1.

49. a. *Sample answer:* You need to add the deposits, and subtract the withdrawals.

Estimate: $83 + 50 - 75 - 13 + 113 - 13 - 22 = 123$

The estimated balance is $123.

b. Exact:

$83.27 + 50 - 75.35 - 12.95 + 112.81 - 13.08 - 21.98$
$= 122.92$

The exact balance is $122.92.

c. The next transaction was a withdrawal.

$$122.92 - x = 101.25$$
$$122.92 - x - 122.92 = 101.25 - 122.92$$
$$-x = -21.67$$
$$x = 21.67$$

The amount of the withdrawal was $21.67.

50.
$$15.9994$$
$$1.0079$$
$$\underline{+\,1.0079}$$
$$18.0152$$

The mass of a mole of water is 18.0152 grams.

51. a.

Fraction pairs	$\frac{1}{3}, \frac{2}{3}$	$\frac{1}{6}, \frac{5}{6}$	$\frac{4}{9}, \frac{5}{9}$	$\frac{3}{11}, \frac{8}{11}$
Decimal pairs	$0.\overline{3}, 0.\overline{6}$	$0.1\overline{6}, 0.8\overline{3}$	$0.\overline{4}, 0.\overline{5}$	$0.\overline{27}, 0.\overline{72}$
Fraction sum	1	1	1	1
Decimal sum	$0.\overline{9}$	$0.\overline{9}$	$0.\overline{9}$	$0.\overline{9}$

b. Another name for $0.\overline{9}$ is 1.

Chapter 5, *continued*

continued

Mixed Review

52. $-\dfrac{8}{9} \cdot \left(\dfrac{-5}{7}\right) = \dfrac{-8 \cdot (-5)}{9 \cdot 7} = \dfrac{40}{63}$

53. $-5\dfrac{3}{7} \cdot \dfrac{21}{22} = \dfrac{-38}{7} \cdot \dfrac{21}{22}$

$\qquad = \dfrac{-38 \cdot 21}{7 \cdot 22}$

$\qquad = \dfrac{-\overset{19}{\cancel{38}} \cdot \overset{3}{\cancel{21}}}{\underset{1}{\cancel{7}} \cdot \underset{11}{\cancel{22}}}$

$\qquad = \dfrac{-57}{11}$

$\qquad = -5\dfrac{2}{11}$

54. $-5 \div \left(\dfrac{-2}{3}\right) = \dfrac{-5}{1} \cdot \left(\dfrac{-3}{2}\right) = \dfrac{-5 \cdot (-3)}{1 \cdot 2} = \dfrac{15}{2} = 7\dfrac{1}{2}$

55. $6\dfrac{5}{12} \div 2\dfrac{3}{4} = \dfrac{77}{12} \div \dfrac{11}{4}$

$\qquad = \dfrac{77}{12} \cdot \dfrac{4}{11}$

$\qquad = \dfrac{77 \cdot 4}{12 \cdot 11}$

$\qquad = \dfrac{\overset{7}{\cancel{77}} \cdot \overset{1}{\cancel{4}}}{\underset{3}{\cancel{12}} \cdot \underset{1}{\cancel{11}}}$

$\qquad = \dfrac{7}{3}$

$\qquad = 2\dfrac{1}{3}$

56. $-12^0 = -1$

57. $3^{-2} \cdot 3^5 = 3^{-2+5} = 3^3 = 27$

58. $\dfrac{b^{-4}}{b^{10}} = b^{-4-10} = b^{-14} = \dfrac{1}{b^{14}}$

59. $\dfrac{32m^{-8}}{8m^2} = 4m^{-8-2} = 4m^{-10} = \dfrac{4}{m^{10}}$

60. B; $1810 = 1.81 \times 10^3$

Lesson 5.7

5.7 Guided Practice (pp. 265–266)

1.
$$\begin{array}{r} -7.39 \\ \times\quad 2.1 \\ \hline 739 \\ 14\,78 \\ \hline -15.519 \end{array}$$

Check: $-7.39 \cdot 2.1 \approx -7 \cdot 2 = -14$ ✓

2.
$$\begin{array}{r} 19.62 \\ \times\quad 5.07 \\ \hline 1\,3734 \\ 0\,000 \\ 98\,10 \\ \hline 99.4734 \end{array}$$

Check: $19.62 \cdot 5.07 \approx 20 \cdot 5 = 100$ ✓

3.
$$\begin{array}{r} 1.13 \\ \times\quad 0.04 \\ \hline 0.0452 \end{array}$$

Check: $1.13 \cdot 0.04 \approx 1 \cdot 0 = 0$ ✓

4.
$$\begin{array}{r} -0.85 \\ \times\quad -8 \\ \hline 6.80 \end{array}$$

Check: $-0.85 \cdot (-8) \approx -1 \cdot (-8) = 8$ ✓

5.
$0.04\overline{)1.6} \longrightarrow$
$$\begin{array}{r} 40 \\ 4\overline{)160} \\ 16 \\ \hline 00 \\ 0 \\ \hline 0 \end{array}$$

Check: $40 \cdot 0.04 = 1.6$ ✓

6.
$0.79\overline{)0.632} \longrightarrow$
$$\begin{array}{r} 0.8 \\ 79\overline{)63.2} \\ 63.2 \\ \hline 0 \end{array}$$

Check: $0.8 \cdot 0.8 = 0.64$ ✓

7.
$-0.65\overline{)-13} \longrightarrow$
$$\begin{array}{r} 20 \\ -65\overline{)-1300} \\ 130 \\ \hline 00 \\ 0 \\ \hline 0 \end{array}$$

Check: $20 \cdot (-0.7) = -14$ ✓

8.
$-4.5\overline{)-4.365} \longrightarrow$
$$\begin{array}{r} 0.97 \\ -45\overline{)-43.65} \\ 40\,5 \\ \hline 3\,15 \\ 3\,15 \\ \hline 0 \end{array}$$

Check: $1 \cdot (-5) = -5$ ✓

9.
$1.56\overline{)0.3744} \longrightarrow$
$$\begin{array}{r} 0.24 \\ 156\overline{)37.44} \\ 31\,2 \\ \hline 6\,24 \\ 6\,24 \\ \hline 0 \end{array}$$

Check: $0.2 \cdot 2 = 0.4$ ✓

10.
$2.7\overline{)-0.0108} \longrightarrow$
$$\begin{array}{r} -0.004 \\ 27\overline{)-0.108} \\ 108 \\ \hline 0 \end{array}$$

Check: $-0.004 \cdot 3 = -0.012$ ✓

5.7 Exercises (pp. 267–269)

Skill Practice

1. In 0.0745, the digit "7" is the leading digit.

2.
$$\text{divisor} \longrightarrow 9\overline{)7.2} \quad \overset{\text{quotient}}{\underset{\text{dividend}}{}}$$

$0.8 \leftarrow$ quotient

$9\overline{)7.2} \leftarrow$ dividend

3.
$$\begin{array}{r} 7.8 \\ \times\quad 2.6 \\ \hline 4\,68 \\ 15\,6 \\ \hline 20.28 \end{array}$$

Check: $7.8 \cdot 2.6 \approx 8 \cdot 3 = 24$ ✓

4.
$$\begin{array}{r} 3.75 \\ \times\ \ -0.4 \\ \hline -1.500 \end{array}$$

Check: $3.75 \cdot (-0.4) \approx 4 \cdot (-0.5) = -2$ ✓

5.
$$\begin{array}{r} -8.2 \\ \times\ 0.7 \\ \hline -5.74 \end{array}$$

Check : $-8.2 \cdot 0.7 \approx -8 \times 1 = -8$ ✓

6.
$$1.25\overline{)0.5} \longrightarrow 125\overline{)50.0}$$
$$\begin{array}{r} 0.4 \\ \underline{50\ 0} \\ 0 \end{array}$$

Check: $0.5 \div 1 = 0.5$ ✓

7.
$$\begin{array}{r} 25 \\ \times\ 0.2 \\ \hline 5.0 \end{array}$$

Check: $25 \cdot 0.2 \approx 30 \cdot 0.2 = 6$ ✓

8.
$$\begin{array}{r} 2.4 \\ \times\ 0.3 \\ \hline 0.72 \end{array}$$

Check: $2.4 \cdot 0.3 \approx 2.5 \times 0.3 = 0.75$ ✓

9.
$$1.1\overline{)13.2} \longrightarrow 11\overline{)132}$$
$$\begin{array}{r} 12 \\ \underline{11} \\ 22 \\ \underline{22} \\ 0 \end{array}$$

Check: $13 \div 1 = 13$ ✓

10.
$$\begin{array}{r} 13.65 \\ \times\ \ 1.1 \\ \hline 1\ 365 \\ 13\ 65 \\ \hline 15.015 \end{array}$$

Check: $13.65 \cdot 1.1 \approx 14 \times 1 = 14$ ✓

11.
$$1.2\overline{)4.8} \longrightarrow 12\overline{)48}$$
$$\begin{array}{r} 4 \\ \underline{48} \\ 0 \end{array}$$

Check: $5 \div 1 = 5$ ✓

12.
$$0.07\overline{)4.9} \longrightarrow 7\overline{)490}$$
$$\begin{array}{r} 70 \\ \underline{49} \\ 00 \end{array}$$

Check: $5 \div 0.1 = 50$ ✓

13.
$$-3.2\overline{)-8} \longrightarrow -32\overline{)-80.0}$$
$$\begin{array}{r} 2.5 \\ \underline{64} \\ 16\ 0 \\ \underline{16\ 0} \\ 0 \end{array}$$

Check: $3 \cdot (-3) = -9$ ✓

14.
$$-0.1\overline{)5} \longrightarrow -1\overline{)50}$$
$$\begin{array}{r} -50 \\ \underline{5} \\ 00 \end{array}$$

Check: $50 \div (-1) = -50$ ✓

15.
$$\begin{array}{r} 5.41 \\ \times\ 0.35 \\ \hline 2705 \\ 1\ 623 \\ \hline 1.8935 \end{array}$$

Check: $5.41 \cdot 0.35 \approx 5 \cdot 0.4 = 2$ ✓

16.
$$0.56\overline{)4.844} \longrightarrow 56\overline{)484.40}$$
$$\begin{array}{r} 8.65 \\ \underline{448} \\ 36\ 4 \\ \underline{33\ 6} \\ 2\ 80 \\ \underline{2\ 80} \\ 0 \end{array}$$

Check: $9 \cdot 0.6 = 5.4$ ✓

17.
$$0.38\overline{)-0.57} \longrightarrow 38\overline{)-57.0}$$
$$\begin{array}{r} -1.5 \\ \underline{38} \\ 19\ 0 \\ \underline{19\ 0} \\ 0 \end{array}$$

Check: $-2 \cdot 0.4 = -0.8$ ✓

18.
$$\begin{array}{r} -2.687 \\ \times\ \ (-9) \\ \hline 24.183 \end{array}$$

Check: $-2.687 \cdot (-9) \approx -3 \cdot (-9) = 27$ ✓

19.
$$4.3\overline{)-37.41} \longrightarrow 43\overline{)-374.1}$$
$$\begin{array}{r} -8.7 \\ \underline{344} \\ 30\ 1 \\ \underline{30\ 1} \\ 0 \end{array}$$

Check: $-9 \cdot 4 = -36$ ✓

20.
$$\begin{array}{r} 0.098 \\ \times\ -\ 0.55 \\ \hline 4\ 90 \\ 49\ 0 \\ \hline -0.05390 \end{array}$$

Check: $0.098 \cdot (-0.55) \approx 0.1 \cdot (-0.6) = -0.06$ ✓

21.
$$\begin{array}{r} 6.025 \\ \times\ \ 48.2 \\ \hline 1\ 2050 \\ 48\ 200 \\ 241\ 00 \\ \hline 290.4050 \end{array}$$

Check: $6.025 \cdot 48.2 \approx 6 \times 50 = 300$ ✓

22.
$$0.925\overline{)1.11} \longrightarrow 925\overline{)1110.0}$$
$$\begin{array}{r} 1.2 \\ \underline{925} \\ 185\ 0 \\ \underline{185\ 0} \\ 0 \end{array}$$

Check: $1 \cdot 0.9 = 0.9$ ✓

23. The error occurred when the decimal point was only moved two places, it should be moved three places. The correct answer is 33.252.

24. The error occurred when the zero was not used as a placeholder. The quotient should be 0.024.

25. D; $35 \div 0.5 = 70$

The other 3 expressions equal 0.7.

26. D;

$$0.42\overline{)-0.67} \quad \longrightarrow \quad 42\overline{)-67.0}$$

$$\begin{array}{r} -1.5 \\ 42\overline{)-67.0} \\ \underline{42} \\ 25\,0 \\ \underline{21\,0} \\ 4\,0 \end{array}$$

The quotient is less than -1.

27. $\quad 9 = \dfrac{a}{-0.9}$

$-0.9(9) = \dfrac{a}{-0.9} \cdot (-0.9)$

$-8.1 = a$

28. $\quad \dfrac{c}{4.5} = 0.16$

$4.5 \cdot \dfrac{c}{4.5} = 4.5 \cdot 0.16$

$c = 0.72$

29. $\quad -2.8 = \dfrac{p}{6.2}$

$-2.8(6.2) = \dfrac{p}{6.2} \cdot 6.2$

$-17.36 = p$

30. $-5t = 0.085$

$\dfrac{-5t}{-5} = \dfrac{0.085}{-5}$

$t = -0.017$

31. $1.2w = 0.321$

$\dfrac{1.2w}{1.2} = \dfrac{0.321}{1.2}$

$w = 0.2675$

32. $-8.2y = -3.3$

$\dfrac{-8.2y}{-8.2} = \dfrac{-3.3}{-8.2}$

$y = 0.40\overline{2439}$

33. $0.13z = -0.0544$

$\dfrac{0.13z}{0.13} = \dfrac{-0.0544}{0.13}$

$z = -0.418\ldots$

34. $\quad \dfrac{g}{-7.2} = -0.022$

$\dfrac{g}{-7.2} \cdot (-7.2) = -0.022(-7.2)$

$g = 0.1584$

35. $-25.2z = 15.0012$

$\dfrac{-25.2z}{-25.2} = \dfrac{15.0012}{-25.2}$

$z = -0.595\ldots$

36. $105.4 \div 29.8 \quad \underline{\ ?\ } \quad 20.4 \div 5.1$

$\quad 105 \div 30 \qquad 20 \div 5$

$\qquad 3.5 \quad \underline{\ <\ } \quad 4$

37. $3.8 \div (-2.1) \quad \underline{\ ?\ } \quad -1.8 \div 6.4$

$\quad 4 \div (-2) \qquad -2 \div 6$

$\qquad -2 \quad \underline{\ <\ } \quad -0.\overline{3}$

38. $3.4^3 + 5.1 \div 1.7 - 4.89 = 39.304 + 5.1 \div 1.7 - 4.89$

$\qquad\qquad\qquad\qquad = 39.304 + 3 - 4.89$

$\qquad\qquad\qquad\qquad = 37.414$

39. $6.2 \cdot (18.77 - 6.27) + 9.1^2 = 6.2 \cdot 12.5 + 9.1^2$

$\qquad\qquad\qquad\qquad\qquad = 6.2 \cdot 12.5 + 82.81$

$\qquad\qquad\qquad\qquad\qquad = 77.5 + 82.81$

$\qquad\qquad\qquad\qquad\qquad = 160.31$

40. 125, 100, 80, 64, . . .

The pattern is multiply the previous number by 0.8.

$125 \cdot 0.8 = 100;\ 100 \cdot 0.8 = 80;\ 80 \cdot 0.8 = 64;\ 64 \cdot 0.8 = 51.2;\ 51.2 \cdot 0.8 = 40.96$

The next two numbers in the pattern are 51.2 and 40.96.

41. $1, -0.5, 0.25, -0.125, \ldots$

The pattern is multiply the previous number by -0.5.

$1 \cdot (-0.5) = -0.5;\ -0.5 \cdot (-0.5) = 0.25;$
$0.25 \cdot (-0.5) = -0.125;\ -0.125 \cdot (-0.5) = 0.0625;$
$0.0625 \cdot (-0.5) = -0.03125$

The next two numbers in the pattern are 0.0625 and -0.03125.

42. $\dfrac{0.5 \cdot 10}{2 \cdot 10} = \dfrac{5}{20} = \dfrac{1}{4}$

43. $\dfrac{1.75 \cdot 100}{3.5 \cdot 100} = \dfrac{175}{350} = \dfrac{1}{2}$

44. $\dfrac{0.75 \cdot 100}{2.25 \cdot 100} = \dfrac{75}{225} = \dfrac{1}{3}$

45. $\dfrac{4.8 \cdot 10}{12 \cdot 10} = \dfrac{48}{120} = \dfrac{2}{5}$

Problem Solving

46. a. Baby's weight = $0.038 \times$ Mother's weight

b. $b = 0.038 \cdot 3600$

$b = 136.8$ pounds

c. $136.8 \div 0.038 = 3600$

47.

x	1	0.1	0.01	0.001	0.0001
87	87	8.7	0.87	0.087	0.0087
356	356	35.6	3.56	0.356	0.0356
1200	1200	120	12	1.2	0.12

Each time you multiply the number in the left most column, you move the decimal one place to the left.

48. B;

$$0.89\overline{)14.75} \quad \longrightarrow \quad 89\overline{)1475.0}$$

$$\begin{array}{r} 16.5 \\ 89\overline{)1475.0} \\ \underline{89} \\ 585 \\ \underline{534} \\ 51\,0 \\ \underline{44\,5} \\ 6\,5 \end{array}$$

You can buy 16 packages of balloons.

49. Yes, 4.6 divided by 0.23, is the same as 460 divided by 23 because both the dividend and the divisor have been multiplied by 100. The quotient will be the same because the problems are equivalent.

50. a. $\$75 \div 19.95 \approx 3.76$

Check: $75 \div 20 = 3.75 \ \checkmark$

You can buy 3 full boxes of bulbs.

b. Multiply $3 \times 19.95 = \$59.85$ to find out how much money 3 boxes of bulbs cost. Subtract $75 - 59.85 = 15.15$, to find out how much money you can spend on individual bulbs. Divide $15.15 \div 1.2 = 12.625$ to find out how many bulbs you can buy individually. So, you can buy 12 bulbs.

51. 1.3^1 has 1 decimal place.

1.3^2, or 1.69, has 2 decimal places.

1.3^3, or 2.197, has 3 decimal places.

1.3^7, or 6.2748517, has 7 decimal places.

The exponent of a number that has one decimal place is the same as the number of decimal places because you would have to move the decimal point over that number of places when you multiply.

52. $15.5 \div 2.5$

$$2.5\overline{)15.5} \longrightarrow \begin{array}{r} 6.2 \\ 25\overline{)155.0} \\ \underline{150} \\ 5\,0 \\ \underline{5\,0} \\ 0 \end{array}$$

The lava flows at an average rate of 6.2 miles per hour. Your answer is reasonable because rounding to leading digits gives $20 \div 3 = 6.\overline{6}$ which is close to 6.2.

53. To London from Boston: $\frac{3285}{6.25} = 525.6$ miles per hour

To Boston from London: $\frac{3285}{7.5} = 438$ miles per hour

The faster speed is $525.6 - 438$, or 87.6 miles per hour faster than the slower. The faster speed is $\frac{525.6}{438}$, or 1.2 times as fast as the slow.

54. To find the cost to mail a letter that weighs 3.5 ounces, we can add $.37 for the first ounce, to 3($.23$) for the next 2.5 ounces.

$0.37 + 3(0.23) = 0.37 + 0.69 = 1.06$

It will cost $1.06 to mail the letter.

55. To find the width of the water subtract the walkway width from the total width. Repeat using the length.

Width: $99.4 - 24.6 - 24.6 = 50.2$ ft

Length: $139.8 - 24.6 - 24.6 = 90.6$ ft

Use $A = \ell w$ to determine the area.

$A = 50.2 \cdot 90.6$

$A = 4548.12$

The area of the water is 4548.12 square feet.

56. $4 \cdot 0.001 = 0.004$

To make 4 microns appear to be 1 millimeter wide, you can divide $1 \div 0.004$ to get 250. You would have to magnify the bacteria 250 times.

57. $1 \text{ inch} = 2.54 \text{ cm}$

$V = 8 \text{ in.}^3$

To find the volume of the cube in cubic centimeters, cube 2.54 cm, then multiply your answer by 8.

$(2.54^3) \cdot 8 = 131.1$

The volume is 131.1cm^3.

Mixed Review

58. $\frac{9}{4} = 2.25 \qquad 2\frac{3}{10} = 2.3 \qquad \frac{11}{5} = 2.2$

From least to greatest, the numbers are $2, \frac{11}{5}, \frac{9}{4}, 2\frac{3}{10},$ 2.32, and 2.5.

59. $-\frac{26}{5} = -5\frac{1}{5} = -5.2 \qquad -4\frac{9}{10} = -4.9$

From least to greatest, the numbers are $-5.25, -\frac{26}{5},$ $-5.1, -5,$ and $-4\frac{9}{10}.$

60. $-\frac{9}{20} = -0.45 \qquad -\frac{3}{8} = -0.375 \qquad -\frac{5}{12} = 0.41\overline{6}$

From least to greatest, the numbers are $-0.46, -\frac{9}{20},$ $-\frac{5}{12}, -0.4,$ and $-\frac{3}{8}.$

61. $\frac{15}{8} = 1.875 \qquad 1\frac{6}{7} = 1.\overline{857142} \qquad \frac{11}{6} = 1.8\overline{3}$

From least to greatest, the numbers are $1.79, \frac{11}{6}, 1.85,$ $1\frac{6}{7},$ and $\frac{15}{8}.$

62. $6.89 \times 10^9 = 6,890,000,000$

63. $1.3 \times 10^{-12} = 0.0000000000013$

64. $7.405 \times 10^{-6} = 0.000007405$

65. $3.48 \times 10^6 = 3,480,000$

66. *Sample answer:* You can set up an equation to determine how many cups of butter you will need.

$$\frac{2}{3} = x \div \frac{1}{4}$$

$$\frac{2}{3} \cdot \frac{1}{4} = \left(x \div \frac{1}{4}\right) \cdot \frac{1}{4}$$

$$\frac{\overset{1}{2} \cdot 1}{3 \cdot \underset{2}{4}} = x$$

$$\frac{1}{6} = x$$

You will need $\frac{1}{6}$ cups of butter.

Chapter 5, *continued*

Lesson 5.8

Investigation (pp. 270–271)

1. Mean

$$= \frac{4.2 + 6.1 + 3.8 + 4.1 + 10.2 + 9.6 + 6.1 + 7.3 + 2.1 + 2.4 + 9.8}{11}$$

$$= \frac{65.7}{11}$$

$$\approx 5.9\overline{72}$$

  2.1, 2.4, 3.8, 4.1, 4.2, 6.1, 6.1, 7.3, 9.6, 9.8, 10.2

  Median = 6.1

  Mode = 6.1

2. Mean

$$= \frac{105 + 121 + 42 + 78 + 77 + 63 + 108 + 32 + 33 + 121 + 64}{11}$$

$$= \frac{844}{11}$$

$$= 76.\overline{72}$$

  32, 33, 42, 63, 64, 77, 78, 105, 108, 121, 121

  Median = 77

  Mode = 121

3. Mean $= \dfrac{2\frac{1}{2} + 7\frac{3}{4} + 9\frac{1}{4} + 7\frac{1}{2} + 4\frac{3}{8} + 7\frac{3}{4} + 3\frac{7}{8}}{7}$

$$= \frac{43}{7}$$

$$\approx 6\frac{1}{7}$$

  $2\frac{1}{2}, 3\frac{7}{8}, 4\frac{3}{8}, 7\frac{1}{2}, 7\frac{3}{4}, 7\frac{3}{4}, 9\frac{1}{4}$

  Median $= 7\frac{1}{2}$

  Mode $= 7\frac{3}{4}$

4. Mean $= \dfrac{56.4 + 25.1 + 24.3 + 56.4 + 48.7 + 59.2 + 37.9}{7}$

$$= \frac{308}{7}$$

$$= 44$$

  24.3, 25.1, 37.9, 48.7, 56.4, 56.4, 59.2

  Median: 48.7

  Mode: 56.4

5. *Sample answer:* It will increase the mean because it will greatly increase the sum used to find the mean. It is unlikely to affect the mode.

6. Provide a few more boxes than the longest known name. It is better to have too many boxes than too few.

5.8 Guided Practice (pp. 272–273)

1. Mean $= \dfrac{-3 + 44 + (-11) + 9 + (-21)}{5} = \dfrac{18}{5} = 3.6$

  The mean temperature is 3.6°C.

2. Mean $= \dfrac{12\frac{1}{2} + 14\frac{3}{4} + 20\frac{1}{2} + 16\frac{3}{4}}{4} = \dfrac{64.5}{4} = 16\frac{1}{8}$

  The mean length is $16\frac{1}{8}$ inches.

3. 10, 13, 14, 15, 17, 18, 20, 22, 24

  Median = 17

  Mode = none

  Range = 24 − 10 = 14

4. 4, 4, 4, 5, 7, 9, 9, 9, 10, 14

  Median $= \dfrac{7 + 9}{2} = \dfrac{16}{2} = 8$

  Modes = 4 and 9

  Range = 14 − 4 = 10

5. 1, 1, 1, 2, 3, 4, 4, 9, 10, 10

  Median : $\dfrac{3 + 4}{2} = 3.5$

  Mean: $\dfrac{1 + 1 + 1 + 2 + 3 + 4 + 4 + 9 + 10 + 10}{10} = \dfrac{45}{10} = 4.5$

  Mode: 1

  Sample answer: The median best represents the data because most of the data is around 3.5

5.8 Exercises (pp. 274–278)

Skill Practice

1. The *mean* is 8.

  $\dfrac{2 + 4 + 6 + 6 + 9 + 10 + 12 + 15}{8} = \dfrac{64}{8} = 8$

2. The *mode* is 6.

3. The *range* is 13: 15 − 2 = 13.

4. Mean $= \dfrac{115 + 157 + 289 + 185 + 164 + 225 + 185 + 208}{8}$

$$= \frac{1528}{8}$$

$$= 191$$

  115, 157, 164, 185, 185, 208, 225, 289

  Median = 185

  Mode = 185

  Range = 289 − 115 = 174

5. Mean $= \dfrac{16 + 23 + 11 + 6 + 15 + 23 + 17 + 16}{8}$

$$= \frac{127}{8}$$

$$= 15.875 \text{ km}$$

  6, 11, 15, 16, 16, 17, 23, 23

  Median = 16 km

  Modes = 16 km and 23 km

  Range = 23 − 6 = 17 km

Chapter 5, *continued*

6. Mean $= \dfrac{-71 + (-56) + (-62) + (-44) + (-56) + (-47)}{6}$

$= \dfrac{-336}{6}$

$= -56$ in.

$-71, -62, -56, -56, -47, -44$

Median $= \dfrac{-56 + (-56)}{2} = -56$ in.

Mode $= -56$ in.

Range $= -44 - (-71) = 27$ in.

7. Mean

$= \dfrac{-2 + 0 + 3 + 1 + 0 + (-1) + 2 + (-2) + (-3) + 0 + 4 + 1}{12}$

$= \dfrac{3}{12}$

$= \dfrac{1}{4}$

$-3, -2, -2, -1, 0, 0, 0, 1, 1, 2, 3, 4$

Median $= 0$

Mode $= 0$

Range $= 4 - (-3) = 7$

8. Mean $= \dfrac{127 + (-8) + 436 + 508 + (-23) + 47}{6}$

$= \dfrac{1087}{6}$

≈ 181.2 ft

$-23, -8.47, 127, 436, 508$

Median $= \dfrac{47 + 127}{2} = \dfrac{174}{2} = 87$ ft

Mode $=$ none

Range $= 508 - (-23) = 531$ ft

9. Mean $= \dfrac{2000 + 1872 + 2112 + 2255 + 2080 + 1795 + 1977}{7}$

$= \dfrac{14{,}091}{7}$

$= 2013$

$1795, 1872, 1977, 2000, 2080, 2112, 2255$

Median $= 2000$

Mode $=$ none

Range $= 2255 - 1795 = 460$

10. Mean $= \dfrac{10\frac{3}{4} + 9\frac{1}{2} + 8\frac{7}{8} + 10\frac{1}{2} + 8\frac{3}{8} + 10\frac{1}{2}}{6}$

$= \dfrac{58.5}{6}$

$= 9\frac{3}{4}$ in.

$8\frac{3}{8}, 8\frac{7}{8}, 9\frac{1}{2}, 10\frac{1}{2}, 10\frac{1}{2}, 10\frac{3}{4}$

Median $= \dfrac{9\frac{1}{2} + 10\frac{1}{2}}{2} = \dfrac{20}{2} = 10$ in.

Mode $= 10\frac{1}{2}$ in.

Range $= 10\frac{3}{4} - 8\frac{3}{8} = 2\frac{3}{8}$ in.

11. Mean $= \dfrac{20 + (-11) + 72 + (-1) + 9 + 51 + 17 + (-5)}{8}$

$= \dfrac{152}{8}$

$= 19°$

$-11, -5, -1, 9, 17, 20, 51, 72$

Median $= \dfrac{9 + 17}{2} = 13°$

Mode $=$ none

Range $= 72 - (-11) = 83°$

12. Mean $= \dfrac{156 + 212 + 538 + 77 + 388 + 419 + 212}{7}$

$= \dfrac{2002}{7}$

$= 286$

$77, 156, 212, 212, 388, 419, 538$

Median $= 212$

Mode $= 212$

Range $= 461$

13. The data set has two modes, 5 and 8.

14. A; $\dfrac{45 + 56 + 50 + 43 + 56 + 64 + 36}{7} = 50$

$36, 43, 45, 50, 56, 56, 64$

Median: 50

15. Mean $= \dfrac{23 + 20 + 30 + 22 + 24 + 23 + 24}{7}$

$= \dfrac{166}{7}$

$= 23.71$

$20, 22, 23, 23, 24, 24, 30$

Median $= 23$

Mode $= 23$ and 24

The averages that best represent the data is the mean and median.

16. Mean $= \dfrac{94 + 47 + 34 + 45 + 48 + 38}{6}$

$= \dfrac{306}{6}$

$= 51$

$34, 38, 45, 47, 48, 94$

Median $= 46$

Mode $=$ none

The average that best represent the data is the median.

17. Mean $= \dfrac{25 + 58 + 88 + 74 + 21 + 20 + 72 + 22 + 24}{9}$

$= \dfrac{404}{9}$

$= 44.\overline{8}$

$20, 21, 22, 24, 25, 58, 72, 74, 88$

Median $= 25$

Mode $=$ none

The average that best represents the data is the mean.

Chapter 5, continued

18. Mean

$$= \frac{124 + 152 + 108 + 159 + 116 + 142 + 175 + 167 + 119 + 127 + 112}{11}$$

$$= \frac{1501}{11}$$

$$= 136.\overline{45}$$

108, 112, 116, 119, 124, 127, 142, 152, 159, 167, 175

Median = 127

Mode = none

The average that best represent the data is the median.

19. With red:

Mean

$$= \frac{19 + 16 + 23 + 35 + 28 + 20 + 16 + 36 + 98 + 13 + 26 + 29 + 31}{13}$$

$$= \frac{390}{13}$$

$$= 30$$

13, 16, 16, 19, 20, 23, 26, 28, 29, 31, 35, 36, 98

Median = 26

Mode = 16

Range = 98 − 13 = 85

Without red:

Mean $= \frac{390 - 98}{12} = \frac{292}{12} = 24\frac{1}{3}$

Median = 24.5

Mode = 16

Range = 36 − 13 = 23

The mean and range are much smaller without the 98. The mode is unchanged and the median is slightly smaller.

20. With red:

Mean = (58 + 67 + 94 + 85 + 78 + 76 + 6 + 99 + 100 + 88 + 76 + 2 + 82 + 81 + 94 + 98) ÷ 16

$$= \frac{1184}{16}$$

$$= 74$$

2, 6, 58, 67, 76, 76, 78, 81, 82, 85, 88, 94, 94, 98, 99, 100

Median = 81.5

Modes = 76 and 94

Range = 100 − 2 = 98

Without red:

Mean $= \frac{1184 - 6 - 2}{14} = \frac{1176}{14} = 84$

Median = 83.5

Modes = 76 and 94

Range: 100 − 58 = 42

With 2 and 6 removed, the mean gets much larger, the range gets smaller. The mode stays the same, and the median increases slightly.

21. 63, 52, 49, b, 68, 75, 57; Range = 31

To find the unknown value subtract the range from the greatest value.

b = 75 − 31 = 44

Mean $= \frac{63 + 52 + 49 + 44 + 68 + 75 + 57}{7}$

$$= \frac{408}{7}$$

$$= 58\frac{2}{7}$$

44, 49, 52, 57, 63, 68, 75

Median = 57

Mode = none

22. 17, 96, 54, 48, d, 27; Range = 81

To find the unknown value add the range to the lowest value.

d = 17 + 81 = 98

Mean $= \frac{17 + 96 + 54 + 48 + 98 + 27}{6} = \frac{340}{6} = 56\frac{2}{3}$

17, 27, 48, 54, 96, 98

Median $= \frac{48 + 54}{2} = \frac{102}{2} = 51$

Mode = none

23. 6, 8, 14, 9, 3, c, 12, 5; Median = 7.5

To find the unknown value put the numbers in order least to greatest (knowing the unknown value falls between 6 and 8).

3, 5, 6, c, 8, 9, 12, 14

$\frac{c + 8}{2} = 7.5$

c + 8 = 15

c = 7

Mean $= \frac{3 + 5 + 6 + 7 + 8 + 9 + 12 + 14}{8} = \frac{64}{8} = 8$

Mode = none

Range = 14 − 3 = 11

24. 11, z, 30, 42, 7, 39, 22; Median = 28

To find the unknown value put the numbers in order from least to greatest (knowing the unknown value falls between 22 and 30).

7, 11, 22, z, 30, 39, 42

z = 28 because it is the number in the middle.

Mean $= \frac{7 + 11 + 22 + 28 + 30 + 39 + 42}{7} = \frac{179}{7} = 25\frac{4}{7}$

Mode = none

Range = 42 − 7 = 35

Chapter 5, *continued*

25. 32, 18, 16, *a*, 23, 41;　　　Mean = 28

To find the unknown value set up an equation and set it equal to the mean.

$$\frac{32 + 18 + 16 + a + 23 + 41}{6} = 28$$

$$32 + 18 + 16 + a + 23 + 41 = 168$$

$$130 + a = 168$$

$$a = 38$$

16, 18, 23, 32, 38, 41

$$\text{Median} = \frac{23 + 32}{2} = \frac{55}{2} = 27.5$$

Mode = None

Range = 41 − 16 = 25

26. Mean = $\dfrac{3b + 5b + b + 6b + (-6b) + (-2b)}{6} = \dfrac{7b}{6}$

27. Mean: 11;　　Median: 12;　　Mode: 17;　　Range: 13

Sample answer: The number in the middle is 12. The mode is 17 (there will be 2). To find the lowest number subtract the range from 17 (which is 4). To find the last number set up an equation using the mean.

$$\frac{4 + x + 12 + 17 + 17}{5} = 11$$

$$4 + x + 12 + 17 + 17 = 55$$

$$50 + x = 55$$

$$x = 5$$

The 5 numbers in this set of data are 4, 5, 12, 17, and 17.

28. Mean: 16;　　Median: 15;　　Mode: 15;　　Range: 22

Sample answer: The number in the middle is 15 and also occurs the most often (in the case twice). Pick a value for the greatest number. Use the range to determine the low number value (30 − 22 = 8). To find the last number set up an equation using the mean.

$$\frac{8 + x + 15 + 15 + 30}{5} = 16$$

$$8 + x + 15 + 15 + 30 = 80$$

$$68 + x = 80$$

$$x = 12$$

The 5 numbers in this set of data are 8, 12, 15, 15, and 30.

29. Mean: 5;　　Median: 1;　　Mode: −4;　　Range: 26

Sample answer: The number in the middle is 1. The mode is −4 (There will be 2). To find the highest number add the range to −4 (which is 22). To find the last number set up an equation using the mean.

$$\frac{-4 + (-4) + 1 + x + 22}{5} = 5$$

$$-4 + (-4) + 1 + x + 22 = 25$$

$$x + 15 = 25$$

$$x = 10$$

The 5 numbers in the set of data are −4, −4, 1, 10, and 22.

Problem Solving

30. a. 22:45 = 22(60) + 45 = 1320 + 45 = 1365 seconds

21:56 = 21(60) + 56 = 1260 + 56 = 1316 seconds

21:03 = 21(60) + 3 = 1260 + 3 = 1263 seconds

20:33 = 20(60) + 33 = 1200 + 33 = 1233 seconds

20:28 = 20(60) + 28 = 1200 + 28 = 1228

b. 1365 + 1316 + 1263 + 1233 + 1228 = 6405 seconds

$$\frac{1365 + 1316 + 1263 + 1233 + 1228}{5} = \frac{6405}{5}$$

$$= 1281 \text{ seconds}$$

c.
```
      21 R21
60)1281
     120
      81
      60
      21
```

21 : 21

31. Mean

$$= \frac{49{,}646 + 49{,}646 + 55{,}820 + 55{,}863 + 56{,}018 + 49{,}707 + 49{,}589}{7}$$

$$= \frac{366{,}289}{7}$$

$$= 52{,}327$$

49,589, 49,646, 49,646, 49,707, 55,820, 55,863, 56,018

Median = 49,707

Mode = 49,646

The mean best represents the attendance data because the median and the mode are too low.

32. Kendra: Mean = $\dfrac{8 + 10 + 9 + 9 + 10 + 12 + 10 + 11}{8}$

$$= \frac{79}{8}$$

$$= 9\frac{7}{8}$$

8, 9, 9, 10, 10, 10, 11, 12

Median = 10

Mode = 10

Range = 12 − 8 = 4

Jade: Mean = $\dfrac{8 + 5 + 9 + 12 + 13 + 10 + 7 + 11}{8}$

$$= \frac{75}{8}$$

$$= 9\frac{3}{8}$$

5, 7, 8, 9, 10, 11, 12, 13

Median = $\dfrac{9 + 10}{2}$ = 9.5

Mode = none

Range = 13 − 5 = 8

Kendra is the more consistent player because her averages are higher and she has a smaller range.

Chapter 5, *continued*

33. *Sample answer:* The median; there are equally many salaries above and below it, so it should reflect the most likely salary for me in each career.

34. A; Mean

$$= \frac{8 + 9 + 11 + 12 + 14 + 14 + 15 + 16 + 17 + 17 + 18 + 20}{12}$$

$$= \frac{171}{12}$$

$$= 14.25$$

Median $= \frac{14 + 15}{2} = 14.5$

Modes $= 14$ and 17

The averages that best represent the data are the mean and median because the values are close to each other. The mode is the value 17, which is about halfway between the mean and the highest quiz score.

35. Mean $= \frac{-81 + (-141) + (-100) + (-67) + (-120) + (-73)}{6}$

$$= \frac{-582}{6}$$

$$= -97$$

The mean distance is -97 meters.

36. *Sample answer:* 5, 6, 8, 8

Mean $= \frac{5 + 6 + 8 + 8}{4}$

$$= \frac{27}{4}$$

$$= 6.75$$

Mode $= 8$

37. Jerry substituted the value of a and then found the mean using the numbers. Roberta found the mean before substituting the value;

Both Jerry and Roberta have a correct method. Roberta's method is faster, and involves less multiplication.

38. To find out how many points you need to score in the third game, you can use the following equation.

$$\frac{125 + 113 + x}{3} = 126$$

$$3\left(\frac{125 + 113 + x}{3}\right) = 3 \cdot 126$$

$$238 + x = 378$$

$$238 + x - 238 = 378 - 238$$

$$x = 140$$

You need 140 points in the third game.

39. The average depth of the lake does not reflect its deepest part. There could be a part of the lake that is too deep for wading.

40. The outlier in the set of data is 592.

With outlier:

Mean $= \frac{318 + 390 + 592 + 388 + 375 + 350 + 410 + 395}{8}$

$$= \frac{3218}{8}$$

$$= 402\frac{1}{4}$$

318, 350, 375, 388, 390, 395, 410, 592

Median $= \frac{388 + 390}{2} = 389$

Mode $=$ none

Without outlier:

Mean $= \frac{3218 - 592}{7}$

$$= \frac{2626}{7}$$

$$= 375\frac{1}{7}$$

Median $= 388$

Mode $=$ none

The mean is most affected by the outlier because the outlier makes the sum of the terms much larger.

41. Isaac: $\frac{9.6 + 9.6 + 9.65 + 9.65}{4} = \frac{38.5}{4} = 9.625$

Carl: $\frac{9.7 + 9.7 + 9.8 + 9.8}{4} = \frac{39}{4} = 9.75$

Kurt: $\frac{9.55 + 9.6 + 9.75 + 9.8}{4} = \frac{38.7}{4} = 9.675$

First place was awarded to Carl, second place to Kurt, and third place to Isaac.

42. Isaac: $\frac{9.6 + 9.6 + 9.6 + 9.65 + 9.8 + 9.65}{6} = \frac{57.9}{6} = 9.65$

Carl: $\frac{9.8 + 9.8 + 9.7 + 9.7 + 9.7 + 9.8}{6} = \frac{58.5}{6} = 9.75$

Kurt: $\frac{9.55 + 9.4 + 9.8 + 9.75 + 9.8 + 9.6}{6} = \frac{57.9}{6} = 9.65$

No, the top 3 gymnasts would not be the same. Isaac and Kurt would have tied for second place.

43. It removes the chance of an extremely high or low scores affecting the mean.

44. a. With outlier:

Mean $= \frac{1 + 7 + 7 + 8 + 8 + 8 + 8 + 8 + 9 + 9}{10}$

$$= \frac{73}{10}$$

$$= 7.3$$

Median $= 8$

Mode $= 8$

Without outlier:

Mean $= \frac{73 - 1}{9} = 8$

Median $= 8$

Mode $= 8$

b. Removing the outlier increases the mean while the median and mode stay the same.

45. a.

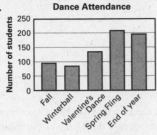

Dance Attendance

b. Mean $= \dfrac{97 + 88 + 133 + 210 + 198}{5} = \dfrac{726}{5} = 145.2$

88, 97, 133, 198, 210

Median $= 133$

c. *Sample answer:* Mean; the mean will give you data on total attendance, which is necessary when money issues are at hand.

d. To find out how much money was collected, we need to know the price per ticket.

46. $(15 + 8 + 7 + 10 + 12 + 4 + 20 + 13 + 7 + 7 + 5 + 3 + 10 + 14 + x) \div 15 = 10$

$$\frac{135 + x}{15} = 10$$

$$15 \cdot \left(\frac{135 + x}{15}\right) = 15 \cdot 10$$

$$135 + x = 150$$

$$135 - 135 + x = 150 - 135$$

$$x = 15$$

To have a mean of 10 points per game you need 15 points in your final game. You have already scored 7 points, so you need 8 more points.

Mixed Review

47.
$$3x - 28 = -37$$
$$3x - 28 + 28 = -37 + 28$$
$$3x = -9$$
$$\frac{3x}{3} = \frac{-9}{3}$$
$$x = -3$$

48.
$$-8 + 2x = -24$$
$$-8 + 2x + 8 = -24 + 8$$
$$2x = -16$$
$$\frac{2x}{2} = \frac{-16}{2}$$
$$x = -8$$

49.
$$-7x + 14 = 84$$
$$-7x + 14 - 14 = 84 - 14$$
$$-7x = 70$$
$$\frac{-7x}{-7} = \frac{70}{-7}$$
$$x = -10$$

50.
$$\frac{x}{5} - 10 = -10$$
$$\frac{x}{5} - 10 + 10 = -10 + 10$$
$$\frac{x}{5} = 0$$
$$\frac{x}{5} \cdot 5 = 0 \cdot 5$$
$$x = 0$$

51.
$$2 - \frac{x}{6} = -11$$
$$2 - \frac{x}{6} - 2 = -11 - 2$$
$$-\frac{x}{6} = -13$$
$$-\frac{x}{6} \cdot (-6) = -13(-6)$$
$$x = 78$$

52.
$$-\frac{x}{4} + 12 = 16$$
$$-\frac{x}{4} + 12 - 12 = 16 - 12$$
$$-\frac{x}{4} = 4$$
$$-4 \cdot \left(-\frac{x}{4}\right) = -4 \cdot 4$$
$$x = -16$$

53. $-3(13) = -39$

54. $-40(-5) = 200$

55. $4(-11) = -44$

56. $-19(0) = 0$

57. C; $(-3)^{-4} = \dfrac{1}{(-3)^4} = \dfrac{1}{81}$

Quiz 5.5–5.8 (p. 278)

1. $4.25 = 4\dfrac{25}{100} = 4\dfrac{1}{4}$

2.
$$\begin{array}{r} 0.44\ldots \\ 9\overline{)4.00} \\ \underline{3\ 6} \\ 40 \\ \underline{36} \\ 4 \end{array}$$
$$\frac{4}{9} = 0.\overline{4}$$

3. $0.58 = \dfrac{58}{100} = \dfrac{29}{50}$

4. Let $x = 0.\overline{2}$.
$$10x = 2.22\ldots$$
$$-x = 0.22\ldots$$
$$9x = 2$$
$$x = \frac{2}{9}$$

5. $-2.301 + 8.4 = 8.4 - 2.301$
$$\begin{array}{r} 8.400 \\ -\ 2.301 \\ \hline 6.099 \end{array}$$

6.
$$\begin{array}{r} 15.250 \\ +\ 9.636 \\ \hline 24.886 \end{array}$$

7.
$$\begin{array}{r} 14.650 \\ -\ 3.608 \\ \hline 11.042 \end{array}$$

8. $3.02 - (-0.225) = 3.02 + 0.225$
$$\begin{array}{r} 3.020 \\ +\ 0.225 \\ \hline 3.245 \end{array}$$

9.
$$\begin{array}{r} -15.3 \\ \times\ 0.48 \\ \hline 1\ 224 \\ 6\ 12 \\ \hline -7.344 \end{array}$$

10.
$$\begin{array}{r} 3.88 \\ \times\ 0.9 \\ \hline 3.492 \end{array}$$

11.
$$2.7\overline{)0.162} \longrightarrow \begin{array}{r} 0.06 \\ 27\overline{)1.62} \\ \underline{1\ 62} \\ 0 \end{array}$$

12.
$$0.225\overline{)2.07} \longrightarrow \begin{array}{r} 9.2 \\ 225\overline{)2070.0} \\ \underline{2025} \\ 45\ 0 \\ \underline{45\ 0} \\ 0 \end{array}$$

Chapter 5, *continued*

13.
$$\begin{array}{r} 11.75 \\ \times\ 0.02 \\ \hline 0.2350 \end{array}$$

The camel travels 0.235 mile.

14. Mean =

$$\frac{1424 + 1342 + 1071 + 805 + 941 + 1376 + 1819}{7} = \frac{8778}{7}$$
$$= 1254$$

805, 941, 1071, 1342, 1376, 1424, 1819

Median = 1342

Mode = none

Range = 1819 − 805 = 1014

Brain Game (p. 278)

If the mode is $1.50, then $1.50 must be the price of at least 2 items. The median is $1.65. One item costs $.10 more than the median, so that item is $1.75. From here, we can write an equation to find the price of the fifth item.

$$\frac{1.50 + 1.50 + 1.65 + 1.75 + x}{5} = 1.68$$
$$\frac{6.40 + x}{5} = 1.68$$
$$5 \cdot \frac{6.40 + x}{5} = 1.68 \cdot 5$$
$$6.40 + x = 8.40$$
$$x = 8.40 - 6.40$$
$$x = 2$$

The prices of the items in the cart, in order from least to greatest, are $1.50, $1.50, $1.65, $1.75, and $2.

Mixed Review of Problem Solving (p. 279)

1. a. $18 \times 0.1 = 1.8$

The phone call cost Rebecca $1.80.

b. $18 \times 0.05 = 0.9$

The phone call cost Rebecca $.90.

c.
$$\begin{array}{r} 1.80 \\ -\ 0.90 \\ \hline 0.90 \end{array}$$

The difference between the 2 calls is $.90.

2. $A = \ell w$

$8.96 = 3.2w$

$2.8 = w$

$p = 2\ell + 2w$

$p = 2(3.2) + 2(2.8)$

$p = 6.4 + 5.6$

$p = 12$

The perimeter of the rectangular garden is 12 meters.

3. Mean = $\dfrac{18 + 15 + 7 + 10 + 32 + 28 + 17 + 21 + 94}{9}$

$$= \frac{242}{9}$$
$$= 26\frac{8}{9}$$

7, 10, 15, 17, 18, 21, 28, 32, 94

Median = 18

Mode = none

The median is most representative of the session lengths because there is no mode and the 94 raises the mean too high.

4. a. Comedy: $\dfrac{2}{5} = 0.4$

Drama: $\dfrac{1}{8} = 0.125$

Action: $\dfrac{5}{16} = 0.3125$

b. Comedy: $8.00 \cdot 0.4 = 320$

Drama: $800 \cdot 0.125 = 100$

Action: $800 \cdot 0.3125 = 250$

To find how many more people picked the most popular over the least popular, subtract the two numbers.

$320 - 100 = 220$

The difference is 220 people.

c. $800 - 320 - 100 - 250 = 130$

The number of people that didn't choose one of these types of movies is 130 people.

5. *Sample answer:* 5, 5, 8, 10, 10, 10; Because the total number is an even number, the median must be the average of the 3rd and 4th values $(8 + 10) \div 2 = 9$. To keep the mode 10, another one is added. You then multiply the mean by the total number of values to get the sum, $8 \cdot 6 = 48$. Subtract the three values already chosen, $48 - 8 - 10 - 10 = 20$. This is the sum of the 3 values. The last value must be greater than or equal to 10. Using 10 for the last value leaves a sum of 10 to split between the first two values, 5 and 5.

6. Find out how many total pounds of grapes you are buying by adding $(2.3 + 1.5 = 3.8)$. Then multiply this amount by how much one pound costs. $(1.3 \times 3.8 = 4.94)$ So, you spend $4.94 on grapes.

7. a. The distance from Fourth and A to Third and D is 4 blocks. Each block is 0.2 miles.

$0.2 \times 4 = 0.8$

The shortest trip is 0.8 mile.

b. The first fifth of a mile cost $2.50 and $.40 for each additional fifth: $2.50 + (0.4 \times 3) = \$3.70$. It will cost $3.70.

c. The previous cost was $3.70. You wait 8 minutes at $.27 per minute $(8 \cdot 0.27 = 2.16)$. You continue on for another 4 blocks at $.40 a block $(0.4 \cdot 4 = 1.6)$. Add these totals: $3.70 + 2.16 + 1.60 = 7.46$

The trip will cost you $7.46.

8.

$$\frac{2}{9}$$

$$\begin{array}{r} 0.22\ldots \\ 9\overline{)2.00} \\ \underline{1\ 8} \\ 20 \\ \underline{18} \\ 2 \end{array}$$

$$\frac{2}{9} = 0.\overline{2}$$

You can determine the result by placing a 0 between the decimal and 2 for every 0 in the denominator.

9. Find the perimeter of the rectangles A and B.

Rectangle A: $P = 2(9.3) + 2(7.5) = 18.6 + 15 = 33.6$ ft

Rectangle B: $P = 2(27.9) + 2(22.5) = 55.8 + 45$

$$= 100.8 \text{ ft}$$

$$\frac{\text{Rect. } B}{\text{Rect. } A} = \frac{100.8}{33.6} = 3$$

The perimeter of Rectangle B is 3 times greater than the perimeter of Rectangle A.

Since the area is the product of length and width each multiplied by 3, ℓw is multiplied by 9, $(3\ell)(3w) = 9\ell w$. So the area of Rectangle B is 9 times greater than the area of Rectangle A.

Chapter 5 Review (pp. 280–284)

1. The fractions $\frac{3}{5}$ and $\frac{5}{3}$ are *reciprocals* or *multiplicative inverses* because their product is 1.

2. If the remainder of the quotient $\frac{a}{b}$ is 0, then the decimal form of $\frac{a}{b}$ is a *terminating decimal*.

3. You can use *front-end estimation* when you do not need to find an exact sum of a group of decimals.

4. A value that occurs most often in a data set is a *mode*.

5. A number that can be written as $\frac{a}{b}$, where a and b are integers and $b \neq 0$, is a *rational number*.

6. $\frac{8}{9} + \frac{4}{9} = \frac{8+4}{9} = \frac{12}{9} = 1\frac{1}{3}$

7. $3\frac{5}{8} - 1\frac{7}{8} = \frac{29}{8} - \frac{15}{8} = \frac{14}{8} = 1\frac{3}{4}$

8. $\frac{3}{10} - \frac{7}{10} - \frac{9}{10} = \frac{3-7-9}{10} = \frac{-13}{10} = -\frac{13}{10}$

9. $\frac{4}{7} + \frac{2}{7} + \frac{6}{7} = \frac{4+2+6}{7} = \frac{12}{7} = 1\frac{5}{7}$

10. $\frac{6n}{18} - \frac{2n}{18} = \frac{6n-2n}{18} = \frac{4n}{18} = \frac{2n}{9}$

11. $-\frac{4n}{6} + \frac{3n}{6} = \frac{-4n+3n}{6} = -\frac{n}{6}$

12. $\frac{8n}{11} + \frac{4n}{11} = \frac{8n+4n}{11} = \frac{12n}{11}$

13. $-\frac{7n}{9} - \frac{5n}{9} = \frac{-7n-5n}{9} = \frac{-12n}{9} = -\frac{4n}{3}$

14. $\frac{3}{5} + \frac{2}{3} = \frac{9}{15} + \frac{10}{15} = \frac{19}{15} = 1\frac{4}{15}$

15. $\frac{3}{5} + \frac{1}{4} = \frac{12}{20} + \frac{5}{20} = \frac{17}{20}$

16. $6\frac{2}{7} + \left(-7\frac{1}{8}\right) = 6\frac{16}{56} + \left(-7\frac{7}{56}\right) = \frac{352}{56} + \left(-\frac{399}{56}\right) = -\frac{47}{56}$

17. $\frac{5v}{3} + \frac{4v}{5} = \frac{25v}{15} + \frac{12v}{15} = \frac{37v}{15}$

18. $\frac{8}{9} - \frac{2}{5} = \frac{40}{45} - \frac{18}{45} = \frac{22}{45}$

19. $\frac{7}{12} - \left(-\frac{5}{8}\right) = \frac{14}{24} - \left(-\frac{15}{24}\right) = \frac{29}{24} = 1\frac{5}{24}$

20. $3\frac{1}{3} - 1\frac{1}{4} = \frac{10}{3} - \frac{5}{4} = \frac{40}{12} - \frac{15}{12} = \frac{25}{12} = 2\frac{1}{12}$

21. $\frac{8x}{17} - \frac{x}{2} = \frac{16x}{34} - \frac{17x}{34} = -\frac{x}{34}$

22. $111\frac{5}{6} - 107\frac{1}{3} = 111\frac{5}{6} - 107\frac{2}{6}$

$$= (111 - 107) + \left(\frac{5}{6} - \frac{2}{6}\right)$$

$$= 4\frac{3}{6}$$

$$= 4\frac{1}{2}$$

East High School took $4\frac{1}{2}$ hours longer to build their robot.

23. $-\frac{5}{8} \cdot \frac{2}{5} = \frac{-5 \cdot 2}{8 \cdot 5} = \frac{\overset{-1}{\cancel{-5}} \cdot \overset{1}{\cancel{2}}}{\underset{4}{\cancel{8}} \cdot \underset{1}{\cancel{5}}} = -\frac{1}{4}$

24. $-\frac{9}{5} \cdot \left(-\frac{11}{15}\right) = \frac{-9 \cdot (-11)}{5 \cdot 15} = \frac{\overset{-3}{\cancel{-9}} \cdot (-11)}{5 \cdot \underset{5}{\cancel{15}}} = \frac{33}{25} = 1\frac{8}{25}$

25. $-\frac{1}{3} \cdot \frac{2}{7} = \frac{-1 \cdot 2}{3 \cdot 7} = \frac{-2}{21} = -\frac{2}{21}$

26. $\frac{3}{8} \cdot \left(-\frac{12}{13}\right) = \frac{3 \cdot (-12)}{8 \cdot 13} = \frac{3 \cdot (\overset{-3}{\cancel{-12}})}{\underset{2}{\cancel{8}} \cdot 13} = -\frac{9}{26}$

27. $8\frac{2}{3} \cdot (-3) = \frac{26}{3} \cdot (-3) = \frac{26 \cdot (\overset{-1}{\cancel{-3}})}{\underset{1}{\cancel{3}} \cdot 1} = -26$

28. $-7\frac{4}{9} \cdot \left(-\frac{1}{4}\right) = \frac{-67 \cdot (-1)}{9 \cdot 4} = \frac{67}{36} = 1\frac{31}{36}$

29. $-6\frac{3}{7} \cdot 2\frac{1}{2} = -\frac{45}{7} \cdot \frac{5}{2} = \frac{-45 \cdot 5}{7 \cdot 2} = -\frac{225}{14} = -16\frac{1}{14}$

30. $4 \cdot \left(-3\frac{5}{12}\right) = 4 \cdot \left(-\frac{41}{12}\right)$

$$= \frac{4 \cdot (-41)}{1 \cdot 12}$$

$$= \frac{\overset{1}{\cancel{4}} \cdot (-41)}{1 \cdot \underset{3}{\cancel{12}}}$$

$$= -\frac{41}{3}$$

$$= -13\frac{2}{3}$$

31. $\frac{13}{18} \div \frac{5}{6} = \frac{13}{18} \cdot \frac{6}{5} = \frac{13 \cdot 6}{18 \cdot 5} = \frac{13 \cdot \overset{1}{\cancel{6}}}{\underset{3}{\cancel{18}} \cdot 5} = \frac{13}{15}$

32. $\frac{7}{22} \div \frac{1}{11} = \frac{7}{22} \cdot \frac{11}{1} = \frac{7 \cdot 11}{22 \cdot 1} = \frac{7 \cdot \overset{1}{\cancel{11}}}{\underset{2}{\cancel{22}} \cdot 1} = \frac{7}{2} = 3\frac{1}{2}$

33. $\frac{2}{3} \div \left(-\frac{1}{6}\right) = \frac{2}{3} \cdot \left(-\frac{6}{1}\right) = \frac{2 \cdot (-6)}{3 \cdot 1} = \frac{2 \cdot (\overset{-2}{\cancel{-6}})}{\underset{1}{\cancel{3}} \cdot 1} = -4$

34. $-\frac{4}{5} \div \left(-\frac{1}{2}\right) = -\frac{4}{5} \cdot \left(-\frac{2}{1}\right) = \frac{-4 \cdot (-2)}{5 \cdot 1} = \frac{8}{5} = 1\frac{3}{5}$

35. $2\frac{3}{4} \div 1\frac{1}{3} = \frac{11}{4} \div \frac{4}{3} = \frac{11 \cdot 3}{4 \cdot 4} = \frac{33}{16} = 2\frac{1}{16}$

36. $\frac{9}{21} \div 5 = \frac{9}{21} \div \frac{5}{1} = \frac{9}{21} \cdot \frac{1}{5} = \frac{9}{105} = \frac{3}{35}$

37. $5\frac{8}{11} \div \left(-\frac{3}{4}\right) = \frac{63}{11} \cdot \left(-\frac{4}{3}\right)$

$= \frac{\overset{21}{\cancel{63}} \cdot (-4)}{11 \cdot \underset{1}{\cancel{3}}}$

$= -\frac{84}{11}$

$= -7\frac{7}{11}$

38. $12\frac{1}{2} \div 4\frac{1}{6} = \frac{25}{2} \div \frac{25}{6} = \frac{25}{2} \cdot \frac{6}{25} = \frac{\overset{1}{\cancel{25}} \cdot \overset{3}{\cancel{6}}}{\underset{1}{\cancel{2}} \cdot \underset{1}{\cancel{25}}} = 3$

39. $12\frac{1}{2} \div 8 = \frac{25}{2} \div \frac{8}{1} = \frac{25}{2} \cdot \frac{1}{8} = \frac{25 \cdot 1}{2 \cdot 8} = \frac{25}{16} = 1\frac{9}{16}$

Each person will run $1\frac{9}{16}$ mile.

40. $\frac{3}{5}$
$$\begin{array}{r} 0.6 \\ 5\overline{)3.0} \\ \underline{3\,0} \\ 0 \end{array}$$

41. $-\frac{7}{8}$
$$\begin{array}{r} -0.875 \\ 8\overline{)-7.000} \\ \underline{6\,4} \\ 60 \\ \underline{56} \\ 40 \\ \underline{40} \\ 0 \end{array}$$

42. Let $x = -0.\overline{23}$.

$100x = -23.23\ldots$

$\underline{-\quad x = \;\;-0.23\ldots}$

$99x = -23$

$x = -\frac{23}{99}$

43. $3.45 = 3\frac{45}{100} = 3\frac{9}{20}$

44. $\frac{2}{9}$
$$\begin{array}{r} 0.\overline{2} \\ 9\overline{)2.0} \\ \underline{1\,8} \\ 2 \end{array}$$

45. Let $x = 2.\overline{65}$.

$100x = 265.65\ldots$

$\underline{-\quad x = \;\;\;\;2.65\ldots}$

$99x = 263$

$x = \frac{263}{99}$

$x = 2\frac{65}{99}$

46. $0.16 = \frac{16}{100} = \frac{4}{25}$

47. $-\frac{3}{11}$
$$\begin{array}{r} -0.\overline{27} \\ 11\overline{)-3.00} \\ \underline{2\,2} \\ 80 \\ \underline{77} \\ 3 \end{array}$$

48.
$$\begin{array}{r} 1.2 \\ +\ 0.67 \\ \hline 1.87 \end{array}$$

49.
$$\begin{array}{r} 33.2 \\ +\ 9.398 \\ \hline 42.598 \end{array}$$

50.
$$\begin{array}{r} 3.160 \\ -\ 1.845 \\ \hline 1.315 \end{array}$$

51.
$$\begin{array}{r} 90.30 \\ +\ 7.81 \\ \hline 98.11 \end{array}$$

$90.3 - (-7.81) = 90.3 + 7.81 = 98.11$

52.
$$\begin{array}{r} 20.68 \\ +\ 5.20 \\ \hline 25.88 \end{array}$$

53.
$$\begin{array}{r} 0.103 \\ +\ 0.700 \\ \hline 0.803 \end{array}$$

54.
$$\begin{array}{r} 9.600 \\ -\ 3.555 \\ \hline 6.045 \end{array}$$

55.
$$\begin{array}{r} -4.230 \\ +\ -8.093 \\ \hline -12.323 \end{array}$$

56.
$$\begin{array}{r} 6.24 \\ \times\ 0.375 \\ \hline 3120 \\ 4368\ \\ 1\,872\ \ \\ \hline 2.34000 \end{array}$$

57.
$$\begin{array}{r} 3.348 \\ \times\ \ 0.9 \\ \hline 3.0132 \end{array}$$

58. $66.96 \div (-2.7) \longrightarrow$
$$\begin{array}{r} -2\,4.8 \\ -2.7\overline{)66.9\,6} \\ \underline{54\ \ \ } \\ 12\,9 \\ \underline{10\,8} \\ 2\,1\,6 \\ \underline{2\,1\,6} \\ 0 \end{array}$$

59. $18.91 \div 9.455 \longrightarrow$
$$\begin{array}{r} 2. \\ 9.455\overline{)18.910} \\ \underline{18\,910} \\ 0 \end{array}$$

60. $40.25\overline{)144.9} \longrightarrow$
$$\begin{array}{r} 3.6 \\ 4025\overline{)14{,}490.0} \\ \underline{12\,075\ \ } \\ 2\,415\,0 \\ \underline{2\,415\,0} \\ 0 \end{array}$$

The mass of the house cat is 3.6 kilograms.

61. Mean $= \dfrac{-7 + (-1) + 0 + 8 + 4 + 2 + (-7) + 2}{8} = \frac{1}{8}°C$

$-7, -7, -1, 0, 2, 2, 4, 8$

Median $= \dfrac{0 + 2}{2} = \frac{2}{2} = 1°C$

Modes $= -7°C$ and $2°C$

Range $= 8 - (-7) = 15°C$

Chapter 5, *continued*

62. Mean $= \dfrac{14.6 + 19.2 + 11 + 16.5 + 12 + 11 + 10.9}{7}$

$= \dfrac{95.2}{7}$

$= 13.6$ m

10.9, 11, 11, 12, 14.6, 16.5, 19.2

Median $= 12$ m

Mode: $= 11$ m

Range: $19.2 - 10.9 = 8.3$ m

63. Mean $= \dfrac{7 + 8.3 + 17.1 + 4.8 + 3.9 + 7 + 4.8 + 13.1}{8}$

$= \dfrac{66}{8}$

$= 8.25$ km

3.9, 4.8, 4.8, 7, 7, 8.3, 13.1, 17.1

Median $= \dfrac{7 + 7}{2} = \dfrac{14}{2} = 7$ km

Modes $= 4.8$ km and 7 km

Range $= 17.1 - 3.9 = 13.2$ km

64. Mean $= \dfrac{2.4 + 1 + 3.7 + 1.4 + 1.3 + 2.5 + 2 + 2.5}{8}$

$= \dfrac{16.8}{8}$

$= 2.1$

1, 1.3, 1.4, 2, 2.4, 2.5, 2.5, 3.7

Median $= \dfrac{2 + 2.4}{2} = \dfrac{4.4}{2} = 2.2$

Modes $= 2.5$

Range $= 3.7 - 1 = 2.7$

Chapter 5 Test (p. 285)

1. $4\dfrac{5}{11} - 2\dfrac{6}{11} = 3\dfrac{16}{11} - 2\dfrac{6}{11} = (3 - 2) + \left(\dfrac{16}{11} - \dfrac{6}{11}\right) = 1\dfrac{10}{11}$

2. $\dfrac{9}{16} - \left(-\dfrac{11}{16}\right) = \dfrac{9 - (-11)}{16} = \dfrac{20}{16} = \dfrac{5}{4} = 1\dfrac{1}{4}$

3. $-\dfrac{5}{6} + \dfrac{1}{8} = -\dfrac{20}{24} + \dfrac{3}{24} = \dfrac{-20 + 3}{24} = -\dfrac{17}{24}$

4. $\dfrac{3}{7} + \left(-\dfrac{8}{21}\right) + \dfrac{2}{3} = \dfrac{9}{21} + \left(-\dfrac{8}{21}\right) + \dfrac{14}{21}$

$= \dfrac{9 + (-8) + 14}{21}$

$= \dfrac{15}{21}$

$= \dfrac{5}{7}$

5. $\dfrac{2}{9} \cdot (-4) = \dfrac{2}{9} \cdot \dfrac{-4}{1} = \dfrac{2 \cdot (-4)}{9 \cdot 1} = -\dfrac{8}{9}$

6. $\dfrac{5}{2} \cdot \dfrac{4}{15} = \dfrac{5 \cdot 4}{2 \cdot 15} = \dfrac{\overset{1}{\cancel{5}} \cdot \overset{2}{\cancel{4}}}{\underset{1}{\cancel{2}} \cdot \underset{3}{\cancel{15}}} = \dfrac{2}{3}$

7. $3\dfrac{1}{2} \div 2 = \dfrac{7}{2} \div \dfrac{2}{1} = \dfrac{7}{2} \cdot \dfrac{1}{2} = \dfrac{7}{4} = 1\dfrac{3}{4}$

8. $7\dfrac{3}{4} \div 2\dfrac{7}{12} = \dfrac{31}{4} \div \dfrac{31}{12} = \dfrac{31}{4} \cdot \dfrac{12}{31} = \dfrac{\cancel{31} \cdot \overset{3}{\cancel{12}}}{\underset{1}{\cancel{4}} \cdot \cancel{31}} = 3$

9.
```
   0.35
20)7.00
   6 0
   ───
   1 00
   1 00
   ────
      0
```

10.
```
   0.075
40)3.000
   2 80
   ───
    200
    200
    ───
      0
```

11. $0.0082 = \dfrac{82}{10{,}000} = \dfrac{41}{5000}$

12. Let $x = 0.4$.

$10x = 4.44\ldots$

$-\ \ x = 0.44\ldots$

$\overline{\ \ 9x = 4\qquad}$

$x = \dfrac{4}{9}$

13.
```
  6.200
− 5.984
──────
  0.216
```

14.
```
   2.608
+ 12.930
───────
  15.538
```

15.
```
              2.4
0.333)0.7992  →  333)799.2
                   666
                   ───
                   133 2
                   133 2
                   ─────
                       0
```

16.
```
   −34.69
 ×   12.7
 ────────
   24 283
   69 38
  346 9
 ─────────
 −440.563
```

17.
```
   3.64
 + 14.2
 ──────
  17.84
```

18.
```
    0.123
 ×   4.53
 ────────
      369
      615
      492
 ────────
  0.55719
```

19.
```
  15.68
−  4.94
──────
  10.74
```

20.
```
                    6.3
3.7611 ÷ 0.597  →  597)3761.1
                      3582
                      ────
                      179 1
                      179 1
                      ─────
                          0
```

21. When $x = -4.1$:

$0.2x = 0.2(-4.1) = -0.82$

$\dfrac{x}{0.2} = \dfrac{-4.1}{0.2} = -20.5$

When $x = 0.06$:

$0.2x = 0.2(0.06) = 0.012$

$\dfrac{x}{0.2} = \dfrac{0.06}{0.2} = 0.3$

When $x = 1.8$:

$0.2x = 0.2(1.8) = 0.36$

$\dfrac{x}{0.2} = \dfrac{1.8}{0.2} = 9$

22. $3\frac{1}{4} - 1\frac{4}{5} = 3\frac{5}{20} - 1\frac{16}{20}$

$$= 2\frac{25}{20} - 1\frac{16}{20}$$

$$= (2 - 1) + \left(\frac{25}{20} - \frac{16}{20}\right)$$

$$= 1 + \frac{9}{20}$$

$$= 1\frac{9}{20}$$

You spent $1\frac{9}{20}$ hours doing homework yesterday.

$1\frac{9}{20} \cdot 60 = \frac{29}{20} \cdot \frac{60}{1} = \frac{29 \cdot 60}{20 \cdot 1} = \frac{29 \cdot \overset{3}{\cancel{60}}}{\underset{1}{\cancel{20}} \cdot 1} = 87$

$1\frac{9}{20}$ hours is equal to 87 minutes.

23. $3\frac{3}{4} \div \frac{5}{12} = \frac{15}{4} \div \frac{5}{12} = \frac{15}{4} \cdot \frac{12}{5} = \frac{\overset{3}{\cancel{15}} \cdot \overset{3}{\cancel{12}}}{\underset{1}{\cancel{4}} \cdot \underset{1}{\cancel{5}}} = 9$

You can read 9 chapters.

24. $0.086 \cdot 1{,}000{,}000{,}000 = 86{,}000{,}000$

$0.077 \cdot 1{,}000{,}000{,}000 = 77{,}000{,}000$

$86{,}000{,}000 - 77{,}000{,}000 = 9{,}000{,}000$

The sale is $9,000,000 greater for frozen bagels.

25. $0.43 \cdot 1{,}000{,}000{,}000 = 430{,}000{,}000$

$86{,}000{,}000 + 77{,}000{,}000 + 430{,}000{,}000 = 593{,}000{,}000$

The total sales of bagels is $593,000,000.

26.
```
      116
  ×  0.645
      580
     4 64
    69 6
   74.820
```

It costs $74.82 for 116 therms of gas.

27. Mean $= \dfrac{2 + 5 + 3 + 7 + 10 + 9 + 8 + 7 + 6 + 7 + 6 + 2}{12}$

$$= \frac{72}{12}$$

$$= 6 \text{ h}$$

2, 2, 3, 5, 6, 6, 7, 7, 7, 8, 9, 10

Median $= \dfrac{6 + 7}{2} = \dfrac{13}{2} = 6.5 \text{ h}$

Mode = 7 h

Range: $10 - 2 = 8$ h

28. $\dfrac{15{,}514 + 17{,}328 + 13{,}697 + x}{4} = 15{,}271$

$15{,}514 + 17{,}328 + 13{,}697 + x = 61{,}084$

$46{,}539 + x = 61{,}084$

$x = 14{,}545$

14,545 people visited the park the fourth week.

Standardized Test Preparation (pp. 286–287)

1. This student should receive full credit because an appropriate equation is written, work is shown accurately and correctly, and the answer is correct.

2. This student should receive partial credit because all the work is done correct, but the wrong beginning equation is used.

Standardized Test Practice (pp. 288–289)

1. To find out how much change Kwame would receive without the discounts, multiply each individual discount and add the amount together. Subtract this total from the original amount of change.

$46.30 - (4 \cdot 0.90 + 8 \cdot 0.45 + 5 \cdot 1.35 + 2 \cdot 2.40)$

$46.30 - (3.60 + 3.60 + 6.75 + 4.80)$

$46.30 - 18.75$

27.55

Kwame would receive $27.55 change without the discount.

2. No, the committee's idea will not work because 18 snowflakes will only cover a square 3 feet by 3 feet, which is 9 square feet. Two snowflakes cover each square foot. The total ceiling area is 75 feet times 75 feet, or 5625 square feet. The commitee will need $5625 \div 9 \cdot 18$, or 11,250 snowflakes. At 50 per bag, they will need $11{,}250 \div 50$, or 225 bags. Each bag costs $1.89 each, for a total of $225 \cdot 1.89$, or $425.25. The commitee's budget is only $250.

3. Multiply $1\frac{3}{4}$ cups times 8 batches to see how much total flour you need.

$1\frac{3}{4} \cdot 8 = \frac{7}{4} \cdot \frac{8}{1} = \frac{7 \cdot 8}{4 \cdot 1} = \frac{7 \cdot \overset{2}{\cancel{8}}}{\underset{1}{\cancel{4}} \cdot 1} = 14$

Yes you will have enough flour to make 8 batches.

4. Your patio: $= A = \ell w$

$$A = 6.4 \cdot 5.2$$

$$A = 33.28 \text{ ft}^2$$

Your friend's patio: $A = \ell w$

$$A = 5.8 \cdot 5.8$$

$$A = 33.64 \text{ ft}^2$$

Since $33.28 < 33.64$, your friend's patio has a greater area than your patio.

5. $\dfrac{4}{5} \cdot \dfrac{3}{4} + \dfrac{1}{4} \cdot \dfrac{1}{2} = \dfrac{4 \cdot 3}{5 \cdot 4} + \dfrac{1 \cdot 1}{4 \cdot 2}$

$$= \frac{\overset{1}{\cancel{4}} \cdot 3}{5 \cdot \underset{1}{\cancel{4}}} + \frac{1 \cdot 1}{4 \cdot 2}$$

$$= \frac{3}{5} + \frac{1}{8}$$

$$= \frac{24}{40} + \frac{5}{40}$$

$$= \frac{29}{40}$$

The team won $\frac{29}{40}$ of the season.

Chapter 5, *continued*

6. $\dfrac{5+1+4+2+0+5+4+4+x}{9} = 3$

$5 + 1 + 4 + 2 + 0 + 5 + 4 + 4 + x = 27$

$25 + x = 27$

$x = 2$

Farah hit 2 home runs to make the mean 3.

0, 1, 2, 2, 4, 4, 4, 5, 5

Median $= 4$

Two players hit more home runs than the median.

7. $\sqrt{324} = 18$

The garden will have dimensions of 18 yards or 54 feet. Since each side of the garden (54 feet) is greater than one side of the city park, (50.25 feet), this is not possible.

8. All numbers except 1 and 15 will divide and cancel each other out, so the answer is $\dfrac{1}{15}$.

9. $3\dfrac{3}{5} \div 20 = \dfrac{18}{5} \div 20 = \dfrac{18}{5} \cdot \dfrac{1}{20} = \dfrac{18 \cdot 1}{5 \cdot 20} = \dfrac{\overset{9}{\cancel{18}} \cdot 1}{5 \cdot \underset{10}{\cancel{20}}} = \dfrac{9}{50}$

No, there is not enough to give each student $\dfrac{1}{5}$ of the bag. You can give each student $\dfrac{9}{50}$ of a bag.

10. Mean $= \dfrac{90 + 91 + 83 + 90 + 80 + 97 + 90 + 100}{8}$

$= \dfrac{721}{8}$

$= 90.125$

80, 83, 90, 90, 90, 91, 97, 100

Median $= \dfrac{90 + 90}{2} = 90$

Mode $= 90$

All 3 averages represent the scores the best because they are all approximately 90, and most of the test scores are close to 90.

11. C; $-1\dfrac{1}{2} \cdot \dfrac{9}{20} = -\dfrac{3}{2} \cdot \dfrac{9}{20} = \dfrac{-3 \cdot 9}{2 \cdot 20} = \dfrac{-27}{40}$

12. B; $16 \div 1.8$

$$
\begin{array}{r}
8.8 \\
1.8\overline{)160.0} \\
\underline{144} \\
160 \\
\underline{144} \\
16
\end{array}
$$

You can fill the pepper grinder 8 times.

13. D; $\dfrac{8}{23} \approx 0.35$

14. $60 \div 3\dfrac{1}{3} = 60 \div \dfrac{10}{3} = 60 \cdot \dfrac{3}{10} = \dfrac{60 \cdot 3}{1 \cdot 10} = \dfrac{\overset{6}{\cancel{60}} \cdot 3}{1 \cdot \underset{1}{\cancel{10}}} = 18$

You can bike 18 miles in one hour.

15.

$$
0.75\overline{)15} \quad \longrightarrow \quad
\begin{array}{r}
20 \\
75\overline{)1500} \\
\underline{150} \\
00 \\
\underline{0} \\
0
\end{array}
$$

16. 2, 4, 4, 5, 7, 8, 10, 12

Median $= \dfrac{5+7}{2} = \dfrac{12}{2} = 6$

The median is 6.

17. $3\dfrac{1}{2} \div \dfrac{1}{4} = \dfrac{7}{2} \div \dfrac{1}{4} = \dfrac{7}{2} \cdot \dfrac{4}{1} = \dfrac{7 \cdot 4}{2 \cdot 1} = \dfrac{7 \cdot \overset{2}{\cancel{4}}}{\underset{1}{\cancel{2}} \cdot 1} = 14$

You must run 14 times around the track.

18. $940 \cdot \dfrac{3}{10} = 282$

$940 \cdot \dfrac{7}{20} = 329$

$940 - 282 - 329 = 329$

There are 329 students in the 8th grade.

19. a. Sugar: $\dfrac{12 \text{ g}}{\text{serving}} > \dfrac{5 \text{ g}}{\text{serving}}$

Fiber: $\dfrac{6 \text{ g}}{\text{serving}} > \dfrac{4 \text{ g}}{\text{serving}}$

Sugar: $\dfrac{12 \text{ g}}{54 \text{ g}} = \dfrac{2}{9} > \dfrac{5 \text{ g}}{30 \text{ g}} = \dfrac{1}{6}$

Fiber: $\dfrac{6 \text{ g}}{54 \text{ g}} = \dfrac{1}{9} < \dfrac{4 \text{ g}}{30 \text{ g}} = \dfrac{2}{15}$

b. Comparing per gram makes more sense nutritionally. Because the units are the same, this comparison is more accurate.

20. Mean

$= \dfrac{17 + 16 + 19 + 20 + 17 + 18 + 17 + 15 + 16 + 19 + 20}{11}$

$= \dfrac{194}{11}$

$= 17.\overline{63}$

15, 16, 16, 17, 17, 17, 18, 19, 19, 20, 20

Median $= 17$

To make the median 17.5, Tonya must complete at least 18 assignments, because the media would be $\dfrac{17+18}{2}$.

$17.5 = (17 + 16 + 19 + 20 + 17 + 18 + 17 + 15 + 16 + 19 + 20 + x) \div 12$

$210 = 17 + 16 + 19 + 20 + 17 + 18 + 17 + 15 + 16 + 19 + 20 + x$

$210 = 194 + x$

$16 = x$

To make the mean 17.5, Tonya must complete 16 assignments.

Chapter 6

Chapter Get-Ready Games (pp. 290–291)

Check students' work.

Stop and Think (p. 291)

1. The best number to roll is 4 because 4 is the solution of the two equations $5x + 1 = 21$ and $11 - 2x = 3$. The second best number to roll is 2 because 2 is the solution of $-7 - x = -9$.

2. 4; Solve each equation and count the number of spaces on the board that have 5 as a solution.

Review Prerequisite Skills (p. 292)

1. The *perimeter* of a figure is the sum of its side lengths.

2. The four *inequality* symbols are $<$, $>$, $\leq$, and $\geq$.

3. To divide by a fraction, you multiply by its *reciprocal*.

4. Terms that have identical variable parts raised to the same power are *like terms*.

5. $3 - 2x + 4 = -2x + 7$

6. $4x + 5 + x - 1 = 5x + 4$

7. $-2(3x + 1) - 2 = -6x - 2 - 2 = -6x - 4$

8. $5(x - 4) - x = 5x - 20 - x = 4x - 20$

9.
$$2x - 1 = 3$$
$$2x - 1 + 1 = 3 + 1$$
$$2x = 4$$
$$\frac{2x}{2} = \frac{4}{2}$$
$$x = 2$$
Check: $2(2) - 1 \stackrel{?}{=} 3$
$$4 - 1 \stackrel{?}{=} 3$$
$$3 = 3 \checkmark$$

10.
$$-3x - 2 = 7$$
$$-3x - 2 + 2 = 7 + 2$$
$$-3x = 9$$
$$\frac{-3x}{-3} = \frac{9}{-3}$$
$$x = -3$$
Check: $-3(-3) - 2 \stackrel{?}{=} 7$
$$9 - 2 \stackrel{?}{=} 7$$
$$7 = 7 \checkmark$$

11.
$$4 - x = 12$$
$$4 - x - 4 = 12 - 4$$
$$-x = 8$$
$$\frac{-x}{-1} = \frac{8}{-1}$$
$$x = -8$$
Check: $4 - (-8) \stackrel{?}{=} 12$
$$4 + 8 \stackrel{?}{=} 12$$
$$12 = 12 \checkmark$$

12.
$$13 = 2x + 3$$
$$13 - 3 = 2x + 3 - 3$$
$$10 = 2x$$
$$\frac{10}{2} = \frac{2x}{2}$$
$$5 = x$$
Check: $13 \stackrel{?}{=} 2(5) + 3$
$$13 \stackrel{?}{=} 10 + 3$$
$$13 = 13 \checkmark$$

13.
$$-5x + 6 = -9$$
$$-5x + 6 - 6 = -9 - 6$$
$$-5x = -15$$
$$\frac{-5x}{-5} = \frac{-15}{-5}$$
$$x = 3$$
Check: $-5(3) + 6 \stackrel{?}{=} -9$
$$-15 + 6 \stackrel{?}{=} -9$$
$$-9 = -9 \checkmark$$

14.
$$8 - x = -3$$
$$8 - x - 8 = -3 - 8$$
$$-x = -11$$
$$\frac{-x}{-1} = \frac{-11}{-1}$$
$$x = 11$$
Check: $8 - 11 \stackrel{?}{=} -3$
$$-3 = -3 \checkmark$$

15.
$$17 = 4x + 1$$
$$17 - 1 = 4x + 1 - 1$$
$$16 = 4x$$
$$\frac{16}{4} = \frac{4x}{4}$$
$$4 = x$$
Check: $17 \stackrel{?}{=} 4(4) + 1$
$$17 \stackrel{?}{=} 16 + 1$$
$$17 = 17 \checkmark$$

16.
$$3x - 5 = 10$$
$$3x - 5 + 5 = 10 + 5$$
$$3x = 15$$
$$\frac{3x}{3} = \frac{15}{3}$$
$$x = 5$$
Check: $3(5) - 5 \stackrel{?}{=} 10$
$$15 - 5 \stackrel{?}{=} 10$$
$$10 = 10 \checkmark$$

17.
$$x + 5 < 18$$
$$x + 5 - 5 < 18 - 5$$
$$x < 13$$

18.
$$x - 4 \geq -6$$
$$x - 4 + 4 \geq -6 + 4$$
$$x \geq -2$$

19.
$$17 + x > 19$$
$$17 + x - 17 > 19 - 17$$
$$x > 2$$

20.
$$-4 + x \leq -9$$
$$-4 + x + 4 \leq -9 + 4$$
$$x \leq -5$$

21. $5x \geq 30$
$$\frac{5x}{5} \geq \frac{30}{5}$$
$$x \geq 6$$

22. $-6x \leq 54$
$$\frac{-6x}{-6} \geq \frac{54}{-6}$$
$$x \geq -9$$

23. $\frac{4}{5}x > 20$
$$\frac{4}{5}x \cdot \frac{5}{4} > 20 \cdot \frac{5}{4}$$
$$x > \frac{20}{1} \cdot \frac{5}{4}$$
$$x > 25$$

Chapter 6, *continued*

24. $\frac{2}{3}x \le 12$

$$\frac{2}{3}x \cdot \frac{3}{2} \le 12 \cdot \frac{3}{2}$$

$$x \le \frac{12}{1} \cdot \frac{3}{2}$$

$$x \le 18$$

Lesson 6.1

6.1 Guided Practice (pp. 293–295)

1. Let x represent the number of packs of each type of flower.

$3 petunia seeds		$4 balloon flower seeds		
Cost per pack $\cdot$	Number of packs $+$	Cost per pack $\cdot$	Number of packs $=$	Total cost

$$3x + 4x = 42$$
$$7x = 42$$
$$\frac{7x}{7} = \frac{42}{7}$$
$$x = 6$$

You buy 6 packs of petunia seeds and 6 packs of balloon flower seeds.

2. $-6 = 11w - 5w$

$$-6 = 6w$$
$$\frac{-6}{6} = \frac{6w}{6}$$
$$-1 = w$$

Check: $-6 \stackrel{2}{=} 11(-1) - 5(-1)$

$$-6 \stackrel{2}{=} -11 + 5$$
$$-6 = -6 \checkmark$$

3. $4p + 10 + p = 25$

$$5p + 10 = 25$$
$$5p + 10 - 10 = 25 - 10$$
$$5p = 15$$
$$\frac{5p}{5} = \frac{15}{5}$$
$$p = 3$$

Check: $4(3) + 10 + 3 \stackrel{2}{=} 25$

$$12 + 10 + 3 \stackrel{2}{=} 25$$
$$25 = 25 \checkmark$$

4. $-8r - 2 + 7r = -9$

$$-r - 2 = -9$$
$$-r - 2 + 2 = -9 + 2$$
$$-r = -7$$
$$\frac{-r}{-1} = \frac{-7}{-1}$$
$$r = 7$$

Check: $-8(7) - 2 + 7(7) \stackrel{2}{=} -9$

$$-56 - 2 + 49 \stackrel{2}{=} -9$$
$$-9 = -9 \checkmark$$

5. $3(x - 9) = -39$

$$3x - 27 = -39$$
$$3x - 27 + 27 = -39 + 27$$
$$3x = -12$$
$$\frac{3x}{3} = \frac{-12}{3}$$
$$x = -4$$

Check: $3(-4 - 9) \stackrel{2}{=} -39$

$$3(-13) \stackrel{2}{=} -39$$
$$-39 = -39 \checkmark$$

6. $z + 4(6 - z) = 21$

$$z + 24 - 4z = 21$$
$$-3z + 24 = 21$$
$$-3z + 24 - 24 = 21 - 24$$
$$-3z = -3$$
$$\frac{-3z}{-3} = \frac{-3}{-3}$$
$$z = 1$$

Check: $1 + 4(6 - 1) \stackrel{2}{=} 21$

$$1 + 4(5) \stackrel{2}{=} 21$$
$$21 = 21 \checkmark$$

7. $8 = -7(y + 1) + 2y$

$$8 = -7y - 7 + 2y$$
$$8 = -5y - 7$$
$$8 + 7 = -5y - 7 + 7$$
$$15 = -5y$$
$$\frac{15}{-5} = \frac{-5y}{-5}$$
$$-3 = y$$

Check: $8 \stackrel{2}{=} -7(-3 + 1) + 2(-3)$

$$8 \stackrel{2}{=} -7(-2) + (-6)$$
$$8 \stackrel{2}{=} 14 + (-6)$$
$$8 = 8 \checkmark$$

8. $\frac{2y + 4}{5} = 6$

$$\frac{2y + 4}{5} \cdot 5 = 6 \cdot 5$$
$$2y + 4 = 30$$
$$2y + 4 - 4 = 30 - 4$$
$$2y = 26$$
$$\frac{2y}{2} = \frac{26}{2}$$
$$y = 13$$

9. $\frac{3x - 1}{8} = 4$

$$\frac{3x - 1}{8} \cdot 8 = 4 \cdot 8$$
$$3x - 1 = 32$$
$$3x - 1 + 1 = 32 + 1$$
$$3x = 33$$
$$\frac{3x}{3} = \frac{33}{3}$$
$$x = 11$$

Check: $\frac{2(13) + 4}{5} \overset{?}{=} 6$

$\frac{26 + 4}{5} \overset{?}{=} 6$

$\frac{30}{5} \overset{?}{=} 6$

$6 = 6$ ✓

Check: $\frac{3(11) - 1}{8} \overset{?}{=} 4$

$\frac{33 - 1}{8} \overset{?}{=} 4$

$\frac{32}{8} \overset{?}{=} 4$

$4 = 4$ ✓

10. $\frac{9 - z}{8} = 3$

$\frac{9 - z}{8} \cdot 8 = 3 \cdot 8$

$9 - z = 24$

$9 - z - 9 = 24 - 9$

$-z = 15$

$\frac{-z}{-1} = \frac{15}{-1}$

$z = -15$

Check: $\frac{9 - (-15)}{8} \overset{?}{=} 3$

$\frac{24}{8} \overset{?}{=} 3$

$3 = 3$ ✓

6.1 Exercises (pp. 295–297)

Skill Practice

1. The like terms in the expression $5x + 6 - 2 - 9x$ are $5x$ and $-9x$, and 6 and -2.

2. $3(x + 4) = 3x + 12$

3. $8b + 2b = 10$

$10b = 10$

$\frac{10b}{10} = \frac{10}{10}$

$b = 1$

Check: $8(1) + 2(1) \overset{?}{=} 10$

$8 + 2 \overset{?}{=} 10$

$10 = 10$ ✓

4. $-n + 8n = 35$

$7n = 35$

$\frac{7n}{7} = \frac{35}{7}$

$n = 5$

Check: $-5 + 8(5) \overset{?}{=} 35$

$-5 + 40 \overset{?}{=} 35$

$35 = 35$ ✓

5. $7y - 3y - 8 = -32$

$4y - 8 = -32$

$4y - 8 + 8 = -32 + 8$

$4y = -24$

$\frac{4y}{4} = \frac{-24}{4}$

$y = -6$

Check $7(-6) - 3(-6) - 8 \overset{?}{=} -32$

$-42 + 18 - 8 \overset{?}{=} -32$

$-32 = -32$ ✓

6. $4x - 7 - 7x = -1$

$-3x - 7 = -1$

$-3x - 7 + 7 = -1 + 7$

$-3x = 6$

$\frac{-3x}{-3} = \frac{6}{-3}$

$x = -2$

Check: $4(-2) - 7 - 7(-2) \overset{?}{=} -1$

$-8 - 7 + 14 \overset{?}{=} -1$

$-1 = -1$ ✓

7. $-2z + 6z - 9 = 15$

$4z - 9 = 15$

$4z - 9 + 9 = 15 + 9$

$4z = 24$

$\frac{4z}{4} = \frac{24}{4}$

$z = 6$

Check: $-2(6) + 6(6) - 9 \overset{?}{=} 15$

$-12 + 36 - 9 \overset{?}{=} 15$

$15 = 15$ ✓

8. $-22 + 3k + 6 = -28$

$3k - 16 = -28$

$3k - 16 + 16 = -28 + 16$

$3k = -12$

$\frac{3k}{3} = \frac{-12}{3}$

$k = -4$

Check: $-22 + 3(-4) + 6 \overset{?}{=} -28$

$-22 - 12 + 6 \overset{?}{=} -28$

$-28 = -28$ ✓

9. $5(w - 7) = -15$

$5w - 35 = -15$

$5w - 35 + 35 = -15 + 35$

$5w = 20$

$\frac{5w}{5} = \frac{20}{5}$

$w = 4$

Check: $5(4 - 7) \overset{?}{=} -15$

$5(-3) \overset{?}{=} -15$

$-15 = -15$ ✓

10. $-2(m + 7) = -22$

$-2m - 14 = -22$

$-2m - 14 + 14 = -22 + 14$

$-2m = -8$

$\frac{-2m}{-2} = \frac{-8}{-2}$

$m = 4$

Chapter 6, continued

Check: $-2(4 + 7) \stackrel{?}{=} -22$

$$-2(11) \stackrel{?}{=} -22$$

$$-22 = -22 \checkmark$$

11. $5(3 - 2n) + 5n = 65$

$$15 - 10n + 5n = 65$$

$$15 - 5n = 65$$

$$15 - 5n - 15 = 65 - 15$$

$$-5n = 50$$

$$\frac{-5n}{-5} = \frac{50}{-5}$$

$$n = -10$$

Check: $5[3 - 2(-10)] + 5(-10) \stackrel{?}{=} 65$

$$5(23) - 50 \stackrel{?}{=} 65$$

$$115 - 50 \stackrel{?}{=} 65$$

$$65 = 65 \checkmark$$

12. $m + 3(m - 4) = 16$

$$m + 3m - 12 = 16$$

$$4m - 12 = 16$$

$$4m - 12 + 12 = 16 + 12$$

$$4m = 28$$

$$\frac{4m}{4} = \frac{28}{4}$$

$$m = 7$$

Check: $7 + 3(7 - 4) \stackrel{?}{=} 16$

$$7 + 3(3) \stackrel{?}{=} 16$$

$$7 + 9 \stackrel{?}{=} 16$$

$$16 = 16 \checkmark$$

13. $-4 = -1 - 3(2p + 3)$

$$-4 = -1 - 6p - 9$$

$$-4 = -10 - 6p$$

$$-4 + 10 = -10 - 6p + 10$$

$$6 = -6p$$

$$\frac{6}{-6} = \frac{-6p}{-6}$$

$$-1 = p$$

Check: $-4 \stackrel{?}{=} -1 - 3[2(-1) + 3]$

$$-4 \stackrel{?}{=} -1 - 3(1)$$

$$-4 = -4 \checkmark$$

14. $2z - 4(9 - 3z) = 62$

$$2z - 36 + 12z = 62$$

$$14z - 36 = 62$$

$$14z - 36 + 36 = 62 + 36$$

$$14z = 98$$

$$\frac{14z}{14} = \frac{98}{14}$$

$$z = 7$$

Check: $2(7) - 4[9 - 3(7)] \stackrel{?}{=} 62$

$$14 - 4(-12) \stackrel{?}{=} 62$$

$$14 + 48 \stackrel{?}{=} 62$$

$$62 = 62 \checkmark$$

15. The negative sign of -2 was not distributed to the term -4.

$$3x - 2(x - 4) = 5$$

$$3x - 2x + 8 = 5$$

$$x + 8 = 5$$

$$x + 8 - 8 = 5 - 8$$

$$x = -3$$

16. B; $3 + 8v - 9v = 21$

$$3 - v = 21$$

$$3 - v - 3 = 21 - 3$$

$$-v = 18$$

$$\frac{-v}{-1} = \frac{18}{-1}$$

$$v = -18$$

17. $\dfrac{6k + 2}{4} = 2$

$$\frac{6k + 2}{4} \cdot 4 = 2 \cdot 4$$

$$6k + 2 = 8$$

$$6k + 2 - 2 = 8 - 2$$

$$6k = 6$$

$$\frac{6k}{6} = \frac{6}{6}$$

$$k = 1$$

18. $\dfrac{2b + 8}{5} = -12$

$$\frac{2b + 8}{5} \cdot 5 = -12 \cdot 5$$

$$2b + 8 = -60$$

$$2b + 8 - 8 = -60 - 8$$

$$2b = -68$$

$$\frac{2b}{2} = \frac{-68}{2}$$

$$b = -34$$

19. $\dfrac{-c - 5}{8} = 4$

$$\frac{-c - 5}{8} \cdot 8 = 4 \cdot 8$$

$$-c - 5 = 32$$

$$-c - 5 + 5 = 32 + 5$$

$$-c = 37$$

$$\frac{-c}{-1} = \frac{37}{-1}$$

$$c = -37$$

20. $\dfrac{-g + 4}{7} = 6$

$$\frac{-g + 4}{7} \cdot 7 = 6 \cdot 7$$

$$-g + 4 = 42$$

$$-g + 4 - 4 = 42 - 4$$

$$-g = 38$$

$$\frac{-g}{-1} = \frac{38}{-1}$$

$$g = -38$$

21. $\dfrac{5 - 2d}{7} = 7$

$$\frac{5 - 2d}{7} \cdot 7 = 7 \cdot 7$$

$$5 - 2d = 49$$

$$5 - 2d - 5 = 49 - 5$$

$$-2d = 44$$

$$\frac{-2d}{-2} = \frac{44}{-2}$$

$$d = -22$$

22. $\dfrac{9 - 3h}{5} = -6$

$$\frac{9 - 3h}{5} \cdot 5 = -6 \cdot 5$$

$$9 - 3h = -30$$

$$9 - 3h - 9 = -30 - 9$$

$$-3h = -39$$

$$\frac{-3h}{-3} = \frac{-39}{-3}$$

$$h = 13$$

Chapter 6, *continued*

23.
$$\frac{5a-2}{3} = -9$$
$$\frac{5a-2}{3} \cdot 3 = -9 \cdot 3$$
$$5a - 2 = -27$$
$$5a - 2 + 2 = -27 + 2$$
$$5a = -25$$
$$\frac{5a}{5} = \frac{-25}{5}$$
$$a = -5$$

24.
$$\frac{4m-16}{12} = -3$$
$$\frac{4m-16}{12} \cdot 12 = -3 \cdot 12$$
$$4m - 16 = -36$$
$$4m - 16 + 16 = -36 + 16$$
$$4m = -20$$
$$\frac{4m}{4} = \frac{-20}{4}$$
$$m = -5$$

25.
$$5y + 8 - 2y + 9y = -16$$
$$12y + 8 = -16$$
$$12y + 8 - 8 = -16 - 8$$
$$12y = -24$$
$$\frac{12y}{12} = \frac{-24}{12}$$
$$y = -2$$
Check: $5(-2) + 8 - 2(-2) + 9(-2) \stackrel{?}{=} -16$
$$-10 + 8 + 4 - 18 \stackrel{?}{=} -16$$
$$-16 = -16 ✓$$

26.
$$8k - 7k - 16 - 3k = -21$$
$$-2k - 16 = -21$$
$$-2k - 16 + 16 = -21 + 16$$
$$-2k = -5$$
$$\frac{-2k}{-2} = \frac{-5}{-2}$$
$$k = \frac{5}{2}$$
Check: $8\left(\frac{5}{2}\right) - 7\left(\frac{5}{2}\right) - 16 - 3\left(\frac{5}{2}\right) \stackrel{?}{=} -21$
$$20 - 17\frac{1}{2} - 16 - 7\frac{1}{2} \stackrel{?}{=} -21$$
$$-21 = -21 ✓$$

27.
$$7(t + 4) - 3(1 + t) = -19$$
$$7t + 28 - 3 - 3t = -19$$
$$4t + 25 = -19$$
$$4t + 25 - 25 = -19 - 25$$
$$4t = -44$$
$$\frac{4t}{4} = \frac{-44}{4}$$
$$t = -11$$

Check: $7(-11 + 4) - 3[1 + (-11)] \stackrel{?}{=} -19$
$$7(-7) - 3(-10) \stackrel{?}{=} -19$$
$$-49 + 30 \stackrel{?}{=} -19$$
$$-19 = -19 ✓$$

28.
$$-(6 - c) + 3(2c - 7) = 1$$
$$-6 + c + 6c - 21 = 1$$
$$7c - 27 = 1$$
$$7c - 27 + 27 = 1 + 27$$
$$7c = 28$$
$$\frac{7c}{7} = \frac{28}{7}$$
$$c = 4$$
Check: $-(6 - 4) + 3[2(4) - 7] \stackrel{?}{=} 1$
$$-2 + 3(1) \stackrel{?}{=} 1$$
$$1 = 1 ✓$$

29.
$$9z + 5(8 + z) - 6(2z - 7) = 40$$
$$9z + 40 + 5z - 12z + 42 = 40$$
$$2z + 82 = 40$$
$$2z + 82 - 82 = 40 - 82$$
$$2z = -42$$
$$\frac{2z}{2} = \frac{-42}{2}$$
$$z = -21$$
Check: $9(-21) + 5[8 + (-21)] - 6[2(-21) - 7] \stackrel{?}{=} 40$
$$-189 + 5(-13) - 6(-49) \stackrel{?}{=} 40$$
$$-189 - 65 + 294 \stackrel{?}{=} 40$$
$$40 = 40 ✓$$

30.
$$4a + 7(2a - 5) - 5(3a + 1) = 50$$
$$4a + 14a - 35 - 15a - 5 = 50$$
$$3a - 40 = 50$$
$$3a - 40 + 40 = 50 + 40$$
$$3a = 90$$
$$\frac{3a}{3} = \frac{90}{3}$$
$$a = 30$$
Check: $4(30) + 7[2(30) - 5] - 5[3(30) + 1] \stackrel{?}{=} 50$
$$120 + 7(55) - 5(91) \stackrel{?}{=} 50$$
$$120 + 385 - 455 \stackrel{?}{=} 50$$
$$50 = 50 ✓$$

Chapter 6, *continued*

31.
$$A = \tfrac{1}{2}bh$$
$$228 = \tfrac{1}{2}(x + 11)(19)$$
$$228 = \tfrac{1}{2}(19x + 209)$$
$$2 \cdot 228 = 2 \cdot \tfrac{1}{2}(19x + 209)$$
$$456 = 19x + 209$$
$$456 - 209 = 19x + 209 - 209$$
$$247 = 19x$$
$$\frac{247}{19} = \frac{19x}{19}$$
$$13 = x$$

32.
$$A = \tfrac{1}{2}bh$$
$$918 = \tfrac{1}{2} \cdot 51(x - 9)$$
$$918 = \tfrac{1}{2}(51x - 459)$$
$$2 \cdot 918 = 2 \cdot \tfrac{1}{2}(51x - 459)$$
$$1836 = 51x - 459$$
$$1836 + 459 = 51x - 459 + 459$$
$$2295 = 51x$$
$$\frac{2295}{51} = \frac{51x}{51}$$
$$45 = x$$

33. In the rectangle, the length is $x + 8$, or 13.
$$x + 8 = 13$$
$$x + 8 - 8 = 13 - 8$$
$$x = 5$$
So, the width when $x = 5$ is $x - 1 = 5 - 1$, or 4.
$$P = 2\ell + 2w = 2(13) + 2(4)$$
$$= 26 + 8 = 34 \text{ units}$$
For the triangle to have the same perimeter, you can write an equation.
$$P = a + b + c$$
$$34 = y - 1 + y + 6 + y + 5$$
$$34 = 3y + 10$$
$$34 - 10 = 3y + 10 - 10$$
$$24 = 3y$$
$$\frac{24}{3} = \frac{3y}{3}$$
$$8 = y$$
For the rectangle and the triangle to have the same perimeter, which is 34 units, $x = 5$ and $y = 8$.

34. If x is the first integer, the next four consecutive integers would be $x + 1, x + 2, x + 3,$ and $x + 4$.
$$\frac{x + (x + 1) + (x + 2) + (x + 3) + (x + 4)}{4} = 60$$
$$\frac{5x + 10}{4} = 60$$
$$\frac{5x + 10}{4} \cdot 4 = 60 \cdot 4$$
$$5x + 10 = 240$$
$$5x + 10 - 10 = 240 - 10$$
$$5x = 230$$
$$\frac{5x}{5} = \frac{230}{5}$$
$$x = 46$$
The 5 consecutive integers are 46, 47, 48, 49, and 50.

Problem Solving

35. a. $8(70 + x) = 2560$

b.
$$8(70 + x) = 2560$$
$$560 + 8x = 2560$$
$$560 + 8x - 560 = 2560 - 560$$
$$8x = 2000$$
$$\frac{8x}{8} = \frac{2000}{8}$$
$$x = 250$$
Check: $8(70 + 250) \stackrel{?}{=} 2560$
$$8(320) \stackrel{?}{=} 2560$$
$$2560 = 2560 \checkmark$$
250 people bought their tickets at the gate.

36.
$$13x + 9x + 10x = 352$$
$$32x = 352$$
$$\frac{32x}{32} = \frac{352}{32}$$
$$x = 11$$
Each T-shirt costs \$11.

37. Using a ruler, $\ell = 35$ mm and $w = 10$ mm.
$$P = 2\ell + 2w$$
$$= 2(35) + 2(10)$$
$$= 70 + 20$$
$$= 90 \text{ mm}$$
$$4(x - 8) = 90$$
$$4x - 32 = 90$$
$$4x - 32 + 32 = 90 + 32$$
$$4x = 122$$
$$\frac{4x}{4} = \frac{122}{4}$$
$$x = 30.5$$

38. A; Because x represents the dollars per hour you charge for painting and you paint for 12 hours, $12x$ represents the amount of money you earn painting. Because $x + 5$ represents the dollars per hour you charge for hanging wallpaper and you hang wallpaper for 15 hours, $15(x + 5)$ represents the amount of money you earn hanging wallpaper.

$$12x + 15(x + 5) = 1020$$

39. Let x represent the number of hours you volunteer next month. For the mean, you add the number of hours you volunteered each month and then divide by 3, the number of months you volunteered. The equation $\frac{9 + 14 + x}{3} = 10$ gives you the number of hours x you need to volunteer next month to have a monthly mean of 10 hours.

40. $26 - 5 - 2 = 19$

Sara has $19 after she buys the teapot and the spare teacup. She spends $3 for a pair. $6 \times 3 = 18$

Sara buys 6 pairs.

$19 - 18 = 1$

Sara has $1 left, so she can afford a $.50 teaspoon.

41.

$$\begin{pmatrix} \text{Money} \\ \text{already} \\ \text{saved} \end{pmatrix} + \begin{pmatrix} \text{Babysitting} \\ \text{money} \end{pmatrix} + \begin{pmatrix} \text{Cashier} \\ \text{money} \end{pmatrix} \begin{pmatrix} \text{Number} \\ \text{of weeks} \end{pmatrix} - \begin{pmatrix} \text{Money} \\ \text{spent} \\ \text{on} \\ \text{lunches} \end{pmatrix} \cdot \begin{pmatrix} \text{Number} \\ \text{of} \\ \text{weeks} \end{pmatrix} = \begin{pmatrix} \text{Price} \\ \text{of} \\ \text{bike} \end{pmatrix}$$

$$25 + (15 + 25)w - 10w = 235$$
$$25 + 40w - 10w = 235$$
$$25 + 30w = 235$$
$$25 + 30w - 25 = 235 - 25$$
$$30w = 210$$
$$\frac{30w}{30} = \frac{210}{30}$$
$$w = 7$$

In 7 weeks, you will have enough money saved.

42. $3(x + 2) - 3 = 9$
$$3x + 6 - 3 = 9$$
$$3x + 3 = 9$$
$$3x + 3 - 3 = 9 - 3$$
$$3x = 6$$
$$\frac{3x}{3} = \frac{6}{3}$$
$$x = 2$$

Yes, it is possible to solve the equation without using the distributive property.

Sample answer:
$$3(x + 2) - 3 = 9$$
$$3(x + 2) - 3 + 3 = 9 + 3$$
$$3(x + 2) = 12$$
$$\frac{3(x + 2)}{3} = \frac{12}{3}$$
$$x + 2 = 4$$
$$x + 2 - 2 = 4 - 2$$
$$x = 2$$

43. *Sample answer:*
$$-3(6x + 4) = 24$$
$$-18x - 12 = 24$$
$$-18x - 12 + 12 = 24 + 12$$
$$-18x = 36$$
$$\frac{-18x}{-18} = \frac{36}{-18}$$
$$x = -2$$

Mixed Review

44. $P = 2\ell + 2w = 2(15) + 2(7) = 30 + 14 = 44$

The perimeter of the rectangle is 44 centimeters.

45. $P = 2\ell + 2w = 2(14) + 2(21) = 28 + 42 = 70$

The perimeter of the rectangle is 70 feet.

46. Because -5 is greater than -6, $1.54 \times 10^{-5} > 1.54 \times 10^{-6}$.

47. Because $3.75 < 5.7$, $3.75 \times 10^4 < 5.7 \times 10^4$.

48. B; 100   101   101   105   105   112

$$\text{Median} = \frac{101 + 105}{2} = \frac{206}{2} = 103$$

Lesson 6.2

Activity (p. 298)

1. $2x + 7 = 3x + 2$

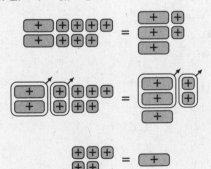

The solution is 5.

Chapter 6, continued

2. $4x - 1 = x - 7$

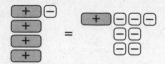

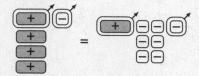

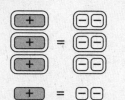

The solution is -2.

3. $5x - 2 = 3x + 6$

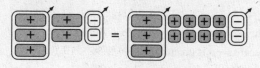

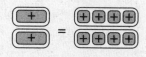

The solution is 4.

6.2 Guided Practice (pp. 299–300)

1.
$$55 + 3x = 8x$$
$$55 + 3x - 3x = 8x - 3x$$
$$55 = 5x$$
$$\frac{55}{5} = \frac{5x}{5}$$
$$11 = x$$

2.
$$9x = 12x - 9$$
$$9x - 12x = 12x - 9 - 12x$$
$$-3x = -9$$
$$\frac{-3x}{-3} = \frac{-9}{-3}$$
$$x = 3$$

3.
$$-15x + 120 = 15x$$
$$-15x + 120 + 15x = 15x + 15x$$
$$120 = 30x$$
$$\frac{120}{30} = \frac{30x}{30}$$
$$4 = x$$

4.
$$4a + 5 = a + 11$$
$$4a + 5 - a = a + 11 - a$$
$$3a + 5 = 11$$
$$3a + 5 - 5 = 11 - 5$$
$$3a = 6$$
$$\frac{3a}{3} = \frac{6}{3}$$
$$a = 2$$

5.
$$3n + 7 = 2n - 1$$
$$3n + 7 - 2n = 2n - 1 - 2n$$
$$n + 7 = -1$$
$$n + 7 - 7 = -1 - 7$$
$$n = -8$$

6.
$$-6c + 1 = -9c + 7$$
$$-6c + 1 + 9c = -9c + 7 + 9c$$
$$3c + 1 = 7$$
$$3c + 1 - 1 = 7 - 1$$
$$3c = 6$$
$$\frac{3c}{3} = \frac{6}{3}$$
$$c = 2$$

7.
$$28 - 3s = 5s - 12$$
$$28 - 3s - 5s = 5s - 12 - 5s$$
$$28 - 8s = -12$$
$$28 - 8s - 28 = -12 - 28$$
$$-8s = -40$$
$$\frac{-8s}{-8} = \frac{-40}{-8}$$
$$s = 5$$

8.
$$4(w - 9) = 7w + 18$$
$$4w - 36 = 7w + 18$$
$$4w - 36 - 7w = 7w + 18 - 7w$$
$$-3w - 36 = 18$$
$$-3w - 36 + 36 = 18 + 36$$
$$-3w = 54$$
$$\frac{-3w}{-3} = \frac{54}{-3}$$
$$w = -18$$

9.
$$2(y + 4) = -3y - 7$$
$$2y + 8 = -3y - 7$$
$$2y + 8 + 3y = -3y - 7 + 3y$$
$$5y + 8 = -7$$
$$5y + 8 - 8 = -7 - 8$$
$$5y = -15$$
$$\frac{5y}{5} = \frac{-15}{5}$$
$$y = -3$$

Chapter 6, _continued_

10. Let n represent the number of lessons you take.

$$12(n - 4) = 8n + 20$$
$$12n - 48 = 8n + 20$$
$$12n - 48 - 8n = 8n + 20 - 8n$$
$$4n - 48 = 20$$
$$4n - 48 + 48 = 20 + 48$$
$$4n = 68$$
$$\frac{4n}{4} = \frac{68}{4}$$
$$n = 17$$

Your friend takes $n - 4$, or $17 - 4 = 13$ lessons. Your friend pays the same total amount as you for 13 lessons.

6.2 Exercises (pp. 300–302)

Skill Practice

1. The perimeter of the figure is the distance all around the figure.

2.
$$7x = x + 18$$
$$7x - x = x + 18 - x$$
$$6x = 18$$
$$\frac{6x}{6} = \frac{18}{6}$$
$$x = 3$$

3.
$$7m = 4m + 21$$
$$7m - 4m = 4m + 21 - 4m$$
$$3m = 21$$
$$\frac{3m}{3} = \frac{21}{3}$$
$$m = 7$$

4.
$$30 - 2s = 4s$$
$$30 - 2s + 2s = 4s + 2s$$
$$30 = 6s$$
$$\frac{30}{6} = \frac{6s}{6}$$
$$5 = s$$

5.
$$81 + 2k = 5k$$
$$81 + 2k - 2k = 5k - 2k$$
$$81 = 3k$$
$$\frac{81}{3} = \frac{3k}{3}$$
$$27 = k$$

6.
$$13q - 48 = -3q$$
$$13q - 48 - 13q = -3q - 13q$$
$$-48 = -16q$$
$$\frac{-48}{-16} = \frac{-16q}{-16}$$
$$3 = q$$

7.
$$-11r = -4r + 56$$
$$-11r + 4r = -4r + 56 + 4r$$
$$-7r = 56$$
$$\frac{-7r}{-7} = \frac{56}{-7}$$
$$r = -8$$

8.
$$5z - 43 = 2z + 80$$
$$5z - 43 - 2z = 2z + 80 - 2z$$
$$3z - 43 = 80$$
$$3z - 43 + 43 = 80 + 43$$
$$3z = 123$$
$$\frac{3z}{3} = \frac{123}{3}$$
$$z = 41$$

9.
$$16y - 43 = 4y + 65$$
$$16y - 43 - 4y = 4y + 65 - 4y$$
$$12y - 43 = 65$$
$$12y - 43 + 43 = 65 + 43$$
$$12y = 108$$
$$\frac{12y}{12} = \frac{108}{12}$$
$$y = 9$$

10.
$$8f + 11 = -7f - 19$$
$$8f + 11 + 7f = -7f - 19 + 7f$$
$$15f + 11 = -19$$
$$15f + 11 - 11 = -19 - 11$$
$$15f = -30$$
$$\frac{15f}{15} = \frac{-30}{15}$$
$$f = -2$$

11.
$$-1 + 11a = 6 - 3a$$
$$-1 + 11a + 3a = 6 - 3a + 3a$$
$$-1 + 14a = 6$$
$$-1 + 14a + 1 = 6 + 1$$
$$14a = 7$$
$$\frac{14a}{14} = \frac{7}{14}$$
$$a = \frac{1}{2}$$

12.
$$9b - 10 = -b - 18$$
$$9b - 10 + b = -b - 18 + b$$
$$10b - 10 = -18$$
$$10b - 10 + 10 = -18 + 10$$
$$10b = -8$$
$$\frac{10b}{10} = \frac{-8}{10}$$
$$b = -\frac{4}{5}$$

13.
$$14s - 28 = 4s + 7$$
$$14s - 28 - 4s = 4s + 7 - 4s$$
$$10s - 28 = 7$$
$$10s - 28 + 28 = 7 + 28$$
$$10s = 35$$
$$\frac{10s}{10} = \frac{35}{10}$$
$$s = 3\frac{1}{2}$$

14. C; $5x + 14 = 3x - 12$
$$5x + 14 - 3x = 3x - 12 - 3x$$
$$2x + 14 = -12$$
$$2x + 14 - 14 = -12 - 14$$
$$2x = -26$$
$$\frac{2x}{2} = \frac{-26}{2}$$
$$x = -13$$

15.
$$3x - 10 = 2x - 3$$
$$3x - 10 - 2x = 2x - 3 - 2x$$
$$x - 10 = -3$$
$$x - 10 + 10 = -3 + 10$$
$$x = 7$$
The length is $2 \cdot 7 - 3$, or 11 units.
$P = 2\ell + 2w = 2(11) + 2(7) = 22 + 14 = 36$
The perimeter of the rectangle is 36 units.

16.
$$3x = 7x - 12$$
$$3x - 7x = 7x - 12 - 7x$$
$$-4x = -12$$
$$\frac{-4x}{-4} = \frac{-12}{-4}$$
$$x = 3$$
The length of each side is $3 \cdot 3$, or 9 units.
$P = a + b + c = 9 + 9 + 9 = 27$
The perimeter of the triangle is 27 units.

17.
$$2x + 10 = 3x - 7$$
$$2x + 10 - 2x = 3x - 7 - 2x$$
$$10 = x - 7$$
$$10 + 7 = x - 7 + 7$$
$$17 = x$$
The length of each side is $3 \cdot 17 - 7$, or 44 units.
$P = a + b + c = 44 + 44 + 44 = 132$
The perimeter of the triangle is 132 units.

18. The value of x, 8, is not the width.
The width is $3(8) + 6$, or 30 units.
$P = 2(20) + 2(30) = 40 + 60 = 100$
The perimeter of the rectangle is 100 units.

19.
$$3(t - 7) = 6t$$
$$3t - 21 = 6t$$
$$3t - 21 - 3t = 6t - 3t$$
$$-21 = 3t$$
$$\frac{-21}{3} = \frac{3t}{3}$$
$$-7 = t$$

20.
$$-3h = 9(2 - 3h)$$
$$-3h = 18 - 27h$$
$$-3h + 27h = 18 - 27h + 27h$$
$$24h = 18$$
$$\frac{24h}{24} = \frac{18}{24}$$
$$h = \frac{3}{4}$$

21.
$$3(j + 4) = -2j + j$$
$$3j + 12 = -j$$
$$3j + 12 - 3j = -j - 3j$$
$$12 = -4j$$
$$\frac{12}{-4} = \frac{-4j}{-4}$$
$$-3 = j$$

22.
$$5(t + 7) = 2(2t + 7)$$
$$5t + 35 = 4t + 14$$
$$5t + 35 - 4t = 4t + 14 - 4t$$
$$t + 35 = 14$$
$$t + 35 - 35 = 14 - 35$$
$$t = -21$$

23.
$$2(c + 6) = 5(c + 12)$$
$$2c + 12 = 5c + 60$$
$$2c + 12 - 2c = 5c + 60 - 2c$$
$$12 = 3c + 60$$
$$12 - 60 = 3c + 60 - 60$$
$$-48 = 3c$$
$$\frac{-48}{3} = \frac{3c}{3}$$
$$-16 = c$$

24.
$$6(s - 4) = 3(s + 9)$$
$$6s - 24 = 3s + 27$$
$$6s - 24 - 3s = 3s + 27 - 3s$$
$$3s - 24 = 27$$
$$3s - 24 + 24 = 27 + 24$$
$$3s = 51$$
$$\frac{3s}{3} = \frac{51}{3}$$
$$s = 17$$

25. $-2.5(2g + 6) = 3g - 6g$

$-5g - 15 = -3g$

$-5g - 15 + 5g = -3g + 5g$

$-15 = 2g$

$\dfrac{-15}{2} = \dfrac{2g}{2}$

$-7.5 = g$

26. $2(p + 2) = 1.8p - 2 - 0.2(p + 5)$

$2p + 4 = 1.8p - 2 - 0.2p - 1$

$2p + 4 = 1.6p - 3$

$2p + 4 - 2p = 1.6p - 3 - 2p$

$4 = -0.4p - 3$

$4 + 3 = -0.4p - 3 + 3$

$7 = -0.4p$

$\dfrac{7}{-0.4} = \dfrac{-0.4p}{-0.4}$

$-17.5 = p$

27. true; $x + 8 = 6x - 7$

$x + 8 - x = 6x - 7 - x$

$8 = 5x - 7$

$8 + 7 = 5x - 7 + 7$

$15 = 5x$

$\dfrac{15}{5} = \dfrac{5x}{5}$

$3 = x$

$x + 8 = 3 + 8 = 11$

$6x - 7 = 6(3) - 7 = 11$

All 4 sides are 11 units.

28. false; each side is 11 units. So the area is $A = s^2 = 11^2 = 121$ square units.

29. C; $5.8 - 3x = 9x - 0.2$

$5.8 - 3x + 3x = 9x - 0.2 + 3x$

$5.8 = 12x - 0.2$

$5.8 + 0.2 = 12x - 0.2 + 0.2$

$6 = 12x$

$\dfrac{6}{12} = \dfrac{12x}{2}$

$0.5 = x$

Lengths of three sides of triangle C are:

$5.8 - 3(0.5) = 4.3$

$9(0.5) - 0.2 = 4.3$

$5(0.5) + 0.8 = 3.3$

The lengths of 2 of the sides are 4.3 units and the length of the third side is 3.3 units. So, the triangle does not have all three sides equal in length.

30. *Sample answer:* $2(5x + 1) = -7x + 2 + 17x$

$10x + 2 = -7x + 2 + 17x$

$10x + 2 = 10x + 2$

$10x + 2 - 10x = 10x + 2 - 10x$

$2 = 2$

$2 - 2 = 2 - 2$

$0 = 0$

There are many solutions of the equation because any value of x satisfies the equation.

Problem Solving

31. B; Let x represent the number of minutes.

Cost of one card				Cost of other card	
Rate per minute	Number of minutes	+ 4 · Weekly rate	=	Rate per minute	Number of minutes

$0.018x + 4(0.25) = 0.029x$

32. No, you can also begin by collecting constant terms on the same side.

33. Let x represent the number of tickets.

Cost for nonmember				Cost for member	
Price per ticket	Number of tickets	=	Price per ticket	Number of tickets	+ Membership fee

$35x = 30x + 25$

$35x - 30x = 30x + 25 - 30x$

$5x = 25$

$\dfrac{5x}{5} = \dfrac{25}{5}$

$x = 5$

A member and a nonmember pay the same amount for 5 tickets.

34. Let x represent the number of minutes.

	Joseph				Nia
Rate ·	Number of minutes	+	Pieces already cut	= Rate ·	Number of minutes

$3x + 72 = 9x$

$3x + 72 - 3x = 9x - 3x$

$72 = 6x$

$\dfrac{72}{6} = \dfrac{6x}{6}$

$12 = x$

It will take Nia 12 minutes it catch up to Joseph.

35. Let x represent the cost of a single balloon.

Bought in dozens and singly

$$\begin{array}{c}\text{Cost} \\ \text{per} \\ \text{dozen}\end{array} \cdot \begin{array}{c}\text{Number} \\ \text{of} \\ \text{dozens}\end{array} + \begin{array}{c}\text{Number} \\ \text{of single} \\ \text{balloons}\end{array} \cdot \begin{array}{c}\text{Cost of} \\ \text{a single} \\ \text{balloon}\end{array}$$

Bought singly

$$= \begin{array}{c}\text{Number} \\ \text{of single} \\ \text{balloons}\end{array} \cdot \begin{array}{c}\text{Cost of} \\ \text{a single} \\ \text{balloon}\end{array}$$

$$8 \cdot 7 + 5x = 75x$$
$$56 + 5x = 75x$$
$$56 + 5x - 5x = 75x - 5x$$
$$56 = 70x$$
$$\frac{56}{70} = \frac{70x}{70}$$
$$0.8 = x$$

The cost of a single balloon is $.80.

$8 \cdot 7 + 5x = 56 + 5(0.8) = 56 + 4 = 60.$

You have $60.

36. Let w represent the number of weeks.

David   Emily

$$\begin{array}{c}\text{Amount} \\ \text{saved} \\ \text{per} \\ \text{week}\end{array} \cdot \begin{array}{c}\text{Number} \\ \text{of} \\ \text{weeks}\end{array} + \begin{array}{c}\text{Amount} \\ \text{already} \\ \text{have}\end{array} = \begin{array}{c}\text{Amount} \\ \text{saved} \\ \text{per} \\ \text{week}\end{array} \cdot \begin{array}{c}\text{Number} \\ \text{of} \\ \text{weeks}\end{array} + \begin{array}{c}\text{Amount} \\ \text{already} \\ \text{have}\end{array}$$

$$8w + 26 = 4w + 58$$
$$8w + 26 - 4w = 4w + 58 - 4w$$
$$4w + 26 = 58$$
$$4w + 26 - 26 = 58 - 26$$
$$4w = 32$$
$$\frac{4w}{4} = \frac{32}{4}$$
$$w = 8$$

In 8 weeks, David and Emily will have the same amount of money.

$$8w + 26 = 2(4w + 58)$$
$$8w + 26 = 8w + 116$$
$$8w + 26 - 8w = 8w + 116 - 8w$$
$$26 = 116$$

Because $26 = 116$ is a false statement, David will never have twice the amount of money that Emily has.

37. Let n represent one number.

Let $30 - n$ represent the other number.

$$3n = 4(30 - n) + 6$$
$$3n = 120 - 4n + 6$$
$$3n = 126 - 4n$$
$$3n + 4n = 126 - 4n + 4n$$
$$7n = 126$$
$$\frac{7n}{7} = \frac{126}{7}$$
$$n = 18$$
$$30 - 18 = 12$$

The two numbers are 18 and 12.

38. $a = c$ and $b \neq d$

Example:
$$7x + 2 = 7x + 9$$
$$7x + 2 - 7x = 7x + 9 - 7x$$
$$2 = 9$$

Mixed Review

39. The LCD of $\frac{1}{2}$, $\frac{2}{3}$, and $\frac{5}{6}$ is $2 \cdot 3$, or 6.

40. The LCD of $\frac{2}{9}$, $\frac{3}{4}$, and $\frac{11}{12}$ is $2^2 \cdot 3^2$, or 36.

41. The LCD of $\frac{4}{5}$, $\frac{1}{2}$, and $\frac{3}{70}$ is $2 \cdot 5 \cdot 7$, or 70.

42.
$$\begin{array}{r} 7.310 \\ + 2.248 \\ \hline 9.558 \end{array}$$

43.
$$\begin{array}{r} 10.26 \\ - 3.72 \\ \hline 6.54 \end{array}$$

44.
$$\begin{array}{r} 16.508 \\ + 4.530 \\ \hline 21.038 \end{array}$$

45. $3b - 5b = -14$
$$-2b = -14$$
$$\frac{-2b}{-2} = \frac{-14}{-2}$$
$$b = 7$$

46. $5c + 24 - 3c = 2$
$$2c + 24 = 2$$
$$2c + 24 - 24 = 2 - 24$$
$$2c = -22$$
$$\frac{2c}{2} = \frac{-22}{2}$$
$$c = -11$$

47.
$$4(x - 7) = 4$$
$$4x - 28 = 4$$
$$4x - 28 + 28 = 4 + 28$$
$$4x = 32$$
$$\frac{4x}{4} = \frac{32}{4}$$
$$x = 8$$

48.
$$3(2z - 3) = 75$$
$$6z - 9 = 75$$
$$6z - 9 + 9 = 75 + 9$$
$$6z = 84$$
$$\frac{6z}{6} = \frac{84}{6}$$
$$z = 14$$

49. $7x - 2(x - 11) = -23$

$7x - 2x + 22 = -23$

$5x + 22 = -23$

$5x + 22 - 22 = -23 - 22$

$5x = -45$

$\dfrac{5x}{5} = \dfrac{-45}{5}$

$x = -9$

50. $\quad \dfrac{y + 3}{5} = 10$

$\dfrac{y + 3}{5} \cdot 5 = 10 \cdot 5$

$y + 3 = 50$

$y + 3 - 3 = 50 - 3$

$y = 47$

51. D; $\quad 55 - 2x = -43$

$55 - 2x - 55 = -43 - 55$

$-2x = -98$

$\dfrac{-2x}{-2} = \dfrac{-98}{-2}$

$x = 49$

Lesson 6.3

6.3 Guided Practice (pp. 303–304)

1. Let w represent the cost of one tube of wax.

You				Your friend		
Cost of goggles	+ Number of wax tubes	• Cost of one wax tube	= Cost of helmet	+ Number of wax tubes	• Cost of one wax tube

$39.95 + 4w = 54.95 + 2w$

$39.95 + 2w = 54.95$

$2w = 15$

$\dfrac{2w}{2} = \dfrac{15}{2}$

$w = 7.5$

Each tube of wax costs $7.50.

2. $\quad -1.7k + 6.7k = 13.1$

$(-1.7k + 6.7k)10 = (13.1)10$

$-17k + 67k = 131$

$50k = 131$

$\dfrac{50k}{50} = \dfrac{131}{50}$

$k = 2.62$

3. $\quad 1.2n - 0.24 = 0.7n$

$(1.2n - 0.24)100 = (0.7n)100$

$120n - 24 = 70n$

$-24 = -50n$

$\dfrac{-24}{-50} = \dfrac{-50n}{-50}$

$0.48 = n$

4. $\quad 8.3 - 8y = 1.2y + 6$

$(8.3 - 8y)10 = (1.2y + 6)10$

$83 - 80y = 12y + 60$

$83 = 92y + 60$

$23 = 92y$

$\dfrac{23}{92} = \dfrac{92y}{92}$

$0.25 = y$

5. $\quad \dfrac{4}{5}x + 3 = -\dfrac{7}{10}$

$\left(\dfrac{4}{5}x + 3\right)10 = \left(-\dfrac{7}{10}\right)10$

$\left(\dfrac{4}{5}x\right)10 + (3)10 = \left(\dfrac{-7}{10}\right)10$

$\dfrac{4 \cdot \overset{2}{10}}{\underset{1}{5}}x + 30 = -\dfrac{7 \cdot \overset{1}{10}}{\underset{1}{10}}$

$8x + 30 = -7$

$8x = -37$

$\dfrac{8x}{8} = \dfrac{-37}{8}$

$x = -\dfrac{37}{8}$ or $-4\dfrac{5}{8}$

6. $2s - 1\dfrac{1}{4}s = \dfrac{1}{3}$

$\dfrac{3}{4}s = \dfrac{1}{3}$

$\left(\dfrac{3}{4}s\right)12 = \dfrac{1}{3}(12)$

$\dfrac{3 \cdot \overset{3}{12}}{\underset{1}{4}}s = \dfrac{1 \cdot \overset{4}{12}}{\underset{1}{3}}$

$9s = 4$

$\dfrac{9s}{9} = \dfrac{4}{9}$

$s = \dfrac{4}{9}$

7. $\quad \dfrac{5}{6}v + \dfrac{5}{8} = \dfrac{3}{8}v$

$\left(\dfrac{5}{6}v + \dfrac{5}{8}\right)24 = \left(\dfrac{3}{8}v\right)24$

$\left(\dfrac{5}{6}v\right)24 + \left(\dfrac{5}{8}\right)24 = \left(\dfrac{3}{8}v\right)24$

$\dfrac{5 \cdot \overset{4}{24}}{\underset{1}{6}}v + \dfrac{5 \cdot \overset{3}{24}}{\underset{1}{8}} = \dfrac{3 \cdot \overset{3}{24}}{\underset{1}{8}}$

$20v + 15 = 9v$

$15 = -11v$

$\dfrac{15}{-11} = \dfrac{-11v}{-11}$

$-\dfrac{15}{11}$ or $-1\dfrac{4}{11} = v$

6.3 Exercises (pp. 305–307)

Skill Practice

1. Twenty-four is the *least common denominator* of $\dfrac{1}{4}, \dfrac{5}{6}$, and $\dfrac{3}{8}$.

2. The process of multiplying both sides of the equation $2.4 + 0.2x = 5$ by 10 is used to *clear* decimals.

3. $1.5a - 1.2 = 1.8a$

$(1.5a - 1.2)10 = (1.8a)10$

$15a - 12 = 18a$

$-12 = 3a$

$\dfrac{-12}{3} = \dfrac{3a}{3}$

$-4 = a$

4. $5.85b = 8.68 + 3.68b$

$5.85b(100) = (8.68 + 3.68b)100$

$585b = 868 + 368b$

$217b = 868$

$\dfrac{217b}{217} = \dfrac{868}{217}$

$b = 4$

5. $0.5c + 3.49 - 2c = 4$

$(0.5c + 3.49 - 2c)100 = 4(100)$

$50c + 349 - 200c = 400$

$-150c + 349 = 400$

$-150c = 51$

$\dfrac{-150c}{-150} = \dfrac{51}{-150}$

$c = -0.34$

6. $r + 8.2 + 0.4r = -8.6$

$(r + 8.2 + 0.4r)10 = -8.6(10)$

$10r + 82 + 4r = -86$

$14r + 82 = -86$

$14r = -168$

$\dfrac{14r}{14} = \dfrac{-168}{14}$

$r = -12$

7. $1.5s - 1.2 - s = 0.5$

$(1.5s - 1.2 - s)10 = (0.5)10$

$15s - 12 - 10s = 5$

$5s - 12 = 5$

$5s = 17$

$\dfrac{5s}{5} = \dfrac{17}{5}$

$s = 3.4$

8. $5.3 + u = 3.2u - 2.7$

$(5.3 + u)10 = (3.2u - 2.7)10$

$53 + 10u = 32u - 27$

$53 - 22u = -27$

$-22u = -80$

$\dfrac{-22u}{-22} = \dfrac{-80}{-22}$

$u = 3.\overline{63}$

9. $4.93 - 9.20v = 0.66v$

$(4.93 - 9.20v)100 = 0.66v(100)$

$493 - 920v = 66v$

$493 = 986v$

$\dfrac{493}{986} = \dfrac{986v}{986}$

$0.5 = v$

10. $7.6a + 9.6 = 1.2a$

$(7.6a + 9.6)10 = (1.2a)10$

$76a + 96 = 12a$

$96 = -64a$

$\dfrac{96}{-64} = \dfrac{-64a}{-64}$

$-1.5 = a$

11. $\dfrac{3}{8}m + \dfrac{7}{8} = 2m$

$\left(\dfrac{3}{8}m + \dfrac{7}{8}\right)8 = (2m)8$

$\left(\dfrac{3}{8}m\right)8 + \left(\dfrac{7}{8}\right)8 = (2m)8$

$\dfrac{3 \cdot \overset{1}{\cancel{8}}}{\underset{1}{\cancel{8}}}m + \dfrac{7 \cdot \overset{1}{\cancel{8}}}{\underset{1}{\cancel{8}}} = 16m$

$3m + 7 = 16m$

$7 = 13m$

$\dfrac{7}{13} = \dfrac{13m}{13}$

$\dfrac{7}{13} = m$

12. $\dfrac{3}{4} - \dfrac{1}{2}b = -3b$

$\left(\dfrac{3}{4} - \dfrac{1}{2}b\right)4 = (-3b)4$

$\left(\dfrac{3}{4}\right)4 - \left(\dfrac{1}{2}b\right)4 = (-3b)4$

$\dfrac{3 \cdot \overset{1}{\cancel{4}}}{\underset{1}{\cancel{4}}} - \dfrac{1 \cdot \overset{2}{\cancel{4}}}{\underset{1}{\cancel{2}}}b = -12b$

$3 - 2b = -12b$

$3 = -10b$

$\dfrac{3}{-10} = \dfrac{-10b}{-10}$

$-\dfrac{3}{10} = b$

Chapter 6, continued

13.
$$-\frac{4}{15}n + \frac{2}{3} = \frac{2}{5}n$$

$$\left(-\frac{4}{15}n + \frac{2}{3}\right)15 = \left(\frac{2}{5}n\right)15$$

$$\left(-\frac{4}{15}n\right)15 + \left(\frac{2}{3}\right)15 = \left(\frac{2}{5}n\right)15$$

$$\frac{-4 \cdot \cancel{15}}{\cancel{15}}n + \frac{2 \cdot \cancel{15}^5}{\cancel{3}_1} = \frac{2 \cdot \cancel{15}^3}{\cancel{5}_1}n$$

$$-4n + 10 = 6n$$

$$10 = 10n$$

$$\frac{10}{10} = \frac{10n}{10}$$

$$1 = n$$

14.
$$p - \frac{4}{9}p = -\frac{7}{9}$$

$$\left(p - \frac{4}{9}p\right)9 = \left(-\frac{7}{9}\right)9$$

$$(p)9 - \left(\frac{4}{9}p\right)9 = \left(-\frac{7}{9}\right)9$$

$$9p - \frac{4 \cdot \cancel{9}^1}{\cancel{9}_1}p = -\frac{7 \cdot \cancel{9}^1}{\cancel{9}_1}$$

$$9p - 4p = -7$$

$$5p = -7$$

$$\frac{5p}{5} = \frac{-7}{5}$$

$$p = -\frac{7}{5} \text{ or } -1\frac{2}{5}$$

15.
$$-\frac{1}{5}p + \frac{3}{4}p = 11$$

$$\left(-\frac{1}{5}p + \frac{3}{4}p\right)20 = (11)20$$

$$\left(-\frac{1}{5}p\right)20 + \left(\frac{3}{4}p\right)20 = (11)20$$

$$\frac{-1 \cdot \cancel{20}^4}{\cancel{5}_1}p + \frac{3 \cdot \cancel{20}^5}{\cancel{4}_1}p = 220$$

$$-4p + 15p = 220$$

$$11p = 220$$

$$\frac{11p}{11} = \frac{220}{11}$$

$$p = 20$$

16.
$$\frac{1}{6}x + \frac{2}{3}x = 1$$

$$\left(\frac{1}{6}x + \frac{2}{3}x\right)6 = (1)6$$

$$\left(\frac{1}{6}x\right)6 + \left(\frac{2}{3}x\right)6 = (1)6$$

$$\frac{1 \cdot \cancel{6}^1}{\cancel{6}_1}x + \frac{2 \cdot \cancel{6}^2}{\cancel{3}_1}x = 6$$

$$x + 4x = 6$$

$$5x = 6$$

$$\frac{5x}{5} = \frac{6}{5}$$

$$x = \frac{6}{5} \text{ or } 1\frac{1}{5}$$

17.
$$\frac{3}{10} - w = \frac{4}{5} - \frac{3}{5}w$$

$$\left(\frac{3}{10} - w\right)10 = \left(\frac{4}{5} - \frac{3}{5}w\right)10$$

$$\left(\frac{3}{10}\right)10 - (w)10 = \left(\frac{4}{5}\right)10 - \left(\frac{3}{5}w\right)10$$

$$\frac{3 \cdot \cancel{10}^1}{\cancel{10}_1} - 10w = \frac{4 \cdot \cancel{10}^2}{\cancel{5}_1} - \frac{3 \cdot \cancel{10}^2}{\cancel{5}_1}w$$

$$3 - 10w = 8 - 6w$$

$$3 = 8 + 4w$$

$$-5 = 4w$$

$$\frac{-5}{4} = \frac{4w}{4}$$

$$-\frac{5}{4} \text{ or } -1\frac{1}{4} = w$$

18.
$$\frac{7}{4}z - \frac{1}{6} = \frac{17}{6} + \frac{3}{4}z$$

$$\left(\frac{7}{4}z - \frac{1}{6}\right)12 = \left(\frac{17}{6} + \frac{3}{4}z\right)12$$

$$\left(\frac{7}{4}z\right)12 - \left(\frac{1}{6}\right)12 = \left(\frac{17}{6}\right)12 + \left(\frac{3}{4}z\right)12$$

$$\frac{7 \cdot \cancel{12}^3}{\cancel{4}_1}z - \frac{1 \cdot \cancel{12}^2}{\cancel{6}_1} = \frac{17 \cdot \cancel{12}^2}{\cancel{6}_1} + \frac{3 \cdot \cancel{12}^3}{\cancel{4}_1}z$$

$$21z - 2 = 34 + 9z$$

$$12z - 2 = 34$$

$$12z = 36$$

$$\frac{12z}{12} = \frac{36}{12}$$

$$z = 3$$

19. The error occurred when $1.5x$ and $1.6x$ were multiplied by 10, but 0.25 was multiplied by 100.

$$1.5x + 0.25 = 1.6x$$

$$(1.5x + 0.25)100 = (1.6x)100$$

$$150x + 25 = 160x$$

$$25 = 10x$$

$$\frac{25}{10} = \frac{10x}{10}$$

$$2.5 = x$$

20. C; $\left(3.75x - \frac{1}{2}\right)8 = \left(1.125 - \frac{9}{4}x\right)8$

$$30x - 4 = 9 - 18x$$

21. Multiply each side of the equation by 1000 to clear the decimals.

$$-4.42x + 0.9 = -9.070 - 0.432x$$

$$(-4.42x + 0.9)1000 = (-9.070 - 0.432x)1000$$

$$-4420x + 900 = -9070 - 432x$$

$$900 = -9070 + 3988x$$

$$9970 = 3988x$$

$$\frac{9970}{3988} = \frac{3988x}{3988}$$

$$2.5 = x$$

Chapter 6, *continued*

22. Multiply each side of the equation by 10,000 to clear the decimals.

$$0.025(x + 4) = 1.2415$$
$$0.025x + 0.1 = 1.2415$$
$$(0.025x + 0.1)10{,}000 = (1.2415)10{,}000$$
$$250x + 1000 = 12{,}415$$
$$250x = 11{,}415$$
$$\frac{250x}{250} = \frac{11{,}415}{250}$$
$$x = 45.66$$

23. Multiply each side of the equation by 45 to clear the fractions.

$$6\frac{4}{5}n - \frac{8}{9} = \frac{7}{15}n$$
$$\frac{34}{5}n - \frac{8}{9} = \frac{7}{15}n$$
$$\left(\frac{34}{5}n - \frac{8}{9}\right)45 = \left(\frac{7}{15}n\right)45$$
$$306n - 40 = 21n$$
$$-40 = -285n$$
$$\frac{-40}{-285} = \frac{-285n}{-285}$$
$$\frac{8}{57} = n$$

24. Multiply each side of the equation by 40 to clear the fractions.

$$\frac{3}{8} + \frac{9}{20}m = \frac{23}{20} + \frac{7}{8}m$$
$$\left(\frac{3}{8} + \frac{9}{20}m\right)40 = \left(\frac{23}{20} + \frac{7}{8}m\right)40$$
$$\left(\frac{3}{8}\right)40 + \left(\frac{9}{20}m\right)40 = \left(\frac{23}{20}\right)40 + \left(\frac{7}{8}m\right)40$$
$$15 + 18m = 46 + 35m$$
$$15 = 46 + 17m$$
$$-31 = 17m$$
$$\frac{-31}{17} = \frac{17m}{17}$$
$$\frac{-31}{17} \text{ or } -1\frac{14}{17} = m$$

25. Multiply each side of the equation by 10 to eliminate the fractions and decimals.

$$5\frac{3}{10} - 0.2x = \frac{1}{5}x + 0.8$$
$$\left(5\frac{3}{10} - 0.2x\right)10 = \left(\frac{1}{5}x + 0.8\right)10$$
$$\left(\frac{53}{10}\right)10 - (0.2x)10 = \left(\frac{1}{5}x\right)10 + (0.8)10$$
$$53 - 2x = 2x + 8$$
$$53 - 4x = 8$$
$$-4x = -45$$
$$\frac{-4x}{-4} = \frac{-45}{-4}$$
$$x = \frac{45}{4} \text{ or } 11\frac{1}{4} \text{ or } 11.25$$

26. Multiply each side of the equation by 4 to clear the fractions and decimals.

$$1.25(x - 9) = \frac{13}{4}$$
$$1.25x - 11.25 = \frac{13}{4}$$
$$(1.25x - 11.25)4 = \left(\frac{13}{4}\right)4$$
$$(1.25x)4 - (11.25)4 = 13$$
$$5x - 45 = 13$$
$$5x = 58$$
$$\frac{5x}{5} = \frac{58}{5}$$
$$x = \frac{58}{5} \text{ or } 11\frac{3}{5} \text{ or } 11.6$$

27. Multiply each side of the equation by 8 to clear the fractions and decimals.

$$\frac{1}{2}x - 3 + 0.625x = 5$$
$$\left(\frac{1}{2}x - 3 + 0.625x\right)8 = (5)8$$
$$\left(\frac{1}{2}x\right)8 - (3)8 + (0.625x)8 = 40$$
$$4x - 24 + 5x = 40$$
$$9x - 24 = 40$$
$$9x = 64$$
$$\frac{9x}{9} = \frac{64}{9}$$
$$x = \frac{64}{9} \text{ or } 7\frac{1}{9} \text{ or } 7.\overline{1}$$

28. Multiply each side of the equation by 8 to clear the fractions and decimals.

$$2.25 - 3z = 0.375 - \frac{3}{4}z$$
$$(2.25 - 3z)8 = \left(0.375 - \frac{3}{4}z\right)8$$
$$(2.25)8 - (3z)8 = (0.375)8 - \left(\frac{3}{4}z\right)8$$
$$18 - 24z = 3 - 6z$$
$$18 - 18z = 3$$
$$-18z = -15$$
$$\frac{-18z}{-18} = \frac{-15}{-18}$$
$$z = \frac{5}{6} \text{ or } 0.8\overline{3}$$

29. *Sample answer:* $5x - 3 = 18$; $5x = 21$; $x = 4\frac{1}{5}$

30.
$$\frac{7}{2a} - \frac{5}{4} = \frac{1}{a}$$

$$\left(\frac{7}{2a} - \frac{5}{4}\right)4a = \left(\frac{1}{a}\right)4a$$

$$\left(\frac{7}{2a}\right)4a - \left(\frac{5}{4}\right)4a = \left(\frac{1}{a}\right)4a$$

$$14 - 5a = 4$$

$$-5a = -10$$

$$\frac{-5a}{-5} = \frac{-10}{-5}$$

$$a = 2$$

Check: $\dfrac{7}{2(2)} - \dfrac{5}{4} \stackrel{?}{=} \dfrac{1}{2}$

$$\frac{7}{4} - \frac{5}{4} \stackrel{?}{=} \frac{1}{2}$$

$$\frac{2}{4} \stackrel{?}{=} \frac{1}{2}$$

$$\frac{1}{2} = \frac{1}{2} \checkmark$$

31.
$$\frac{3}{4x} = \frac{1}{2x} - \frac{7}{12}$$

$$\left(\frac{3}{4x}\right)12x = \left(\frac{1}{2x} - \frac{7}{12}\right)12x$$

$$\frac{3}{4x}(12x) = \left(\frac{1}{2x}\right)12x - \left(\frac{7}{12}\right)12x$$

$$9 = 6 - 7x$$

$$3 = -7x$$

$$\frac{3}{-7} = \frac{-7x}{-7}$$

$$-\frac{3}{7} = x$$

Check: $\dfrac{3}{4\left(-\frac{3}{7}\right)} \stackrel{?}{=} \dfrac{1}{2\left(-\frac{3}{7}\right)} - \dfrac{7}{12}$

$$\frac{3}{-\frac{12}{7}} \stackrel{?}{=} \frac{1}{-\frac{6}{7}} - \frac{7}{12}$$

$$-\frac{7}{4} \stackrel{?}{=} -\frac{7}{6} - \frac{7}{12}$$

$$-\frac{7}{4} = -\frac{7}{4} \checkmark$$

32.
$$1.8 - \frac{3}{8y} = \frac{9}{10y} - 6$$

$$\left(1.8 - \frac{3}{8y}\right)40y = \left(\frac{9}{10y} - 6\right)40y$$

$$(1.8)40y - \left(\frac{3}{8y}\right)40y = \left(\frac{9}{10y}\right)40y - (6)40y$$

$$72y - 15 = 36 - 240y$$

$$312y - 15 = 36$$

$$312y = 51$$

$$\frac{312y}{312} = \frac{51}{312}$$

$$y = \frac{17}{104}$$

Check: $1.8 - \dfrac{3}{8\left(\frac{17}{104}\right)} \stackrel{?}{=} \dfrac{9}{10\left(\frac{17}{104}\right)} - 6$

$$1.8 - \frac{3}{\frac{17}{13}} \stackrel{?}{=} \frac{9}{\frac{85}{52}} - 6$$

$$\frac{9}{5} - \frac{39}{17} \stackrel{?}{=} \frac{468}{85} - 6$$

$$-\frac{42}{85} = -\frac{42}{85} \checkmark$$

33.
$$3\frac{4}{9} - \frac{2}{3c} = 6\left(\frac{1}{c} + 3\right)$$

$$3\frac{4}{9} - \frac{2}{3c} = \frac{6}{c} + 18$$

$$\left(\frac{31}{9} - \frac{2}{3c}\right)9c = \left(\frac{6}{c} + 18\right)9c$$

$$\left(\frac{31}{9}\right)9c - \left(\frac{2}{3c}\right)9c = \left(\frac{6}{c}\right)9c + (18)9c$$

$$31c - 6 = 54 + 162c$$

$$-131c - 6 = 54$$

$$-131c = 60$$

$$\frac{-131c}{-131} = \frac{60}{-131}$$

$$c = -\frac{60}{131}$$

Check: $3\dfrac{4}{9} - \dfrac{2}{3\left(-\frac{60}{131}\right)} \stackrel{?}{=} 6\left(\dfrac{1}{-\frac{60}{131}} + 3\right)$

$$3\frac{4}{9} - \frac{2}{-\frac{180}{131}} \stackrel{?}{=} 6\left(-\frac{131}{60} + 3\right)$$

$$\frac{31}{9} - \left(-\frac{131}{90}\right) \stackrel{?}{=} -\frac{131}{10} + 18$$

$$\frac{49}{10} = \frac{49}{10} \checkmark$$

Problem Solving

34. D; Let x represent the cost of one ticket.

You		Your friend	
Number of tickets $\cdot$	Cost of a ticket	= Cost of a T-shirt $+$	Cost of a ticket

$$10x = 13.5 + x$$

35. Let x represent the number of pounds of Swiss cheese and the number of pounds of turkey.

Swiss Cheese		Turkey		
Cost per pound $\cdot$	Number of pounds $+$	Cost per pound $\cdot$	Number of pounds $=$	Total cost

$$3.96x + 4.76x = 13.08$$

$$(3.96x + 4.76x)100 = (13.08)100$$

$$396x + 476x = 1308$$

$$872x = 1308$$

$$\frac{872x}{872} = \frac{1308}{872}$$

$$x = 1.5$$

You buy 1.5 pounds each of Swiss cheese and turkey.

36. Let x represent the cost of one pint of potato salad.

Rosh

| Cost of plates and cups | + | Number of pints of potato salad | · | Cost of one pint of potato salad |

Arlene

| = | Cost of watermelons | + | Number of pints of potato salad | · | Cost of one pint of potato salad |

$$19.1 + 5x = 15.55 + 6x$$
$$(19.1 + 5x)100 = (15.55 + 6x)100$$
$$1910 + 500x = 1555 + 600x$$
$$1910 - 100x = 1555$$
$$-100x = -355$$
$$\frac{-100x}{-100} = \frac{-355}{-100}$$
$$x = 3.55$$

The cost of one pint of potato salad is $3.55.

37. *Sample answer:* Sally and Peter leave the same location driving in opposite directions at a rate of r miles per hour. After Sally drives 2.1 hours and Peter drives 0.4 hour, they are 127.5 miles apart. What is the rate r?

$$2.1r + 0.4r = 127.5$$
$$(2.1r + 0.4r)10 = (127.5)10$$
$$21r + 4r = 1275$$
$$25r = 1275$$
$$\frac{25r}{25} = \frac{1275}{25}$$
$$r = 51$$

The solution represents the rate at which Sally and Peter are driving, which is 51 miles per hour.

38. a. Let x represent the cost of one yard of fabric.

| Cost of pattern | + | (Number of yards of red fabric + Number of yards of purple fabric |

| + | Number of yards of blue fabric) | · | Cost of one yard of fabric | = | Total cost |

$$7 + \left(\frac{3}{4} + 2\frac{1}{2} + \frac{7}{8}\right)x = 23.5$$
$$\left[7 + \left(\frac{3}{4} + \frac{5}{2} + \frac{7}{8}\right)x\right]8 = 23.5(8)$$
$$56 + (6 + 20 + 7)x = 188$$
$$56 + 33x = 188$$
$$33x = 132$$
$$\frac{33x}{33} = \frac{132}{33}$$
$$x = 4$$

b. The cost of one yard of fabric is $4. You spend $\frac{3}{4} \cdot 4$, or $3 on red fabric, $2\frac{1}{2} \cdot 4$, or $10 on purple fabric, and $\frac{7}{8} \cdot 4$, or $3.50 on blue fabric.

39. Yes, you will get the correct answer. An advantage is that

you don't have to find the LCD. A disadvantage is that the equation will contain larger numbers to work with.

40. a.
$$6.95x - 2.13 = 1.8x + 3.07$$
$$(6.95x - 2.13)100 = (1.8x + 3.07)100$$
$$695x - 213 = 180x + 307$$
$$515x - 213 = 307$$
$$515x = 520$$
$$\frac{515x}{515} = \frac{520}{515}$$
$$x = \frac{104}{103} \text{ or } 1\frac{1}{103} \text{ or about } 1.0097$$

b. *Sample answer:*

You can estimate the solution by using the equation:
$$7x - 2 = 2x + 3$$
$$5x - 2 = 3$$
$$5x = 5$$
$$\frac{5x}{5} = \frac{5}{5}$$
$$x = 1$$

This estimation method is useful as a check of reasonableness.

41. Let x represent the area of the entire lawn.

You

| Fraction you mow | · | Area of entire lawn | + |

Sister

| Fraction your sister mows | · | Area of entire lawn | = | Area you and your sister mow |

$$\frac{1}{3}x + \frac{2}{5}x = 121 \cdot 30$$
$$\frac{1}{3}x + \frac{2}{5}x = 3630$$
$$\left(\frac{1}{3}x + \frac{2}{5}x\right)15 = (3630)15$$
$$\left(\frac{1}{3}x\right)15 + \left(\frac{2}{5}x\right)15 = (3630)15$$
$$5x + 6x = 54,450$$
$$11x = 54,450$$
$$\frac{11x}{11} = \frac{54,450}{11}$$
$$x = 4950$$

The area of the entire lawn is 4950 square feet. There are $4950 - 3630$, or 1320 square feet left to mow. The length of the section left to mow is $1320 \div 30$, or 44 feet.

42. a. $x - \frac{1}{2}x - \frac{1}{4}x - 4 = 5$

b.
$$x - \frac{1}{2}x - \frac{1}{4}x - 4 = 5$$
$$\left(x - \frac{1}{2}x - \frac{1}{4}x - 4\right)4 = (5)4$$
$$(x)4 - \left(\frac{1}{2}x\right)4 - \left(\frac{1}{4}x\right)4 - (4)4 = (5)4$$
$$4x - 2x - x - 16 = 20$$
$$x - 16 = 20$$
$$x = 36$$

You start with $36.

c. By working backwards you could find how much

Chapter 6, *continued*

money you started with. Because you have $5 left, you had $9 before you bought popcorn. This is also the amount you spent on the movie ticket, so you had $18 before you bought the movie ticket. That is also the amount you deposited, so you started with $36.

d. *Sample answer:* They are alike in that both use the amounts in the problem. They are different because one starts with an equation and the other starts with the final amount.

43. $\dfrac{3.756(5) + x}{6} = x + 2.872$

$\dfrac{18.78 + x}{6} = x + 2.872$

$\left(\dfrac{18.78 + x}{6}\right)6 = (x + 2.872)6$

$18.78 + x = 6x + 17.232$

$1.548 + x = 6x$

$1.548 = 5x$

$\dfrac{1.548}{5} = \dfrac{5x}{5}$

$0.3096 = x$

In June, 0.31 inch of rain fell.

44. Let w represent the width of the rectangle. Let $2\frac{2}{3}w$ represent the length, ℓ.

$P = 2\ell + 2w$

$2\left(2\frac{2}{3}w\right) + 2w = 3\left(2\frac{2}{3}w\right) - 2\frac{1}{2}$

$2\left(\frac{8}{3}w\right) + 2w = 3\left(\frac{8}{3}w\right) - \frac{5}{2}$

$\frac{16}{3}w + 2w = 8w - \frac{5}{2}$

$\left(\frac{16}{3}w + 2w\right)6 = \left(8w - \frac{5}{2}\right)6$

$\left(\frac{16}{3}w\right)6 + (2w)6 = (8w)6 - \left(\frac{5}{2}\right)6$

$32w + 12w = 48w - 15$

$44w = 48w - 15$

$-4w = -15$

$\dfrac{-4w}{-4} = \dfrac{-15}{-4}$

$w = 3.75$

The width of the rectangle is 3.75 units.

$A = \ell \cdot w$

$\ell = 2\frac{2}{3} \cdot 3.75 = \frac{8}{3} \cdot 3.75 = 10$ units

$A = 10 \cdot 3.75 = 37.5$

The area of the rectangle is 37.5 square units.

Mixed Review

45. $A = \frac{1}{2}bh$

$= \frac{1}{2}\left(\frac{1}{2}\right)(4)$

$= 1$

46. $A = \frac{1}{2}bh$

$15 = \frac{1}{2}\left(\frac{5}{6}\right)h$

$15 = \frac{5}{12}h$

$15 \cdot \frac{12}{5} = \frac{5}{12}h \cdot \frac{12}{5}$

$36 = h$

47. $A = \frac{1}{2}bh$

$22 = \frac{1}{2}b(2.5)$

$22 = 1.25b$

$\dfrac{22}{1.25} = \dfrac{1.25b}{1.25}$

$17.6 = b$

48. $A = \frac{1}{2}bh$

$9 = \frac{1}{2}(4.5)h$

$9 = 2.25h$

$\dfrac{9}{2.25} = \dfrac{2.25h}{2.25}$

$4 = h$

49. $A = \frac{1}{2}bh$

$2.1 = \frac{1}{2}b(6)$

$2.1 = 3b$

$\dfrac{2.1}{3} = \dfrac{3b}{3}$

$0.7 = b$

50. $A = \frac{1}{2}bh$

$= \frac{1}{2}(3.25)(8)$

$= 13$

51. $6n + 12 = 2n$

$12 = -4n$

$\dfrac{12}{-4} = \dfrac{-4n}{-4}$

$-3 = n$

52. $16 - 3s = 2s - 14$

$16 = 5s - 14$

$30 = 5s$

$\dfrac{30}{5} = \dfrac{5s}{5}$

$6 = s$

53. $-3(w - 7) = 5w + 3$

$-3w + 21 = 5w + 3$

$21 = 8w + 3$

$18 = 8w$

$\dfrac{18}{8} = \dfrac{8w}{8}$

$2\frac{1}{4} = w$

54. D; $9(8 + x) = 72 + 9x$

Quiz 6.1–6.3 (p. 308)

1. $2(x + 16) = 46$

$2x + 32 = 46$

$2x = 14$

$\dfrac{2x}{2} = \dfrac{14}{2}$

$x = 7$

2. $79 = 10x - 23 + 7x$

$79 = 17x - 23$

$102 = 17x$

$\dfrac{102}{17} = \dfrac{17x}{17}$

$6 = x$

Chapter 6, continued

3. $-108 - 9x = -16(x + 5)$
$-108 - 9x = -16x - 80$
$-108 = -7x - 80$
$-28 = -7x$
$\dfrac{-28}{-7} = \dfrac{-7x}{-7}$
$4 = x$

4. $12n = 17 - 22n$
$34n = 17$
$\dfrac{34n}{34} = \dfrac{17}{34}$
$n = \dfrac{1}{2}$

5. $\dfrac{x + 8}{3} = -4$
$\dfrac{x + 8}{3} \cdot 3 = -4 \cdot 3$
$x + 8 = -12$
$x = -20$

6. $\dfrac{2x - 1}{5} = 7$
$\dfrac{2x - 1}{5} \cdot 5 = 7 \cdot 5$
$2x - 1 = 35$
$2x = 36$
$\dfrac{2x}{2} = \dfrac{36}{2}$
$x = 18$

7. $27.2m + 15.7 = -85.94 + 0.8m$
$(27.2m + 15.7)100 = (-85.94 + 0.8m)100$
$2720m + 1570 = -8594 + 80m$
$2640m + 1570 = -8594$
$2640m = -10{,}164$
$\dfrac{2640m}{2640} = \dfrac{-10{,}164}{2640}$
$m = -3.85$

8. $14.6p + 34.25 = 11.8p + 45.45$
$(14.6p + 34.25)100 = (11.8p + 45.45)100$
$1460p + 3425 = 1180p + 4545$
$280p + 3425 = 4545$
$280p = 1120$
$\dfrac{280p}{280} = \dfrac{1120}{280}$
$p = 4$

9. $\dfrac{1}{2}v + \dfrac{11}{12} - \dfrac{5}{4}v = -\dfrac{5}{12}$
$\left(\dfrac{1}{2}v + \dfrac{11}{12} - \dfrac{5}{4}v\right)12 = \left(-\dfrac{5}{12}\right)12$
$\left(\dfrac{1}{2}v\right)12 + \left(\dfrac{11}{12}\right)12 - \left(\dfrac{5}{4}v\right)12 = \left(-\dfrac{5}{12}\right)12$
$6v + 11 - 15v = -5$
$-9v + 11 = -5$
$-9v = -16$
$\dfrac{-9v}{-9} = \dfrac{-16}{-9}$
$v = \dfrac{16}{9} \text{ or } 1\dfrac{7}{9}$

10. $2\dfrac{5}{6} - \dfrac{1}{3}w = w + \dfrac{1}{6}$
$\left(\dfrac{17}{6} - \dfrac{1}{3}w\right)6 = \left(w + \dfrac{1}{6}\right)6$
$\left(\dfrac{17}{6}\right)6 - \left(\dfrac{1}{3}w\right)6 = (w)6 + \left(\dfrac{1}{6}\right)6$
$17 - 2w = 6w + 1$
$17 - 8w = 1$
$-8w = -16$
$\dfrac{-8w}{-8} = \dfrac{-16}{-8}$
$w = 2$

11. $4y - 12 = y + 3$
$3y - 12 = 3$
$3y = 15$
$\dfrac{3y}{3} = \dfrac{15}{3}$
$y = 5$

The length of the rectangle is $y + 3 = 5 + 3$, or 8 feet.

$2x - 3 = 7x - 18$
$-3 = 5x - 18$
$15 = 5x$
$\dfrac{15}{5} = \dfrac{5x}{5}$
$3 = x$

The width is $2x - 3 = 2(3) - 3$, or 3 feet.
$P = 2\ell + 2w = 2(8) + 2(3) = 16 + 6 = 22$
The perimeter of the rectangle is 22 feet.

12. a. $235 + (30 + 40)x = 445$
$235 + 70x = 445$
$70x = 210$
$\dfrac{70x}{70} = \dfrac{210}{70}$
$x = 3$

You can buy 3 pairs of ink cartridges for the printer.

b. $\$40 \cdot 3 = \$120$

You will spend $120 on color ink cartridges.

Brain Game (p. 308)

1. $2g - 7 - 3g = -12$
$-g - 7 = -12$
$-g = -5$
$\dfrac{-g}{-1} = \dfrac{-5}{-1}$
$g = 5$

2. $4n + 1 = 9n - 4$
$1 = 5n - 4$
$5 = 5n$
$\dfrac{5}{5} = \dfrac{5n}{5}$
$1 = n$

3.
$$1.6q + 13 = 5 - 2.4q$$
$$(1.6q + 13)10 = (5 - 2.4q)10$$
$$16q + 130 = 50 - 24q$$
$$40q + 130 = 50$$
$$40q = -80$$
$$\frac{40q}{40} = \frac{-80}{40}$$
$$q = -2$$

4. $12 = -2r - 12 + 8r$
$$12 = 6r - 12$$
$$24 = 6r$$
$$\frac{24}{6} = \frac{6r}{6}$$
$$4 = r$$

5.
$$\frac{9}{16}\ell - \frac{9}{8} = \frac{3}{8}\ell$$
$$\left(\frac{9}{16}\ell - \frac{9}{8}\right)16 = \left(\frac{3}{8}\ell\right)16$$
$$\left(\frac{9}{16}\ell\right)16 - \left(\frac{9}{8}\right)16 = \left(\frac{3}{8}\ell\right)16$$
$$9\ell - 18 = 6\ell$$
$$-18 = -3\ell$$
$$\frac{-18}{-3} = \frac{-3\ell}{-3}$$
$$6 = \ell$$

6. $a - 2(a + 1) = 3$
$$a - 2a - 2 = 3$$
$$-a - 2 = 3$$
$$-a = 5$$
$$\frac{-a}{-1} = \frac{5}{-1}$$
$$a = -5$$

7.
$$\frac{9}{10}n + \frac{1}{5} = \frac{7}{10}n + \frac{3}{5}$$
$$\left(\frac{9}{10}n + \frac{1}{5}\right)10 = \left(\frac{7}{10}n + \frac{3}{5}\right)10$$
$$\left(\frac{9}{10}n\right)10 + \left(\frac{1}{5}\right)10 = \left(\frac{7}{10}n\right)10 + \left(\frac{3}{5}\right)10$$
$$9n + 2 = 7n + 6$$
$$2n + 2 = 6$$
$$2n = 4$$
$$\frac{2n}{2} = \frac{4}{2}$$
$$n = 2$$

8. $i + 4 - 7i = 10$
$$4 - 6i = 10$$
$$-6i = 6$$
$$\frac{-6i}{-6} = \frac{6}{-6}$$
$$i = -1$$

9.
$$7 - 2.65t = -4.4t$$
$$(7 - 2.65t)100 = (-4.4t)100$$
$$700 - 265t = -440t$$
$$700 = -175t$$
$$\frac{700}{-175} = \frac{-175t}{-175}$$
$$-4 = t$$

The city is Arlington.

Mixed Review of Problem Solving (p. 309)

1. a.   You

$$\underset{\text{ringtones}}{\text{Number of}} \cdot \underset{\text{ringtone}}{\text{Cost of a}} + \underset{\text{of cover}}{\text{Cost}}$$

Kaylee

$$= \underset{\text{ringtones}}{\text{Number of}} \cdot \underset{\text{ringtone}}{\text{Cost of a}} + \underset{\text{of antenna}}{\text{Cost}}$$

b.
$$5c + 9.99 = 3c + 15.97$$
$$(5c + 9.99)100 = (3c + 15.97)100$$
$$500c + 999 = 300c + 1597$$
$$200c + 999 = 1597$$
$$200c = 598$$
$$\frac{200c}{200} = \frac{598}{200}$$
$$c = 2.99$$

Each ringtone costs $2.99.

c. $3c + 15.97 = 3(2.99) + 15.97 = 8.97 + 15.97 = 24.94$

Kaylee pays $24.94.

2. a. Cypress: 15 ft = 180 in.

Oak: 22 ft = 264 in.
$$180 + 30x = 264 + 10x$$
$$180 + 20x = 264$$
$$20x = 84$$
$$\frac{20x}{20} = \frac{84}{20}$$
$$x = 4.2$$

It will take 4.2 years for the trees to be the same height.

$$180 + 30x = 180 + 30(4.2) = 180 + 126 = 306$$

306 in. = 25.5 ft

This height is 25.5 ft.

b. 5 ft = 60 in.
$$30x = 60 + 10x$$
$$20x = 60$$
$$\frac{20x}{20} = \frac{60}{20}$$
$$x = 3$$

It will take 3 more years for the bald cypress tree to be 5 feet taller than the bur oak tree.

3. $2 \times 6 + 9x = 138$

$12 + 9x = 138$

$9x = 126$

$\dfrac{9x}{9} = \dfrac{126}{9}$

$x = 14$

The other log must to be 14 feet.

The fence consists of 3 sides of the 2×6 rectangle ($2 + 6 + 2 = 10$ feet), 3 feet on the left of the 2×6 rectangle, and the length opposite the 14 foot log.

$10 + 3 + 14 = 27$ ft

There are 27 feet of fence that border the garden.

4. $x + 3 = 2x + 1$

$3 = x + 1$

$2 = x$

Each side of the triangle is $x + 3 = 2 + 3$, or 5 units.

$P = a + b + c = 5 + 5 + 5 = 15$

The perimeter of the triangle is 15 units.

5. Answers will vary.

6. $\dfrac{1}{3}x + \dfrac{1}{2}x = 900$

$\left(\dfrac{1}{3}x + \dfrac{1}{2}x\right)6 = (900)6$

$\left(\dfrac{1}{3}x\right)6 + \left(\dfrac{1}{2}x\right)6 = 5400$

$2x + 3x = 5400$

$5x = 5400$

$\dfrac{5x}{5} = \dfrac{5400}{5}$

$x = 1080$

$1080 - 900 = 180$

Rita drove 180 miles.

Al drove $\dfrac{1}{2}(1080)$, or 540 miles.

You drove $\dfrac{1}{3}(1080)$, or 360 miles.

Al drove the farthest.

7. a.

Number of shirts at $8 each		Number of shirts after the first 2 shirts		Total amount spent
Number of shirts at $8 each	Cost of each of the first 2 shirts	Number of shirts after the first 2 shirts	Cost of every shirt after the second shirt	= Total amount spent

b. $2 \cdot 8 + (n - 2)5 = 36$

$16 + 5n - 10 = 36$

$5n + 6 = 36$

$5n = 30$

$\dfrac{5n}{5} = \dfrac{30}{5}$

$n = 6$

You buy 6 shirts.

c. You spent a total of $36 for 6 shirts, so the mean cost per shirt is $36 \div 6$, or $6.

Lesson 6.4

Investigation (pp. 310–311)

1.

Object	$\dfrac{C}{d}$
water bottle	$\dfrac{206 \text{ mm}}{65 \text{ mm}} \approx 3.17$
tuna can	$\dfrac{264 \text{ mm}}{84 \text{ mm}} \approx 3.14$
clock	$\dfrac{549 \text{ mm}}{174 \text{ mm}} \approx 3.16$
quarter	$\dfrac{74 \text{ mm}}{24 \text{ mm}} \approx 3.08$
mug	$\dfrac{261 \text{ mm}}{82 \text{ mm}} \approx 3.18$

2. The numbers in the new column are all about the same.

Explore 2

Step 1 $\dfrac{3.17 + 3.14 + 3.16 + 3.08 + 3.18}{5} = \dfrac{15.73}{5} = 3.146$

Step 2 All of the means should be about 3.14.

Step 3 $\dfrac{C}{d} = 3.14$

$\dfrac{C}{d} \cdot d = 3.14 \cdot d$

$C = 3.14d$

3. $C = 3.14(64) = 200.96$

The circumference of the circle is 200.96 millimeters.

4. $C = 3.14(140) = 439.6$

The circumference of the circle is 439.6 millimeters.

5. $C = 3.14(36) = 113.04$

The circumference of the circle is 113.04 centimeters.

6. $C = 3.14(20) = 62.8$

The circumference of the circle is 62.8 centimeters.

7. $C = 3.14(4) = 12.56$

The circumference of the circle is 12.56 inches.

8. $C = 3.14(1.25) = 3.925$

The circumference of the circle is 3.925 inches.

9. $C = 3.14d$

$\dfrac{C}{3.14} = \dfrac{3.14d}{3.14}$

$\dfrac{C}{3.14} = d$

6.4 Guided Practice (pp. 313–314)

1. $C = 2\pi r \approx 2\left(\dfrac{22}{7}\right)\!\left(\overset{4}{\cancel{28}}\right) = 176$

The circumference is about 176 miles. Use $\dfrac{22}{7}$ for π because 28 is divisible by 7.

Chapter 6, *continued*

2. $C = 2\pi r \approx 2(3.14)(9.5) = 59.66$

The circumference is about 59.66 meters. Use 3.14 for π because 9.5 is not divisible by 7.

3. $C = \pi d \approx 3.14(16) = 50.24$

The circumference is about 50.24 centimeters. Use 3.14 for π because 16 is not divisible by 7.

4. $C = \pi d \approx 3.14(32) = 100.48$

The circumference is about 100.48 inches. Use 3.14 for π because 32 is not divisible by 7.

5. $C = \pi d \approx \dfrac{22}{7}\overset{20}{(1\cancel{4}0)} = 440$

The circumference is about 440 feet. Use $\dfrac{22}{7}$ for π because 140 is divisible by 7.

6. $C = 2\pi r \approx 2(3.14)(1.5) = 9.42$

The circumference is about 9.42 kilometers. Use 3.14 for π because 1.5 is not divisible by 7.

7.
$$C = \pi d$$
$$462 \approx \frac{22}{7}d$$
$$462 \cdot \frac{7}{22} = \frac{22}{7}d \cdot \frac{7}{22}$$
$$147 = d$$

The diameter is about 147 feet.

8.
$$C = 2\pi r$$
$$38 \approx 2(3.14)r$$
$$38 = 6.28r$$
$$\frac{38}{6.28} = \frac{6.28r}{6.28}$$
$$6.05 \approx r$$

The radius is about 6.05 inches. Use 3.14 for π because 38 is not divisible by 22.

6.4 Exercises (pp. 314–317)

Skill Practice

1.

radius

diameter

2. The distance around a circle is its *circumference*.

3. $C = 2\pi r \approx 2(3.14)(10) = 62.8$

The circumference is about 62.8 millimeters. Use 3.14 because 10 is not divisible by 7.

4. $C = 2\pi r \approx 2\left(\dfrac{22}{7}\right)\left(3\dfrac{1}{2}\right) \approx 2\left(\dfrac{\overset{11}{\cancel{22}}}{\underset{1}{\cancel{7}}}\right)\left(\dfrac{\overset{1}{\cancel{7}}}{\underset{1}{\cancel{2}}}\right) = 22$

The circumference is about 22 feet. Use $\dfrac{22}{7}$ because 7 is divisible by 7.

5. $C = \pi d \approx 3.14(100) = 314$

The circumference is about 314 centimeters. Use 3.14 for π because 100 is not divisible by 7.

6. $C = 2\pi r \approx 2\left(\dfrac{22}{\underset{1}{\cancel{7}}}\right)(\overset{3}{\cancel{21}}) = 132$

The circumference is about 132 feet. Use $\dfrac{22}{7}$ because 21 is divisible by 7.

7. $C = \pi d \approx \left(\dfrac{22}{\underset{1}{\cancel{7}}}\right)(\overset{2}{\cancel{14}}) = 44$

The circumference is about 44 inches. Use $\dfrac{22}{7}$ because 14 is divisible by 7.

8. $C = \pi d \approx 3.14(20) = 62.8$

The circumference is about 62.8 miles. Use 3.14 because 20 is not divisible by 7.

9. $C = \pi d \approx \dfrac{22}{\underset{1}{\cancel{7}}}(\overset{9}{\cancel{63}}) = 198$

The circumference is about 198 millimeters. Use $\dfrac{22}{7}$ because 63 is divisible by 7.

10. $C = \pi d \approx \dfrac{22}{\underset{1}{\cancel{7}}}(\overset{8}{\cancel{56}}) = 176$

The circumference is about 176 meters. Use $\dfrac{22}{7}$ because 56 is divisible by 7.

11. $C = 2\pi r \approx 2\left(\dfrac{22}{\underset{1}{\cancel{7}}}\right)(\overset{6}{\cancel{42}}) = 264$

The circumference is about 264 feet. Use $\dfrac{22}{7}$ because 42 is divisible by 7.

12. The diameter is 4.5 inches, not the radius, so the formula $C = \pi d$ should be used.

$C = \pi d \approx 3.14(4.5) = 14.13$

The circumference is about 14.13 inches.

13.
$$C = \pi d$$
$$66 \approx \frac{22}{7}d$$
$$66 \cdot \frac{7}{22} = \frac{22}{7}d \cdot \frac{7}{22}$$
$$22 = d$$

The diameter is about 22 inches.

14.
$$C = 2\pi r$$
$$3.14 \approx 2(3.14)r$$
$$3.14 = 6.28r$$
$$\frac{3.14}{6.28} = \frac{6.28r}{6.28}$$
$$0.5 = r$$

The radius is about 0.5 meter.

15. $C = \pi d$

$$33 \approx \frac{22}{7}d$$

$$33 \cdot \frac{7}{22} = \frac{22}{7}d \cdot \frac{7}{22}$$

$$10.5 = d$$

The diameter is about 10.5 kilometers.

16. $C = 2\pi r$

$$628 \approx 2(3.14)r$$

$$628 = 6.28r$$

$$\frac{628}{6.28} = \frac{6.28r}{6.28}$$

$$100 = r$$

The radius is about 100 centimeters.

17. $C = 2\pi r$

$$9.42 \approx 2(3.14)(r)$$

$$9.42 = 6.28r$$

$$\frac{9.42}{6.28} = \frac{6.28r}{6.28}$$

$$1.5 = r$$

The radius is about 1.5 centimeters.

18. $C = \pi d$

$$330 \approx \frac{22}{7}d$$

$$330 \cdot \frac{7}{22} = \frac{22}{7}d \cdot \frac{7}{22}$$

$$105 = d$$

The diameter is about 105 yards.

19. $C = 2\pi r$

$$157 \approx 2(3.14)r$$

$$157 = 6.28r$$

$$\frac{157}{6.28} = \frac{6.28r}{6.28}$$

$$25 = r$$

The radius is about 25 yards.

20. $C = \pi d$

$$235.5 \approx 3.14d$$

$$\frac{235.5}{3.14} = \frac{3.14d}{3.14}$$

$$75 = d$$

The diameter is about 75 centimeters.

21. $C = 2\pi r$

$$44 \approx 2\left(\frac{22}{7}\right)r$$

$$44 = \frac{44}{7}r$$

$$44 \cdot \frac{7}{44} = \frac{44}{7}r \cdot \frac{7}{44}$$

$$7 = r$$

The radius is about 7 meters.

22. C; $C = 2\pi r \approx 2(3.14)(8) = 50.24$

23. $d = 2$ cm

$C = \pi d \approx 3.14(2) = 6.28$

The circumference is about 6.28 centimeters.

Check: Estimate: $3.14(2) \approx 3(2) = 6$, so 6.28 is reasonable.

24. $d = 0.75$ in.

$C = \pi d \approx 3.14(0.75) = 2.355$

The circumference is about 2.355 inches.

Check: Estimate: $3.14(0.75) \approx 3(1) = 3$, so 2.355 is reasonable.

25. $r = 7$ mm

$C = 2\pi r \approx 2(3.14)(7) = 43.96$

The circumference is about 43.96 millimeters.

Check: Estimate: $2(3.14)(7) \approx 2(3)(7) = 42$, so 43.96 is reasonable.

26. $C = \pi d \approx 3.14(5) = 15.7$

There are 4 half circles or 2 whole circles, so $2(15.7) = 31.4$. The perimeter of the figure is 31.4 centimeters.

27. $C = \pi d \approx 3.14(3) = 9.42$

Two half circles make 1 whole circle.

$9.42 + 6 + 6 = 21.42$

The perimeter of the figure is 21.42 feet.

28. $C = \pi d \approx 3.14(7) = 21.98$

Two half circles make 1 whole circle.

$21.98 + 9 + 9 = 39.98$

The perimeter of the figure is 39.98 inches.

29.

$C = \pi d$	Circumference formula
$\dfrac{C}{d} = \dfrac{\pi d}{d}$	Division property of equality
$\dfrac{C}{d} = \pi$	Simplify.

If $C = \pi d$, then $\pi = \dfrac{C}{d}$.

30.

$C = \pi d$	Circumference formula
$\dfrac{C}{\pi} = \dfrac{\pi d}{\pi}$	Division property of equality
$\dfrac{C}{\pi} = d$	Simplify.

If $C = \pi d$, then $d = \dfrac{C}{\pi}$.

31.

$C = 2\pi r$	Circumference formula
$\dfrac{C}{2\pi} = \dfrac{2\pi r}{2\pi}$	Division property of equality
$\dfrac{C}{2\pi} = r$	Simplify.

If $C = 2\pi r$, then $r = \dfrac{C}{2\pi}$.

Chapter 6, *continued*

32. $C = 2\pi r$ Circumference formula

$\dfrac{C}{2r} = \dfrac{2\pi r}{2r}$ Division property of equality

$\dfrac{C}{2r} = \pi$ Simplify.

If $C = 2\pi r$, then $\pi = \dfrac{C}{2r}$.

33. $C = 2\pi r$

$75.36 \approx 2(3.14)(x + 9)$

$75.36 = 6.28\,(x + 9)$

$75.36 = 6.28x + 56.52$

$18.84 = 6.28x$

$\dfrac{18.84}{6.28} = \dfrac{6.28x}{6.28}$

$3 = x$

The value of x is 3 m.

34. $C = \pi d$

$109.9 \approx 3.14(2x + 17)$

$109.9 = 6.28x + 53.38$

$56.52 = 6.28x$

$\dfrac{56.52}{6.28} = \dfrac{6.28x}{6.28}$

$9 = x$

The value of x is 9 m.

35. $C = \pi d$

$94.2 \approx 3.14(x + 20)$

$94.2 = 3.14x + 62.8$

$31.4 = 3.14x$

$\dfrac{31.4}{3.14} = \dfrac{3.14x}{3.14}$

$10 = x$

The value of x is 10 m.

Problem Solving

36. $C = \pi d \approx 3.14(96) = 301.44$

The circumference is about 301.44 feet.

37. $C = 2\pi r \approx 2\left(\dfrac{22}{7}\right)(3.5) = 22$

The circumference of the first gear is about 22 inches.

The radius of the second gear is 3(3.5), or 10.5 inches.

$C = 2\pi r \approx 2\left(\dfrac{22}{7}\right)(10.5) = 66$

The circumference of the second gear is about 66 inches.

The circumference of the second gear is 3 times as great as the circumference of the first gear.

38. Yes, your friend's approximation of 12 feet is reasonable. Estimate by using 36 feet for the circumference and 3 for π.

$d = \dfrac{C}{\pi} = \dfrac{36}{3} = 12.$

39. The circumference of the clock face is about 72 feet 3 inches, or 72.25 feet.

$C = \pi d$

$72.25 \approx 3.14d$

$\dfrac{72.25}{3.14} = \dfrac{3.14d}{3.14}$

$23.01 \approx d$

The diameter of the clock face is about 23 feet.

40. *Circumnavigate* means to navigate around an object. This is like the definition of circumference in that it involves going *around* an object as circumference is the distance *around* a circle.

41. Answers will vary.

42. $C = \pi d$

$12.2 \approx 3.14d$

$24 = 3.14d$

$\dfrac{24}{3.14} = \dfrac{3.14d}{3.14}$

$7.64 \approx d$

The diameter of the leg opening is 7.64 inches.

43. B; hoop:

$C = \pi d$

$56.5 \approx 3.14d$

$\dfrac{56.5}{3.14} = \dfrac{3.14d}{3.14}$

$18 \text{ in.} \approx d$

basketball: $C = \pi d$

$28.5 \approx 3.14d$

$\dfrac{28.5}{3.14} = \dfrac{3.14d}{3.14}$

$9 \text{ in.} \approx d$

The approximate difference between the diameter of the hoop and the diameter of the basketball is $18 - 9$, or 9 inches.

44. $C = 2\pi r$

$r = 1\colon C = 2\pi(1) = 2\pi$ m

$r = 2\colon C = 2\pi(2) = 4\pi$ m

$r = 4\colon C = 2\pi(4) = 8\pi$ m

$r = 8\colon C = 2\pi(8) = 16\pi$ m

$r = 16\colon C = 2\pi(16) = 32\pi$ m

The circumference of a circle doubles as its radius doubles.

The circumference of a circle triples as its radius triples. This is because circumference is measured in linear units.

45. $C = 2\pi r \approx 2(3.14)(2) = 12.56$

Sample answer: The perimeter of the square is between 13 and 37. The square's perimeter is closer to 13 because the square is closer in size to the smaller circle.

46 a. $C = 2\pi r \approx 2(3.14)(3963) \approx 24{,}900$

The circumference of Earth is about 24,900 miles.

b.
$$\begin{array}{r} 29{,}000 \\ -24{,}900 \\ \hline 4100 \end{array}$$

Mike Horn traveled about 4100 miles farther.

c.
$$C = 2\pi r$$
$$29{,}000 \approx 2(3.14)r$$
$$29{,}000 = 6.28r$$
$$\frac{29{,}000}{6.28} = \frac{6.28r}{6.28}$$
$$4618 \approx r$$

The radius of Earth would be about 4618 miles. This radius is about 655 miles greater than the actual radius.

d. *Sample answer:* He probably had to go around mountains, lakes, and so on.

47. $C = \pi d \approx 3.14(26) = 81.64$

The circumference of the wheel is about 81.64 inches.

1 mi = 5280 ft = 63,360 in.

63,360 in. $\times$ 6 = 380,160 in.

6 mi = 380,160 in.

$$\frac{380{,}160}{81.64} \approx 4657$$

The wheel will make approximately 4657 rotations.

48. a. The diameter is 2 • 5, or 10 units.

$$C = \pi d = 10\pi$$

$$\frac{10\pi}{2} = 5\pi, \frac{10\pi}{3}, \frac{10\pi}{4} = \frac{5\pi}{2}, \frac{10\pi}{5} = 2\pi$$

b. $\ell = \dfrac{10\pi}{n + 1}$

c. $\ell = \dfrac{10\pi}{11 + 1} = \dfrac{10\pi}{12} = \dfrac{5\pi}{6}$

Mixed Review

49.
$$-15 + x \le 8$$
$$-15 + x + 15 \le 8 + 15$$
$$x \le 23$$

50.
$$r + 11 > 6$$
$$r + 11 - 11 > 6 - 11$$
$$r > -5$$

51.
$$-4a \ge -8$$
$$\frac{-4a}{-4} \le \frac{-8}{-4}$$
$$a \le 2$$

52–54.

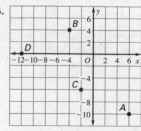

55. $(5 \times 10^9) \times (4 \times 10^{15})$

$= 5 \times 4 \times 10^9 \times 10^{15}$ Commutative property of multiplication

$= (5 \times 4) \times (10^9 \times 10^{15})$ Associative property of multiplication

$= 20 \times 10^{24}$ Product of powers property

$= 2 \times 10^1 \times 10^{24}$ Write 20 in scientific notation.

$= 2 \times 10^{25}$ Product of powers property

Lesson 6.5

6.5 Guided Practice (p. 319)

1.
$$-7z + 15 \ge 57$$
$$-7z + 15 - 15 \ge 57 - 15$$
$$-7z \ge 42$$
$$\frac{-7z}{-7} \le \frac{42}{-7}$$
$$z \le -6$$

2.
$$11n + 36 < 3n - 4$$
$$11n + 36 - 3n < 3n - 4 - 3n$$
$$8n + 36 < -4$$
$$8n + 36 - 36 < -4 - 36$$
$$8n < -40$$
$$\frac{8n}{8} < \frac{-40}{8}$$
$$n < -5$$

3.
$$9(y - 2) > -16$$
$$9y - 18 > -16$$
$$9y - 18 + 18 > -16 + 18$$
$$9y > 2$$
$$\frac{9y}{9} > \frac{2}{9}$$
$$y > \frac{2}{9}$$

4.
$$10x - (5x + x + 50) \ge 200$$
$$10x - (6x + 50) \ge 200$$
$$10x - 6x - 50 \ge 200$$
$$4x - 50 \ge 200$$
$$4x - 50 + 50 \ge 200 + 50$$
$$4x \ge 250$$
$$\frac{4x}{4} \ge \frac{250}{4}$$
$$x \ge 62.5$$

At least 63 people need to attend the bowling night.

Chapter 6, *continued*

Skill Practice

1. The inequality symbols have the following meanings:

　$<$　less than

　$>$　greater than

　$\leq$　less than or equal to

　$\geq$　greater than or equal to

2. When you solve an inequality, you reverse the inequality symbol when multiplying or dividing by a *negative* number.

3.　$4a + 7 \geq 11$

$4a + 7 - 7 \geq 11 - 7$

$4a \geq 4$

$\dfrac{4a}{4} \geq \dfrac{4}{4}$

$a \geq 1$

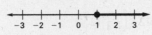

4.　$16 < 3b + 22$

$16 - 22 < 3b + 22 - 22$

$-6 < 3b$

$\dfrac{-6}{3} < \dfrac{3b}{3}$

$-2 < b$

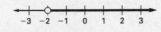

5.　$7 - 2p \geq -5$

$7 - 2p - 7 \geq -5 - 7$

$-2p \geq -12$

$\dfrac{-2p}{-2} \leq \dfrac{-12}{-2}$

$p \leq 6$

6.　$-3y + 2 < -16$

$-3y + 2 - 2 < -16 - 2$

$-3y < -18$

$\dfrac{-3y}{-3} > \dfrac{-18}{-3}$

$y > 6$

7.　$-2w + 6 < 2$

$-2w + 6 - 6 < 2 - 6$

$-2w < -4$

$\dfrac{-2w}{-2} > \dfrac{-4}{-2}$

$w > 2$

8.　$26s \leq 3s + 69$

$26s - 3s \leq 3s + 69 - 3s$

$23s \leq 69$

$\dfrac{23s}{23} \leq \dfrac{69}{23}$

$s \leq 3$

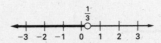

9.　$12c + 12 > 48c$

$12c + 12 - 12c > 48c - 12c$

$12 > 36c$

$\dfrac{12}{36} > \dfrac{36c}{36}$

$\dfrac{1}{3} > c$

10.　$5x - 14 \leq 2x + 7$

$5x - 14 - 2x \leq 2x + 7 - 2x$

$3x - 14 \leq 7$

$3x - 14 + 14 \leq 7 + 14$

$3x \leq 21$

$\dfrac{3x}{3} \leq \dfrac{21}{3}$

$x \leq 7$

11.　$5 - 4z > 17 - z$

$5 - 4z + 4z > 17 - z + 4z$

$5 > 17 + 3z$

$5 - 17 > 17 + 3z - 17$

$-12 > 3z$

$\dfrac{-12}{3} > \dfrac{3z}{3}$

$-4 > z$

12.　$10 \geq 5(3 + t)$

$10 \geq 15 + 5t$

$10 - 15 \geq 15 + 5t - 15$

$-5 \geq 5t$

$\dfrac{-5}{5} \geq \dfrac{5t}{5}$

$-1 \geq t$

Chapter 6, *continued*

13.
$$2(5 + n) \le 6$$
$$10 + 2n \le 6$$
$$10 + 2n - 10 \le 6 - 10$$
$$2n \le -4$$
$$\frac{2n}{2} \le \frac{-4}{2}$$
$$n \le -2$$

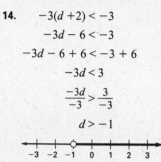

14.
$$-3(d + 2) < -3$$
$$-3d - 6 < -3$$
$$-3d - 6 + 6 < -3 + 6$$
$$-3d < 3$$
$$\frac{-3d}{-3} > \frac{3}{-3}$$
$$d > -1$$

15.
$$10a > -5(a + 6)$$
$$10a > -5a - 30$$
$$10a + 5a > -5a - 30 + 5a$$
$$15a > -30$$
$$\frac{15a}{15} > \frac{-30}{15}$$
$$a > -2$$

16.
$$2(5x - 4) \le 8(x + 1)$$
$$10x - 8 \le 8x + 8$$
$$10x - 8 - 8x \le 8x + 8 - 8x$$
$$2x - 8 \le 8$$
$$2x - 8 + 8 \le 8 + 8$$
$$2x \le 16$$
$$\frac{2x}{2} \le \frac{16}{2}$$
$$x \le 8$$

17.
$$4(6k - 4) \ge 7k - (2k - 3)$$
$$24k - 16 \ge 7k - 2k + 3$$
$$24k - 16 \ge 5k + 3$$
$$24k - 16 - 5k \ge 5k + 3 - 5k$$
$$19k - 16 \ge 3$$
$$19k - 16 + 16 \ge 3 + 16$$
$$19k \ge 19$$
$$\frac{19k}{19} \ge \frac{19}{19}$$
$$k \ge 1$$

18. B; $-3b + 9 - 11b < 65$
$$-14b + 9 < 65$$
$$-14b + 9 - 9 < 65 - 9$$
$$-14b < 56$$
$$\frac{-14b}{-14} > \frac{56}{-14}$$
$$b > -4$$

19. When dividing each side of an inequality by a negative number you reverse the direction of the inequality symbol.
$$9 - 2x \le 3$$
$$-2x \le -6$$
$$\frac{-2x}{-2} \ge \frac{-6}{-2}$$
$$x \ge 3$$

20. $\frac{2}{3}x + \frac{4}{3} - \frac{3}{4}x < -\frac{3}{4}$

Multiply each side by 12.
$$\left(\frac{2}{3}x + \frac{4}{3} - \frac{3}{4}x\right)12 < \left(-\frac{3}{4}\right)12$$
$$\left(\frac{2}{3}x\right)12 + \left(\frac{4}{3}\right)12 - \left(\frac{3}{4}x\right)12 < \left(-\frac{3}{4}\right)12$$
$$8x + 16 - 9x < -9$$
$$-x + 16 < -9$$
$$-x < -25$$
$$\frac{-x}{-1} > \frac{-25}{-1}$$
$$x > 25$$

21. $\frac{2}{3}y + 18 \ge 5 - \frac{4}{7}y$

Multiply each side by 21.
$$\left(\frac{2}{3}y + 18\right)21 \ge \left(5 - \frac{4}{7}y\right)21$$
$$\left(\frac{2}{3}y\right)21 + (18)21 \ge (5)21 - \left(\frac{4}{7}y\right)21$$
$$14y + 378 \ge 105 - 12y$$
$$26y + 378 \ge 105$$
$$26y \ge -273$$
$$\frac{26y}{26} \ge \frac{-273}{26}$$
$$y \ge -10.5$$

22. $\frac{1}{2}k - 6 \ge -\frac{1}{6}k$

Multiply each side by 6.
$$\left(\frac{1}{2}k - 6\right)6 \ge \left(-\frac{1}{6}k\right)6$$
$$\left(\frac{1}{2}k\right)6 - (6)6 \ge \left(-\frac{1}{6}k\right)6$$
$$3k - 36 \ge -k$$
$$-36 \ge -4k$$
$$\frac{-36}{-4} \le \frac{-4k}{-4}$$
$$9 \le k$$

23. $\frac{1}{3}m - \frac{1}{2}m > -4$

Multiply each side by 6.

$\left(\frac{1}{3}m - \frac{1}{2}m\right)6 > (-4)6$

$\left(\frac{1}{3}m\right)6 - \left(\frac{1}{2}m\right)6 > (-4)6$

$2m - 3m > -24$

$-m > -24$

$\frac{-m}{-1} < \frac{-24}{-1}$

$m < 24$

24. $3.7z \le 33.32 - 3.1z$

Multiply each side by 100.

$(3.7z)100 \le (33.32 - 3.1z)100$

$370z \le 3332 - 310z$

$680z \le 3332$

$\frac{680z}{680} \le \frac{3332}{680}$

$z \le 4.9$

25. $-0.6y - 3.79 + 5.2y < 19.67$

Multiply each side by 100.

$(-0.6y - 3.79 + 5.2y)100 < (19.67)100$

$-60y - 379 + 520y < 1967$

$460y - 379 < 1967$

$460y < 2346$

$\frac{460y}{460} < \frac{2346}{460}$

$y < 5.1$

26. $0.05a + 9.367 - 1.65a \le 4.183$

Multiply each side by 1000.

$(0.05a + 9.367 - 1.65a)1000 \le (4.183)1000$

$50a + 9367 - 1650a \le 4183$

$-1600a + 9367 \le 4183$

$-1600a \le -5184$

$\frac{-1600a}{-1600} \ge \frac{-5184}{-1600}$

$a \ge 3.24$

27. $2.3x - 52.46 \le -0.9(x - 117)$

$2.3x - 52.46 \le -0.9x + 105.3$

Multiply each side by 100.

$(2.3x - 52.46)100 \le (-0.9x + 105.3)100$

$230x - 5246 \le -90x + 10{,}530$

$320x - 5246 \le 10{,}530$

$320x \le 15{,}776$

$\frac{320x}{320} \le \frac{15{,}776}{320}$

$x \le 49.3$

28.
$C = 2\pi r$

$2\pi r < 5 + 2r$

$2(3.14)r < 5 + 2r$

$6.28r < 5 + 2r$

$4.28r < 5$

$\frac{4.28r}{4.28} < \frac{5}{4.28}$

$r < 1.17$

Sample answer:

Examples: $r = 1$, $r = 1.1$

Nonexamples: $r = 1.2$, $r = 2$

29.
$-13 < 3x - 4 < 8$

$-13 + 4 < 3x - 4 + 4 < 8 + 4$

$-9 < 3x < 12$

$\frac{-9}{3} < \frac{3x}{3} < \frac{12}{3}$

$-3 < x < 4$

30.
$9 < -x + 6 \le 17$

$9 - 6 < -x + 6 - 6 \le 17 - 6$

$3 < -x \le 11$

$\frac{3}{-1} > \frac{-x}{-1} \ge \frac{11}{-1}$

$-11 \le x < -3$

31.
$2 \le 2(x + 4) < 20$

$2 \le 2x + 8 < 20$

$2 - 8 \le 2x + 8 - 8 < 20 - 8$

$-6 \le 2x < 12$

$\frac{-6}{2} \le \frac{2x}{2} < \frac{12}{2}$

$-3 \le x < 6$

32. $|a| \ge 2$

$a \ge 2$ or $a \le -2$

Problem Solving

33. a. $925 + 25p \ge 2500$

b.
$925 + 25p \ge 2500$

$925 + 25p - 925 \ge 2500 - 925$

$25p \ge 1575$

$\frac{25p}{25} \ge \frac{1575}{25}$

$p \ge 63$

You need at least 63 more pledges.

Chapter 6, *continued*

34. B; $0.25 + 0.10m \le 1.65$

$(0.25 + 0.10m)100 \le (1.65)100$

$25 + 10m \le 165$

$10m \le 140$

$\dfrac{10m}{10} \le \dfrac{140}{10}$

$m \le 14$

You can talk no more than 14 minutes.

35. $16{,}000 + 150d > 18{,}550$

$16{,}000 + 150d - 16{,}000 > 18{,}550 - 16{,}000$

$150d > 2550$

$\dfrac{150d}{150} > \dfrac{2550}{150}$

$d > 17$

You need to catch more than 17 discs to have a new high score.

36. Solving a multi-step inequality is similar to solving a multi-step equation in that when they involve addition or subtraction, the same steps are used to isolate the variable.

Solving a multi-step inequality is different from solving a multi-step equation in that when an inequality involves multiplication or division by a negative number, the inequality symbol must be reversed.

37. $350 + 0.2x \ge 500$

$350 + 0.2x - 350 \ge 500 - 350$

$0.2x \ge 150$

$\dfrac{0.2x}{0.2} \ge \dfrac{150}{0.2}$

$x \ge 750$

Jade has to sell at least $750 worth of clothes to earn at least $500.

$350 + 0.15x \ge 500$

$0.15x \ge 150$

$\dfrac{0.15x}{0.15} \ge \dfrac{150}{0.15}$

$x \ge 1000$

Jade has to sell at least $1000 worth of clothes to earn at least $500.

38. a. The number of magazines that need to be produced and sold to cover or exceed the overhead costs.

b. $3.95m - 1.20m \ge 25{,}000$

$2.75m \ge 25{,}000$

$\dfrac{2.75m}{2.75} \ge \dfrac{25{,}000}{2.75}$

$m \ge 9090.91$

The publisher needs to produce and sell at least 9091 magazines each month to make a profit.

c. $3.95m - 1.10m \ge 24{,}000$

$2.85m \ge 24{,}000$

$\dfrac{2.85m}{2.85} \ge \dfrac{24{,}000}{2.85}$

$m \ge 8421.05$

Sample answer: The publisher will need to produce and sell 670 fewer magazines each month to make a profit.

39. $20{,}000 > 2.75h + 3500$

$16{,}500 > 2.75h$

$\dfrac{16{,}500}{2.75} > \dfrac{2.75h}{2.75}$

$6000 > h$

The base height of a *Strato* cloud is less than 6000 feet.

40. It is an *Alto* cloud because its base is higher than the base of a *Strato* cloud and lower than the base of a *Cirro* cloud.

41. The range of base heights is $6000 < h < 20{,}000$.

42. $d < 120$ cannot be correct because you have only $25 to spend. The cost of 119 drinks is $357.

43. $d \le 0$ cannot be correct because you cannot buy a negative number of drinks.

44. $d \ge 4$ cannot be correct because you cannot buy an unlimited number of drinks.

45. $ax + b < c$

$ax < c - b$ Subtraction Property of Inequality

$x < \dfrac{c - b}{a}$ if $a > 0$ Division Property of Inequality

$x > \dfrac{c - b}{a}$ if $a < 0$

Mixed Review

46. $\dfrac{13}{x}$

47. $x - 480$

48. You can make the following sandwiches with white bread:

white, turkey, mustard

white, turkey, mayonnaise

white, turkey, neither

white, ham, mustard

white, ham, mayonnaise

white, ham, neither

white, roast beef, mustard

white, roast beef, mayonnaise

white, roast beef, neither

There are 9 possible sandwiches with white bread, so there are also 9 possible sandwiches with wheat bread. You can make 18 different sandwiches.

Use the strategy *Make a List* because you can list all of the possibilities.

Chapter 6, *continued*

49. C; $3.3c - 2.1 = 7.8$

$(3.3c \quad 2.1)10 = (7.8)10$

$33c - 21 = 78$

$33c = 99$

$\dfrac{33c}{33} = \dfrac{99}{33}$

$c = 3$

Technology Activity 6.5 (p. 323)

1. The solution is all numbers less than 13.

2. The solution is all numbers greater than 3.

3. The solution is all numbers less than or equal to -1.

4. The solution is all numbers less than or equal to -4.

5. The solution is all numbers greater than -3.

6. The solution is all numbers greater than -1.

7. $2(1.50) + 0.25p + 3(0.95) \le 10$

$3 + 0.25p + 2.85 \le 10$

$0.25p + 5.85 \le 10$

The solution is all numbers less than or equal to 16.6. Dani can buy at most 16 pencils.

Lesson 6.6

6.6 Guided Practice (pp. 325–326)

1. $12x + 8 > 125$

$12x > 117$

$x > 9.75$

It doesn't make sense to attend 9.75 games. So, you would have to attend 10 or more games to make buying a season ticket a better value.

2. The difference of a number and 4 is less than

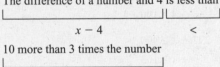

$x - 4 \qquad\qquad\qquad <$

10 more than 3 times the number

$3x + 10$

The inequality is $x - 4 < 3x + 10$.

3. 6 times the sum of a number and 8 is no more than

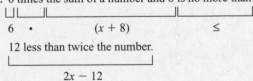

$6 \quad\cdot \qquad\qquad (x + 8) \qquad\qquad \le$

12 less than twice the number.

$2x - 12$

The inequality is $6(x + 8) \le 2x - 12$.

---

4. Let x represent the number of bottles

without membership		with membership	

Cost of a membership	$=$	Number of bottles	$>$	Cost of a bottle	$\cdot$	Number of bottles	$+$	Membership fee

$18x > 15x + 20$

$3x > 20$

$\dfrac{3x}{3} > \dfrac{20}{3}$

$x > 6.\overline{6}$

You cannot buy $6.\overline{6}$ bottles of vitamins. So, you need to buy 7 or more bottles of vitamins each year to make a membership worthwhile.

6.6 Exercises (pp. 326–329)

Skill Practice

1. Yes, it can be translated as an inequality because "is at least" means $\ge$.

2. No, it cannot be translated as an inequality because "is" means $=$. It can be translated as an equation.

3. No, it cannot be translated as an inequality because "is equal to" means $=$. It can be translated as an equation.

4. Yes, it can be translated as an inequality because "is less than" means $<$.

5. $x + 2 \le 6$
$x + 2 - 2 \le 6 - 2$
$x \le 4$

6. $9 < x + 1$
$9 - 1 < x + 1 - 1$
$8 < x$

7. $x - 6 > 14$
$x - 6 + 6 > 14 + 6$
$x > 20$

8. $8x \ge 40$
$\dfrac{8x}{8} \ge \dfrac{40}{8}$
$x \ge 5$

9. $x + 12 < 4$
$x + 12 - 12 < 4 - 12$
$x < -8$

10. $7 > x - 5$
$7 + 5 > x - 5 + 5$
$12 > x$

11. B; $4x + 2 < 18$

12. The phrase "is at least" means $\ge$.

$3(x + 5) \ge 26$

$3x + 15 \ge 26$

$3x \ge 11$

$x \ge 3\frac{2}{3}$

13. A number of ride tickets must be a whole number because you can't buy part of a ride.

14. You can buy a fraction of a pound of ham.

15. A number of hot dogs must be a whole number because you can't buy part of a hot dog.

Chapter 6, *continued*

16. $-16 \le 8(x + 3) < 72$

$-16 \le 8x + 24 < 72$

$-40 \le \quad 8x \quad < 48$

$\dfrac{-40}{8} \le \quad \dfrac{8x}{8} \quad < \dfrac{48}{8}$

$-5 \le \quad x \quad < 6$

17. $12 < 6x - 4 \le 26$

$16 < \quad 6x \quad \le 30$

$\dfrac{16}{6} < \quad \dfrac{6x}{6} \quad \le \dfrac{30}{6}$

$2\dfrac{2}{3} < \quad x \quad \le 5$

Problem Solving

18. a. Let n represent the number of months.

$$\underset{\text{fee}}{\text{Initial}} + \underset{\text{fee}}{\text{Monthly}} \cdot \underset{\text{of months}}{\text{Number}} \le \underset{\text{to spend}}{\text{Amount}}$$

b. $50 + 32n \le 200$

$32n \le 150$

$\dfrac{32n}{32} \le \dfrac{150}{32}$

$n \le 4.6875$

You can be a member for 4 months.

c.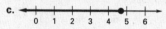

You can afford to be a member for 4 months.

19. B; Let x represent the number of items.

$2x - 55 \ge 100$

20. Let x represent the number of CDs.

$$\underset{\text{of CD}}{\text{Cost}} \cdot \underset{\text{of CDs}}{\text{Number}} + \underset{\text{charges}}{\text{Shipping}} \le \underset{\text{you have}}{\text{Money}}$$

$12x + 4 \le 50$

$12x \le 46$

$\dfrac{12x}{12} \le \dfrac{46}{12}$

$x \le 3.8\overline{3}$

You can't buy part of a CD, so you can buy no more than 3 CDs.

21. Let x represent the number of dances.

Member		Nonmember	

$$\underset{\substack{\text{a dance}}}{\underset{\text{attend}}{\text{Cost to}}} \cdot \underset{\text{of dances}}{\text{Number}} + \underset{\text{fee}}{\text{Membership}} < \underset{\substack{\text{a dance}}}{\underset{\text{attend}}{\text{Cost to}}} \cdot \underset{\text{of dances}}{\text{Number}}$$

$4x + 30 < 6x$

$30 < 2x$

$\dfrac{30}{2} < \dfrac{2x}{2}$

$15 < x$

You have to attend more than 15 dances so that becoming a member will cost less than paying the nonmember rate.

22. Three less than a number can be translated as $x - 3$, which is a phrase. Three is less than a number can be translated as $3 < x$, which is a sentence.

23. *Sample answer:* You want to spend no more than \$31 on CDs. How many \$8 CDs can you buy if you spend \$5 on lunch?

$5 + 8x \le 31$

$8x \le 26$

$\dfrac{8x}{8} \le \dfrac{26}{8}$

$x \le 3.25$

You can't buy part of a CD, so you can buy no more than 3 CDs.

24. Let h represent the number of hours.

$$\underset{\substack{\text{ground}}}{\underset{\text{covering}}{\underset{\text{snow already}}{\text{Amount of}}}} + \underset{\text{rate}}{\text{Falling}} \cdot \underset{\text{of hours}}{\text{Number}} \ge \underset{\substack{\text{cancelled}}}{\underset{\text{school to be}}{\underset{\text{snow for}}{\text{Amount of}}}}$$

$2 + 0.5h \ge 6$

$0.5h \ge 4$

$\dfrac{0.5h}{0.5} \ge \dfrac{4}{0.5}$

$h \ge 8$

In 8 hours, there will be at least 6 inches of snow. Eight hours after 7 P.M. is 3 A.M.

Because there will be at least 6 inches of snow at 3 A.M., school will be cancelled.

25. $\dfrac{90 + 92 + 115 + x}{4} \ge 100$

$\dfrac{297 + x}{4} \ge 100$

$\dfrac{297 + x}{4} \cdot 4 \ge 100 \cdot 4$

$297 + x \ge 400$

$x \ge 103$

You need a score of 103 or higher in the next game.

26. Let x represent the number of hours over 30.

$30(6.5) + 1.5(6.5)x > 273$

$195 + 9.75x > 273$

$9.75x > 78$

$\dfrac{9.75x}{9.75} > \dfrac{78}{9.75}$

$x > 8$

You must work more than 8 hours of overtime to make more than \$273 in a week.

Chapter 6, continued

27. girth $= 2h + 2w = 2(15) + 2(12) = 30 + 24 = 54$

Let x represent the number of boxes.

$$\underset{\substack{\text{Length} \\ \text{of a box}}}{\fbox{}} \cdot \underset{\substack{\text{Number} \\ \text{of boxes}}}{\fbox{}} + \underset{\text{Girth}}{\fbox{}} \le \underset{\substack{\text{Total length} \\ \text{and girth}}}{\fbox{}}$$

$$6x + 54 \le 108$$

$$6x \le 54$$

$$\frac{6x}{6} \le \frac{54}{6}$$

$$x \le 9$$

You could wrap no more than 9 boxes as one package.

28. a. Total cost of a ride with Town Taxi:

$$2 + (0.40)\left(\tfrac{1}{5}n\right)$$

Total cost of a ride with City Cab:

$$2.50 + (0.15)\left(\tfrac{1}{10}n\right)$$

b. *Sample answer:* No, because Town Taxi charges $.40 for every $\frac{1}{5}$ mi, and City Cab charges $.15 for every $\frac{1}{10}$ mi, which is $.30 every $\frac{1}{5}$ mi. So, the total cost for Town Taxi could end up being more than the total cost for City Cab depending on how far they travel.

c. *Sample answer:* Distances greater than or equal to 8 mi.

$$2.5 + (0.15)\left(\tfrac{1}{10}n\right) < 2 + 0.4\left(\tfrac{1}{5}n\right)$$

$$2.5 + 0.015n < 2 + 0.08n$$

$$2.5 < 2 + 0.065n$$

$$0.5 < 0.065n$$

$$\frac{0.5}{0.065} < \frac{0.065n}{0.065}$$

$$7.7 < n \text{ or } n > 7.7$$

Testing $n = 7$ and $n = 8$ in both inequalities shows that City Cab is cheaper when $n = 8$.

So the total cost for City Cab is less than the total cost for Town Taxi for distances greater than or equal to 8 miles.

29. $216 \le x + x + 2 \le 232$

$$216 \le \quad 2x + 2 \quad \le 232$$

$$214 \le \quad 2x \quad \le 230$$

$$\frac{214}{2} \le \quad \frac{2x}{2} \quad \le \frac{230}{2}$$

$$107 \le \quad x \quad \le 115$$

Possible pairs of consecutive odd integers: 107 and 109, 109 and 111, 111 and 113, 113 and 115, and 115 and 117. The sum of 107 and 109 is 216, and the sum of 115 and 117 is 232.

Mixed Review

30. $\dfrac{15}{18} = \dfrac{15 \div 3}{18 \div 3} = \dfrac{5}{6}$

31. $\dfrac{-7}{42} = \dfrac{-7 \div 7}{42 \div 7} = \dfrac{-1}{6} = -\dfrac{1}{6}$

32. $\dfrac{24}{-168} = \dfrac{24 \div 24}{-168 \div 24} = \dfrac{1}{-7} = -\dfrac{1}{7}$

33.
$$6a - 15 \le 27$$
$$6a - 15 + 15 \le 27 + 15$$
$$6a \le 42$$
$$\frac{6a}{6} \le \frac{42}{6}$$
$$a \le 7$$

34.
$$-9 < 5 - 7k$$
$$-9 - 5 < 5 - 7k - 5$$
$$-14 < -7k$$
$$\frac{-14}{-7} > \frac{-7k}{-7}$$
$$2 > k \text{ or } k < 2$$

35.
$$2p + 24 > 10p$$
$$2p + 24 - 2p > 10p - 2p$$
$$24 > 8p$$
$$\frac{24}{8} > \frac{8p}{8}$$
$$3 > p \text{ or } p < 3$$

36. C;
$$A = \ell w$$
$$42 = 7w$$
$$\frac{42}{7} = \frac{7w}{7}$$

$$w = 6$$
$$p = 2\ell + 2w$$
$$p = 2(7) + 2(6) = 14 + 12 = 26$$

The perimeter of the rectangle is 26 meters.

Quiz 6.4–6.6 (p. 329)

1. $C = \pi d \approx \dfrac{22}{7}(28) = 88$

The circumference is about 88 inches.

2.
$$C = \pi d$$
$$132 \approx \frac{22}{7}d$$
$$132 \cdot \frac{7}{22} = \frac{22}{7}d \cdot \frac{7}{22}$$
$$42 = d$$

The diameter is about 42 feet.

3.
$$C = 2\pi r$$
$$150 \approx 2(3.14)r$$
$$150 = 6.28r$$
$$\frac{150}{6.28} = \frac{6.28r}{6.28}$$
$$23.89 = r$$

The radius is about 23.89 centimeters.

4.
$$-8a - 10 > 14$$
$$-8a - 10 + 10 > 14 + 10$$
$$-8a > 24$$
$$\frac{-8a}{-8} < \frac{24}{-8}$$
$$a < -3$$

5.
$$3z \le 35 - 2z$$
$$3z + 2z \le 35 - 2z + 2z$$
$$5z \le 35$$
$$\frac{5z}{5} \le \frac{35}{5}$$
$$z \le 7$$

6.
$$5b \geq 2(b + 2.25)$$
$$5b \geq 2b + 4.5$$
$$5b - 2b \geq 2b + 4.5 - 2b$$
$$3b \geq 4.5$$
$$\frac{3b}{3} \geq \frac{4.5}{3}$$
$$b \geq 1.5$$

7.
$$6x - 2 \geq 40$$
$$6x - 2 + 2 \geq 40 + 2$$
$$6x \geq 42$$
$$\frac{6x}{6} \geq \frac{42}{6}$$
$$x \geq 7$$

8.
$$5(4 + x) > 10$$
$$20 + 5x > 10$$
$$20 + 5x - 20 > 10 - 20$$
$$5x > -10$$
$$\frac{5x}{5} > \frac{-10}{5}$$
$$x > -2$$

9.
$$33,600 + (2500 + 1700)x > 54,000$$
$$33,600 + 4200x > 54,000$$
$$4200x > 20,400$$
$$\frac{4200x}{4200} > \frac{20,400}{4200}$$
$$x > 4.86$$

You must go through at least 5 levels to beat your high score.

Mixed Review of Problem Solving (p. 330)

1. a. Front wheel: $C = \pi d \approx (3.14)(50) = 157$ in.

Rear wheel: $C = \pi d \approx (3.14)(17) = 53.38$ in.

The front wheel circumference is 157 in. and the rear wheel circumference is 53.38 in.

b. The rear wheel will take about 3 rotations for every one rotation of the front wheel.

Sample answer: $157 \div 53.38 = 2.9$

c. Change 157 in. to 13.083 ft by dividing by 12. Change 53.38 in to 4.448 ft by dividing by 12.

Front wheel: $2000 \div 13.083 = 153$ rotations

Rear wheel: $2000 \div 4.448 = 450$ rotations

2. *Sample answer:* The perimeter consists of two halves of a circle with a diameter of 74 m plus two segments of length 85 m: $(3.14)(74) + 2(85)$

$$= 232.36 + 170$$
$$= 402.36$$

The perimeter of the track is approximately 402.36 m.

3.
$$2.5(130) + 0.5(x) \geq 668$$
$$325 + 0.5x \geq 668$$
$$325 + 0.5x - 325 \geq 668 - 325$$
$$0.5x \geq 343$$
$$\frac{0.5x}{0.5} \geq \frac{343}{0.5}$$
$$x \geq 686$$

The pretzel shop must sell at least 686 pretzel bites to make $668.

4. Answers will vary.

5.
$$47 < (1.25)n$$
$$\frac{47}{1.25} < \frac{1.25n}{1.25}$$
$$37.6 < n$$
$$n > 37.6$$

Sample answer: If you ride the subway at least 38 times, it is less expensive if you buy the monthly pass.

6. $C = \pi d$

Largest doll: $24 = 3.14(d)$

$$\frac{24}{3.14} = \frac{3.14d}{3.14}$$
$$d = 7.64 \text{ cm}$$

So its radius is $7.64 \div 2 = 3.82$ cm. The radii of the next 3 dolls are 3.82×0.7, 3.82×0.7^2, and 3.82×0.7^3. The next doll (5th) is $3.82 \times 0.7^4 = 0.92$. The 5th doll's radius is about 0.9 cm.

7. a.
$$380n > 760 + 70n + 720$$
$$380n > 1480 + 70n$$
$$380n - 70n > 1480 + 70n - 70n$$
$$310n > 1480$$
$$\frac{310n}{310} > \frac{1480}{310}$$
$$n > 4.8$$

Isaac must sell at least 5 chairs to make a profit.

b.
$$380n > 760 + 70n + 720 + 155n$$
$$380n > 1480 + 225n$$
$$380n - 225n > 1480 + 225n - 225n$$
$$155n > 1480$$
$$\frac{155n}{155} > \frac{1480}{155}$$
$$n > 9.5$$

Isaac must sell at least 10 chairs to make a profit.

c. Isaac's income: $8 \times 380 = \$3040$

Isaac's expenses:

rent	+	materials	+	expenses	+	apprentice
760	+	8×70	+	720	+	5×155
760	+	560	+	720	+	775

$$\$2815$$

Since Isaac's income, $3040, is greater than his expenses, $2815, he made a profit.

Chapter 6, *continued*

1. The set of all points in a plane that are the same distance from a fixed point called the center is a *circle*.

2. You can approximate π with the decimal 3.14 or the fraction $\frac{22}{7}$.

3. B   **4.** A   **5.** C

6. $6a + 8 - 14a = 96$

$-8a + 8 = 96$

$-8a + 8 - 8 = 96 - 8$

$-8a = 88$

$\dfrac{-8a}{-8} = \dfrac{88}{-8}$

$a = -11$

7. $18 + 4(p - 9) = 6$

$18 + 4p - 36 = 6$

$4p - 18 = 6$

$4p - 18 + 18 = 6 + 18$

$4p = 24$

$\dfrac{4p}{4} = \dfrac{24}{4}$

$p = 6$

8. $4(12 + z) - z = -192$

$48 + 4z - z = -192$

$48 + 3z = -192$

$48 + 3z - 48 = -192 - 48$

$3z = -240$

$\dfrac{3z}{3} = \dfrac{-240}{3}$

$z = -80$

9. $12 + 5(b - 7) = 2$

$12 + 5b - 35 = 2$

$5b - 23 = 2$

$5b - 23 + 23 = 2 + 23$

$5b = 25$

$\dfrac{5b}{5} = \dfrac{25}{5}$

$b = 5$

10. $\dfrac{a + 4}{3} = 10$

$\left(\dfrac{a + 4}{3}\right)3 = (10)3$

$a + 4 = 30$

$a + 4 - 4 = 30 - 4$

$a = 26$

11. $\dfrac{-5c - 12}{4} = 2$

$\left(\dfrac{-5c - 12}{4}\right)4 = 2(4)$

$-5c - 12 = 8$

$-5c - 12 + 12 = 8 + 12$

$-5c = 20$

$\dfrac{-5c}{-5} = \dfrac{20}{-5}$

$c = -4$

12. $-7b + 10 = -11 - 4b$

$-7b + 4b + 10 = -11 - 4b + 4b$

$-3b + 10 = -11$

$-3b + 10 - 10 = -11 - 10$

$-3b = -21$

$\dfrac{-3b}{-3} = \dfrac{-21}{-3}$

$b = 7$

13. $5(m - 9) = -27 - 4m$

$5m - 45 = -27 - 4m$

$5m - 45 + 4m = -27 - 4m + 4m$

$9m - 45 = -27$

$9m - 45 + 45 = -27 + 45$

$9m = 18$

$\dfrac{9m}{9} = \dfrac{18}{9}$

$m = 2$

14. $6(t - 5) = 2(t + 5)$

$6t - 30 = 2t + 10$

$6t - 30 - 2t = 2t + 10 - 2t$

$4t - 30 = 10$

$4t - 30 + 30 = 10 + 30$

$4t = 40$

$\dfrac{4t}{4} = \dfrac{40}{4}$

$t = 10$

15. $3(11 + c) = 19 + c$

$33 + 3c = 19 + c$

$33 + 3c - c = 19 + c - c$

$33 + 2c = 19$

$33 + 2c - 33 = 19 - 33$

$2c = -14$

$\dfrac{2c}{2} = \dfrac{-14}{2}$

$c = -7$

Chapter 6, *continued*

16.
$$2q + 17 = 19q - 51$$
$$2q + 17 - 2q = 19q - 51 - 2q$$
$$17 = 17q - 51$$
$$17 + 51 = 17q - 15 + 51$$
$$68 = 17q$$
$$\frac{68}{17} = \frac{17q}{17}$$
$$4 = q$$

17.
$$2 - (a - 4) = -2(a - 1)$$
$$2 - a + 4 = -2a + 2$$
$$-a + 6 = -2a + 2$$
$$-a + 6 + 2a = -2a + 2 + 2a$$
$$a + 6 = 2$$
$$a + 6 - 6 = 2 - 6$$
$$a = -4$$

18.
$$2w + 50 = 3w - 87$$
$$2w + 50 - 2w = 3w - 87 - 2w$$
$$50 = w - 87$$
$$50 + 87 = w - 87 + 87$$
$$137 = w$$

There are 137 women's rowing teams.

19.
$$-3.5a - 11.4 + 9.9a = 3$$
$$(-3.5a - 11.4 + 9.9a)10 = 3(10)$$
$$-35a - 114 + 99a = 30$$
$$64a - 114 = 30$$
$$64a - 114 + 114 = 30 + 114$$
$$64a = 144$$
$$\frac{64a}{64} = \frac{144}{64}$$
$$a = 2.25$$

20.
$$\frac{11}{16}n - 3 + \frac{1}{4}n = \frac{7}{4}$$
$$\left(\frac{11}{16}n - 3 + \frac{1}{4}n\right)16 = \frac{7}{4}(16)$$
$$\frac{11}{16}n(16) - 3(16) + \frac{1}{4}n(16) = \frac{7}{4}(16)$$
$$11n - 48 + 4n = 28$$
$$15n - 48 = 28$$
$$15n - 48 + 48 = 28 + 48$$
$$15n = 76$$
$$\frac{15n}{15} = \frac{76}{15}$$
$$n = 5\frac{1}{15}$$

21.
$$5s + 3\frac{1}{8} = \frac{5}{24} - 2s$$
$$\left(5s + 3\frac{1}{8}\right)24 = \left(\frac{5}{24} - 2s\right)24$$
$$5s(24) + \frac{25}{8}(24) = \frac{5}{24}(24) - 2s(24)$$
$$120s + 75 = 5 - 48s$$
$$120s + 75 + 48s = 5 - 48s + 48s$$
$$168s + 75 = 5$$
$$168s + 75 - 75 = 5 - 75$$
$$168s = -70$$
$$\frac{168s}{168} = \frac{-70}{168}$$
$$s = -\frac{5}{12}$$

22.
$$\frac{2}{3}b + \frac{4}{5} = \frac{1}{6}b + 2\frac{3}{10}$$
$$\left(\frac{2}{3}b + \frac{4}{5}\right)30 = \left(\frac{1}{6}b + \frac{23}{10}\right)30$$
$$\left(\frac{2}{3}b\right)30 + \left(\frac{4}{5}\right)30 = \left(\frac{1}{6}b\right)30 + \left(\frac{23}{10}\right)30$$
$$20b + 24 = 5b + 69$$
$$20b + 24 - 5b = 5b + 69 - 5b$$
$$15b + 24 = 69$$
$$15b + 24 - 24 = 69 - 24$$
$$15b = 45$$
$$\frac{15b}{15} = \frac{45}{15}$$
$$b = 3$$

23.
$$16.7m - 167.2 = 60.8 + 2.45m$$
$$(16.7m - 167.2)100 = (60.8 + 2.45m)100$$
$$1670m - 16{,}720 = 6080 + 245m$$
$$1670m - 16{,}720 - 245m = 6080 + 245m - 245m$$
$$1425m - 16{,}720 = 6080$$
$$1425m - 16{,}720 + 16{,}720 = 6080 + 16{,}720$$
$$1425m = 22{,}800$$
$$\frac{1425m}{1425} = \frac{22{,}800}{1425}$$
$$m = 16$$

24.
$$-8 + 4.6r = 4r - 2.6$$
$$(-8 + 4.6r)10 = (4r - 2.6)10$$
$$-80 + 46r = 40r - 26$$
$$-80 + 46r - 40r = 40r - 26 - 40r$$
$$-80 + 6r = -26$$
$$-80 + 6r + 80 = -26 + 80$$
$$6r = 54$$
$$\frac{6r}{6} = \frac{54}{6}$$
$$r = 9$$

Chapter 6, *continued*

25. $12x = 4.56 - 12(0.05)$

$12x = 4.56 - 0.60$

$12x = 3.96$

$\dfrac{12x}{12} = \dfrac{3.96}{12}$

$x = 0.33$

You paid $.33 for each can before the deposit.

26. $C = 2\pi r \approx 2\left(\dfrac{22}{7}\right)(21) = 132$

The circumference is about 132 feet.

27. $C = \pi d$

$62.8 \approx 3.14d$

$\dfrac{62.8}{3.14} = \dfrac{3.14d}{3.14}$

$20 = d$

The diameter is about 20 millimeters.

28. $C = 2\pi r$

$12 \approx 2(3.14)r$

$12 = 6.28r$

$\dfrac{12}{6.28} = \dfrac{6.28r}{6.28}$

$1.91 \approx r$

The radius is about 1.91 inches.

29. $C = \pi d$

$66 \approx \left(\dfrac{22}{7}\right)d$

$66 \cdot \dfrac{7}{22} = \left(\dfrac{22}{7}\right)d \cdot \left(\dfrac{7}{22}\right)$

$\dfrac{\overset{3}{\cancel{66}} \cdot 7}{1 \cdot \underset{1}{\cancel{22}}} = d$

$21 = d$

The diameter is about 21 feet.

30. $C = 2\pi r$

$100.48 \approx 2(3.14)r$

$100.48 = 6.28r$

$\dfrac{100.48}{6.28} = \dfrac{6.28r}{6.28}$

$16 = r$

The radius is about 16 centimeters.

31. $C = \pi d$

$C \approx (3.14)(1)$

$C = 3.14$

The circumference is about 3.14 miles.

32. $C = 2\pi r$

$C \approx 2\left(\dfrac{22}{7}\right)(7)$

$C = 44$

The circumference is about 44 inches.

33. $C = \pi d$

$440 \approx \left(\dfrac{22}{7}\right)(d)$

$440 \cdot \dfrac{7}{22} = \left(\dfrac{22}{7}\right)d \cdot \dfrac{7}{22}$

$140 = d$

The diameter is about 140 meters.

34. $C = 2\pi r$

$176 \approx 2\left(\dfrac{22}{7}\right)(r)$

$176 = \left(\dfrac{44}{7}\right)r$

$176 \cdot \dfrac{7}{44} = \left(\dfrac{44}{7}\right)r \cdot \dfrac{7}{44}$

$28 = r$

The radius is about 28 centimeters.

35. $C = \pi d \approx 3.14(89) = 279.46$

The circumference is about 279.46 feet.

36. $-5 < 3x + 16$

$-5 - 16 < 3x + 16 - 16$

$-21 < 3x$

$\dfrac{-21}{3} < \dfrac{3x}{3}$

$-7 < x$

37. $m + 4(5 - m) > -7$

$m + 20 - 4m > -7$

$-3m + 20 > -7$

$-3m + 20 - 20 > -7 - 20$

$-3m > -27$

$\dfrac{-3m}{-3} < \dfrac{-27}{-3}$

$m < 9$

38. $6 - (g - 7) \le 6 - 8g$

$6 - g + 7 \le 6 - 8g$

$13 - g \le 6 - 8g$

$13 - g + 8g \le 6 - 8g + 8g$

$13 + 7g \le 6$

$13 + 7g - 13 \le 6 - 13$

$7g \le -7$

$\dfrac{7g}{7} \le \dfrac{-7}{7}$

$g \le -1$

39. $14 - 3x \le 11$

$14 - 3x - 14 \le 11 - 14$

$-3x \le 3$

$\dfrac{-3x}{-3} \ge \dfrac{-3}{-3}$

$x \ge 1$

40.
$$7(15 - x) \geq 56$$
$$105 - 7x \geq 56$$
$$105 - 7x - 105 \geq 56 - 105$$
$$-7x \geq -49$$
$$\frac{-7x}{-7} \leq \frac{-49}{-7}$$
$$x \leq 7$$

41.
$$2x + 116 \geq 250$$
$$2x + 116 - 116 \geq 250 - 116$$
$$2x \geq 134$$
$$\frac{2x}{2} \geq \frac{134}{2}$$
$$x \geq 67$$

The chorus needs to sell at least 67 tickets.

Chapter 6 Test (p. 335)

1.
$$-3z + 17 + 12z = 11$$
$$9z + 17 = 11$$
$$9z + 17 - 17 = 11 - 17$$
$$9z = -6$$
$$\frac{9z}{9} = \frac{-6}{9}$$
$$z = -\frac{2}{3}$$

2.
$$m - 6(m + 10) = 50$$
$$m - 6m - 60 = 50$$
$$-5m - 60 = 50$$
$$-5m - 60 + 60 = 50 + 60$$
$$-5m = 110$$
$$\frac{-5m}{-5} = \frac{110}{-5}$$
$$m = -22$$

3.
$$7(12 - r) = -84$$
$$84 - 7r = -84$$
$$84 - 7r - 84 = -84 - 84$$
$$-7r = -168$$
$$\frac{-7r}{-7} = \frac{-168}{-7}$$
$$r = 24$$

4.
$$3b + 4 = b - 4$$
$$3b + 4 - b = b - 4 - b$$
$$2b + 4 = -4$$
$$2b + 4 - 4 = -4 - 4$$
$$2b = -8$$
$$\frac{2b}{2} = \frac{-8}{2}$$
$$b = -4$$

5.
$$-25 - a = 2a + 20$$
$$-25 - a - 2a = 2a + 20 - 2a$$
$$-25 - 3a = 20$$
$$-25 - 3a + 25 = 20 + 25$$
$$-3a = 45$$
$$\frac{-3a}{-3} = \frac{45}{-3}$$
$$a = -15$$

6.
$$3(2x - 11) = 3(x + 10)$$
$$6x - 33 = 3x + 30$$
$$6x - 33 - 3x = 3x + 30 - 3x$$
$$3x - 33 = 30$$
$$3x - 33 + 33 = 30 + 33$$
$$3x = 63$$
$$\frac{3x}{3} = \frac{63}{3}$$
$$x = 21$$

7.
$$\frac{3x - 5}{10} = 7$$
$$10 \cdot \frac{(3x - 5)}{10} = 7 \cdot 10$$
$$3x - 5 = 70$$
$$3x - 5 + 5 = 70 + 5$$
$$3x = 75$$
$$\frac{3x}{3} = \frac{75}{3}$$
$$x = 25$$

8.
$$\frac{-3r + 54}{5} = 2r + 3$$
$$5\left(\frac{-3r + 54}{5}\right) = 5(2r + 3)$$
$$-3r + 54 = 10r + 15$$
$$-13r + 54 = 15$$
$$-13r = -39$$
$$\frac{-13r}{-13} = \frac{-39}{-13}$$
$$r = 3$$

9.
$$\frac{3}{5}w = 5w + \frac{22}{25}$$
$$\frac{3}{5}w(25) = \left(5w + \frac{22}{25}\right)25$$
$$\frac{3}{5}w(25) = 5w(25) + \frac{22}{25}(25)$$
$$15w = 125w + 22$$
$$-110w = 22$$
$$\frac{-110w}{-110} = \frac{22}{-110}$$
$$w = -\frac{1}{5}$$

10. $C = \pi d \approx 3.14(12.3) = 38.622$

The circumference is about 38.622 millimeters.

11.

$$C = 2\pi r$$

$$?? \approx 2\left(\frac{22}{7}\right)r$$

$$22 = \frac{44}{7}r$$

$$\frac{7}{44} \cdot 22 = \frac{7}{44} \cdot \frac{44}{7}r$$

$$\frac{7}{2} = r$$

$$3\frac{1}{2} = r$$

The radius is about $3\frac{1}{2}$ inches.

12.

$$C = \pi d$$

$$9.42 \approx 3.14d$$

$$\frac{9.42}{3.14} = \frac{3.14d}{3.14}$$

$$3 = d$$

The diameter is about 3 feet.

13.

$$6n + 19 \le 7$$

$$6n + 19 - 19 \le 7 - 19$$

$$6n \le -12$$

$$\frac{6n}{6} \le \frac{-12}{6}$$

$$n \le -2$$

14.

$$10 - 3x > 25$$

$$10 - 3x - 10 > 25 - 10$$

$$-3x > 15$$

$$\frac{-3x}{-3} < \frac{15}{-3}$$

$$x < -5$$

15.

$$9c - 8 \ge 3c + 16$$

$$9c - 8 - 3c \ge 3c + 16 - 3c$$

$$6c - 8 \ge 16$$

$$6c - 8 + 8 \ge 16 + 8$$

$$6c \ge 24$$

$$\frac{6c}{6} \ge \frac{24}{6}$$

$$c \ge 4$$

16.

$$3(k + 3) > k - 1$$

$$3k + 9 > k - 1$$

$$3k + 9 - k > k - 1 - k$$

$$2k + 9 > -1$$

$$2k + 9 - 9 > -1 - 9$$

$$2k > -10$$

$$\frac{2k}{2} > \frac{-10}{2}$$

$$k > -5$$

17.

$$8y + 3y + 36 \le 124$$

$$11y + 36 \le 124$$

$$11y + 36 - 36 \le 124 - 36$$

$$11y \le 88$$

$$\frac{11y}{11} \le \frac{88}{11}$$

$$y \le 8$$

18.

$$w - 4(w + 5) < -8$$

$$w - 4w - 20 < -8$$

$$-3w - 20 < -8$$

$$-3w - 20 + 20 < -8 + 20$$

$$-3w < 12$$

$$\frac{-3w}{-3} > \frac{12}{-3}$$

$$w > -4$$

19.

$$9 + 11x \le 4$$

$$9 + 11x - 9 \le 4 - 9$$

$$11x \le -5$$

$$\frac{11x}{11} \le \frac{-5}{11}$$

$$x \le -\frac{5}{11}$$

20.

$$2x - 13 < x + 8$$

$$2x - 13 - x < x + 8 - x$$

$$x - 13 < 8$$

$$x - 13 + 13 < 8 + 13$$

$$x < 21$$

21.

$$7(12 - x) \ge 14$$

$$84 - 7x \ge 14$$

$$84 - 7x - 84 \ge 14 - 84$$

$$-7x \ge -70$$

$$\frac{-7x}{-7} \le \frac{-70}{-7}$$

$$x \le 10$$

22.

$$15.95 + 5p = 10p + 4.2$$

$$11.75 + 5p = 10p$$

$$11.75 = 5p$$

$$\frac{11.75}{5} = p$$

$$2.35 = p$$

Each pair of socks costs $2.35.

23.

$$1647 + 7471 + x = 7x + 700$$

$$9118 + x = 7x + 700$$

$$9118 = 6x + 700$$

$$\frac{8418}{6} = \frac{6x}{6}$$

$$1403 = x$$

There were 1403 newspapers published that were not daily or weekly.

24. The length of the string attached to the ball is the height of the pole minus the diameter of the ball: $10 - 2 = 8$ ft, 8 ft $\times$ 12 in. = 96 in., 96 in. $-$ 8.4 in. = 87.6 in., 87.6 $\div$ 12 in. = 7.3 ft.

The longest path point P can make is a circle whose circumference is the length of the string.

$C = 2\pi r \approx 2(3.14)(7.3) \approx 45.8$

The circumference is about 45.8 ft.

25.
$$2.2(4.5) + 1.7x \le 15$$
$$9.9 + 1.7x \le 15$$
$$9.9 + 1.7x - 9.9 \le 15 - 9.9$$
$$1.7x \le 5.1$$
$$\frac{1.7x}{1.7} \le \frac{5.1}{1.7}$$
$$x \le 3$$

You can buy no more than 3 lb.

Standardized Test Preparation (pp. 336–337)

1. *Sample answer:* This student should receive full credit. The solution answers all 3 parts of the question correctly, and the work shown provides explanation for the answers.

Standardized Test Practice (pp. 338–339)

1. a. $d = rt$

$$12 = 8(t)$$
$$\frac{12}{8} = \frac{8t}{8}$$
$$t = 1.5$$

It will take Rick 1 hr 30 min.

b. $1.5 - 0.5 = 1$ hr

Rick's rate: 9 miles per hour

$9 \cdot 1 = 9$

Tran will ride 9 miles when Rick reaches 12 miles.

c. Let x represent the additional amount of time.

Tran has gone 9 mi and Rick has gone 12 mi.

Tran's total: $(9x + 9)$ mi

Rick's total: $(8x + 12)$ mi

Tran will catch up to Rick when the total distances are equal.

$$9x + 9 = 8x + 12$$
$$9x + 9 - 8x = 8x + 12 - 8x$$
$$x + 9 = 12$$
$$x + 9 - 9 = 12 - 9$$
$$x = 3$$

It will take 3 more hours for Tran to catch up to Rick.

2. a. *Sample answer:* The minimum number of pizzas that need to be sold to exceed the overhead costs.

b. Price per pizza $\cdot$ No. of pizzas $-$ Cost of ingredients $\cdot$ No. of pizzas $>$ Overhead costs

$$7.95x - 2.25x > 5000$$
$$5.7x > 5000$$
$$\frac{5.7x}{5.7} > \frac{5000}{5.7}$$
$$x > 877.2$$

c. The store must sell at least 878 pizzas to make its overhead.

3. a. $x - \frac{2}{3}x - \frac{1}{2}\left(x - \frac{2}{3}x\right) - 15 = 7$

b.
$$\left(x - \frac{2}{3}x - \frac{1}{2}\left(x - \frac{2}{3}x\right) - 15\right)6 = (7)(6)$$
$$6(x) - \left(\frac{2}{3}x\right)(6) - \left(\frac{1}{2}x\right)(6) + \left(\frac{1}{3}x\right)(6) - 15(6) = 42$$
$$6x - 4x - 3x + 2x - 90 = 42$$
$$x - 90 = 42$$
$$x - 90 + 90 = 42 + 90$$
$$x = 132$$

You start with $132.

c. Another way to solve this problem is by working backwards. You have $7 + 15 = 22$ before you buy the shirt. That is what you spent at the amusement park, so you had $44 before you went to the park. That is $\frac{1}{3}$ the original amount, so you started with $3 \times 44 = \$132$.

d. *Sample answer:* The methods are alike because both follow a series of steps. The methods are different because one starts with an equation, the other starts with the final amount of money.

4. a. Original price $\times$ 1st 3 shirts $+$ Discount price $\times$ No. of shirts $=$ Total cost

b.
$$12 \times 3 + 10(x - 3) = 56$$
$$36 + 10(x - 3) = 56$$
$$36 + 10x - 30 = 56$$
$$10x + 6 = 56$$
$$10x + 6 - 6 = 56 - 6$$
$$10x = 50$$
$$\frac{10x}{10} = \frac{50}{10}$$
$$x = 5$$

You buy 5 pairs of shorts.

c. You pay $56 for 5 pairs of shorts, and $56 \div 5 = 11.2$. The mean cost is $11.20.

5. a. $C = \pi d \approx (3.14)(2) \approx 6.28$

The circumference is about 6.28 m.

b. Each table needs 6.28 meters of ribbon, so divide 40 meters by 6.28 meter ($40 \div 6.28 = 6.4$). Since it does not make sense to trim part of table, there is enough ribbon for 6 tables.

c. You will need a total of 62.8 meters (6.28 × 10) of ribbon to do all ten tables. You already used 40 meters. Subtract 40 meters from 62.8 meters (62.8 − 40 = 22.8). You will need another 23 meters to fully trim all the tables.

6. C;

$$C = \pi d$$
$$38 \approx (3.14)(d)$$
$$\frac{38}{3.14} = \frac{3.14d}{3.14}$$
$$d \approx 12.1$$

The pen's diameter is about 12.1 feet.

7. D; $3 + 2(x − 3) = 15$

$$3 + 2x − 6 = 15$$
$$2x − 3 = 15$$
$$2x − 3 + 3 = 15 + 3$$
$$2x = 18$$
$$\frac{2x}{2} = \frac{18}{2}$$
$$x = 9$$

The car was parked 9 hours.

8. A;

$$10(6.02x + 5.1) = (0.7 + 22)10$$
$$60.2x + 51 = 7 + 220$$

60.2 is still a decimal.

9. $0.1x + 0.5(9) + 0.75(4) = 20$

$$(0.1x + 4.5 + 3)10 = 20(10)$$
$$x + 45 + 30 = 200$$
$$x + 75 = 200$$
$$x = 125$$

Rajev used 125 minutes.

10. $9x − 4 = 2(3x + 4)$

$$9x − 4 = 6x + 8$$
$$3x − 4 = 8$$
$$3x = 12$$
$$\frac{3x}{3} = \frac{12}{3}$$
$$x = 4$$

The sides have a length of $9(4) − 4$, or 32 units.

$$P = a + b + c = 32 + 32 + 32 = 96 \text{ units}$$

11. 20 ft + 4 ft = 24 ft

$$C = 2\pi r$$
$$C \approx 2(3.14)(24)$$
$$C \approx 151$$

The circumference of the deck is 151 ft.

12. *Sample answer:*

John: x quarters

Justin: $2x + 5$ quarters

Jason: $3x$ quarters

$$2x + 5 = 3x$$
$$2x + 5 − 2x = 3x − 2x$$
$$5 = x$$

John has 5 quarters and 5($.25) = $1.25.

13. If Michelle babysits for x hours, she will have $(22 + 5x)$ dollars. She needs at least $75.

$$22 + 5x \geq 75$$
$$22 + 5x − 22 \geq 75 − 22$$
$$5x \geq 53$$
$$\frac{5x}{5} \geq \frac{53}{5}$$
$$x \geq 10.6$$

If she charges for whole number of hours, Michelle needs to babysit for 11 hours.

14. *Sample answers:*

$$\begin{array}{r} \overset{5}{6} : \overset{60}{\cancel{00}} \\ -2 : 15 \\ \hline 3 \text{ hrs. } 45 \text{ min.} \end{array}$$

Each quarter pays 30 minutes, so she needs to pay for 4 hours, which is 8 half hours. Trish will need 8 quarters not 7 quarters. She will need 1 more.

15. Let x represent the amount of car sales.

$$300 + 0.02x \geq 1500$$
$$(300 + 0.02x)100 \geq (1500)(100)$$
$$30{,}000 + 2x \geq 150{,}000$$
$$30{,}000 + 2x − 30{,}000 \geq 150{,}000 − 30{,}000$$
$$2x \geq 120{,}000$$
$$\frac{2x}{2} \geq \frac{120{,}000}{2}$$
$$x \geq 60{,}000$$

The salesperson has to sell at least $60,000 worth of cars to earn at least $1500.

Chapter 7

Chapter Get-Ready Games (pp. 340–341)

1. Path with the least number of points:

$$7\text{?} \div x = 8 \longrightarrow x + 7 = 11 \longrightarrow x \div 4 = 3$$
$$\longrightarrow x - 1 = 3 \longrightarrow 7x = 7 \longrightarrow 9 - x = 8$$
$$\longrightarrow 64 \div x = 8 \longrightarrow x + 8 = 19 \longrightarrow 3x = 27$$
$$\longrightarrow 10 - x = 6 \longrightarrow 2x = 14 \longrightarrow 14 - x = 8$$

2. Correct path:

$$6.3 \div 0.9 \longrightarrow 7 + 1.8 \longrightarrow 8.8 \times 3.5$$
$$\longrightarrow 30.8 - 5.8 \longrightarrow 25 \div 1.25 \longrightarrow 20 + 6.3$$
$$\longrightarrow 26.3 \times 0.4 \longrightarrow 10.52 + 1.2 \longrightarrow 11.72 \div 4$$
$$\longrightarrow 2.93$$

Stop and Think (p. 341)

1. When dividing decimals, you move the decimal point in both the divisor and dividend the same number of places. Then divide. As with whole numbers, it is then possible to get a whole number or decimal answer. Therefore it is not true to say that when dividing decimals you can never get a whole number. For example, $4.75 \div 0.25 = 19$.

2. There are 3 different paths through the *Video Maze* that do not cover the same ground more than once.

Review Prerequisite Skills (p. 342)

1. The fraction $\frac{1}{2}$ is in *simplest form*, but $\frac{2}{4}$ is not.

2. The fractions $\frac{2}{3}$ and $\frac{4}{6}$ are *equivalent fractions*.

3. A mathematical sentence that shows two expressions have the same value is called an *equation*.

4. $\dfrac{x}{7} = 3$

$7 \cdot \dfrac{x}{7} = 7 \cdot 3$

$x = 21$

5. $\dfrac{x}{-2} = 4$

$-2 \cdot \dfrac{x}{-2} = -2 \cdot 4$

$x = -8$

6. $-9x = 108$

$\dfrac{-9x}{-9} = \dfrac{108}{-9}$

$x = -12$

7. $8x = 56$

$\dfrac{8x}{8} = \dfrac{56}{8}$

$x = 7$

8. $\dfrac{\text{Fraction of socks}}{\text{that are black}} = \dfrac{\text{Number of black socks}}{\text{Total number of socks}} = \dfrac{6}{15} = \dfrac{2}{5}$

9. $\dfrac{15}{75} = \dfrac{\overset{1}{\cancel{3}} \cdot \overset{1}{\cancel{5}}}{\cancel{3} \cdot \cancel{5} \cdot 5} = \dfrac{1}{5}$

10. $\dfrac{12}{60} = \dfrac{\overset{1}{\cancel{2}} \cdot \overset{1}{\cancel{2}} \cdot \overset{1}{\cancel{3}}}{\cancel{2} \cdot \cancel{2} \cdot \cancel{3} \cdot 5} = \dfrac{1}{5}$

11. $\dfrac{9ab}{36a} = \dfrac{\overset{1}{\cancel{3}} \cdot \overset{1}{\cancel{3}} \cdot \overset{1}{\cancel{a}} \cdot b}{2 \cdot 2 \cdot \cancel{3} \cdot \cancel{3} \cdot \cancel{a}} = \dfrac{b}{4}$

12. $\dfrac{18n^3}{36n} = \dfrac{2 \cdot \overset{1}{\cancel{3}} \cdot \overset{1}{\cancel{3}} \cdot \overset{1}{\cancel{n}} \cdot n \cdot n}{\cancel{2} \cdot 2 \cdot \cancel{3} \cdot \cancel{3} \cdot \cancel{n}} = \dfrac{n^2}{2}$

13. From least to greatest, the numbers are -1.11, -0.25, 0, $\frac{1}{3}$, $\frac{9}{8}$, and $\frac{12}{9}$.

14. From least to greatest, the numbers are $-\frac{7}{8}$, -0.02, $\frac{1}{12}$, 0.34, 1.28, and $\frac{10}{3}$.

Lesson 7.1

Activity (p. 343)

1.

Side length	2	4	5
Perimeter	8	16	20
$\dfrac{\text{Side length}}{\text{Perimeter}}$	$\dfrac{2}{8} = \dfrac{1}{4}$	$\dfrac{4}{16} = \dfrac{1}{4}$	$\dfrac{5}{20} = \dfrac{1}{4}$

2. All the fractions in the table equal $\frac{1}{4}$.

3. The perimeter of a square is four times its side length s.

7.1 Guided Practice (p. 344)

1. $\dfrac{\text{Expert-only trails}}{\text{Easy trails}} = \dfrac{11}{15}$

The ratio can be written as $\frac{11}{15}$, $11 : 15$, or 11 to 15.

2. $\dfrac{\text{Easy trails}}{\text{Difficult trails}} = \dfrac{15}{7}$

The ratio can be written as $\frac{15}{7}$, $15 : 7$, or 15 to 7.

3. $\dfrac{2 \text{ gal}}{1 \text{ sec}} = \dfrac{2 \text{ gal}}{1 \text{ sec}} \cdot \dfrac{60 \text{ sec}}{1 \text{ min}} = \dfrac{120 \text{ gal}}{1 \text{ min}}$

120 gallons of water are pumped in one minute.

4. $\dfrac{114 \text{ points}}{6 \text{ games}} = \dfrac{114 \div 6}{6 \div 6} = \dfrac{19}{1}$

The unit rate is 19 points per game.

5. $\dfrac{365 \text{ people}}{5 \text{ months}} = \dfrac{365 \div 5}{5 \div 5} = \dfrac{73}{1}$

The unit rate is 73 people per month.

6. $\dfrac{329 \text{ miles}}{10 \text{ gallons}} = \dfrac{329 \div 10}{10 \div 10} = \dfrac{32.9}{1}$

The unit rate is 32.9 miles per gallon.

7. $\dfrac{-49 \text{ m}}{14 \text{ sec}} = \dfrac{-49 \div 14}{14 \div 14} = \dfrac{-3.5}{1}$

The unit rate is -3.5 meters per second.

7.1 Exercises (pp. 345–346)

Skill Practice

1. A ratio uses division to compare two numbers, whereas a rate is a ratio of two quantities that have different units.

2. "Three gallons to $4.50" and "five gallons to $7.50" are equivalent *rates*.

3. $\dfrac{33}{22} = \dfrac{3 \cdot \cancel{11}}{2 \cdot \cancel{11}} = \dfrac{3}{2}$

The ratio can be written as $\frac{3}{2}$, $3 : 2$, or 3 to 2.

4. $\dfrac{20}{25} = \dfrac{4 \cdot \cancel{5}}{5 \cdot \cancel{5}} = \dfrac{4}{5}$

The ratio can be written as $\frac{4}{5}$, $4 : 5$, or 4 to 5.

5. $\dfrac{27}{42} = \dfrac{9 \cdot \cancel{3}}{14 \cdot \cancel{3}} = \dfrac{9}{14}$

The ratio can be written as $\frac{9}{14}$, $9 : 14$, or 9 to 14.

Chapter 7, continued

6. $\dfrac{-12}{4} = \dfrac{-3 \cdot \cancel{4}}{1 \cdot \cancel{4}} = \dfrac{-3}{1}$

The ratio can be written as $\dfrac{-3}{1}$, $-3:1$, or -3 to 1.

7. 51 to $17 = \dfrac{51}{17} = \dfrac{3 \cdot \cancel{17}}{1 \cdot \cancel{17}} = \dfrac{3}{1}$

The ratio can be written as $\dfrac{3}{1}$, $3:1$, or 3 to 1.

8. $26:39 = \dfrac{26}{39} = \dfrac{2 \cdot \cancel{13}}{3 \cdot \cancel{13}} = \dfrac{2}{3}$

The ratio can be written as $\dfrac{2}{3}$, $2:3$, or 2 to 3.

9. $28:6 = \dfrac{28}{6} = \dfrac{2 \cdot 14}{2 \cdot 3} = \dfrac{14}{3}$

The ratio can be written as $\dfrac{14}{3}$, $14:3$, or 14 to 3.

10. 35 to $49 = \dfrac{35}{49} = \dfrac{5 \cdot \cancel{7}}{7 \cdot \cancel{7}} = \dfrac{5}{7}$

The ratio can be written as $\dfrac{5}{7}$, $5:7$, or 5 to 7.

11. $\dfrac{60 \text{ miles}}{\text{hour}} = \dfrac{60 \text{ miles}}{\cancel{\text{hour}}} \cdot \dfrac{1 \cancel{\text{ hour}}}{60 \text{ minutes}} = \dfrac{1 \text{ mile}}{\text{minute}}$

12. $\dfrac{32 \text{ ounces}}{\text{serving}} = \dfrac{32 \cancel{\text{ ounces}}}{\text{serving}} \cdot \dfrac{1 \text{ pound}}{16 \cancel{\text{ ounces}}} = \dfrac{2 \text{ pounds}}{\text{serving}}$

13. $\dfrac{105 \text{ min}}{\text{game}} = \dfrac{105 \cancel{\text{ min}}}{\text{game}} \cdot \dfrac{1 \text{ h}}{60 \cancel{\text{ min}}} = \dfrac{1.75 \text{ h}}{\text{game}}$

14. $\dfrac{\$1.44}{\text{ft}} = \dfrac{\$1.44}{\cancel{\text{ft}}} \cdot \dfrac{3 \cancel{\text{ ft}}}{1 \text{ yd}} = \dfrac{\$4.32}{\text{yd}}$

15. $\dfrac{50 \text{ feet}}{\text{second}} = \dfrac{50 \text{ feet}}{\cancel{\text{second}}} \cdot \dfrac{60 \cancel{\text{ seconds}}}{1 \text{ min}} = \dfrac{3000 \text{ ft}}{\text{min}}$

16. $\dfrac{87 \text{ cents}}{30 \text{ inches}} = \dfrac{87 \text{ cents}}{30 \cancel{\text{ inches}}} \cdot \dfrac{12 \cancel{\text{ inches}}}{1 \text{ ft}} = \dfrac{34.8 \text{ cents}}{\text{ft}}$

17. $\dfrac{15 \text{ min}}{\text{quarter}} = \dfrac{15 \cancel{\text{ min}}}{\text{quarter}} \cdot \dfrac{1 \text{ hour}}{60 \cancel{\text{ min}}} = \dfrac{0.25 \text{ hour}}{\text{quarter}}$

18. $\dfrac{20 \text{ miles}}{\text{hour}} = \dfrac{20 \cancel{\text{ miles}}}{\text{hour}} \cdot \dfrac{5280 \text{ ft}}{1 \cancel{\text{ mile}}} = \dfrac{105{,}600 \text{ ft}}{\text{hour}}$

19. $\dfrac{24 \text{ adults}}{6 \text{ cars}} = \dfrac{24 \div 6}{6 \div 6} = \dfrac{4}{1}$

The unit rate is 4 adults per car.

20. $\dfrac{80 \text{ miles}}{4 \text{ hours}} = \dfrac{80 \div 4}{4 \div 4} = \dfrac{20}{1}$

The unit rate is 20 miles per hour.

21. $\dfrac{18 \text{ degrees}}{6 \text{ minutes}} = \dfrac{18 \div 6}{6 \div 6} = \dfrac{3}{1}$

The unit rate is 3 degrees per minute.

22. $\dfrac{610 \text{ rotations}}{5 \text{ minutes}} = \dfrac{610 \div 5}{5 \div 5} = \dfrac{122}{1}$

The unit rate is 122 rotations per minute.

23. $\dfrac{50 \text{ ounces}}{5 \text{ servings}} = \dfrac{50 \div 5}{5 \div 5} = \dfrac{10}{1}$

The unit rate is 10 ounces per serving.

24. $\dfrac{-75 \text{ feet}}{20 \text{ seconds}} = \dfrac{-75 \div 20}{20 \div 20} = \dfrac{-3.75}{1}$

The unit rate is -3.75 feet per second.

25. $\dfrac{-34 \text{ meters}}{8 \text{ seconds}} = \dfrac{-34 \div 8}{8 \div 8} = \dfrac{-4.25}{1}$

The unit rate is -4.25 meters per second.

26. $\dfrac{3 \text{ pounds}}{\$2} = \dfrac{3 \div 2}{2 \div 2} = \dfrac{1.5}{1}$

The unit rate is 1.5 pounds per dollar.

27. The wrong fractional form of 1 week to 7 days was used to find an equivalent rate.

$\dfrac{14 \text{ times}}{\text{day}} \cdot \dfrac{7 \text{ days}}{\text{week}} = \dfrac{98 \text{ times}}{\text{week}}$

28. B; $\dfrac{232 \text{ mi}}{4 \text{ h}} = \dfrac{(232 \div 4) \text{ mi}}{(4 \div 4) \text{ h}} = \dfrac{58 \text{ mi}}{\text{h}}$

$\dfrac{174 \text{ mi}}{3 \text{ h}} = \dfrac{(174 \div 3) \text{ mi}}{(3 \div 3) \text{ h}} = \dfrac{58 \text{ mi}}{\text{h}}$

29. The ratio 3 to 12 can be written as $\dfrac{3}{12} = \dfrac{1 \cdot \cancel{3}}{4 \cdot \cancel{3}} = \dfrac{1}{4}$.

The ratio 2 to 6 can be written as $\dfrac{2}{6} = \dfrac{1 \cdot \cancel{2}}{\cancel{2} \cdot 3} = \dfrac{1}{3}$.

Because $\dfrac{1}{4} \ne \dfrac{1}{3}$, the ratios are not equivalent.

30. The ratio $6:18$ can be written as $\dfrac{6}{18} = \dfrac{1 \cdot \cancel{6}}{3 \cdot \cancel{6}} = \dfrac{1}{3}$.

The ratio $10:30$ can be written as $\dfrac{10}{30} = \dfrac{1 \cdot \cancel{10}}{3 \cdot \cancel{10}} = \dfrac{1}{3}$.

Because $\dfrac{1}{3} = \dfrac{1}{3}$, the ratios are equivalent.

31. The ratio $15:35$ can be written as $\dfrac{15}{35} = \dfrac{3 \cdot \cancel{5}}{\cancel{5} \cdot 7} = \dfrac{3}{7}$.

The ratio $18:42$ can be written as $\dfrac{18}{42} = \dfrac{3 \cdot \cancel{6}}{\cancel{6} \cdot 7} = \dfrac{3}{7}$.

Because $\dfrac{3}{7} = \dfrac{3}{7}$, the ratios are equivalent.

32. Because the ratios are equivalent and $8 \cdot 2 = 16$, $x \cdot 2 = 4$. So, $x = 2$.

33. Because the ratios are equivalent and $9 \cdot 3 = 27$, $c \cdot 3 = 30$. So, $c = 10$.

34. Because the ratios are equivalent and $\dfrac{2}{5} \cdot 15 = 6$, $\dfrac{2}{5} \cdot n = 10$. So, $n = 25$.

35. Because the ratios are equivalent and $\dfrac{2}{3} \cdot 18 = 12$, $\dfrac{2}{3} \cdot z = 2$. So, $z = 3$.

36. $\dfrac{8}{x} = \dfrac{x}{18}$

$\left(\dfrac{x}{8}\right)\left(\dfrac{8}{x}\right) = \left(\dfrac{x}{8}\right)\left(\dfrac{x}{18}\right)$

$1 = \dfrac{x^2}{144}$

Because $12^2 = 144$ and $144 \div 144 = 1$, $x = 12$.

37. $\dfrac{16}{y} = \dfrac{y}{4}$

$\left(\dfrac{y}{16}\right)\left(\dfrac{16}{y}\right) = \left(\dfrac{y}{16}\right)\left(\dfrac{y}{4}\right)$

$1 = \dfrac{y^2}{64}$

Because $8^2 = 64$ and $64 \div 64 = 1$, $y = 8$.

Chapter 7, continued

38. $\dfrac{3}{a} = \dfrac{a}{27}$

$\left(\dfrac{a}{3}\right)\left(\dfrac{3}{a}\right) = \left(\dfrac{a}{3}\right)\left(\dfrac{a}{27}\right)$

$1 = \dfrac{a^2}{81}$

Because $9^2 = 81$ and $81 \div 81 = 1$, $a = 9$.

39. $\dfrac{t}{2} = \dfrac{18}{t}$

$\left(\dfrac{2}{t}\right)\left(\dfrac{t}{2}\right) = \left(\dfrac{2}{t}\right)\left(\dfrac{18}{t}\right)$

$1 = \dfrac{36}{t^2}$

Because $6^2 = 36$ and $36 \div 36 = 1$, $t = 6$.

40. $\dfrac{6}{9} = \dfrac{2 \cdot \cancel{3}}{\cancel{3} \cdot 3} = \dfrac{2}{3}, \dfrac{10}{15} = \dfrac{2 \cdot \cancel{5}}{3 \cdot \cancel{5}} = \dfrac{2}{3}$

So, $\dfrac{6}{9}$ and $\dfrac{10}{15}$ are equivalent ratios.

$\dfrac{6}{10} = \dfrac{2 \cdot 3}{2 \cdot 5} = \dfrac{3}{5}, \dfrac{9}{15} = \dfrac{\cancel{3} \cdot 3}{\cancel{3} \cdot 5} = \dfrac{3}{5}$

So, $\dfrac{6}{10}$ and $\dfrac{9}{15}$ are equivalent ratios.

$\dfrac{15}{10} = \dfrac{3 \cdot \cancel{5}}{2 \cdot \cancel{5}} = \dfrac{3}{2}, \dfrac{9}{6} = \dfrac{3 \cdot \cancel{3}}{2 \cdot \cancel{3}} = \dfrac{3}{2}$

So, $\dfrac{15}{10}$ and $\dfrac{9}{6}$ are equivalent ratios.

$\dfrac{15}{9} = \dfrac{\cancel{3} \cdot 5}{\cancel{3} \cdot 3} = \dfrac{5}{3}, \dfrac{10}{6} = \dfrac{2 \cdot 5}{2 \cdot 3} = \dfrac{5}{3}$

So, $\dfrac{15}{9}$ and $\dfrac{10}{6}$ are equivalent ratios.

Problem Solving

41. Write the ratio of the screen's length to its width. Then determine whether the ratio is equivalent to $4 : 3$ or $16 : 9$.

42. You would predict that $\dfrac{1}{10}$ of your math class is left-handed by assuming that the ratio of left-handed people in your class to all people in your class is equivalent to the ratio of left-handed people to all people.

43. $\dfrac{4 \text{ times}}{\text{hour}} = \dfrac{4 \text{ times}}{1 \text{ hour}} \cdot \dfrac{24 \text{ hours}}{1 \text{ day}} \cdot \dfrac{7 \text{ days}}{1 \text{ week}} = \dfrac{672 \text{ times}}{1 \text{ week}}$

The clock chimes 672 times in a week.

44. $\dfrac{\$47.25}{7 \text{ hours}} = \dfrac{47.25 \div 7}{7 \div 7} = \dfrac{6.75}{1}$

You are paid $6.75 per hour.

45. B; $\dfrac{\$11.70}{10 \text{ pounds}} = \dfrac{11.70 \div 10}{10 \div 10} = \dfrac{\$1.17}{\text{pound}}$

$\dfrac{\$23.40}{20 \text{ pounds}} = \dfrac{23.40 \div 20}{20 \div 20} = \dfrac{\$1.17}{\text{pound}}$

$\dfrac{\$35.10}{30 \text{ pounds}} = \dfrac{35.10 \div 30}{30 \div 30} = \dfrac{\$1.17}{\text{pound}}$

Because the ratios are equivalent, store B prices its oranges using a constant unit rate.

46. You can compare the speeds of the animals by writing each rate as a unit rate.

Greyhound:

$\dfrac{330 \text{ ft}}{5 \text{ sec}} = \dfrac{(330 \div 5) \text{ ft}}{(5 \div 5) \text{ sec}} = \dfrac{66 \text{ ft}}{\text{sec}}$

Roadrunner:

$\dfrac{75 \text{ ft}}{3 \text{ sec}} = \dfrac{(75 \div 3) \text{ ft}}{(3 \div 3) \text{ sec}} = \dfrac{25 \text{ ft}}{\text{sec}}$

Cheetah:

$\dfrac{198 \text{ ft}}{2 \text{ sec}} = \dfrac{(198 \div 2) \text{ ft}}{(2 \div 2) \text{ sec}} = \dfrac{99 \text{ ft}}{\text{sec}}$

The cheetah is the fastest animal and the roadrunner is the slowest animal.

47. If Elliot has 40 pretzels and Colin has 8, the ratio is 40 to 8. This ratio can be written as $\dfrac{40}{8} = \dfrac{40 \div 8}{8 \div 8} = \dfrac{5}{1}$, or 5 to 1.

If Elliot gives 4 pretzels to Colin, then Elliot now has $40 - 4 = 36$ pretzels and Colin has $8 + 4 = 12$ pretzels, making the ratio 36 to 12. This ratio can be written as $\dfrac{36}{12} = \dfrac{36 \div 12}{12 \div 12} = \dfrac{3}{1}$, or 3 to 1.

Mixed Review

48. $3c = 18$

$\dfrac{3c}{3} = \dfrac{18}{3}$

$c = 6$

49. $9x = -81$

$\dfrac{9x}{9} = \dfrac{-81}{9}$

$x = -9$

50. $\dfrac{v}{4} = -2$

$4 \cdot \dfrac{v}{4} = 4 \cdot -2$

$v = -8$

51. $\dfrac{n}{10} = 8$

$10 \cdot \dfrac{n}{10} = 10 \cdot 8$

$n = 80$

52. $10y + 4 < 24$

$10y < 20$

$y < 2$

53. A; $C = 2\pi r$

$39.25 \approx 2(3.14)r$

$39.25 \approx 6.28r$

$\dfrac{39.25}{6.28} \approx r$

$6.25 \approx r$

The radius of the circle is about 6.25 feet.

Lesson 7.2

Investigation (p. 347)

Steps 1–4. Answers will vary.

1. A good answer will include a clear scale drawing and accurate measurements.

Chapter 7, continued

2. No; A good answer will include data from the scale drawing and will conclude that the ratio of the areas is the same as the ratio of the sides squared.

3. *Sample answer:* If different scales were used in the same drawing, the drawing would appear distorted because it would be stretched either horizontally or vertically.

7.2 Guided Practice (pp. 348–350)

1.

	Ants	Person
Carries	0.005 oz	x lb
Weight	0.0001 oz	100 lb

$$\frac{0.005}{0.0001} = \frac{x}{100}$$

$$\frac{0.005}{0.0001} \cdot 100 = \frac{x}{100} \cdot 100$$

$$5000 = x$$

If human strength were proportional to that of an ant, a 100 pound person could carry 5000 pounds.

2. $\dfrac{n}{12} = \dfrac{3}{4}$

$12 \cdot \dfrac{n}{12} = 12 \cdot \dfrac{3}{4}$

$n = 9$

3. $\dfrac{50}{20} = \dfrac{z}{16}$

$16 \cdot \dfrac{50}{20} = 16 \cdot \dfrac{z}{16}$

$40 = z$

4. $\dfrac{25}{3} = \dfrac{t}{51}$

$51 \cdot \dfrac{25}{3} = 51 \cdot \dfrac{t}{51}$

$425 = t$

5. $\dfrac{6}{c} = \dfrac{54}{99}$

$6 \cdot 99 = c \cdot 54$

$594 = 54c$

$\dfrac{594}{54} = \dfrac{54c}{54}$

$11 = c$

Check: $\dfrac{6}{11} \overset{?}{=} \dfrac{54}{99}$

$6 \cdot 99 \overset{?}{=} 11 \cdot 54$

$594 = 594$ ✓

6. $\dfrac{n}{14} = \dfrac{63}{84}$

$n \cdot 84 = 14 \cdot 63$

$84n = 882$

$\dfrac{84n}{84} = \dfrac{882}{84}$

$n = 10.5$

Check: $\dfrac{10.5}{14} \overset{?}{=} \dfrac{63}{84}$

$10.5 \cdot 84 \overset{?}{=} 14 \cdot 63$

$882 = 882$ ✓

7. $\dfrac{2.1}{0.9} = \dfrac{27.3}{y}$

$2.1 \cdot y = 0.9 \cdot 27.3$

$2.1y = 24.57$

$\dfrac{2.1y}{2.1} = \dfrac{24.57}{2.1}$

$y = 11.7$

Check: $\dfrac{2.1}{0.9} \overset{?}{=} \dfrac{27.3}{11.7}$

$2.1 \cdot 11.7 \overset{?}{=} 0.9 \cdot 27.3$

$24.57 = 24.57$ ✓

8. $\dfrac{16.2}{67.4} = \dfrac{x}{134.8}$

$16.2 \cdot 134.8 = 67.4 \cdot x$

$2183.76 = 67.4x$

$\dfrac{2183.76}{67.4} = \dfrac{67.4x}{67.4}$

$32.4 = x$

Check: $\dfrac{16.2}{67.4} \overset{?}{=} \dfrac{32.4}{134.8}$

$16.2 \cdot 134.8 \overset{?}{=} 67.4 \cdot 32.4$

$2183.76 = 2183.76$ ✓

9. $\dfrac{8}{a} = \dfrac{0.4}{0.62}$

$8 \cdot 0.62 = a \cdot 0.4$

$4.96 = 0.4a$

$\dfrac{4.96}{0.4} = \dfrac{0.4a}{0.4}$

$12.4 = a$

Check: $\dfrac{8}{12.4} \overset{?}{=} \dfrac{0.4}{0.62}$

$8 \cdot 0.62 \overset{?}{=} 12.4 \cdot 0.4$

$4.96 = 4.96$ ✓

10. $\dfrac{b}{1.8} = \dfrac{49.6}{14.4}$

$b \cdot 14.4 = 1.8 \cdot 49.6$

$14.4b = 89.28$

$\dfrac{14.4b}{14.4} = \dfrac{89.28}{14.4}$

$b = 6.2$

Check: $\dfrac{6.2}{1.8} \overset{?}{=} \dfrac{49.6}{14.4}$

$6.2 \cdot 14.4 \overset{?}{=} 1.8 \cdot 49.6$

$89.28 = 89.28$ ✓

11. Scale $= \dfrac{\text{Height of strawberry model}}{\text{Height of actual strawberry}}$

$\dfrac{25 \text{ ft}}{3 \text{ in.}} = \dfrac{15 \text{ ft}}{h \text{ in.}}$

$25h = 45$

$h = 1.8$

The height of the actual strawberry was 1.8 inches.

7.2 Exercises (pp. 350–353)

Skill Practice

1. Set the cross products of the proportion equal to one another by using the cross products property. Then solve the resulting equation.

Chapter 7, *continued*

2. The relationship between a model's dimensions and the actual object's dimensions is given by the *scale*.

0. $\dfrac{1}{2} = \dfrac{r}{6}$ Check: $\dfrac{1}{2} \overset{?}{=} \dfrac{3}{6}$

$6 \cdot \dfrac{1}{2} = 6 \cdot \dfrac{x}{6}$ $\dfrac{1}{2} = \dfrac{1}{2}$ ✓

$3 = x$

4. $\dfrac{c}{10} = \dfrac{3}{5}$ Check: $\dfrac{6}{10} \overset{?}{=} \dfrac{3}{5}$

$10 \cdot \dfrac{c}{10} = 10 \cdot \dfrac{3}{5}$ $\dfrac{3}{5} = \dfrac{3}{5}$ ✓

$c = 6$

5. $\dfrac{h}{4} = \dfrac{45}{20}$ Check: $\dfrac{9}{4} \overset{?}{=} \dfrac{45}{20}$

$4 \cdot \dfrac{h}{4} = 4 \cdot \dfrac{45}{20}$ $\dfrac{9}{4} = \dfrac{9}{4}$ ✓

$h = 9$

6. $\dfrac{3}{8} = \dfrac{x}{32}$ Check: $\dfrac{3}{8} \overset{?}{=} \dfrac{12}{32}$

$32 \cdot \dfrac{3}{8} = 32 \cdot \dfrac{x}{32}$ $\dfrac{3}{8} = \dfrac{3}{8}$ ✓

$12 = x$

7. B; $\dfrac{12}{15} = \dfrac{x}{25}$

$25 \cdot \dfrac{12}{15} = 25 \cdot \dfrac{x}{25}$

$20 = x$

8. $\dfrac{3}{4} \overset{?}{=} \dfrac{6}{8}$

$3 \cdot 8 \overset{?}{=} 4 \cdot 6$

$24 = 24$

The ratios form a proportion.

9. $\dfrac{1}{2} \overset{?}{=} \dfrac{2}{5}$

$1 \cdot 5 \overset{?}{=} 2 \cdot 2$

$5 \neq 4$

The ratios do not form a proportion.

10. $\dfrac{14}{21} \overset{?}{=} \dfrac{26}{39}$

$14 \cdot 39 \overset{?}{=} 21 \cdot 26$

$546 = 546$

The ratios form a proportion.

11. $\dfrac{15}{45} \overset{?}{=} \dfrac{45}{135}$

$15 \cdot 135 \overset{?}{=} 45 \cdot 45$

$2025 = 2025$

The ratios form a proportion.

12. $\dfrac{2}{3} = \dfrac{4}{z}$

$2 \cdot z = 3 \cdot 4$

$2z = 12$

$z = 6$

13. $\dfrac{6}{a} = \dfrac{3}{1}$

$6 \cdot 1 = a \cdot 3$

$6 = 3a$

$2 = a$

14. $\dfrac{39}{13} = \dfrac{9}{d}$

$39 \cdot d = 13 \cdot 9$

$39d = 117$

$d = 3$

15. $\dfrac{68}{12} = \dfrac{51}{p}$

$68 \cdot p = 12 \cdot 51$

$68p = 612$

$p = 9$

16. $\dfrac{17}{12} = \dfrac{k}{36}$

$17 \cdot 36 = 12 \cdot k$

$612 = 12k$

$51 = k$

17. $\dfrac{2}{5} = \dfrac{c}{20}$

$2 \cdot 20 = 5 \cdot c$

$40 = 5c$

$8 = c$

18. $\dfrac{7.2}{m} = \dfrac{2.4}{1.8}$

$7.2 \cdot 1.8 = m \cdot 2.4$

$12.96 = 2.4m$

$5.4 = m$

19. $\dfrac{256}{9.6} = \dfrac{1.6}{g}$

$256 \cdot g = 9.6 \cdot 1.6$

$256g = 15.36$

$g = 0.06$

20. $\dfrac{67.2}{g} = \dfrac{16.8}{3.3}$

$67.2 \cdot 3.3 = g \cdot 16.8$

$221.76 = 16.8g$

$13.2 = g$

21. $\dfrac{t}{29.4} = \dfrac{5.5}{4.2}$

$t \cdot 4.2 = 29.4 \cdot 5.5$

$4.2t = 161.7$

$t = 38.5$

22. $\dfrac{f}{5.4} = \dfrac{483}{18.9}$

$f \cdot 18.9 = 5.4 \cdot 483$

$18.9f = 2608.2$

$f = 138$

23. $\dfrac{712}{8.8} = \dfrac{x}{18.7}$

$712 \cdot 18.7 = 8.8 \cdot x$

$13,314.4 = 8.8x$

$1513 = x$

24. The cross products were found incorrectly.

$\dfrac{3}{9} = \dfrac{12}{m}$

$3 \cdot m = 9 \cdot 12$

$3m = 108$

$m = 36$

25. Scale $= \dfrac{\text{Height of building model}}{\text{Height of actual building}}$

$\dfrac{3 \text{ in.}}{50 \text{ ft}} = \dfrac{h \text{ in.}}{100 \text{ ft}}$

$3 \cdot 100 = 50 \cdot h$

$300 = 50h$

$6 = h$

The model's height is 6 inches.

26. Scale $= \dfrac{\text{Height of building model}}{\text{Height of actual building}}$

$\dfrac{3 \text{ in.}}{50 \text{ ft}} = \dfrac{h \text{ in.}}{240 \text{ ft}}$

$3 \cdot 240 = 50 \cdot h$

$720 = 50h$

$14.4 = h$

The model's height is 14.4 inches.

27. Scale $= \dfrac{\text{Height of building model}}{\text{Height of actual building}}$

$\dfrac{3 \text{ in.}}{50 \text{ ft}} = \dfrac{h \text{ in.}}{316 \text{ ft}}$

$3 \cdot 316 = 50 \cdot h$

$948 = 50h$

$18.96 = h$

The model's height is 18.96 inches.

Chapter 7, continued

28. Scale = $\dfrac{\text{Height of building model}}{\text{Height of actual building}}$

$\dfrac{3 \text{ in.}}{50 \text{ ft}} = \dfrac{h \text{ in.}}{545 \text{ ft}}$

$3 \cdot 545 = 50 \cdot h$

$1635 = 50h$

$32.7 = h$

The model's height is 32.7 inches.

29. $\dfrac{2}{x+2} = \dfrac{18}{27}$

$2 \cdot 27 = (x+2)18$

$54 = 18x + 36$

$18 = 18x$

$1 = x$

30. $\dfrac{x-2}{8} = \dfrac{30}{40}$

$(x-2)40 = 8 \cdot 30$

$40x - 80 = 240$

$40x = 320$

$x = 8$

31. $\dfrac{9}{5} = \dfrac{36}{x-3}$

$9(x-3) = 5 \cdot 36$

$9x - 27 = 180$

$9x = 207$

$x = 23$

32. $\dfrac{5}{x} = \dfrac{7}{x+4}$

$5(x+4) = x \cdot 7$

$5x + 20 = 7x$

$20 = 2x$

$10 = x$

33. $\dfrac{x}{5} = \dfrac{3x-4}{7}$

$x \cdot 7 = 5(3x-4)$

$7x = 15x - 20$

$0 = 8x - 20$

$20 = 8x$

$2.5 = x$

34. $\dfrac{3-5x}{4} = \dfrac{x+5}{9}$

$(3-5x) \cdot 9 = 4(x+5)$

$27 - 45x = 4x + 20$

$27 = 49x + 20$

$7 = 49x$

$\dfrac{7}{49} = x$

$\dfrac{1}{7} = x$

35. $\dfrac{4}{x-5} = \dfrac{3}{2x}$

$4 \cdot 2x = (x-5) \cdot 3$

$8x = 3x - 15$

$5x = -15$

$x = -3$

$\dfrac{3}{2x} = \dfrac{y}{21}$

$\dfrac{3}{2(-3)} = \dfrac{y}{21}$

$\dfrac{3}{-6} = \dfrac{y}{21}$

$3 \cdot 21 = -6 \cdot y$

$63 = -6y$

$-10.5 = y$

Check: $\dfrac{4}{x-5} = \dfrac{3}{2x} = \dfrac{y}{21}$

$\dfrac{4}{-3-5} \stackrel{?}{=} \dfrac{3}{2(-3)} \stackrel{?}{=} \dfrac{-10.5}{21}$

$\dfrac{4}{-8} \stackrel{?}{=} \dfrac{3}{-6} \stackrel{?}{=} \dfrac{-10.5}{21}$

$-\dfrac{1}{2} = -\dfrac{1}{2} = -\dfrac{1}{2} \checkmark$

36. $\dfrac{7}{b-36} = \dfrac{28}{b}$

$7 \cdot b = (b-36) \cdot 28$

$7b = 28b - 1008$

$-21b = -1008$

$b = 48$

$\dfrac{a}{72} = \dfrac{28}{b}$

$\dfrac{a}{72} = \dfrac{28}{48}$

$a \cdot 48 = 72 \cdot 28$

$48a = 2016$

$a = 42$

Check: $\dfrac{7}{b-36} = \dfrac{a}{72} = \dfrac{28}{b}$

$\dfrac{7}{48-36} \stackrel{?}{=} \dfrac{42}{72} \stackrel{?}{=} \dfrac{28}{48}$

$\dfrac{7}{12} = \dfrac{7}{12} = \dfrac{7}{12} \checkmark$

37. $\dfrac{8}{p-10} = \dfrac{16}{p-5}$

$8(p-5) = (p-10) \cdot 16$

$8p - 40 = 16p - 160$

$-40 = 8p - 160$

$120 = 8p$

$15 = p$

$\dfrac{16}{p-5} = \dfrac{n+8}{p}$

$\dfrac{16}{15-5} = \dfrac{n+8}{15}$

$\dfrac{16}{10} = \dfrac{n+8}{15}$

$16 \cdot 15 = 10(n+8)$

$240 = 10n + 80$

$160 = 10n$

$16 = n$

Check: $\dfrac{8}{p-10} = \dfrac{16}{p-5} = \dfrac{n+8}{p}$

$\dfrac{8}{15-10} \stackrel{?}{=} \dfrac{16}{15-5} \stackrel{?}{=} \dfrac{16+8}{15}$

$\dfrac{8}{5} \stackrel{?}{=} \dfrac{16}{10} \stackrel{?}{=} \dfrac{24}{15}$

$\dfrac{8}{5} = \dfrac{8}{5} = \dfrac{8}{5} \checkmark$

38. Yes, $\dfrac{a}{c} = \dfrac{b}{d}$. Using cross products you get $ad = bc$. Then divide each side by d, and then by c to get $\dfrac{a}{c} = \dfrac{b}{d}$.
No, $\dfrac{d}{a} \neq \dfrac{c}{b}$. *Sample answer:* Let $a = 3$, $b = 6$, $c = 4$, and $d = 8$; $\dfrac{3}{6} = \dfrac{4}{8}$ but $\dfrac{d}{a} = \dfrac{8}{3}$, $\dfrac{c}{b} = \dfrac{4}{6} = \dfrac{2}{3}$, and $\dfrac{d}{a} \neq \dfrac{c}{b}$.

Problem Solving

39. Because 1 min = 60 sec, set up the proportion as follows:

$\dfrac{88 \text{ ft}}{2 \text{ sec}} = \dfrac{x \text{ ft}}{60 \text{ sec}}$

$88 \cdot 60 = 2 \cdot x$

$5280 = 2x$

$2640 = x$

The car travels 2640 feet in one minute.

40. $\dfrac{54 \text{ dollars}}{3 \text{ lawns}} = \dfrac{x \text{ dollars}}{5 \text{ lawns}}$

$54 \cdot 5 = 3 \cdot x$

$270 = 3x$

$90 = x$

You would earn $90 if you mowed 5 lawns.

Chapter 7, *continued*

41. If you write 10 pounds to $16 as the fraction $\frac{10}{16}$ and write an equivalent fraction with 5 in the numerator, the denominator is 8, because $\frac{10}{16} = \frac{10 \div 2}{16 \div 2} = \frac{5}{8}$.

So, you can see that 5 pounds of pasta costs $8.

42. $\text{Scale} = \dfrac{\text{Height of drawing}}{\text{Height of actual building}}$

$\dfrac{1 \text{ in.}}{80 \text{ ft}} = \dfrac{h \text{ in.}}{853 \text{ ft}}$

$1 \cdot 853 = 80 \cdot h$

$853 = 80h$

$10.6625 = h$

$\text{Scale} = \dfrac{\text{Width of drawing}}{\text{Width of actual building}}$

$\dfrac{1 \text{ in.}}{80 \text{ ft}} = \dfrac{w \text{ in.}}{145 \text{ ft}}$

$1 \cdot 145 = 80 \cdot w$

$145 = 80w$

$1.8125 = w$

The drawing will fit on a regular $8\frac{1}{2} \times 11$ sheet of paper. Using the scale 1 in. : 80 ft, the height of the drawing of the Transamerica Building will be 10.6625 inches and the width will be 1.8125 inches.

43. a. $\text{Scale} = \dfrac{\text{Length of drawing}}{\text{Length of actual car}}$

$\dfrac{1 \text{ in.}}{40 \text{ in.}} = \dfrac{\ell \text{ in.}}{215 \text{ in.}}$

$1 \cdot 215 = 40 \cdot \ell$

$215 = 40\ell$

$5.375 = \ell$

$\text{Scale} = \dfrac{\text{Width of drawing}}{\text{Width of actual car}}$

$\dfrac{1 \text{ in.}}{40 \text{ in.}} = \dfrac{w \text{ in.}}{76 \text{ in.}}$

$1 \cdot 76 = 40 \cdot w$

$76 = 40w$

$1.9 = w$

$\text{Scale} = \dfrac{\text{Height of drawing}}{\text{Height of actual car}}$

$\dfrac{1 \text{ in.}}{40 \text{ in.}} = \dfrac{h \text{ in.}}{54 \text{ in.}}$

$1 \cdot 54 = 40 \cdot h$

$54 = 40h$

$1.35 = h$

The length of the car for your drawing is 5.375 inches, the width is 1.9 inches, and the height is 1.35 inches.

b. Check drawings.

44. C; $\dfrac{0.25 \text{ in.}}{20 \text{ mi}} = \dfrac{2 \text{ in.}}{r \text{ mi}}$

$0.25x = 40$

$x = 160$

It is about 160 miles from Montgomery to Atlanta.

45. The actual wingspan of the space shuttle orbiter or the actual length is needed so there is only one unknown value in a proportion.

46. a. Use the fact that 1 pound = 16 ounces.

$\dfrac{2{,}000{,}000 \text{ flowers}}{16 \text{ ounces}} = \dfrac{x \text{ flowers}}{10 \text{ ounces}}$

$20{,}000{,}000 = 16x$

$1{,}250{,}000 = x$

About 1,250,000 flowers are visited to make 10 ounces of honey.

b. Use the fact that 1 pound = 16 ounces.

$\dfrac{55{,}000 \text{ mi}}{16 \text{ ounces}} = \dfrac{x \text{ mi}}{10 \text{ ounces}}$

$550{,}000 = 16x$

$34{,}375 = x$

The bees fly about 34,375 miles to make 10 ounces of honey.

c. To find the mean, divide the number of flowers visited by the number of miles flown by the bees.

$\dfrac{\text{Mean number of}}{\text{flowers visited}} = \dfrac{\text{Number of flowers visited}}{\text{Number of miles}}$

$= \dfrac{2{,}000{,}000 \text{ flowers}}{55{,}000 \text{ mi}}$

$\approx \dfrac{36.4 \text{ flowers}}{\text{mi}}$

About 36.4 flowers are visited in one mile.

47. $\approx \dfrac{1 \text{ cm}}{450 \text{ ft}}$

48. *Sample answers:*

Constitution Hill $\approx$ 2600 ft

Piccadilly St. $\approx$ 2400 ft

Queen's Walk $\approx$ 1500 ft

$P \approx 2600 + 2400 + 1500 = 6500$

The perimeter of the park is about 6500 feet.

Base of triangular region $\approx$ 2600 ft

Height of triangular region $\approx$ 1400 ft

$A \approx \frac{1}{2}bh = \frac{1}{2}(2600)(1400) = \frac{1}{2} \cdot 3{,}640{,}000 = 1{,}820{,}000$

The area of the park is about 1,820,000 square feet.

49. *Sample answer:* Convert the dimensions of the park from feet to yards.

Base ≈ 2600 ft $= 2600$ ft $\times \dfrac{1 \text{ yd}}{3 \text{ ft}} = 866\frac{2}{3}$ yd

Height ≈ 1400 ft $= 1400$ ft $\times \dfrac{1 \text{ yd}}{3 \text{ ft}} = 466\frac{2}{3}$ yd

$A = \frac{1}{2}bh$

$= \frac{1}{2}\left(866\frac{2}{3}\right)\left(466\frac{2}{3}\right)$

$= \frac{1}{2}\left(\frac{2600}{3}\right)\left(\frac{1400}{3}\right)$

$\approx 202{,}222 \text{ yd}^2$

Cost $= 0.36(202{,}222) \approx 72{,}800$

It would cost about \$72,800 to cover all of The Green Park with the grass seed.

50. The team has played $4 + 6 = 10$ games. So, the ratio of wins to total games played is $\frac{4}{10}$. Let x be the number of remaining games the team wins. Because this number is equal to the number of remaining games played, the ratio becomes $\frac{4 + x}{10 + x}$. To make the playoffs, this ratio must equal 75%, or 0.75.

$\dfrac{4 + x}{10 + x} = 0.75$

$\dfrac{4 + x}{10 + x} = \dfrac{0.75}{1}$

$4 + x = (10 + x) \cdot 0.75$

$4 + x = 7.5 + 0.75x$

$4 + 0.25x = 7.5$

$0.25x = 3.5$

$x = 14$

There must be 14 games left in the schedule for your team to make the playoffs.

51. Consider a diagram of the situation.

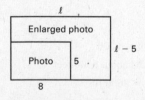

Using the diagram, set up a proportion as follows:

$\dfrac{5}{8} = \dfrac{\ell - 5}{\ell}$

$5 \cdot \ell = 8(\ell - 5)$

$5\ell = 8\ell - 40$

$-3\ell = -40$

$\ell = \dfrac{40}{3}$

The length of the enlarged photo is $\frac{40}{3}$ inches and the width is $\frac{40}{3} - 5 = \frac{25}{3}$ inches.

$P = 2\ell + 2w$

$= 2\left(\dfrac{40}{3}\right) + 2\left(\dfrac{25}{3}\right)$

$= \dfrac{80}{3} + \dfrac{50}{3}$

$= \dfrac{130}{3}$

$= 43\dfrac{1}{3}$

$A = \ell w = \left(\dfrac{40}{3}\right)\left(\dfrac{25}{3}\right) = \dfrac{1000}{9} = 111\dfrac{1}{9}$

The perimeter of the enlarged photo is $43\frac{1}{3}$ inches and the area is $111\frac{1}{9}$ square inches.

Mixed Review

52. $\dfrac{13}{104} \times 100 = \dfrac{13 \times 100}{104} = \dfrac{1300}{104} = 12\dfrac{1}{2} = 12.5$

53. $\dfrac{16}{80} \times 100 = \dfrac{16 \times 100}{80} = \dfrac{1600}{80} = 20$

54. $\dfrac{37}{100} \times 82 = \dfrac{37 \times 82}{100} = \dfrac{3034}{100} = 30\dfrac{17}{50} = 30.34$

55. $\dfrac{15}{100} \times 68 = \dfrac{15 \times 68}{100} = \dfrac{1020}{100} = 10\dfrac{1}{5} = 10.2$

56. $\dfrac{105}{28} \times 100 = \dfrac{105 \times 100}{28} = \dfrac{10{,}500}{28} = 375$

57. $\dfrac{291}{97} \times 100 = \dfrac{291 \times 100}{97} = \dfrac{29{,}100}{97} = 300$

58. $\dfrac{42 \text{ people}}{14 \text{ taxis}} = \dfrac{42 \div 14}{14 \div 14} = \dfrac{3}{1}$

The unit rate is 3 people per taxi.

59. $\dfrac{258 \text{ miles}}{6 \text{ hours}} = \dfrac{258 \div 6}{6 \div 6} \approx \dfrac{43}{1}$

The unit rate is 43 people per hour.

60. $\dfrac{36 \text{ dogs}}{18 \text{ households}} = \dfrac{36 \div 18}{18 \div 18} = \dfrac{2}{1}$

The unit rate is 2 dogs per household.

61. C

Lesson 7.3

7.3 Guided Practice (pp. 354–355)

1. $\dfrac{63}{75} = \dfrac{p}{100}$

$\dfrac{63}{75} \cdot 100 = \dfrac{p}{100} \cdot 100$

$84 = p$

63 is 84% of 75.

2. $\dfrac{84}{70} = \dfrac{p}{100}$

$100 \cdot \dfrac{84}{70} = 100 \cdot \dfrac{p}{100}$

$120 = p$

84 is 120% of 70.

3. $\dfrac{a}{75} = \dfrac{16}{100}$

$\dfrac{a}{75} \cdot 75 = \dfrac{16}{100} \cdot 75$

$a = 12$

12 is 16% of 75.

4. $\dfrac{a}{92} = \dfrac{35}{100}$

$\dfrac{a}{92} \cdot 92 = \dfrac{35}{100} \cdot 92$

$a = 32.2$

32.2 is 35% of 92.

5. $\dfrac{260}{b} = \dfrac{325}{100}$

$260 \cdot 100 = 325 \cdot b$

$26{,}000 = 325b$

$80 = b$

260 is 325% of 80.

6. $\dfrac{a}{65} = \dfrac{0.5}{100}$

$65 \cdot \dfrac{a}{65} = 65 \cdot \dfrac{0.5}{100}$

$a = 0.325$

0.325 is 0.5% of 65.

16. $\dfrac{179.2}{h} = \dfrac{32}{100}$

$17{,}920 = 32b$

$560 = b$

179.2 is 32% of 560.

17 A; $\dfrac{a}{90} = \dfrac{20}{100}$

$90 \cdot \dfrac{a}{90} = 90 \cdot \dfrac{20}{100}$

$a = 18$

$18 is 20% of $90.

18. The values of a and b are substituted incorrectly.

$\dfrac{12}{60} = \dfrac{p}{100}$

$100 \cdot \dfrac{12}{60} = \dfrac{p}{100} \cdot 100$

$20 = p$

20% of 60 is 12.

7.3 Exercises (pp. 356–358)

Skill Practice

1. Another way to say "25 songs of 100" is to say "25 *percent* of the songs."

2. In the sentence "30 is 75% of 40," 40 is the base.

3. $\dfrac{209}{b} = \dfrac{38}{100}$

$20{,}900 = 38b$

$550 = b$

209 is 38% of 550.

19. *Sample answers:*

Three percent problems in which you find the percent:

2 is what percent of 10?

15 is what percent of 50?

25 is what percent of 50?

Three percent problems in which you find the part:

What number is 40% of 80?

What number is 75% of 90?

What number is 90% of 20?

Three percent problems in which you find the base:

5 is 25% of what number?

12 is 50% of what number?

90 is 200% of what number?

4. $\dfrac{6}{75} = \dfrac{p}{100}$

$100 \cdot \dfrac{6}{75} = 100 \cdot \dfrac{p}{100}$

$8 = p$

6 is 8% of 75.

5. $\dfrac{5}{125} = \dfrac{p}{100}$

$100 \cdot \dfrac{5}{125} = 100 \cdot \dfrac{p}{100}$

$4 = p$

5 is 4% of 125.

6. $\dfrac{481}{b} = \dfrac{52}{100}$

$48{,}100 = 52b$

$925 = b$

481 is 52% of 925.

7. $\dfrac{a}{245} = \dfrac{45}{100}$

$100a = 11{,}025$

$a = 110.25$

110.25 is 45% of 245.

8. $\dfrac{a}{120} = \dfrac{30}{100}$

$120 \cdot \dfrac{a}{120} = 120 \cdot \dfrac{30}{100}$

$a = 36$

36 is 30% of 120.

9. $\dfrac{756}{840} = \dfrac{p}{100}$

$100 \cdot \dfrac{756}{840} = 100 \cdot \dfrac{p}{100}$

$90 = p$

756 is 90% of 840.

10. $\dfrac{39}{50} = \dfrac{p}{100}$

$100 \cdot \dfrac{39}{50} = 100 \cdot \dfrac{p}{100}$

$78 = p$

39 is 78% of 50.

11. $\dfrac{918}{b} = \dfrac{170}{100}$

$91{,}800 = 170b$

$540 = b$

918 is 170% of 540.

12. $\dfrac{111}{740} = \dfrac{p}{100}$

$100 \cdot \dfrac{111}{740} = 100 \cdot \dfrac{p}{100}$

$15 = p$

111 is 15% of 740.

13. $\dfrac{567}{420} = \dfrac{p}{100}$

$100 \cdot \dfrac{567}{420} = 100 \cdot \dfrac{p}{100}$

$135 = p$

567 is 135% of 420.

14. $\dfrac{a}{150} = \dfrac{520}{100}$

$100a = 78{,}000$

$a = 780$

780 is 520% of 150.

15. $\dfrac{a}{700} = \dfrac{0.36}{100}$

$100a = 252$

$a = 2.52$

2.52 is 0.36% of 700.

20. $\dfrac{a}{120} = \dfrac{30}{100}$

$100a = 3600$

$a = 36$

$\dfrac{a}{30} = \dfrac{120}{100}$

$100a = 3600$

$a = 36$

30% of 120 = 120% of 30.

21. $\dfrac{a}{80} = \dfrac{20}{100}$

$100a = 1600$

$a = 16$

$\dfrac{a}{50} = \dfrac{40}{100}$

$100a = 2000$

$a = 20$

20% of 80 < 40% of 50.

22. $\dfrac{a}{140} = \dfrac{15}{100}$

$100a = 2100$

$a = 21$

$\dfrac{a}{24} = \dfrac{75}{100}$

$100a = 1800$

$a = 18$

15% of 140 > 75% of 24.

23. $\dfrac{a}{80} = \dfrac{25}{100}$

$100a = 2000$

$a = 20$

$\dfrac{a}{12} = \dfrac{125}{100}$

$100a = 1500$

$a = 15$

25% of 80 > 125% of 12.

24. $\dfrac{a}{30} = \dfrac{150}{100}$

$100a = 4500$

$a = 45$

$\dfrac{a}{48} = \dfrac{75}{100}$

$100a = 3600$

$a = 36$

150% of 30 > 75% of 48.

Chapter 7, *continued*

25. $\dfrac{a}{400} = \dfrac{10}{100}$ $\qquad\qquad$ $\dfrac{a}{160} = \dfrac{25}{100}$

$\qquad\ 100a = 4000$ $\qquad\qquad\quad 100a = 4000$

$\qquad\qquad a = 40$ $\qquad\qquad\qquad\ a = 40$

10% of 400 = 25% of 160.

26. $\dfrac{a}{8y} = \dfrac{50}{100}$ $\qquad$ **27.** $\dfrac{3y}{b} = \dfrac{60}{100}$

$\quad 8y \cdot \dfrac{a}{8y} = 8y \cdot \dfrac{50}{100}$ $\qquad\quad 300y = 60b$

$\qquad\qquad a = 4y$ $\qquad\qquad\qquad 5y = b$

28. $\dfrac{34}{b} = \dfrac{20}{100}$ $\qquad\qquad$ $\dfrac{170}{b} = \dfrac{85}{100}$

$\quad 3400 = 20b$ $\qquad\qquad 17{,}000 = 85b$

$\quad\ \ 170 = b$ $\qquad\qquad\qquad\ 200 = b$

85% of 20% of 200 is 34.

29. $\dfrac{46}{b} = \dfrac{25}{100}$ $\qquad\qquad$ $\dfrac{184}{b} = \dfrac{115}{100}$

$\ 4600 = 25b$ $\qquad\qquad 18{,}400 = 115b$

$\quad\ 184 = b$ $\qquad\qquad\qquad 160 = b$

115% of 25% of 160 is 46.

Problem Solving

30. a. $\dfrac{a}{b} = \dfrac{p}{100}$

$\quad$ **b.** $\dfrac{89}{356} = \dfrac{p}{100}$

$\quad$ **c.** $100 \cdot \dfrac{89}{356} = 100 \cdot \dfrac{p}{100}$

$\qquad\qquad\quad 25 = p$

Twenty-five percent of the people surveyed like to draw.

31. $\dfrac{\text{Number that finished}}{\text{Number that ran}} = \dfrac{p}{100}$

$\qquad\quad \dfrac{19{,}236}{23{,}513} = \dfrac{p}{100}$

$\quad 100 \cdot \dfrac{19{,}236}{23{,}513} = 100 \cdot \dfrac{p}{100}$

$\qquad\qquad 81.8 \approx p$

About 81.8% of the runners finished the race.

32. B; $\dfrac{34}{100} = \dfrac{\text{Number of green stickers}}{\text{Total number of stickers}}$

$\qquad \dfrac{34}{100} = \dfrac{g}{150}$

33. $\dfrac{a}{60} = \dfrac{75}{100}$

$\quad 60 \cdot \dfrac{a}{60} = 60 \cdot \dfrac{75}{100}$

$\qquad\qquad a = 45$

About 45 pounds of a 60 pound child's weight is water.

34. $\dfrac{\text{Students in club}}{\text{Students in school}} = \dfrac{p}{100}$

$\qquad\qquad \dfrac{560}{875} = \dfrac{p}{100}$

$\quad 100 \cdot \dfrac{560}{875} = 100 \cdot \dfrac{p}{100}$

$\qquad\qquad 64 = p$

64% of the students in your school belong to a club.

To check your answer, estimate 560 to be 600 and 875 to be 1000. Write 600 of 1000 as the fraction $\dfrac{600}{1000}$. This fraction is equal to $\dfrac{60}{100} = 60\%$. So, your answer seems reasonable.

35. $\dfrac{a}{24} = \dfrac{167}{100}$

$\quad 24 \cdot \dfrac{a}{24} = 24 \cdot \dfrac{167}{100}$

$\qquad\qquad a = 40.08$

The crocodile was about 40 feet long.

$40 - 24 = 16$

The ancient crocodile was about 16 feet longer than today's crocodile.

36. Because you are multiplying 400 by 0.1, move the decimal point in 400 one place to the left.

37. Number of people who didn't wear a red shirt = $80 - 32 = 48$

$\qquad \dfrac{48}{80} = \dfrac{p}{100}$

$\quad 100 \cdot \dfrac{48}{80} = 100 \cdot \dfrac{p}{100}$

$\qquad\qquad 60 = p$

Sixty percent of the 80 people did not wear a red shirt to school.

38. $\dfrac{32}{b} = \dfrac{80}{100}$

$\quad 3200 = 80b$

$\qquad 40 = b$

Because 32 is 80% of 40, the maximum number of points on the quiz is 40.

$\qquad \dfrac{a}{40} = \dfrac{90}{100}$

$\quad 100a = 3600$

$\qquad a = 36$

Because 90% of 40 is 36, you need $36 - 32 = 4$ more points to earn a score of 90%.

39. *Sample answer:* Your average points scored in a basketball season is 120% of your average points scored last season.

40. Convert 3 feet 4 inches to inches.

3 ft 4 in. = (3 × 12) in. + 4 in. = 40 in.

$$\frac{\text{Model height}}{\text{Actual height}} = \frac{p}{100}$$

$$\frac{1 \text{ in.}}{40 \text{ in.}} = \frac{p}{100}$$

$$100 \cdot \frac{1}{40} = 100 \cdot \frac{p}{100}$$

$$2.5 = p$$

The height of the model is about 3% of the actual height.

41. a. Mary Anne:

$$A = \ell w = 30 \cdot 32 = 960$$

Josefina:

$$A = \ell w = 58 \cdot 18 = 1044$$

So far, Mary Anne has mowed 960 square feet and Josefina has mowed 1044 square feet.

b. Mary Anne's section:

Total area $= \ell w = 40 \cdot 40 = 1600$ ft^2

$$\frac{\text{Area mowed so far}}{\text{Total area}} = \frac{p}{100}$$

$$\frac{960}{1600} = \frac{p}{100}$$

$$96{,}000 = 1600p$$

$$60 = p$$

Mary Anne has mowed 60% of her section.

Josefina's section:

Total area $= \ell w = 60 \cdot 30 = 1800$ ft^2

$$\frac{\text{Area mowed so far}}{\text{Total area}} = \frac{p}{100}$$

$$\frac{1044}{1800} = \frac{p}{100}$$

$$104{,}400 = 1800p$$

$$58 = p$$

Josefina has mowed 58% of her section.

So, Mary Anne has mowed the greatest percent of her section.

c. Unmowed portion of back lawn $= 1800 - 1044$

$$= 756 \text{ ft}^2$$

$$\frac{a}{756} = \frac{5}{100}$$

$$100a = 3780$$

$$a = 37.8$$

5% of the unmowed portion, 756 square feet, is 37.8 square feet. Josefina has $756 - 37.8 = 718.2$ square feet left to mow.

Josefina mows $1044 + 718.2 = 1762.2$ square feet.

Total area of lawn $= 1600 + 1800 = 3400$ ft^2

$$\frac{\text{Area Josefina mows}}{\text{Total area}} = \frac{p}{100}$$

$$\frac{1762.2}{3400} = \frac{p}{100}$$

$$176{,}220 = 3400p$$

$$51.8 \approx p$$

Josefina mows about 51.8% of the entire lawn.

42. 64% reduction first:

$$\frac{\text{new length}}{\text{original length}} = \frac{p}{100}$$

$$\frac{a}{10} = \frac{64}{100}$$

$$10 \cdot \frac{a}{10} = 10 \cdot \frac{64}{100}$$

$$a = 6.4 \text{ in.}$$

$$\frac{\text{new width}}{\text{original width}} = \frac{p}{100}$$

$$\frac{a}{8} = \frac{64}{100}$$

$$8 \cdot \frac{a}{8} = 8 \cdot \frac{64}{100}$$

$$a = 5.12 \text{ in.}$$

78% reduction:

$$\frac{\text{new length}}{64\text{\%-reduced length}} = \frac{p}{100}$$

$$\frac{a}{6.4} = \frac{78}{100}$$

$$6.4 \cdot \frac{a}{6.4} = 6.4 \cdot \frac{78}{100}$$

$$a = 4.992 \text{ in.}$$

$$\frac{\text{new width}}{64\text{\%-reduced width}} = \frac{p}{100}$$

$$\frac{a}{5.12} = \frac{78}{100}$$

$$5.12 \cdot \frac{a}{5.12} = 5.12 \cdot \frac{78}{100}$$

$$a = 3.9936 \text{ in.}$$

New area $= \ell w = (4.992)(3.9936) \approx 19.94$ in.^{2}

78% reduction first:

$$\frac{\text{new length}}{\text{original length}} = \frac{p}{100}$$

$$\frac{a}{10} = \frac{78}{100}$$

$$10 \cdot \frac{a}{10} = 10 \cdot \frac{78}{100}$$

$$a = 7.8 \text{ in.}$$

$$\frac{\text{new width}}{\text{original width}} = \frac{p}{100}$$

$$\frac{a}{8} = \frac{78}{100}$$

$$a = 6.24 \text{ in.}$$

64% reduction:

$$\frac{\text{new length}}{78\%\text{-reduced length}} = \frac{p}{100}$$

$$\frac{a}{7.8} = \frac{64}{100}$$

$$a = 4.992 \text{ in.}$$

$$\frac{\text{new width}}{78\%\text{-reduced width}} = \frac{p}{100}$$

$$\frac{a}{6.24} = \frac{64}{100}$$

$$a = 3.9936 \text{ in.}$$

New area $= \ell w = (4.992)(3.9936) \approx 19.94 \text{ in.}^2$

The areas are the same.

43. $\dfrac{\text{New pay rate}}{\text{Original pay rate}} = \dfrac{120}{100}$

$$\frac{a}{b} = \frac{120}{100}$$

$$100a = 120b$$

$$a = 1.2b$$

The first option results in a pay rate that is 1.2 times the original pay rate.

$$\frac{\text{Option 2 rate}}{\text{New pay rate}} = \frac{80}{100}$$

$$\frac{c}{1.2b} = \frac{80}{100}$$

$$100c = 96b$$

$$c = 0.96b$$

The second option results in a pay rate that is 0.96 times the original pay rate. So, choosing the second option enables the worker to make less money than before the raise.

Mixed Review

44–47. *Sample answers given.*

44. $\dfrac{48}{72} = \dfrac{48 \div 24}{72 \div 24} = \dfrac{2}{3}; \dfrac{48}{72} = \dfrac{48 \div 12}{72 \div 12} = \dfrac{4}{6}$

The fractions $\dfrac{2}{3}$ and $\dfrac{4}{6}$ are equivalent to $\dfrac{48}{72}$.

45. $\dfrac{21}{28} = \dfrac{21 \div 7}{28 \div 7} = \dfrac{3}{4}; \dfrac{3}{4} = \dfrac{3 \times 2}{4 \times 2} = \dfrac{6}{8}$

The fractions $\dfrac{3}{4}$ and $\dfrac{6}{8}$ are equivalent to $\dfrac{21}{28}$.

46. $\dfrac{18}{54} = \dfrac{18 \div 18}{54 \div 18} = \dfrac{1}{3}; \dfrac{18}{54} = \dfrac{18 \div 6}{54 \div 6} = \dfrac{3}{9}$

The fractions $\dfrac{1}{3}$ and $\dfrac{3}{9}$ are equivalent to $\dfrac{18}{54}$.

47. $\dfrac{75}{125} = \dfrac{75 \div 25}{125 \div 25} = \dfrac{3}{5}; \dfrac{3}{5} = \dfrac{3 \times 2}{5 \times 2} = \dfrac{6}{10}$

The fractions $\dfrac{3}{5}$ and $\dfrac{6}{10}$ are equivalent to $\dfrac{75}{125}$.

48. $1.86 = \dfrac{186}{100} = 1\dfrac{86}{100} = 1\dfrac{43}{50}$

49. $8.714 = \dfrac{8714}{1000} = 8\dfrac{714}{1000} = 8\dfrac{357}{500}$

50. $0.624 = \dfrac{624}{1000} = \dfrac{78}{125}$

51. $3.28 = \dfrac{328}{100} = 3\dfrac{28}{100} = 3\dfrac{7}{25}$

52.

$$\begin{array}{r} 0.0\,2\,3 \\ \times \quad 8.4\,5 \\ \hline 1\,1\,5 \\ 9\,2 \\ 1\,8\,4 \\ \hline 0.1\,9\,4\,3\,5 \end{array}$$

53.

$$\begin{array}{r} 4\,7.1 \\ \times\,0.9\,6 \\ \hline 2\,8\,2\,6 \\ 4\,2\,3\,9 \\ \hline 4\,5.2\,1\,6 \end{array}$$

54.

$$8.2\overline{)11.48} \longrightarrow 82\overline{)114.8}$$
$$\begin{array}{r} 1.4 \\ \hline 82\,)\overline{114.8} \\ 82 \\ \hline 32\,8 \\ 32\,8 \\ \hline 0 \end{array}$$

55.

$$6.4\overline{)17.92} \longrightarrow 64\overline{)179.2}$$
$$\begin{array}{r} 2.8 \\ \hline 64\,)\overline{179.2} \\ 128 \\ \hline 51\,2 \\ 51\,2 \\ \hline 0 \end{array}$$

56. A; $2(10) + 2h = 30$

$$20 + 2h = 30$$

$$2h = 10$$

$$h = 5$$

You and your friend can buy at most 5 hot dogs.

Lesson 7.4

7.4 Guided Practice (pp. 360–361)

1. $35\% = 35 \div 100 = .35 = 0.35$

$$35\% = \frac{35}{100} = \frac{35 \div 5}{100 \div 5} = \frac{7}{20}$$

2. $140\% = 140 \div 100 = 1.40 = 1.4$

$$140\% = \frac{140}{100} = \frac{140 \div 20}{100 \div 20} = \frac{7}{5} = 1\frac{2}{5}$$

3. $0.75\% = 0.75 \div 100 = .0075 = 0.0075$

$$0.75\% = \frac{0.75}{100}$$

$$= \frac{0.75 \times 100}{100 \times 100}$$

$$= \frac{75}{10,000}$$

$$= \frac{75 \div 25}{10,000 \div 25}$$

$$= \frac{3}{400}$$

4. $12.12\% = 12.12 \div 100 = .1212 = 0.1212$

$12.12\% = \dfrac{12.12}{100}$

$= \dfrac{12.12 \times 100}{100 \times 100}$

$= \dfrac{1212}{10,000}$

$= \dfrac{1212 \div 4}{10,000 \div 4}$

$= \dfrac{303}{2500}$

5. $0.9 = (0.9 \times 100)\% = 090. = 90\%$

6. $5.04 = (5.04 \times 100)\% = 504. = 504\%$

7.
$\dfrac{1}{20} = \dfrac{p}{100}$

$100 \cdot \dfrac{1}{20} = 100 \cdot \dfrac{p}{100}$

$5 = p$

$\dfrac{1}{20} = 5\%$

8.
$\dfrac{3}{8} = \dfrac{p}{100}$

$100 \cdot \dfrac{3}{8} = 100 \cdot \dfrac{p}{100}$

$37.5 = p$

$\dfrac{3}{8} = 37.5\%$

9. $41\% = 0.41$

$\dfrac{9}{20} = 0.45$

The numbers ordered from least to greatest are 0.389, 41%, and $\dfrac{9}{20}$.

10. $\dfrac{9}{10} = 0.9$

$95\% = 0.95$

The numbers ordered from least to greatest are 0.099, $\dfrac{9}{10}$, and 95%.

11. $145\% = 1.45$

$\dfrac{7}{5} = 1.4$

The numbers ordered from least to greatest are $\dfrac{7}{5}$, 145%, and 1.5.

7.4 Exercises (pp. 361–364)

Skill Practice

1. In a circle graph, the sum of the percents is 100%.

In a circle graph, the sum of the fractions is 1.

2. $80\% = 80\% = 0.8$

3. $12.5\% = 12.5\% = 0.125$

4. $7.5\% = 07.5\% = 0.075$

5. $110\% = 110\% = 1.1$

6. $1.05\% = 01.05\% = 0.0105$

7. $44.55\% = 44.55\% = 0.4455$

8. $0.4\% = 00.4\% = 0.004$

9. $0.78\% = 00.78\% = 0.0078$

10. $187.09\% = 187.09\% = 1.8709$

11. $0.08\% = 00.08\% = 0.0008$

12. $0.09 = 0.09 = 9\%$

13. $1.27 = 1.27 = 127\%$

14. $0.7 = 0.70 = 70\%$

15. $2.1 = 2.10 = 210\%$

16. $4 = 400 = 400\%$

17. $0.51 = 0.51 = 51\%$

18. $0.003 = 0.003 = 0.3\%$

19. $0.057 = 0.057 = 5.7\%$

20. $0.039 = 0.039 = 3.9\%$

21. $0.004 = 0.004 = 0.4\%$

22. The decimal is incorrectly written as a fraction.

$0.001 = 0.001 = 0.1\%$

23. $40\% = \dfrac{40}{100} = \dfrac{2}{5}$

24. $87\% = \dfrac{87}{100}$

25. $32.5\% = \dfrac{32.5}{100} = \dfrac{325}{1000} = \dfrac{13}{40}$

26. $5\% = \dfrac{5}{100} = \dfrac{1}{20}$

27. $124\% = \dfrac{124}{100} = 1\dfrac{24}{100} = 1\dfrac{6}{25}$

28. $1\% = \dfrac{1}{100}$

29. $4.2\% = \dfrac{4.2}{100} = \dfrac{42}{1000} = \dfrac{21}{500}$

30. $200.2\% = \dfrac{200.2}{100} = \dfrac{2002}{1000} = 2\dfrac{1}{500}$

31. $8.03\% = \dfrac{8.03}{100} = \dfrac{803}{10,000}$

32. $0.07\% = \dfrac{0.07}{100} = \dfrac{7}{10,000}$

33.
$\dfrac{5}{8} = \dfrac{p}{100}$

$100 \cdot \dfrac{5}{8} = 100 \cdot \dfrac{p}{100}$

$62.5 = p$

$\dfrac{5}{8} = 62.5\%$

34.
$\dfrac{3}{2} = \dfrac{p}{100}$

$100 \cdot \dfrac{3}{2} = 100 \cdot \dfrac{p}{100}$

$150 = p$

$\dfrac{3}{2} = 150\%$

Chapter 7, *continued*

35. $\dfrac{1}{80} = \dfrac{p}{100}$

$100 \cdot \dfrac{1}{80} = 100 \cdot \dfrac{p}{100}$

$1.25 = p$

$\dfrac{1}{80} = 1.25\%$

36. $\dfrac{3}{20} = \dfrac{p}{100}$

$100 \cdot \dfrac{3}{20} = 100 \cdot \dfrac{p}{100}$

$15 = p$

$\dfrac{3}{20} = 15\%$

37. $\dfrac{31}{10} = \dfrac{p}{100}$

$100 \cdot \dfrac{31}{10} = 100 \cdot \dfrac{p}{100}$

$310 = p$

$\dfrac{31}{10} = 310\%$

38. $\dfrac{4}{800} = \dfrac{p}{100}$

$100 \cdot \dfrac{4}{800} = 100 \cdot \dfrac{p}{100}$

$0.5 = p$

$\dfrac{4}{800} = 0.5\%$

39. $\dfrac{4}{50} = \dfrac{p}{100}$

$100 \cdot \dfrac{4}{50} = 100 \cdot \dfrac{p}{100}$

$8 = p$

$\dfrac{4}{50} = 8\%$

40. $\dfrac{117}{200} = \dfrac{p}{100}$

$100 \cdot \dfrac{117}{200} = 100 \cdot \dfrac{p}{100}$

$58.5 = p$

$\dfrac{117}{200} = 58.5\%$

41. $\dfrac{7}{16} = \dfrac{p}{100}$

$100 \cdot \dfrac{7}{16} = 100 \cdot \dfrac{p}{100}$

$43.75 = p$

$\dfrac{7}{16} = 43.75\%$

42. $\dfrac{11}{12} = \dfrac{p}{100}$

$100 \cdot \dfrac{11}{12} = 100 \cdot \dfrac{p}{100}$

$91\dfrac{2}{3} = p$

$\dfrac{11}{12} = 91\dfrac{2}{3}\%$

43. $\dfrac{1}{4} = 0.25$

$26\% = 0.26$

So, $\dfrac{1}{4} < 26\%$.

44. $450\% = 4.5$

$\dfrac{9}{2} = 4.5$

So, $450\% = \dfrac{9}{2}$.

45. $\dfrac{13}{25} = 0.52$

So, $\dfrac{13}{25} > 0.5$.

46. $\dfrac{17}{200} = 0.085$

So, $0.0825 < \dfrac{17}{200}$.

47. $27\% = 0.27$

$\dfrac{1}{5} = 0.2$

So, $27\% > \dfrac{1}{5}$.

48. $\dfrac{7}{20} = 0.35$

$35\% = 0.35$

So, $\dfrac{7}{20} = 35\%$.

49. $4.5\% = 0.045$

So, $4.5\% = 0.045$.

50. $3.83\% = 0.0383$

So, $3.83\% < 0.383$.

51. $101\% = 1.01$

So, $101\% > 0.101$.

52. $\dfrac{9}{40} = 0.225$

$22\% = 0.22$

$\dfrac{41}{125} = 0.328$

The numbers ordered from least to greatest are 22%, $\dfrac{9}{40}$, 0.228, 0.3, and $\dfrac{41}{125}$.

53. $6.5\% = 0.065$

$\dfrac{9}{50} = 0.18$

$66\% = 0.66$

The numbers ordered from least to greatest are 6.5%, $\dfrac{9}{50}$, 0.5, 0.65, and 66%.

54. $\dfrac{4}{7} \approx 0.571$

$58\% = 0.58$

$0.58\% = 0.0058$

The numbers from least to greatest are 0.58%, 0.058, $\dfrac{4}{7}$, 58%, and 58.

55. $212\% = 2.12$

$\dfrac{21}{100} = 0.21$

$\dfrac{21}{10} = 2.1$

The numbers ordered from least to greatest are $\dfrac{21}{100}$, 0.212, $\dfrac{21}{10}$, 212%, and 21.2.

56. $\dfrac{11}{15} = 0.73$

$7.3\% = 0.073$

$\dfrac{75}{100} = 0.75$

$0.73\% = 0.0073$

The numbers ordered from least to greatest are 0.73%, 7.3%, 0.73, $\dfrac{11}{15}$, and $\dfrac{75}{100}$.

57. $\dfrac{12}{25} = 0.48$

$480\% = 4.8$

$4.8\% = 0.048$

The numbers ordered from least to greatest are 4.8%, $\dfrac{12}{25}$, 0.484, 480%, and 4.84.

58. B; $2.5\% = 0.025$

$\dfrac{2}{7} \approx 0.286$

The numbers ordered from least to greatest are 2.5%, 0.25, and $\dfrac{2}{7}$.

Chapter 7, *continued*

59. A: $\frac{9}{8} = 1.125 = 112.5\%$

B: $\frac{5}{4} = 1.25 = 125\%$

C: $\frac{7}{4} = 1.75 = 175\%$

D: $\frac{31}{20} = 1.55 = 155\%$

The fraction in choice A is not like the others when written as a percent.

60. $\frac{1}{4} = 0.25 = 25\%$

$\frac{1}{5} = 0.20 = 20\%$

Because $20\% < 25\%$, $\frac{1}{5} < \frac{1}{4}$. So, $\frac{1}{5} < 25\%$.

61.   45%   4.5%

62. $33\frac{1}{3}\%$ $3\frac{1}{3}\%$

63.   20%   2%

64.   75%   7.5%

 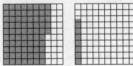

65. $\frac{a}{120} = \frac{30}{100}$ $\qquad$ $\frac{a}{36} = \frac{50}{100}$

$100a = 3600$ $\qquad$ $100a = 1800$

$a = 36$ $\qquad\qquad$ $a = 18$

So, 50% of 30% of 120 is 18.

$\frac{3}{20}(120) = 18$

So, $\frac{3}{20}$ of 120 is 18.

Yes, 50% of 30% of 120 is the same as $\frac{3}{20}$ of 120.

Problem Solving

66. Spanish was the most popular language.

67. $\frac{1}{20} = \frac{p}{100}$

$100 \cdot \frac{1}{20} = 100 \cdot \frac{p}{100}$

$5 = p$

5% of the students studied German.

68. $\frac{9}{50} + \frac{1}{20} = \frac{18}{100} + \frac{5}{100}$

$= \frac{23}{100}$

$= 23\%$

23% of the students studied French or German.

69. $100\% - 69\% = 31\%$

31% of the students did not study Spanish.

70. $\frac{18}{48} = \frac{p}{100}$

$100 \cdot \frac{18}{48} = 100 \cdot \frac{p}{100}$

$37.5 = p$

37.5% of the people sleep 8 hours a night.

71. a. $\frac{\text{Red cars}}{\text{Total cars}} = \frac{9}{25} = 0.36 = 36\%$

36% of the cars in the lot are red.

$\frac{\text{Cars that are not red}}{\text{Total cars}} = \frac{25 - 9}{25}$

$= \frac{16}{25}$

$= 0.64$

$= 64\%$

64% of the cars in the lot are not red.

b. To determine the percent of cars that are not black given the number of white cars, add the number of white cars to the number of red cars and divide by 25. Another way is to find the percent of cars that are white and add it to the percent of cars that are red.

72. If a fraction is greater than 1, then the equivalent percent is greater than 100% because 1 is equal to 100%. So, anything greater than 1 is greater than 100%.

73. $\frac{17}{20} = 0.85$; $\frac{1}{2} = 0.5$; $\frac{19}{50} = 0.38$; $79\% = 0.79$

The numbers ordered from least to greatest are $\frac{19}{50}$, $\frac{1}{2}$, 0.7, 79%, and $\frac{17}{20}$.

Check:

Chapter 7, continued

74. A circle graph cannot be used because the percents do not add up to 100%. A bar graph would be an appropriate way to display the data.

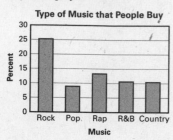

75. *Sample answer:* A percent should not be greater than 100 when a store is offering a percent discount off of an item.

76. B; Use the fact that 1 mile = 1760 yards.

$$\frac{100}{1760} = \frac{p}{100}$$

$$100 \cdot \frac{100}{1760} = 100 \cdot \frac{p}{100}$$

$$5.7 \approx p$$

A football field is about 5.7% of a mile.

77.

$$\frac{2}{15} = 0.1\overline{3} = 13\frac{1}{3}\%$$

$$\frac{5}{12} = 0.41\overline{6} = 41\frac{2}{3}\%$$

$$13\frac{1}{3}\% + 41\frac{2}{3}\% = 55\%$$

55% of the people prefer Brand A or Brand B.

$$100\% - 55\% = 45\%$$

45% of the remaining people prefer Brand C or have no preference.

$$80\% \text{ of } 45\% = 0.80(0.45) = 0.36 = 36\%$$

36% of the people prefer Brand C.

$$55\% + 36\% = 91\%$$

$$100\% - 91\% = 9\%$$

9% of the people surveyed have no preference.

Mixed Review

78.
$$\begin{array}{r} 0.13 \\ \times\ \ 9 \\ \hline 1.17 \end{array}$$

79.
$$\begin{array}{r} 0.41 \\ \times\ \ 11 \\ \hline 41 \\ 4\ 1 \\ \hline 4.51 \end{array}$$

80.
$$\begin{array}{r} 4.5 \\ \times\ \ 9 \\ \hline 40.5 \end{array}$$

81.
$$\begin{array}{r} 1.98 \\ \times\ \ 6 \\ \hline 11.88 \end{array}$$

82. Strategy: Work Backward

Use this strategy because you want to find out how much money you started with when you know how much money you have now.

Money made after working for 4 hours.

↓

−$5.75 for movie

↓

−$2 for popcorn

↓

+$3 from sister

↓

$19.75

$19.75 − $3 = $16.25

↓

$16.25 + $2 = $18.25

↓

$18.25 + $5.75 = $24

$$\frac{\$24}{4\text{ h}} = \$6 \text{ per hour}$$

You were paid $6 per hour.

83. D; $10 + 4x < 31$

$$10 + 4(6) \overset{?}{<} 31$$

$$10 + 24 \overset{?}{<} 31$$

$$34 \not< 31$$

Quiz 7.1–7.4 (p. 364)

1. $\dfrac{\text{Gorillas}}{\text{Sheep}} = \dfrac{6}{2} = \dfrac{3}{1}$

2. $\dfrac{\text{Monkeys}}{\text{Camels}} = \dfrac{2}{4} = \dfrac{1}{2}$

3. $\dfrac{\text{Bears}}{\text{Lions}} = \dfrac{5}{1}$

4. $\dfrac{a}{72} = \dfrac{5}{6}$

$$6a = 360$$
$$a = 60$$

5. $\dfrac{2}{3} = \dfrac{7}{x}$

$$2x = 21$$
$$x = 10.5$$

6. $\dfrac{18}{27} = \dfrac{y}{3}$

$$54 = 27y$$
$$2 = y$$

7. $\dfrac{6}{8} = \dfrac{b}{28}$

$$168 = 8b$$
$$21 = b$$

8. $\dfrac{12}{c} = \dfrac{23}{92}$

$$1104 = 23c$$
$$48 = c$$

9. $\dfrac{z}{8} = \dfrac{95}{19}$

$$19z = 760$$
$$z = 40$$

10. $\dfrac{a}{29} = \dfrac{40}{100}$

$$29 \cdot \frac{a}{29} = 29 \cdot \frac{40}{100}$$

$$a = 11.6$$

You save $11.60.

Chapter 7, *continued*

11. Flowers planted $= 12 + 9 + 6 + 3 = 30$

You planted 30 flowers.

12. $\dfrac{\text{Daffodils}}{\text{All flowers}} = \dfrac{p}{100}$

$$\dfrac{9}{30} = \dfrac{p}{100}$$

$$100 \cdot \dfrac{9}{30} = 100 \cdot \dfrac{p}{100}$$

$$30 = p$$

30% of the flower bed is daffodils.

13. $\dfrac{a}{30} = \dfrac{70}{100}$

$$30 \cdot \dfrac{a}{30} = 30 \cdot \dfrac{70}{100}$$

$$a = 21$$

Because $12 + 9 = 21$, carnations and daffodils combine to equal 70%.

Mixed Review of Problem Solving (p. 365)

1. a. $\dfrac{\text{Free throws made}}{\text{Free throws attempted}} = \dfrac{p}{100}$

$$\dfrac{x}{15} = \dfrac{60}{100}$$

b. $\dfrac{x}{15} = \dfrac{60}{100}$

$$100x = 900$$

$$x = 9$$

$$9 = 1 + 2 + t$$

$$9 = 3 + t$$

$$6 = t$$

Alma made 6 free throws in the third game.

2. a. Maximum length = Total length − Margin lengths

$$= 11 - (0.5 + 0.5)$$

$$= 11 - 1$$

$$= 10$$

The maximum possible length of the enlarged design is 10 inches.

b. $\dfrac{\text{Enlarged length}}{\text{Original length}} = \dfrac{p}{100}$

$$\dfrac{10}{8} = \dfrac{p}{100}$$

$$1000 = 8p$$

$$125 = p$$

The enlarged length will be 125% of the original length.

c. Scale $= \dfrac{\text{Width of enlarged design}}{\text{Width of original design}}$

$$\dfrac{10 \text{ in.}}{8 \text{ in.}} = \dfrac{w \text{ in.}}{5 \text{ in.}}$$

$$50 = 8w$$

$$6.25 = w$$

The width of the enlarged design is 6.25 inches.

3. *Sample answer:*

$\dfrac{\text{Days in school}}{\text{Total school days}} = \dfrac{8}{10}$, 8 to 10, 8 : 10

4. $\dfrac{\text{Water weight}}{\text{Total weight}} = \dfrac{p}{100}$

$$\dfrac{a}{12} = \dfrac{95}{100}$$

$$100a = 1140$$

$$a = 11.4$$

11.4 pounds of a 12 pound watermelon is water. So, $12 - 11.4 = 0.6$ pound of the watermelon is not water.

5. a. Red car:

$$\dfrac{1.15 \text{ mi}}{1 \text{ min}} = \dfrac{1.15 \text{ mi}}{1 \text{ min}} \cdot \dfrac{60 \text{ min}}{1 \text{ h}} = \dfrac{69 \text{ mi}}{\text{h}}$$

Blue car:

$$\dfrac{0.02 \text{ mi}}{1 \text{ sec}} = \dfrac{0.02 \text{ mi}}{1 \text{ sec}} \cdot \dfrac{60 \text{ sec}}{1 \text{ min}} \cdot \dfrac{60 \text{ min}}{1 \text{ h}} = \dfrac{72 \text{ mi}}{\text{h}}$$

Because 72 miles per hour is faster than 69 miles per hour, you know that 0.02 mile per second is faster than 1.15 miles per minute.

b. All of the rates in this problem are unit rates because they all have a denominator of 1 unit.

6. a. $0.9\% = 0.009$

$$\dfrac{1}{4} = 0.25$$

$$60\% = 0.60$$

The responses in order from the one chosen the most to the one chosen the least are Saturday, Friday, Sunday, and Wednesday.

b. Saturday: 60%

Friday: $\dfrac{1}{4} = 0.25 = 25\%$

$$60\% + 25\% = 85\%$$

85% of the students chose the two most favored days of the week.

c. Add up the percents given and subtract the sum from 100%.

$$0.9\% + 25\% + 60\% + 10\% = 95.9\%$$

$$100\% - 95.9\% = 4.1\%$$

4.1% of the students surveyed were not included in the results listed.

7. $\dfrac{\text{Additional copies produced by new machine}}{\text{Copies produced by old machine}} = \dfrac{p}{100}$

$$\dfrac{a}{10} = \dfrac{223}{100}$$

$$100a = 2230$$

$$a = 22.3$$

The new machine produces 22.3 more copies per minute. So, the new machine produces $10 + 22.3 = 32.3$ copies per minute.

Chapter 7, continued

8. $\text{Scale} = \dfrac{\text{Height of model}}{\text{Height of actual building}}$

$\dfrac{1 \text{ in.}}{200 \text{ ft}} = \dfrac{h \text{ in.}}{1046 \text{ ft}}$

$1046 = 200h$

$5.23 = h$

Width of model $= h - 4.23 = 5.23 - 4.23 = 1$

The width of the model is 1 inch.

Lesson 7.5

7.5 Guided Practice (p. 367)

1. The change is a decrease.

$p = \dfrac{50 - 36}{50} = \dfrac{14}{50} = 0.28 = 28\%$

The percent of decrease is 28%.

2. The change is an increase.

$p = \dfrac{29.5 - 10}{10} = \dfrac{19.5}{10} = 1.95 = 195\%$

The percent of increase is 195%.

3. The change is an increase.

$p = \dfrac{110 - 90}{90} = \dfrac{20}{90} = 0.\overline{2} = 22.\overline{2}\%$

The percent of increase is $22.\overline{2}\%$.

4. Decrease $= 11\%$ of $59,084$

$\qquad = 0.11(59,084)$

$\qquad = 6499.24$

New amount $= 59,084 - 6499.24$

$\qquad\qquad = 52,584.76$

$\qquad\qquad \approx 53,000$

About 53,000 people visited the park in November.

7.5 Exercises (pp. 368–369)

Skill Practice

1. When the original amount is less than the new amount, the percent of change is called an *increase*.

2. The change is an increase.

$p = \dfrac{16 - 10}{10} = \dfrac{6}{10} = 0.6 = 60\%$

The percent of increase is 60%.

3. The change is a decrease.

$p = \dfrac{360 - 352}{360} = \dfrac{8}{360} = 0.0\overline{2} = 2.\overline{2}\%$

The percent of decrease is 2%.

4. The change is a decrease.

$p = \dfrac{33,300 - 31,080}{33,300} = \dfrac{2220}{33,300} = 0.0\overline{6} = 6.\overline{6}\%$

The percent of decrease is 7%.

5. The change is an increase.

$p = \dfrac{13,908 - 12,200}{12,200} = \dfrac{1708}{12,200} = 0.14 = 14\%$

The percent of increase is 14%.

6. The change is a decrease.

$p = \dfrac{50 - 45}{50} = \dfrac{5}{50} = 0.1 = 10\%$

The percent of decrease is 10%.

7. The change is an increase.

$p = \dfrac{420 - 350}{350} = \dfrac{70}{350} = 0.2 = 20\%$

The percent of increase is 20%.

8. C; $p = \dfrac{3 - 1}{1} = \dfrac{2}{1} = 2 = 200\%$

The percent of increase is 200%.

9. Increase $= 4\%$ of $1100 = 0.04(1100) = 44$

New amount $= 1100 + 44 = 1144$

The new amount is 1144.

10. Decrease $= 13\%$ of $24,700 = 0.13(24,700) = 3211$

New amount $= 24,700 - 3211 = 21,489$

The new amount is 21,489.

11. Increase $= 60\%$ of $8 = 0.6(8) = 4.8$

New amount $= 8 + 4.8 = 12.8$

The new amount is 12.8.

12. Decrease $= 30\%$ of $65 = 0.3(65) = 19.5$

New amount $= 65 - 19.5 = 45.5$

The new amount is 45.5.

13. Decrease $= 12.5\%$ of $88,000 = 0.125(88,000) = 11,000$

New amount $= 88,000 - 11,000 = 77,000$

The new amount is 77,000.

14. Increase $= 14.6\%$ of $26,000 = 0.146(26,000) = 3796$

New amount $= 26,000 + 3796 = 29,796$

The new amount is 29,796.

15. Your friend did not add the increase to the original number. Multiplying a number by 5 and adding the product to the original number is a 500% increase.

16. $p = \dfrac{4x - x}{x} = \dfrac{3x}{x} = 3 = 300\%$

The percent of increase is 300%.

17. $p = \dfrac{9b - 6b}{6b} = \dfrac{3b}{6b} = \dfrac{1}{2} = 0.5 = 50\%$

The percent of increase is 50%.

18. $p = \dfrac{5d - d}{d} = \dfrac{4d}{d} = 4 = 400\%$

The percent of increase is 400%.

19. $p = \dfrac{6h - 4h}{4h} = \dfrac{2h}{4h} = \dfrac{1}{2} = 0.5 = 50\%$

The percent of increase is 50%.

20. $p = \dfrac{y - \frac{3}{8}y}{y} = \dfrac{\frac{5}{8}y}{y} = \dfrac{5}{8} = 0.625 = 62.5\%$

The percent of decrease is 62.5%.

Chapter 7, *continued*

21. $p = \dfrac{4.5a - 2.25a}{1.5a} = \dfrac{2.25a}{1.5a} = \dfrac{1}{2} = 0.5 = 50\%$

The percent of decrease is 50%.

22. $p = \dfrac{5m - 4.5m}{5m} = \dfrac{0.5m}{5m} = 0.1 = 10\%$

The percent of decrease is 10%.

23. $p = \dfrac{z - \frac{3}{4}z}{z} = \dfrac{\frac{1}{4}z}{z} = \dfrac{1}{4} = 0.25 = 25\%$

The percent of decrease is 25%.

24. Let a be the number.

New amount after increase $= a + 0.5a = 1.5a$

New amount after decrease $= 1.5a - 0.5(1.5a)$
$$= 1.5a - 0.75a = 0.75a$$

$p = \dfrac{a - 0.75a}{a} = \dfrac{0.25a}{a} = 25\%$

The percent of change from the original number to the final number is 25%.

Problem Solving

25. a. Increase $= 69\%$ of $130{,}000$
$$= (0.69)(130{,}000)$$
$$= 89{,}700$$

New amount $= 130{,}000 + 89{,}700$
$$= 219{,}700$$

There were 219,700 tennis courts in 1985.

b. Increase $= 9\%$ of $219{,}700$
$$= (0.09)(219{,}700)$$
$$= 19{,}773$$

The amount of the second increase is 19,773.

c. New amount $= 219{,}700 + 19{,}773$
$$= 239{,}473$$

There were 239,473 tennis courts in 1995.

26. $p = \dfrac{291{,}049{,}000 - 260{,}255{,}000}{260{,}255{,}000}$

$= \dfrac{30{,}794{,}000}{260{,}255{,}000}$

$\approx 11.8\%$

The percent of increase in population was about 11.8%.

27. B; Decrease $= 10\%$ of $\$170$
$$= 0.10(170)$$
$$= 17$$

New amount $= \$170 - \$17 = \$153$

Decrease $= 10\%$ of $\$153 = 0.10(153) = 15.30$

New amount $= \$153 - \$15.30 = \$137.70$

The camera will cost $137.70.

28. Decrease $= 51\%$ of $46{,}650$
$$= 0.51(46{,}650)$$
$$= 23{,}791.5$$

New amount $= 46{,}650 - 23{,}791.5 = 22{,}858.5$

In 2004, about 23,000 tons of hazelnuts were produced in the United States. A little less than half as many tons were produced in 2004 as in 1997.

29. Let a be the number.

$p = \dfrac{a - \frac{1}{4}a}{a} = \dfrac{\frac{3}{4}a}{a} = 75\%$

The percent of decrease is 75%.

30. Let a be the number.

$p = \dfrac{a - \frac{a}{5}}{a} = \dfrac{\frac{4}{5}a}{a} = \dfrac{4}{5} = 80\%$

Dividing a number by 5 is a decrease of 80%.

31. New length $= 6 + 0.5(6) = 6 + 3 = 9$ in.

New width $= 4 + 0.5(4) = 4 + 2 = 6$ in.

The new dimensions will be 9 inches by 6 inches.

Old area $= 6(4) = 24$ in.^{2}

New area $= 9(6) = 54$ in.^{2}

$p = \dfrac{54 - 24}{24} = \dfrac{30}{24} = \dfrac{5}{4} = 125\%$

The percent of increase in the area is 125%. So, the increase in area is greater than 50%.

32. New height $= 3 + 1(3) = 3 + 3 = 6$ cm

New base $= 4 + 1(4) = 4 + 4 = 8$ cm

Old area $= \dfrac{1}{2}(4)(3) = \dfrac{1}{2}(12) = 6$ cm^2

New area $= \dfrac{1}{2}(8)(6) = \dfrac{1}{2}(48) = 24$ cm^2

$p = \dfrac{24 - 6}{6} = \dfrac{18}{6} = 3 = 300\%$

The percent of increase in the area is 300%.

33. Increase $= 0.117(60) = 7.02$

Amount in 2002 $= 60 + 7.02 = 67.02$

Assuming the increase is about the same each year from 2001 to 2007, use an increase of 11.7% to find the number of hours each year until 2007.

Increase $= 0.117(67.02) \approx 7.84$

Amount in 2003 $\approx 67.02 + 7.84 = 74.86$

Increase $= 0.117(74.86) \approx 8.76$

Amount in 2004 $\approx 74.86 + 8.76 = 83.62$

Increase $= 0.117(83.62) \approx 9.78$

Amount in 2005 $\approx 83.62 + 9.78 = 93.4$

Increase $= 0.117(93.4) \approx 10.93$

Amount in 2006 $\approx 93.4 + 10.93 = 104.33$

Chapter 7, *continued*

Increase $= 0.117(104.33) \approx 12.21$

Amount in 2007 $\approx 104.33 + 12.21 = 116.54$

So, you should expect each person to spend about 117 hours playing video games in 2007.

34. Percent of change $= \dfrac{2000 \text{ population} - 1990 \text{ population}}{1990 \text{ population}}$

$$0.093 = \dfrac{1,953,631 - a}{a}$$

$$0.093a = 1,953,631 - a$$

$$1.093a = 1,953,631$$

$$a \approx 1,787,403$$

The actual population in 1990 was about 1,787,403. So, 1,772,000 is a reasonable estimate for the population of Houston in 1990.

Mixed Review

35.
$$\begin{array}{r} 4.412 \\ \times\ \ 0.36 \\ \hline 26472 \\ 1\ 3236 \\ \hline 1.58832 \end{array}$$

36. $-6.7 \cdot 0.8 = -5.36$

37.
$$\begin{array}{r} -0.91 \\ \times\ \ \ 0.35 \\ \hline 455 \\ 273 \\ \hline -0.3185 \end{array}$$

38.
$$14.2 + 1.4x = -5.4$$
$$14.2 + 1.4x - 14.2 = -5.4 - 14.2$$
$$1.4x = -19.6$$
$$\dfrac{1.4x}{1.4} = \dfrac{-19.6}{1.4}$$
$$x = -14$$

39.
$$0.2s - 1.3 = 0.3$$
$$0.2s - 1.3 + 1.3 = 0.3 + 1.3$$
$$0.2s = 1.6$$
$$\dfrac{0.2s}{0.2} = \dfrac{1.6}{0.2}$$
$$s = 8$$

40.
$$1.14y - 2 = y + 1.64$$
$$1.14y - 2 + 2 = y + 1.64 + 2$$
$$1.14y = y + 3.64$$
$$1.14y - y = y + 3.64 - y$$
$$0.14y = 3.64$$
$$\dfrac{0.14y}{0.14} = \dfrac{3.64}{0.14}$$
$$y = 26$$

41. B; Median: 3, 4, **6**, **7**, 7, 9

Median $= \dfrac{6 + 7}{2} = \dfrac{13}{2} = 6.5$

Lesson 7.6

7.6 Guided Practice (pp. 370–372)

1. Discount $= 10\%$ of $\$25 = 0.1(25) = 2.5$

Sale price $= 25 - 2.5 = 22.5$

The sale price is $22.50.

2. Discount $= 30\%$ of $\$85.50 = 0.3(85.5) = 25.65$

Sale price $= 85.50 - 25.65 = 59.85$

The sale price is $59.85.

3. Discount $= 20\%$ of $\$14.20$

$\qquad = 0.2(14.2)$

$\qquad = 2.84$

Sale price $= 14.20 - 2.84 = 11.36$

The sale price is $11.36.

4. Discount $= 25\%$ of $\$136.24$

$\qquad = 0.25(136.24)$

$\qquad = 34.06$

Sale price $= 136.24 - 34.06 = 102.18$

The sale price is $102.18.

5. Markup $= 85\%$ of $\$64 = 0.85(64) = 54.4$

Retail price $= 64 + 54.4 = 118.4$

The retail price is $118.40.

6. Markup $= 110\%$ of $\$35 = 1.1(35) = 38.5$

Retail price $= 35 + 38.5 = 73.5$

The retail price is $73.50.

7. Sales tax $= 5\%$ of $\$8.90 = 0.05(8.9) \approx 0.45$

Total cost $= 8.90 + 0.45 = 9.35$

The total cost is $9.35.

8. Sales tax $= 7\%$ of $\$54.07 = 0.07(54.07) \approx 3.78$

Total cost $= 54.07 + 3.78 = 57.85$

The total cost is $57.85.

9. Tip $= 15\%$ of $\$35 = 0.15(35) = 5.25$

Sales tax $= 6\%$ of $\$35 = 0.06(35) = 2.1$

Total cost $= 35 + 5.25 + 2.1 = 42.35$

The total cost of the meal is $42.35.

7.6 Exercises (pp. 372–374)

Skill Practice

1. To find the retail price, add the *markup* to the wholesale price.

2. The sale price is the original price minus the *discount*.

3. Discount $= 15\%$ of $\$60 = 0.15(60) = 9$

Sale price $= 60 - 9 = 51$

The sale price is $51.

4. Discount $= 60\%$ of $\$28.50 = 0.6(28.5) = 17.1$

Sale price $= 28.5 - 17.1 = 11.4$

The sale price is $11.40.

5. Markup $= 65\%$ of $\$25 = 0.65(25) = 16.25$

Retail price $= 25 + 16.25 = 41.25$

The retail price is $41.25.

6. Markup = 140% of $14.50 = 1.4(14.5) = 20.3

Retail price = 14.5 + 20.3 = 34.8

The retail price is $34.80.

7. Discount = 30% of $42 = 0.3(42) = 12.6

Sale price = 42 − 12.6 = 29.4

The sale price is $29.40.

8. Markup = 110% of $19 = 1.1(19) = 20.9

Retail price = 19 + 20.9 = 39.9

The retail price is $39.90.

9. C; Markup = 130% of $16.49 = 1.3(16.49) ≈ 21.44

Retail price = 16.49 + 21.44 = 37.93

The retail price is $37.93.

10. Sales tax = 6% of $72 = 0.06(72) = 4.32

Total cost = 72 + 4.32 = 76.32

The total cost is $76.32.

11. Sales tax = 5.5% of $58.40 = 0.055(58.4) ≈ 3.21

Total cost = 58.4 + 3.21 = 61.61

The total cost is $61.61.

12. Sales tax = 7% of $8.40 = 0.07(8.4) ≈ 0.59

Total cost = 8.40 + 0.59 = 8.99

The total cost is $8.99.

13. Sales tax = 6.5% of $258.20 = 0.065 (258.2) ≈ 16.78

Total cost = 258.20 + 16.78 = 274.98

The total cost is $274.98.

14. Tip = 18% of $28.50 = 0.18(28.5) = 5.13

Sales tax = 4.5% of $28.50 = 0.045(28.5) ≈ 1.28

Total cost = 28.50 + 5.13 + 1.28 = 34.91

The total cost is $34.91.

15. Tip = 20% of $18 = 0.2(18) = 3.6

Sales tax = 5% of $18 = 0.05(18) = 0.9

Total cost = 18 + 3.6 + 0.9 = 22.5

The total cost is $22.50.

16. The sales tax is on the sale price, not the original price.

Discount = 5% of $28 = 0.05(28) = 1.4

Sale price = 28 − 1.40 = 26.60

Sales tax = 5% of $26.60 = 0.05(26.6) = 1.33

Total cost = 26.60 + 1.33 = 27.93

The total cost is $27.93.

17. The new price is a discount.

$$p = \frac{32 - 24}{32} = \frac{8}{32} = \frac{1}{4} = 25\%$$

The percent of discount is 25%.

Discount = 25% of $96 = 0.25(96) = 24

New price = 96 − 24 = 72

The new price for a $96 item with a 25% discount is $72.

18. The new price is a discount.

$$p = \frac{45 - 40.50}{45} = \frac{4.5}{45} = \frac{1}{10} = 10\%$$

The percent of discount is 10%.

Discount = 10% of $96 = 0.1(96) = 9.6

New price = 96 − 9.60 = 86.40

The new price for a $96 item with a 10% discount is $86.40.

19. The new price is a markup.

$$p = \frac{33.25 - 19}{19} = \frac{14.25}{19} = 0.75 = 75\%$$

The percent of markup is 75%.

Markup = 75% of $96 = 0.75(96) = 72

New price = 96 + 72 = 168

The new price for a $96 item with a 75% markup is $168.

20. The new price is a markup.

$$p = \frac{121 - 55}{55} = \frac{66}{55} = \frac{6}{5} = 120\%$$

The percent of markup is 120%.

Markup = 120% of $96 = 1.2(96) = 115.2

New price = 96 + 115.20 = 211.20

The new price for a $96 item with a 120% markup is $211.20.

21. The new price is a markup.

$$p = \frac{22.5 - 12.5}{12.5} = \frac{10}{12.5} = 0.8 = 80\%$$

The percent of markup is 80%.

Markup = 80% of $96 = 0.8(96) = 76.8

New price = 96 + 76.80 = 172.80

The new price for a $96 item with an 80% markup is $172.80.

22. The new price is a discount.

$$p = \frac{199.99 - 119.99}{199.99} = \frac{80}{199.99} ≈ 0.4 = 40\%$$

The percent of discount is 40%.

Discount = 40% of $96 = 0.4(96) = 38.4

New price = 96 − 38.40 = 57.60

The new price for a $96 item with a 40% discount is $57.60.

23. $43 = 0.075(p - 0.2p) + p - 0.2p$

$43 = 0.075(0.8p) + 0.8p$

$43 = 0.06p + 0.8p$

$43 = 0.86p$

$50 = p$

The original price is $50.

Chapter 7, *continued*

24.
$$126 = 0.05(150 - 150d) + 150 - 150d$$
$$126 = 7.5 - 7.5d + 150 - 150d$$
$$126 = 157.5 - 157.5d$$
$$-31.5 = -157.5d$$
$$0.2 = d$$

The discount is 20%.

25.
$$63.96 = t(75 - 0.18 \cdot 75) + 75 - 0.18 \cdot 75$$
$$63.96 = t(75 - 13.5) + 75 - 13.5$$
$$63.96 = 61.5t + 61.5$$
$$2.46 = 61.5t$$
$$0.04 = t$$

The sales tax is 4%.

Problem Solving

26. Sales tax = 4% of $25.75 = 0.04(25.75) = 1.03

Total cost = 25.75 + 1.03 = 26.78

The total cost is $26.78.

27. Tip = 20% of $30 = 0.2(30) = 6

Sales tax = 6% of $30 = 0.06(30) = 1.8

Total cost = 30 + 6 + 1.8 = 37.8

The total cost of the meal is $37.80.

28. B; Discount = 15% of $12.95 = 0.15(12.95) ≈ 1.94

Sale price = 12.95 − 1.94 = 11.01

Sales tax = 6% of $11.01 = 0.06(11.01) ≈ 0.66

Total cost = 11.01 + 0.66 = 11.67

The total cost of the book is $11.67.

29. D; Total bill = 20.88 + 0.05(20.88) + 0.2(20.88)
$$\approx 20.88 + 1.04 + 4.18$$
$$= 26.10$$

Cost per person = 26.1 ÷ 3 = 8.7

Each person should pay $8.70.

30. Round $42 down to $40. Because $25\% = \frac{1}{4}$, multiply 40 by $\frac{1}{4}$ to get $10. Then subtract $10 from $42 to get an estimated sale price of $32.

31. Tip = 15% of $24.20 = 0.15(24.2) = 3.63

Total cost = 24.2 + 3.63 = $27.83

Tip = 20% of $24.20 = 0.2(24.2) = 4.84

Total cost = 24.2 + 4.84 = $29.04

Sample answer: People usually round to the nearest dollar rather than leaving the exact amount because they don't have the change.

32. Markup = Wholesale price · percent
$$0.12 = 3p$$
$$0.04 = p$$

The percent markup is 4%.

33. Markup = 75% of $15 = 0.75(15) = 11.25

Retail price = 15 + 11.25 = 26.25

Discount = 20% of $26.25 = 0.2(26.25) = 5.25

Sale price = 26.25 − 5.25 = 21

The sale price of the shirt is $21.

34. Amount of tip = 15 − 12.6 = 2.4
$$\frac{2.4}{12.6} = \frac{p}{100}$$
$$100 \cdot \frac{2.4}{12.6} = 100 \cdot \frac{p}{100}$$
$$19\% \approx p$$

You gave a tip of about 19%. So, the tip is less than 20%.

35. Amount of discount = 26 − 16.9 = 9.1
$$\frac{9.1}{26} = \frac{p}{100}$$
$$100 \cdot \frac{9.1}{26} = 100 \cdot \frac{p}{100}$$
$$35 = p$$

The percent of discount is 35%.

Discount = 35% of $59 = 0.35(59) = 20.65

Sale price = 59 − 20.65 = 38.35

A $59 DVD boxed set with a 35% discount costs $38.35.

36. Markup = 115% of $12 = 1.15(12) = 13.8

Retail price = 12 + 13.8 = 25.8

Discount = 15% of $25.80 = 0.15(25.8) = 3.87

Sale price = 25.8 − 3.87 = 21.93

Tax = 4.5% of $21.93 = 0.045(21.93) ≈ 0.99

Final cost = 21.93 + 0.99 = 22.92

The final cost of the basketball is $22.92.

37. No. The second discount is 60% of the sale price, not 60% of the original price.

38. Let w be the wholesale price.
$$30.78 = (1.25w + w) - 0.1(1.25w + w)$$
$$30.78 = 2.25w - 0.125w - 0.1w$$
$$30.78 = 2.025w$$
$$15.2 = w$$

The wholesale price was $15.20.

39. Let b be the bill before tax and tip.
$$33 = b + 0.04b + 0.16b$$
$$33 = 1.2b$$
$$27.5 = b$$

The food bill before tax and tip was $27.50.

Mixed Review

40.
$$2.4b = 108$$
$$\frac{2.4b}{2.4} = \frac{108}{2.4}$$
$$b = 45$$

41.
$$8.5y = 51$$
$$\frac{8.5y}{8.5} = \frac{51}{8.5}$$
$$y = 6$$

42. $3.5x = 140$

$\dfrac{3.5x}{3.5} = \dfrac{140}{3.5}$

$x = 40$

44. $6.5a = 286$

$\dfrac{6.5a}{6.5} = \dfrac{286}{6.5}$

$a = 44$

46. $4.2m = 84$

$\dfrac{4.2m}{4.2} = \dfrac{84}{4.2}$

$m = 20$

48. $\quad 4a = a + 9$

$4a - a = a + 9 - a$

$3a = 9$

$\dfrac{3a}{3} = \dfrac{9}{3}$

$a = 3$

49. $\quad n - 2 = 2n - 9$

$n - 2 - n = 2n - 9 - n$

$-2 = n - 9$

$-2 + 9 = n - 9 + 9$

$7 = n$

50. $\quad j = 4(j - 12)$

$j = 4j - 48$

$j - 4j = 4j - 48 - 4j$

$-3j = -48$

$\dfrac{-3j}{-3} = \dfrac{-48}{-3}$

$j = 16$

51. $\quad 6k + 9 = 11k - 1$

$6k + 9 - 6k = 11k - 1 - 6k$

$9 = 5k - 1$

$9 + 1 = 5k - 1 + 1$

$10 = 5k$

$\dfrac{10}{5} = \dfrac{5k}{5}$

$2 = k$

52. $\quad \dfrac{a}{80} = \dfrac{35}{100}$

$80 \cdot \dfrac{a}{80} = 80 \cdot \dfrac{35}{100}$

$a = 28$

28 is 35% of 80.

43. $1.6d = 384$

$\dfrac{1.6d}{1.6} = \dfrac{384}{1.6}$

$d = 240$

45. $1.3k = 39$

$\dfrac{1.3k}{1.3} = \dfrac{39}{1.3}$

$k = 30$

47. $3.6n = 270$

$\dfrac{3.6n}{3.6} = \dfrac{270}{3.6}$

$n = 75$

53. $\quad \dfrac{308}{440} = \dfrac{p}{100}$

$100 \cdot \dfrac{308}{440} = 100 \cdot \dfrac{p}{100}$

$70 = p$

308 is 70% of 440.

54. C; $p\% = \dfrac{75 - 45}{45} = \dfrac{30}{45} = \dfrac{2}{3} = 66\frac{2}{3}\%$

Lesson 7.7

7.7 Guided Practice (pp. 375–376)

1. $a = p\% \cdot b$

$= 45\% \cdot 700$

$= 0.45 \cdot 700$

$= 315$

45% of 700 is 315.

2. $a = p\% \cdot b$

$= 110\% \cdot 320$

$= 1.1 \cdot 320$

$= 352$

110% of 320 is 352.

3. $a = p\% \cdot b$

$= 0.5\% \cdot 450$

$= 0.005 \cdot 450$

$= 2.25$

0.5% of 450 is 2.25.

4. $\quad a = p\% \cdot b$

$6.4 = 62.5\% \cdot b$

$6.4 = 0.625 \cdot b$

$10.24 = b$

6.4 is 62.5% of 10.24.

5. $\quad a = p\% \cdot b$

$15 = p\% \cdot 120$

$0.125 = p\%$

$12.5\% = p$

15 is 12.5% of 120.

6. $I = Prt$

$= (500)(0.035)(2)$

$= 35$

You will earn $35 in interest.

7.7 Exercises (pp. 377–379)

Skill Practice

1. The amount earned or paid for the use of money is called *interest*.

2. To find simple interest, multiply the annual rate written as a decimal, the time in years, and the *principal*.

3. $a = p\% \cdot b$

$= 46\% \cdot 900$

$= 0.46 \cdot 900$

$= 414$

414 is 46% of 900.

4. $\quad a = p\% \cdot b$

$205 = p\% \cdot 250$

$0.82 = p\%$

$82\% = p$

205 is 82% of 250.

5. $\quad a = p\% \cdot b$

$132 = 24\% \cdot b$

$132 = 0.24 \cdot b$

$550 = b$

132 is 24% of 550.

6. $a = p\% \cdot b$

$a = 95\% \cdot 420$

$a = 0.95 \cdot 420$

$a = 399$

399 is 95% of 420.

7. $a = p\% \cdot b$

$= 120\% \cdot 55$

$= 1.2 \cdot 55$

$= 66$

66 is 120% of 55.

8. $a = p\% \cdot b$

$= 0.4\% \cdot 150$

$= 0.004 \cdot 150$

$= 0.6$

0.6 is 0.4% of 150.

9. $\quad a = p\% \cdot b$

$115 = 46\% \cdot b$

$115 = 0.46 \cdot b$

$250 = b$

115 is 46% of 250.

10. $\quad a = p\% \cdot b$

$26 = 130\% \cdot b$

$26 = 1.3 \cdot b$

$20 = b$

26 is 130% of 20.

11. $\quad a = p\% \cdot b$

$62.4 = 80\% \cdot b$

$62.4 = 0.8 \cdot b$

$78 = b$

62.4 is 80% of 78.

12. $\quad a = p\% \cdot b$

$289.25 = 89\% \cdot b$

$289.25 = 0.89 \cdot b$

$325 = b$

289.25 is 89% of 325.

13.

$a = p\% \cdot b$

$3 = p\% \cdot 600$

$0.005 = p\%$

$0.5\% = p$

3 is 0.5% of 600.

14.

$a = p\% \cdot b$

$291.04 = p\% \cdot 856$

$0.34 = p\%$

$34\% = p$

291.04 is 34% of 856.

15. When using 60% in an equation, the decimal point needs to be moved two places to the left.

$54 = 0.6 \cdot b$

$90 = b$

54 is 60% of 90.

16. $I = Prt = (250)(0.02)(3) = 15$

$15 in simple interest will be earned.

17. $I = Prt = (940)(0.035)\left(\dfrac{30}{12}\right) = 82.25$

$82.25 in simple interest will be earned.

18. $I = Prt = (620)(0.03)\left(\dfrac{20}{12}\right) = 31$

$31 in simple interest will be earned.

19. $0.6 \cdot 60 = 0.9 \cdot x$

$36 = 0.9x$

$40 = x$

60% of 60 = 90% of 40

20. $0.2 \cdot 70 = p\% \cdot 280$

$14 = p\% \cdot 280$

$0.05 = p\%$

$5\% = p$

20% of 70 = 5% of 280

21. $0.005 \cdot 140 = p\% \cdot 70$

$0.7 = p\% \cdot 70$

$0.01 = p\%$

$1\% = p$

0.5% of 140 = 1% of 70

22. $1.6 \cdot 25 = 0.8 \cdot x$

$40 = 0.8x$

$50 = x$

160% of 25 = 80% of 50

23. C; $\dfrac{\text{Amount after}}{\text{2 years}} = \dfrac{\text{Original}}{\text{amount}} + \dfrac{\text{Interest}}{\text{earned}}$

$= 450 + 450(0.045)(2)$

24. $I = Prt$

$12.5 = 500 \cdot r \cdot \dfrac{6}{12}$

$12.5 = 250r$

$0.05 = r$

The annual interest rate is 5%.

25. $I = Prt$

$89.25 = 850 \cdot 0.0525 \cdot t$

$89.25 = 44.625t$

$2 = t$

The time is 2 years.

26. $I = Prt$

$260 = P \cdot 0.065 \cdot 4$

$260 = 0.26P$

$1000 = P$

The principal is $1000.

27. $I = Prt$

$320 = P \cdot 0.08 \cdot 2$

$320 = 0.16P$

$2000 = P$

The principal is $2000.

28. $I = 100xy$

If interest doubles, the expression for interest becomes $100(2x)(y) = 200xy$. Then using $\dfrac{1}{2}y$, the interest is the same as before: $200x\left(\dfrac{1}{2}y\right) = 100xy$. If the number of years is greater than $\dfrac{1}{2}y$, the interest is more than before. If the number of years is less than $\dfrac{1}{2}y$, the interest is less than before.

Problem Solving

29. **a.** $I = Prt$

b. $100 = P(0.03)(0.5)$

c. $100 = 0.015P$

$6666.67 \approx P$

You must put about $6666.67 in the savings account.

30. $a = p\% \cdot b$

$= 30.7\% \cdot 365$

$= 0.307 \cdot 365$

≈ 112

Charlotte has about 112 days of precipitation.

31. D; $a = p\% \cdot b$

$63.60 = 30\% \cdot b$

$63.60 = 0.3 \cdot b$

$212 = b$

The regular price of the jacket was $212.00.

32. $a = p\% \cdot b$

$6 = 37.5\% \cdot b$

$6 = 0.375 \cdot b$

$16 = b$

There are 16 theaters in Vicki's city.

$\dfrac{6}{b} = \dfrac{37.5}{100}$

$600 = 37.5b$

$16 = b$

There are 16 theaters in Vicki's city.

Sample answer: The methods are similar, but there is an extra step in the proportion, multiplying 6 by 100.

33. $I = Prt$

$I = 1200(0.095)\left(\dfrac{15}{12}\right)$

$= 142.5$

Total amount $= 1200 + 142.5 = 1342.5$

You pay $142.50 in interest and you pay the bank a total of $1342.50.

34. **a.** $a = p\% \cdot b$

$= 15.7\% \cdot 171,100,000$

$= 0.157 \cdot 171,100,000$

$= 26,862,700$

$\approx 26,900,000$

About 26,900,000 acres of Texas is cropland.

Chapter 7, continued

b. $a = p\% \cdot b$

$10,500 = p\% \cdot 26,900,000$

$0.0004 \approx p\%$

$0.04\% = p$

About 0.04% of cropland in Texas is planted with peppers.

35. The solutions are the same. You can rewrite $\frac{3}{100}$ as 3%.

The original equation can then be written as $\frac{12}{b} = 3\%$.

Multiplying both sides by b then gives $12 = 3\% \cdot b$.

36. $I = Prt$

$50 = P \cdot 0.04 \cdot 5$

$50 = 0.2P$

$250 = P$

You must deposit $250 in the account.

37.

	5%	10%	15%
22	1.1	2.2	3.3
50	2.5	5	7.5
76	3.8	7.6	11.4

5% of a number is half of 10% of the number. 15% of a number is the sum of 5% and 10% of the number.

Let n be a positive number.

5% of $n = \frac{1}{2}$(10% of n)

15% of n = 10% of n + 5% of n

20% of n = 2(10% of n) and so on.

38. *Sample answers:*

$I = Prt$ $I = Prt$

$39 \stackrel{?}{=} (260)(0.05)(3)$ $39 \stackrel{?}{=} (500)(0.026)(3)$

$39 = 39$ $39 = 39$

A principal of $260 and a simple interest rate of 5% pays $39 in interest over a 3 year period, as does a principal of $500 and a simple interest rate of 2.6%.

39. 1st year's interest = $500(0.04)(1) = 20$

Amount in account after 1st year = $500 + 20$

$= 520$

2nd year's interest = $520(0.04)(1) = 20.8$

Amount in account after 2nd year = $520 + 20.8$

$= 540.8$

3rd year's interest = $540.8(0.04)(1) \approx 21.63$

Amount in account after 3rd year = $540.8 + 21.63$

$= 562.43$

4th year's interest = $562.43(0.04)(1) \approx 22.50$

Amount in account after 4th year = $562.43 + 22.50$

$= 584.93$

5th year's interest = $584.93(0.04)(1) \approx 23.40$

Amount in account after 5th year = $584.93 + 23.40$

$= 608.33$

6th year's interest = $608.33(0.04)(1) \approx 24.33$

Amount in account after 6th year = $608.33 + 24.33$

$= 632.66$

40. Amount in certificate of deposit

$= 1000 + 1000(0.036)\left(\frac{6}{12}\right)$

$= 1000 + 18$

$= \$1018$

1st month's interest = $1000(0.0022)(1) = 2.20$

Amount in account after 1st month = $1000 + 2.20$

$= \$1002.20$

2nd month's interest = $1002.20(0.0022)(1) \approx 2.20$

Amount in account after 2nd month = $1002.20 + 2.20$

$= \$1004.40$

3rd month's interest = $1004.40(0.0022)(1) \approx 2.21$

Amount in account after 3rd month = $1004.40 + 2.21$

$= \$1006.61$

4th month's interest = $1006.61(0.0022)(1) \approx 2.21$

Amount in account after 4th month = $1006.61 + 2.21$

$= \$1008.82$

5th month's interest = $1008.82(0.0022)(1) \approx 2.22$

Amount in account after 5th month = $1008.82 + 2.22$

$= \$1011.04$

6th month's interest = $1011.04(0.0022)(1) \approx 2.22$

Amount in account after 6th month = $1011.04 + 2.22$

$= \$1013.26$

7th month's interest = $1013.26(0.0022)(1) \approx 2.23$

Amount in account after 7th month = $1013.26 + 2.23$

$= \$1015.49$

8th month's interest = $1015.49(0.0022)(1) \approx 2.23$

Amount in account after 8th month = $1015.49 + 2.23$

$= \$1017.72$

9th month's interest = $1017.72(0.0022)(1) \approx 2.24$

Amount in account after 9th month = $1017.72 + 2.24$

$= \$1019.96$

So, after leaving your money in the savings account for about 9 months, you will earn the same amount as by investing in the CD.

Mixed Review

41. $\frac{6}{8} = \frac{2 \cdot 3}{2 \cdot 2 \cdot 2} = \frac{3}{4}$

The ratio $\frac{6}{8}$ can be written as $\frac{3}{4}$, 3 to 4, and 3 : 4.

Chapter 7, continued

42. $\dfrac{33}{55} = \dfrac{3 \cdot \cancel{11}}{5 \cdot \cancel{11}} = \dfrac{3}{5}$

The ratio 33 to 55 can be written as $\dfrac{3}{5}$, 3 to 5, and $3:5$.

43. $\dfrac{64}{16} = \dfrac{4 \cdot \cancel{16}}{1 \cdot \cancel{16}} = \dfrac{4}{1}$

The ratio $64:16$ can be written as $\dfrac{4}{1}$, 4 to 1, and $4:1$.

44. $\dfrac{7}{56} = \dfrac{\cancel{7}}{\cancel{7} \cdot 8} = \dfrac{1}{8}$

The ratio $\dfrac{7}{56}$ can be written as $\dfrac{1}{8}$, 1 to 8, and $1:8$.

45.
$$-3x - 2 \le 4 - x$$
$$-3x + x - 2 \le 4 - x + x$$
$$-2x - 2 \le 4$$
$$-2x - 2 + 2 \le 4 + 2$$
$$-2x \le 6$$
$$\dfrac{-2x}{-2} \ge \dfrac{6}{-2}$$
$$x \ge -3$$

46. Discount = 15% of $15.95 = 0.15(15.95) \approx 2.39$

Sale price = $15.95 - 2.39 = 13.56$

Cost of 2 DVDs = $2(13.56) = 27.12$

Sales tax = 6% of $27.12 = 0.06(27.12) \approx 1.63$

Total cost = $27.12 + 1.63 = 28.75$

You have enough money because the cost of the two DVDs with the discount and after sales tax is $28.75.

Brain Game (p. 379)

Let s be the size of an object. If you shrink the object to 40% of its original size, then the new size is $0.4s$ because

$$\dfrac{a}{s} = \dfrac{40}{100}$$

$$a = 0.4s$$

To return the object of size $0.4s$ to its original size s, you need to answer the question, "s is what percent of $0.4s$?"

$$\dfrac{s}{0.4s} = \dfrac{p}{100}$$

$$250\% = p$$

To get the object back to its original size, set the zapper at 250%.

If you enlarge the object by 60% of its original size, then the new size is $1.6s$ because

$$\dfrac{a}{s} = \dfrac{160}{100}$$

$$a = 1.6s$$

To return the object of size $1.6s$ to its original size s, you need to answer the question, "s is what percent of $1.6s$?"

$$\dfrac{s}{1.6s} = \dfrac{p}{100}$$

$$62.5\% = p$$

To get the object back to its original size, set the shrink zapper at 62.5%.

Technology Activity 7.7 (p. 380)

1. $7577.03   **2.** $7571.20   **3.** $3744.89

4. Your balance after 5 years: $1824.98

Friend's simple interest: $I = Prt = (1500)(0.04)(5) = 300$

Friend's balance after 5 years = $1500 + 300 = 1800

After 5 years, your balance is $24.98 greater than your friend's balance.

5. Your balance after 10 years: $12,695.39

Sister's simple interest: $I = Prt$
$$= (10{,}000)(0.025)(10)$$
$$= 2500$$

Sister's balance after 10 years: $10{,}000 + 2500 = $12{,}500$

After 10 years, your balance is $195.39 greater than your sister's balance.

Lesson 7.8

Activity (p. 381)

Answers will vary.

7.8 Guided Practice (p. 383)

1. $P(\text{Rolling a number} > 3) = \dfrac{16 + 14 + 18}{100}$
$$= \dfrac{48}{100}$$
$$= 0.48$$
$$= 48\%$$

The experimental probability of rolling a number greater than 3 is 48%.

$P(\text{Rolling a number} > 3) = \dfrac{3}{6} = \dfrac{1}{2} = 0.5 = 50\%$

The theoretical probability of rolling a number greater than 3 is 50%.

2. $\dfrac{1}{150} \times 25{,}000 \approx 167$

You could expect about 167 buttons in a shipment of 25,000 to be defective.

7.8 Exercises (pp. 383–386)

Skill Practice

1. The favorable outcomes for rolling an even number on a number cube are *2, 4, and 6*.

Chapter 7, *continued*

2. Theoretical probability is a ratio of the number of favorable outcomes to the number of possible outcomes for outcomes that are equally likely to occur. Experimental probability is a ratio of the number of favorable outcomes to the total number of outcomes based on the results of actually performing an experiment.

3. Number of tiles in bag = 10 + 7 + 6 + 5 + 2 = 30 tiles

$P(A) = \dfrac{10}{30} = \dfrac{1}{3}$

The probability of drawing an A is $\dfrac{1}{3}$.

4. $P(I) = \dfrac{6}{30} = \dfrac{1}{5}$

The probability of drawing an I is $\dfrac{1}{5}$.

5. Number of I's and O's in bag = 6 + 5 = 11

$P(I \text{ or } O) = \dfrac{11}{30}$

The probability of drawing an I or an O is $\dfrac{11}{30}$.

6. Number of E's and U's in bag = 7 + 2 = 9

$P(E \text{ or } U) = \dfrac{9}{30} = \dfrac{3}{10}$

The probability of drawing an E or a U is $\dfrac{3}{10}$.

7. $P(Z) = \dfrac{0}{30} = 0$

The probability of drawing a Z is 0.

8. Number of vowels in bag = 10 + 7 + 6 + 5 + 2 = 30

$P(\text{vowel}) = \dfrac{30}{30} = 1$

The probability of drawing a vowel is 1.

9. $P(\text{rolling a 4}) = \dfrac{50}{250} = 0.2 = 20\%$

The experimental probability of rolling a 4 is 20%.

10. $P(\text{rolling a 2}) = \dfrac{42}{250} = 0.168 = 16.8\%$

The experimental probability of rolling a 2 is 16.8%.

11. Number of rolls greater than 3 = 50 + 35 + 35 = 120

$P(\text{rolling a number greater than 3}) = \dfrac{120}{250} = 0.48 = 48\%$

The experimental probability of rolling a number greater than 3 is 48%.

12. Number of rolls that are odd numbers
= 40 + 48 + 35 = 123

$P(\text{rolling an odd number}) = \dfrac{123}{250} = 0.492 = 49.2\%$

The experimental probability of rolling an odd number is 49.2%.

13. All the numbers are divisible by 1, so the experimental probability of rolling a number divisible by 1 is 100%.

14. $P(\text{yellow}) = \dfrac{3}{15} = \dfrac{1}{5}$

$\dfrac{1}{5} \times 120 = 24$

You can predict that there are 24 yellow marbles in the bag.

15. $P(\text{green}) = \dfrac{5}{15} = \dfrac{1}{3}$

$\dfrac{1}{3} \times 120 = 40$

You can predict that there are 40 green marbles in the bag.

16. $P(\text{red}) = \dfrac{7}{15}$

$\dfrac{7}{15} \times 120 = 56$

You can predict that there are 56 red marbles in the bag.

17. $P(\text{blue}) = \dfrac{0}{15} = 0$

$0 \times 120 = 0$

You can predict that there are no blue marbles in the bag.

18. The denominator of the fraction should be the total number of spins, not the number of blue spins.

Experimental probability of spinning red = $\dfrac{7}{20}$.

19. B; $P(\text{rolling a multiple of 3}) = \dfrac{2}{6} = \dfrac{1}{3}$

20. $P(\text{not rolling a 2}) = \dfrac{5}{6} = 0.8\overline{3} = 83.\overline{3}\%$

The probability of not rolling a 2 is $83.\overline{3}\%$.

21. $P(\text{not rolling a number less than 3}) = \dfrac{4}{6} = \dfrac{2}{3} = 66.\overline{6}\%$

The probability of not rolling a number less than 3 is $66.\overline{6}\%$.

22. $P(\text{not spinning purple}) = \dfrac{6}{8} = \dfrac{3}{4} = 0.75 = 75\%$

The probability of not spinning purple is 75%.

23. $P(\text{not spinning purple, red, or yellow}) = \dfrac{1}{8} = 0.125 = 12.5\%$

The probability of not spinning purple, red, or yellow is 12.5%.

24. Spinning green is unlikely because there is only 1 green section out of 8 sections. So, the probability of spinning green is $\dfrac{1}{8}$, or 12.5%.

25. Possible outcomes of tossing two coins:

Heads, Heads

Heads, Tails

Tails, Heads

Tails, Tails

There are 4 possible outcomes, and one of the outcomes is two tails. So, the probability of getting two tails is $\dfrac{1}{4}$, or 25%.

Chapter 7, continued

26. Possible outcomes of rolling two number cubes:

Roll 1	Roll 2	Sum
1	1	2
1	2	3
1	3	4
1	4	5
1	5	6
1	6	7
2	1	3
2	2	4
2	3	5
2	4	6
2	5	7
2	6	8
3	1	4
3	2	5
3	3	6
3	4	7
3	5	8
3	6	9

Roll 1	Roll 2	Sum
4	1	5
4	2	6
4	3	7
4	4	8
4	5	9
4	6	10
5	1	6
5	2	7
5	3	8
5	4	9
5	5	10
5	6	11
6	1	7
6	2	8
6	3	9
6	4	10
6	5	11
6	6	12

There are 36 possible outcomes, and 7 of the outcomes have a sum that is a multiple of 5. The probability that the sum of the numbers is a multiple of 5 is $\frac{7}{36}$, or $19.\overline{4}\%$.

Problem Solving

27. a. Check drawings.

b. Total socks = 4 + 12 + 8 = 24

$P(\text{picking white}) = \frac{4}{24} = \frac{1}{6} = 0.1\overline{6} = 16.\overline{6}\%$

$P(\text{picking black}) = \frac{12}{24} = \frac{1}{2} = 0.5 = 50\%$

$P(\text{picking brown}) = \frac{8}{24} = \frac{1}{3} = 0.\overline{3} = 33.3\%$

28. The coins are all different sizes, which can affect the likelihood of a coin choice. For example, you are probably more likely to choose a larger coin than a smaller coin. Because theoretical probability assumes all outcomes are equally likely, it cannot be used.

29. $P(\text{longer second toe}) = \frac{409}{896} \approx 0.4565 = 45.65\%$

The probability that a randomly chosen person from the survey has a longer second toe is 46%.

30. C; $P(\text{preferring dogs to cats}) = \frac{24}{40} = \frac{3}{5} = 0.6$

31. $P(\text{moving 5 spaces}) = \frac{1}{6}$

$\frac{1}{6} \times 50 = \frac{25}{3} = 8\frac{1}{3}$

You can predict that you will move exactly 5 spaces about 8 times in 50 spins.

32. Sharon: $P(\text{hit}) = \frac{7}{20} = 0.35 = 35\%$

Erica: $P(\text{hit}) = \frac{10}{35} \approx 0.29 = 29\%$

Because 35% > 29%, Sharon is more likely to get a hit her next time at bat.

33. a. Check work.

b. Answers will vary.

34. *Sample answer:* In a drawer full of white socks, choosing a white sock is certain to occur. Choosing a blue sock from the same drawer cannot occur.

35. $P(\text{left-handed child}) = 10\% = 0.10$

$0.10 \times 500 = 50$

You would expect 50 children to be left-handed if both parents are right-handed.

$P(\text{left-handed child}) = 20\% = 0.20$

$0.20 \times 500 = 100$

You would expect 100 children to be left-handed if only the mom is left-handed.

$P(\text{right-handed child}) = 60\% = 0.60$

$0.60 \times 500 = 300$

You would expect 300 children to be right-handed if both parents are left-handed.

$P(\text{right-handed child}) = 90\% = 0.90$

$0.90 \times 500 = 450$

You would expect 450 children to be right-handed if only the dad is left-handed.

36. a. $P(\text{landing heads up}) = \frac{1}{2}$

$\frac{1}{2} \times 20 = 10$

You can predict that the coin will land heads up 10 times in 20 tosses.

b. *Sample answer:*

1	2	3	4	5	6	7	8	9	10
H	H	H	T	H	T	T	T	T	H

11	12	13	14	15	16	17	18	19	20
T	H	T	H	T	T	T	T	H	H

c. $P(\text{landing heads up}) = \frac{9}{20}$

The results from part (a) and part (b) were not the same. The experimental probability of a coin landing heads up is $\frac{9}{20}$.

Chapter 7, *continued*

d. *Sample answer:* Theoretical probability and experimental probability are not always the same, but they should be close.

37. *Sample answer:* The store should order mostly pink and purple T-shirts and very few blue and orange T-shirts.

38. The results of his previous roll do not affect his next roll. The probability of rolling any selected number is always $\frac{1}{6}$.

39. There are 4 possible outcomes: choosing two girls, choosing two boys, choosing a girl and a boy, and choosing a boy and a girl. So, the probability of choosing two boys is $\frac{1}{4}$.

Out of 100 times, about $\frac{1}{4} \times 100 = 25$ of them should be two boys.

40. The game favors you because there are three prime numbers on a number cube, 2, 3, and 5, and only two composite numbers on a number cube, 4 and 6.

Sample answer: To make the game fair, include the number 1 with composite numbers. This way you and your friend both have 3 chances of winning.

Mixed Review

41.
$$10 + 9y = -8 + 3y$$
$$10 + 9y - 3y = -8 + 3y - 3y$$
$$10 + 6y = -8$$
$$10 - 10 + 6y = -8 - 10$$
$$6y = -18$$
$$\frac{6y}{6} = \frac{-18}{6}$$
$$y = -3$$
Check: $10 + 9(-3) \stackrel{?}{=} -8 + 3(-3)$
$$10 - 27 \stackrel{?}{=} -8 - 9$$
$$-17 = -17 ✓$$

42.
$$3f + 6 = 6f - 18$$
$$3f - 3f + 6 = 6f - 18 - 3f$$
$$6 = 3f - 18$$
$$6 + 18 = 3f - 18 + 18$$
$$24 = 3f$$
$$\frac{24}{3} = \frac{3f}{3}$$
$$8 = f$$
Check: $3(8) + 6 \stackrel{?}{=} 6(8) - 18$
$$24 + 6 \stackrel{?}{=} 48 - 18$$
$$30 = 30 ✓$$

43.
$$7(t + 4) + 2(t - 5) = 90$$
$$7t + 28 + 2t - 10 = 90$$
$$9t + 18 = 90$$
$$9t + 18 - 18 = 90 - 18$$
$$9t = 72$$
$$\frac{9t}{9} = \frac{72}{9}$$
$$t = 8$$
Check: $7(8 + 4) + 2(8 - 5) \stackrel{?}{=} 90$
$$7(12) + 2(3) \stackrel{?}{=} 90$$
$$84 + 6 \stackrel{?}{=} 90$$
$$90 = 90 ✓$$

44.
$$8 - c + 5(c - 1) = 180$$
$$8 - c + 5c - 5 = 180$$
$$4c + 3 = 180$$
$$4c + 3 - 3 = 180 - 3$$
$$4c = 177$$
$$\frac{4c}{4} = \frac{177}{4}$$
$$c = 44.25$$
Check: $8 - 44.25 + 5(44.25 - 1) \stackrel{?}{=} 180$
$$8 - 44.25 + 5(43.25) \stackrel{?}{=} 180$$
$$8 - 44.25 + 216.25 \stackrel{?}{=} 180$$
$$180 = 180 ✓$$

45. $I = Prt = (750)(0.027)\left(\frac{30}{12}\right) \approx 50.63$

You will earn $50.63 in interest.

46. B

Quiz 7.5–7.8 (p. 386)

1. The change is an increase.

$p = \dfrac{138 - 120}{120} = \dfrac{18}{120} = 0.15 = 15\%$

The percent of increase is 15%.

2. The change is a decrease.

$p = \dfrac{260 - 169}{260} = \dfrac{91}{260} = 0.35 = 35\%$

The percent of decrease is 35%.

3. Markup = 50% of $20 = 0.5(20) = 10$
Retail price = $20 + 10 = 30$
Sales tax = 5% of $30 = 0.05(30) = 1.5$
Total cost = $30 + 1.5 = 31.5$
The total cost of the shirt is $31.50.

4. $a = p\% \cdot b$
$$75 = 125\% \cdot b$$
$$75 = 1.25 \cdot b$$
$$60 = b$$
75 is 125% of 60.

5. $a = p\% \cdot b$
$$552.5 = p\% \cdot 85,000$$
$$0.0065 = p\%$$
$$0.65\% = p$$
552.5 is 0.65% of 85,000.

Chapter 7, *continued*

6. $a = p\% \cdot b$

$\quad = 25\% \cdot 10.5$

$\quad = 0.25 \cdot 10.5$

$\quad = 2.625$

The koala absorbs 2.625 ounces of fiber.

7. $P(\text{red}) = \dfrac{3}{8}$

$\quad \dfrac{3}{8} \times 40 = 15$

You can predict that the spinner will land on red 15 times.

8. $P(\text{blue}) = \dfrac{4}{8} = \dfrac{1}{2}$

$\quad \dfrac{1}{2} \times 40 = 20$

You can predict that the spinner will land on blue 20 times.

9. $P(\text{yellow}) = \dfrac{1}{8}$

$\quad \dfrac{1}{8} \times 40 = 5$

You can predict that the spinner will land on yellow 5 times.

10. $P(\text{white}) = \dfrac{0}{8} = 0$

$\quad 0 \times 40 = 0$

You can predict that the spinner will land on white 0 times.

Mixed Review of Problem Solving (p. 387)

1. a. One discounted sweater costs

$\quad (\$81.20 - \$40.40) \div 2 = \$40.80 \div 2 = \$20.40.$

Three discounted sweaters cost

$3(\$20.40) = \$61.20.$

b. The pair of pants cost $\$81.20 - \$61.20 = \$20.$

c. $\dfrac{\text{Cost of pants}}{\text{Final bill}} = \dfrac{p}{100}$

$\quad \dfrac{20}{81.20} = \dfrac{p}{100}$

$\quad 2000 = 81.20p$

$\quad 25 \approx p$

About 25% of the final bill is the cost of the pants.

2. Markup $= 25\%$ of $\$8 = 0.25(8) = 2$

New price $= 8 + 2 = \$10$

Discount $= p\%$ of $\$10$

New price $=$ Old price $-$ Discount

$\quad 8 = 10 - p\% \cdot 10$

$\quad -2 = -p\% \cdot 10$

$\quad 2 = p\% \cdot 10$

$\quad 0.2 = p\%$

$\quad 20\% = p$

The store must discount the oil by 20%.

3. $P(\text{not spinning yellow}) = \dfrac{7}{8}$

The probability of not spinning yellow on the spinner is $\dfrac{7}{8}$.

4. Total number of marbles $= 5 + 2 + 3 = 10$

$\quad P(\text{red}) = \dfrac{2}{10} = 0.2$

The probability that you will choose a red marble is 0.2.

5. Change received: $30 - 22.20 = \$7.80$

Minimum tip $= 15\%$ of $\$22.20 = 0.15(22.2) = 3.33$

Maximum tip $= 20\%$ of $\$22.20 = 0.2(22.2) = 4.44$

A tip that is between 15% and 20% would be between $3.33 and $4.44. If Jay and Gia do not use the $5 bill, they will only have $2.80 left in change. So, they cannot use the change they are given without having to ask that the $5 bill be exchanged for ones.

6. Current compensation: $10.50(160) - 210 = \$1470$

Plan A: $11.50(160) - 210 = \$1630$

Percent increase: $p\% = \dfrac{1630 - 1470}{1470} = \dfrac{160}{1470} \approx 10.9\%$

Plan B:

Increase in hourly rate $= 10\%$ of $\$10.50$

$\quad\quad\quad\quad\quad\quad\quad\quad\quad = 0.1(10.5) = 1.05$

New hourly rate $= 10.50 + 1.05 = 11.55$

New monthly compensation: $11.55(160) - 210 = \$1638$

Percent increase: $p\% = \dfrac{1638 - 1470}{1470} = \dfrac{168}{1470} \approx 11.4\%$

Plan C: If the company pays her insurance, then her new monthly compensation is $10.50(160) = \$1680.$

Percent increase: $p\% = \dfrac{1680 - 1470}{1470} = \dfrac{210}{1470} \approx 14.3\%$

Plan A offers an increase in her hourly rate, which brings her salary to $1840 minus $210 for insurance, or $1630. Plan B also offers an increase in her hourly rate, which brings her salary to $1848 minus $210 for insurance, or $1638. Plan C offers to pay her insurance but keeps her monthly salary at $1680. So, plan C offers Angie the greatest percent increase in her total compensation, an increase of about 14.3%.

7. *Sample answer:* If Arthur starts with 10 kilograms of food, and it grows 50%, it will be $10 + 0.5(10) = 15$ kilograms in one week. If he uses 50% of the food to feed the turtle, he will have $15 - 0.5(15) = 7.5$ kilograms. The next week, the food will grow to $7.5 + 0.5(7.5) = 11.25$ kilograms. After feeding the turtle, he will have $11.25 - 0.5(11.25) = 5.625$ kilograms. The amount of food decreases over time.

Chapter 7, *continued*

8. *Sample answer:*

After 1 year: $I = Prt = (300)(0.023)(1) = 6.9$

Amount in account $= 300 + 6.9 = \$306.90$

After 2 years: $I = Prt = (300)(0.023)(2) = 13.8$

Amount in account $= 300 + 13.8 = \$313.80$

After 3 years: $I = Prt = (300)(0.023)(3) = 20.7$

Amount in account $= 300 + 20.7 = \$320.70$

9. *Sample answer:*

There are 3 even numbers on a number cube. So, the probability of rolling an even number is $\frac{3}{6} = \frac{1}{2}$. There are 3 odd numbers on a number cube. So, the probability of rolling an odd number is $\frac{3}{6} = \frac{1}{2}$. There are 3 numbers that are less than 4 on a number cube. So, the probability of rolling a number less than 4 is $\frac{3}{6} = \frac{1}{2}$.

Chapter 7 Review (pp. 388–392)

1. If you write $\frac{180 \text{ miles}}{3 \text{ hours}}$ as $\frac{60 \text{ miles}}{1 \text{ hour}}$, you have written the rate as a *unit rate*.

2. A ratio whose denominator is 100 is a *percent*.

3. The theoretical probability of an event is the ratio of the number of *favorable outcomes* to the number of *possible outcomes* when all outcomes are equally likely.

4. The increase in the wholesale price of an item is a *markup*.

5. A decrease in the price of an item is a *discount*.

6. C **7.** B **8.** A

9. $\dfrac{\text{Shaded squares}}{\text{Unshaded squares}} = \dfrac{5}{5} = \dfrac{1 \cdot \cancel{5}}{1 \cdot \cancel{5}} = \dfrac{1}{1}$

10. $\dfrac{\text{Shaded squares}}{\text{Unshaded squares}} = \dfrac{6}{8} = \dfrac{\cancel{2} \times 3}{\cancel{2} \times 4} = \dfrac{3}{4}$

11. $\dfrac{30 \text{ feet}}{4 \text{ seconds}} = \dfrac{30 \div 4}{4 \div 4} = \dfrac{7.5}{1}$

The unit rate is 7.5 feet per second.

12. $\dfrac{\$3.36}{2 \text{ gallons}} = \dfrac{3.36 \div 2}{2 \div 2} = \dfrac{1.68}{1}$

The unit rate is $1.68 per gallon.

13. $\dfrac{72 \text{ people}}{4 \text{ groups}} = \dfrac{72 \div 4}{4 \div 4} = \dfrac{18}{1}$

The unit rate is 18 people per group.

14. $\dfrac{90 \text{ miles}}{4 \text{ hours}} = \dfrac{90 \div 4}{4 \div 4} = \dfrac{22.5}{1}$

The unit rate is 22.5 miles per hour.

15. $\dfrac{28 \text{ feet}}{2 \text{ seconds}} = \dfrac{28 \div 2}{2 \div 2} = \dfrac{14}{1}$

The unit rate is 14 feet per second.

16. $\dfrac{48 \text{ points}}{4 \text{ quarters}} = \dfrac{48 \div 4}{4 \div 4} = \dfrac{12}{1}$

The unit rate is 12 points per quarter.

17. $\dfrac{356 \text{ kilometers}}{8 \text{ hours}} = \dfrac{356 \div 8}{8 \div 8} = \dfrac{44.5}{1}$

The unit rate is 44.5 kilometers per hour.

18. $\dfrac{\$17.25}{5 \text{ pounds}} = \dfrac{17.25 \div 5}{5 \div 5} = \dfrac{3.45}{1}$

The unit rate is $3.45 per pound.

19. Emily:

$5 \text{ min } 30 \text{ sec} = \left(5 + \dfrac{30}{60}\right) \text{ min} = 5.5 \text{ min}$

$\dfrac{1600 \text{ m}}{5.5 \text{ min}} = \dfrac{(1600 \div 5.5) \text{ m}}{(5.5 \div 5.5) \text{ min}} \approx \dfrac{290.9 \text{ m}}{\text{min}}$

Megan:

$2 \text{ min } 40 \text{ sec} = \left(2 + \dfrac{40}{60}\right) \text{ min} = 2\tfrac{2}{3} \text{ min}$

$\dfrac{800 \text{ m}}{2\frac{2}{3} \text{ min}} = \dfrac{\left(800 \div 2\frac{2}{3}\right) \text{ m}}{\left(2\frac{2}{3} \div 2\frac{2}{3}\right) \text{ min}} = \dfrac{300 \text{ m}}{\text{min}}$

Megan has the faster average speed.

20. $\dfrac{5}{13} = \dfrac{18}{c}$

$5c = 13 \cdot 18$

$5c = 234$

$c = 46.8$

21. $\dfrac{48}{54} = \dfrac{x}{6}$

$48 \cdot 6 = 54 \cdot x$

$288 = 54x$

$5.\overline{3} = x$

22. $\dfrac{n}{12} = \dfrac{7}{8}$

$n \cdot 8 = 12 \cdot 7$

$8n = 84$

$n = 10.5$

23. $\dfrac{25}{b+1} = \dfrac{5}{2}$

$25 \cdot 2 = (b + 1) \cdot 5$

$50 = 5b + 5$

$45 = 5b$

$9 = b$

24. $\text{Scale} = \dfrac{\text{Distance on map}}{\text{Actual distance}}$

$\dfrac{1 \text{ in.}}{10 \text{ mi}} = \dfrac{n \text{ in.}}{105 \text{ mi}}$

$1 \cdot 105 = 10 \cdot n$

$105 = 10n$

$10.5 = n$

The distance between the cities on the map is 10.5 inches.

25. $\dfrac{\$12}{3 \text{ dogs}} = \dfrac{\$x}{5 \text{ dogs}}$

$12 \cdot 5 = 3 \cdot x$

$60 = 3x$

$20 = x$

You earn $20 for walking 5 dogs.

26. $\dfrac{51 \text{ pages}}{45 \text{ min}} = \dfrac{x \text{ pages}}{1 \text{ h}}$

$\dfrac{51 \text{ pages}}{45 \text{ min}} = \dfrac{x \text{ pages}}{60 \text{ min}}$

$51 \cdot 60 = 45 \cdot x$

$3060 = 45x$

$68 = x$

You can read 68 pages in an hour.

Chapter 7, *continued*

27. $\dfrac{72}{1200} = \dfrac{p}{100}$

$7200 = 1200p$

$6 = p$

72 is 6% of 1200.

28. $\dfrac{a}{26} = \dfrac{95}{100}$

$100a = 2470$

$a = 24.7$

24.7 is 95% of 26.

29. $\dfrac{\text{People who read for fun}}{\text{Total people surveyed}} = \dfrac{p}{100}$

$\dfrac{146}{270} = \dfrac{p}{100}$

$100 \cdot \dfrac{146}{270} = 100 \cdot \dfrac{p}{100}$

$54 \approx p$

About 54% of the people surveyed like to read for fun.

30. $74\% = 74\% = 0.74$

$74\% = \dfrac{74}{100} = \dfrac{37}{50}$

31. $3.8\% = 03.8\% = 0.038$

$3.8\% = \dfrac{3.8}{100} = \dfrac{38}{1000} = \dfrac{19}{500}$

32. $16.8\% = 16.8\% = 0.168$

$16.8\% = \dfrac{16.8}{100} = \dfrac{168}{1000} = \dfrac{21}{125}$

33. $130\% = 130\% = 1.3$

$130\% = \dfrac{130}{100} = \dfrac{13}{10}$

34. $\dfrac{3}{5} = 0.6 = 0.60 = 60\%$

35. $\dfrac{5}{2} = 2.5 = 2.50\% = 250\%$

36. $0.02 = 0.02\% = 2\%$

37. $18.6 = 18.60\% = 1860\%$

38. $\dfrac{\text{People who like pork chops}}{\text{Total people surveyed}} = \dfrac{p}{100}$

$\dfrac{18}{72} = \dfrac{p}{100}$

$100 \cdot \dfrac{18}{72} = 100 \cdot \dfrac{p}{100}$

$25 = p$

25% of the people surveyed like pork chops.

39. The change is a decrease.

$p\% = \dfrac{50 - 35}{50} = \dfrac{15}{50} = 0.3 = 30\%$

The percent of decrease is 30%.

40. The change is an increase.

$p\% = \dfrac{220 - 90}{90} = \dfrac{130}{90} = 1.\overline{4} = 144.\overline{4}\%$

The percent of increase is 144%.

41. $p = \dfrac{984 - 800}{800} = \dfrac{184}{800} = \dfrac{23}{100} = 23\%$

The percent of increase is 23%.

42. Markup = 70% of $30 = 0.7(30) = 21$

Retail price = $30 + 21 = 51$

The retail price is $51.

43. Discount = 18% of $72 = 0.18(72) = 12.96$

Sale price = $72 - 12.96 = 59.04$

The sale price is $59.04.

44. Tip = 15% of $14.99 = 0.15(14.99) \approx 2.25$

Sales tax = 3% of $14.99 = 0.03(14.99) \approx 0.45$

Total cost = $14.99 + 2.25 + 0.45 = 17.69$

You spent about $17.69.

45. $a = p\% \cdot b$

$72 = 75\% \cdot b$

$72 = 0.75b$

$96 = b$

72 is 75% of 96.

46. $a = p\% \cdot b$

$a = 34\% \cdot 856$

$a = 0.34(856)$

$a = 291.04$

291.04 is 34% of 856.

47. $I = Prt = 460(0.035)(3) = 48.3$

In 3 years, $48.30 in interest is earned.

48. $I = Prt = 1540(0.0275)(3) = 127.05$

In 3 years, $127.05 in interest is earned.

49. Number of marbles in bag = $8 + 5 + 4 = 17$

$P(\text{red}) = \dfrac{8}{17} \approx 0.47 = 47\%$

The probability of drawing a red marble is about 47%.

$P(\text{yellow}) = \dfrac{5}{17} \approx 0.29 = 29\%$

The probability of drawing a yellow marble is about 29%.

$P(\text{blue}) = \dfrac{4}{17} \approx 0.24 = 24\%$

The probability of drawing a blue marble is about 24%.

50. $P(\text{rolling a } 5) = \dfrac{30}{200} = \dfrac{3}{20} = 0.15 = 15\%$

The probability of rolling a 5 is 15%.

51. Number of rolls less than 5 = $35 + 28 + 46 + 27 = 136$

$P(\text{rolling a number less than 5}) = \dfrac{136}{200} = 0.68 = 68\%$

The probability of rolling a number less than 5 is 68%.

52. Number of rolls divisible by 3 = $46 + 34 = 80$

$P(\text{rolling a number divisible by 3}) = \dfrac{80}{200} = 0.4 = 40\%$

The probability of rolling a number divisible by 3 is 40%.

Chapter 7 Test (p. 393)

1. $\dfrac{\text{Shaded squares}}{\text{Unshaded squares}} = \dfrac{15}{10}$, or $\dfrac{3}{2}$

2. $\dfrac{\text{Shaded squares}}{\text{Unshaded squares}} = \dfrac{12}{18}$, or $\dfrac{2}{3}$

3. $\dfrac{\text{Shaded squares}}{\text{Unshaded squares}} = \dfrac{17}{3}$

Chapter 7, continued

4. $\dfrac{\text{Shaded squares}}{\text{Unshaded squares}} = \dfrac{14}{21}$, or $\dfrac{2}{3}$

5. $\dfrac{156 \text{ miles}}{3 \text{ hours}} = \dfrac{(156 \div 3) \text{ miles}}{(3 \div 3) \text{ hours}} = \dfrac{52 \text{ miles}}{1 \text{ hour}}$

6. $\dfrac{18 \text{ servings}}{6 \text{ people}} = \dfrac{(18 \div 6) \text{ servings}}{(6 \div 6) \text{ people}} = \dfrac{3 \text{ servings}}{1 \text{ person}}$

7. $\dfrac{448 \text{ cycles}}{5 \text{ days}} = \dfrac{(448 \div 5) \text{ cycles}}{(5 \div 5) \text{ days}} = \dfrac{89.6 \text{ cycles}}{1 \text{ day}}$

8. $\dfrac{525 \text{ meters}}{21 \text{ seconds}} = \dfrac{(525 \div 21) \text{ meters}}{(21 \div 21) \text{ seconds}} = \dfrac{25 \text{ meters}}{1 \text{ second}}$

9. $\dfrac{12}{16} = \dfrac{18}{a}$

$12a = 16 \cdot 18$

$12a = 288$

$a = 24$

10. $\dfrac{15}{6} = \dfrac{d}{4}$

$4 \cdot \dfrac{15}{6} = 4 \cdot \dfrac{d}{4}$

$10 = d$

11. $\dfrac{9}{n} = \dfrac{21}{14}$

$9 \cdot 14 = n \cdot 21$

$126 = 21n$

$6 = n$

12. $\dfrac{t-3}{12} = \dfrac{11}{6}$

$(t-3) \cdot 6 = 12 \cdot 11$

$6t - 18 = 132$

$6t = 150$

$t = 25$

13. $\dfrac{a}{120} = \dfrac{320}{100}$

$100a = 38,400$

$a = 384$

384 is 320% of 120.

14. $\dfrac{a}{700} = \dfrac{0.5}{100}$

$100a = 350$

$a = 3.5$

3.5 is 0.5% of 700.

15. $\dfrac{19}{50} = \dfrac{p}{100}$

$1900 = 50p$

$38 = p$

19 is 38% of 50.

16. $\dfrac{192}{32} = \dfrac{p}{100}$

$19,200 = 32p$

$600 = p$

192 is 600% of 32.

17. $\dfrac{27}{b} = \dfrac{8}{100}$

$2700 = 8b$

$337.5 = b$

27 is 8% of 337.5.

18. $\dfrac{5.1}{b} = \dfrac{30}{100}$

$510 = 30b$

$17 = b$

5.1 is 30% of 17.

19. $0.7\% = 00.7\% = 0.007$

$0.7\% = \dfrac{0.7}{100} = \dfrac{7}{1000}$

20. $419\% = 419\% = 4.19$

$419\% = \dfrac{419}{100} = 4\dfrac{19}{100}$

21. $8\% = 08\% = 0.08$

$8\% = \dfrac{8}{100} = \dfrac{2}{25}$

22. $7.8\% = 07.8\% = 0.078$

$7.8\% = \dfrac{7.8}{100} = \dfrac{78}{1000} = \dfrac{39}{500}$

23. $p = \dfrac{40 - 36}{40} = \dfrac{4}{10} = \dfrac{1}{10} = 10\%$

The percent of decrease is 10%.

24. $p = \dfrac{324 - 225}{225} = \dfrac{99}{225} = \dfrac{11}{25} = 44\%$

The percent of increase is 44%.

25. $p = \dfrac{258 - 6.45}{258} = \dfrac{251.55}{258} = 0.975 = 97.5\%$

The percent of decrease is 97.5%.

26. Number of letters = 9

Number of E's = 4

$P(\text{drawing an E}) = \dfrac{4}{9}$

The probability of drawing an E is $\dfrac{4}{9}$.

27. Number of S's = 2

$P(\text{drawing an S}) = \dfrac{2}{9}$

The probability of drawing an S is $\dfrac{2}{9}$.

28. $\text{Scale} = \dfrac{\text{Distance on map}}{\text{Actual distance}}$

$\dfrac{1 \text{ cm}}{150 \text{ km}} = \dfrac{6.7 \text{ cm}}{d \text{ km}}$

$d = 150 \cdot 6.7$

$d = 1005$

The actual distance between Miami and Columbia is about 1005 kilometers.

29. $a = p\% \cdot b$

$102 = 34\% \cdot b$

$102 = 0.34 \cdot b$

$300 = b$

300 people were surveyed.

30. Sales tax = 6.5% of 26 = 0.065(26) = 1.69

Tip = 16% of 26 = 0.16(26) = 4.16

Total cost = 26 + 1.69 + 4.16 = 31.85

The total cost of the meal is $31.85.

31. $a = p\% \cdot b = 30\% \cdot 4.5 = 0.3(4.5) = 1.35$

$7(1.35) = 9.45$

About 9.45 pounds of waste are recycled per person per week.

Standardized Test Preparation (p. 395)

1. The percent discount cannot be more than 100% because then the cost would be less than zero. So, choice D can be eliminated.

2. The total cost cannot be less than the cost of the television because tax is added to the cost. So, choice A can be eliminated.

Standardized Test Practice (pp. 396–397)

1. A; $P(\text{Wood}) = \dfrac{9}{9 + 15} = \dfrac{9}{24} = \dfrac{9 \div 3}{24 \div 3} = \dfrac{3}{8}$

Chapter 7, *continued*

2. B; $p\% = \dfrac{315 - 280}{280} = \dfrac{35}{280} = 0.125 = 12.5\%$

The percent of increase is 12.5%.

3. C; Markup = 60% of $8.40 = 0.6(8.4) = 5.04$

Retail price = $8.40 + 5.04 = 13.44$

The retail price is $13.44.

4. B; Tip = 18% of $15.35 = 0.18(15.35) \approx 2.76$

Because $2.75 is close to $2.76, you should leave $2.75 as a tip.

5. B; $4\% = \dfrac{\$31.20 - \text{original}}{\text{original}}$

$$0.04 = \dfrac{31.20 - x}{x}$$

$$0.04 \cdot x = \dfrac{31.20 - x}{x} \cdot x$$

$$0.04x = 31.20 - x$$

$$0.04x + x = 31.20 - x + x$$

$$1.04x = 31.20$$

$$\dfrac{1.04x}{1.04} = \dfrac{31.20}{1.04}$$

$$x = 30$$

The cost before the increase was $30.

6. D; $\dfrac{\text{Quarters}}{\text{Nickels}} = \dfrac{\text{Quarters}}{\text{Nickels}}$

$$\dfrac{35}{n} = \dfrac{5}{7}$$

7. A; $\dfrac{1040 \text{ words}}{15 \text{ minutes}} = \dfrac{1040 \div 15}{15 \div 15} = \dfrac{69.\overline{3}}{1}$

Lauren's typing speed is $69.\overline{3}$ words per minute.

8. C; $I = Prt = (100)(5\%)(5) = (100)(0.05)(5) = 25$

Balance = $100 + $25 = 125

9. C; $\dfrac{10 \text{ feet}}{4 \text{ seconds}} = \dfrac{10 \div 4}{4 \div 4} = \dfrac{2.5 \text{ feet}}{1 \text{ second}}$

10. C; $\dfrac{\text{Length of model}}{\text{Length of actual building}} = \dfrac{\text{Height of model}}{\text{Height of actual building}}$

$$\dfrac{11 \text{ in.}}{231 \text{ ft}} = \dfrac{3 \text{ in.}}{h \text{ ft}}$$

$$11h = 693$$

$$h = 63$$

The actual building is 63 feet tall.

11. C; There are 11 numbers with a 4 in them from 31 to 50 and there are 20 numbers.

$P(\text{choosing a number with a 4}) = \dfrac{11}{20}$

The probability that the house you choose has a 4 in its number is $\dfrac{11}{20}$.

12. C; Number of marbles in bag = $3 + 8 + 13 = 24$

$P(\text{yellow}) = \dfrac{8}{24} = \dfrac{1}{3}$

The probability that the marble is yellow is $\dfrac{1}{3}$.

13. $0.5 = \dfrac{1}{2}$; $0.05 = \dfrac{1}{20}$

The least whole number by which you can multiply each side of the equation to clear the fractions and decimals is 20.

14. There are $5 + 4 + 3 + 2 = 14$ total marbles in the bowl. Because there are 4 green marbles, there are 10 marbles that are not green.

$P(\text{not green}) = \dfrac{10}{14} = \dfrac{5}{7}$

The probability that Kim's marble is not green is $\dfrac{5}{7}$.

15. $P(\text{blue}) = \dfrac{6}{24} = \dfrac{1}{4}$

$$\dfrac{1}{4} \times 75 \approx 19$$

You can predict that there are about 19 blue marbles in the bag.

16. The distance measured on the map from Lake Point to Oak Glen is 1.25 inches.

$\text{Scale} = \dfrac{\text{Distance on map}}{\text{Actual distance}}$

$$\dfrac{0.5 \text{ in.}}{10 \text{ mi}} = \dfrac{1.25 \text{ in.}}{d \text{ mi}}$$

$$0.5d = 12.5$$

$$d = 25$$

The actual distance from Lake Point to Oak Glen is about 25 miles. This distance is likely to be less than the actual distance because the road curves on the map.

17. The discount off the first watch Amber found:

10% of $35.95 = 0.10(35.95) \approx 3.60

The sale price of the first watch:

$35.95 - $3.60 = 32.35

The sale price of the first watch including sales tax:

$32.35 + 8\%$ of $32.35 = 32.35 + 0.08(32.35)$

$$\approx 32.35 + 2.59$$

$$= \$34.94$$

The discount off the second watch Amber found:

20% of $38.25 = 0.20(38.25) = 7.65

The sale price of the second watch:

$38.25 - $7.65 = 30.60

The sale price of the second watch including sales tax:

$30.60 + 8\%$ of $30.60 = 30.60 + 0.08(30.60)$

$$\approx 30.60 + 2.45$$

$$= \$33.05$$

The second watch Amber found costs less than the first watch because the first watch costs $34.94 and the second watch costs $33.05.

18. a. 21% of the total number of people is 504 people.

$$\frac{a}{b} = \frac{p}{100}$$

$$\frac{504}{b} = \frac{21}{100}$$

$$504 \cdot 100 = 21 \cdot b$$

$$50{,}400 = 21b$$

$$\frac{50{,}400}{21} = \frac{21b}{21}$$

$$2400 = b$$

2400 people participated in the poll.

b. 13% of 2400 people chose rodeo star as a career. So, 13% of 2400 = 0.13(2400) = 312 people chose a career as a rodeo star.

c. 35% of the 2400 total people chose veterinarian as a career.

35% of 2400 = 0.35(2400) = 840 people chose a career as a veterinarian.

312 people chose a career as a rodeo star.

840 + 312 = 1152 people chose a career as either a veterinarian or a rodeo star.

d. *Sample answer:* The careers with greater percents will probably be about the same, but the careers with lesser percents may change because a difference of one or two people would change the percent quite a bit.

19. Cindy found the sum of the percents. Instead, you must find the discounted price of each item and then add the prices.

The sale price of the coat is

$78 − 20% of 78 = 78 − 0.2(78) = 78 − 15.6 = $62.40.

The sale price of the sweater is

$36 − 10% of 36 = 36 − 0.1(36) = 36 − 3.6 = $32.40.

The total cost of the items before sales tax is

$62.40 + $32.40 = $94.80.

Sales tax = 4% of $94.80 = 0.04(94.8) ≈ 3.79

The total cost of the items after sales tax is $94.80 + $3.79 = $98.59.

Cumulative Review, Chs. 1–7 (pp. 398–399)

1. $66 - 11 \times 5 = 66 - 55 = 11$

2. $8 \div (3.5 + 0.5) = 8 \div 4 = 2$

3. $17 + (3 \times 4)^2 = 17 + 12^2 = 17 + 144 = 161$

4. $8 \times 6 \div 2^4 = 8 \times 6 \div 16 = 48 \div 16 = 3$

5. $(-3 + 11) + 5 = 8 + 5 = 13$

6. $(14 - 8) - 13 = 6 - 13 = 6 + (-13) = -7$

7. $-3(8 + 6) = -3(8) + (-3)(6)$

$$= -24 - 18$$
$$= -24 + (-18)$$
$$= -42$$

8. $-5(-3 - 7) = -5(-3) + (-5)(-7)$

$$= 15 + 35$$
$$= 50$$

9. $(-5 \cdot 8) \cdot 4 = (-40) \cdot 4 = -160$

10. $\frac{104}{39} = \frac{104 \div 13}{39 \div 13} = \frac{8}{3}$

11. $-\frac{32}{102} = -\left(\frac{32 \div 2}{102 \div 2}\right) = -\frac{16}{51}$

12. $-\frac{9abc}{12a} = -\frac{\overset{3}{\cancel{9}} \cdot 3 \cdot \overset{1}{\cancel{a}} \cdot b \cdot c}{\underset{1}{\cancel{12}} \cdot 4 \cdot \underset{1}{\cancel{a}}} = -\frac{3bc}{4}$

13. $\frac{21bcd}{7bc} = \frac{3 \cdot \overset{1}{\cancel{7}} \cdot \overset{1}{\cancel{b}} \cdot \overset{1}{\cancel{c}} \cdot d}{\underset{1}{\cancel{7}} \cdot \underset{1}{\cancel{b}} \cdot \underset{1}{\cancel{c}}} = 3d$

14. $\frac{\$5.97}{yd} = \frac{\$5.97}{1\ \cancel{yd}} \cdot \frac{1\ \cancel{yd}}{3\ ft} = \frac{\$1.99}{ft}$

15. $\frac{30\ mi}{h} = \frac{30\ mi}{1\ \cancel{h}} \cdot \frac{1\ \cancel{h}}{60\ min} = \frac{0.5\ mi}{min}$

16. $\frac{4\ oz}{serving} = \frac{4\ \cancel{oz}}{serving} \cdot \frac{1\ lb}{16\ \cancel{oz}} = \frac{0.25\ lb}{serving}$

17. $\frac{180\ ft}{sec} = \frac{180\ ft}{1\ \cancel{sec}} \cdot \frac{60\ \cancel{sec}}{1\ min} = \frac{10{,}800\ ft}{min}$

18. $7x^{-4} = \frac{7}{x^4}$

19. $a^{-6} \cdot a^4 = a^{-6+4} = a^{-2} = \frac{1}{a^2}$

20. $\frac{8w^{-6}}{24w^2} = \frac{8}{24}w^{-6-2} = \frac{8}{24}w^{-8} = \frac{8}{24w^8} = \frac{1}{3w^8}$

21. $\frac{16r^{-2}}{4r^3} = \frac{16}{4}r^{-2-3} = \frac{16}{4}r^{-5} = \frac{16}{4r^5} = \frac{4}{r^5}$

22. $-55 + (-43) = -98$

23. $0 + (-144) = -144$

24. $-21 - 33 = -21 + (-33) = -54$

25. $-17 - (-67) = -17 + 67 = 50$

26. $-5(-16) = 80$

27. $3(-8)(10) = -24(10) = -240$

28. $\frac{-51}{-17} = 3$

29. $\frac{0}{-25} = 0$

30. $-9\frac{3}{4} + 4\frac{2}{3} = -9\frac{9}{12} + 4\frac{8}{12}$

$$= (-9 + 4) + \left(-\frac{9}{12} + \frac{8}{12}\right)$$

$$= -5\frac{1}{12}$$

31. $-\frac{19x}{25} - \frac{11x}{25} = \frac{-19x - 11x}{25} = \frac{-30x}{25} = -\frac{6x}{5}$

32. $\frac{3}{c} - \frac{7}{2c} = \frac{6}{2c} - \frac{7}{2c} = \frac{6 - 7}{2c} = -\frac{1}{2c}$

33. $\frac{9}{21} \cdot \frac{7}{5} = \frac{9 \cdot 7}{21 \cdot 5} = \frac{63}{105} = \frac{3}{5}$

34. $12\frac{1}{2} \cdot \frac{6}{25} = \frac{25}{2} \cdot \frac{6}{25} = \frac{\overset{1}{\cancel{25}} \cdot \overset{3}{\cancel{6}}}{2 \cdot \underset{1}{\cancel{25}}} = 3$

35. $\frac{13}{18} \div \frac{5}{6} = \frac{13}{18} \cdot \frac{6}{5} = \frac{13 \cdot \overset{1}{\cancel{6}}}{\underset{3}{\cancel{18}} \cdot 5} = \frac{13}{15}$

36. $5\frac{8}{11} \div \left(-\frac{3}{4}\right) = \frac{63}{11} \div \left(-\frac{3}{4}\right)$

$\qquad = \frac{63}{11} \cdot \frac{4}{-3}$

$\qquad = \frac{\overset{-21}{\cancel{63}} \cdot 4}{11 \cdot (\underset{1}{\cancel{-3}})}$

$\qquad = -\frac{84}{11} = -7\frac{7}{11}$

37. $16.7 \cdot (-3.2) \longrightarrow$

$$
\begin{array}{r}
16.7 \\
\times\ -3.2 \\
\hline
3\ 34 \\
50\ 1 \\
\hline
-53.44
\end{array}
$$

38. $43.4 \cdot 0.13 \longrightarrow$

$$
\begin{array}{r}
43.4 \\
\times\ 0.13 \\
\hline
1\ 302 \\
4\ 34 \\
\hline
5.642
\end{array}
$$

39.
$3.434 \div 8.08 \longrightarrow 8.08)\overline{3.434} = 808)\overline{343.400}$

$$
\begin{array}{r}
0.425 \\
\hline
323\ 2 \\
20\ 20 \\
16\ 16 \\
4\ 040 \\
4\ 040 \\
\hline
0
\end{array}
$$

40. $8 = b - (-6)$

$\quad 8 = b + 6$

$8 - 6 = b + 6 - 6$

$\quad 2 = b$

41. $9y = -63$

$\quad \frac{9y}{9} = \frac{-63}{9}$

$\quad y = -7$

42. $2c - 5 = 17$

$2c - 5 + 5 = 17 + 5$

$\quad 2c = 22$

$\quad \frac{2c}{2} = \frac{22}{2}$

$\quad c = 11$

43. $d + 3.4 \le 9.1$

$d + 3.4 - 3.4 \le 9.1 - 3.4$

$\quad d \le 5.7$

44. $\frac{1}{3}x > -2$

$3 \cdot \frac{1}{3}x > -2 \cdot 3$

$\quad x > -6$

45. $7 - 2y \le 11$

$7 - 2y - 7 \le 11 - 7$

$\quad -2y \le 4$

$\quad \frac{-2y}{-2} \ge \frac{4}{-2}$

$\quad y \ge -2$

46.
$$x = 5(2x + 3)$$
$$x = 10x + 15$$
$$x - 15 = 10x + 15 - 15$$
$$x - 15 = 10x$$
$$x - 15 - x = 10x - x$$
$$-15 = 9x$$
$$\frac{-15}{9} = \frac{9x}{9}$$
$$-\frac{5}{3} = x, \text{ or } -1\frac{2}{3} = x$$

47.
$$6 - \frac{2}{5}a > 2$$
$$6 - \frac{2}{5}a - 6 > 2 - 6$$
$$-\frac{2}{5}a > -4$$
$$\left(-\frac{5}{2}\right)\left(-\frac{2}{5}a\right) < -4\left(-\frac{5}{2}\right)$$
$$a < 10$$

48.
$$2(3k + 1) \le 5k - 30$$
$$6k + 2 \le 5k - 30$$
$$6k + 2 - 5k \le 5k - 30 - 5k$$
$$k + 2 \le -30$$
$$k + 2 - 2 \le -30 - 2$$
$$k \le -32$$

49. $0.43 = 0.43 = 43\%$

50. $0.003 = 0.003 = 0.3\%$

51. $\frac{3}{10} = \frac{3 \cdot 10}{10 \cdot 10} = \frac{30}{100} = 30\%$

52. $\frac{29}{20} = \frac{29 \cdot 5}{20 \cdot 5} = \frac{145}{100} = 145\%$

53. $P(\text{choosing a vowel}) = \frac{2}{6} = \frac{1}{3}$

The probability of choosing a vowel is $\frac{1}{3}$.

54. $P(\text{drawing a number less than 4}) = \frac{3}{4}$

The probability of drawing a number less than 4 is $\frac{3}{4}$.

55. Cost of clothes $= 3(45 - 10) + 2(35 - 5)$

$\qquad = 3(35) + 2(30)$

$\qquad = 105 + 60$

$\qquad = 165$

The cost of the clothes is $165.

56. Change in stock $= 25(0.56) + 45(-1.8) + 60(-0.50)$

$\qquad = 14 - 81 - 30$

$\qquad = 14 + (-81) + (-30)$

$\qquad = -67 + (-30)$

$\qquad = -97$

The total change in value of your uncle's stock is $-$97.

Chapter 7, *continued*

57.
$$80 + 40w = 320$$
$$80 + 40w - 80 = 320 - 80$$
$$40w = 240$$
$$\frac{40w}{40} = \frac{240}{40}$$
$$w = 6$$

It will take 6 weeks to save enough money to buy the camera if you save $40 a week.

$$80 + 35w = 320$$
$$80 + 35w - 80 = 320 - 80$$
$$35w = 240$$
$$\frac{35w}{35} = \frac{240}{35}$$
$$w \approx 7$$

It will take 7 weeks to save enough money to buy the camera if you save $35 a week.

58. Method 1:

Multiples of 8: 8, 16, **24**, 32, . . .

Multiples of 12: 12, **24**, 36, 48, . . .

The LCM of 8 and 12 is 24.

Method 2:

$$8 = 2^3$$
$$12 = 2^2 \cdot 3$$

The LCM of 8 and 12 is $2^3 \cdot 3$, or 24.

After 24 seconds, both shooters go off at the same time.

59. Hippopotamus weight − Gentoo penguin weight

$$= 66 - 0.29$$
$$= 65.71$$

The hippopotamus weighs 65.71 pounds more than the gentoo penguin.

60. Polar bear weight − Giant panda weight $= 1.32 - 0.25$
$$= 1.07$$

The polar bear weighs 1.07 pounds more than the giant panda.

61. $A = \ell w = 34.5(11.5) = 396.75$

The iceberg covered an area of about 396.75 square miles.

62.
$$26 + x \geq 75$$
$$26 + x - 26 \geq 75 - 26$$
$$x \geq 49$$

You must sell 49 subscriptions in the last week. The mean number of subscriptions you have to sell per day is $49 \div 7 = 7$.

63. $\dfrac{\text{Students who chose oral report}}{\text{Total students surveyed}} = \dfrac{p}{100}$

$$\frac{36}{300} = \frac{p}{100}$$
$$3600 = 300p$$
$$12 = p$$

12% of the students chose an oral report.

64. $\dfrac{\text{Students who chose visual project}}{\text{Total students surveyed}} = \dfrac{105}{300} = \dfrac{7}{20}$

$\frac{7}{20}$ of students chose a visual project.

65. Visual project: $\dfrac{105}{300} = \dfrac{105 \div 3}{300 \div 3} = \dfrac{35}{100} = 35\%$

Writing a paper: $\dfrac{96}{300} = \dfrac{96 \div 3}{300 \div 3} = \dfrac{32}{100} = 32\%$

Taking a test: $\dfrac{63}{300} = \dfrac{63 \div 3}{300 \div 3} = \dfrac{21}{100} = 21\%$

Taking a test was chosen by 21% of the students.

Chapter 8

Chapter Get-Ready Games (pp. 400–401)

Check student's work.

Stop and Think (p. 401)

Check student's work.

2. There are 169 points on each grid, not including the borders. I found this answer by multiplying the number of horizontal grid lines from -6 to 6 on the y-axis (13) by the number of vertical grid lines from -6 to 6 on the x-axis (13); $13 \times 13 = 169$.

Review Prerequisite Skills (p. 402)

1. The object is a line.   2. The object is a point.

3. The object is a ray.

4. A unit for measuring angles is a *degree*.

5. The angle is 50°.   6. The angle is 120°.

7. The angle is 90°.   8. The angle is 35°.

9. The angle is 60°.   10. The angle is 180°.

11.
$$\begin{array}{c} 0.25 \text{ in.} : 6 \text{ in.} \\ \times\, 4 \quad \times\, 4 \\[4pt] 1 \text{ in.} : 24 \text{ in.} \\ \times\, 3.5 \quad \times\, 3.5 \\[4pt] 3.5 \text{ in.} : 84 \text{ in.} \end{array}$$

$$84 \,\cancel{\text{in.}} \left(\frac{1 \text{ ft}}{12 \,\cancel{\text{in.}}} \right) = 7 \text{ ft}$$

The giant crayon is 84 inches, or 7 feet long.

Lesson 8.1

8.1 Guided Practice (pp. 403–405)

1. $m\angle 1 + m\angle 2 = 79° + 101° = 180°$

   $\angle 1$ and $\angle 2$ are supplementary.

2. $m\angle 1 + m\angle 2 = 64° + 36° = 100°$

   $\angle 1$ and $\angle 2$ are neither supplementary nor complementary.

3. $m\angle 1 + m\angle 2 = 52° + 38° = 90°$

   $\angle 1$ and $\angle 2$ are complementary.

4. $m\angle 1 + m\angle 2 = 44° + 46° = 90°$

   $\angle 1$ and $\angle 2$ are complementary.

5. $m\angle 1 + m\angle 2 = 53° + 47° = 100°$

   $\angle 1$ and $\angle 2$ are neither supplementary nor complementary.

6. $m\angle 1 + m\angle 2 = 95° + 85° = 180°$

   $\angle 1$ and $\angle 2$ are supplementary.

7. $\angle 7$ and the 137° angle are vertical angles. Their measures are equal, so $m\angle 7 = 137°$.

   $m\angle 6 + 137° = 180°$

   $\qquad m\angle 6 = 43°$

   $\angle 6$ and $\angle 8$ are vertical angles. Their measures are equal, so $m\angle 8 = 43°$.

8. $\angle 10$ and the 54° angle are vertical angles. Their measures are equal, so $m\angle 10 = 54°$.

   $m\angle 9 + 54° = 180°$

   $\qquad m\angle 9 = 126°$

   $\angle 9$ and $\angle 11$ are vertical angles. Their measures are equal, so $m\angle 11 = 126°$

9. $\angle 2$ and the 85° angle are corresponding angles. Their measures are equal, so $m\angle 2 = 85°$.

10. $m\angle 3 + 85° = 180°$

    $\qquad m\angle 3 = 95°$

11. $\angle 2$ and $\angle 4$ are vertical angles. Their measures are equal, so $m\angle 4 = 85°$.

12. $\angle 4$ and the 85° angle are alternate exterior angles. Their measures are equal, so $m\angle 4 = 85°$.

    $m\angle 1 + m\angle 4 = 180°$

    $m\angle 1 + 85° = 180°$

    $\quad m\angle 1 = 95°$

8.1 Exercises (pp. 406–408)

Skill Practice

1. The sum of the measures of two *supplementary* angles is 180°.

2. Two lines that intersect to form a right angle are called *perpendicular*.

3. $m\angle 1 + m\angle 2 = 62° + 118° = 180°$

   $\angle 1$ and $\angle 2$ are supplementary.

4. $m\angle 1 + m\angle 2 = 51° + 39° = 90°$

   $\angle 1$ and $\angle 2$ are complementary.

5. $m\angle 1 + m\angle 2 = 90°$ 6. $m\angle 3 + m\angle 4 = 180°$

   $56° + m\angle 2 = 90°$ $\quad m\angle 3 + 71° = 180°$

   $\qquad m\angle 2 = 34°$ $\qquad m\angle 3 = 109°$

7. $m\angle 5 + m\angle 6 = 180°$ 8. $m\angle 7 + m\angle 8 = 90°$

   $22° + m\angle 6 = 180°$ $\quad m\angle 7 + 84° = 90°$

   $\qquad m\angle 6 = 158°$ $\qquad m\angle 7 = 6°$

9. B; $m\angle 2 + m\angle 3 = 90°$, so they are complementary.

10. $\angle 2$ and the 45° angle are vertical angles. Their measures are equal, so $m\angle 2 = 45°$.

    $m\angle 1 + 45° = 180°$

    $\qquad m\angle 1 = 135°$

    $\angle 1$ and $\angle 3$ are vertical angles. Their measures are equal, so $m\angle 3 = 135°$.

11. $\angle 1$ and the 80° angle are vertical angles. Their measures are equal, so $m\angle 1 = 80°$.

    $m\angle 2 + 80° = 180°$

    $\qquad m\angle 2 = 100°$

    $\angle 2$ and $\angle 3$ are vertical angles. Their measures are equal, so $m\angle 3 = 100°$.

Chapter 8, continued

12. $m\angle 6 = 44°$

$m\angle 6 + m\angle 3 = 180°$

$44° + m\angle 3 = 180°$

$m\angle 3 = 136°$

$m\angle 1 = m\angle 3 = m\angle 5 = m\angle 7 = 136°$

$m\angle 2 = m\angle 4 = m\angle 6 = 44°$

13. $m\angle 4 = 106°$

$m\angle 3 + m\angle 4 = 180°$

$m\angle 3 + 106° = 180°$

$m\angle 3 = 74°$

$m\angle 1 = m\angle 3 = m\angle 5 = m\angle 8 = m\angle 9 = m\angle 11 = 74°$

$m\angle 2 = m\angle 4 = m\angle 6 = m\angle 7 = m\angle 10 = 106°$

14. Vertical angles are equal, not supplementary. So, $m\angle 2 = 112°$.

15. B;

$m\angle 1 + m\angle 2 = 21° + 69° = 90°$

$m\angle 3 + m\angle 4 = 12° + 68° = 80°$

$m\angle 5 + m\angle 6 = 79° + 11° = 90°$

$m\angle 7 + m\angle 8 = 45° + 45° = 90°$

Each pair of angles,

$\angle 1$ and $\angle 2$, $\angle 5$ and $\angle 6$, and $\angle 7$ and $\angle 8$ are complementary.

$\angle 3$ and $\angle 4$ are not complementary.

16–19. The types of angle pairs may vary.

16. $\angle 1$ and the 65° angle are vertical angles. So, $m\angle 1 = 65°$.

17.

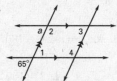

$\angle a$ and $\angle 2$ are supplementary and $\angle a$ and the 65° angle are corresponding angles.

$m\angle a = 65°$

$m\angle a + m\angle 2 = 180°$

$65° + m\angle 2 = 180°$

$m\angle 2 = 115°$

18.

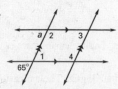

$\angle a$ and the 65° angle are corresponding angles. $\angle a$ and $\angle 3$ are also corresponding angles. $m\angle a = m\angle 3 = 65°$

19.

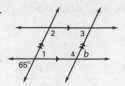

$\angle b$ and the 65° angle are alternate exterior angles and $\angle 4$ and $\angle b$ are supplementary.

$m\angle b = 65°$

$m\angle b + m\angle 4 = 180°$

$65° + m\angle 4 = 180°$

$m\angle 4 = 115°$

20. The opposite angles are equal, and adjacent angles are supplementary.

21. Two angles are *sometimes* supplementary. For example, $150° + 30° = 180°$, but $150° + 20° \neq 180°$.

22. Vertical angles *never* have different measures. Vertical angles are equal.

23. Perpendicular lines *always* form four right angles. Perpendicular lines form a right angle. The angles that are vertical to the angle or supplementary to the angle are also right angles.

24. $m\angle 1 + m\angle 2 = 180°$

$(5x + 15) + 28x = 180$

$33x + 15 = 180$

$33x = 165$

$x = 5$

$m\angle 1 = (5(5) + 15)° = (25 + 15)° = 40°$

$m\angle 2 = 28(5)° = 140°$

25. $m\angle 6 + m\angle 3 = 180°$

$(100 - 10y) + 45y = 180$

$35y + 100 = 180$

$35y = 80$

$y = 2\frac{2}{7}$

$m\angle 3 = 45\left(2\frac{2}{7}\right)° = 102\frac{6}{7}°$

$m\angle 6 = \left[100 - 10\left(2\frac{2}{7}\right)\right]° = \left(100 - 22\frac{6}{7}\right)° = 77\frac{1}{7}°$

26. $m\angle 5 = m\angle 4$

$11n - 13 = 7n + 39$

$4n - 13 = 39$

$4n = 52$

$n = 13$

$m\angle 4 = m\angle 5 = (11(13) - 13)° = (143 - 13)° = 130°$

27. $\angle B$ and $\angle C$ are supplementary and $m\angle C = 4 \cdot m\angle B$.

$m\angle B + m\angle C = 180°$

$m\angle B + 4 \cdot m\angle B = 180°$

$5 \cdot m\angle B = 180$

$m\angle B = 36°$

Chapter 8, continued

Problem Solving

28. ∠1 and the 60° angle are vertical angles. So,
m∠1 = 60°.

m∠2 + 60° = 180°

  m∠2 = 120°

∠2 and ∠3 are vertical angles. So, m∠2 = m∠3 = 120°.

29. *Sample answer:* Six pairs of vertical angles are formed by a line intersecting 3 parallel lines.

At each of the three parallel lines, 2 pairs of vertical angles are formed. So, the total is 6 pairs.

Example:

30. ∠1 and ∠2 are supplementary angles. To find m∠2, subtract m∠1 = 135° from 180°. So, m∠2 = 45°.

31. Check student's work.

Sample answer:

Complementary angles:

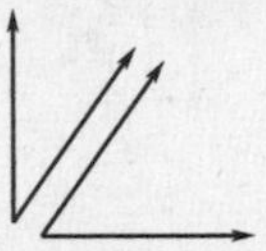

Supplementary angles:

Neither supplementary nor complementary angles:

32. *Sample answer:*

The measure of the angle is about 25°. So, its complement is about 90° − 25° = 65°.

33. C;

∠1 and ∠3 are vertical angles and m∠1 = 120°.
So, m∠1 = m∠3 = 120°.

m∠1 + m∠3 = 120° + 120° = 240°

34. *Sample answer:* If two complementary angles have the same angle measure, let x° represent each angle's measure. Then set up an equation using the fact that the angles are complements.

x° + x° = 90°

  2x = 90

  x = 45

So, each angle measures 45°.

35.

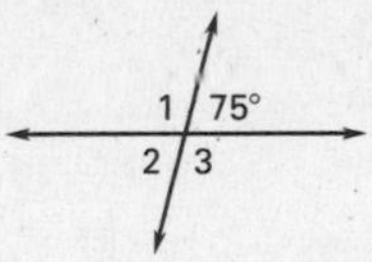

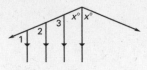

∠2 and the 75° angle are vertical angles. Their measures are equal, so m∠2 = 75°.

m∠1 + 75° = 180°

  m∠1 = 105°

∠1 and ∠3 are vertical angles. Their measures are equal, so m∠3 = 105°.

36. *Sample answer:* The following real-world situations involving perpendicular lines are the horizontal and vertical bars of a football goal post, the baseball paths of a baseball in field, and the lines that form the squares of a checkerboard.

37. The vertical support that divides the peak forms two angles of equal measures. Let x° represent the measure of each angle.

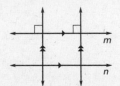

x° + x° = 135°

  2x = 135

  x = 67.5°

Each of ∠1, ∠2, and ∠3 is a corresponding angle with the 67.5° angle. So, m∠1 = m∠2 = m∠3 = 67.5°.

38. *Sample drawing:*

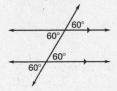

The figure contains 16 right angles. By using corresponding angles, alternate interior angles, or alternate exterior angles you can determine that each of the four intersections form four rights angles. So, there are a total of 4 × 4 = 16 right angles.

39. *Sample answer:*

There are four 60° angles in the figure.

40. *Sample drawing:*

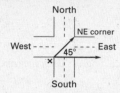

The man is standing on the southwest corner.

41. $(0.5x + 45)° + (2x + 60)° = 180°$

$$2.5x + 105 = 180$$
$$2.5x = 75$$
$$x = 30°$$
$$(0.5x + 45)° + 90° + m = 180°$$
$$0.5(30°) + 45° + 90° + m = 180°$$
$$15° + 45° + 90° + m = 180°$$
$$m = 30°$$

The unknown angle measure between Mulberry Street and Walnut Street is 30°.

Mixed Review

42. $2x + 7x = 90$

$$9x = 90$$
$$\frac{9x}{9} = \frac{90}{9}$$
$$x = 10$$

43. $10x - 7x + 120 = 360$

$$3x + 120 = 360$$
$$3x + 120 - 120 = 360 - 120$$
$$3x = 240$$
$$\frac{3x}{3} = \frac{240}{3}$$
$$x = 80$$

44. $x + 3x + 45 = 180$

$$4x + 45 = 180$$
$$4x + 45 - 45 = 180 - 45$$
$$4x = 135$$
$$\frac{4x}{4} = \frac{135}{4}$$
$$x = 33\frac{3}{4}$$

45. $A = \frac{1}{2}bh = \left(\frac{1}{2}\right)(3)(2) = 3$

The area of the triangle is 3 square inches.

46. $A = \frac{1}{2}bh = \left(\frac{1}{2}\right)(9)(4) = 18$

The area of the triangle is 18 square centimeters.

47. $A = \frac{1}{2}bh = \left(\frac{1}{2}\right)(13)(5) = 32.5$

The area of the triangle is 32.5 square feet.

48. D;

$$53.72\% = 53.72 \div 100$$
$$= 0.5372$$

8.1 Extension (p. 410)

1.

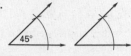

2.

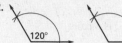

3.

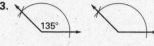

4.

5. 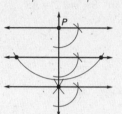 **6.**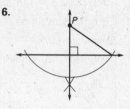

7.

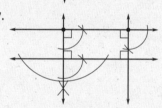

8.

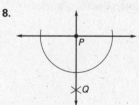

Lesson 8.2

8.2 Guided Practice (p. 412)

1. The triangle has two sides of equal length, so it is an isosceles triangle.

2. The triangle's sides are all of equal length, so it is an isosceles and equilateral triangle.

3. The triangle has no sides of equal length, so it is a scalene triangle.

4. The triangle's sides are all of equal length, so it is an isosceles and equilateral triangle.

5. The triangle has two sides of equal length, so it is an isosceles triangle.

6. The triangle has no sides of equal length, so it is a scalene triangle.

Chapter 8, *continued*

7. $x° + 40° + 88° = 180°$

$\qquad x + 128 = 180$

$\qquad\qquad x = 52$

The triangle has three acute angles, so it is an acute triangle.

8.2 Exercises (pp. 413–415)

Skill Practice

1. A *scalene* triangle has no sides of equal length.

2. An *isosceles* triangle has at least two sides of equal length.

3. The angle is an acute angle.

4. The angle is a right angle.

5. The angle is an obtuse angle.

6. The triangle has no sides of equal length, so it is a scalene triangle.

7. The triangle's sides are all of equal length, so it is an isosceles and equilateral triangle.

8. The triangle has two sides of equal length, so it is an isosceles triangle.

9. The triangle has two sides of equal length, so it is an isosceles triangle.

10. The triangle has three sides of equal length, so it is an isosceles and equilateral triangle.

11. The triangle has no sides of equal length, so it is a scalene triangle.

12. The triangle is not an acute triangle because it does not have three acute angles. The triangle has one right angle, so it is a right triangle.

13. $x° + 43° + 79° = 180°$

$\qquad x + 122 = 180$

$\qquad\qquad x = 58$

The triangle has three acute angles, so it is an acute triangle.

14. $66° + 90° + x° = 180°$

$\qquad 156 + x = 180$

$\qquad\qquad x = 24$

The triangle has one right angle, so it is a right triangle.

15. $x° + 32° + 116° = 180°$

$\qquad x + 148 = 180$

$\qquad\qquad x = 32$

The triangle has one obtuse angle, so it is an obtuse triangle.

16. A; $x° + 110° + 40° = 180°$

$\qquad\quad x + 150 = 180$

$\qquad\qquad\quad x = 30$

17. $43° + 48° + 90° = 181°$

The angles add up to more than 180°, so the angles do not form a triangle.

18. $1.5° + 0.5° + 178° = 180°$

The angles add up to 180°, so they can form a triangle.

19. $21.3° + 56.7° + 102° = 180°$

The angles add up to 180°, so they can form a triangle.

20. $45° + 45° + x° = 180°$

$\qquad 90 + x = 180$

$\qquad\qquad x = 90$

The other unknown angle measures are 45° and 90°.

The triangle has one right angle, so it is a right triangle.

21. $x° + x° + 40° = 180°$

$\qquad 2x + 40 = 180$

$\qquad\quad 2x = 140$

$\qquad\qquad x = 70$

The other unknown angle measures are 70° and 70°.

The triangle has three acute angles, so it is an acute triangle.

22. All three sides are of equal lengths so all three angles have equal measures.

The other unknown angle measures are 60° and 60°.

The triangle has three acute angles, so it is an acute triangle.

23. $x° + (4x - 10)° + 90° = 180°$

$\qquad x + 4x - 10 + 90 = 180$

$\qquad\qquad 5x + 80 = 180$

$\qquad\qquad\quad 5x = 100$

$\qquad\qquad\qquad x = 20$

$(4x - 10)° = (4(20) - 10)° = (80 - 10)° = 70°$

The angles of the triangle are 90°, 20°, and 70°.

24. $x° + (3x + 10)° + 70° = 180°$

$\qquad x + 3x + 10 + 70 = 180$

$\qquad\qquad 4x + 80 = 180$

$\qquad\qquad\quad 4x = 100$

$\qquad\qquad\qquad x = 25$

$(3x + 10)° = (3(25) + 10)° = (75 + 10)° = 85°$

The angles of the triangle are 25°, 70°, and 85°.

25. $(x + 30)° + (90 - x)° + 2x° = 180°$

$\qquad x + 30 + 90 - x + 2x = 180$

$\qquad\qquad\quad 2x + 120 = 180$

$\qquad\qquad\qquad\quad 2x = 60$

$\qquad\qquad\qquad\qquad x = 30$

$(x + 30)° = (30 + 30)° = 60°$

$(90 - x)° = (90 - 30)° = 60°$

$2x° = 2(30)° = 60°$

The angles of the triangle are all 60°.

26. $m\angle 1 + 35° + 70° = 180°$

$\qquad m\angle 1 + 105° = 180°$

$\qquad\qquad m\angle 1 = 75°$

$\angle 2$ and the 35° angle are vertical angles. Their measures are equal, so $m\angle 2 = 35°$.

$\angle 1$ and $\angle 4$ are alternate interior angles, so $m\angle 1 = m\angle 4 = 75°$.

$m\angle 3 + m\angle 2 + m\angle 4 = 180°$

$\qquad m\angle 3 + 35° + 75° = 180°$

$\qquad\qquad m\angle 3 + 110° = 180°$

$\qquad\qquad\qquad m\angle 3 = 70°$

27. $m\angle BAC + 50° + 120° = 180°$

$\qquad m\angle BAC + 170° = 180°$

$\qquad\qquad m\angle BAC = 10°$

$m\angle ACD + 120° = 180°$

$\qquad m\angle ACD = 60°$

$m\angle CAD + m\angle ACD + 90° = 180°$

$\qquad m\angle CAD + 60° + 90° = 180°$

$\qquad\qquad m\angle CAD + 150° = 180°$

$\qquad\qquad\qquad m\angle CAD = 30°$

$m\angle FAE + 50° + 120° = 180°$

$\qquad m\angle FAE + 170° = 180°$

$\qquad\qquad m\angle FAE = 10°$

$m\angle AED + 120° = 180°$

$\qquad m\angle AED = 60°$

$m\angle DAE + m\angle AED + 90° = 180°$

$\qquad m\angle DAE + 60° + 90° = 180°$

$\qquad\qquad m\angle DAE + 150° = 180°$

$\qquad\qquad\qquad m\angle DAE = 30°$

$\triangle ABC$ and $\triangle AEC$ are formed with angles measuring 50°, 120°, and 10°. Because one angle is an obtuse angle, the triangles are obtuse triangles.

$\triangle ACD$ and $\triangle AED$ are formed with angles measuring $180° - 120° = 60°$, 90°, and 30°. Because one angle is a right angle, the triangles are right triangles.

$\triangle ABD$ and $\triangle AFD$ are formed with angles measuring 50°, 90°, and $10° + 30° = 40°$. Because one angle is a right angle, the triangles are right triangles.

$\triangle ACE$ is formed with angles measuring 60°, 60°, and 60°. Because all three angles are acute angles, the triangle is an acute triangle.

$\triangle ABF$ is formed with angles measuring 50°, 50°, and $10° + 30° + 10° + 30° = 80°$. Because all three angles are acute, the triangle is an acute triangle.

$\triangle ABE$ and $\triangle AFC$ are formed with angles measuring 50°, 60°, and $10 + 30 + 30 = 70°$. Because all three angles are acute, the triangle is an acute triangle.

Use the fact that in an isosceles triangle, the sides opposite the angles of equal measure have the same length. Because $m\angle B = m\angle F$, $\triangle ABF$ is isosceles. Because $m\angle ACE = m\angle AEC$, $\triangle ACE$ is isosceles.

Problem Solving

28. There are two sides of equal length, so the triangle is an isosceles triangle.

29. The angles of an equiangular triangle are all $x°$. Therefore they add up to $3x°$. This equals 180°. So divide 180° by 3 to find the measure of each angle. Each angle is 60°.

30. A right triangle cannot be equilateral. *Sample answer:* A right triangle has only one right angle, so the other two angles have a sum of 90°. All three angles do not have an equal measure, so it cannot be equilateral.

31. Two angles are supplementary if their sum is 180°. Three angles form a triangle if their sum is 180°. Two angles cannot be supplementary in a triangle because the measure of the third angle would have to be 0° which is impossible.

32. The angle formed between the tower and the ground is a right angle, so the triangle is a right triangle.

All three sides have different lengths, so the triangle is scalene.

33. B;

$m\angle C$ is greater than $m\angle B$, $78° > 54°$.

$m\angle B$ is greater than $m\angle A$, $54° > 48°$.

$m\angle A$ is greater than $40°$, $48° > 40°$.

34. *Sample answer:* $\triangle ABC$ and $\triangle DEF$ are possible, $\triangle GHI$ is impossible, because the two shorter sides cannot meet to form the third vertex.

35. $x° + 65° = 360°$

$\qquad x = 295$

The angle is a reflex angle.

36. $x° + 230° = 360°$

$\qquad x = 130$

The angle is an obtuse angle.

37. $x° + 110° = 360°$

$\qquad x = 250$

The angle is a reflex angle.

38. 1, 1, 8

1, 2, 7

1, 3, 6

1, 4, 5

2, 2, 6

2, 3, 5

2, 4, 4

3, 3, 4

Only the sets containing 3, 3, 4 and 2, 4, 4 can be the lengths of the sides of a triangle.

In a triangle, the sum of the 2 shorter sides must be greater than the longest side.

Chapter 8, *continued*

Mixed Review

39. $P = 2\ell + 2w$

$124 = 2(48) + 2w$

$124 = 96 + 2w$

$28 = 2w$

$14 = w$

The width of the rectangle is 14 centimeters.

40. $A = \ell w$

$105 = 7\ell$

$15 = \ell$

The length of the rectangle is 15 inches.

41. $A = \ell w$

$216 = 24w$

$9 = w$

The width of the rectangle is 9 meters.

42. $P = 2\ell + 2w$

$144 = 2\ell + 2(16)$

$144 = 2\ell + 32$

$112 = 2\ell$

$56 = \ell$

The length of the rectangle is 56 feet.

43. $0.292 \times 510{,}072{,}000 = 148{,}941{,}024$

The total land area of Earth is 148,941,024 square kilometers.

44. C;

Find the amount of the discount.

20% of $20 = $0.20(20) = 4$

Find the sale price.

$20 - $4 = 16

Find the amount of the sales tax.

4% of $16 = $0.04(16) = 0.64$

Find the total cost of the backpack.

$16 + $.64 = 16.64

Lesson 8.3

8.3 Guided Practice (p. 417)

1. The quadrilateral has exactly one pair of parallel sides. So, it is a trapezoid.

2. $90° + 90° + 115° + x° = 360°$

$295 + x = 360$

$x = 65$

8.3 Exercises (pp. 417–419)

Skill Practice

1. A quadrilateral with exactly 1 pair of parallel sides is a *trapezoid*.

2. A parallelogram with 4 right angles is a *rectangle*.

3. The quadrilateral is a trapezoid.

4. The quadrilateral is a rectangle.

5. The quadrilateral is a rhombus.

6–8. Measurements may vary.

6. Side lengths: 1.3 cm and 2.5 cm

The quadrilateral is a parallelogram.

7. Side lengths: 1.6 cm

The quadrilateral is a rhombus.

8. Side lengths: 1.3 cm

The quadrilateral is a square.

9. $110° + 71° + 70° + x° = 360°$

$251 + x = 360$

$x = 109$

10. $x° + 60° + 95° + 100° = 360°$

$x + 255 = 360$

$x = 105$

11. $x° + 140° + 70° + 85° = 360°$

$x + 295 = 360$

$x = 65$

12. $100° + 80° + 40° + x° = 360°$

$220 + x = 360$

$x = 140$

$140° + y° = 180°$

$y = 40$

13. $115° + x° = 180°$

$x = 65$

$90° + 90° + 65° + y° = 360°$

$245 + y = 360$

$y = 115$

14. $54° + 54° + x° = 180°$

$108 + x = 180$

$x = 72$

$72° + 105° + 110° + y° = 360°$

$287 + y = 360$

$y = 73$

15. *Sample answer:* The error is that a diagonal cannot be a side of a figure. So, the diagonals of $ABCD$ are $\overline{AC}$ and $\overline{BD}$.

16. C;

The sum of the angles in a quadrilateral is 360°. If a quadrilateral has 3 acute angles, the fourth angle must be obtuse.

Chapter 8, *continued*

17. $58° + 62° + (24x + 1)° + (25x − 6)° = 360°$

$58 + 62 + 24x + 1 + 25x − 6 = 360°$

$49x + 115 = 360$

$49x = 245$

$x = 5$

$m\angle E = (24x + 1)° = (24(5) + 1)° = 121°$

$m\angle H = (25x − 6)° = (25(5) − 6)° = (125 − 6)°$

$= 119°$

18. $x° + (3x + 13)° + (x + 1)° + (4x − 14)° = 360°$

$x + 3x + 13 + x + 1 + 4x − 14 = 360$

$9x = 360$

$x = 40$

$m\angle L = (x + 1)° = (40 + 1)° = 41°$

$m\angle M = (4x − 14)°$

$= (4(40) − 14)°$

$= (160 − 14)°$

$= 146°$

$m\angle K = (3x + 13)°$

$= (3(40) − 13)°$

$= (120 − 13)°$

$= 133°$

$m\angle J = x° = 40°$

19. A rhombus is *always* a parallelogram.

Sample answer: A rhombus is a parallelogram with four equal sides.

20. A rectangle is *sometimes* a square.

Sample answer: All squares are rectangles, but not all rectangles are squares.

21. A square is *always* a parallelogram.

Sample answer: A square is a parallelogram with 4 equal sides and 4 right angles.

22. A triangle is *never* a quadrilateral.

Sample answer: A triangle has 3 sides and a quadrilateral has 4 sides.

23. A trapezoid is *never* a parallelogram.

Sample answer: A trapezoid has exactly 1 pair of parallel sides and a parallelogram has 2 pairs of parallel sides.

24. A quadrilateral is *sometimes* a rectangle.

Sample answer: A rectangle is a quadrilateral, but not all quadrilaterals are rectangles.

25. Because the sum of the angles in a quadrilateral is 360°,

$x = 360 − (60 + 122 + 90) = 360 − 272 = 88$,

$z = 180 − x = 180 − 88 = 92$, and

$y = 360 − [(180 − 60) + 90 + z]$

$= 360 − (120 + 90 + 92)$

$= 360 − 302$

$= 58.$

Problem Solving

26. The quadrilaterals in the design are dark blue rectangles, red squares, green trapezoids, light blue parallelograms, purple parallelograms, and yellow trapezoids.

27. A quadrilateral has at most, 2 diagonals.

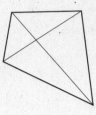 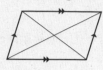

28. $x° + (x + 80)° + x° + (x + 80)° = 360°$

$x + x + 80 + x + x + 80 = 360$

$4x + 160 = 360$

$4x = 200$

$x = 50$

The angle measures are 50°, 50° + 80° = 130°, 50°, and 50° + 80° = 130°.

29. The figure is a rhombus. *Sample answer:* All sides of the figure have equal lengths because all the side lengths of an equilateral triangle are equal. The opposite sides are parallel.

30. The greatest number of obtuse angles a quadrilateral can have is 3.

Sample answer: If a quadrilateral had 4 obtuse angles, the sum would be greater than 360°. This isn't possible because the sum of the angle measures in a quadrilateral is 360°.

31. A quadrilateral cannot have three 60° angles.

Sample answer: If the measures of three angles were 60°, the measure of the fourth angle would have to be $360° − 3(60°) = 180°$. A 180° angle is a straight line. So, the figure would only have 3 district sides, not 4.

32. a. *HAJG* and *GJEF* are trapezoids because each has exactly one pair of parallel sides. *ABCJ* and *JCDE* are parallelograms because each has two pairs of parallel sides.

Explanations may vary.

$\angle 1$ and the 130° angle are supplementary angles. So,

$m\angle 1 + 130° = 180°$

$m\angle 1 = 50°.$

$\angle 2$ and the 130° angle are vertical angles. So,

$m\angle 2 = 130°.$

$\angle 3$ and $\angle 1$ are vertical angles. So,

$m\angle 1 = m\angle 3 = 50°.$

Chapter 8, *continued*

∠5 and ∠3 are alternate interior angles. So, $m\angle 3 = m\angle 5 = 50°$.

∠4 and the 130° angle are alternate interior angles. So, $m\angle 4 = 130°$.

∠4 and ∠6 are corresponding angles. ∠2 and ∠7 are corresponding angles. ∠9 and the 130° angle are corresponding angles. ∠3 and ∠10 are corresponding angles. ∠10 and ∠8 are also corresponding angles. So,

$m\angle 4 = m\angle 6 = 130°$,

$m\angle 2 = m\angle 7 = 130°$,

$m\angle 9 = 130°$,

$m\angle 3 = m\angle 10 = 50°$, and

$m\angle 10 = m\angle 8 = 50°$.

Because *HAJG* is a quadrilateral,

$105° + m\angle 4 + m\angle 3 + m\angle 13 = 360°$

$105° + 130° + 50° + m\angle 13 = 360°$

$285° + m\angle 13 = 360°$

$m\angle 13 = 75°$.

∠12 and ∠13 are supplementary angles. So,

$m\angle 12 + m\angle 13 = 180°$

$m\angle 12 + 75° = 180°$

$m\angle 12 = 105°$.

Because *GJEF* is a quadrilateral,

$m\angle 12 + m\angle 2 + m\angle 10 + m\angle 11 = 360°$

$105° + 130° + 150° + m\angle 11 = 360°$

$285° + m\angle 11 = 360°$

$m\angle 11 = 75°$.

b. *Sample answer:* The measures of opposite angles of a parallelogram are equal. The consecutive angles in a parallelogram are supplementary.

For example:

In parallelogram *JCDE*,

$m\angle 1 = m\angle 8 = 50°$,

$m\angle 7 = m\angle 9 = 130°$,

$m\angle 1 + m\angle 9 = 50° + 130° = 180°$,

$m\angle 1 + m\angle 7 = 50° + 130° = 180°$,

$m\angle 9 + m\angle 8 = 130° + 50° = 180°$,

and

$m\angle 7 + m\angle 8 = 132° + 50° = 180°$.

Mixed Review

33. $17° + 92° + x° = 180°$

$109 + x = 180$

$x = 71$

The measure of the third angle is 71°.

34. $26° + 34° + x° = 180°$

$60 + x = 180$

$x = 120$

The measure of the third angle is 120°.

35. $61° + 68° + x° = 180°$

$129 + x = 180$

$x = 51$

The measure of the third angle is 51°.

36. $72° + 81° + x° = 180°$

$153 + x = 180$

$x = 27$

The measure of the third angle is 27°.

37. 430% of $130 = 4.30(130)$

$= 559$

38. B;

$40° + x° = 90°$

$x = 50$

Lesson 8.4

Activity (p. 420)

Steps 1–3.

Shape		
Number of Sides	4	5
Number of Diagonal Lines	1	2
Number of Triangles Formed	2	3
Sum of Angle Measures	360°	540°

Shape				
Number of Sides	6	7	8	10
Number of Diagonal Lines	3	4	5	7
Number of Triangles Formed	4	5	6	8
Sum of Angle Measures	720°	900°	1080°	1440°

Chapter 8, continued

8.4 Guided Practice (p. 421)

1. A 9-gon has 9 sides, so use $n = 9$.

$$(n - 2) \cdot 180° = (9 - 2) \cdot 180°$$
$$= 1260°$$

The sum of the angle measures in a 9-gon is 1260°.

2. A regular heptagon has 7 sides, so use $n = 7$.

$$\frac{(n - 2) \cdot 180°}{n} = \frac{(7 - 2) \cdot 180°}{7} = \frac{900°}{7} \quad 128.6°$$

The measure of one angle in a regular heptagon is about 128.6°.

8.4 Exercises (pp. 422–424)

Skill Practice

1. A *polygon* is a closed figure with sides that are line segments that intersect only at their endpoints.

2. A *regular polygon* is a closed figure with sides that are line segments of equal length meeting only at their endpoints, and with all angles of equal measure.

3. The figure is a polygon, but it is not regular. Its angles and sides have different measures.

4. The figure is not a polygon. The figure does not have line segments as sides.

5. The figure is a regular polygon.

6. A 12-gon has 12 sides, so use $n = 12$.

$$(n - 2) \cdot 180° = (12 - 2) \cdot 180° = 1800°$$

The sum of the angle measures in a 12-gon is 1800°.

7. A 16-gon has 16 sides, so use $n = 16$.

$$(n - 2) \cdot 180° = (16 - 2) \cdot 180° = 2520°$$

The sum of the angle measures in a 16-gon is 2520°.

8. An 11-gon has 11 sides, so use $n = 11$.

$$(n - 2) \cdot 180° = (11 - 2) \cdot 180° = 1620°$$

The sum of the angle measures in an 11-gon is 1620°.

9. An 20-gon has 20 sides, so use $n = 20$.

$$(n - 2) \cdot 180° = (20 - 2) \cdot 180° = 3240°$$

The sum of the angle measures in a 20-gon is 3240°.

10. The error is multiplying 180° by the number of sides of the polygon. Instead, use the equation to find the sum of the angles. It is $(n - 2) \cdot 180° = (6 - 2) \cdot 180° = 4 \cdot 180° = 720°$.

11. A regular 10-gon has 10 sides, so use $n = 10$.

$$\frac{(n - 2) \cdot 180°}{n} = \frac{(10 - 2) \cdot 180°}{10} = \frac{1440°}{10} = 144°$$

The measure of one angle in a regular 10-gon is 144°.

12. A regular 14-gon has 14 sides, so use $n = 14$.

$$\frac{(n - 2) \cdot 180°}{n} = \frac{(14 - 2) \cdot 180°}{14} = \frac{2160°}{14} \approx 154.3°$$

The measure of one angle in a regular 14-gon is about 154°.

13. A regular 15-gon has 15 sides, so use $n = 15$.

$$\frac{(n - 2) \cdot 180°}{n} = \frac{(15 - 2) \cdot 180°}{15} = \frac{2340°}{15} = 156°$$

The measure of one angle in a regular 15-gon is 156°.

14. B; The sum of the angle measures in a pentagon:

$$(n - 2) \cdot 180° = (5 - 2) \cdot 180° = 3(180°) = 540°$$
$$90° + 85° + 120° + 130° + x° = 540$$
$$425 + x = 540$$
$$x = 115$$

15. The sum of the measures of a hexagon is 720°.

$$x° + 2x° + 2x° + x° + 2x° + 2x° = 720°$$
$$10x = 720$$
$$x = 72$$

$$2(x) = 2(72)$$
$$2x = 144$$

$m\angle R = 72°$, $m\angle L = 144°$, $m\angle M = 144°$, $m\angle N = 72°$, $m\angle P = 144°$, $m\angle Q = 144°$

16. The sum of the measures of a pentagon is 540°.

$$x° + 150° + 150° + x° + 2x° = 540°$$
$$4x + 300 = 540$$
$$4x = 240$$
$$x = 60$$

$$2(x) = 2(60)$$
$$2x = 120$$

$m\angle K = 60°$, $m\angle H = 60°$, $m\angle J = 120°$

17. The sum of the measures of a pentagon is 540°.

$m\angle E = m\angle ABC$

$$90° + m\angle E + 90° + m\angle ABC + 90° = 540°$$
$$90° + m\angle E + 90° + m\angle E + 90° = 540°$$
$$2m\angle E + 270° = 540°$$
$$2m\angle E = 270°$$
$$m\angle E = 135°$$

$m\angle E = m\angle ABC = 135°$

$x = 180 - m\angle ABC$

$x = 180 - 135$

$x = 45$

$m\angle E = 135°$, $m\angle ABC = 135°$

18. A;

The sum of the measures of a pentagon is 540°. To be a regular pentagon, the two missing angles must have the same measures as the other three angles.

$$3(107°) + x° + x° = 540°$$
$$321 + 2x = 540$$
$$2x = 219$$
$$x = 109.5°$$

Because $109.5° \neq 107$, the pentagon is not regular.

Chapter 8, *continued*

19. $(n - 2) \cdot 180° = 1980°$

$n - 2 = 11$

$n = 13$

The polygon is a 13-gon.

20. $(n - 2) \cdot 180° = 2520°$

$n - 2 = 14$

$n = 16$

The polygon is a 16-gon.

21. $(n - 2) \cdot 180° = 2880°$

$n - 2 = 16$

$n = 18$

The polygon is an 18-gon.

22. $(n - 2) \cdot 180° = 3600°$

$n - 2 = 20$

$n = 22$

The polygon is a 22-gon.

23. *Sample answer:* According to the formula, you can tell that the measure of each interior angle of a regular polygon must be greater than 0° but less than 180°. The greatest whole number less than 180 is 179. So, you must find the number of sides that make each interior angle equal to 179°.

$\dfrac{(n - 2) \cdot 180°}{n} = 179°$

$(n - 2) \cdot 180 = 179n$

$180(n - 2) = 179n$

$180n - 180(2) = 179n$

$180n - 360 = 179n$

$n - 360 = 0$

$n = 360$

The greatest number of sides that a regular polygon can have and produce a whole number angle measure is 360.

Problem Solving

24. The swimming pool design is a polygon because it is a closed figure whose sides are line segments intersecting only at endpoints.

25. The swimming pool design is not a polygon. It does not have line segments as sides.

26. The swimming pool design is a polygon because it is a closed figure whose sides are line segments intersecting only at endpoints.

27. *Sample answer:* Some of the rocks are pentagons and hexagons.

28. B;

The top of the table is a regular polygon with 7 sides, so use $n = 7$.

$\dfrac{(n - 2) \cdot 180°}{n} = \dfrac{(7 - 2) \cdot 180°}{7} = \dfrac{900°}{7} \approx 128.6°$

The measure of one angle of the table is about 128.6°.

29. *Sample answer:* Cut off the vertices without intersecting the cuts.

Check student's work.

30. *Sample answer:*

31. The figure eight is not a polygon. *Sample answer:* Its sides are not line segments and it encloses two separate regions.

32. a. $m\angle a = 180° - 50° = 130°$

$m\angle b = 180° - 60° = 120°$

$m\angle c = 180° - 70° = 110°$

$m\angle d = 180° - 90° = 90°$

$m\angle e = 180° - 90° = 90°$

$m\angle f = 180° - 90° = 90°$

$m\angle g = 180° - 90° = 90°$

$m\angle h = 180° - 108° = 72°$

$m\angle j = 180° - 108° = 72°$

$m\angle k = 180° - 108° = 72°$

$m\angle l = 180° - 108° = 72°$

$m\angle m = 180° - 108° = 72°$

b. Triangle:

$m\angle a + m\angle b + m\angle c = 130° + 120° + 110° = 360°$

The sum of the exterior angle measures of the triangle is 360°.

Rectangle:

$m\angle d + m\angle e + m\angle f + m\angle g = 90° + 90° + 90° + 90°$
$= 360°$

The sum of the exterior angle measures of the rectangle is 360°.

Pentagon:

$m\angle h + m\angle j + m\angle k + m\angle l + m\angle m$
$= 72° + 72° + 72° + 72° + 72°$
$= 360°$

The sum of the exterior angle measures of the pentagon is 360°.

c. The sum of the exterior angle measure of a polygon is 360°.

33.

Shape	Diagonal
Quadrilateral	
	2
Pentagon	
	5
Hexagon	
	9

$$2, \quad 5, \quad 9, \ldots$$
$$+3 \quad +4$$

To get the next number in the pattern, add 5 to 9.

$5 + 9 = 14$

So a heptagon has 14 diagonals.

34. You can make a base marker that is a regular polygon with each angle measuring 135°, but not 145°. *Sample answer:* A regular octagon has interior angle measures of

$$\frac{(8-2) \cdot 180°}{8} = 135°.$$

A regular 10-gon has interior angle measures of

$$\frac{(10-2) \cdot 180°}{10} = 144°$$

and a regular 11-gon has interior angle measures of

$$\frac{(11-2) \cdot 180°}{11} \approx 147.27°.$$

There is no regular polygon that has interior angle measures between 144° and 147.27°, so 145° is not possible.

35. Let x represent the measure of each interior angle. So the expressions $0.25x$ and $180 - x$ both represent the measure of each exterior angle.

$0.25x = 180 - x$

$1.25x = 180$

$x = 144$

Interior angle measures: 144°

Exterior angle measures: $0.25(144°) = 36°$

Because the sum of the exterior angles of a n-sided polygon is 360;

$36n = 360$

$n = 10$

The polygon has 10 sides and is a regular 10-gon.

36. Let x represent of each exterior angle of a regular pentagon.

$5x = 360$

$x = 72$

A n-sided polygon has an interior angle measure sum that is $15(72°) = 1080°$.

$(n - 2) \cdot 180° = 1080°$

$n - 2 = 6$

$n = 8$

The polygon is an octagon.

Mixed Review

37. $x° + 90° + 90° + 90° = 360°$

$x + 270 = 360$

$x = 90$

The measure of the fourth angle is 90°.

38. $x° + 87° + 93° + 87° = 360°$

$x + 267 = 360$

$x = 93$

The measure of the fourth angle is 93°.

39. $x° + 39° + 141° + 13° = 360°$

$x + 193 = 360$

$x = 167$

The measure of the fourth angle is 167°.

40. $x° + 90° + 80° + 90° = 360°$

$x + 260 = 360$

$x = 100$

The measure of the fourth angle is 100°.

41. $98\% = \dfrac{98}{100} = \dfrac{49}{50}$

42. $141.3\% = \dfrac{1413}{1000} = 1\dfrac{413}{1000}$

43. $0.14\% = \dfrac{14}{10,000} = \dfrac{7}{5000}$

44. $7.6\% = \dfrac{76}{1000} = \dfrac{19}{250}$

45. $0.45\% = \dfrac{45}{10,000} = \dfrac{9}{2000}$

46. $18.2\% = \dfrac{182}{1000} = \dfrac{91}{500}$

47. $0.98\% = \dfrac{98}{1000} = \dfrac{49}{5000}$

48. $156\% = \dfrac{156}{100} = 1\dfrac{56}{100} = 1\dfrac{14}{25}$

Chapter 8, continued

49. C;

49. C;

Find the amount of markup.

$25.70 - 12.50 = 13.20$

Find the percent markup.

% markup $\cdot$ 12.5 = 13.2

% markup $= \frac{13.2}{12.5} = 1.056$

The percent markup is $1.056 = 1.056 \times 100 = 105.6\%$.

Quiz 8.1–8.4 (p. 424)

1. $m\angle 1 + m\angle 2 = 32° + 148° = 180°$

The sum of the measures of the angles is 180°, so they are supplementary.

2. $m\angle 3 + m\angle 4 = 59° + 41° = 100°$

The sum of the measures of the angles is 100°, so they are neither supplementary nor complementary.

3. $m\angle 5 + m\angle 6 = 12° + 78° = 90°$

The sum of the measures of the angles is 90°, so they are complementary.

4. $m\angle 7 + m\angle 8 = 116° + 64° = 180°$

The sum of the measures of the angles is 180°, so they are supplementary.

5. $m\angle A + m\angle B = 73° + 117° = 190°$

The sum of the measures of the angles is 190°, so they are neither supplementary nor complementary.

6. $m\angle C + m\angle D = 48° + 42° = 90°$

The sum of the measures of the angles is 90°, so they are complementary.

7. $23° + 57° + 95° = 175°$

The angles in a triangle cannot have these measures because their sum does not equal 180°.

8. $64.6° + 77.3° + 38.1° = 180°$

The angles in a triangle can have these measures because they add up to 180°. The triangle is acute and scalene.

9. $155° + 24.9° + 0.1° = 180°$

The angles in a triangle can have these measures because they add up to 180°. The triangle is obtuse and scalene.

10. $50° + 55° + 130° + x° = 360°$

$$235 + x = 360$$
$$x = 125$$

11. $3x° + x° = 180°$

$$4x = 180$$
$$x = 45$$

12. $(n - 2) \cdot 180° = (6 - 2) \cdot 180° = 4(180°) = 720°$

$112° + 135° + 107° + 144° + 90° + x° = 720°$

$$588 + x = 720$$
$$x = 132$$

13. The figure in Exercise 10 is a trapezoid.

The figure is Exercise 12 is a hexagon.

Mixed Review of Problem Solving (p. 425)

1. a. The figure has 5 sides, so it is a pentagon.

  b. $(n - 2) \cdot 180° = (5 - 2) \cdot 180° = 540°$

  The sum of the angle measures is 540°.

  c. $115° + (2x + 35)° + 110° + 130° + x° = 540°$

$$3x + 390 = 540$$
$$3x = 150$$
$$x = 50$$

  $2x + 35 = 2(50) + 35 = 135$

  The unknown angle measures are 50° and 135°.

  d. The polygon is not regular because the angles do not have the same measure.

2.

The segment divides the octagon into the hexagons.

$(n - 2) \cdot 180° = (6 - 2) \cdot 180° = 720°$

The sum of the measures in each polygon is 720°.

3. a. The black polygon is a triangle, the blue polygons are trapezoids, and the yellow polygon is a pentagon.

  b. Method 1: $x°$ is supplementary to 30°, so $x° = 180° - 30° = 150°$.

  Method 2: The sum of the interior angles in a quadrilateral is 360.

$$x° + 30° + 90° + 90° = 360°$$
$$x + 210 = 360$$
$$x = 150$$

4. *Sample answer:* The triangle at the left is isosceles, so the angles opposite the sides of equal length are also equal. The third angle and the $x°$ angle are vertical angles.

  So, $75° + 75° + x° = 180°$

$$150 + x = 180$$
$$x = 30.$$

5. *Sample answer:*

6. *Sample answer:* All four sides of a rhombus are always equal. The angles of a rhombas are sometimes right angles.

Chapter 8, continued

7. a. Any two of the following pair of supplementary
angles: ∠1 and ∠2, ∠2 and ∠3, ∠3 and ∠4, ∠4
and ∠1

Vertical angles: ∠1 and ∠3, ∠2 and ∠4

b. $m\angle 3 = m\angle 1 = 20°$

c. $m\angle 4 + m\angle 3 = 180°$

$m\angle 4 + 30° = 180°$

$m\angle 4 = 150°$

d. Explanations may vary. ∠3 gets smaller because ∠1
gets smaller and $m\angle 3 = m\angle 1$. ∠2 and ∠4 are vertical
angles, so they have the same measure, ∠1 and ∠2
are supplements, so as $m\angle 1$ decrease, $m\angle 2$ increases
approaching 180°.

8.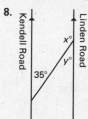

Because 35° and ∠y are alternate interior angles,
$m\angle y = 35°$.

Because ∠x and ∠y are supplementary angles,
$m\angle x + m\angle y = 180°$

$m\angle x + 35° = 180°$

$m\angle x = 145°$

Vida's left turn measures 145°.

9. The sum of the 3 angles of the isoceles triangle is 180°.

The other four angles are 90°, 90°, 360° − 90° = 270°,
and 360° − 90° = 270°.

The sum of the measures of the angles in the sign are
180° + 90° + 90° + 270° + 270° = 900°.

Lesson 8.5

8.5 Investigation (p. 426)

1. *Sample answer:*

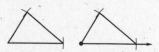

2. *Sample answer:*

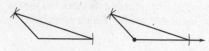

3. *Sample answer:*

4. The measures of the angles of the copied triangles have
the same measures of the angles as the original.

Sample answer: The angles are equal because the
triangles have the same size and same shape.

5. *Sample answer:* The angles in the same position in each
triangle have the same measures.

8.5 Guided Practice (pp. 427–429)

1. Corresponding angles: ∠E and ∠Q, ∠F and ∠R, ∠G
and ∠N, ∠H and ∠P

Corresponding sides: $\overline{EF}$ and $\overline{QR}$, $\overline{FG}$ and $\overline{RN}$, and $\overline{GH}$
and $\overline{NP}$, $\overline{HE}$ and $\overline{PQ}$

2. $\overline{ST}$ and $\overline{KJ}$ are corresponding sides, so they have the same
measure.

The length of $\overline{ST}$ is 10m.

3. ∠T and ∠J are corresponding angles, so they have the
same measure.

$m\angle T = m\angle J = 31°$

4. ∠R and ∠L are corresponding angles, so they have the
same measure.

$m\angle R = m\angle L = 25°$

5. The triangles are congruent by Side-Angle-Side.

6. The triangles are not necessarily congruent because SSS,
SAS, or ASA do not apply.

8.5 Exercises (pp. 429–432)

Skill Practice

1. Two angles with the same measure are *congruent*.

2. Sides and angles that are in the same position in different
figures are called *corresponding parts*.

3. Congruent pairs of angles:

∠N ≅ ∠R	∠M ≅ ∠Q
∠K ≅ ∠S	∠L ≅ ∠P

4. $m\angle S = m\angle K = 90°$

5. The length of $\overline{NK}$ is 12 inches.

6. $m\angle R = m\angle N = 60°$

7. $m\angle C = m\angle F = 80°$

8. The length of $\overline{AF}$ is 3 centimeters.

9. $m\angle A = m\angle D = 100°$

10. The length of $\overline{HC}$ is 4 centimeters.

11. △ABC ≅ △LMK by Side-Angle-Side.

△GHJ ≅ △PQN by Side-Side-Side.

12. The error is in the name of the triangles.

△ABC ≅ △DFE by Side-Angle-Side.

13. C;

∠C ≅ ∠G

$5x + 15 = 105$

$5x = 90$

$x = 18$

Chapter 8, continued

14. The triangles are congruent by Side-Side-Side.

$$x - 6 = 4$$
$$x = 10$$

15. The triangles are congruent by Angle-Side-Angle.

$$2x + 6 = 32$$
$$2x = 26$$
$$x = 13$$

16. The triangles are congruent by Angle-Side-Angle.

$$(2x - 24)° = x°$$
$$x = 24$$

17. *Sample answer:*

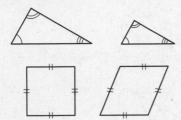

18. No.

Sample answer:

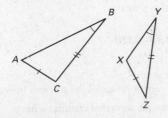

Problem Solving

19. Each individual hexagon is regular, so all of the sides are congruent in each hexagon. Because one length of a hexagon is equal to one length of another hexagon (by the picture), all of the lengths of the hexagons are congruent. Each hexagon is regular, so all of the angles are congruent. All of the hexagons are congruent because their corresponding sides and angles are congruent.

20. The red triangles in the kite are congruent by Side-Angle-Side. You know two sides are 5 inches. The other side is shared so it is the same measure for both triangles. The angle in between is the same because the lines are perpendicular.

21. The red triangles in the kite are congruent by Side-Side-Side. They share a side, there is a pair of 7-foot sides and a pair of 4-foot sides.

22. *Sample answer:* Equality and congruent mean something is exactly the same about two figures. They are different because equality means "the same value" and congruence means "the same size."

23. The sum of the angle measures of a pentagon is 540°.

$$90° + 90° + m\angle X + m\angle X + 105° = 540°$$
$$285° + 2m\angle X = 540°$$
$$2m\angle X = 255°$$
$$m\angle X = 127.5°$$

Because $m\angle 1 = m\angle X$, $m\angle 1 = 127.5°$.

24. *Sample answer:* You have to show SSS, SAS, or ASA to show two triangles are congruent. In each case, you must have at least 3 pairs of congruent corresponding parts to establish congruence. If two triangles are congruent, then 3 pairs of sides are congruent and 3 pairs of angles are congruent. So a total of 6 pairs of corresponding parts are congruent.

25. B;

$\overline{CB}$ is not congruent to $\overline{AD}$.

26. $\triangle ABC \cong \triangle AED$ by SAS. Then $\overline{AC} \cong \overline{AD}$ because they are corresponding parts in the congruent triangles, $\triangle ACD$ is isosceles because it has two congruent sides.

27. The triangles are not necessarily congruent because SSS, SAS, or ASA do not apply. So, you cannot conclude another pair of congruent angles are present.

28. *Sample answer:*

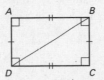

$\overline{AD} \cong \overline{CB}$, $\angle A \cong \angle C$, and $\overline{AB} \cong \overline{CD}$. So, $\triangle ADB \cong \triangle CBD$ by SAS.

29. *Sample answer:* You can show the triangles are congruent if you know that the third sides of the two triangles are congruent or if you know that the angles between the two 7 foot sides in each triangle are congruent.

30. a.

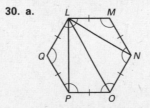

$\triangle LMN \cong \triangle LQP$ by SAS.

b. Corresponding congruent angles: $\angle Q$ and $\angle M$, $\angle MLN$ and $\angle QLP$, $\angle MNL$ and $\angle QPL$

Corresponding congruent sides: $\overline{LM}$ and $\overline{LQ}$, $\overline{LN}$ and $\overline{LP}$, $\overline{MN}$ and $\overline{QP}$

c. $\triangle LPO \cong \triangle LNO$ by SSS.

31. The congruent corresponding parts in the two triangles are $\overline{AC} \cong \overline{TD}$, $\overline{TA} \cong \overline{AT}$, and $\angle CAT \cong \angle DTA$. So, $\triangle ACT \cong \triangle TDA$ by SAS.

Chapter 8, continued

Mixed Review

32–35.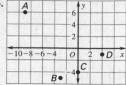

36. There are 20 numbers that are multiples of 5.

$$P(5) = \frac{20}{100} = \frac{1}{5}$$

The probability the number is a multiple of 5 is $\frac{1}{5}$.

37. 1.25% of 400 = $0.0125 \times 400 = 5$

5 is 1.25% of 400.

38. 65% of 91 = $0.65 \times 91 = 59.15$

59.15 is 65% of 91.

39. The sum of the angle measures of a quadrilateral is 360°.

$$109° + 72° + 76° + x° = 360°$$
$$257 + x = 360$$
$$x = 103$$

The value of x is 103.

40. The sum of the angle measures of a pentagon is 540°.

$$101° + 90° + 90° + 101° + x° = 540°$$
$$382 + x = 540$$
$$x = 158$$

The value of x is 158.

41. C;

$$\frac{(n-2) \cdot 180°}{n} = \frac{(18-2) \cdot 180°}{18} = 160°$$

Lesson 8.6

8.6 Guided Practice (pp. 433–435)

1. The figure is *not* a reflecion.

2.

Original		Image
(x, y)	$\longrightarrow$	$(-x, y)$
$J(0, 1)$	$\longrightarrow$	$J'(0, 1)$
$K(0, 4)$	$\longrightarrow$	$K'(0, 4)$
$L(5, 2)$	$\longrightarrow$	$L'(-5, 2)$

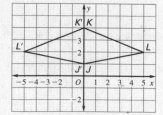

3.

Original		Image
(x, y)	$\longrightarrow$	$(x, -y)$
$S(-3, 2)$	$\longrightarrow$	$S'(-3, -2)$
$T(-1, 4)$	$\longrightarrow$	$T'(-1, -4)$
$U(-4, 5)$	$\longrightarrow$	$U'(-4, -5)$
$V(-5, 3)$	$\longrightarrow$	$V'(-5, -3)$

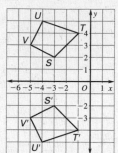

4.

A square has 4 lines of symmetry. A rhombus that is not a square has 2 lines of symmetry.

8.6 Exercises (pp. 435–438)

Skill Practice

1. A *reflection* creates a mirror image of the original figure.

2. A *transformation* is an operation that changes a figure into another figure.

3. The figure is *not* a reflection.

4. The figure is a reflection.

5. The figure is *not* a reflection.

6.

Original		Image
(x, y)	$\longrightarrow$	$(x, -y)$
$A(3, 6)$	$\longrightarrow$	$A'(3, -6)$
$B(6, 3)$	$\longrightarrow$	$B'(6, -3)$
$C(5, 0)$	$\longrightarrow$	$C'(5, 0)$
$D(1, 1)$	$\longrightarrow$	$D'(1, -1)$

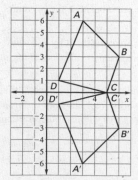

Chapter 8, *continued*

7.

Original		Image
(x, y)	$\longrightarrow$	$(x, -y)$
$Q(-1, 3)$	$\longrightarrow$	$Q'(-1, -3)$
$R(-3, 6)$	$\longrightarrow$	$R'(-3, -6)$
$S(-6, 4)$	$\longrightarrow$	$S'(-6, -4)$
$T(-6, 0)$	$\longrightarrow$	$T'(-6, 0)$

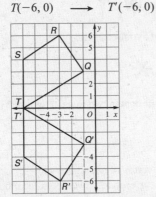

8.

Original		Image
(x, y)	$\longrightarrow$	$(-x, y)$
$B(2, -1)$	$\longrightarrow$	$B'(-2, -1)$
$C(5, 0)$	$\longrightarrow$	$C'(-5, 0)$
$D(7, -2)$	$\longrightarrow$	$D'(-7, -2)$
$E(0, -6)$	$\longrightarrow$	$E'(0, -6)$

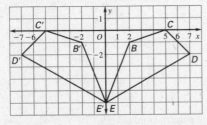

9. The error is that the coordinates of the image are those for a reflection in the the *y*-axis, not the *x*-axis.

Original		Image
(x, y)	$\longrightarrow$	$(x, -y)$
$A(4, 5)$	$\longrightarrow$	$A'(4, -5)$
$B(2, 0)$	$\longrightarrow$	$B'(2, 0)$
$C(6, 2)$	$\longrightarrow$	$C'(6, -2)$

10. C;

Figure C is a reflection of figure D in the *x*-axis.

11. D;

Figure A has 4 lines of symmetry.

12.

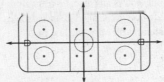

The figure has 2 lines of symmetry.

13.

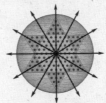

The figure has 6 lines of symmetry.

14.

The figure has 1 line of symmetry.

15. *Sample answer:* The polygon is an obtuse scalene triangle. There is more than one possible polygon, any scalene triangle has no lines of symmetry.

16. *Sample answer:* The polygon is an equilateral triangle. This is the only possible polygon that has 3 lines of symmetry.

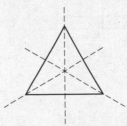

17. *Sample answer:* The polygon is a rectangle. There is one other possible polygon, a rhombus is a quadrilateral with exactly two lines of symmetry.

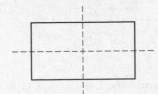

18. *Sample answer:* The polygon is an isosceles trapezoid. There are other possible polygons, any kite or isosceles trapezoid is a quadrilateral with only one line of symmetry.

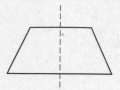

19.

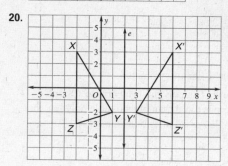

20.

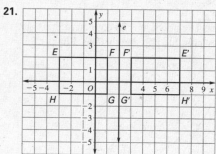

21.

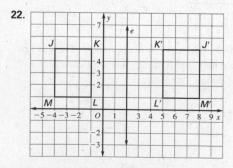

22.

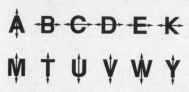

23. Letters with no line of symmetry: F, G, J, L, N, P, Q, R, S, Z

F G J L N

P Q R S Z

Letters with one line of symmetry: A, B, C, D, E, K, M, T, U, V, W, Y

A B C D E K

M T U V W Y

Letters with two lines of symmetry: H, I, O, X

H I O X

No capital letters have more than two lines of symmetry.

Problem Solving

24. Check work.

25. *Sample answer:* If each vertex of one figure with coordinates (x, y) has a corresponding vertex in the other figure with coordinates $(-x, y)$, then the figures are reflections of each other in the y-axis.

26. D;

Reflect in x-axis

$(x, y) \longrightarrow (x, -y)$

$R(-4, 3) \longrightarrow R'(-4, -3)$

27. *Sample answer:*

More than one pattern is possible.

28. a–b.

Sides	3	4	5
Regular Polygon			
Lines of Symmetry	3	4	5

Sides	6	8
Regular Polygon		
Lines of Symmetry	6	8

c. The number of sides of a regular polygon is equal to the number of lines of symmetry.

29. *Sample answer:*

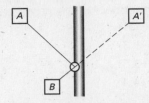

This method can be used in playing pool, where you have to bounce the cue ball against a wall in order to hit the ball into a pocket.

30. *Sample answer:* TOT, MOM, BIB

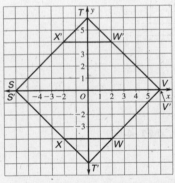

31.

Original		Image
(x, y)	$\longrightarrow$	$(x, -y)$
$S(-6, 0)$	$\longrightarrow$	$S'(-6, 0)$
$T(0, 6)$	$\longrightarrow$	$T'(0, -6)$
$V(6, 0)$	$\longrightarrow$	$V'(6, 0)$
$W(2, -4)$	$\longrightarrow$	$W'(2, 4)$
$X(-2, -4)$	$\longrightarrow$	$X'(-2, 4)$

The figure has only 1 line of symmetry, the *y*-axis.

32. a–b.

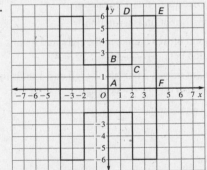

ABCDEF is a hexagon.

c. The figure is a polygon with 12 sides, a 12-gon.

33. Check student's graphs.

$\triangle ABC \cong \triangle EFG$. The fold line is the line $y = x$.

If $\triangle ABC$ is the original and $\triangle EFG$ is the image, the transformation is $(x, y) \longrightarrow (y, x)$.

34.

Original		2nd Polygon		3rd Polygon
(x, y)	$\longrightarrow$	$(x, -y)$	$\longrightarrow$	$(-x, y)$
$A(1, -2)$	$\longrightarrow$	$A'(1, 2)$	$\longrightarrow$	$A''(-1, 2)$
$B(5, -1)$	$\longrightarrow$	$B'(5, 1)$	$\longrightarrow$	$B''(-5, 1)$
$C(8, -4)$	$\longrightarrow$	$C'(8, 4)$	$\longrightarrow$	$C''(-8, 4)$
$D(7, -7)$	$\longrightarrow$	$D'(7, 7)$	$\longrightarrow$	$D''(-7, 7)$
$E(4, -8)$	$\longrightarrow$	$E'(4, 8)$	$\longrightarrow$	$E''(-4, 8)$

The third polygon is not a reflection of the original polygon. There is no single line of reflection that will reflect the original to the third.

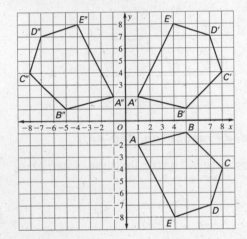

Mixed Review

35. $(x + 1, y + 2) = (-2 + 1, 3 + 2) = (-1, 5)$

36. $(x - 2, y + 8) = (-2 - 2, 3 + 8) = (-4, 11)$

37. $(x - 3, y - 3) = (-2 - 3, 3 - 3) = (-5, 0)$

The points plotted in a coordinate plane for Exercises 35–37.

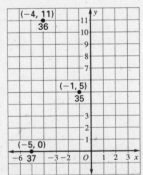

38. 0.8% of 500 = 0.008 × 500 = 4

4 is 0.8% of 500.

Chapter 8, continued

39. $756 = p\%$ of 270

   $756 = p(270)$

   $\dfrac{756}{270} = p$

   $2.8 = p$

   $280\% = p\%$

   756 is 280% of 270.

40. B;

   $(n - 2) \cdot 180° = (9 - 2) \cdot 180° = 7 \cdot 180° = 1260°$

   The sum of the angle measures of a 9-gon is 1260°.

Brain Game (p. 438)

"… the eye sees not itself but by reflection …"

Lesson 8.7

Activity (p. 439)

Steps 1–2.

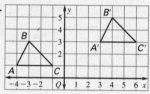

Step 3. $(x, y) \longrightarrow (x + 7, y + 2)$

8.7 Guided Practice (pp. 440–441)

1. Each point moves 5 units to the left and 4 units down,
$(x, y) \longrightarrow (x - 5, y - 4)$.

2.
Original		Solution
(x, y)	$\longrightarrow$	$(y, -x)$
$A(1, 1)$	$\longrightarrow$	$A'(1, -1)$
$B(3, 1)$	$\longrightarrow$	$B'(1, -3)$
$C(3, 3)$	$\longrightarrow$	$C'(3, -3)$
$D(1, 4)$	$\longrightarrow$	$D'(4, -1)$

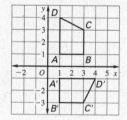

3.
Original		Solution
(x, y)	$\longrightarrow$	$(-y, x)$
$A(1, 1)$	$\longrightarrow$	$A'(-1, 1)$
$B(3, 1)$	$\longrightarrow$	$B'(-1, 3)$
$C(3, 3)$	$\longrightarrow$	$C'(-3, 3)$
$D(1, 4)$	$\longrightarrow$	$D'(-4, 1)$

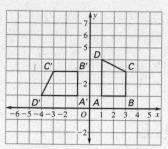

4.
Original		Solution
(x, y)	$\longrightarrow$	$(-x, -y)$
$A(1, 1)$	$\longrightarrow$	$A'(-1, -1)$
$B(3, 1)$	$\longrightarrow$	$B'(-3, -1)$
$C(3, 3)$	$\longrightarrow$	$C'(-3, -3)$
$D(1, 4)$	$\longrightarrow$	$D'(-1, -4)$

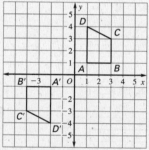

8.7 Exercises (pp. 441–444)

Skill Practice

1. The transformation is a reflection.

2. The transformation is a translation.

3. The transformation is a rotation.

4. Each point moves 5 units to the right and 4 units up. The translation is $(x, y) \longrightarrow (x + 5, y + 4)$.

5. Each point moves 5 units to the left and 3 units up. The translation is $(x, y) \longrightarrow (x - 5, y + 3)$.

6.

Original		Image
(x, y)	$\longrightarrow$	$(x - 5, y + 1)$
$P(0, -1)$	$\longrightarrow$	$P'(-5, 0)$
$Q(3, -1)$	$\longrightarrow$	$Q'(-2, 0)$
$R(5, -3)$	$\longrightarrow$	$R'(0, -2)$

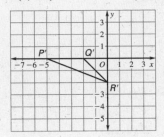

7.

Original		Image
(x, y)	$\longrightarrow$	$(x + 1, y - 6)$
$L(4, 2)$	$\longrightarrow$	$L'(5, -4)$
$M(0, 3)$	$\longrightarrow$	$M'(1, -3)$
$N(1, 1)$	$\longrightarrow$	$N'(2, -5)$

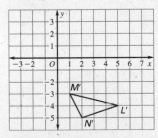

8. *Sample answer:* The triangle was rotated counter clockwise, instead of clockwise. To rotate $\triangle JKL$ 90° clockwise, switch the coordinates and then multiply the new y–coordinate by -1.

(x, y)	$\longrightarrow$	$(y, -x)$
$J(-4, -3)$	$\longrightarrow$	$J'(-3, 4)$
$K(-2, 0)$	$\longrightarrow$	$K'(0, 2)$
$L(1, 2)$	$\longrightarrow$	$L'(2, -1)$

The vertices of $\triangle J'K'L'$ should be $J'(-3, 4)$, $K'(0, 2)$, and $L'(2, -1)$.

9. a–c.

Original		Image
(x, y)	$\longrightarrow$	$(-y, x)$
$R(-2, -1)$	$\longrightarrow$	$R'(1, -2)$
$S(-5, -2)$	$\longrightarrow$	$S'(2, -5)$
$T(-4, 2)$	$\longrightarrow$	$T'(-2, -4)$

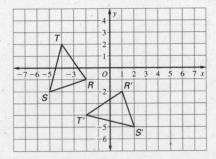

10. 180° rotation:

Original		Image
(x, y)	$\longrightarrow$	$(-x, -y)$
$R(-2, -1)$	$\longrightarrow$	$R'(2, 1)$
$S(-5, -2)$	$\longrightarrow$	$S'(5, 2)$
$T(-4, 2)$	$\longrightarrow$	$T'(4, -2)$

90° clockwise rotation:

Original		Image
(x, y)	$\longrightarrow$	$(y, -x)$
$R(-2, -1)$	$\longrightarrow$	$R''(-1, 2)$
$S(-5, -2)$	$\longrightarrow$	$S''(-2, 5)$
$T(-4, 2)$	$\longrightarrow$	$T''(2, 4)$

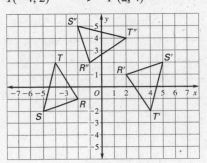

11.

Original		Image
(x, y)	$\longrightarrow$	$(-x, -y)$
$L(2, 0)$	$\longrightarrow$	$L'(-2, 0)$
$M(2, 3)$	$\longrightarrow$	$M'(-2, -3)$
$N(6, 0)$	$\longrightarrow$	$N'(-6, 0)$

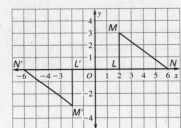

12.

Original		Image
(x, y)	$\longrightarrow$	$(-y, x)$
$L(2, 0)$	$\longrightarrow$	$L'(0, 2)$
$M(2, 3)$	$\longrightarrow$	$M'(-3, 2)$
$N(6, 0)$	$\longrightarrow$	$N'(0, 6)$

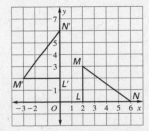

Chapter 8, continued

13.

Original		Image
(x, y)	$\longrightarrow$	$(x - 3, y - 4)$
$L(2, 0)$	$\longrightarrow$	$L'(-1, -4)$
$M(2, 3)$	$\longrightarrow$	$M'(-1, -1)$
$N(6, 0)$	$\longrightarrow$	$N'(3, -4)$

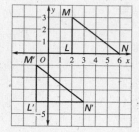

14.

Original		Image		Image
(x, y)	$\longrightarrow$	$(-x, -y)$	$\longrightarrow$	$(x + 1, y + 1)$
$L(2, 0)$	$\longrightarrow$	$L'(-2, 0)$	$\longrightarrow$	$L''(-1, 1)$
$M(2, 3)$	$\longrightarrow$	$M'(-2, -3)$	$\longrightarrow$	$M''(-1, -2)$
$N(6, 0)$	$\longrightarrow$	$N'(-6, 0)$	$\longrightarrow$	$N''(-5, 1)$

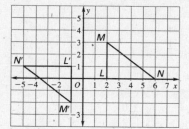

15.

Original		Image		Image
(x, y)	$\longrightarrow$	$(x + 3, y)$	$\longrightarrow$	$(-(x + 3), -y)$
$L(2, 0)$			$\longrightarrow$	$L'(-5, 0)$
$M(2, 3)$			$\longrightarrow$	$M'(-5, -3)$
$N(6, 0)$			$\longrightarrow$	$N'(-9, 0)$

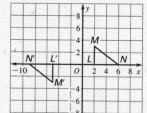

16.

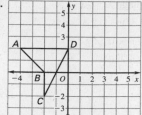

a.

(x, y)	$\longrightarrow$	$(x, -y)$
$A(-4, 2)$	$\longrightarrow$	$A'(-4, -2)$
$B(-2, 0)$	$\longrightarrow$	$B'(-2, 0)$
$C(-2, -2)$	$\longrightarrow$	$C'(-2, 2)$
$D(0, 2)$	$\longrightarrow$	$D'(0, -2)$

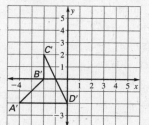

b.

(x, y)	$\longrightarrow$	$(x + 4, y)$
$A'(-4, -2)$	$\longrightarrow$	$A''(0, -2)$
$B'(-2, 0)$	$\longrightarrow$	$B''(2, 0)$
$C'(-2, 2)$	$\longrightarrow$	$C''(2, 2)$
$D'(0, -2)$	$\longrightarrow$	$D''(4, -2)$

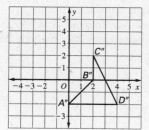

c.

(x, y)	$\longrightarrow$	$(-x, -y)$
$A''(0, -2)$	$\longrightarrow$	$A'''(0, 2)$
$B''(2, 0)$	$\longrightarrow$	$B'''(-2, 0)$
$C''(2, 2)$	$\longrightarrow$	$C'''(-2, -2)$
$D''(4, -2)$	$\longrightarrow$	$D'''(-4, 2)$

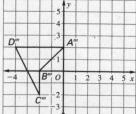

Chapter 8, *continued*

17. *Blue* to *red* translation: $(x, y) \longrightarrow (x + 4, y - 4)$;
reflection: in line $y = x$; rotation: $180°$;

Blue to red: (1) Reflect in x-axis then reflect in y-axis;
(2) Make two $90°$ clockwise rotations; (3) Make two $90°$ counterclockwise rotations.

18. *Sample answer:* A $180°$ rotation is $(x, y) \longrightarrow (-x, -y)$ and a $90°$ clockwise rotation is $(x, y) \longrightarrow (y, -x)$. So applying both rotations is $(x, y) \longrightarrow (-x, -y) \longrightarrow (-y, x)$, which is the same as a $90°$ counterclockwise rotation.

Problem Solving

19. $360 \div 8 = 45$

A rotation of $45°$, $2(45) = 90°$, $3(45) = 135°$, $4(45) = 180°$, $5(45) = 225°$, $6(45) = 270°$, $7(45) = 315°$, in the clockwise or counter clockwise direction, will produce an image identical in shape to the original figure.

20. The transformation is a translation.

21. The transformation is a reflection.

22. The transformation is a rotation.

23. The transformation is a translation.

24. The transformation is a reflection.

25. The transformation is a rotation.

26. *Sample answer:* Assume x and y represent positive numbers, and point A could have coordinates $(-x, y)$. After a $180°$ rotation, $A(-x, y) \longrightarrow A'(x, -y)$, and point A' lies in Quadrant IV. Point B could have coordinates $(x, -y)$. After a $90°$ clockwise rotation, $B(x, -y) \longrightarrow B'(-y, -x)$, and point B' lies in Quandrat III.

27. Each image has rotational symmetry. The least angle of rotation can be found by dividing $360°$ by the number of lines of symmetry.

The least angle of symmetry in the first image is $360 \div 6 = 60°$.

The least angle of symmetry in the second image is $360 \div 5 = 72°$.

The least angle of symmetry in the third image is $360 \div 9 = 40°$.

28. *Sample answer:* The first image would be the same because it has a horizontal line of symmetry.

The second and third image would not be the same because they do not have a horizontal line of symmetry.

29. *Sample answer:* Yes, a figure can have rotational symmetry without having line symmetry.

For example, the origami pinwheel in Exercise 19 has rotational symmetry but not line symmetry.

30. B;

Figure 10

90° clockwise rotation:

31. *Sample answer:*

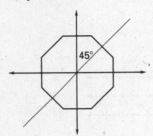

32.

Original	Image	Image
$(x, y) \longrightarrow$	$(y, -x) \longrightarrow$	$(-y, -x)$
$(-1, 2)$		$(-2, 1)$
$(-2, 1)$		$(-1, 2)$
$(-3, 2)$		$(-2, 3)$
$(-4, 1)$		$(-1, 4)$
$(-4, 4)$		$(-4, 4)$
$(-3, 3)$		$(-3, 3)$
$(-2, 4)$		$(-4, 2)$
$(-1, 3)$		$(-3, 1)$

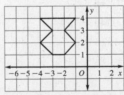

The rule for the doubled transformation performed is $(x, y) \longrightarrow (y, -x)$.

Sample answer: The coordinates are switched and the opposites are taken. This is because the rotation is $(x, y) \longrightarrow (y, -x)$, and then the reflection is $(y, -x) \longrightarrow (-y, -x)$.

Chapter 8, continued

33. *Sample answer:* The single transformation is 90° counterclockwise, $(x, y) \longrightarrow (-y, x)$. The first reflection is $(x, y) \longrightarrow (y, x)$ and the reflection in the y-axis is $(x, y) \longrightarrow (-x, y)$. combining the two is $(x, y) \longrightarrow (y, x) \longrightarrow (-y, x)$;

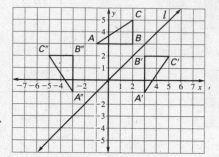

34. Work backwards.

Image			Original
$(-y, -x) \longrightarrow$	$(y, -x)$	$\longrightarrow$	(x, y)
$(1, 2)$	$\longrightarrow$		$(-2, -1)$
$(3, 3)$	$\longrightarrow$		$(-3, -3)$
$(3, -1)$	$\longrightarrow$		$(1, -3)$

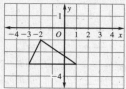

Mixed Review

35. $\dfrac{a}{25} = \dfrac{24}{200}$

$200a = 600$

$a = 3$

36. $\dfrac{32}{9} = \dfrac{c}{108}$

$3456 = 9c$

$384 = c$

37. $\dfrac{7}{60} = \dfrac{154}{d}$

$9240 = 7d$

$1320 = d$

38. $x° + 90° + 40.5° = 180°$

$x + 130.5 = 180$

$x = 49.5$

The value of x is 49.5. The triangle has one right angle, so it is a right triangle.

39. $x° + 27° + 35° = 180°$

$x + 62 = 180$

$x = 118$

The value of x is 118. The triangle has one obtuse angle, so it is an obtuse triangle.

40. $x° + 50.2° + 55° = 180°$

$x + 105.2 = 180$

$x = 74.8$

The value of x is 74.8. The triangle has three acute angles, so it is an acute triangle.

41. A;

Mean: $\dfrac{28 + 39 + 39 + 43 + 45 + 45 + 45 + 48}{8} = \dfrac{332}{8} = 41.5$

8.7 Extension (p. 446)

1. The figure does not tessellate.

2. The figure tessellates.

3. The figure does not tessellate.

4. The figure was rotated 90° counterclockwise each time.

5.

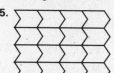

6. *Sample answer:*

The tessellation was created by a translation of the polygon.

7. *Sample answer:*

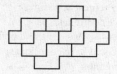

The tessellation was created by a translation of the polygon.

8. *Sample answer:*

The tessellation was created by a reflection and translation of the polygon.

9. *Sample answer:*

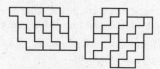

10. *Sample answer:*

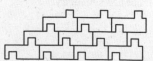

11. *Sample answer:*

Chapter 8, continued

Lesson 8.8

8.8 Guided Practice (pp. 448–449)

1. Rectangles A and E are similar.

2. $\dfrac{AB}{FG} = \dfrac{AD}{FJ}$

   $\dfrac{8}{4} = \dfrac{16}{x}$

   $8x = 64$

   $x = 8$

   The value of x is 8 meters.

3. $\dfrac{x \text{ feet}}{6 \text{ feet}} = \dfrac{18 \text{ feet}}{9 \text{ feet}}$

   $x = 12$

   The tree is 12 feet tall.

   Check: $\dfrac{12}{6} = \dfrac{18}{9} = 2$ ✓

   The answer is reasonable.

4. Scale factor of 2:

Original		Image
(x, y)	$\longrightarrow$	$(2x, 2y)$
$R(1, 1)$	$\longrightarrow$	$R'(2, 2)$
$S(3, 2)$	$\longrightarrow$	$S'(6, 4)$
$T(2, 3)$	$\longrightarrow$	$T'(4, 6)$

   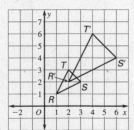

8.8 Exercises (pp. 450–454)

Skill Practice

1. The *scale factor* of a dilation is the ratio of corresponding side lengths.

2. A polygon and its image after dilation are always *similar polygons*.

3. The corrsponding angles are congruent.

   $\dfrac{25 \text{ ft}}{10 \text{ ft}} = \dfrac{25 \text{ ft}}{10 \text{ ft}} = \dfrac{25 \text{ ft}}{10 \text{ ft}}$

   The corresponding sides are proportional. So, the figures are similar.

4. The corresponding angles are congruent.

   $\dfrac{7.5 \text{ m}}{3 \text{ m}} = \dfrac{5 \text{ m}}{2 \text{ m}}$

   The corresponding sides are proportional. So, the figures are similar.

5. The corresponding angles are congruent.

   $\dfrac{10}{5} = \dfrac{8}{4} = \dfrac{6}{3}$

   The corresponding sides are proportional. So, the figures are similar.

6. The corresponding angles are congruent.

   $\dfrac{4}{4} = \dfrac{1}{1}$ $\dfrac{5}{5} = \dfrac{1}{1}$

   $\dfrac{6}{4} = \dfrac{3}{2}$ $\dfrac{9}{7}$

   The corresponding sides are not proportional.

   $\dfrac{1}{1} \neq \dfrac{3}{2} \neq \dfrac{9}{7}$

   So, the figures are not similar.

7. $\dfrac{DE}{AB} = \dfrac{DF}{AC}$

   $\dfrac{6}{x} = \dfrac{9}{6}$

   $36 = 9x$

   $4 = x$

   The value of x is 4 inches.

8. $m\angle K = m\angle G = 40°$

   The value of $x°$ is 40°.

9. $\dfrac{DF}{JL} = \dfrac{FG}{LK}$

   $\dfrac{3}{x} = \dfrac{4}{3}$

   $9 = 4x$

   $\dfrac{9}{4} = x$

   $2\dfrac{1}{4} = x$

   The value of x is $2\dfrac{1}{4}$ feet.

10. $\dfrac{NP}{ST} = \dfrac{MN}{RS}$

    $\dfrac{2}{x} = \dfrac{6}{9}$

    $18 = 6x$

    $3 = x$

    The value of x is 3 inches.

Chapter 8, continued

11. Original   Image

$(x, y) \longrightarrow (3x, 3y)$

$W(2, 2) \longrightarrow W'(6, 6)$

$X(0, 4) \longrightarrow X'(0, 12)$

$Y(4, 6) \longrightarrow Y'(12, 18)$

$Z(6, 0) \longrightarrow Z'(18, 0)$

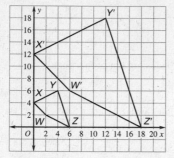

12. Original   Image

$(x, y) \longrightarrow \left(\frac{1}{2}x, \frac{1}{2}y\right)$

$B(0, -2) \longrightarrow B'(0, -1)$

$C(4, 2) \longrightarrow C'(2, 1)$

$D(2, 6) \longrightarrow D'(1, 3)$

$E(-2, 6) \longrightarrow E'(-1, 3)$

$F(-4, 2) \longrightarrow F'(-2, 1)$

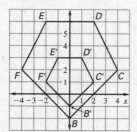

13. Original   Image

$(x, y) \longrightarrow \left(\frac{3}{4}x, \frac{3}{4}y\right)$

$R(8, 8) \longrightarrow R'(6, 6)$

$S(-4, 4) \longrightarrow S'(-3, 3)$

$T(-4, -4) \longrightarrow T'(-3, -3)$

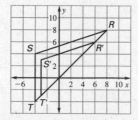

14. Original   Image

$(x, y) \longrightarrow (4x, 4y)$

$L(2, -2) \longrightarrow L'(8, -8)$

$M(4, 2) \longrightarrow M'(16, 8)$

$N(-3, 2) \longrightarrow N'(-12, 8)$

$P(-1, -2) \longrightarrow P'(-4, -8)$

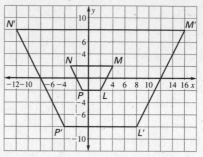

15. Original   Image

$(x, y) \longrightarrow (1.5x, 1.5y)$

$G(-2, -6) \longrightarrow G'(-3, -9)$

$H(-8, -8) \longrightarrow H'(-12, -12)$

$J(-6, -2) \longrightarrow J'(-9, -3)$

$K(0, 0) \longrightarrow K'(0, 0)$

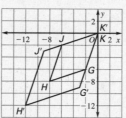

16. Original   Image

$(x, y) \qquad (1.75x, 1.75y)$

$K(24, 6) \qquad K'(42, 10.5)$

$L(8, 10) \qquad L'(14, 17.5)$

$M(8, 0) \qquad M'(14, 0)$

$N(0, 18) \qquad N'(0, 31.5)$

$P(20, 22) \qquad P'(35, 38.5)$

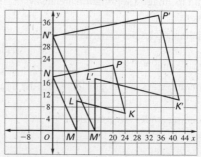

17. *Sample answer:*

The error is that the student did not multiply both coordinates by 3.

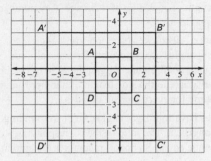

18. D;

Add point Q on $\overline{AB}$, point R on $\overline{BC}$, point S on $\overline{AC}$, where $BQ = QA$, $BR = RC$, and $AS = SC$.

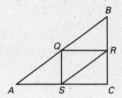

$BA = 2 \cdot ED$, $BC = 2 \cdot EF$, $AC = 2 \cdot DF$, $\angle B \cong \angle E$, $\angle A \cong \angle D$, and $\angle C \cong \angle F$ because $\triangle ABC \sim \triangle DEF$ by a scale factor of $\frac{1}{2}$.

$\triangle BQR \cong \triangle QAS \cong \triangle RSC \cong \triangle EDF$ by SAS

$\triangle BQR \cong \triangle SRQ$ by AAA

Area of $\triangle ABC$ = Area of $\triangle BQR$ + Area of $\triangle QAS$
$\qquad\qquad$ + Area of $\triangle SRQ$ + Area of $\triangle RSC$

$\qquad\qquad$ = 4(Area of $\triangle EDF$)

Therefore, $\dfrac{\text{Area of } \triangle EDF}{\text{Area of } \triangle ABC} = \dfrac{1}{4}$.

The area of $\triangle DEF$ is $\frac{1}{4}$ as great as the area of $\triangle ABC$.

19. $A(4, 6) \longrightarrow D\left(4 \cdot \frac{1}{2} = 2, 6 \cdot \frac{1}{2} = 3\right)$

$B(8, 8) \longrightarrow E\left(8 \cdot \frac{1}{2} = 4, 8 \cdot \frac{1}{2} = 4\right)$

$C(12, 4) \longrightarrow F\left(12 \cdot \frac{1}{2} = 6, 4 \cdot \frac{1}{2} = 2\right)$

$(x, y) \longrightarrow \left(\frac{1}{2}x, \frac{1}{2}y\right)$

The scale factor is $\frac{1}{2}$.

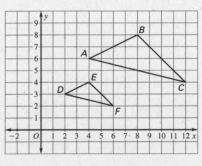

20.
$$G(1, 4) \longrightarrow K(1 \cdot 3 = 3, 4 \cdot 3 = 12)$$
$$H(6, 4) \longrightarrow L(6 \cdot 3 = 18, 4 \cdot 3 = 12)$$
$$I(6, 1) \longrightarrow M(6 \cdot 3 = 18, 1 \cdot 3 = 3)$$
$$J(1, 1) \longrightarrow N(1 \cdot 3 = 3, 1 \cdot 3 = 3)$$
$$(x, y) \longrightarrow (3x, 3y)$$

The scale factor is 3.

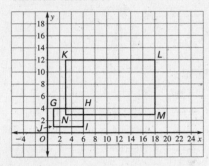

21.
$P(4, 8)$	$T(4 \cdot 2 = 8, 8 \cdot 2 = 16)$
$Q(8, 8)$	$U(8 \cdot 2 = 16, 8 \cdot 2 = 16)$
$R(8, 2)$	$V(8 \cdot 2 = 16, 2 \cdot 2 = 4)$
$S(4, 2)$	$W(4 \cdot 2 = 8, 2 \cdot 2 = 4)$

The scale factor is 2.

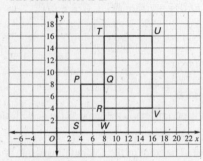

22. $\dfrac{8 \text{ m}}{4 \text{ m}} = \dfrac{6 \text{ m}}{3 \text{ m}} = 2$

$\triangle ACE \sim \triangle ABF$

The scale factor is 2.

23. $\dfrac{y}{4.5} = \dfrac{3}{2}$

$\quad 2y = 13.5$

$\quad y = 6.75$

The value of y is 6.75 centimeters.

$m\angle A + 96° + 90° + 150° + m\angle D = 540°$

$m\angle A + 96° + 90° + 150° + m\angle J = 540°$

$m\angle A + 96° + 90° + 150° + 150° = 540°$

$\qquad\qquad\quad m\angle A + 486 = 540°$

$\qquad\qquad\qquad\qquad m\angle A = 54°$

$m\angle A = m\angle F$, so $x = 54$.

24. $2x = 88$

$\quad\ x = 44$

The hexagon has 6 sides, so $n = 6$.

$(n - 2) \cdot 180° = (6 - 2) \cdot 180° = 720°$

$y° + y° + 88° + y° + y° + 88° = 720°$

$\qquad\qquad\qquad 4y + 176 = 720$

$\qquad\qquad\qquad\qquad\ 4y = 544$

$\qquad\qquad\qquad\qquad\ \ y = 136$

The values of x and y are 44 and 136.

Problem Solving

25. $A(-1, 2) \quad\longrightarrow\quad E(-1 \cdot 4 = -4, 2 \cdot 4 = 8)$

$\quad B(3, 2) \quad\longrightarrow\quad F(3 \cdot 4 = 12, 2 \cdot 4 = 8)$

$\quad C(3, -1) \quad\longrightarrow\quad G(3 \cdot 4 = 12, -1 \cdot 4 = -4)$

$\quad D(-1, -1) \quad\longrightarrow\quad H(-1 \cdot 4 = 4, -1 \cdot 4 = -4)$

$\quad (x, y) \quad\longrightarrow\quad (4x, 4y)$

The scale factor is 4.

Perimeter of $ABCD = AB + BC + CD + AD$

$\qquad\qquad\qquad\quad = 4 + 3 + 4 + 3$

$\qquad\qquad\qquad\quad = 14$ units

Perimeter of $EFGH = EF + FG + GH + EH$

$\qquad\qquad\qquad\quad = 16 + 12 + 16 + 12$

$\qquad\qquad\qquad\quad = 56$ units

Compare perimeters.

$\dfrac{\text{perimeter of } EFGH}{\text{perimeter of } ABCD} = \dfrac{56}{14} = 4$

The ratio of the perimeters is the same as the scale factor.

26. The diagram is not drawn to scale.

Sample answer: The front of the colored illustration is taller and more narrow than the assembly diagram.

27. D;

$\dfrac{x \text{ ft}}{5 \text{ ft}} = \dfrac{15 \text{ ft}}{3 \text{ ft}}$

$\quad 3x = 75$

$\quad\ \ x = 25$

The height of the flagpole is 25 feet.

28. *Sample answer:* The estimation is reasonable. The scale factor is $\dfrac{2.8}{1.4} = 2$. The length of $\overline{AB}$ is about 4 meters, so the length of $\overline{EF}$ is about $2 \cdot 4 = 8$ meters.

29. Two triangles that are congruent are also similar.

Sample answer: Congruent means same size and same shape. If they have same shape, they are similar.

30. $\dfrac{x \text{ ft}}{5.5 \text{ ft}} = \dfrac{140 \text{ ft}}{28 \text{ ft}}$

$\quad 28x = 770$

$\qquad x = 27.5$

The sand castle is about 27.5 feet tall.

31. The image will be identical to the original polygon.

Sample answer: If the scale factor is 1, then the length of each side of the original polygon is multiplied by 1 to find the length of each side of its image. Any number times 1 is equal to itself.

32. *Sample answer:* All squares have four right angles, so corresponding angles are congruent. Because all four sides of a square are the same length, the ratio of the side length of one square to the side length of another square will be the same for every pairing of sides.

All rectangles have four right angles, so corresponding angles are congruent. The ratio of the corresponding sides may not be equal. So not all rectangles are similar.

33. *Sample answer:* The area of $ABCD$ is 80 square inches, so $AD = 80 \div 10 = 8$ inches. The scale factor is $\dfrac{5}{10} = \dfrac{1}{2}$, so $WY = \dfrac{1}{2}$ and $AD = \dfrac{1}{2}(8) = 4$ inches. Then the area of $WXYZ$ is $(5 \text{ in.})(4 \text{ in.}) = 20$ square inches.

34. The scale factor is $\dfrac{30}{10} = 3$. So, the perimeter of $\triangle VWX$ is 3 times the perimeter of $\triangle RST$.

35. $\dfrac{100 \text{ mm}}{36 \text{ mm}} = \dfrac{25}{6}$

The scale factor is $\dfrac{25}{6}$.

36. *Sample answer:* $\angle M \cong \angle N$ and $\angle L \cong \angle O$ because they are alternate interior angles. $\angle MQL \cong \angle NQO$ because they are vertical angles. So, the corresponding angles are congruent.

$\dfrac{ML}{NO} = \dfrac{MQ}{NQ} = \dfrac{LQ}{OQ} = \dfrac{1}{2}$

The corresponding sides are proportional so the triangles are similar.

37. $ABDF \sim CDFH \sim EFHJ \sim GHJL \sim IJLK \sim LKMN \sim OKMP$. They are all similar because all of the angles are congruent right angles, and the sides of every rectangle are in the ratio $8 : 5$.

38. *Sample answer:* Using the formula for the area of a trapezoid. $ABCD$,

$\quad 51 = \dfrac{1}{2}x(7 + 10)$

$102 = 17x$

$\quad 6 = x.$

So $x = 6$ centimeters. The scale factor is $\dfrac{3.5}{7} = \dfrac{1}{2}$, so

$ST = \dfrac{1}{2}(6) = 3$ cm and

$UT = \dfrac{1}{2}(CD) = \dfrac{1}{2}(7 + 3) = 5$ cm.

$RSTU$ is a trapezoid, so its area is

$\dfrac{1}{2}(ST)(RS + UT) = \dfrac{1}{2}(3)(3.5 + 5) = 12.75$ square centimeters.

Chapter 8, continued

Mixed Review

39. $5^3 = 5 \cdot 5 \cdot 5 = 125$

40. $2^4 = 2 \cdot 2 \cdot 2 \cdot 2 = 16$

41. $0^2 = 0 \cdot 0 = 0$

42. $1^9 = 1 \cdot 1 \cdot 1 \cdot 1 \cdot 1 \cdot 1 \cdot 1 \cdot 1 \cdot 1 = 1$

43. Strategy: Make a List.

1st Scoop	2nd Scoop
1. Vanilla	Vanilla
2. Vanilla	Chocolate
3. Vanilla	Mint Chip
4. Vanilla	Cookie Crumble
5. Vanilla	Strawberry
6. Chocolate	Chocolate
7. Chocolate	Mint Chip
8. Chocolate	Cookie Crumble
9. Chocolate	Strawberry
10. Mint Chip	Mint Chip
11. Mint Chip	Cookie Crumble
12. Mint Chip	Strawberry
13. Cookie Crumble	Cookie Crumble
14. Cookie Crumble	Strawberry
15. Strawberry	Strawberry

There are 15 possibilities of 2 scoop ice cream cones.

Make a list to visually see all the different possibilities and to be able to count them.

44. B;

Original		Image
(x, y)	$\longrightarrow$	$(x, -y)$
$A(1, 4)$	$\longrightarrow$	$A'(1, -4)$
$B(3, 3)$	$\longrightarrow$	$B'(3, -3)$
$C(1, 1)$	$\longrightarrow$	$C'(1, -1)$

Quiz 8.5–8.8 (p. 454)

1. $m\angle B = m\angle E = x°$

$m\angle B + 62° + 34° = 180°$

$x° + 62° + 34° = 180°$

$x + 96 = 180$

$x = 84$

2. $\dfrac{6}{4} = \dfrac{x}{7}$

$42 = 4x$

$10.5 = x$

3. translation

4. reflection

5. rotation

6. translation

7.

Original		Image
(x, y)	$\longrightarrow$	$(4x, 4y)$
$A(1, 1)$	$\longrightarrow$	$A'(4, 4)$
$B(2, 3)$	$\longrightarrow$	$B'(8, 12)$
$C(3, 0)$	$\longrightarrow$	$C'(12, 0)$

Original		Image
(x, y)	$\longrightarrow$	$(x + 2, y - 3)$
$A'(4, 4)$	$\longrightarrow$	$A''(6, 1)$
$B'(8, 12)$	$\longrightarrow$	$B''(10, 9)$
$C'(12, 0)$	$\longrightarrow$	$C''(14, -3)$

Original		Image
(x, y)	$\longrightarrow$	$(-x, y)$
$A''(6, 1)$	$\longrightarrow$	$A'''(-6, 1)$
$B''(10, 9)$	$\longrightarrow$	$B'''(-10, 9)$
$C''(14, -3)$	$\longrightarrow$	$C'''(-14, -3)$

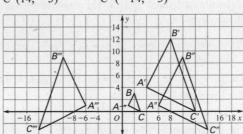

Mixed Review of Problem Solving (p. 455)

1. a. $\dfrac{1}{4}$ in. $\cdot\ 24 = 6$ in.

$\dfrac{1}{2}$ in. $\cdot\ 24 = 12$ in.

The full-sized license plate is 6 inches high and 12 inches wide.

b. Perimeter of model license plate $= 2\left(\dfrac{1}{4}\right) + 2\left(\dfrac{1}{2}\right) = 1\dfrac{1}{2}$ in.

c. Method 1: Use the scale factor: $1\dfrac{1}{2}$ inches is $\dfrac{1}{24}$ of the perimeter of the actual license plate, which is

$24\left(1\dfrac{1}{2}\right) = 36$ inches.

Method 2: Use the actual dimensions of the license plate to calculate the perimeter.
So, $P = 2\ell + 2w = 2(6) + 2(12) = 36$ inches.

d. Method 1: The license plate on the second car has a height of $\dfrac{1}{4}\left(\dfrac{1}{4}\right) = \dfrac{1}{16}$ inch and a width of $\dfrac{1}{4}\left(\dfrac{1}{2}\right) = \dfrac{1}{8}$ inch, so the perimeter is $2\left(\dfrac{1}{16} + \dfrac{1}{8}\right) = 2\left(\dfrac{3}{16}\right) = \dfrac{3}{8}$ inch.

Method 2: The perimeter is $\dfrac{1}{4}$ of the perimeter of the license plate of the first model, or $\dfrac{1}{4}\left(1\dfrac{1}{2}\right) = \dfrac{3}{8}$ inches.

Method 3: The scale factor for the second model is $\dfrac{1}{24}\left(\dfrac{1}{4}\right) = \dfrac{1}{96}$ of the actual car, so the perimeter of the license plate is $\dfrac{1}{96}(36) = \dfrac{3}{8}$ inch.

2. Check student's work.

3.

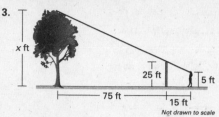

x ft

25 ft

5 ft

75 ft

15 ft

Not drawn to scale

$$\frac{x \text{ ft}}{25 \text{ ft}} = \frac{75 \text{ ft}}{15 \text{ ft}}$$

$$15x = 1875$$

$$x = 125$$

The tree is 125 feet tall.

4. *Sample answer:*

For each triangle, two sides are congruent sides of the rhombus and the third side is the diagonal, so the triangles are congruent by SSS. This explanation works for either diagonal.

5. a. Translate figure A by $(x, y) \longrightarrow (x + 4, y)$. Then rotate it 90° clockwise.

b. Rotate figure A by 90° clockwise. Then translate it by $(x, y) \longrightarrow (x, y - 4)$.

c. *Sample answer:*

The common point of rotation would be $(-2, -2)$. The point $(-2, 1)$ on the blue figure is 3 units vertically from $(-2, -2)$, and the corresponding point $(1, -2)$ on the red figure is 3 units horizontally from $(-2, -2)$. So the blue figure would transform to the red figure by a rotation of 90° clockwise, centered at $(-2, -2)$. The point would have to lie in Quadrant III.

Chapter 8 Review (pp. 456–460)

1. D

2. C

3. B

4. A

5. Two angles whose measures have a sum of 90° are *complementary* angles.

6. Two lines on the same plane that never intersect are *parallel*.

7. A *heptagon* is a polygon with seven sides.

8. A figure has *line symmetry* if one half of the figure is a mirror image of the other half.

9. $\angle 1$ and the 109° angle are vertical angles. Their measures are equal, so $m\angle 1 = 109°$.

10. $m\angle 1 + 50° = 180°$

$m\angle 1 = 130°$

11. $m\angle 1 + 65° + 90° = 180°$

$m\angle 1 + 155° = 180°$

$m\angle 1 = 25°$

12. $\angle 1$ and the 125° angle are supplementary angles. So,

$m\angle 1 + 125° = 180°$

$m\angle 1 = 55°$.

$\angle 2$ and the 135° angle are supplementary angles. So,

$m\angle 2 + 135° = 180°$

$m\angle 2 = 45°$.

$\angle 3$ and $\angle 1$ are alternate interior angles.

So, $m\angle 3 = m\angle 1 = 55°$.

The sum of the interior angles of a triangle is 180°. So,

$m\angle 1 + m\angle 2 + m\angle 4 = 180°$

$55° + 45° + m\angle 4 = 180°$

$100° + m\angle 4 = 180°$

$m\angle 4 = 80°$.

$\angle 5$ and $\angle 2$ are alternate interior angles. So,

$m\angle 5 = m\angle 2 = 45°$.

13. $90° + 64° + x° = 180°$

$154 + x = 180$

$x = 26$

Because the triangle has one right angle, it is a right triangle.

14. $17° + 55° + x° = 180°$

$72 + x = 180$

$x = 108$

Because the triangle has one obtuse angle, it is an obtuse triangle.

15. $40° + 52° + x° = 180°$

$92 + x = 180$

$x = 88$

Because the triangle has three acute angles, it is an acute triangle.

16. The quadrilateral is a trapezoid.

$90° + 90° + 60° + x° = 360°$

$240 + x = 360$

$x = 120$

17. The quadrilateral is a parallelogram.

$120° + 120° + x° + x° = 360°$

$240 + x + x = 360$

$240 + 2x = 360$

$2x = 120$

$x = 60$

18. The quadrilateral is a trapezoid.

$140° + x° + 60° + 42° = 360°$

$x + 242 = 360$

$x = 118$

19. Because a 12-gon has 12 sides, use $n = 12$.

$$\frac{(n - 2) \cdot 180°}{n} = \frac{(12 - 2) \cdot 180°}{12} = 150°$$

The measure of one angle in a regular 12-gon is 150°.

20. Because a hexagon has six sides, use $n = 6$.

$(n - 2) \cdot 180° = (6 - 2) \cdot 180° = 720°$

The sum of the angle measures in a hexagon is 720°.

21. $\triangle ABC \cong \triangle GFH$ by Side-Angle-Side.

$\overline{AB} \cong \overline{GF}$

$\angle B \cong \angle F$

$\overline{BC} \cong \overline{FH}$

22. $\triangle XYZ \cong \triangle RST$ by Angle-Side-Angle.

$\angle X \cong \angle R$

$\overline{XZ} \cong \overline{RT}$

$\angle Z \cong \angle T$

23. $\triangle LMN \cong \triangle PQR$ by Side-Angle-Side.

$\overline{LN} \cong \overline{PR}$

$\angle N \cong \angle R$

$\overline{NM} \cong \overline{RQ}$

24. $\triangle TUV \cong \triangle WXY$ by Side-Side-Side.

$\overline{TU} \cong \overline{WX}$

$\overline{UV} \cong \overline{XY}$

$\overline{TV} \cong \overline{WY}$

25. Original   Image

$(x, y) \longrightarrow (-x, y)$

$A(1, 3) \longrightarrow A'(-1, 3)$

$B(4, 3) \longrightarrow B'(-4, 3)$

$C(3, 1) \longrightarrow C'(-3, 1)$

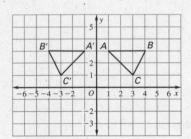

26.

The jet has one line of symmetry.

27.

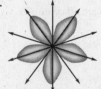

The flower has five lines of symmetry.

28. The bicycle does not have any lines of symmetry.

29. Original   Image

$(x, y) \longrightarrow (x - 2, y + 1)$

$K(3, 1) \longrightarrow K'(1, 2)$

$L(1, 4) \longrightarrow L'(-1, 5)$

$M(3, 3) \longrightarrow M'(1, 4)$

30. Original   Image

$(x, y) \longrightarrow (-x, -y)$

$K(3, 1) \longrightarrow K'(-3, -1)$

$L(1, 4) \longrightarrow L'(-1, -4)$

$M(3, 3) \longrightarrow M'(-3, -3)$

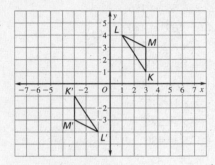

31. $\dfrac{x \text{ feet}}{20 \text{ feet}} = \dfrac{60 \text{ feet}}{25 \text{ feet}}$

$25x = 1200$

$x = 48$

The building is 48 feet tall.

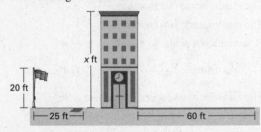

32. The perimeter of *PQRS* is
$2(40) + 2(10) = 100$ centimeters.

The perimeter of *JKLM* is 20 centimeters. So, the scale
factor is $\dfrac{20}{100} = \dfrac{1}{5}$.

Using the scale factor, the length of *JKLM* is
$\dfrac{1}{5}(40) = 8$ centimeters and the width of *JKLM* is
$\dfrac{1}{5}(10) = 2$ centimeters.

Chapter 8 Test (p. 461)

1. $m\angle 2 + 40° = 180°$

$m\angle 2 = 140°$

$\angle 1$ and the 40° angle are vertical angles. Their measures
are equal, so $m\angle 1 = 40°$.

$\angle 2$ and $\angle 3$ are vertical angles. Their measures are equal,
so $m\angle 3 = m\angle 2 = 140°$.

2. $m\angle 2 + 150° = 180°$

$\qquad m\angle 2 = 30°$

$\angle 1$ and the 120° angle are vertical angles. Their measures are equal, so $m\angle 1 = 120°$.

$\angle 3$ and the 30° angle are vertical angles. Their measures are equal, so $m\angle 3 = 30°$.

3. $\angle 1$ and the 48° angle are vertical angles. Their measures are equal, so $m\angle 1 = 48°$.

$\angle 3$ and the 56° angle are vertical angles. Their measures are equal, so $m\angle 3 = 56°$.

$m\angle 1 + m\angle 2 + m\angle 3 = 180°$

$48° + m\angle 2 + 56° = 180°$

$\qquad m\angle 2 + 109° = 180°$

$\qquad\qquad m\angle 2 = 76°$

4. $m\angle 1 + 145° + 18° = 180°$

$\qquad m\angle 1 + 163° = 180°$

$\qquad\qquad m\angle 1 = 17°$

5. $m\angle 1 + 90° + 45° = 180°$

$\qquad m\angle 1 + 135° = 180°$

$\qquad\qquad m\angle 1 = 45°$

6. $m\angle 1 + 70° + 40° = 180°$

$\qquad m\angle 1 + 110° = 180°$

$\qquad\qquad m\angle 1 = 70°$

7. The quadrilateral is a rectangle.

8. The quadrilateral is a rhombus.

9. The quadrilateral is a trapezoid.

10. A square has 4 sides, so $n = 4$.

$$\frac{(n-2)}{n} \cdot 180° = \frac{(4-2)}{4} \cdot 180° = \frac{1}{2} \cdot 180° = 90°$$

The measure of one angle of a square is 90°.

11. A regular octagon has 8 sides, so $n = 8$.

$$\frac{(n-2)}{n} \cdot 180° = \frac{(8-2)}{8} \cdot 180° = \frac{6}{8} \cdot 180° = 135°$$

The measure of one angle of a regular octagon is 135°.

12. A regular 9-gon has 9 sides, so $n = 9$.

$$\frac{(n-2)}{n} \cdot 180° = \frac{(9-2)}{9} \cdot 180° = \frac{7 \cdot 180°}{9} \cdot 140°$$

The measure of one angle of a regular 9-gon is 140°.

13. $x + 6 = 5x - 2$

$\qquad 6 = 4x - 2$

$\qquad 8 = 4x$

$\qquad 2 = x$

The value of x is 2.

14.

Original		Solution
(x, y)	$\longrightarrow$	$(-x, -y)$
$A(1, 3)$	$\longrightarrow$	$A'(-1, -3)$
$B(4, 3)$	$\longrightarrow$	$B'(-4, -3)$
$C(4, 1)$	$\longrightarrow$	$C'(-4, -1)$
$D(2, 1)$	$\longrightarrow$	$D'(-2, -1)$

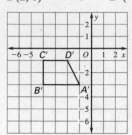

15.

Original		Solution
(x, y)	$\longrightarrow$	$(x - 5, y + 3)$
$R(1, 0)$	$\longrightarrow$	$R'(-4, 3)$
$S(3, -1)$	$\longrightarrow$	$S'(-2, 2)$
$T(3, -3)$	$\longrightarrow$	$T'(-2, 0)$
$U(1, -3)$	$\longrightarrow$	$U'(-4, 0)$

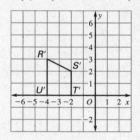

16. $\dfrac{75 \text{ in.}}{x \text{ in.}} = \dfrac{108 \text{ in.}}{96 \text{ in.}}$

$\qquad 6912 = 108x$

$\qquad\quad 64 = x$

Martha is 64 inches tall.

17. $\dfrac{5 \text{ cm}}{12.5 \text{ cm}} = \dfrac{12 \text{ cm}}{x \text{ cm}}$

$\qquad\quad 5x = 150$

$\qquad\quad\; x = 30$

$\dfrac{5 \text{ cm}}{12.5 \text{ cm}} = \dfrac{15 \text{ cm}}{y \text{ cm}}$

$\qquad\quad 5y = 187.5$

$\qquad\quad\; y = 37.5$

The lengths of the other two sides are 30 centimeters and 37.5 centimeters.

The perimeter of the original triangle is $5 + 12 + 15 = 32$ centimeters.

The perimeter of the similar triangle is $12.5 + 30 + 37.5 = 80$ centimeters.

The scale factor is $\dfrac{80}{32} = 2.5$.

Chapter 8, *continued*

1. C;

$\angle 3$ and $\angle 4$ are complementary angles.

2. A;

$\angle 1$ and $\angle 2$ are vertical angles.

3. C;

$\angle 1$ is a right angle.

Standardized Test Practice (pp. 464–465)

1. D;

Perpendicular lines are formed by two consecutive sides of a rectangular window pane.

2. C;

Each angle of a regular octagon is
$$\frac{(n-2) \cdot 180°}{n} = \frac{(8-2) \cdot 180°}{8} = 135.$$
So, $x° = z° = 135°$ and $x + z = 135 + 135 = 270$.

3. B;

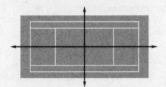

The tennis court has 2 lines of symmetry.

4. D;

$$m\angle A + m\angle B = 180°$$
$$118° + m\angle B = 180°$$
$$m\angle B = 62°$$
$$m\angle B + m\angle C = 180°$$
$$62° + m\angle C = 180°$$
$$m\angle C = 118°$$

5. D

6. B;

The sum of the interior angles of a pentagon is $(5-2) \cdot 180° = 540°$ and each angle measures $540 \div 5 = 108°$.

$$x = y = 108$$
$$x + y = 108 + 108$$
$$= 216 \neq 144$$
$$2x + y = 2(108) + 108$$
$$= 324$$

7. A; A 9-gon has 9 sides so, $n = 9$.

$(n-2) \cdot 180° = (9-2) \cdot 180° = 7 \cdot 180° = 1260°$

8. D;

The figure has 4 lines of symmetry.

9. C

10. D;

Vertical angles are *always* congruent.

11. D;

A 12–gon has 12 sides, so $n = 12$.

$$\frac{(n-2) \cdot 180°}{n} = \frac{(12-2) \cdot 180°}{12} = 150$$

An octagon has 8 sides, so $n = 8$.

$$\frac{(n-2) \cdot 180°}{n} = \frac{(8-2) \cdot 180°}{8} = 135°$$

The sum of the angles is $150° + 135° = 285°$.

12. $90° + 61° + x° = 180°$

$$151 + x = 180$$
$$x = 29$$

13. $\dfrac{AB}{BC} = \dfrac{BD}{CD}$

$$\frac{AB}{5 \text{ cm}} = \frac{6 \text{ cm}}{4 \text{ cm}}$$
$$4(AB) = 30$$
$$AB = 7.5 \text{ cm}$$

14. $x° + 105° + (x + 1)° = 180°$

$$2x + 106 = 180$$
$$2x = 74$$
$$x = 37$$
$$m\angle C = (x + 1)° = (37 + 1)° = 38°$$

15. *Sample answer:* The measure of the unmarked angle in the left triangle is $x°$ because vertical angles are congruent. Then

$$65° + 65° + x° = 180°$$
$$130 + x = 180$$
$$x = 50.$$

Chapter 8, continued

16. *Sample answer:* We know that $m\angle A = 50°$, $m\angle B = m\angle Q = 90°$, and $AB = QP = 2m$. So,

$$40° + 90° + m\angle P = 180°$$
$$130° + m\angle P = 180°$$
$$m\angle P = 50°$$

Because $m\angle A = m\angle P = 50°$, $AB = PQ = 2m$, and $m\angle B = m\angle Q = 90°$, we can conclude that

$\angle A \cong \angle P$

$AB \cong PQ$

$\angle B \cong \angle Q$.

So, $\triangle ABC \cong \triangle PQR$ by Angle-Side-Angle.

All corresponding parts of congruent figures are congruent. So, the corresponding angles are congruent and the corresponding sides have a 1 : 1 ratio. So, $\triangle ABC \sim \triangle PQR$.

17.

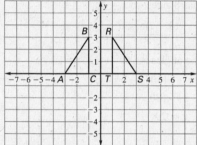

Sample answer:

Method 1: $AC = ST = 2$ units, $m\angle C = m\angle T = 90°$, and $BC = RT = 3$ units. So, $\triangle ABC \cong \triangle SRT$ by Side-Angle-Side.

Method 2:

Because $\triangle ABC$ is a reflection of $\triangle RST$ in the *y*-axis, $\triangle BAC$ is an identical mirror image of $\triangle RST$. So, $\triangle BAC \cong \triangle RST$.

18. a. $16 \text{ in.} \left(\dfrac{1}{4}\right) = 4 \text{ in.}$

$24 \text{ in.} \left(\dfrac{1}{4}\right) = 6 \text{ in.}$

The dimensions of the reduced photo are 4 inches by 6 inches.

b. *Sample answer:* If each page is $5 + 5 = 10$ inches by 3 inches, the 4 inch by 6 inch photo will not fit. If each page is 5 inches by $3 + 3 = 6$ inches, the 4 inch by 6 inch photo will fit.

So, if the picture will fit or not depends on whether the album holds the pictures stacked horizontally or vertically.

c. Area of photo is $(4)(6) = 24 \text{ in}^2$.

The area of the matte and the photo is $11 \text{ in}^2. + 24 \text{ in}^2. = 35 \text{ in}^2$.

The matte is 7 inches long. So,

$A = \ell w$

$35 = 7w$

$5 = w$.

The width or height of the matte is 5 inches.

19. a.

Original	Image
(x, y)	$(2x, 2y)$
$A(-2, 0)$	$A'(-4, 0)$
$B(-2, 4)$	$B'(-4, 8)$
$C(-6, 8)$	$C'(-12, 16)$
$D(-12, 6)$	$D'(-24, 12)$

The vertices are $A'(-4, 0)$, $B'(-4, 8)$, $C'(-12, 16)$, and $D'(-24, 12)$.

b.

Original	Image
(x, y)	$\left(\dfrac{1}{4}x, \dfrac{1}{4}y\right)$
$A'(-4, 0)$	$A''(-1, 0)$
$B'(-4, 8)$	$B''(-1, 2)$
$C'(-12, 16)$	$C''(-3, 4)$
$D'(-24, 12)$	$D''(-6, 3)$

The vertices are $A''(-1, 0)$, $B''(-1, 2)$, $C''(-3, 4)$, and $D''(-6, 3)$.

c. The scale factor that change $ABCD$ to $A'' B'' C'' D''$ is the product of the two scale factors, $2\left(\dfrac{1}{4}\right) = \dfrac{1}{2}$.

Chapter 9

Chapter Get-Ready Games (pp. 466–467)

1. Turn the left wheel 4 times and turn the right wheel 6 times.

$5^4 = 625$ $\qquad$ $4^4 = 256$ $\qquad$ $2^7 = 128$

2. 1 and a: $180° − 90° − 60° = 30°$

2 and c: $180° − 90° − 45° = 45°$

3 and b: $180° − 90° − 65° = 25°$

4 and e: $180° − 90° − 55° = 35°$

5 and d: $180° − 90° − 30° = 60°$

Stop and Think (p. 467)

1. $4^4 = 4 \cdot 4 \cdot 4 \cdot 4$

$\quad = (2 \cdot 2) \cdot (2 \cdot 2) \cdot (2 \cdot 2) \cdot (2 \cdot 2)$

$\quad = 2^8$

or $4^4 = (2 \cdot 2)^4 = (2^2)^4 = 2^8$

2. The sum of the measures of the angles of a triangle is $180°$. The sum of the given angle measures is $185°$. So, these angles cannot form a triangle.

Review Prerequisite Skills (p. 468)

1. isosceles triangle $\qquad$ **2.** scalene triangle

3. equilateral triangle

4. A right triangle, when classified by its side lengths, may *not* be an *equilateral* triangle.

5. $4^2 + 3^2 = 16 + 9 = 25$

6. $14^2 − 5^2 = 196 − 25 = 171$

7. $27^2 − 3^2 = 729 − 9 = 720$

8. $2^2 + 6^2 = 4 + 36 = 40$

9. $6^2 − 3^2 = 36 − 9 = 27$

10. $10^2 − 5^2 = 100 − 25 = 75$

11. $5^2 + 6^2 = 25 + 36 = 61$

12. $7^2 + 3^2 = 49 + 9 = 58$

13. $x° + (2x − 30)° = 90°$

$\qquad x + 2x − 30 = 90$

$\qquad\qquad 3x = 120$

$\qquad\qquad\quad x = 40$

$2x − 30 = 2(40) − 30 = 80 − 30 = 50$

The measures of the angles are $40°$, $50°$, and $90°$.

14. $x° + x° + 4x° = 180°$

$\qquad\qquad 6x = 180$

$\qquad\qquad\ x = 30$

$4x = 4(30) = 120$

The measures of the angles are $30°$, $30°$, and $120°$.

15. $(2x − 50)° + (x + 20)° + 2x° = 180°$

$\qquad\qquad\qquad 5x − 30 = 180$

$\qquad\qquad\qquad\quad 5x = 210$

$\qquad\qquad\qquad\quad\ x = 42$

$2x − 50 = 2(42) − 50 = 84 − 50 = 34$

$x + 20 = 42 + 20 = 62$

$2x = 2(42) = 84$

The measures of the angles are $34°$, $62°$, and $84°$.

Lesson 9.1

Activity (p. 469)

Step 1.

Area of square (square units)	1	4	9	16	25	36
Side length (units)	1	2	3	4	5	6

Step 2. Area (square units) side length (units)

49	7
64	8
100	10
400	20

Step 3. The side length of a square with an area of 81 square units is 9 units. The side length of a square with an area of 100 square units is 10 units. So, the side length of a square with an area between 81 and 100 square units is between 9 and 10 units.

9.1 Guided Practice (pp. 470–471)

1. $\sqrt{4} = 2$ because $2^2 = 4$.

2. $\sqrt{0} = 0$ because $0^2 = 0$.

3. $−\sqrt{36} = −6$ because $(−6)^2 = 36$.

4. $−\sqrt{81} = −9$ because $(−9)^2 = 81$.

5. Because 23 is between $16 = 4^2$ and $25 = 5^2$, $\sqrt{23}$ is between 4 and 5. Because $4.5^2 = 20.25$ and $23 > 20.25$, $\sqrt{23} \approx 5$.

6. Because 41 is between $36 = 6^2$ and $49 = 7^2$, $\sqrt{41}$ is between 6 and 7. Because $6.5^2 = 42.25$ and $41 < 42.25$, $\sqrt{41} \approx 6$.

7. $\sqrt{\dfrac{25}{81}} = \dfrac{5}{9}$ because $\left(\dfrac{5}{9}\right)^2 = \dfrac{25}{81}$. So, $\sqrt{\dfrac{25}{81}} \approx 1$.

8. $\sqrt{0.36} = 0.6$ because $(0.6)^2 = 0.36$. So, $\sqrt{0.36} \approx 1$.

9. $\sqrt{236} \approx 15.4$ $\qquad$ **10.** $\sqrt{11} \approx 3.3$

11. $−\sqrt{20.96} \approx −4.6$ $\qquad$ **12.** $−\sqrt{3590} \approx −59.9$

13. $t^2 = 36$

$\quad t = \pm\sqrt{36}$

$\quad t = \pm 6$

Check: $t = −6$: $(−6)^2 \overset{?}{=} 36$

$\qquad\qquad\qquad 36 = 36$ ✓

$\qquad\quad t = 6$: $6^2 \overset{?}{=} 36$

$\qquad\qquad\qquad 36 = 36$ ✓

14. $k^2 = 121$

$\quad k = \pm\sqrt{121}$

$\quad k = \pm 11$

Check: $k = −11$: $(−11)^2 \overset{?}{=} 121$

$\qquad\qquad\qquad\quad 121 = 121$ ✓

$\qquad\quad k = 11$: $11^2 \overset{?}{=} 121$

$\qquad\qquad\qquad\quad 121 = 121$ ✓

Chapter 9, continued

15.
$$y^2 - 15 = 10$$
$$y^2 - 15 + 15 = 10 + 15$$
$$y^2 = 25$$
$$y = \pm\sqrt{25}$$
$$y = \pm5$$

Check: $y = -5$: $(-5)^2 - 15 \stackrel{?}{=} 10$
$$25 - 15 \stackrel{?}{=} 10$$
$$10 = 10 \checkmark$$
$$y = 5: 5^2 - 15 \stackrel{?}{=} 10$$
$$25 - 15 \stackrel{?}{=} 10$$
$$10 = 10 \checkmark$$

16.
$$x^2 + 7 = 16$$
$$x^2 + 7 - 7 = 16 - 7$$
$$x^2 = 9$$
$$x = \pm\sqrt{9}$$
$$x = \pm3$$

Check: $x = -3$: $(-3)^2 + 7 \stackrel{?}{=} 16$
$$9 + 7 \stackrel{?}{=} 16$$
$$16 = 16 \checkmark$$
$$x = 3: 3^2 + 7 \stackrel{?}{=} 16$$
$$9 + 7 \stackrel{?}{=} 16$$
$$16 = 16 \checkmark$$

9.1 Exercises (pp. 472–474)

Skill Practice

1. A number b is a square root of c if $b^2 = c$.

2. The number 121 is a perfect square because the square root of 121 is an integer, 11.

3. $-\sqrt{1} = -1$ because $(-1)^2 = 1$.

4. $\sqrt{100} = 10$ because $10^2 = 100$.

5. $\sqrt{144} = 12$ because $12^2 = 144$.

6. $-\sqrt{16} = -4$ because $(-4)^2 = 16$.

7. The answer is missing a negative sign; $-\sqrt{49} = -7$ because $(-7)^2 = 49$.

8. Because 33 is between $25 = 5^2$ and $36 = 6^2$, $\sqrt{33}$ is between 5 and 6. Because $5.5^2 = 30.25$ and $33 > 30.25$, $\sqrt{33} \approx 6$.

9. Because 14 is between $9 = 3^2$ and $16 = 4^2$, $\sqrt{14}$ is between 3 and 4. Because $3.5^2 = 12.25$ and $14 > 12.25$, $\sqrt{14} \approx 4$.

10. Because 117 is between $100 = 10^2$ and $121 = 11^2$, $\sqrt{117}$ is between 10 and 11. Because $10.5^2 = 110.25$ and $117 > 110.25$, $\sqrt{117} \approx 11$.

11. Because 52 is between $49 = 7^2$ and $64 = 8^2$, $\sqrt{52}$ is between 7 and 8. Because $7.5^2 = 56.25$ and $52 < 56.25$, $\sqrt{52} \approx 7$.

12. Because 74 is between $64 = 8^2$ and $81 = 9^2$, $\sqrt{74}$ is between 8 and 9. Because $8.5^2 = 72.25$ and $74 > 72.25$, $\sqrt{74} \approx 9$.

13. Because 22 is between $16 = 4^2$ and $25 = 5^2$, $\sqrt{22}$ is between 4 and 5. Because $4.5^2 = 20.25$ and $22 > 20.25$, $\sqrt{22} \approx 5$.

14. Because 48 is between $36 = 6^2$ and $49 = 7^2$, $\sqrt{48}$ is between 6 and 7. Because $6.5^2 = 42.25$ and $48 > 42.25$, $\sqrt{48} \approx 7$.

15. Because 123 is between $121 = 11^2$ and $144 = 12^2$, $\sqrt{123}$ is between 11 and 12. Because $11.5^2 = 132.25$ and $121 < 132.25$, $\sqrt{123} \approx 11$.

16. $-\sqrt{34.6} \approx -5.9$ 17. $\sqrt{43.56} \approx 6.6$

18. $\sqrt{2440} \approx 49.4$ 19. $-\sqrt{6204} \approx -78.8$

20. A; $13^2 = 169$; Because 165 is the closest to 169, $\sqrt{165} \approx 13$.

21. $x^2 = 0$
$$x = \pm\sqrt{0}$$
$$x = 0$$
Check: $x = 0$: $0^2 \stackrel{?}{=} 0$
$$0 = 0 \checkmark$$

22. $b^2 = 49$
$$b = \pm\sqrt{49}$$
$$b = \pm7$$
Check: $b = -7$: $(-7)^2 \stackrel{?}{=} 49$
$$49 = 49 \checkmark$$
$$b = 7: 7^2 \stackrel{?}{=} 49$$
$$49 = 49 \checkmark$$

23. $y^2 = 81$
$$y = \pm\sqrt{81}$$
$$y = \pm9$$
Check: $y = -9$: $(-9)^2 \stackrel{?}{=} 81$
$$81 = 81 \checkmark$$
$$y = 9: 9^2 \stackrel{?}{=} 81$$
$$81 = 81 \checkmark$$

24.
$$z^2 - 169 = 0$$
$$z^2 - 169 + 169 = 0 + 169$$
$$z^2 = 169$$
$$z = \pm\sqrt{169}$$
$$z = \pm13$$
Check: $z = -13$: $(-13)^2 - 169 \stackrel{?}{=} 0$
$$169 - 169 \stackrel{?}{=} 0$$
$$0 = 0 \checkmark$$
$$z = 13: 13^2 - 169 \stackrel{?}{=} 0$$
$$169 - 169 \stackrel{?}{=} 0$$
$$0 = 0 \checkmark$$

25. $y^2 + 7 = 56$

$y^2 + 7 - 7 = 56 - 7$

$y^2 = 49$

$y = \pm\sqrt{49}$

$y = \pm 7$

Check: $y = -7$: $(-7)^2 + 7 \stackrel{?}{=} 56$

$49 + 7 \stackrel{?}{=} 56$

$56 = 56$ ✓

$y = 7$: $7^2 + 7 \stackrel{?}{=} 56$

$49 + 7 \stackrel{?}{=} 56$

$56 = 56$ ✓

26. $a^2 + 12 = 48$

$a^2 + 12 - 12 = 48 - 12$

$a^2 = 36$

$a = \pm\sqrt{36}$

$a = \pm 6$

Check: $a = -6$: $(-6)^2 + 12 \stackrel{?}{=} 48$

$36 + 12 \stackrel{?}{=} 48$

$48 = 48$ ✓

$a = 6$: $6^2 + 12 \stackrel{?}{=} 48$

$36 + 12 \stackrel{?}{=} 48$

$48 = 48$ ✓

27. $n^2 - 27 = 94$

$n^2 - 27 + 27 = 94 + 27$

$n^2 = 121$

$n = \pm\sqrt{121}$

$n = \pm 11$

Check: $n = -11$: $(-11)^2 - 27 \stackrel{?}{=} 94$

$121 - 27 \stackrel{?}{=} 94$

$94 = 94$ ✓

$n = 11$: $11^2 - 27 \stackrel{?}{=} 94$

$121 - 27 \stackrel{?}{=} 94$

$94 = 94$ ✓

28. $y^2 - 31 = 36$

$y^2 - 31 + 31 = 36 + 31$

$y^2 = 67$

$y = \pm\sqrt{67}$

$y \approx \pm 8.19$

Check: $y = -8.19$: $(-8.19)^2 - 31 \stackrel{?}{=} 36$

$67.0761 - 31 \stackrel{?}{=} 36$

$36.0761 \approx 36$ ✓

$y = 8.19$: $8.19^2 - 31 \stackrel{?}{=} 36$

$67.0761 - 31 \stackrel{?}{=} 36$

$36.0761 \approx 36$ ✓

29. $62 + z^2 = 198$

$62 + z^2 - 62 = 198 - 62$

$z^2 = 136$

$z = \pm\sqrt{136}$

$z \approx \pm 11.66$

Check: $z = -11.66$: $62 + (-11.66)^2 \stackrel{?}{=} 198$

$62 + 135.9556 \stackrel{?}{=} 198$

$197.9556 \approx 198$ ✓

$z = 11.66$: $62 + 11.66^2 \stackrel{?}{=} 198$

$62 + 135.9556 \stackrel{?}{=} 198$

$197.9556 \approx 198$ ✓

30. $c^2 - 0.35 = 1.65$

$c^2 - 0.35 + 0.35 = 1.65 + 0.35$

$c^2 = 2$

$c = \pm\sqrt{2}$

$c \approx \pm 1.41$

Check: $c = -1.41$: $(-1.41)^2 - 0.35 \stackrel{?}{=} 1.65$

$1.9881 - 0.35 \stackrel{?}{=} 1.65$

$1.6381 \approx 1.65$ ✓

$c = 1.41$: $(1.41)^2 - 0.35 \stackrel{?}{=} 1.65$

$1.9881 - 0.35 \stackrel{?}{=} 1.65$

$1.6381 \approx 1.65$ ✓

31. $58 + m^2 = 253$

$58 + m^2 - 58 = 253 - 58$

$m^2 = 195$

$m = \pm\sqrt{195}$

$m \approx \pm 13.96$

Check: $m = -13.96$: $58 + (-13.96)^2 \stackrel{?}{=} 253$

$58 + 194.8816 \stackrel{?}{=} 253$

$252.8816 \approx 253$ ✓

$m = 13.96$: $58 + (13.96)^2 \stackrel{?}{=} 253$

$58 + 194.8816 \stackrel{?}{=} 253$

$252.8816 \approx 253$ ✓

32. $k^2 - 0.17 = 0.64$

$k^2 - 0.17 + 0.17 = 0.64 + 0.17$

$k^2 = 0.81$

$k = \pm\sqrt{0.81}$

$k = \pm 0.9$

Check: $k = -0.9$: $(-0.9)^2 - 0.17 \stackrel{?}{=} 0.64$

$0.81 - 0.17 \stackrel{?}{=} 0.64$

$0.64 = 0.64$ ✓

$k = 0.9$: $(0.9)^2 - 0.17 \stackrel{?}{=} 0.64$

$0.81 - 0.17 \stackrel{?}{=} 0.64$

$0.64 = 0.64$ ✓

33.
$$m^2 + 0.38 = 1.82$$
$$m^2 + 0.38 - 0.38 = 1.82 - 0.38$$
$$m^2 = 1.44$$
$$m = \pm\sqrt{1.44}$$
$$m = \pm 1.2$$

Check: $m = -1.2$: $(-1.2)^2 + 0.38 \stackrel{?}{=} 1.82$
$$1.44 + 0.38 \stackrel{?}{=} 1.82$$
$$1.82 = 1.82 \checkmark$$

$m = 1.2$: $(1.2)^2 + 0.38 \stackrel{?}{=} 1.82$
$$1.44 + 0.38 \stackrel{?}{=} 1.82$$
$$1.82 = 1.82 \checkmark$$

34.
$$p^2 + 0.06 = 1.27$$
$$p^2 + 0.06 - 0.06 = 1.27 - 0.06$$
$$p^2 = 1.21$$
$$p = \pm\sqrt{1.21}$$
$$p = \pm 1.1$$

Check: $p = -1.1$: $(-1.1)^2 + 0.06 \stackrel{?}{=} 1.27$
$$1.21 + 0.06 \stackrel{?}{=} 1.27$$
$$1.27 = 1.27 \checkmark$$

$p = 1.1$: $(1.1)^2 + 0.06 \stackrel{?}{=} 1.27$
$$1.21 + 0.06 \stackrel{?}{=} 1.27$$
$$1.27 = 1.27 \checkmark$$

35.
$$s^2 - 0.52 = 1.44$$
$$s^2 - 0.52 + 0.52 = 1.44 + 0.52$$
$$s^2 = 1.96$$
$$s = \pm\sqrt{1.96}$$
$$s = \pm 1.4$$

Check: $s = -1.4$: $(-1.4)^2 - 0.52 \stackrel{?}{=} 1.44$
$$1.96 - 0.52 \stackrel{?}{=} 1.44$$
$$1.44 = 1.44 \checkmark$$

$s = 1.4$: $(1.4)^2 - 0.52 \stackrel{?}{=} 1.44$
$$1.96 - 0.52 \stackrel{?}{=} 1.44$$
$$1.44 = 1.44 \checkmark$$

36. Square roots are *sometimes* whole numbers.

37. Square roots of perfect squares are *always* integers.

38. A number *never* has more than two square roots.

39. When $a = 5$ and $b = 5$:
$$\sqrt{a^2 - b^2} = \sqrt{5^2 - 5^2} = \sqrt{25 - 25} = \sqrt{0} = 0$$

40. When $a = 10$ and $b = 8$:
$$\sqrt{a^2 - b^2} = \sqrt{10^2 - 8^2} = \sqrt{100 - 64} = \sqrt{36} = 6$$

41. When $a = 15$ and $b = 12$:
$$\sqrt{a^2 - b^2} = \sqrt{15^2 - 12^2} = \sqrt{225 - 144} = \sqrt{81} = 9$$

42. $-\sqrt{\dfrac{1}{4}} = -\sqrt{\dfrac{1}{2} \cdot \dfrac{1}{2}} = -\dfrac{1}{2}$

43. $\sqrt{\dfrac{16}{25}} = \sqrt{\dfrac{4}{5} \cdot \dfrac{4}{5}} = \dfrac{4}{5}$

44. $-\sqrt{\dfrac{81}{100}} = -\sqrt{\dfrac{9}{10} \cdot \dfrac{9}{10}} = -\dfrac{9}{10}$

45. $\sqrt{\dfrac{144}{169}} = \sqrt{\dfrac{12}{13} \cdot \dfrac{12}{13}} = \dfrac{12}{13}$

46. $\sqrt{1.44} = \sqrt{1.2 \cdot 1.2} = 1.2$

47. $\sqrt{1.96} = \sqrt{1.4 \cdot 1.4} = 1.4$

48. $-\sqrt{0.25} = -\sqrt{0.5 \cdot 0.5} = -0.5$

49. $\sqrt{11.56} = \sqrt{3.4 \cdot 3.4} = 3.4$

50. $\sqrt{\sqrt{625}} = \sqrt{25} = 5$

51. $-\sqrt{\sqrt{1296}} = -\sqrt{36} = -6$

52. $-\sqrt{\sqrt{\sqrt{256}}} = -\sqrt{\sqrt{16}} = -\sqrt{4} = -2$

53. $\sqrt{\sqrt{\sqrt{4096}}} = \sqrt{\sqrt{64}} = \sqrt{8} \approx 2.83$

Problem Solving

54. a. Let x = side length of fabric.
$$x^2 = 729$$
b. $x = \pm\sqrt{729}$

c. $x = 27$

The length of one side of the pillow is 27 inches.

55. C; Let s = side length of plot.
$$s^2 = 6250$$
$$s = \sqrt{6250}$$
$$s \approx 79.1 \text{ yd}$$

56. *Sample answer:* Find the length of one side by taking the square root of the area. Then multiply the length of the side by 4 to find the perimeter.

Because $s \approx 79.1$, perimeter $= 4s \approx 4(79.1) = 316.4$. The perimeter of the land is about 316 yards.

57. Tablecloth: $\dfrac{50}{12} = 4\dfrac{1}{6}$

So, the tablecloth is $4\dfrac{1}{6}$ ft by $4\dfrac{1}{6}$ ft.

Let s = side length of table.
$$s^2 = 21.5$$
$$s = \sqrt{21.5}$$
$$s \approx 4.64$$

The tablecloth will not cover the table because $4\dfrac{1}{6}$ ft < 4.64 ft.

58. *Sample answer:* Numbers whose square roots are not rational: 2, 3, and $\dfrac{1}{5}$; rational: 1, 4, and $\dfrac{1}{9}$.

59.
$$w^2 = 576$$
$$w = \sqrt{576}$$
$$w = 24 \text{ ft}$$

Area of road: $A = \ell w = 330(24) = 7920$

Area of an intersection: $A = s^2 = 24^2 = 576$

The area of the roadway is
$7920 + 576 + 576 = 9072$ square feet.

Chapter 9, *continued*

60. Disagree; *Sample answer:* A rational number can be written as the quotient of two integers, but $\sqrt{5}$ is not an integer.

61. When $h = 3100$:
$$d = \sqrt{1.5h} = \sqrt{1.5(3100)} = \sqrt{4650} \approx 68.2$$
The ranger can see about 68.2 miles.

62. The formula says you can see about 68 miles. Because Mt. Washington lies above the surrounding land, you can see farther than the formula suggests.

63. When $d = 57.6$:
$$d = \sqrt{1.5h}$$
$$57.6 = \sqrt{1.5h}$$
$$(57.6)^2 = \left(\sqrt{1.5h}\right)^2$$
$$3317.76 = 1.5h$$
$$\frac{3317.76}{1.5} = \frac{1.5h}{1.5}$$
$$2212 \approx h$$
The ranger is about 2212 feet above the surrounding land.

64. $\sqrt{0.36} = 0.6$
$\sqrt{0.0036} = 0.06$
$\sqrt{0.000036} = 0.006$
$\sqrt{0.00000036} = 0.0006$
Each number is 0.1 times the previous number.
$\sqrt{0.0000000036} = 0.00006$

65. *Sample answer:* Choose two integers between which the square root lies. Guess the square root to the tenths' place using the relative distance of the original number from the squares of the two integers. Square your guess to see if it is too large or too small, and then adjust your guess accordingly. The one-place decimal whose square is closest to the original number is the best estimate.

Mixed Review

66. $12.4\% = 0.124$
$\frac{1}{8} = 0.125$
$0.1 = 0.100$
Because $0.100 < 0.124 < 0.125$, the numbers ordered from least to greatest are 0.1, 12.4%, $\frac{1}{8}$.

67. $0.85 = 0.850$
$8.5\% = 0.085$
$\frac{5}{8} = 0.625$
Because $0.085 < 0.625 < 0.850$, the numbers ordered from least to greatest are 8.5%, $\frac{5}{8}$, 0.85.

68. $\frac{3}{4} = 0.75$
$74\% = 0.74$
$0.7 = 0.70$
Because $0.70 < 0.74 < 0.75$, the numbers ordered from least to greatest are 0.7, 74%, $\frac{3}{4}$.

69. (1) Read and Understand
(2) Make a Plan: Draw a Diagram
(3) Solve the Problem:

Determine the number of ways a row of three postage stamps can be torn from a 4 by 3 sheet of stamps.

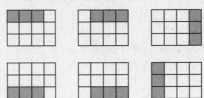

There are 6 ways that a row of 3 attached stamps can be chosen.

70. C;

Money to be used for rides = \$6 − \$2.25 = \$3.75
Number of rides = \$3.75 ÷ \$.75 = 5
Nikki can go on 5 rides.

Lesson 9.2

9.2 Guided Practice (pp. 475–477)

1. The number $\frac{5}{8}$ is rational because it is the quotient of two integers.

2. The number $\sqrt{7}$ is irrational because its decimal form, $2.645751311\ldots$, is a nonrepeating and nonterminating decimal.

3. The number $\sqrt{25}$ is rational because $\sqrt{25} = 5$ and 5 is an integer.

4. The number $\frac{2}{9}$ is rational because it is the quotient of two integers.

5.

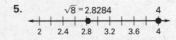

$4 > \sqrt{8}$

6.

$\frac{4}{5} = 0.8$ $\sqrt{\frac{4}{5}} = \sqrt{0.8} \approx 0.894$

$\frac{4}{5} < \sqrt{\frac{4}{5}}$

7.

$\frac{1}{4}$ $\sqrt{\frac{1}{4}} = \frac{1}{2}$

$\frac{1}{4} < \sqrt{\frac{1}{4}}$

8.

$\sqrt{7} \approx 2.646$ 3

$\sqrt{7} < 3$

Chapter 9, continued

9. $0.\overline{52} = 0.525252\ldots$

$0.\overline{525} = 0.525525\ldots$

$0.52\overline{5} = 0.525555\ldots$

$\sqrt{0.276} = 0.525357\ldots$

The decimals from least to greatest are:

$0.525252\ldots, 0.525357\ldots, 0.525525\ldots$, and $0.525555\ldots$

The numbers from least to greatest are:

$0.\overline{52}, \sqrt{0.276}, 0.\overline{525}$, and $0.52\overline{5}$.

10. $1.7 = 1.7000\ldots$

$\sqrt{1.7} = 1.3038\ldots$

$1.\overline{89} = 1.8989\ldots$

$1.\overline{3} = 1.3333\ldots$

The decimals from least to greatest are:

$1.3038\ldots, 1.3333\ldots, 1.7000\ldots$, and $1.8989\ldots$

The numbers from least to greatest are:

$\sqrt{1.7}, 1.\overline{3}, 1.7$, and $1.\overline{89}$.

11. When $h = 15$:

$s = \sqrt{\dfrac{h}{0.019}} = \sqrt{\dfrac{15}{0.019}} \approx 28.10$

The wind speed must be about 28 knots.

9.2 Exercises (pp. 477–480)

Skill Practice

1. Numbers that cannot be written as a quotient of two integers are *irrational*.

2. Together, rational and irrational numbers make up the set of *real numbers*.

3. The number 0.682 is rational because it is a terminating decimal.

4. The number 0.12345 . . . is irrational because it is a nonterminating and nonrepeating decimal.

5. The number $0.\overline{2}$ is rational because it is a repeating decimal.

6. The number 0.30311 is rational because it is a terminating decimal.

7. The number $\sqrt{36}$ is rational because $\sqrt{36} = 6$ and 6 is an integer.

8. The number $\sqrt{62}$ is irrational because its decimal form, 7.87400 . . . , is a nonterminating and nonrepeating decimal.

9. The number $\sqrt{5}$ is irrational because its decimal form, 2.23606 . . . , is a nonterminating and nonrepeating decimal.

10. The number $\sqrt{144}$ is rational because $\sqrt{144} = 12$ and 12 is an integer.

11. The number $\dfrac{9}{46}$ is rational because it is the quotient of two integers.

12. The number $\sqrt{\dfrac{25}{49}}$ is rational because $\sqrt{\dfrac{25}{49}} = \dfrac{5}{7}$ and $\dfrac{5}{7}$ is the quotient of two integers.

13. The number $\sqrt{\dfrac{100}{81}}$ is rational because $\sqrt{\dfrac{100}{81}} = \dfrac{10}{9}$ and $\dfrac{10}{9}$ is the quotient of two integers.

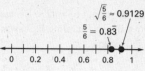

14. The number $\dfrac{22}{31}$ is rational because it is the quotient of two integers.

15. A; It is the only rational number in the group.

16.

$$\sqrt{\dfrac{5}{6}} \approx 0.9129$$
$$\dfrac{5}{6} = 0.8\overline{3}$$

$$\dfrac{5}{6} < \sqrt{\dfrac{5}{6}}$$

17.

$$\sqrt{0.9} \approx 0.9487$$

$$\sqrt{0.9} > 0.9$$

18.

$$\dfrac{3.5}{2.4} = 1.458\overline{3}$$
$$\sqrt{2.25} \approx 1.5$$

$$\sqrt{2.25} > \dfrac{3.5}{2.4}$$

19.

$$\sqrt{4.6} \approx 2.1448 \quad 2.5$$

$$\sqrt{4.6} < 2.5$$

20.

$$\sqrt{6.7} \approx 2.5884 \quad 2.6$$

$$2.6 > \sqrt{6.7}$$

21.

$$\sqrt{\dfrac{8}{11}} \approx 0.8528 \quad \dfrac{9}{10} = 0.9$$

$$\sqrt{\dfrac{8}{11}} < \dfrac{9}{10}$$

22–30. Sample explanations are given.

22. Using mental math, $\sqrt{0.81} = 0.9$.

Because $0.81 < 0.9$, $0.81 < \sqrt{0.81}$.

23. Using estimation, $\sqrt{10} \approx 3$.

Because $5 > 3$, $5 > \sqrt{10}$.

24. Using mental math, $\sqrt{\dfrac{64}{121}} = \dfrac{8}{11}$.

Because $\dfrac{8}{11} = \dfrac{8}{11}$, $\sqrt{\dfrac{64}{121}} = \dfrac{8}{11}$.

25. Using estimation, $\sqrt{\dfrac{16}{3}} \approx 2$.

Because $2 < 5$, $\sqrt{\dfrac{16}{3}} < 5$.

26. Using estimation, $\sqrt{21} \approx 5$.

Because $5 < 7$, $\sqrt{21} < 7$.

27. Using mental math, $-\sqrt{25} = -5$.

Because $-5 = -5$, $-5 = -\sqrt{25}$.

28. Using a calculator, $\sqrt{9.9} \approx 3.15$.

Because $3.15 < 3.3$, $\sqrt{9.9} < 3.3$.

Chapter 9, *continued*

29. Using a calculator, $\sqrt{1.7} \approx 1.304$.

Because $1.3 < 1.304$, $1.3 < \sqrt{1.7}$.

30. Using a calculator, $-\sqrt{1.6} \approx -1.26$.

Because $-0.4 > -1.26$, $-0.4 > -\sqrt{1.6}$.

31. D; $\sqrt{30} \approx 5.48 > 5$

32.

$$-\sqrt{9} = -3 \quad \frac{141}{25} = 5.64 \quad \sqrt{45} \approx 6.71 \quad 8.69$$

The numbers ordered from least to greatest are $-\sqrt{9}$, $\frac{141}{25}$, $\sqrt{45}$, and 8.69.

33. C; $\sqrt{2} \approx 1.41$

$\sqrt{5} \approx 2.24$

34. The decimals ordered from least to greatest are $0.\overline{131}$, $0.1\overline{3}$, 0.133, and $0.1\overline{3}$.

35. The decimals ordered from least to greatest are $0.\overline{262}$, $0.2\overline{6}$, 0.266, and $0.2\overline{6}$.

36. The decimals ordered from least to greatest are $0.4\overline{5}$, 0.455, $0.4\overline{5}$, and $\sqrt{0.68}$.

37. The decimals ordered from least to greatest are $0.3\overline{9}$, 0.399, $0.3\overline{9}$, $\sqrt{0.17}$.

38. $\sqrt{8} \approx 2.828$

The numbers from least to greatest are -4, -3.75, 1.5, and $\sqrt{8}$.

39. $\sqrt{81} = 9$

$\sqrt{220} \approx 14.832$

The numbers from least to greatest are -9, $\sqrt{81}$, 10.3, and $\sqrt{220}$.

40. $-\sqrt{12} \approx -3.464$

$-\sqrt{\frac{1}{4}} = -0.5$

$-\frac{3}{4} = -0.75$

The numbers from least to greatest are -3.5, $-\sqrt{12}$, $-\frac{3}{4}$, and $-\sqrt{\frac{1}{4}}$.

41. $\sqrt{2.5} \approx 1.581$

$\frac{2}{5} = 0.4$

$\sqrt{1.25} \approx 1.118$

The numbers from least to greatest are $\frac{2}{5}$, 1.02, $\sqrt{1.25}$, and $\sqrt{2.5}$.

42. The number $\sqrt{64}$ is rational because $\sqrt{64} = 8$ and 8 is an integer.

43–48. Let $a = 2$, $b = 4$, and $c = 9$.

43. $\sqrt{b + c} = \sqrt{4 + 9} = \sqrt{13} = 3.605551\ldots \approx 3.6$

It is irrational.

44. $\sqrt{c^2 - (a + b)} = \sqrt{9^2 - (2 + 4)}$

$= \sqrt{81 - 6}$

$= \sqrt{75} = 8.66025\ldots$

≈ 8.7

It is irrational.

45. $\sqrt{a^2 - b + c} = \sqrt{2^2 - 4 + 9} = \sqrt{4 - 4 + 9} = \sqrt{9} = 3$

It is rational.

46. $\sqrt{bc + b + c} = \sqrt{4(9) + 4 + 9}$

$= \sqrt{36 + 4 + 9}$

$= \sqrt{49}$

$= 7$

It is rational.

47. $\sqrt{c^2 - b^2 + 1} = \sqrt{9^2 - 4^2 + 1}$

$= \sqrt{81 - 16 + 1}$

$= \sqrt{66}$

$= 8.124038\ldots$

≈ 8.1

It is irrational.

48. $\sqrt{ab + bc - a^2} = \sqrt{2(4) + 4(9) - 2^2}$

$= \sqrt{8 + 36 - 4}$

$= \sqrt{40}$

$= 6.3245\ldots$

≈ 6.3

It is irrational.

49. Irrational; The sum of an irrational number and an integer is irrational.

50. Irrational; The sum of two irrational numbers is irrational.

51. Irrational; The product of an integer and an irrational number is irrational.

52. No; The square root of a negative number is not a real number.

53–58. Let $a = 4$, $b = 3$, $c = 9$, and $d = 5$.

53. $\sqrt{a + c} = \sqrt{4 + 9} = \sqrt{13}$

$\sqrt{a} + \sqrt{c} = \sqrt{4} + \sqrt{9} = 2 + 3 = 5$

$\sqrt{a + c}$ and $\sqrt{a} + \sqrt{c}$ are never equal unless a or c is zero.

54. $\sqrt{a^2} = \sqrt{4^2} = \sqrt{16} = 4$

$(\sqrt{a})^2 = (\sqrt{4})^2 = 2^2 = 4$

$\sqrt{a^2}$ and $(\sqrt{a})^2$ are always equal because $\sqrt{a^2} = \sqrt{aa} = a$ and $(\sqrt{a})^2 = \sqrt{a} \cdot \sqrt{a} = a$.

Chapter 9, *continued*

55. $\sqrt{ac} = \sqrt{4(9)} = \sqrt{36} = 6$

$\sqrt{a} \cdot \sqrt{c} = \sqrt{4} \cdot \sqrt{9} = 2 \cdot 3 = 6$

$\sqrt{ac}$ and $\sqrt{a} \cdot \sqrt{c}$ are always equal because

$(\sqrt{ac})^2 = \sqrt{ac} \cdot \sqrt{ac} = ac$ and

$(\sqrt{a} \cdot \sqrt{c})^2 = \sqrt{a} \cdot \sqrt{c} \cdot \sqrt{a} \cdot \sqrt{c} = ac$.

56. $\sqrt{a^2 + b^2} = \sqrt{4^2 + 3^2} = \sqrt{16 + 9} = \sqrt{25} = 5$

$\sqrt{a^2} + \sqrt{b^2} = \sqrt{4^2} + \sqrt{3^2} = 4 + 3 = 7$

$\sqrt{a^2 + b^2}$ and $\sqrt{a^2} + \sqrt{b^2}$ are never equal unless a or b are zero.

57. $\sqrt{d^2 - a^2} = \sqrt{5^2 - 4^2} = \sqrt{25 - 16} = \sqrt{9} = 3$

$\sqrt{d^2} - \sqrt{a^2} = \sqrt{5^2} - \sqrt{4^2} = 5 - 4 = 1$

$\sqrt{d^2 - a^2}$ and $\sqrt{d^2} - \sqrt{a^2}$ are sometimes equal when $a = d$.

58. $\sqrt{\dfrac{a}{c}} = \sqrt{\dfrac{4}{9}} = \dfrac{2}{3}$

$\dfrac{\sqrt{a}}{\sqrt{c}} = \dfrac{\sqrt{4}}{\sqrt{9}} = \dfrac{2}{3}$

$\sqrt{\dfrac{a}{c}}$ and $\dfrac{\sqrt{a}}{\sqrt{c}}$ are always equal because

$\left(\sqrt{\dfrac{a}{c}}\right)^2 = \sqrt{\dfrac{a}{c}} \cdot \sqrt{\dfrac{a}{c}} = \dfrac{a}{c}$ and

$\left(\dfrac{\sqrt{a}}{\sqrt{c}}\right)^2 = \dfrac{\sqrt{a}\sqrt{a}}{\sqrt{c}\sqrt{c}} = \dfrac{a}{c}$.

59. When $x = 1$: $\sqrt{x + 3} = \sqrt{1 + 3} = \sqrt{4} = 2$; rational.

When $x = 2$: $\sqrt{x + 3} = \sqrt{2 + 3} = \sqrt{5}$; irrational.

$\sqrt{x + 3}$ is sometimes irrational.

60. Because $\sqrt{x^2} = x$, $\sqrt{x^2}$ is never irrational for whole number values of x.

61. When $x = 3$: $\sqrt{x} \div 4 = \sqrt{3} \div 4$; irrational.

When $x = 4$: $\sqrt{x} \div 4 = \sqrt{4} \div 4 = 2 \div 4 = 0.5$; rational.

$\sqrt{x} \div 4$ is sometimes irrational.

62. $\sqrt{x^2} = -x$ for all values of x less than or equal to 0.

Sample answer:

When $x = -5$: $\sqrt{(-5)^2} = \sqrt{25} = 5 = -(-5)$

Problem Solving

63. B; Length of a side: $s = \sqrt{400} = 20$

Perimeter: $P = 4s = 4(20) = 80$

The perimeter is 80 feet which is an integer and therefore a rational, real number.

64. Length of a side: $s^2 = 212$

$s = \sqrt{212}$

$s = 14.5602\ldots$

The side length, $14.5602\ldots$, is irrational.

65. *Sample answer:* 8.2 is rational, and $\sqrt{80}$ is irrational.

66. Let $s =$ side length of the carpet.

$s^2 = 110$

$s = \sqrt{110}$

$s \approx 10.49$

The carpet is 10.49 ft by 10.49 ft. 10.49 is less than 10.5 and 11.2, so the carpet will fit in the room.

67. Let $s =$ side length of a stencil.

$s^2 = 20.25$

$s = \sqrt{20.25}$

$s = 4.5$

Number of stencils in column $= (7.5 \times 12)$ in. $\div 4.5$ in.

$= 90 \div 4.5$

$= 20$

You can place 20 stencils in a column from the top to the bottom of your wall.

68. a. $-0.122333\ldots \approx -0.1$

$\sqrt{7.9} \approx 2.8$

$\dfrac{3\sqrt{7}}{6} \approx 1.3$

$\dfrac{\sqrt{3 + 22}}{4} = \dfrac{\sqrt{25}}{4} = \dfrac{5}{4} \approx 1.3$

$\dfrac{\sqrt{9}}{1} = \dfrac{3}{1} = 3$

$-\dfrac{\sqrt{144}}{2} = -\dfrac{12}{2} = -6$

b.

Rational numbers	Irrational numbers
$\dfrac{\sqrt{9}}{1}$ $\dfrac{\sqrt{3+22}}{4}$ $-\dfrac{\sqrt{144}}{2}$	$-0.122333\ldots$ $\dfrac{3\sqrt{7}}{6}$ $\sqrt{7.9}$

c.

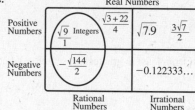

69. $m = 5\sqrt{\dfrac{w}{A}} = 5\sqrt{\dfrac{19.6}{11.71}} \approx 6.5$

The minimum wind speed to fly the kite is about 6.5 miles per hour. No, you can't fly your kite with a wind speed of 6 miles per hour.

70. a. $r = \sqrt{\dfrac{A}{\pi}} = \sqrt{\dfrac{6}{\pi}} \approx 1.4$

The radius of the circle is about 1.4 feet.

b. $r = \sqrt{\dfrac{A}{\pi}} = \sqrt{\dfrac{9\pi}{\pi}} = \sqrt{9} = 3$

The radius of the circle is 3 feet and the diameter is $2(3) = 6$ feet.

c. The area needs to be a product of π and a perfect square for the radius to be an integer.

Chapter 9, *continued*

71. No; *Sample answer:* The decimal shown on the calculator screen could terminate at a higher level of accuracy, or there might be a repeating pattern in the decimal that takes more decimal places to identify than are shown.

72. Let s = side length of large square.

$$\text{Area of large square} - \text{Area of small squares} = \text{Shaded area}$$

$$s^2 - 4(3^2) = 45$$
$$s^2 - 36 = 45$$
$$s^2 - 36 + 36 = 45 + 36$$
$$s^2 = 81$$
$$s = 9$$

The side length of the large square is 9 centimeters, so it is rational.

73. *Sample answer:*

$$\frac{17}{25}, \frac{7}{10}, \frac{18}{25}, \sqrt{0.5}, \sqrt{0.51}, \sqrt{0.52}$$

You could not write all of the rational numbers between these two numbers because you can always create a new number by adding a digit to the end of the decimal form of a rational number between $\frac{2}{3}$ and $\frac{3}{4}$.

Mixed Review

74–81. Let $a = 4$, $b = 3$, and $c = 2$.

74. $a^2 + b^2 = 4^2 + 3^2 = 16 + 9 = 25$

75. $a^2 - b^2 = 4^2 - 3^2 = 16 - 9 = 7$

76. $c + a^2 = 2 + 4^2 = 2 + 16 = 18$

77. $b^2 - b = 3^2 - 3 = 9 - 3 = 6$

78. $a^2 + c = 4^2 + 2 = 16 + 2 = 18$

79. $c^2 - b = 2^2 - 3 = 4 - 3 = 1$

80. $b^2 - a + c = 3^2 - 4 + 2 = 9 - 4 + 2 = 5 + 2 = 7$

81. $a^2 - b^2 + c^2 = 4^2 - 3^2 + 2^2 = 16 - 9 + 4 = 7 + 4 = 11$

82. $5a^2 \cdot 6a^9 = 5 \cdot 6a^{2+9} = 30a^{11}$

83. $d^8 \cdot 4d^5 = 1 \cdot 4d^{8+5} = 4d^{13}$

84. $\dfrac{c^5 \cdot c^3}{c^4} = \dfrac{c^{5+3}}{c^4} = \dfrac{c^8}{c^4} = c^{8-4} = c^4$

85. $\dfrac{-8n^8}{12n^{12}} = -\dfrac{2}{3}n^{8-12} = -\dfrac{2}{3}n^{-4} = \dfrac{-2}{3n^4}$

86. $\dfrac{10m^7}{5m^3} = 2m^{7-3} = 2m^4$

87. $p^5 \cdot p^5 = p^{5+5} = p^{10}$

88. $\dfrac{16r}{r^4} = 16r^{1-4} = 16r^{-3} = \dfrac{16}{r^3}$

89. $\dfrac{36s^{12}}{12s^{36}} = 3s^{12-36} = 3s^{-24} = \dfrac{3}{s^{24}}$

90. Side length of enlarged hexagon = $2 \cdot 15 = 30$ cm.

Perimeter of enlarged hexagon = $6 \cdot 30 = 180$ cm.

The perimeter of the hexagon is 180 centimeters.

Lesson 9.3

Investigation (p. 481)

Step 1. $3^2 + 4^2 = 9 + 16 = 25$

The sum of the areas of the two squares is 25.

Step 2. The length is 5 units. So its area is $5^2 = 25$ square units.

Step 3. Because $3^2 + 4^2 = 5^2$, the areas are the same.

1.

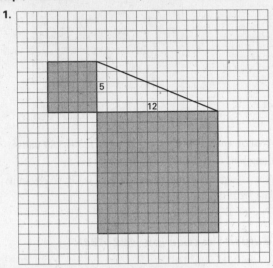

Area of squares = $5^2 + 12^2 = 25 + 144 = 169$ units^2

Length of hypotenuse = 13 units

Area of square with side length of 13 is $13^2 = 169$ units^2

The areas are the same.

2.

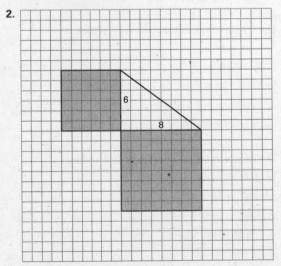

Area of squares = $6^2 + 8^2 = 36 + 64 = 100$ units^2

Length of hypotenuse = 10 units

Area of square with side length of 10 is $10^2 = 100$ units^2

The areas are the same.

3.

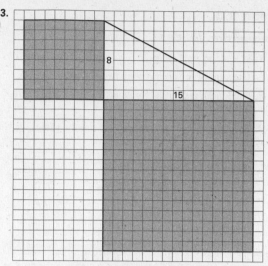

Area of squares $= 8^2 + 15^2 = 64 + 225 = 289$ units^2

Length of hypotenuse $= 17$ units

Area of square with side length of 17 is $17^2 = 289$ units^2

The areas are the same.

4. $a^2 + b^2 = c^2$

9.3 Guided Practice (pp. 482–484)

1.
$$a^2 + b^2 = c^2$$
$$28^2 + 45^2 = c^2$$
$$784 + 2025 = c^2$$
$$2809 = c^2$$
$$\sqrt{2809} = c$$
$$53 = c$$

The length of the hypotenuse is 53 inches.

2.
$$a^2 + b^2 = c^2$$
$$(7.5)^2 + 18^2 = c^2$$
$$56.25 + 324 = c^2$$
$$380.25 = c^2$$
$$\sqrt{380.25} = c$$
$$19.5 = c$$

The length of the hypotenuse is 19.5 inches.

3. $a^2 + b^2 = c^2$
$$a^2 + 8^2 = 16^2$$
$$a^2 + 64 = 256$$
$$a^2 = 192$$
$$a = \sqrt{192}$$
$$a \approx 13.9$$

The length of the leg is about 13.9 meters.

4. $a^2 + b^2 = c^2$
$$9^2 + b^2 = 15^2$$
$$81 + b^2 = 225$$
$$b^2 = 144$$
$$b = \sqrt{144}$$
$$b = 12$$

The length of the leg is 12 feet.

5. $a = 14, b = 17, c = 23$
$$a^2 + b^2 \stackrel{?}{=} c^2$$
$$14^2 + 17^2 \stackrel{?}{=} 23^2$$
$$196 + 289 \stackrel{?}{=} 529$$
$$485 \neq 529$$

It is not a right triangle because $14^2 + 17^2 \neq 23^2$.

9.3 Exercises (pp. 484–486)

Skill Practice

1. In a right triangle, the side opposite the right angle is called the *hypotenuse*.

2. The theorem that relates the lengths of the legs to length of the hypotenuse of a right triangle is the *Pythagorean Theorem*.

3.
$$a^2 + b^2 = c^2$$
$$30^2 + 16^2 = c^2$$
$$900 + 256 = c^2$$
$$1156 = c^2$$
$$\sqrt{1156} = c$$
$$34 = c$$

The length of the hypotenuse is 34 feet.

4.
$$a^2 + b^2 = c^2$$
$$18^2 + 24^2 = c^2$$
$$324 + 576 = c^2$$
$$900 = c^2$$
$$\sqrt{900} = c$$
$$30 = c$$

The length of the hypotenuse is 30 inches.

5.
$$a^2 + b^2 = c^2$$
$$96^2 + 40^2 = c^2$$
$$9216 + 1600 = c^2$$
$$10{,}816 = c^2$$
$$\sqrt{10{,}816} = c$$
$$104 = c$$

The length of the hypotenuse is 104 meters.

6. B; $a^2 + b^2 = c^2$
$$24^2 + 32^2 = c^2$$
$$576 + 1024 = c^2$$
$$1600 = c^2$$
$$\sqrt{1600} = c^2$$
$$40 = c$$

7.
$$a^2 + b^2 = c^2$$
$$90^2 + b^2 = 150^2$$
$$8100 + b^2 = 22{,}500$$
$$b^2 = 14{,}400$$
$$b = \sqrt{14{,}400}$$
$$b = 120$$

The length of the leg is 120 centimeters.

Chapter 9, *continued*

8.
$$a^2 + b^2 = c^2$$
$$a^2 + 25^2 = 35^2$$
$$a^2 + 625 = 1225$$
$$a^2 = 600$$
$$a = \sqrt{600}$$
$$a \approx 24.5$$

The length of the leg is about 24.5 inches.

9.
$$a^2 + b^2 = c^2$$
$$46^2 + b^2 = 50^2$$
$$2116 + b^2 = 2500$$
$$b^2 = 384$$
$$b = \sqrt{384}$$
$$b \approx 19.6$$

The length of the leg is about 19.6 feet.

10. Eight feet was substituted for the wrong variable.
$$a^2 + b^2 = c^2$$
$$6^2 + b^2 = 8^2$$
$$36 + b^2 = 64$$
$$b^2 = 28$$
$$b = \sqrt{28}$$
$$b \approx 5.3$$

The length of the leg is about 5.3 feet.

11. $a = 4, b = 5, c = 7$
$$a^2 + b^2 \stackrel{?}{=} c^2$$
$$4^2 + 5^2 \stackrel{?}{=} 7^2$$
$$16 + 25 \stackrel{?}{=} 49$$
$$41 \neq 49$$

It is not a right triangle.

12. $a = 50, b = 64, c = 80$
$$a^2 + b^2 \stackrel{?}{=} c^2$$
$$50^2 + 64^2 \stackrel{?}{=} 80^2$$
$$2500 + 4096 \stackrel{?}{=} 6400$$
$$6596 \neq 6400$$

It is not a right triangle.

13. $a = 85, b = 204, c = 221$
$$a^2 + b^2 \stackrel{?}{=} c^2$$
$$85^2 + 204^2 \stackrel{?}{=} 221^2$$
$$7225 + 41{,}616 \stackrel{?}{=} 48{,}841$$
$$48{,}841 = 48{,}841$$

It is a right triangle.

14. $a = 1.2, b = 1.6, c = 2$
$$a^2 + b^2 \stackrel{?}{=} c^2$$
$$1.2^2 + 1.6^2 \stackrel{?}{=} 2^2$$
$$1.44 + 2.56 \stackrel{?}{=} 4$$
$$4 = 4$$

It is a right triangle.

15. $a = 6.5, b = 15.6, c = 16.9$
$$a^2 + b^2 \stackrel{?}{=} c^2$$
$$6.5^2 + 15.6^2 \stackrel{?}{=} 16.9^2$$
$$42.25 + 243.36 \stackrel{?}{=} 285.61$$
$$285.61 = 285.61$$

It is a right triangle.

16. $a = 28.8, b = 8.4, c = 31$
$$a^2 + b^2 \stackrel{?}{=} c^2$$
$$28.8^2 + 8.4^2 \stackrel{?}{=} 31^2$$
$$829.44 + 70.56 \stackrel{?}{=} 961$$
$$900 \neq 961$$

It is not a right triangle.

17.
$$a^2 + b^2 = c^2$$
$$(1.5)^2 + b^2 = (2.5)^2$$
$$2.25 + b^2 = 6.25$$
$$b^2 = 4$$
$$b = \sqrt{4}$$
$$b = 2$$

The length of the leg is 2 units.

18.
$$a^2 + b^2 = c^2$$
$$a^2 + 123^2 = (139.4)^2$$
$$a^2 + 15{,}129 = 19{,}432.36$$
$$a^2 = 4303.36$$
$$a = \sqrt{4303.36}$$
$$a = 65.6$$

The length of the leg is 65.6 units.

19.
$$a^2 + b^2 = c^2$$
$$(2.8)^2 + (4.5)^2 = c^2$$
$$7.84 + 20.25 = c^2$$
$$28.09 = c^2$$
$$\sqrt{28.09} = c$$
$$5.3 = c$$

The length of the hypotenuse is 5.3 units.

20.
$$a^2 + b^2 = c^2$$
$$(4.5)^2 + b^2 = (7.5)^2$$
$$20.25 + b^2 = 56.25$$
$$b^2 = 36$$
$$b = \sqrt{36}$$
$$b = 6$$

The length of the leg is 6 units.

21.
$$a^2 + b^2 = c^2$$
$$a^2 + 2^2 = (\sqrt{13})^2$$
$$a^2 + 4 = 13$$
$$a^2 = 9$$
$$a = \sqrt{9}$$
$$a = 3$$

The length of the leg is 3 units.

22.
$$a^2 + b^2 = c^2$$
$$(\sqrt{8})^2 + 1^2 = c^2$$
$$8 + 1 = c^2$$
$$9 = c^2$$
$$\sqrt{9} = c$$
$$3 = c$$

The length of the hypotenuse is 3 units.

23.
$$a^2 + b^2 = c^2$$
$$a^2 + 37.5^2 = 42.5^2$$
$$a^2 + 1406.25 = 1806.25$$
$$a^2 = 400$$
$$a = \sqrt{400}$$
$$a = 20$$

The length of the leg is 20 units.

24.
$$a^2 + b^2 = c^2$$
$$2.5^2 + 6^2 = c^2$$
$$6.25 + 36 = c^2$$
$$42.25 = c^2$$
$$\sqrt{42.25} = c$$
$$6.5 = c$$

The length of the hypotenuse is 6.5 units.

25.
$$a^2 + b^2 = c^2$$
$$2^2 + (\sqrt{21})^2 = c^2$$
$$4 + 21 = c^2$$
$$25 = c^2$$
$$\sqrt{25} = c$$
$$5 = c$$

The length of the hypotenuse is 5 units.

26.
$$a^2 + b^2 = c^2$$
$$(\sqrt{6})^2 + b^2 = (\sqrt{15})^2$$
$$6 + b^2 = 15$$
$$b^2 = 9$$
$$b = \sqrt{9}$$
$$b = 3$$

The length of the leg is 3 units.

27.

$$a^2 + b^2 = c^2$$
$$a^2 + a^2 = 6^2$$
$$2a^2 = 36$$
$$a^2 = 18$$
$$a = \sqrt{18}$$
$$a \approx 4.24$$

The length of each leg is about 4.24 feet.

28. $a = x$, $b = 3x$, $c = \sqrt{5}$
$$a^2 + b^2 = c^2$$
$$x^2 + (3x)^2 = (\sqrt{5})^2$$
$$x^2 + 9x^2 = 5$$
$$10x^2 = 5$$
$$x^2 = 0.5$$
$$x = \sqrt{0.5}$$
$$x \approx 0.71$$

The rectangle is 0.71 feet by $3x = 3(0.71) = 2.13$ feet.

29.
$$a^2 + b^2 = c^2$$
$$(12^2 + 3^2) + 4^2 = c^2$$
$$(144 + 9) + 16 = c^2$$
$$169 = c^2$$
$$\sqrt{169} = c$$
$$13 = c$$

The length of segment AB is 13 units.

Problem Solving

30.
$$a^2 + b^2 = c^2$$
$$8^2 + 4^2 = c^2$$
$$64 + 16 = c^2$$
$$80 = c^2$$
$$\sqrt{80} = c$$
$$8.9 \approx c$$

Each rope should be about 8.9 feet long.

31. The Pythagorean Theorem states that if the triangle is right, then the square of the hypotenuse equals the sum of the squares of the legs. The converse states that if the square of one of the sides of the triangle equals the sum of the squares of the other sides, then the triangle is right. If you want to find the hypotenuse of a triangle whose legs are 3 feet and 4 feet $(\sqrt{x})$, you would use the Pythagorean Theorem.

$$a^2 + b^2 = c^2$$
$$3^2 + 4^2 = c^2$$
$$9 + 16 = c^2$$
$$25 = c^2$$
$$\sqrt{25} = c$$
$$5 = c$$

The hypotenuse is 5 feet $(\sqrt{x})$.

If you want to know whether a triangle with sides 5 feet, 12 feet, and 13 feet, is a right triangle, you would use the converse.

$$a^2 + b^2 \stackrel{?}{=} c^2$$
$$5^2 + 12^2 \stackrel{?}{=} 13^2$$
$$25 + 144 \stackrel{?}{=} 169$$
$$169 = 169 \checkmark$$

It is a right triangle.

Chapter 9, continued

32. A; $a = 5, b = x, c = 13$

$$a^2 + b^2 = c^2$$
$$5^2 + x^2 = 13^2$$
$$25 + x^2 = 169$$
$$x^2 = 144$$
$$x = \sqrt{144}$$
$$x = 12$$

The ladder meets the wall at a height of 12 feet.

33. $a^2 + b^2 = c^2$
$$9^2 + b^2 = (23.8)^2$$
$$81 + b^2 = 566.44$$
$$b^2 = 485.44$$
$$b = \sqrt{485.44}$$
$$b \approx 22.0$$

The wire is attached to the pole about 22.0 meters above the ground.

34. *Sample answer:* If $a^2 + b^2 = c^2$, then the triangle is a right triangle; If an angle is 30°, then it is an acute angle.

35. a. Use the Pythagorean Theorem to find the height of the wall.

$$a^2 + b^2 = c^2$$
$$20^2 + b^2 = 25^2$$
$$400 + b^2 = 625$$
$$b^2 = 225$$
$$b = \sqrt{225}$$
$$b = 15$$

The height of the wall is 15 feet.

The window and wall are similar, so $\dfrac{20}{3\frac{1}{3}} = \dfrac{15}{y}$,

and $y = 2.5$ ft.

The window is 2.5 feet tall.

b. The window and the wall are similar, so $\dfrac{20}{3\frac{1}{3}} = \dfrac{25}{a}$,

and $a = 4\frac{1}{6}$.

The window's diagonal is $4\frac{1}{6}$ feet. Then use the Pythagorean Theorem to find the height of the window:

$$a^2 + b^2 = c^2$$
$$\left(3\frac{1}{3}\right)^2 + b^2 = \left(4\frac{1}{6}\right)^2$$
$$11\frac{1}{9} + b^2 = 17\frac{13}{36}$$
$$b^2 = 6.25$$
$$b = \sqrt{6.25}$$
$$b = 2.5$$

The height of the window is 2.5 feet.

36. a.

b. $a^2 + b^2 = c^2$
$$4^2 + 5^2 = c^2$$
$$16 + 25 = c^2$$
$$41 = c^2$$
$$\sqrt{41} = c$$
$$6.4 \approx c$$

It is about 6.4 miles from the campsite to the creek.

c. Eric's route: $3.5 + 4 + 1.5 = 9$ miles

It is about $9 - 6.4 = 2.6$ miles shorter to walk in a straight line.

37. *Sample answer:* The length of the longest side is always less than the sum of the lengths of the two shorter sides.

38. Yes; $a^2 + b^2 \overset{?}{=} c^2$
$$a^2 + 5^2 \overset{?}{=} \left(\sqrt{a^2 + 25}\right)^2$$
$$a^2 + 25 = a^2 + 25 ✓$$

The triangle formed by two of the sides is right. A quadrilateral with at least one pair of equal sides opposite each other and at least one right angle is a rectangle.

Mixed Review

39. $x^2 = 49$
$$x = \pm\sqrt{49} = \pm 7$$
Check: $x = -7$: $(-7)^2 \overset{?}{=} 49$
$$49 = 49 ✓$$
$$x = 7: (7)^2 \overset{?}{=} 49$$
$$49 = 49 ✓$$

40. $a^2 + 12 = 15$
$$a^2 + 12 - 12 = 15 - 12$$
$$a^2 = 3$$
$$a = \pm\sqrt{3}$$
Check: $a = -\sqrt{3}$: $(-\sqrt{3})^2 + 12 \overset{?}{=} 15$
$$3 + 12 \overset{?}{=} 15$$
$$15 = 15 ✓$$
$$a = \sqrt{3}: (\sqrt{3})^2 + 12 \overset{?}{=} 15$$
$$3 + 12 \overset{?}{=} 15$$
$$15 = 15 ✓$$

Chapter 9, continued

41.
$$y^2 - 11 = 0$$
$$y^2 - 11 + 11 = 0 + 11$$
$$y^2 = 11$$
$$y = \pm\sqrt{11}$$
Check: $y = -\sqrt{11}: \left(-\sqrt{11}\right)^2 - 11 \stackrel{?}{=} 0$
$$11 - 11 \stackrel{?}{=} 0$$
$$0 = 0 \checkmark$$
$$y = \sqrt{11}: \left(\sqrt{11}\right)^2 - 11 \stackrel{?}{=} 0$$
$$11 - 11 \stackrel{?}{=} 0$$
$$0 = 0 \checkmark$$

42.
$$z^2 - 2 = 79$$
$$z^2 - 2 + 2 = 79 + 2$$
$$z^2 = 81$$
$$z = \pm\sqrt{81}$$
$$z = \pm 9$$
Check: $z = -9: (-9)^2 - 2 \stackrel{?}{=} 79$
$$81 - 2 \stackrel{?}{=} 79$$
$$79 = 79 \checkmark$$
$$z = 9: 9^2 - 2 \stackrel{?}{=} 79$$
$$81 - 2 \stackrel{?}{=} 79$$
$$79 = 79 \checkmark$$

43. $L(1, 5) \rightarrow L'(3, 15)$
$M(4, 2) \rightarrow M'(12, 6)$
$N(0, 0) \rightarrow N'(0, 0)$

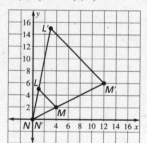

44. C;
$$m\angle A + m\angle B + m\angle C + m\angle D = 360°$$
$$58° + 64° + 123° + m\angle D = 360°$$
$$245° + m\angle D = 360°$$
$$m\angle D = 115°$$

Lesson 9.4

9.4 Guided Practice (pp. 487–488)

1.
$$a^2 + b^2 = x^2$$
$$0.5^2 + 0.9^2 = x^2$$
$$0.25 + 0.81 = x^2$$
$$1.06 = x^2$$
$$1.0 \approx x$$

It is about 1 mile to your friend's house from your house.

2.
$$a^2 + b^2 = c^2$$
$$0.4^2 + 0.6^2 = c^2$$
$$0.16 + 0.36 = c^2$$
$$0.52 = c^2$$
$$\sqrt{0.52} = c$$
$$0.7 \approx c$$

It is about 0.7 mile to the marina from your house by boat.

3.
$$70^2 + h^2 = 74^2$$
$$4900 + h^2 = 5476$$
$$h^2 = 576$$
$$h = \sqrt{576}$$
$$h = 24$$
Perimeter $= 70 + 74 + 24 = 168$
Area $= \frac{1}{2}bh = \frac{1}{2}(70)(24) = 840$

The perimeter of the triangle is 168 feet and the area is 840 square feet.

4.
$$a^2 + b^2 = c^2$$
$$6^2 + 24^2 \stackrel{?}{=} 25^2$$
$$36 + 576 \stackrel{?}{=} 625$$
$$612 \neq 625$$

Because $6^2 + 24^2 \neq 25^2$, the side lengths do not form a Pythagorean triple.

9.4 Exercises (pp. 489–491)

Skill Practice

1. The integers 5, 12, and 13 form a *Pythagorean triple* because $5^2 + 12^2 = 13^2$.

2.
$$a^2 + b^2 = c^2$$
$$12^2 + 16^2 = c^2$$
$$144 + 256 = c^2$$
$$400 = c^2$$
$$20 = c$$
Perimeter $= 12 + 16 + 20 = 48$
Area $= \frac{1}{2}bh = \frac{1}{2}(12)(16) = 96$

The perimeter is 48 centimeters and the area is 96 square centimeters.

3.
$$a^2 + b^2 = c^2$$
$$20^2 + b^2 = 25^2$$
$$400 + b^2 = 625$$
$$b^2 = 225$$
$$b = 15$$
Perimeter $= 20 + 15 + 25 = 60$
Area $= \frac{1}{2}bh = \frac{1}{2}(20)(15) = 150$

The perimeter is 60 feet and the area is 150 square feet.

Chapter 9, *continued*

4.
$$a^2 + b^2 = c^2$$
$$a^0 + 4.2^0 = 5.8^2$$
$$a^2 + 17.64 = 33.64$$
$$a^2 = 16$$
$$a = 4$$

Perimeter = $4.2 + 5.8 + 4 = 14$

Area = $\frac{1}{2}bh = \frac{1}{2}(4.2)(4) = 8.4$

The perimeter is 14 kilometers and the area is 8.4 square kilometers.

5.
$$a^2 + b^2 = c^2$$
$$4.8^2 + 3.6^2 = c^2$$
$$23.04 + 12.96 = c^2$$
$$36 = c^2$$
$$6 = c$$

Perimeter = $4.8 + 3.6 + 6 = 14.4$

Area = $\frac{1}{2}bh = \frac{1}{2}(4.8)(3.6) = 8.64$

The perimeter is 14.4 inches and the area is 8.64 square inches.

6.
$$a^2 + b^2 = c^2$$
$$60^2 + b^2 = 601.5^2$$
$$3600 + b^2 = 361,802.25$$
$$b^2 = 358,202.25$$
$$b = 598.5$$

Perimeter = $60 + 601.5 + 598.5 = 1260$

Area = $\frac{1}{2}bh = \frac{1}{2}(60)(598.5) = 17,955$

The perimeter is 1260 yards and the area is 17,955 square yards.

7.
$$a^2 + b^2 = c^2$$
$$a^2 + 117^2 = 125^2$$
$$a^2 + 13,689 = 15,625$$
$$a^2 = 1936$$
$$a = 44$$

Perimeter = $117 + 125 + 44 = 286$

Area = $\frac{1}{2}bh = \frac{1}{2}(117)(44) = 2574$

The perimeter is 286 meters and the area is 2574 square meters.

8.
$$a^2 + b^2 = c^2$$
$$1.1^2 + 6^2 = c^2$$
$$1.21 + 36 = c^2$$
$$37.21 = c^2$$
$$6.1 = c$$

Perimeter = $1.1 + 6 + 6.1 = 13.2$

Area = $\frac{1}{2}bh = \frac{1}{2}(1.1)(6) = 3.3$

The perimeter is 13.2 centimeters and the area is 3.3 square centimeters.

9.
$$a^2 + b^2 = c^2$$
$$15^2 + b^2 = 25^2$$
$$225 + b^2 = 625$$
$$b^2 = 400$$
$$b = 20$$

Perimeter = $15 + 20 + 25 = 60$

Area = $\frac{1}{2}bh = \frac{1}{2}(15)(20) = 150$

The perimeter is 60 yards and the area is 150 square yards.

10. C;
$$a^2 + b^2 = c^2$$
$$3.6^2 + 7.7^2 = c^2$$
$$12.96 + 59.29 = c^2$$
$$72.25 = c^2$$
$$8.5 = c$$

Perimeter = $3.6 + 7.7 + 8.5 = 19.8$

11. The hypotenuse was used in the area formula instead of the missing leg.
$$a^2 + b^2 = c^2$$
$$a^2 + 2.1^2 = 5.3^2$$
$$a^2 + 4.41 = 28.09$$
$$a^2 = 23.68$$
$$a \approx 4.9$$

$A = \frac{1}{2}bh = \frac{1}{2}(4.9)(2.1) \approx 5.1$

The area is about 5.1 square feet.

12.
$$a^2 + b^2 = c^2$$
$$9^2 + 36^2 \stackrel{?}{=} 41^2$$
$$81 + 1296 \stackrel{?}{=} 1681$$
$$1377 \neq 1681$$

The numbers do not form a Pythagorean triple.

13.
$$a^2 + b^2 = c^2$$
$$55^2 + 48^2 \stackrel{?}{=} 73^2$$
$$3025 + 2304 \stackrel{?}{=} 5329$$
$$5329 = 5329$$

The numbers form a Pythagorean triple.

14.
$$a^2 + b^2 = c^2$$
$$39^2 + 80^2 \stackrel{?}{=} 89^2$$
$$1521 + 6400 \stackrel{?}{=} 7921$$
$$7921 = 7921$$

The numbers form a Pythagorean triple.

15.
$$a^2 + b^2 = c^2$$
$$45^2 + 96^2 \stackrel{?}{=} 104^2$$
$$2025 + 9216 \stackrel{?}{=} 10,816$$
$$11,241 \neq 10,816$$

The numbers do not form a Pythagorean triple.

Chapter 9, continued

16. $A = \frac{1}{2}bh$

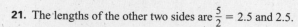

$24 = \frac{1}{2}(6)h$

$24 = 3h$

$8 = h$

$8^2 + 6^2 = c^2$

$100 = c^2$

$10 = c$

Perimeter $= 8 + 6 + 10 = 24$

The perimeter is 24 meters.

17. $A = \frac{1}{2}bh$

$46.2 = \frac{1}{2}(8.8)h$

$46.2 = 4.4h$

$10.5 = h$

$8.8^2 + 10.5^2 = c^2$

$77.44 + 110.25 = c^2$

$187.69 = c^2$

$13.7 = c$

Perimeter $= 8.8 + 10.5 + 13.7 = 33$

The perimeter is 33 miles.

18. $A = \frac{1}{2}bh$

$546 = \frac{1}{2}(84)h$

$546 = 42h$

$13 = h$

$84^2 + 13^2 = c^2$

$7056 + 169 = c^2$

$7225 = c^2$

$85 = c$

Perimeter $= 84 + 13 + 85 = 182$

The perimeter is 182 centimeters.

19. The lengths of the other two sides are $\frac{10}{2} = 5$ and 5.

$a^2 + b^2 = c^2$

$5^2 + 5^2 \overset{?}{=} \left(\sqrt{50}\right)^2$

$25 + 25 \overset{?}{=} 50$

$50 = 50 \checkmark$

Yes, it is a right triangle.

20. The lengths of the other two sides are $\frac{\sqrt{32}}{2}$ and $\frac{\sqrt{32}}{2}$.

$a^2 + b^2 = c^2$

$\left(\frac{\sqrt{32}}{2}\right)^2 + \left(\frac{\sqrt{32}}{2}\right)^2 \overset{?}{=} 4^2$

$\frac{32}{4} + \frac{32}{4} \overset{?}{=} 16$

$8 + 8 \overset{?}{=} 16$

$16 = 16$

Yes, it is a right triangle.

21. The lengths of the other two sides are $\frac{5}{2} = 2.5$ and 2.5.

$a^2 + b^2 = c^2$

$2.5^2 + 2.5^2 \overset{?}{=} \left(\sqrt{13}\right)^2$

$6.25 + 6.25 \overset{?}{=} 13$

$12.5 \neq 13$

No, it is not a right triangle.

22. Yes; *Sample answer:* When you multiply the length of each side of a right triangle by the same positive integer, you create another triangle that is similar to the first. Similar triangles have congruent angles, so the new triangle is also a right triangle, and the new numbers form a Pythagorean triple.

23. With $b = a$, find c.

$a^2 + a^2 = c^2$

$2a^2 = c^2$

$\sqrt{2a^2} = c$

$\sqrt{2aa} = c$

$a\sqrt{2} = c$

So, perimeter $= a + a + a\sqrt{2} = 2a + a\sqrt{2}$.

When $a = 9$:

$P = 2a + a\sqrt{2} = 2(9) + 9\sqrt{2} \approx 18 + 12.7 = 30.7$ units

24. $d = \sqrt{(u - s)^2 + (v - t)^2}$

$= \sqrt{(5 - 0)^2 + (0 - (-12))^2}$

$= \sqrt{25 + 144}$

$= 13$

25. $d = \sqrt{(u - s)^2 + (v - t)^2}$

$= \sqrt{(5 - (-2))^2 + (-6 - 4)^2}$

$= \sqrt{49 + 100}$

≈ 12.2

26. $d = \sqrt{(u - s)^2 + (v - t)^2}$

$= \sqrt{(3 - 1)^2 + (4 - 6)^2}$

$= \sqrt{4 + 4}$

≈ 2.8

27. $d = \sqrt{(u - s)^2 + (v - t)^2}$

$= \sqrt{(3 - (-4))^2 + (3 - 7)^2}$

$= \sqrt{49 + 16}$

≈ 8.1

28. $d = \sqrt{(u - s)^2 + (v - t)^2}$

$= \sqrt{(-5 - 6)^2 + (-1 - (-3))^2}$

$= \sqrt{121 + 4}$

≈ 11.2

29. $d = \sqrt{(u - s)^2 + (v - t)^2}$

$= \sqrt{(1 - (-2))^2 + (9 - 0)^2}$

$= \sqrt{9 + 81}$

≈ 9.5

30.
$$a^2 + b^2 = c^2$$
$$(u - s)^2 + (v - t)^2 = d^2$$
$$\sqrt{(u - s)^2 + (v - t)^2} = d$$

Problem Solving

31. a–b.

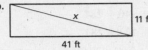

c. $41^2 + 11^2 = x^2$

$1681 + 121 = x^2$

$1802 = x^2$

$\sqrt{1802} = x$

$42.4 \approx x$

Tina swims about 42.4 feet.

32.

$500^2 + h^2 = 747^2$

$250,000 + h^2 = 558,009$

$h^2 = 308,009$

$h \approx 555$ ft

The Washington Monument is about 555 feet high.

33. *Sample answer:* It is easier to use indirect measurement if one of the distances is difficult or impossible to measure, such as the distance over a body of water or the height of a tall building. It is better to use direct measurement when all of the lengths are easy to measure, such as the dimensions of a doorway.

34. A;

$10^2 + 15^2 = x^2$

$100 + 225 = x^2$

$325 = x^2$

$18 \approx x$

The measurement of x is about 18 inches.

35. a.

	a	b	c	Perimeter	Area
$\triangle ABC$	3	4	5	12	6
$\triangle DEF$	6	8	10	24	24
$\triangle TUV$	9	12	15	36	54

b. Draw and label three right triangles:

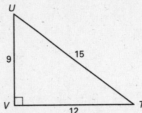

By comparing the diagrams, you can see that the perimeters are two and three times those of the original triangle. However, if you imagine placing the original triangle on the others, you can see that the areas are more than two and three times the original area.

36.

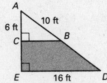

Length of BC:

$6^2 + (BC)^2 = 10^2$

$36 + (BC)^2 = 100$

$(BC)^2 = 64$

$BC = 8$ ft

Length of CE:

Use the fact that $\triangle ABC \sim \triangle ADE$.

$$\frac{BC}{DE} = \frac{AC}{AE}$$

$$\frac{8}{16} = \frac{6}{6 + CE}$$

$8(6 + CE) = 16(6)$

$48 + 8 \cdot CE = 96$

$8 \cdot CE = 48$

$CE = 6$

Area of $\triangle ADE$:

$A = \frac{1}{2}bh = \frac{1}{2}(16)(12) = 96$

Area of $\triangle ABC$:

$A = \frac{1}{2}bh = \frac{1}{2}(8)(6) = 24$

Area of $CBDE$:

$96 - 24 = 72$

The area of the shaded region is 72 square feet.

Chapter 9, *continued*

Mixed Review

37. $x° + 90° + 60° = 180°$

$x° + 150° = 180°$

$x° = 30°$

38. $x° + 90° + 45° = 180°$

$x° + 135° = 180°$

$x° = 45°$

39. $x° + 90° + 15° = 180°$

$x° + 105° = 180°$

$x° = 75°$

40. $x° + 90° + 81° = 180°$

$x° + 171° = 180°$

$x° = 9°$

41. Reflection of figure in y-axis:

$(x, y) \rightarrow (-x, y)$

$A(-3, 3) \rightarrow A'(3, 3)$

$B(-3, 6) \rightarrow B'(3, 6)$

$C(-5, 3) \rightarrow C'(5, 3)$

$D(-6, 1) \rightarrow D'(6, 1)$

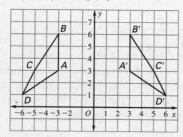

42. A; $-\sqrt{625} = -25$ because $(-25)^2 = 625$

Quiz 9.1–9.4 (p. 491)

1. $\sqrt{50} \approx 7.1$

2. $\sqrt{18} \approx 4.2$

3. $-\sqrt{160} \approx -12.6$

4. $\sqrt{462} \approx 21.5$

5. $x^2 = 400$

$x = \pm\sqrt{400}$

$x = \pm20$

Check: $x = -20$: $(-20)^2 \stackrel{?}{=} 400$

$400 = 400$ ✓

$x = 20$: $20^2 \stackrel{?}{=} 400$

$400 = 400$ ✓

6. $b^2 - 11 = -2$

$b^2 = 9$

$b = \pm\sqrt{9}$

$b = \pm3$

Check:

$b = -3$: $(-3)^2 - 11 \stackrel{?}{=} -2$

$9 - 11 \stackrel{?}{=} -2$

$-2 = -2$ ✓

$b = 3$: $3^2 - 11 \stackrel{?}{=} -2$

$9 - 11 \stackrel{?}{=} -2$

$-2 = -2$ ✓

7. $m^2 + 140 = 284$

$m^2 = 144$

$m = \pm\sqrt{144}$

$m = \pm12$

Check:

$m = -12$: $(-12)^2 + 140 \stackrel{?}{=} 284$

$144 + 140 \stackrel{?}{=} 284$

$284 = 284$ ✓

$m = 12$: $12^2 + 140 \stackrel{?}{=} 284$

$144 + 140 \stackrel{?}{=} 284$

$284 = 284$ ✓

8. $a^2 + b^2 = c^2$

$12^2 + 16^2 = c^2$

$144 + 256 = c^2$

$400 = c^2$

$\sqrt{400} = c$

$20 = c$

The length of the hypotenuse is 20 meters.

9. $a^2 + b^2 = c^2$

$9^2 + b^2 = 41^2$

$81 + b^2 = 1681$

$b^2 = 1600$

$b = 40$

Perimeter $= 9 + 40 + 41 = 90$

Area $= \frac{1}{2}bh = \frac{1}{2}(9)(40) = 180$

The perimeter is 90 feet and the area is 180 square feet.

10. $a^2 + b^2 = c^2$

$5^2 + 12^2 \stackrel{?}{=} 15^2$

$25 + 144 \stackrel{?}{=} 225$

$169 \neq 225$

The numbers do not form a Pythagorean triple.

11. $a^2 + b^2 = c^2$

$60^2 + 91^2 \stackrel{?}{=} 109^2$

$3600 + 8281 \stackrel{?}{=} 11{,}881$

$11{,}881 = 11{,}881$

The numbers form a Pythagorean triple.

12. $a^2 + b^2 = c^2$

$11^2 + 40^2 \stackrel{?}{=} 41^2$

$121 + 1600 \stackrel{?}{=} 1681$

$1721 \neq 1681$

The numbers do not form a Pythagorean triple.

Chapter 9, continued

Mixed Review of Problem Solving (p. 492)

1. a. $r: a^2 + b^2 = c^2$

$$1^2 + 1^2 = r^2$$
$$1 + 1 = r^2$$
$$2 = r^2$$
$$\sqrt{2} = r$$

$s: a^2 + b^2 = c^2$

$$1^2 + (\sqrt{2})^2 = s^2$$
$$1 + 2 = s^2$$
$$3 = s^2$$
$$\sqrt{3} = s$$

$t: a^2 + b^2 = c^2$

$$1^2 + (\sqrt{3})^2 = t^2$$
$$1 + 3 = t^2$$
$$4 = t^2$$
$$2 = t$$

$u: a^2 + b^2 = c^2$

$$1^2 + 2^2 = u^2$$
$$1 + 4 = u^2$$
$$5 = u^2$$
$$\sqrt{5} = u$$

b. Perimeter $= 5(1) + \sqrt{5} \approx 5 + 2.2 \approx 7.2$

Area of each triangle:

$$A = \frac{1}{2}bh = \frac{1}{2}(1)(1) = 0.5$$

$$A = \frac{1}{2}bh = \frac{1}{2}(\sqrt{2})(1) \approx 0.7$$

$$A = \frac{1}{2}bh = \frac{1}{2}(\sqrt{3})(1) \approx 0.9$$

$$A = \frac{1}{2}bh = \frac{1}{2}(2)(1) = 1$$

Area of design $\approx 0.5 + 0.7 + 0.9 + 1 = 3.1$

The perimeter of the design is about 7.2 units and the area is about 3.1 square units.

2. a.

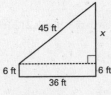

7 m

7.5 m

b. $a^2 + b^2 = c^2$

$$7^2 + 7.5^2 = c^2$$
$$49 + 56.25 = c^2$$
$$105.25 = c^2$$
$$\sqrt{105.25} = c$$

Because 105.25 is between $100 = 10^2$ and $121 = 11^2$, $\sqrt{105.25}$ is between 10 and 11. Use guess and check with values between 10 and 11 to find that $\sqrt{105.25} \approx 10.3$ meters.

c. Irrational; $\sqrt{105.25}$ cannot be expressed as the ratio of two integers.

3.

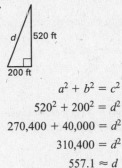

d / 520 ft

200 ft

$$a^2 + b^2 = c^2$$
$$520^2 + 200^2 = d^2$$
$$270{,}400 + 40{,}000 = d^2$$
$$310{,}400 = d^2$$
$$557.1 \approx d$$

Distance between you and your friend − height of the observation deck $\approx 557.1 - 520 = 37.1$ feet

4. Use the diagram.

45 ft

x

6 ft   6 ft

36 ft

$$a^2 + b^2 = c^2$$
$$x^2 + 36^2 = 45^2$$
$$x^2 + 1296 = 2025$$
$$x^2 = 729$$
$$x = 27$$

The top of the banner is $27 + 6 = 33$ feet from the floor, so the bottom of the banner is $33 - 3 = 30$ feet from the floor.

5. *Sample answer:* $0.43040040004000004\ldots$; it is irrational because it is nonrepeating and nonterminating.

6. $a^2 + b^2 = c^2$

$$78^2 + 36^2 = c^2$$
$$6084 + 1296 = c^2$$
$$7380 = c^2$$
$$85.9 \approx c$$

Because the diagonal of the doorway is about 85.9 inches, the table top with a diameter of $2(41) = 82$ inches can fit through the doorway.

7. Bottom triangle: $a^2 + b^2 = c^2$

$$a^2 + 24^2 = 28^2$$
$$a^2 + 576 = 784$$
$$a^2 = 208$$
$$a \approx 14.422$$

Area of bottom half: $A = \frac{1}{2}bh \approx \frac{1}{2}(2(14.422))(24) \approx 346.1$

Area of top half: $A = \frac{1}{2}bh \approx \frac{1}{2}(2(14.422))(8) \approx 115.4$

The area of the kite is about $346.1 + 115.4 \approx 462$ square inches.

8. a. No; The side length of the rug is $\sqrt{100} = 10$ feet. Because $10 > 9$, the rug is too wide for her room.

Chapter 9, continued

b. $A = \pi r^2$

$100 = \pi r^2$

$\dfrac{100}{\pi} = \dfrac{\pi r^2}{\pi}$

$31.8 \approx r^2$

$5.64 \approx r$

The diameter is about $2(5.64) \approx 11.3$ feet. Because $11.3 > 9$, the rug is too wide for her room.

c. Yes; *Sample answer:* 9 feet by $11\frac{1}{9}$ feet.

Lesson 9.5

9.5 Guided Practice (pp. 493–495)

1. hypotenuse = leg $\cdot \sqrt{2} = 150 \cdot \sqrt{2} \approx 212$

The diagonal distance across the park is about 212 feet.

2. hypotenuse = 2 $\cdot$ shorter leg

$50 = 2x$

$25 = x$

longer leg = shorter leg $\cdot \sqrt{3}$

$y = 25 \cdot \sqrt{3}$

$y = 25\sqrt{3}$

The shorter leg is 25 inches and the longer leg is $25\sqrt{3}$ inches.

3. longer leg = shorter leg $\cdot \sqrt{3}$

$7\sqrt{3} = x \cdot \sqrt{3}$

$7 = x$

hypotenuse = 2 $\cdot$ shorter leg

$y = 2 \cdot 7$

$y = 14$

The shorter leg is 7 meters and the hypotenuse is 14 meters.

4. hypotenuse = 2 $\cdot$ shorter leg

$4 = 2x$

$2 = x$

longer leg = shorter leg $\cdot \sqrt{3}$

$y = 2 \cdot \sqrt{3}$

$y = 2\sqrt{3}$

The shorter leg is 2 centimeters and the longer leg is $2\sqrt{3}$ centimeters.

5. longer leg = shorter leg $\cdot \sqrt{3}$

$15\sqrt{3} = x \cdot \sqrt{3}$

$15 = x$

hypotenuse = 2 $\cdot$ shorter leg

$y = 2 \cdot 15$

$y = 30$

The distance from the top of the pyramid to the boat is 30 feet.

9.5 Exercises (pp. 495–497)

Skill Practice

1. A 45°-45°-90° triangle is an *isosceles right* triangle.

2. The length of the hypotenuse is $\sqrt{2}$ times the length of a leg.

3. hypotenuse = leg $\cdot \sqrt{2}$

$9\sqrt{2} = x \cdot \sqrt{2}$

$9 = x$

The length of a leg is 9 meters.

4. hypotenuse = leg $\cdot \sqrt{2}$

$28\sqrt{2} = x \cdot \sqrt{2}$

$28 = x$

The length of a leg is 28 centimeters.

5. hypotenuse = leg $\cdot \sqrt{2}$

$z = 30\sqrt{2}$

The length of the hypotenuse is $30\sqrt{2}$ feet.

6. hypotenuse = leg $\cdot \sqrt{2}$

$z = 6\sqrt{2}$

The length of the hypotenuse is $6\sqrt{2}$ centimeters.

7. hypotenuse = leg $\cdot \sqrt{2}$

$10\sqrt{2} = x \cdot \sqrt{2}$

$10 = x$

The length of a leg is 10 inches.

8. hypotenuse = leg $\cdot \sqrt{2}$

$15\sqrt{2} = x \cdot \sqrt{2}$

$15 = x$

The length of a leg is 15 feet.

9. She multiplied by $\sqrt{3}$ instead of $\sqrt{2}$.

hypotenuse = leg $\cdot \sqrt{2} = 8\sqrt{2}$ in.

10. hypotenuse = 2 $\cdot$ shorter leg

$22 = 2x$

$11 = x$

longer leg = shorter leg $\cdot \sqrt{3}$

$y = 11 \cdot \sqrt{3}$

$y = 11\sqrt{3}$

The shorter leg is 11 inches and the longer leg is $11\sqrt{3}$ inches.

11. longer leg = shorter leg $\cdot \sqrt{3}$

$17\sqrt{3} = x \cdot \sqrt{3}$

$17 = x$

hypotenuse = 2 $\cdot$ shorter leg

$z = 2 \cdot 17$

$z = 34$

The shorter leg is 17 centimeters and the hypotenuse is 34 centimeters.

12. hypotenuse = 2 · shorter leg
$$z = 2 \cdot 36$$
$$z = 72$$
longer leg = shorter leg · $\sqrt{3}$
$$y = 36 \cdot \sqrt{3}$$
$$y = 36\sqrt{3}$$
The hypotenuse is 72 meters and the longer leg is $36\sqrt{3}$ meters.

13. hypotenuse = 2 · shorter leg
$$16 = 2x$$
$$8 = x$$
longer leg = shorter leg · $\sqrt{3}$
$$y = 8 \cdot \sqrt{3}$$
$$y = 8\sqrt{3}$$
The shorter leg is 8 meters and the longer leg is $8\sqrt{3}$ meters.

14. hypotenuse = 2 · shorter leg
$$23 = 2x$$
$$\frac{23}{2} = x$$
$$11\frac{1}{2} = x$$
longer leg = shorter leg · $\sqrt{3}$
$$y = \frac{23}{2} \cdot \sqrt{3}$$
$$y = \frac{23\sqrt{3}}{2}$$
The shorter leg is $11\frac{1}{2}$ feet and the longer leg is $\frac{23\sqrt{3}}{2}$ feet.

15. hypotenuse = 2 · shorter leg
$$65 = 2x$$
$$\frac{65}{2} = x$$
$$32\frac{1}{2} = x$$
longer leg = shorter leg · $\sqrt{3}$
$$y = \frac{65}{2} \cdot \sqrt{3}$$
$$y = \frac{65\sqrt{3}}{2}$$
The shorter leg is $32\frac{1}{2}$ centimeters and the longer leg is $\frac{65\sqrt{3}}{2}$ centimeters.

16. C; hypotenuse = 2 · shorter leg
$$10\sqrt{3} = 2x$$
$$5\sqrt{3} = x$$

17. hypotenuse = leg · $\sqrt{2}$
$$\sqrt{2} = x \cdot \sqrt{2}$$
$$1 = x$$
The perimeter is $4(1) = 4$ inches.

18. hypotenuse = 2 · shorter leg
$$2 = 2x$$
$$1 = x$$
longer leg = shorter leg · $\sqrt{3} = 1 \cdot \sqrt{3} = \sqrt{3}$
The perimeter is $1 + 1 + \sqrt{3} + \sqrt{3} \approx 5$ feet.

19. In the 45°-45°-90° triangle:
hypotenuse = leg · $\sqrt{2} = 4 \cdot \sqrt{2} = 4\sqrt{2}$
In the 30°-60°-90° triangle:
hypotenuse = 2 · shorter leg
$$4\sqrt{2} = 2x$$
$$2\sqrt{2} = x$$
$$2.8 \approx x$$
longer leg = shorter leg · $\sqrt{3}$
$$= 2\sqrt{2} \cdot \sqrt{3}$$
$$= 2\sqrt{2}\sqrt{3}$$
$$\approx 4.9$$
The perimeter is about $4 + 4 + 2.8 + 4.9 \approx 16$ millimeters.

20. Length of *AC*:
$$AC = AB \cdot \sqrt{3} = 11\sqrt{3} \text{ m}$$
Length of *BC*:
$$BC = 2 \cdot AB = 2 \cdot 11 = 22 \text{ m}$$
Length of *XZ*:
$$\frac{AB}{XY} = \frac{AC}{XZ}$$
$$\frac{11}{6} = \frac{11\sqrt{3}}{XZ}$$
$$11 \cdot XZ = 6(11\sqrt{3})$$
$$XZ = 6\sqrt{3} \text{ m}$$
Length of *YZ*:
$$\frac{AB}{XY} = \frac{BC}{YZ}$$
$$\frac{11}{6} = \frac{22}{YZ}$$
$$11 \cdot YZ = 6 \cdot 22$$
$$YZ = 12 \text{ m}$$
Area of $\triangle XYZ$: $A = \frac{1}{2}bh = \frac{1}{2}(6\sqrt{3})(6) = 18\sqrt{3}$
The area of $\triangle XYZ$ is $18\sqrt{3}$ square meters.

Chapter 9, *continued*

21. Length of *AD*:

$AB = 2 \cdot AD$

$8 = 2AD$

$4 = AD$

Length of *AC*:

$AC = 2AB = 2(8) = 16$

Length of *DC*: $DC = AC - AD = 16 - 4 = 12$

Length of *BD*:

$BD = AD \cdot \sqrt{3} = 4 \cdot \sqrt{3} = 4\sqrt{3}$

Length of *BC*:

$BC = 2BD = 2\left(4\sqrt{3}\right) = 8\sqrt{3}$

The three 30°-60°-90° triangles are $\triangle ABC$, $\triangle ADB$, and $\triangle BDC$.

Area of $\triangle ABC = \frac{1}{2}bh = \frac{1}{2}\left(8\sqrt{3}\right)(8) = 32\sqrt{3}$ units^2

Area of $\triangle ADB = \frac{1}{2}bh = \frac{1}{2}(4)\left(4\sqrt{3}\right) = 8\sqrt{3}$ units^2

Area of $\triangle BDC = \frac{1}{2}bh = \frac{1}{2}\left(4\sqrt{3}\right)(12) = 24\sqrt{3}$ units^2

The area of $\triangle ADB$ is $\frac{1}{4}$ the area of $\triangle ABC$. The area of $\triangle BDC$ is $\frac{3}{4}$ the area of $\triangle ABC$. The area of $\triangle ADB$ is $\frac{1}{3}$ the area of $\triangle BDC$.

Problem Solving

22. C; hypotenuse = leg $\cdot \sqrt{2}$

$20 = x\sqrt{2}$

$\dfrac{20}{\sqrt{2}} = x$

$14.1 \approx x$

23. hypotenuse = 2 $\cdot$ shorter leg

$230 = 2 \cdot x$

$115 = x$

The subway station is 115 feet below the ground.

24. No; The angles of an equilateral triangle are all 60°.

25. *Sample answer:*

hypotenuse = 2 $\cdot$ shorter leg

$\quad = 2(1)$

$\quad = 2$ inches

longer leg = shorter leg $\cdot \sqrt{3}$

$\quad = 1\left(\sqrt{3}\right)$

$\quad = \sqrt{3}$

$\quad \approx 1.73$ inches

26.

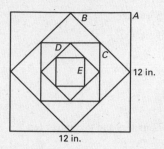

Perimeter of square $A = 4(12) = 48$ in.

Side length of square *B*:

hypotenuse = leg $\cdot \sqrt{2} = 6\sqrt{2}$

Perimeter of square $B = 4\left(6\sqrt{2}\right) \approx 34$ in.

Side length of square *C*:

hypotenuse = leg $\cdot \sqrt{2} = \left(3\sqrt{2}\right) \cdot \sqrt{2} = 6$

Perimeter of square $C = 4(6) = 24$ in.

Side length of square *D*:

hypotenuse = leg $\cdot \sqrt{2} = 3\sqrt{2}$

Perimeter of square $D = 4\left(3\sqrt{2}\right) \approx 17$ in.

Side length of square *E*:

hypotenuse = leg $\cdot \sqrt{2} = \left(\dfrac{3\sqrt{2}}{2}\right)\sqrt{2} = 3$ in.

Perimeter of square $E = 4(3) = 12$ in.

27. Perimeter = $6 + 6 + 6\sqrt{2} = 12 + 6\sqrt{2}$ in.

Perimeters of 4 triangles = $4\left(12 + 6\sqrt{2}\right) = 48 + 24\sqrt{2}$ in.

28. For the $30° - 60° - 90°$ triangle:

hypotenuse = 2 • shorter leg

$2x = 2$ shorter leg

$x =$ shorter leg

longer leg = shorter leg • $\sqrt{3} = x \cdot \sqrt{3} = x\sqrt{3}$

For the $45° - 45° - 90°$ triangle:

each leg = x(same as $30° - 60° - 90°$ shorter leg)

hypotenuse = leg • $\sqrt{2} = x \cdot \sqrt{2} = x\sqrt{2}$

Base of shaded region: $x\sqrt{3} - x$

Area of shaded region = $\frac{1}{2}bh$

$$= \frac{1}{2}(x\sqrt{3} - x)(x)$$

$$= \frac{x^2\sqrt{3} - x^2}{2}$$

$$= \frac{x^2(\sqrt{3} - 1)}{2}$$

29. $x^2 + (x\sqrt{3})^2 \overset{?}{=} (2x)^2$

$x^2 + 3x^2 \overset{?}{=} 4x^2$

$4x^2 = 4x^2$

Sample answer:

$4^2 + (4\sqrt{3})^2 \overset{?}{=} 8^2$

$16 + 16 \cdot 3 \overset{?}{=} 64$

$16 + 48 \overset{?}{=} 64$

$64 = 64$

30. Perimeter $= 6(1.5) = 9$ mm

To find the height of an equilateral triangle, use the diagram and the 30°-60°-90° triangle rule.

longer leg = shorter leg • $\sqrt{3} = 0.75 \cdot \sqrt{3} \approx 1.299$

The height of each triangle is about 1.299 millimeters.

The area of the hexagon = 6 • area of a triangle

$$= 6 \cdot \frac{1}{2}bh$$

$$\approx 6 \cdot \frac{1}{2}(1.5)(1.299)$$

$$\approx 5.8 \text{ square millimeters.}$$

Mixed Review

31. $0.45 = \dfrac{x}{20}$

$0.45 \cdot 20 = \dfrac{x}{20} \cdot 20$

$9 = x$

32. $0.217 = \dfrac{x}{50}$

$0.217 \cdot 50 = \dfrac{x}{50} \cdot 50$

$10.85 = x$

33. $0.4001 = \dfrac{x}{13}$

$0.4001 \cdot 13 = \dfrac{x}{13} \cdot 13$

$5.2013 = x$

34. $\dfrac{28 \text{ people}}{4 \text{ teams}} = \dfrac{(28 \div 4) \text{ people}}{(4 \div 4) \text{ teams}} = \dfrac{7 \text{ people}}{1 \text{ team}}$

35. $\dfrac{60 \text{ meters}}{20 \text{ seconds}} = \dfrac{(60 \div 20) \text{ meters}}{(20 \div 20) \text{ seconds}} = \dfrac{3 \text{ meters}}{1 \text{ second}}$

36. $\dfrac{488 \text{ rotations}}{8 \text{ minutes}} = \dfrac{(488 \div 8) \text{ rotations}}{(8 \div 8) \text{ minutes}} = \dfrac{61 \text{ rotations}}{1 \text{ minute}}$

37. C; $a^2 + 5b = (-8)^2 + 5(-2) = 64 + (-10) = 54$

Lesson 9.6

Investigation (p. 499)

1. $\sin A = \dfrac{12}{15} = \dfrac{4}{5}$

$\cos A = \dfrac{9}{15} = \dfrac{3}{5}$

$\sin B = \dfrac{9}{15} = \dfrac{3}{5}$

$\cos B = \dfrac{12}{15} = \dfrac{4}{5}$

2. $\sin A = \dfrac{6}{10} = \dfrac{3}{5}$

$\cos A = \dfrac{8}{10} = \dfrac{4}{5}$

$\sin B = \dfrac{8}{10} = \dfrac{4}{5}$

$\cos B = \dfrac{6}{10} = \dfrac{3}{5}$

3. $\sin A = \dfrac{15}{17}$

$\cos A = \dfrac{8}{17}$

$\sin B = \dfrac{8}{17}$

$\cos B = \dfrac{15}{17}$

4. $\sin A = \dfrac{24}{25}$

$\cos A = \dfrac{7}{25}$

$\sin B = \dfrac{7}{25}$

$\cos B = \dfrac{24}{25}$

5. $\sin A = \dfrac{35}{37}$

$\cos A = \dfrac{12}{37}$

$\sin B = \dfrac{12}{37}$

$\cos B = \dfrac{35}{37}$

6. $\sin A = \dfrac{3}{3.25}$

$\cos A = \dfrac{1.25}{3.25}$

$\sin B = \dfrac{1.25}{3.25}$

$\cos B = \dfrac{3}{3.25}$

7.

$m\angle A$	$\sin A$	$\cos A$
37°	$\dfrac{3}{5} = 0.6$	$\dfrac{4}{5} = 0.8$
53°	$\dfrac{4}{5} = 0.8$	$\dfrac{3}{5} = 0.6$
62°	$\dfrac{15}{17} \approx 0.88$	$\dfrac{8}{17} \approx 0.47$
67°	$\dfrac{3}{3.25} \approx 0.92$	$\dfrac{1.25}{3.25} \approx 0.38$
71°	$\dfrac{35}{37} \approx 0.95$	$\dfrac{12}{37} \approx 0.32$
74°	$\dfrac{24}{25} = 0.96$	$\dfrac{7}{25} = 0.28$

a. As $m\angle A$ increases from 0° to 90°, the value of sin A *increases.*

b. As $m\angle A$ increases from 0° to 90° the value of cos A *decreases.*

Chapter 9, *continued*

1. $\sin A = \dfrac{\text{opposite}}{\text{hypotenuse}} = \dfrac{8}{17}$

$\cos A = \dfrac{\text{adjacent}}{\text{hypotenuse}} = \dfrac{15}{17}$

$\tan A = \dfrac{\text{opposite}}{\text{adjacent}} = \dfrac{8}{15}$

$\sin C = \dfrac{\text{opposite}}{\text{hypotenuse}} = \dfrac{15}{17}$

$\cos C = \dfrac{\text{adjacent}}{\text{hypotenuse}} = \dfrac{8}{17}$

$\tan C = \dfrac{\text{opposite}}{\text{adjacent}} = \dfrac{15}{8}$

$\tan C$ has a value greater than 1.

2.

$\sin A = \dfrac{\text{opposite}}{\text{hypotenuse}} = \dfrac{2}{2\sqrt{2}} = \dfrac{1}{\sqrt{2}}$

$\cos A = \dfrac{\text{adjacent}}{\text{hypotenuse}} = \dfrac{2}{2\sqrt{2}} = \dfrac{1}{\sqrt{2}}$

$\tan A = \dfrac{\text{opposite}}{\text{adjacent}} = \dfrac{2}{2} = 1$

It doesn't make a difference which 45° angle is chosen because the opposite and adjacent values are the same.

3. $\cos 70° \approx 0.3420$ **4.** $\tan 50° \approx 1.1918$

5. $\sin 25° \approx 0.4226$ **6.** $\tan 7° \approx 0.1228$

7. $\cos B = \dfrac{\text{adjacent}}{\text{hypotenuse}}$

$\cos 40° = \dfrac{x}{6}$

$6 \cdot \cos 40° = 6 \cdot \dfrac{x}{6}$

$4.596 \approx x$

The value of x is about 4.60 feet.

8. $\sin 31° = \dfrac{\text{opposite}}{\text{hypotenuse}}$

$\sin 31° = \dfrac{x}{380}$

$380 \cdot \sin 31° = 380 \cdot \dfrac{x}{380}$

$195.71 \approx x$

The height is about 196 feet.

9. $\tan 16° = \dfrac{\text{opposite}}{\text{adjacent}}$

$\tan 16° = \dfrac{h}{64.2}$

$64.2 \cdot \tan 16° = 64.2 \cdot \dfrac{h}{64.2}$

$18.41 \approx h$

The height is about 18 meters.

1. B **2.** A **3.** C

4. $\sin P = \dfrac{\text{opposite}}{\text{hypotenuse}} = \dfrac{40}{41}$

$\cos P = \dfrac{\text{adjacent}}{\text{hypotenuse}} = \dfrac{9}{41}$

$\tan P = \dfrac{\text{opposite}}{\text{adjacent}} = \dfrac{40}{9}$

$\sin R = \dfrac{\text{opposite}}{\text{hypotenuse}} = \dfrac{9}{41}$

$\cos R = \dfrac{\text{adjacent}}{\text{hypotenuse}} = \dfrac{40}{41}$

$\tan R = \dfrac{\text{opposite}}{\text{adjacent}} = \dfrac{9}{40}$

5. $\sin P = \dfrac{\text{opposite}}{\text{hypotenuse}} = \dfrac{11}{61}$

$\cos P = \dfrac{\text{adjacent}}{\text{hypotenuse}} = \dfrac{60}{61}$

$\tan P = \dfrac{\text{opposite}}{\text{adjacent}} = \dfrac{11}{60}$

$\sin R = \dfrac{\text{opposite}}{\text{hypotenuse}} = \dfrac{60}{61}$

$\cos R = \dfrac{\text{adjacent}}{\text{hypotenuse}} = \dfrac{11}{61}$

$\tan R = \dfrac{\text{opposite}}{\text{adjacent}} = \dfrac{60}{11}$

6. $\sin P = \dfrac{\text{opposite}}{\text{hypotenuse}} = \dfrac{28}{53}$

$\cos P = \dfrac{\text{adjacent}}{\text{hypotenuse}} = \dfrac{45}{53}$

$\tan P = \dfrac{\text{opposite}}{\text{adjacent}} = \dfrac{28}{45}$

$\sin R = \dfrac{\text{opposite}}{\text{hypotenuse}} = \dfrac{45}{53}$

$\cos R = \dfrac{\text{adjacent}}{\text{hypotenuse}} = \dfrac{28}{53}$

$\tan R = \dfrac{\text{opposite}}{\text{adjacent}} = \dfrac{45}{28}$

7. B; $5^2 + 12^2 = c^2$

$169 = c^2$

$13 = c$

$\cos E = \dfrac{\text{adjacent}}{\text{hypotenuse}} = \dfrac{12}{13}$

8. $\tan 51° \approx 1.2349$ **9.** $\sin 80° \approx 0.9848$

10. $\sin 36° \approx 0.5878$ **11.** $\cos 76° \approx 0.2419$

12. $\tan G = \dfrac{\text{opposite}}{\text{adjacent}}$

$\tan 16° = \dfrac{x}{12}$

$0.2867 \approx \dfrac{x}{12}$

$3.4409 = x$

The value of x is about 3.441 inches.

13. $\sin K = \dfrac{\text{adjacent}}{\text{hypotenuse}}$

$\sin 43° = \dfrac{9}{x}$

$x = \dfrac{9}{\sin 43°}$

$x \approx \dfrac{9}{0.6820}$

$x \approx 13.197$

The value of x is about 13.197 centimeters.

14. $\cos L = \dfrac{\text{adjacent}}{\text{hypotenuse}}$

$\cos 8° = \dfrac{x}{21}$

$0.9903 \approx \dfrac{x}{21}$

$20.7963 \approx x$

The value of x is about 20.796 meters.

15. B; $\tan 35° = \dfrac{7}{AC}$

$0.7002 \approx \dfrac{7}{AC}$

$AC \approx \dfrac{7}{0.7002}$

$AC \approx 10$ ft

16. The tangent ratio is the length of the opposite side over the length of the adjacent side, not over the length of the hypotenuse.

$\tan 25° = \dfrac{x}{13}$

$0.4663 \approx \dfrac{x}{13}$

$6.0619 \approx x$

6 cm $\approx x$

17. Length of AC:

$\cos 70.1° = \dfrac{x}{37}$

$0.3404 \approx \dfrac{x}{37}$

$12.5948 \approx x$

$12.6 \approx x$

Perimeter $= 12.6 + 37 + 34.8 = 84.4$

The perimeter is about 84.4 inches.

18. Length of AC:

$\cos 32° = \dfrac{x}{53}$

$0.8480 \approx \dfrac{x}{53}$

$44.944 \approx x$

$44.9 \approx x$

Perimeter $= 44.9 + 28.1 + 53 = 126.0$

The perimeter is about 126.0 meters.

19. Length of BC:

$\cos 64.4° = \dfrac{x}{51}$

$0.4321 \approx \dfrac{x}{51}$

$22.0371 \approx x$

$22.0 \approx x$

Perimeter $= 22 + 46 + 51 = 119$

The perimeter is about 119.0 feet.

20. $\sin A = \dfrac{\text{opposite}}{\text{hypotenuse}} = \dfrac{x+1}{2x-1}$

$\cos A = \dfrac{\text{adjacent}}{\text{hypotenuse}} = \dfrac{x}{2x-1}$

$\tan A = \dfrac{\text{opposite}}{\text{adjacent}} = \dfrac{x+1}{x}$

$\sin B = \dfrac{\text{opposite}}{\text{hypotenuse}} = \dfrac{x}{2x-1}$

$\cos B = \dfrac{\text{adjacent}}{\text{hypotenuse}} = \dfrac{x+1}{2x-1}$

$\tan B = \dfrac{\text{opposite}}{\text{adjacent}} = \dfrac{x}{x+1}$

21. $m\angle C = 180° - 90° - 30° = 60°$

Find BC.

$\tan 30° = \dfrac{BC}{8.7}$

$8.7 \tan 30° = BC$

5 in. $\approx BC$

Find AC.

$8.7^2 + 5^2 = (AC)^2$

$75.69 + 25 = (AC)^2$

$100.69 = (AC)^2$

10 in. $\approx AC$

$\sin C = \dfrac{\text{opposite}}{\text{hypotenuse}} = \dfrac{8.7}{10}$

$\cos C = \dfrac{\text{adjacent}}{\text{hypotenuse}} = \dfrac{5}{10} = \dfrac{1}{2}$

$\tan C = \dfrac{\text{opposite}}{\text{adjacent}} = \dfrac{8.7}{5}$

22. $m\angle C = 180° - 90° - 36° = 54°$

Find BC.

$\sin 36° = \dfrac{BC}{11.5}$

$11.5 \sin 36° = BC$

6.8 m $\approx BC$

Find AB.

$(AB)^2 + 6.8^2 = 11.5^2$

$(AB)^2 + 46.24 = 132.25$

$(AB)^2 = 86.01$

$AB \approx 9.3$ m

$\sin C = \dfrac{\text{opposite}}{\text{hypotenuse}} = \dfrac{9.3}{11.5}$

$\cos C = \dfrac{\text{adjacent}}{\text{hypotenuse}} = \dfrac{6.8}{11.5}$

$\tan C = \dfrac{\text{opposite}}{\text{adjacent}} = \dfrac{9.3}{6.8}$

Chapter 9, continued

23. $m\angle C = 180° - 90° - 19.7° = 70.3°$

Find AB.

$$\cos 19.7° = \frac{AB}{51}$$

$$51 \cos 19.7° = AB$$

$$48.0 \text{ cm} \approx AB$$

Find BC.

$$(BC)^2 + 48^2 = 51^2$$

$$(BC)^2 + 2304 = 2601$$

$$(BC)^2 = 297$$

$$BC \approx 17.2 \text{ cm}$$

$$\sin C = \frac{\text{opposite}}{\text{hypotenuse}} = \frac{48}{51} = \frac{16}{17}$$

$$\cos C = \frac{\text{adjacent}}{\text{hypotenuse}} = \frac{17.2}{51}$$

$$\tan C = \frac{\text{opposite}}{\text{adjacent}} = \frac{48}{17.2}$$

24. $\dfrac{\sin A}{\cos A} = \dfrac{\frac{a}{c}}{\frac{b}{c}} = \dfrac{a}{c} \cdot \dfrac{c}{b} = \dfrac{a}{b} = \tan A$

25. Sometimes; it is true when $m\angle A = m\angle B$.

26. Always; $\sin A = \dfrac{a}{c}$ and $\cos B = \dfrac{a}{c}$.

27. Never; The statement would be true if $\dfrac{a}{c} = \dfrac{a}{b}$ or $b = c$, but because the length of a leg is never equal to the length of the hypotenuse, the statement is never true.

28. Sometimes; Because $\sin A = \dfrac{a}{c}$ and $\cos A = \dfrac{b}{c}$, it is true when $a = b$ making the triangle isosceles.

Problem Solving

29. a.

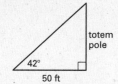

totem pole

42°

50 ft

b. $\tan 42° = \dfrac{\text{opposite}}{\text{adjacent}}$

$$\tan 42° = \frac{x}{50}$$

c. $0.9004 \approx \dfrac{x}{50}$

$$45.02 \approx x$$

The totem pole is about 45 feet tall.

30. $\tan A = \dfrac{15}{8} = \dfrac{\text{opposite}}{\text{adjacent}}$

$$\cos B = \frac{15}{17} = \frac{\text{adjacent}}{\text{hypotenuse}}$$

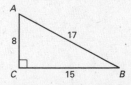

A

8

17

C

15

B

31. $\sin 60° = \dfrac{3}{x}$

$$0.8660 \approx \frac{3}{x}$$

$$x \approx \frac{3}{0.8660}$$

$$x \approx 3.5$$

The scratching post will be about 3.5 feet long.

32. *Sample answer:* Sine is the opposite leg divided by the hypotenuse. Cosine is the adjacent leg divided by the hypotenuse. Tangent is the opposite leg divided by the adjacent leg.

33. a. $\cos 25° = \dfrac{x}{2000}$

$$0.9063 \approx \frac{x}{2000}$$

$$1812.6 \approx x$$

The whale is about 1813 meters along the ocean surface from the point where it started.

b. $\sin 25° = \dfrac{x}{2000}$

$$0.4226 \approx \frac{x}{2000}$$

$$845.2 \approx x$$

The whale found its food at a depth of about 845 meters.

c. $\dfrac{1}{2}$ of deepest known dive $= \dfrac{1}{2}(3000) = 1500$ meters

Because $845 < 1500$, the whale's dive was less than half of the deepest known dive.

34. C; $\tan 60° = \dfrac{10}{x}$

$$\sqrt{3} = \frac{10}{x}$$

$$x = \frac{10}{\sqrt{3}}$$

$$x \approx 5.7735$$

$$A = \frac{1}{2}bh \approx \frac{1}{2}(5.7735)(10) \approx 28.87$$

The area of the boat sail is about 28.87 square feet.

35. *Sample answer:* A 20 foot ramp makes a 10° angle with the ground. How high is the ramp off the ground?

36. a. Starting point: $\tan A = \dfrac{\text{opposite}}{\text{adjacent}} = \dfrac{30}{30}$

Raised position: $\tan A = \dfrac{\text{opposite}}{\text{adjacent}} = \dfrac{60}{30}$

b. As the height increases, the opposite leg's length increases which increases the value of $\tan A$.

c. The measure of angle A decreases as the balloon lands. Because $\cos A = \dfrac{\text{adjacent}}{\text{hypotenuse}}$, as the height decreases the hypotenuse length decreases, and the $\cos A$ increases.

Chapter 9, continued

37. No;

Height of the office building:

$$\tan 60° = \frac{b}{400}$$

$$1.73 \approx \frac{b}{400}$$

$$692 \approx b$$

If we assume that the angle to the top of the apartment complex is also half, 30°:

$$\tan 30° = \frac{a}{400}$$

$$0.577 \approx \frac{a}{400}$$

$$231 \approx a$$

Because the height of the apartment complex, 231 feet, is not half of 692, the angle must not be 30°.

38. No; Because $\sin = \frac{\text{opposite}}{\text{hypotenuse}}$, $\sin x°$ cannot be greater than one because the opposite leg can never be greater than the hypotenuse.

39. Yes; For example: $\tan 60° \approx 1.7$

40. Yes; $\sin 90° = 1$.

41. Yes; $\cos 0° = 1$.

42. Use the diagram and sine ratios to find the height.

$$\sin 50° = \frac{\text{opposite}}{\text{hypotenuse}}$$

$$0.766 \approx \frac{x}{6}$$

$$4.596 \approx x$$

Half of the base:

$$\cos 50° = \frac{\text{adjacent}}{\text{hypotenuse}}$$

$$0.643 \approx \frac{y}{6}$$

$$3.86 \approx y$$

$$A = \frac{1}{2}bh \approx \frac{1}{2}(2(3.86))(4.596) \approx 17.7$$

The area is about 17.7 square meters.

43.

Airplane
33,000 ft   3°
       x   Airport

$$\tan 3° = \frac{33{,}000}{x}$$

$$0.0524 \approx \frac{33{,}000}{x}$$

$$x \approx \frac{33{,}000}{0.0524}$$

$$x \approx 629{,}770.9924 \text{ ft} \approx 119 \text{ mi}$$

The descent must begin about 119 miles from the airport.

Mixed Review

44. $A = s^2 = 6^2 = 36 \text{ ft}^2$

45. $A = \ell w = 20(3) = 60 \text{ cm}^2$

46. $A = \frac{1}{2}bh = \frac{1}{2}(4)(2\sqrt{3}) = 4\sqrt{3} \text{ m}^2$

47.
$$d = rt$$
$$145 = r \cdot 40$$
$$3.625 = r$$
The rate is 3.625 miles per hour.

48.
$$d = rt$$
$$78 = r \cdot 20$$
$$3.9 = r$$
The rate is 3.9 meters per second.

49.
$$d = rt$$
$$768 = r \cdot 15$$
$$51.2 = r$$
The rate is 51.2 kilometers per second.

50. Account with 2.5% interest rate:

$$I = Prt = 1350(0.025)(1.25) \approx \$42.19$$

Account with 4% interest rate:

$$I = Prt = 1350(0.04)(1.25) \approx \$67.50$$

$$67.50 = 1350(0.025)t$$

$$67.50 = 33.75t$$

$$2 = t$$

In two years, the interest on the lesser rate account equals the interest on the higher rate account in 15 months. So you will need 25 months − 15 months = 10 additional months to earn more in interest on the lesser rate account.

Quiz 9.5–9.6 (p. 506)

1. hypotenuse = leg · $\sqrt{2}$
$$15\sqrt{2} = x \cdot \sqrt{2}$$
$$15 = x$$
The value of x is 15 centimeters.

2. hypotenuse = 2 · shorter leg
$$44 = 2x$$
$$22 = x$$
longer leg = shorter leg · $\sqrt{3}$
$$y = 22\sqrt{3}$$
The shorter leg is 22 inches and the longer leg is $22\sqrt{3}$ inches.

3. longer leg = shorter leg · $\sqrt{3}$
$$14\sqrt{3} = x\sqrt{3}$$
$$14 = x$$
hypotenuse = 2 · shorter leg
$$y = 2 \cdot 14$$
$$y = 28$$
The shorter leg is 14 meters and the hypotenuse is 28 meters.

Chapter 9, *continued*

4. $\sin A = \dfrac{\text{opposite}}{\text{hypotenuse}} = \dfrac{64}{80} = \dfrac{4}{5}$

$\cos A = \dfrac{\text{adjacent}}{\text{hypotenuse}} = \dfrac{48}{80} = \dfrac{3}{5}$

$\tan A = \dfrac{\text{opposite}}{\text{adjacent}} = \dfrac{64}{48} = \dfrac{4}{3}$

$\sin B = \dfrac{\text{opposite}}{\text{hypotenuse}} = \dfrac{48}{80} = \dfrac{3}{5}$

$\cos B = \dfrac{\text{adjacent}}{\text{hypotenuse}} = \dfrac{64}{80} = \dfrac{4}{5}$

$\tan B = \dfrac{\text{opposite}}{\text{adjacent}} = \dfrac{48}{64} = \dfrac{3}{4}$

5. $\sin A = \dfrac{\text{opposite}}{\text{hypotenuse}} = \dfrac{42}{58} = \dfrac{21}{29}$

$\cos A = \dfrac{\text{adjacent}}{\text{hypotenuse}} = \dfrac{40}{58} = \dfrac{20}{29}$

$\tan A = \dfrac{\text{opposite}}{\text{adjacent}} = \dfrac{42}{40} = \dfrac{21}{20}$

$\sin B = \dfrac{\text{opposite}}{\text{hypotenuse}} = \dfrac{40}{58} = \dfrac{20}{29}$

$\cos B = \dfrac{\text{adjacent}}{\text{hypotenuse}} = \dfrac{42}{58} = \dfrac{21}{29}$

$\tan B = \dfrac{\text{opposite}}{\text{adjacent}} = \dfrac{40}{42} = \dfrac{20}{21}$

6. $\sin A = \dfrac{\text{opposite}}{\text{hypotenuse}} = \dfrac{32}{40} = \dfrac{4}{5}$

$\cos A = \dfrac{\text{adjacent}}{\text{hypotenuse}} = \dfrac{24}{40} = \dfrac{3}{5}$

$\tan A = \dfrac{\text{opposite}}{\text{adjacent}} = \dfrac{32}{24} = \dfrac{4}{3}$

$\sin B = \dfrac{\text{opposite}}{\text{hypotenuse}} = \dfrac{24}{40} = \dfrac{3}{5}$

$\cos B = \dfrac{\text{adjacent}}{\text{hypotenuse}} = \dfrac{32}{40} = \dfrac{4}{5}$

$\tan B = \dfrac{\text{opposite}}{\text{adjacent}} = \dfrac{24}{32} = \dfrac{3}{4}$

7.

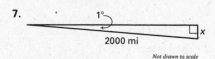

Not drawn to scale

$\sin 1° = \dfrac{x}{2000}$

$0.01745 \approx \dfrac{x}{2000}$

$34.9 \approx x$

The plane will be about 34.9 miles away from the correct path.

Brain Game (p. 506)

$\cos 15° = 0.9659 \rightarrow$ M

$\sin 52° = 0.7880 \rightarrow$ A

$\cos 85° = 0.0872 \rightarrow$ R

$\sin 60° = 0.8660 \rightarrow$ I

$\cos 45° = 0.7071 \rightarrow$ E

$\tan 30° = 0.5774 \rightarrow$ C

$\tan 12° = 0.2126 \rightarrow$ U

$\sin 5° = 0.0872 \rightarrow$ R

$\cos 30° = 0.8660 \rightarrow$ I

$\sin 45° = 0.7071 \rightarrow$ E

MARIE CURIE

Technology Activity 9.6 (p. 507)

1. $\tan^{-1}(0.25) \approx 14.0°$ **2.** $\tan^{-1}(0.14) \approx 8.0°$

3. $\tan^{-1}(0.92) \approx 42.6°$ **4.** $\tan^{-1}(1.05) \approx 46.4°$

5. $\tan^{-1}(24.65) \approx 87.7°$ **6.** $\tan^{-1}(64.25) \approx 89.1°$

7. $\tan^{-1}(32.46)$ has a larger angle because the greater the tangent of an angle, the larger the angle.

8. *Sample answer:*

positive ratio: $\dfrac{3}{4}$ reciprocal: $\dfrac{4}{3}$

$\tan^{-1}\left(\dfrac{3}{4}\right) \approx 36.9°$

$\tan^{-1}\left(\dfrac{4}{3}\right) \approx 53.1°$

Because $36.9 + 53.1 = 90$, the angles are complementary.

Mixed Review of Problem Solving (p. 508)

1. a.

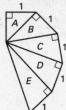

b. hypotenuse of $\triangle A$:

hypotenuse $= \text{leg} \cdot \sqrt{2} = 1 \cdot \sqrt{2} = \sqrt{2}$

hypotenuse of $\triangle B$:

$a^2 + b^2 = c^2$

$\left(\sqrt{2}\right)^2 + 1^2 = c^2$

$2 + 1 = c^2$

$3 = c^2$

$\sqrt{3} = c$

hypotenuse of $\triangle C$:

$a^2 + b^2 = c^2$

$\left(\sqrt{3}\right)^2 + 1^2 = c^2$

$3 + 1 = c^2$

$4 = c^2$

$2 = c$

hypotenuse of $\triangle D$:

$a^2 + b^2 = c^2$

$2^2 + 1^2 = c^2$

$4 + 1 = c^2$

$5 = c^2$

$\sqrt{5} = c$

hypotenuse of $\triangle E$:

$$a^2 + b^2 = c^2$$
$$(\sqrt{5})^2 + 1^2 = c^2$$
$$5 + 1 = c^2$$
$$6 = c^2$$
$$\sqrt{6} = c$$

The hypotenuse of each triangle is $\sqrt{x}$ starting with $x = 2$.

2. a. Length of ascent track:

$$\sin 45° = \frac{\text{opposite}}{\text{hypotenuse}}$$
$$0.707 \approx \frac{300}{a}$$
$$a \approx \frac{300}{0.707}$$
$$a \approx 424$$

Length of descent track:

$$\sin 64° = \frac{\text{opposite}}{\text{hypotenuse}}$$
$$0.899 \approx \frac{300}{d}$$
$$d \approx \frac{300}{0.899}$$
$$d \approx 334$$

The length of the track is about $424 + 334 = 758$ feet.

b. The horizontal length of the ascent is 300 feet, the same as the triangles other leg. Horizontal length of the descent:

$$\tan 64° = \frac{\text{opposite}}{\text{adjacent}}$$
$$2.05 \approx \frac{300}{x}$$
$$x \approx \frac{300}{2.05}$$
$$x \approx 146$$

The horizontal length traveled is about $300 + 146 = 446$ feet.

3. $A = s^2$
$$0.09 = s^2$$
$$0.3 = s$$

The side length of the square, the triangle's hypotenuse, is 0.3 yard.

hypotenuse = 2 • shorter leg

$$0.3 = 2 \cdot x$$
$$0.15 = x$$

The length of the shorter leg is 0.15 yard.

4. $\sin 20° = \frac{\text{opposite}}{\text{hypotenuse}}$

$$0.342 \approx \frac{x}{8}$$
$$2.736 \approx x$$

The height of the top of the ramp is about 2.7 feet.

5. Her shoulder-to-hip length makes a 30° angle with the floor. Use a rule for 30°-60°-90° triangles.

hypotenuse = 2 • shorter leg

$$28 = 2 \cdot x$$
$$14 = x$$

She should lift her shoulders 14 inches off the floor.

6. *Sample answer:*

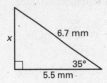

$$\sin 35° = \frac{\text{opposite}}{\text{hypotenuse}}$$
$$0.574 \approx \frac{x}{6.7}$$
$$3.85 \approx x$$

$$\tan 35° = \frac{\text{opposite}}{\text{adjacent}}$$
$$0.7002 \approx \frac{x}{5.5}$$
$$3.85 \approx x$$

The leg opposite the 35° angle is about 3.85 millimeters when found using either method.

7. a. Distance to Kirsten from Jan:

hypotenuse = leg • $\sqrt{2}$ = 500 • $\sqrt{2}$ ≈ 707

Kirsten is about 707 feet from Jan.

b. Distance to Madison from Jan:

hypotenuse = 2 • shorter leg = 2 • 500 = 1000

Madison is about 1000 feet from Jan.

c. Distance to skyscraper from Madison:

longer leg = shorter leg • $\sqrt{3}$ = 500 • $\sqrt{3}$ ≈ 866

Using a rule for 45°-45°-90° triangles, Kirsten is 500 feet from the skyscraper.

So, Kirsten is about $866 - 500 = 366$ feet from Madison.

Chapter 9 Review (pp. 509–512)

1. A rational number can be written as the ratio of two integers, while an irrational number cannot.

2. *Sample answer:*

Rational numbers: 4, $\frac{1}{3}$, and 0.24

Irrational numbers: $\sqrt{5}$, 0.1010010001 . . . , and π.

3. The sum of the squares of the lengths of the legs equals the square of the length of the hypotenuse.

4. *Sample answer:*

4 with roots 2 and -2 : $2(2) = 4$ and $(-2)(-2) = 4$.

16 with roots 4 and -4 : $4(4) = 16$ and $(-4)(-4) = 16$.

121 with roots 11 and -11 : $11(11) = 121$ and $(-11)(-11) = 121$.

5. A *perfect square* is any number that has an integer as its square root.

6. In a right triangle, the side opposite the right angle is the *hypotenuse.*

7. In a 30°-60°-90° triangle, the *shorter* leg is opposite the 30° angle.

8. Sine, cosine, and tangent are *trigonometric* ratios.

9. Reversing the parts of an if-then statement produces a *converse* statement.

10. $\sqrt{94.09} = 9.7$

11. $-\sqrt{784} = -28$

12. $-\sqrt{2125} \approx -46.1$

13. $\sqrt{941} \approx 30.7$

14. $\sqrt{63.42} \approx 8.0$

15. $-\sqrt{1200} \approx -34.6$

16. $\sqrt{861} \approx 29.3$

17. $-\sqrt{306.21} \approx -17.5$

18. $a^2 = 169$
    $a = \pm\sqrt{169}$
    $a = \pm 13$

19. $b^2 - 20 = 101$
    $b^2 = 121$
    $b = \pm\sqrt{121}$
    $b = \pm 11$

20. $c^2 + 25 = 89$
    $c^2 = 64$
    $c = \pm\sqrt{64}$
    $c = \pm 8$

21. $15 + x^2 = 51$
    $x^2 = 36$
    $x = \pm\sqrt{36}$
    $x = \pm 6$

22. $y^2 - 12 = 13$
    $y^2 = 25$
    $y = \pm\sqrt{25}$
    $y = \pm 5$

23. $40 + z^2 = 56$
    $z^2 = 16$
    $z = \pm\sqrt{16}$
    $z = \pm 4$

24. $v^2 + 36 = 85$
    $v^2 = 49$
    $v = \pm\sqrt{49}$
    $v = \pm 7$

25. $214 - w^2 = 60$
    $154 = w^2$
    $\pm\sqrt{154} = w$

26. Let $x =$ the length of one side of the base.
    $x^2 = 2025$
    $x = \sqrt{2025} = 45$
    The length of one side is 45 feet.

27. When $n = 5$:
    $d = \sqrt{2^2 + n^2} = \sqrt{2^2 + 5^2} = \sqrt{4 + 25} = \sqrt{29} \approx 5.4$
    Ken is about 5.4 miles from Central Square.

28. The number $\sqrt{100}$ is rational because $\sqrt{100} = 10$ and 10 is an integer.

29. The number $0.\overline{6}$ is rational because it is a repeating decimal.

30. The number $\frac{16}{25}$ is rational because it is the quotient of two integers.

31. The number $\sqrt{6}$ is irrational because its decimal form, $2.449489\ldots$, is neither terminating nor repeating.

32. The number $\frac{1}{3}$ is rational because it is the quotient of two integers.

33. The number $\sqrt{\frac{27}{3}}$ is rational because $\sqrt{\frac{27}{3}} = \sqrt{9} = 3$ and 3 is an integer.

34. The number $5.\overline{8}$ is rational because it is a repeating decimal.

35. The number $\sqrt{44}$ is irrational because its decimal form, $6.63324\ldots$, is neither terminating nor repeating.

36.
    So, $\sqrt{31} > 4$.

37.
    So, $7 < \sqrt{59}$.

38.
    So, $-9 = -\sqrt{81}$.

39.
    So, $\sqrt{48} > 6.3$.

40. $a^2 + b^2 = c^2$
    $2.4^2 + 0.7^2 = c^2$
    $6.25 = c^2$
    $2.5 = c$

41. $a^2 + b^2 = c^2$
    $a^2 + 24^2 = 40^2$
    $a^2 = 1024$
    $a = 32$

42. $a^2 + b^2 = c^2$
    $8^2 + b^2 = 17^2$
    $b^2 = 225$
    $b = 15$

43. $a^2 + b^2 = c^2$
    $12^2 + 35^2 \overset{?}{=} 37^2$
    $144 + 1225 \overset{?}{=} 1369$
    $1369 = 1369$
    It is a right triangle.

44. $a^2 + b^2 = c^2$
    $15^2 + 48^2 \overset{?}{=} 50^2$
    $225 + 2304 \overset{?}{=} 2500$
    $2529 \neq 2500$
    It is not a right triangle.

45. $a^2 + b^2 = c^2$
    $10^2 + 24^2 \overset{?}{=} 26^2$
    $100 + 576 \overset{?}{=} 676$
    $676 = 676$
    It is a right triangle.

46. $a^2 + b^2 = c^2$
    $21^2 + 50.4^2 = c^2$
    $2981.16 = c^2$
    $54.6 = c$
    Perimeter $= 21 + 50.4 + 54.6 = 126$ inches
    Area $= \frac{1}{2}ab = \frac{1}{2} \times 21 \times 50.4 = 529.2$ square inches

47. $a^2 + b^2 = c^2$
    $a^2 + 63^2 = 225^2$
    $a^2 = 46{,}656$
    $a = 216$
    Perimeter $= 216 + 63 + 225 = 504$ centimeters
    Area $= \frac{1}{2}ab = \frac{1}{2} \times 216 \times 63 = 6804$ square centimeters

Chapter 9, continued

48.
$$a^2 + b^2 = c^2$$
$$12^2 + b^2 = 25.5^2$$
$$b^2 = 506.25$$
$$b = 22.5$$

Perimeter = $12 + 22.5 + 25.5 = 60$ meters

Area = $\frac{1}{2}ab = \frac{1}{2} \times 12 \times 22.5 = 135$ square meters

49.
$$a^2 + b^2 = c^2$$
$$44^2 + 33^2 = c^2$$
$$3025 = c^2$$
$$55 = c$$

Perimeter = $44 + 33 + 55 = 132$ feet

Area = $\frac{1}{2}ab = \frac{1}{2} \times 44 \times 33 = 726$ square feet

50.
$$a^2 + b^2 = c^2$$
$$250^2 + 50^2 = c^2$$
$$65{,}000 = c^2$$
$$254.95 \approx c$$

The top of the tree is about 255 feet away.

51. hypotenuse = leg $\cdot \sqrt{2}$
$$x = 8 \cdot \sqrt{2}$$
$$x = 8\sqrt{2} \text{ in.}$$

52. hypotenuse = leg $\cdot \sqrt{2}$
$$20\sqrt{2} = x \cdot \sqrt{2}$$
$$20 \text{ cm} = x$$

53. hypotenuse = 2 $\cdot$ shorter leg
$$12 = 2 \cdot x$$
$$6 \text{ m} = x$$

longer leg = shorter leg $\cdot \sqrt{3}$
$$y = 6 \cdot \sqrt{3}$$
$$y = 6\sqrt{3} \text{ m}$$

54. Use the 30°-60°-90° triangle rules and the diagram to find h.

longer leg = shorter leg $\cdot \sqrt{3}$
$$h = 3 \cdot \sqrt{3} = 3\sqrt{3}$$
$$A = \frac{1}{2}bh = \frac{1}{2}(6)\left(3\sqrt{3}\right) = 9\sqrt{3}$$

The area of one triangle is $9\sqrt{3}$ square inches.

55. $\sin A = \dfrac{\text{opposite}}{\text{hypotenuse}} = \dfrac{9}{15} = \dfrac{3}{5}$

$\cos A = \dfrac{\text{adjacent}}{\text{hypotenuse}} = \dfrac{12}{15} = \dfrac{4}{5}$

$\tan A = \dfrac{\text{opposite}}{\text{adjacent}} = \dfrac{9}{12} = \dfrac{3}{4}$

$\sin B = \dfrac{\text{opposite}}{\text{hypotenuse}} = \dfrac{12}{15} = \dfrac{4}{5}$

$\cos B = \dfrac{\text{adjacent}}{\text{hypotenuse}} = \dfrac{9}{15} = \dfrac{3}{5}$

$\tan B = \dfrac{\text{opposite}}{\text{adjacent}} = \dfrac{12}{9} = \dfrac{4}{3}$

56. $\sin A = \dfrac{\text{opposite}}{\text{hypotenuse}} = \dfrac{48}{73}$

$\cos A = \dfrac{\text{adjacent}}{\text{hypotenuse}} = \dfrac{55}{73}$

$\tan A = \dfrac{\text{opposite}}{\text{adjacent}} = \dfrac{48}{55}$

$\sin B = \dfrac{\text{opposite}}{\text{hypotenuse}} = \dfrac{55}{73}$

$\cos B = \dfrac{\text{adjacent}}{\text{hypotenuse}} = \dfrac{48}{73}$

$\tan B = \dfrac{\text{opposite}}{\text{adjacent}} = \dfrac{55}{48}$

57. $\sin A = \dfrac{\text{opposite}}{\text{hypotenuse}} = \dfrac{36}{85}$

$\cos A = \dfrac{\text{adjacent}}{\text{hypotenuse}} = \dfrac{77}{85}$

$\tan A = \dfrac{\text{opposite}}{\text{adjacent}} = \dfrac{36}{77}$

$\sin B = \dfrac{\text{opposite}}{\text{hypotenuse}} = \dfrac{77}{85}$

$\cos B = \dfrac{\text{adjacent}}{\text{hypotenuse}} = \dfrac{36}{85}$

$\tan B = \dfrac{\text{opposite}}{\text{adjacent}} = \dfrac{77}{36}$

Chapter 9 Test (p. 513)

1.
$$x^2 = 49$$
$$x = \pm\sqrt{49}$$
$$x = \pm 7$$

2.
$$m^2 + 41 = 162$$
$$m^2 = 121$$
$$m = \pm\sqrt{121}$$
$$m = \pm 11$$

3.
$$n^2 - 63 = 162$$
$$n^2 = 225$$
$$n = \pm\sqrt{225}$$
$$n = \pm 15$$

4.
$$a^2 + 88 = 232$$
$$a^2 = 144$$
$$a = \pm\sqrt{144}$$
$$a = \pm 12$$

5. The number $\sqrt{16}$ is rational because $\sqrt{16} = 4$ and 4 is an integer.

6. The number $\frac{23}{24}$ is rational because it is the quotient of two integers.

7. The number $\sqrt{39}$ is irrational because its decimal form, $6.24499\ldots$, is neither terminating nor repeating.

8. The number $\sqrt{\frac{1}{4}}$ is rational because $\sqrt{\frac{1}{4}} = \frac{1}{2}$ and $\frac{1}{2}$ is the quotient of two integers.

9.

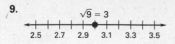

$\sqrt{9} = 3$

$$\sqrt{9} = 3$$

10.

$-11 < -\sqrt{11}$

11.

$\sqrt{12} < 4$

12.
$$a^2 + b^2 = c^2$$
$$6.4^2 + 8^2 = c^2$$
$$40.96 + 64 = c^2$$
$$104.96 = c^2$$
$$10.2 \text{ m} \approx c$$

Area $= \frac{1}{2}bh = \frac{1}{2}(6.4)(8) = 25.6 \text{ m}^2$

Perimeter $= 10.2 + 6.4 + 8 = 24.6 \text{ m}$

13.
$$a^2 + b^2 = c^2$$
$$11^2 + 11^2 = c^2$$
$$121 + 121 = c^2$$
$$242 = c^2$$
$$15.6 \text{ ft} \approx c$$

Area $= \frac{1}{2}bh = \frac{1}{2}(11)(11) = 60.5 \text{ ft}^2$

Perimeter $= 11 + 11 + 15.6 = 37.6 \text{ ft}$

14.
$$a^2 + b^2 = c^2$$
$$120^2 + b^2 = 122^2$$
$$14{,}400 + b^2 = 14{,}884$$
$$b^2 = 484$$
$$b \approx 22 \text{ mm}$$

Area $= \frac{1}{2}bh = \frac{1}{2}(120)(22) = 1320 \text{ mm}^2$

Perimeter $= 122 + 120 + 22 = 264 \text{ mm}$

15.
$$a^2 + b^2 = c^2$$
$$15^2 + 24^2 \stackrel{?}{=} 25^2$$
$$225 + 576 \stackrel{?}{=} 625$$
$$801 \neq 625$$

It is not a right triangle.

16.
$$a^2 + b^2 = c^2$$
$$28^2 + 96^2 \stackrel{?}{=} 100^2$$
$$784 + 9216 \stackrel{?}{=} 10{,}000$$
$$10{,}000 = 10{,}000$$

It is a right triangle.

17.
$$a^2 + b^2 = c^2$$
$$3.6^2 + 5.8^2 \stackrel{?}{=} 5.9^2$$
$$12.96 + 33.64 \stackrel{?}{=} 34.81$$
$$46.6 \neq 34.81$$

It is not a right triangle.

18.
$$a^2 + b^2 = c^2$$
$$22.5^2 + 30^2 \stackrel{?}{=} 37.5^2$$
$$506.25 + 900 \stackrel{?}{=} 1406.25$$
$$1406.25 = 1406.25$$

It is a right triangle.

19.
$$x = 7$$
hypotenuse $=$ leg $\cdot \sqrt{2}$
$$y = 7\sqrt{2}$$

The length of a leg is 7 centimeters and the length of the hypotenuse is $7\sqrt{2}$ centimeters.

20. hypotenuse $=$ leg $\cdot \sqrt{2}$
$$13\sqrt{2} = x\sqrt{2}$$
$$13 = x$$

The length of a leg is 13 feet.

21. longer leg $=$ shorter leg $\cdot \sqrt{3}$
$$6\sqrt{3} = x\sqrt{3}$$
$$6 = x$$

hypotenuse $= 2 \cdot$ shorter leg
$$y = 2 \cdot 6$$
$$y = 12$$

The length of the shorter leg is 6 inches and the length of the hypotenuse is 12 inches.

22. When $\ell = 4$:
$$s = 5.66\sqrt{\ell} = 5.66\sqrt{4} = 5.66(2) = 11.32$$

The maximum walking speed for the ostrich is 11.32 feet per second.

23. hypotenuse $= 2 \cdot$ shorter leg
$$793 = 2x$$
$$396.5 = x$$

The height of the boarding platform is 396.5 feet.

Standardized Test Preparation (p. 515)

1. Full credit; The correct ratio is chosen, the calculations are correct, and the reasoning is fully explained.

2. No credit; No work is shown and the solution does not make sense.

Standardized Test Practice (pp. 516–517)

1.
$$a^2 + b^2 = c^2$$
$$5^2 + 12^2 = c^2$$
$$169 = c^2$$
$$13 = c$$

The diagonal of the garden is 13 feet. Because he has 15 feet of marigolds, he has enough to plant along the diagonal.

Chapter 9, *continued*

2. Use the rules for 30°-60°-90° triangles with the hypotenuse = 100 feet.

hypotenuse − 2 • shorter leg

$$100 = 2x$$

$$50 = x$$

The fire truck can come 50 feet from the building when the ladder is extended.

longer leg = shorter leg • $\sqrt{3}$ = 50 • $\sqrt{3}$ ≈ 86.6 feet

The ladder reaches about 87 + 8 = 95 feet up the building.

3. Let s = side length of the kite.

$$A = s^2$$

$$81 = s^2$$

$$9 = s$$

The side length is 9 feet and the perimeter is 4(9) = 36 feet.

4. Vertical distance at high tide:

$$\cos 78° = \frac{\text{adjacent}}{\text{hypotenuse}}$$

$$0.208 \approx \frac{h}{10}$$

$$2.08 \approx h$$

Vertical distance at low tide:

$$\cos 72° = \frac{\text{adjacent}}{\text{hypotenuse}}$$

$$0.309 \approx \frac{\ell}{10}$$

$$3.09 \approx \ell$$

Vertical distance at low tide − Vertical distance at high tide
= 3.09 − 2.08 = 1.01

The water level rises about 1 foot from low tide to high tide.

5. Yes; For example, if the radius is $\frac{2}{\sqrt{\pi}}$ units, the area is:

$$A = \pi r^2 = \pi \left(\frac{2}{\sqrt{\pi}}\right)^2 = \pi \left(\frac{4}{\pi}\right) = 4 \text{ units}^2.$$

6.

Solve the equation.

$$\tan 4.76° = \frac{\text{opposite}}{\text{adjacent}}$$

$$0.0833 \approx \frac{2}{b}$$

$$b \approx \frac{2}{0.0833}$$

$$b \approx 24$$

The base is about 24 feet long.

7. Use the Pythagorean Theorem.

$$a^2 + b^2 = c^2$$

$$x^2 + 28^2 = 35^2$$

$$x^2 = 441$$

$$x = 21$$

Because Jeff is holding the kite string 3 feet above the ground, the kite is 21 + 3 = 24 feet above the ground. Because 24 > 22, it cannot be reached by the pole.

8. Use the rules for 30°-60°-90° triangles to find how far away you start.

longer leg = shorter leg • $\sqrt{3}$

$$26 = x \cdot \sqrt{3}$$

$$15 \approx x$$

Using the rule for 45°-45°-90° triangles, you end up 26 feet from the base of the pole. You move 26 − 15 = 11 feet.

9. One quarter of the length of the ladder is 2.75 feet. Use the Pythagorean Theorem to find the distance from the base of the ladder to the building.

$$a^2 + b^2 = c^2$$

$$a^2 + 10^2 = 11^2$$

$$a^2 = 21$$

$$a \approx 4.6$$

Because 4.6 > 2.75, the ladder is too far from the wall by 4.6 − 2.75 = 1.85 feet.

10. D;

$$a^2 − 81 = 115$$

$$a^2 = 196$$

$$a = \pm\sqrt{196}$$

$$a = \pm 14$$

11. D;

$$a^2 + b^2 = c^2$$

$$6^2 + 24^2 \stackrel{?}{=} 25^2$$

$$36 + 576 \stackrel{?}{=} 625$$

$$612 \neq 625$$

It is not a Pythagorean triple.

12. A;

$$a^2 + b^2 = c^2$$

$$7^2 + (AC)^2 = 25^2$$

$$(AC)^2 = 576$$

$$AC = 24$$

$$\tan A = \frac{\text{opposite}}{\text{adjacent}} = \frac{7}{24}$$

Chapter 9, *continued*

13. Find the original triangle's hypotenuse.

$$a^2 + b^2 = c^2$$
$$27^2 + 36^2 = c^2$$
$$2025 = c^2$$
$$45 = c$$

Let $h =$ the hypotenuse of the larger triangle. Because the triangles are similar, $\frac{36}{108} = \frac{45}{h}$ and $h = 135$.

The hypotenuse of the larger triangle is 135 inches.

14.
$$a^2 + b^2 = c^2$$
$$28^2 + 21^2 = c^2$$
$$1225 = c^2$$
$$35 = c$$

The television screen is 35 inches.

15. hypotenuse $= \text{leg} \cdot \sqrt{2}$
$$11\sqrt{2} = \text{leg} \cdot \sqrt{2}$$
$$11 = \text{leg}$$

The leg of the right triangle is the square's side length.

Area of napkin: $A = s^2 = 11^2 = 121$

The area of the napkin is 121 square inches.

16. a. $\frac{300 \text{ feet}}{\text{second}} \cdot 10 \text{ seconds} = 3000 \text{ feet}$

The jet travels 3000 feet in 10 seconds.

b. Solve the equation.

$$\sin 15° = \frac{\text{opposite}}{\text{hypotenuse}}$$

$$0.2588 \approx \frac{x}{3000}$$

$$776 \approx x$$

The height of the jet is about 776 feet.

c. You can use the cosine ratio with the answer from part (a): $\cos 15° = \frac{\text{adjacent}}{3000}$. You can use the Pythagorean Theorem to find the horizontal distance.

17. a. $\sin 12° = \frac{\text{opposite}}{\text{hypotenuse}}$

$$0.208 \approx \frac{h}{4810}$$

$$1000.48 \approx h$$

The height of the mountain is about 1000 feet.

b.
$$a^2 + b^2 = c^2$$
$$1000^2 + b^2 = 2000^2$$
$$b^2 = 3{,}000{,}000$$
$$b \approx 1732.05$$

The horizontal distance traveled is about 1732 feet.

c. Distance traveled on the lift:

$$a^2 + b^2 = c^2$$
$$1000^2 + b^2 = 4810^2$$
$$b^2 = 22{,}136{,}100$$
$$b \approx 4704.9$$

The total horizontal distance traveled is about $1732 + 4705 = 6437$ feet. Because 1 mile = 5280 feet, the skier traveled more than 1 mile horizontally.

Chapter 10

Chapter Get-Ready Games (pp. 518–519)

Check students' work.

Stop and Think (p. 519)

1. No. *Sample answer:* You could tell area from circumference and perimeter because area is measured in square units and circumference and perimeter are measured in units. However, you might not be able to tell a perimeter from a circumference if the side lengths of a triangle or rectangle were decimal measures.

2. Check students' work.

Review Prerequisite Skills (p. 520)

1. Quadrilateral $ABCD$ is a parallelogram.

2. $\overline{PQ}$ is the radius of the circle.

3. Quadrilateral $JKLM$ is a trapezoid.

4. To find the area of the shaded region, divide the figure into 2 rectangles.

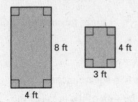

$A = \ell w + \ell w = 4(8) + 3(4) = 32 + 12 = 44$

The area of the shaded region is 44 square feet.

5. To find the area of the shaded region, subtract the area of the triangle from the area of the square.

$A = s^2 - \frac{1}{2}bh = 5^2 - \frac{1}{2}(5)(5) = 25 - 12.5 = 12.5$

The area of the shaded region is 12.5 square centimeters.

6. To find the area of the shaded region, add the area of the triangle to the area of the rectangle.

$A = \frac{1}{2}bh + \ell w = \frac{1}{2}(6)(3) + 6(3) = 9 + 18 = 27$

The area of the shaded region is 27 square inches.

Lesson 10.1

10.1 Guided Practice (pp. 522–523)

1.

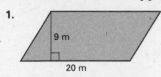

$A = bh = 20(9) = 180$

The parallelogram has an area of 180 square meters.

2.

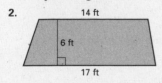

$A = \frac{1}{2}(b_1 + b_2)h = \frac{1}{2}(14 + 17)6 = 93$

The trapezoid has an area of 93 square feet.

---

3. $A = \frac{1}{2}(b_1 + b_2)h = \frac{1}{2}(3 \cdot 6 + 3 \cdot 16)(3 \cdot 3) = 297 \text{ in}^2$

The area is multiplied by $\dfrac{297 \text{ in.}^2}{33 \text{ in.}^2} = 9$.

10.1 Exercises (pp. 523–526)

Skill Practice

1. The area formula for a parallelogram is $A = bh$.

2. The area formula for a triangle is $A = \frac{1}{2}bh$.

3. The area formula for a trapezoid is $A = \frac{1}{2}(b_1 + b_2)h$.

4. $A = bh = 7(5) = 35$

   The parallelogram has an area of 35 square feet.

5. $A = bh = 13(10) = 130$

   The parallelogram has an area of 130 square centimeters.

6. $A = bh = 5(14) = 70$

   The parallelogram has an area of 70 square inches.

7. The incorrect values were used for the base and height.

   $A = bh = 10(5) = 50 \text{ in.}^2$

8. C; $A = bh = 10(4) = 40$

   The parallelogram has an area of 40 square feet.

9.

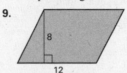

$A = bh = 12(8) = 96$

The parallelogram has an area of 96 square units.

10.

$A = bh = 9(14) = 126$

The parallelogram has an area of 126 square units.

11.

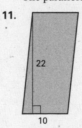

$A = bh = 10(22) = 220$

The parallelogram has an area of 220 square units.

12.

$A = bh = 2(1.5) = 3$

The parallelogram has an area of 3 square units.

13.

$A = bh = 3.2(5) = 16$

The parallelogram has an area of 16 square units.

14.

$A = bh = 12(18) = 216$

The parallelogram has an area of 216 square units.

15. $A = \frac{1}{2}(b_1 + b_2)h = \frac{1}{2}(18 + 9)(12) = 162$

The trapezoid has an area of 162 square inches.

16. $A = \frac{1}{2}(b_1 + b_2)h = \frac{1}{2}(10 + 5)(12) = 90$

The trapezoid has an area of 90 square yards.

17. $A = \frac{1}{2}(b_1 + b_2)h = \frac{1}{2}(54 + 10)(15) = 480$

The trapezoid has an area of 480 square meters.

18.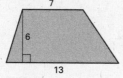

$A = \frac{1}{2}(b_1 + b_2)h = \frac{1}{2}(13 + 7)6 = 60$

The trapezoid has an area of 60 square units.

19.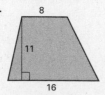

$A = \frac{1}{2}(b_1 + b_2)h = \frac{1}{2}(8 + 16)(11) = 132$

The trapezoid has an area of 132 square units.

20.

$A = \frac{1}{2}(b_1 + b_2)h = \frac{1}{2}(5.5 + 2.5)(3) = 12$

The trapezoid has an area of 12 square units.

21.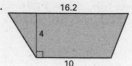

$A = \frac{1}{2}(b_1 + b_2)h = \frac{1}{2}(16.2 + 10)(4) = 52.4$

The trapezoid has an area of 52.4 square units.

22. Quadrilateral *ABCD*:

$A = \frac{1}{2}(b_1 + b_2)h = \frac{1}{2}(14 + 8)(10) = 110 \text{ m}^2$

Quadrilateral *EFGH*:

$A = \frac{1}{2}(b_1 + b_2)h = \frac{1}{2}(7 + 4)(5) = 27.5 \text{ m}^2$

The area of *ABCD* is $\frac{110 \text{ m}^2}{27.5 \text{ m}^2} = 4$ times the area of *EFGH*.

23. Quadrilateral *ABCD*: $A = bh = 4(3) = 12 \text{ ft}^2$

Quadrilateral *EFGH*: $A = bh = 12(9) = 108 \text{ ft}^2$

The area of *EFGH* is $\frac{108 \text{ ft}^2}{12 \text{ ft}^2} = 9$ times the area of *ABCD*.

24. $A = \frac{1}{2}(45 + 37)(16) = 656$

The area of the trapezoid is 656 square inches.

25. To find the total area, find the sum of the areas of the triangle and the rectangle.

$A = \frac{1}{2}bh + \ell w = \frac{1}{2}(24)(12) + 24(9) = 144 + 216 = 360$

The area of the figure is 360 square feet.

26. To find the total area, double the area of one trapezoid.

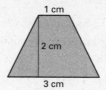

$A = 2\left(\frac{1}{2}(b_1 + b_2)h\right) = 2\left(\frac{1}{2}(1 + 3)(2)\right) = 2(4) = 8$

The area of the figure is 8 square centimeters.

27.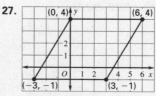

$b = 6$

$h = 5$

$A = bh = 6(5) = 30$

The parallelogram has an area of 30 square units.

28.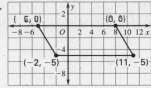

$b = 13$

$h = 5$

$A = bh = 13(5) = 65$

The parallelogram has an area of 65 square units.

29. $A = bh$

$84 = b(12)$

$\dfrac{84}{12} = \dfrac{b(12)}{12}$

$7 = b$

The base is 7 centimeters.

30. $A = bh$

$105 = 15h$

$\dfrac{105}{15} = \dfrac{15h}{15}$

$7 = h$

The height is 7 meters.

31. $A = \frac{1}{2}(b_1 + b_2)h$

$100 = \frac{1}{2}(10 + 15)h$

$100 = 12.5h$

$\dfrac{100}{12.5} = \dfrac{12.5h}{12.5}$

$8 = h$

The height is 8 inches.

32. $A = \frac{1}{2}(b_1 + b_2)h$

$78 = \frac{1}{2}(12 + b_2)6$

$78 = 36 + 3b_2$

$42 = 3b_2$

$\dfrac{42}{3} = \dfrac{3b_2}{3}$

$14 = b_2$

The base is 14 feet.

33. Use the Pythagorean theorem to find the height of the trapezoid.

$h^2 + 9^2 = 15^2$

$h^2 + 81 = 225$

$h^2 = 144$

$h = \sqrt{144}$

$h = 12$ in.

$A = \frac{1}{2}(b_1 + b_2)h = \frac{1}{2}(18 + 27)(12) = 270$

The trapezoid has an area of 270 square inches.

34. Use the Pythagorean theorem to find the height of the parallelogram.

$h^2 + 5^2 = 13^2$

$h^2 + 25 = 169$

$h^2 = 144$

$h = \sqrt{144}$

$h = 12$ m

$A = bh = 30(12) = 360$

The parallelogram has an area of 360 square meters.

35. Use the Pythagorean theorem to find the part of the lower base not known.

$a^2 + 30^2 = 34^2$

$a^2 + 900 = 1156$

$a^2 = 256$

$a = \sqrt{256}$

$a = 16$

$A = \frac{1}{2}(b_1 + b_2)h = \frac{1}{2}(40 + 56)(30) = 1440$

The trapezoid has an area of 1440 square centimeters.

36. $A = \frac{1}{2}(b_1 + b_2)h$

$225 = \frac{1}{2}(2y + y)(10)$

$225 = 15y$

$\frac{225}{15} = \frac{15y}{15}$

$15 = y$

Use the Pythagorean theorem to find x.

$15^2 + 10^2 = x^2$

$225 + 100 = x^2$

$325 = x^2$

$\sqrt{325} = x$

$18.0 \approx x$

So, the value of x is about 18.0 inches and the value of y is 15 inches.

Problem Solving

37. B; $A = \frac{1}{2}(b_1 + b_2)h = \frac{1}{2}(16 + 14)(23) = 345$

The area is 345 square inches.

38. a.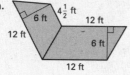

b. Trapezoid:

$A = \frac{1}{2}(b_1 + b_2)h = \frac{1}{2}\left(12 + 4\frac{1}{2}\right)(6) = 49\frac{1}{2}$ ft^2

Parallelogram: $A = bh = 12(6) = 72$ ft^2

c. The area of the figure is $49\frac{1}{2} + 72 = 121\frac{1}{2}$ square feet.

39. $A = \frac{1}{2}(b_1 + b_2)h = \frac{1}{2}(18 + 24)(15) = 315$

The area of the top surface is 315 square inches. Alice needs 315 square inches of tile.

40. *Sample answer:*

41. $b = 23$ mm

$h = 11$ mm

$A = bh = 23(11) = 253$

The parallelogram has an area of 253 square millimeters.

42. *Sample answer:* An isosceles triangle is a triangle with two equal sides, so it makes sense that an isosceles trapezoid is a trapezoid with two equal sides.

43. a. $A = bh = 5(2) = 10$

The parallelogram has an area of 10 square centimeters.

b. When dimensions are doubled:

$A = bh = 10(4) = 40$

The parallelogram has an area of 40 square centimeters. The area was quadrupled when each dimension was doubled.

When dimensions are tripled:

$A = bh = 15(6) = 90$

The parallelogram has an area of 90 square centimeters. The area is 9 times greater than the original area when the dimensions are tripled.

c. $A = (kb)(kh) = k^2bh$

The formula is the original formula times k^2. So, the area is k^2 times the original area.

d. $A = \frac{1}{2}(kb_1 + kb_2)kh = \frac{1}{2}(b_1 + b_2)k^2h$

The formula is the original formula times k^2. So, the area is k^2 times the original area.

44. $A = \frac{1}{2}(b_1 + b_2)h \approx \frac{1}{2}(250 + 500)(300) \approx 112,500$

The state of Nevada has an area of about 112,500 square miles.

45. $A = bh \approx 300(110) \approx 33,000$

The state of Tennessee has an area of about 33,000 square miles.

46.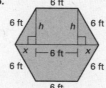

The area of the floor is the sum of the areas of two congruent trapezoids. The trapezoids bisect the angle of the regular hexagon that measures 120°. Use the sine and cosine ratios to find h and x.

$\sin 60° = \frac{h}{6}$

$\cos 60° = \frac{x}{6}$

$6 \cdot \sin 60° = h$

$6 \cdot \cos 60° = x$

$5.196 \approx h$

$6 \cdot \frac{1}{2} = x$

$3 = x$

The base of the trapezoid is $x + 6 + x = 3 + 6 + 3 = 12$ feet.

Chapter 10, *continued*

$A = \frac{1}{2}(b_1 + b_2)h + \frac{1}{2}(b_1 + b_2)h$

$\quad = (b_1 + b_2)h$

$\quad \approx (6 + 12)(5.196)$

$\quad = 93.528$

The area of the floor is about 93.5 square feet.

Mixed Review

47. $C = \pi d \approx 3.14(8) = 25.12$

The circumference is about 25.12 inches.

48. $C = 2\pi r \approx 2(3.14)(3) = 18.84$

The circumference is about 18.84 feet.

49. $C = \pi d \approx 3.14(2.4) = 7.536$

The circumference is about 7.536 centimeters.

50. $\quad a^2 + b^2 = c^2$

$\quad (QR)^2 + 30^2 = 34^2$

$\quad (QR)^2 + 900 = 1156$

$\quad\quad\quad (QR)^2 = 256$

$\quad\quad\quad\quad QR = \sqrt{256}$

$\quad\quad\quad\quad QR = 16$

The length of $\overline{QR}$ is 16 millimeters.

51. $\sin P = \dfrac{\text{opposite}}{\text{hypotenuse}} = \dfrac{16}{34} = \dfrac{8}{17}$

$\cos P = \dfrac{\text{adjacent}}{\text{hypotenuse}} = \dfrac{30}{34} = \dfrac{15}{17}$

$\tan P = \dfrac{\text{opposite}}{\text{adjacent}} = \dfrac{16}{30} = \dfrac{8}{15}$

$\sin R = \dfrac{\text{opposite}}{\text{hypotenuse}} = \dfrac{30}{34} = \dfrac{15}{17}$

$\cos R = \dfrac{\text{adjacent}}{\text{hypotenuse}} = \dfrac{16}{34} = \dfrac{8}{17}$

$\tan R = \dfrac{\text{opposite}}{\text{adjacent}} = \dfrac{30}{16} = \dfrac{15}{8}$

52. D; $\sqrt{26} = 5.09901\ldots,$

which does not repeat nor terminate.

Lesson 10.2

Activity (p. 527)

Step 1. The base is equal to about $\frac{1}{2}$ of the circumference. The height is about equal to the radius.

Step 2. $A = \pi r^2$; $A = bh = \left(\frac{1}{2} \cdot 2\pi r\right) \cdot r = \pi r^2$

10.2 Guided Practice (p. 528)

1. $A = \pi r^2 \approx 3.14(7)^2 \approx 153.86$

The area is about 153.86 square feet.

2. $r = \dfrac{d}{2} = \dfrac{3}{2} = 1.5$ km

$A = \pi r^2 \approx 3.14(1.5)^2 \approx 7.07$

The area is about 7.07 square kilometers.

3. $\quad A = \pi r^2$

$\quad 628 \approx 3.14r^2$

$\quad 200 \approx r^2$

$\quad \sqrt{200} \approx r$

$\quad 14.14 \approx r$

The radius of the circle is about 14.14 centimeters.

4. To find the area of the shaded region, subtract the area of the three circles from the area of the rectangle.

$A = \ell w - 3(\pi r^2)$

$\quad \approx 36(12) - 3(3.14)(6)^2$

$\quad \approx 432 - 339.12$

$\quad \approx 92.88$

The area of the shaded region is about 92.88 square inches.

5. The two half circles at either end of the figure combine to form a circle with a radius of 3 feet.

To find the area of the shaded region, add the area of the circle to the area of the rectangle.

$A = \pi r^2 + \ell w \approx 3.14(3)^2 + 10(6) \approx 28.26 + 60 \approx 88.26$

The area of the shaded region is about 88.26 square feet.

10.2 Exercises (pp. 529–532)

Skill Practice

1. The area of a circle is the product of π and the square of the *radius*.

2. The circumference of a circle is the product of π and the *diameter*.

3. $A = \pi r^2 \approx 3.14(2)^2 \approx 12.56$

The area is about 12.56 square feet.

4. $A = \pi r^2 \approx 3.14(10)^2 \approx 314$

The area is about 314 square centimeters.

5. $A = \pi r^2 \approx 3.14(13.3)^2 \approx 555.43$

The area is about 555.43 square meters.

6. $A = \pi r^2 \approx 3.14(25)^2 \approx 1962.5$

The area is about 1962.5 square yards.

7. $r = \dfrac{d}{2} = \dfrac{17}{2} = 8.5$ mm

$A = \pi r^2 \approx 3.14(8.5)^2 \approx 226.87$

The area is about 226.87 square millimeters.

8. $r = \dfrac{d}{2} = \dfrac{20.8}{2} = 10.4$ cm

$A = \pi r^2 \approx 3.14(10.4)^2 \approx 339.62$

The area is about 339.62 square centimeters.

9. The diameter was incorrectly used as the radius. The radius is 5.5 yards, not 11 yards.

$A = \pi r^2 \approx 3.14(5.5)^2 = 94.985$

The area is about 95 square yards.

10. $A = \pi r^2 \approx 3.14(9)^2 \approx 254.34$

The area is about 254.34 square centimeters.

Chapter 10, continued

11. $A = \pi r^2 \approx 3.14(17)^2 = 907.46$

The area is about 907.46 square feet.

12. $A = \pi r^2 \approx 3.14(30.4)^2 \approx 2901.86$

The area is about 2901.86 square meters.

13. $r = \dfrac{d}{2} = \dfrac{28}{2} = 14$ mm

$A = \pi r^2 \approx 3.14(14)^2 \approx 615.44$

The area is about 615.44 square millimeters.

14. $r = \dfrac{d}{2} = \dfrac{6}{2} = 3$ yd

$A = \pi r^2 \approx 3.14(3)^2 \approx 28.26$

The area is about 28.26 square yards.

15. $r = \dfrac{d}{2} = \dfrac{40.2}{2} = 20.1$ in.

$A = \pi r^2 \approx 3.14(20.1)^2 \approx 1268.59$

The area is about 1268.59 square inches.

16. $A = \pi r^2$

$28.26 \approx 3.14 r^2$

$9 \approx r^2$

$\sqrt{9} \approx r$

$3 \approx r$

The radius of the circle is about 3 feet.

17. $A = \pi r^2$

$3.14 \approx 3.14 r^2$

$1 \approx r^2$

$\sqrt{1} \approx r$

$1 \approx r$

The radius of the circle is about 1 meter.

18. $A = \pi r^2$

$200.96 \approx 3.14 r^2$

$64 \approx r^2$

$\sqrt{64} \approx r$

$8 \approx r$

The radius of the circle is about 8 yards.

19. $A = \pi r^2$

$113.04 \approx 3.14 r^2$

$36 \approx r^2$

$\sqrt{36} \approx r$

$6 \approx r$

The radius of the circle is about 6 inches.

20. $A = \pi r^2$

$12.56 \approx 3.14 r^2$

$4 \approx r^2$

$\sqrt{4} \approx r$

$2 \approx r$

The radius of the circle is about 2 millimeters.

21. $A = \pi r^2$

$254.34 \approx 3.14 r^2$

$81 \approx r^2$

$\sqrt{81} \approx r$

$9 \approx r$

The radius of the circle is about 9 centimeters.

22. $A = \pi r^2$

$907.46 \approx 3.14 r^2$

$289 \approx r^2$

$\sqrt{289} \approx r$

$17 \approx r$

The radius of the circle is about 17 miles.

23. $A = \pi r^2$

$4069.44 \approx 3.14 r^2$

$1296 \approx r^2$

$\sqrt{1296} \approx r$

$36 \approx r$

The radius of the circle is about 36 centimeters.

24. $A = \pi r^2$

$1808.64 \approx 3.14 r^2$

$576 \approx r^2$

$\sqrt{576} \approx r$

$24 \approx r$

The radius of the circle is about 24 feet.

25. $C = 2\pi r$

$18.84 \approx 2(3.14)r$

$3 \approx r$

$A = \pi r^2 \approx 3.14(3)^2 \approx 28.26$

The area is about 28.26 square feet.

26. $C = 2\pi r$

$81.64 \approx 2(3.14)r$

$13 \approx r$

$A = \pi r^2 \approx 3.14(13)^2 \approx 530.66$

The area is about 530.66 square meters.

27. $C = 2\pi r$

$37.68 \approx 2(3.14)r$

$6 \approx r$

$A = \pi r^2 \approx 3.14(6)^2 \approx 113.04$

The area is about 113.04 square centimeters.

28. C; $C = 2\pi r$

$50.24 \approx 2(3.14)r$

$8 \approx r$

$A = \pi r^2 \approx 3.14(8)^2 \approx 200.96$

The area is about 200.96 square millimeters.

29. $r = 10$ mm

$A = \pi r^2 \approx 3.14(10)^2 \approx 314$

The area is about 314 square millimeters.

Chapter 10, continued

30. If the area of a circle is 25π square feet, then the radius is $\sqrt{25}$, or 5 feet.

31. The radii of the circles are equal to the width of the rectangle, 7 millimeters. The length of the rectangle is equivalent to 8 radii, or 56 millimeters.

To find the area of the shaded region, subtract the area of 2 whole circles from the area of the rectangle.

$$A = \ell w - 2(\pi r^2) \approx 56(7) - 2\left(\frac{22}{7}\right)(7)^2 \approx 392 - 308 \approx 84$$

The area of the shaded region is about 84 square millimeters.

32. To find the area of the shaded region, subtract the area of the smaller circle from the area of the larger circle.

$$A \approx 3.14(13)^2 - 3.14(4)^2 \approx 530.66 - 50.24 \approx 480.42$$

The area of the shaded region is about 480.42 square meters.

33. To find the area of the shaded region, subtract the area of the circle from the area of the rectangle.

$$A = \ell w - \pi r^2$$
$$\approx 22(20) - 3.14(8)^2$$
$$\approx 440 - 200.96$$
$$\approx 239.04$$

The area of the shaded region is about 239.04 square inches.

34. To find the area of the shaded region, subtract the area of the circle from the area of the triangle.

$$A = \frac{1}{2}bh - \pi r^2$$
$$\approx \frac{1}{2}(10)(7) - 3.14(2)^2$$
$$\approx 35 - 12.56$$
$$\approx 22.44$$

The area of the shaded region is about 22.44 square kilometers.

35. If $c = a$, then:
$$2\pi r = \pi r^2$$
$$2r = r \cdot r$$
$$2 = r$$

The radius is 2 units.

36. Find the area of the shaded region of the 6 circles.
$$A = \pi\left(\sqrt{6}\right)^2 - \pi\left(\sqrt{5}\right)^2 + \pi(2)^2 - \pi\left(\sqrt{3}\right)^2 + \pi\left(\sqrt{2}\right)^2 - \pi(1)^2$$
$$= 6\pi - 5\pi + 4\pi - 3\pi + 2\pi - 1\pi$$
$$= 3\pi$$

The area of the shaded region for the first 4 circles is $4\pi - 3\pi + 2\pi - \pi = 2\pi$. The area of the shaded region for the first 2 circles is $2\pi - \pi = \pi$.

So, $A = \frac{n\pi}{2}$ where n is an even number of circles in the pattern.

Problem Solving

37. $A = \pi r^2 \approx 3.14(12)^2 \approx 452.16$

About 452.16 square feet of the yard is watered.

38. C; $r = \frac{d}{2} = \frac{18}{2} = 9$ ft

$$A = \pi r^2 \approx 3.14(9)^2 = 254.34$$

About 254 square feet of material is needed.

39. $A \approx 3.14(50)^2 - 3.14(32.5)^2$
$$\approx 7850 - 3316.25$$
$$\approx 4533.375$$

The area of the roof is about 4533.38 square meters.

40. To find the area of the shaded region, subtract the area of a half circle from the area of the rectangle.

$$A = \ell w - \frac{1}{2}\pi r^2$$
$$\approx 3(1.5) - \frac{1}{2}(3.14)(1.5)^2$$
$$\approx 4.5 - 3.5325$$
$$\approx 0.9675$$

The area of the shaded region is about 0.97 square meter.

41. Area of rectangle: $A = \ell w = 4(2) = 8$ ft^2

Area of half circle: $A = \frac{1}{2}\pi r^2 \approx \frac{1}{2}(3.14)(1)^2 = 1.57$ ft^2

The area of the window is about $8 + 1.57 = 9.57 \approx 10$ square feet. It would cost about $10 \times 1.50 = \$15.00$ more to install a double-paned window.

42. The low-emissivity coating costs $10 \times 3.00 = \$30.00$. A double-paned, low-emissivity coating window costs $30 + 15 = \$45$ more.

43. A double-paned window saves $0.60 \times 10 = \$6$ per year. A low-emissivity window saves $0.50 \times 10 = \$5$ per year. Let $y =$ years.
$$11y = 45$$
$$\frac{11y}{11} = \frac{45}{11}$$
$$y \approx 4$$

It will take about 4 years for the extra cost of the double-paned low-emissivity window to be offset by the energy savings.

44.

Radius r	Area of a circle with radius r	Area of a circle with radius $2r$	Area of a circle with radius $3r$	Area of a circle with radius $4r$
2 in.	4π in.^{2}	16π in.^{2}	36π in.^{2}	64π in.^{2}
3 in.	9π in.^{2}	36π in.^{2}	81π in.^{2}	144π in.^{2}
5 in.	25π in.^{2}	100π in.^{2}	225π in.^{2}	400π in.^{2}

When the radius is multiplied by k, the area of the circle is k^2 times greater than the original area.

When radius is multiplied by k:
$$A = \pi(kr)^2 = \pi k^2 r^2 = k^2 \pi r^2$$

Chapter 10, continued

45. a. Smaller disk: $A = \pi r^2 \approx 3.14(3.5)^2 \approx 38.465$ in.^{2}

Larger disk: $A = \pi r^2 \approx 3.14(5)^2 \approx 78.5$ in.^{2}

You can sand about $38.465 \times 5 \approx 192.33$ square inches with the smaller disk and about $78.5 \times 5 = 392.5$ square inches with the larger disk in one minute.

b. Smaller disk: $11,520 \div 192.33 \approx 60$ minutes

Larger disk: $11,520 \div 392.5 \approx 29$ minutes

You would save about $60 - 29 = 31$ minutes by sanding the entire porch with the larger disk.

46. Use the Pythagorean theorem to find the side length of the smaller square.

$$x^2 + x^2 = 20^2$$
$$2x^2 = 400$$
$$x^2 = 200$$
$$x \approx 14 \text{ mm}$$
$$A = s^2 \approx 14^2 \approx 200 \text{ cm}^2$$

Next, find the area of the larger square.

$$A = s^2 = 20^2 = 400 \text{ cm}^2$$

The area of the circle is about halfway between the areas of the squares, or about 300 square centimeters.

You can check the estimate by calculating the area of the circle.

$$A = \pi r^2 \approx 3.14(10)^2 \approx 314 \text{ square centimeters}$$

The estimate is reasonable.

47. Area of square: $A = s^2 = (2r)^2 = 4r^2$

Area of circle: $A = \pi r^2$

Area of the shaded region $= \dfrac{4r^2 - \pi r^2}{4}$

$$4 - \pi = \frac{r^2(4 - \pi)}{4}$$
$$(4 - \pi) \cdot 4 = \frac{r^2(4 - \pi)}{4} \cdot 4$$
$$\frac{(4 - \pi) \cdot 4}{4 - \pi} = \frac{r^2(4 - \pi)}{4 - \pi}$$
$$4 = r^2$$
$$\sqrt{4} = r$$
$$2 = r$$

For the area of the shaded region to be $4 - \pi$, the radius must be 2 inches.

Mixed Review

48. The quadrilateral is a parallelogram with 4 sides of equal length. So, it is a rhombus.

49. The quadrilateral has exactly one pair of parallel sides. So, it is a trapezoid.

50. The quadrilateral is a parallelogram with 4 right angles. So, it is a rectangle.

51. Use the strategy *Make a Table*.

Time in Minutes	15	30	45	60	75	90	105	120
Number of Quarters	1	2	3	4	5	6	7	8

One hour and 40 minutes is equivalent to 100 minutes, so you will use 7 quarters.

A $10 roll of quarters has $10(4) = 40$ quarters.

$$40 - 7 = 33$$

You will have 33 quarters left over.

52. C; $\qquad a^2 + b^2 = c^2$

$$3.6^2 + 4.8^2 \stackrel{?}{=} 6^2$$
$$12.96 + 23.04 \stackrel{?}{=} 36$$
$$36 = 36 \checkmark$$

Brain Game (p. 532)

Center circle: $r = 3$

$A = \pi r^2 = 9\pi$ in.^{2}

Red region: $r = 6$

$A = \pi r^2 - \text{Center circle} = 36\pi - 9\pi = 27\pi$ in.^{2}

Blue region: $r = 9$

$A = \pi r^2 - \text{Red region} - \text{Center circle}$

$\quad = 81\pi - 27\pi - 9\pi$

$\quad = 45\pi$ in.^{2}

Green region: $r = 12$

$A = \pi r^2 - \text{Blue region} - \text{Red region} - \text{Center circle}$

$\quad = 144\pi - 45\pi - 27\pi - 9\pi$

$\quad = 63\pi$ in.^{2}

White region: $r = 15$

$A = \pi r^2 - \text{Green region} - \text{Blue region} - \text{Red region} - \text{Center circle}$

$\quad = 225\pi - 63\pi - 45\pi - 27\pi - 9\pi$

$\quad = 81\pi$ in.^{2}

Score for center circle:

$\dfrac{225\pi}{9\pi} = 25$

Score for red region:

$\dfrac{225\pi}{27\pi} \approx 8$

Score for blue region:

$\dfrac{225\pi}{45\pi} = 5$

Score for green region:

$\dfrac{225\pi}{63\pi} \approx 4$

Score for white region:

$\dfrac{225\pi}{81\pi} \approx 3$

Greg's score:

$8 + 3 + 3 = 14$

Jamie's score:

$5 + 4 + 4 = 13$

Greg's score is higher than Jamie's.

Chapter 10, *continued*

Technology Activity 10.2 (p. 533)

1. When the area of a circle is multiplied by 9, the radius is multiplied by 3.

2. When the area of a circle is multiplied by 16, the radius is multiplied by 4.

3. When the area of a circle is multiplied by 25, the radius is multiplied by 5.

4. When the area of a circle is multiplied by 36, the radius is multiplied by 6.

5. When the area of a circle is doubled, the radius is multiplied by $\sqrt{2}$. If it is tripled, the radius is multiplied by $\sqrt{3}$. If the area of a circle is multiplied by n, then the radius is multiplied by $\sqrt{n}$.

6. The formula for the radius of a circle with area A is

$r = \sqrt{\dfrac{A}{\pi}}$ because:

$$A = \pi r^2$$

$$\frac{A}{\pi} = \frac{\pi r^2}{\pi}$$

$$\frac{A}{\pi} = r^2$$

$$\sqrt{\frac{A}{\pi}} = r$$

Lesson 10.3

10.3 Guided Practice (p. 535)

1. The solid has one triangular base, so it is a triangular pyramid. It is a polyhedron because it is enclosed by polygons.

2. The solid has one circular base, so it is a cone. It is not a polyhedron because a circle is not a polygon.

3. The solid has two octagonal bases that lie in parallel planes, so it is an octagonal prism. It is a polyhedron because it is enclosed by polygons.

4. Method 1: Sketch the solid.

Method 2: Sketch the top, front, and side views.

top   front   side

A rectangular pyramid has 5 faces, 8 edges, and 5 vertices.

10.3 Exercises (pp. 536–538)

Skill Practice

1. C; A solid with two rectangular bases is a rectangular prism.

2. A; A solid with three rectangular faces is a triangular prism.

3. B; A solid with four triangular faces is a rectangular pyramid.

4. The solid is round with no bases, so it is a sphere. It is not a polyhedron because it is not enclosed by polygons.

5. The solid has two rectangular bases that lie in parallel planes, so it is a rectangular prism. It is a polyhedron because it is enclosed by polygons.

6. The solid has two circular bases that lie in parallel planes, so it is a cylinder. It is not a polyhedron because circles are not polygons.

7. The solid has one rectangular base, so it is a rectangular pyramid. It has 5 faces, 8 edges, and 5 vertices.

8. The solid has two pentagonal bases that lie in parallel planes, so it is a pentagonal prism. It has 7 faces, 15 edges, and 10 vertices.

9. The solid has two octagonal bases that lie in parallel planes, so it is an octagonal prism. It has 10 faces, 24 edges, and 16 vertices.

10. A hexagonal pyramid has 12 edges, 6 for the sides of the hexagon and 6 connecting each vertex of the base to the point of the pyramid.

11. Method 1: Sketch the solid.

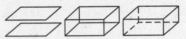

Method 2: Sketch the top, front, and side views.

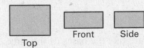

Top   Front   Side

12. Method 1: Sketch the solid.

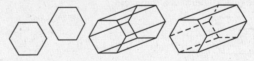

Method 2: Sketch the top, front, and side views.

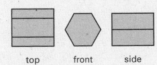

top   front   side

13. Method 1: Sketch the solid.

Method 2: Sketch the top, front, and side views.

top

front   side

14. The solids that form the structures have two pentagonal bases, so they are pentagonal prisms.

15. The structure is formed by a solid with one circular base, or a cone, and a solid with two circular bases, or a cylinder.

16. The structure is formed by a solid with two octagonal bases, or an octagonal prism, and a solid with one octagonal base and triangular faces, or an octagonal pyramid.

17. D; The solid has one rectangular base and triangular faces, so it is a rectangular pyramid.

18.

19.

20. The quadrilateral is a square like the bases of the cube.

21. The quadrilateral is a rectangle.

22. The quadrilateral is a trapezoid.

23. a.

b.

Problem Solving

24. (1)

(2) •

(3)

25. D; It has a base that is a polygon.

26. *Sample answer:* They are alike because they are both polyhedrons and have congruent side lengths and angles of the base. They are different because the pyramid has triangular faces, while the prism has rectangular faces. The pyramid has one base, while the prism has two.

27. *Sample answer:* In your classroom or at home, you find cylinders in pieces of chalk and soup cans. You find cones in an ice cream cone or a funnel. Square prisms are found in dice and food storage containers.

28.

Figure	Number of faces F	Number of vertices V	Number of edges E	$F + V$
pentagonal pyramid	6	6	10	12
rectangular pyramid	5	5	8	10
triangular prism	5	6	9	11
rectangular prism	6	8	12	14

Euler's formula is $E = F + V - 2$.

29. Find the length of the diagonal of the base d.

$$s^2 + s^2 = d^2$$
$$2s^2 = d^2$$
$$\sqrt{2s^2} = d$$
$$s\sqrt{2} = d$$

Find the length of $\overline{AB}$.

$$s^2 + \left(s\sqrt{2}\right)^2 = (AB)^2$$
$$s^2 + 2s^2 = (AB)^2$$
$$3s^2 = (AB)^2$$
$$\sqrt{3s^2} = AB$$
$$s\sqrt{3} = AB$$

30. *Sample answer:* You can divide it into 6 pyramids. The point of each pyramid is at the center of the cube, and the base of each pyramid is a face of the cube.

Mixed Review

31. $A = \frac{1}{2}bh = \frac{1}{2}(3)(5) = 7.5$

The area is 7.5 square feet.

32. $A = \frac{1}{2}bh = \frac{1}{2}(10)(8) = 40$

The area is 40 square inches.

Chapter 10, *continued*

33. $A = \frac{1}{2}bh = \frac{1}{2}(5)(4) = 10$

The area is 10 square meters.

34. $r = \frac{d}{2} = \frac{21}{2}$

$A = \pi r^2 \approx \frac{22}{7}\left(\frac{21}{2}\right)^2 = 346.5$

The area is about 346.5 square inches.

35. A; $\sin A = \frac{\text{opposite}}{\text{hypotenuse}} = \frac{8}{17}$

Quiz 10.1–10.3 (p. 538)

1. $A = bh = 15(8) = 120$

The parallelogram has an area of 120 square centimeters.

2. $A = bh = 6(12) = 72$

The parallelogram has an area of 72 square feet.

3. $A = \frac{1}{2}(b_1 + b_2)h = \frac{1}{2}(9 + 4.5)(6) = 40.5$

The trapezoid has an area of 40.5 square centimeters.

4. $A = \frac{1}{2}(b_1 + b_2)h = \frac{1}{2}(10 + 14)8 = 96$

The trapezoid has an area of 96 square feet.

5. $r = \frac{d}{2} = \frac{22}{2} = 11$ ft

$A = \pi r^2 \approx 3.14(11)^2 \approx 379.94$

The area is about 379.94 square feet.

6. $A = \pi r^2$

$254.34 \approx 3.14r^2$

$81 \approx r^2$

$\sqrt{81} \approx r$

$9 \approx r$

The radius of the circle is about 9 feet.

7. $A = \pi r^2$

$452.16 \approx 3.14r^2$

$144 \approx r^2$

$\sqrt{144} \approx r$

$12 \approx r$

The radius of the circle is about 12 centimeters.

8. $A = \pi r^2$

$78.5 \approx 3.14r^2$

$25 \approx r^2$

$\sqrt{25} \approx r$

$5 \approx r$

The radius of the circle is about 5 meters.

9. The solid has one square base, so it is a square pyramid. It is a polyhedron because it is enclosed by polygons.

10. Method 1: Sketch the solid.

 1.   **2.**   **3.**

Method 2: Sketch the top, front, and side views.

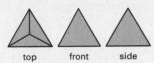

top   front   side

A triangular pyramid has 4 faces, 6 edges, and 4 vertices.

10.3 Extension (p. 540)

1.

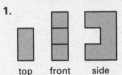

top   front   side

2.

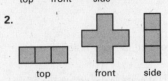

top   front   side

3.

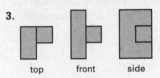

top   front   side

4. 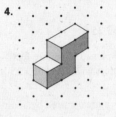   **5.**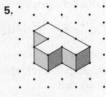

6.

7.

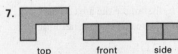

top   front   side

8.

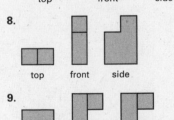

top   front   side

9.

top   front   side

Chapter 10, *continued*

1. a.

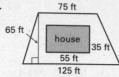

b. To find the area of the lot covered by grass, subtract the area of the house from the area of the lot.

$$A = \frac{1}{2}(b_1 + b_2)h - \ell w$$

$$= \frac{1}{2}(125 + 75)(65) - 55(35)$$

$$= 6500 - 1925$$

$$= 4575$$

The area of the lot covered by grass is 4575 square feet.

c. No; the area covered by grass is the difference of the areas of the lot and the house, no matter where the house is positioned.

2. a. Complete circle sprinkler:

$A = \pi r^2 \approx 3.14(10)^2 = 314$ ft^2

Half-circle sprinkler:

$A = \frac{1}{2}\pi r^2 \approx \frac{1}{2}(3.14)(15)^2 = 353.25$ ft^2

The complete circle sprinkler waters 314 square feet and the half-circle sprinkler waters an area of 353.25 square feet.

b. The half-circle sprinkler covers a greater area by about $353.25 - 314 \approx 39$ square feet.

3. 6; The area of one space is $72 \div 4 = 18$ square feet.

$A = bh$

$18 = b(3)$

$6 = b$

The line dividing each space is 6 meters long.

4. To find the values of b_2 that make the area of the trapezoid greater than the area of the parallelogram, solve the inequality.

$$\frac{1}{2}(b_1 + b_2)h > bh$$

$$\frac{1}{2}(10 + b_2)(30) > 20(30)$$

$$150 + 15b_2 > 600$$

$$15b_2 > 450$$

$$b_2 > 30$$

When b_2 is greater than 30 meters, the area of the trapezoid is greater than the area of the parallelogram.

5. 7; A pentagonal prism has 7 faces, so the candle has 7 faces.

6. *Sample answer:*

Polyhedron with 2 congruent bases:

The solid is a cube.

Solid with 2 congruent bases but is not a polyhedron:

The solid is a cylinder.

7. a. To find the area of the deck, subtract the area of the semicircle from the area of the square.

$$A = s^2 - \frac{1}{2}\pi r^2$$

$$\approx (16)^2 - \frac{1}{2}(3.14)(8)^2$$

$$= 256 - 100.5$$

$$= 155.5$$

The area of the deck is about 155.5 square feet.

b. You need two coats of sealant for a total coverage of about $2 \times 155.5 = 311$ square feet. Since each can of sealant covers 150 square feet, you will need, $311 \div 150 \approx 2.1$, 3 cans.

c. Cost of 3 cans: $3(4.50) = 13.50$

Sales tax: 6% of $13.50 = 0.06(13.50) = 0.81$

Total cost: $13.50 + 0.81 = 14.31$

The sealant will cost $14.31.

8. *Sample answer:*

The solid is a triangular prism.

No; there is no other solid that has two triangular bases and three rectangular faces.

9. The crystal is formed by a solid with two rectangular bases, or a rectangular prism, and two solids each with one rectangular base, or two rectangular pyramids.

top   front   side

Chapter 10, *continued*

Lesson 10.4

10.4 Guided Practice (pp. 544–545)

1.

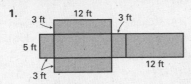

$S = 2B + Ph = 2(12)(5) + [2(12) + 2(5)](3) = 222$

The surface area of the prism is 222 square feet.

2.

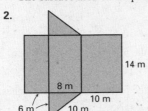

$S = 2B + Ph = 2\left(\frac{1}{2}\right)(6)(8) + (6 + 8 + 10)(14) = 384$

The surface area of the prism is 384 square meters.

3.

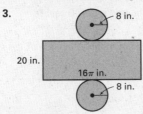

$S = 2\pi r^2 + 2\pi rh = 2\pi(8)^2 + 2\pi(8)(20) \approx 1407.4$

The surface area of the cylinder is about 1407.4 square inches.

4. Lateral surface area $= 2\pi rh = 2\pi(5)(10) \approx 314.16$

The lateral surface area of the cylinder is about 314 square inches.

10.4 Exercises (pp. 545–547)

Skill Practice

1. *Sample answer:* Surface area is the sum of the areas of all the faces and lateral surfaces of a solid.

2. The net of a cylinder is made up of two *circles* and one *rectangle*.

3.

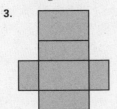

4.

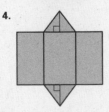

5.

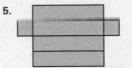

6.

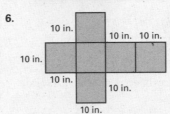

$S = 2B + Ph = 2(10)^2 + 4(10)(10) = 600$

The surface area of the prism is 600 square inches.

7.

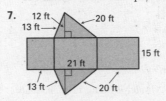

$S = 2B + Ph$

$= 2\left(\frac{1}{2}\right)(21)(12) + (21 + 13 + 20)(15)$

$= 1062$

The surface area of the prism is 1062 square feet.

8.

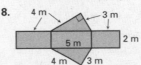

$S = 2B + Ph = 2\left(\frac{1}{2}\right)(3)(4) + (4 + 5 + 3)(2) = 36$

The surface area of the prism is 36 square meters.

9. $S = 2B + Ph = 2(4) + 8(5) = 48$

The surface area of the prism is 48 square inches.

10. $S = 2B + Ph = 2(20) + 12(3) = 76$

The surface area of the prism is 76 square centimeters.

11. $S = 2B + Ph = 2(45) + 30(2.8) = 174$

The surface area of the prism is 174 square yards.

12. $S = 2B + Ph = 2(19.3) + 16(0.5) = 46.6$

The surface area of the prism is 46.6 square meters.

13. D; $S = 2B + Ph = 2(3)(2) + (2(3) + 2(2))(9) = 102 \text{ ft}^2$

14.

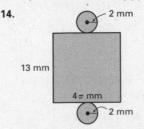

$S = 2\pi r^2 + 2\pi rh = 2\pi(2)^2 + 2\pi(2)(13) \approx 188.5$

The surface area of the cylinder is about 188.5 square millimeters.

15.

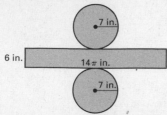

$$S = 2\pi r^2 + 2\pi rh = 2\pi(7)^2 + 2\pi(7)(6) \approx 571.8$$

The surface area of the cylinder is about 571.8 square inches.

16.

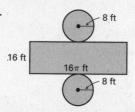

$$S = 2\pi r^2 + 2\pi rh = 2\pi(8)^2 + 2\pi(8)(16) \approx 1206.4$$

The surface area of the cylinder is about 1206.4 square feet.

17.

$$S = 2\pi r^2 + 2\pi rh = 2\pi(6)^2 + 2\pi(6)(2) \approx 301.6$$

Lateral surface area $= 2\pi rh = 2\pi(6)(2) \approx 75.4$

The surface area of the cylinder is about 301.6 square meters and the lateral surface area is about 75.4 square meters.

18.

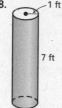

$$S = 2\pi r^2 + 2\pi rh = 2\pi(1)^2 + 2\pi(1)(7) \approx 50.3$$

Lateral surface area $= 2\pi rh = 2\pi(1)(7) \approx 44.0$

The surface area of the cylinder is about 50.3 square feet and the lateral surface area is about 44.0 square feet.

19.

$$S = 2\pi r^2 + 2\pi rh = 2\pi(10)^2 + 2\pi(10)(20) \approx 1885.0$$

Lateral surface area $= 2\pi rh = 2\pi(10)(20) \approx 1256.6$

The surface area of the cylinder is about 1885.0 square centimeters and the lateral surface area is about 1256.6 square centimeters.

20. Square face: $A = 7^2 = 49$

Rectangular face: $A = 7(12) = 84$

$S = 49 + 4(84) = 385$

The area of the net is 385 square meters. It will not form a closed figure when folded unless another base is added.

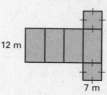

21. Lateral surface area $= Ph = 30(5) = 150$

The lateral surface area of the prism is 150 square feet.

22. Lateral surface area $= Ph = 24(12) = 288$

The lateral surface area of the prism is 288 square inches.

23. Lateral surface area $= Ph = 34(6) = 204$

The lateral surface area of the prism is 204 square centimeters.

24. Lateral surface area $= Ph = 20(7) = 140$

The lateral surface area of the prism is 140 square meters.

25. The lateral surface area does not include the area of the bases.

Lateral surface area $= 2\pi rh = 2\pi(3)(7) \approx 131.9$ in.^{2}

26. The base has edge lengths of 1 foot.

Use the Pythagorean theorem to find the height of the base.

$$h^2 + 0.5^2 = 1^2$$
$$h^2 + 0.25 = 1$$
$$h^2 = 0.75$$
$$h = \sqrt{0.75}$$
$$h \approx 0.87$$

$$S = 2B + Ph = 2\left(\frac{1}{2}\right)(1)(0.87) + (1 + 1 + 1)1 = 3.87$$

Lateral surface area $= Ph = 3(1) = 3$

The surface area of the prism is about 3.9 square feet and the lateral surface area is about 3 square feet.

27. Lateral surface area $= 2\pi rh$

$$4\pi^2 = 2\pi r(2)$$
$$4\pi^2 = 4\pi r$$
$$\frac{4\pi^2}{4\pi} = \frac{4\pi r}{4\pi}$$
$$\pi = r$$

The radius of the cylinder is π feet.

Chapter 10, continued

Problem Solving

28. Answers will vary.

29. $S = 2\pi r^2 + 2\pi rh = 2\pi(35)^2 + 2\pi(35)(224) \approx 56{,}957.1$

The surface area of the Crystal Bridge is about 56,957.1 square feet.

30. C; $S = 2B + Ph = 2(2^2) + 4(2)(2) = 24$

You need at least 24 square feet of wrapping paper.

31. Surface area of the cube:

$S = 2B + Ph = 2(1)^2 + 4(1)(1) = 6 \text{ in.}^2$

Surface area of the cylinder:

$S = 2\pi r^2 + 2\pi rh = 2\pi(0.5)^2 + 2\pi(0.5)(1) \approx 4.71 \text{ in.}^2$

The cube requires more fondue.

32.

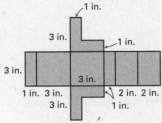

$S = 2B + Ph$

$ = 2(3(1) + 2(1)) + (1 + 3 + 3 + 1 + 2 + 2)(3)$

$ = 46$

The surface area of the solid is 46 square inches.

33.

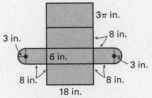

$S = 2B + Ph$

$ = 2\left(\tfrac{1}{2}\pi(3)^2 + 8(6)\right) + (3\pi + 8 + 6 + 8)(18)$

$ \approx 689.9$

The surface area of the mailbox is about 689.9 square inches.

34. *Sample answer:* The lateral surface area of a prism is the sum of the areas of the faces that are not bases. Assume the sides of the base are x, y, and z. The lateral area is $xh + yh + zh$, or $(x + y + z)h$, which is the product of the perimeter and the height.

35. $S = 2B + Ph = 2(s^2) + 4(s)s = 6s^2$

So, the surface area of a cube is $6s^2$.

36. Doubling the height of a prism does not result in doubling the surface area because the increase in height does not affect the area of the bases. However, doubling the height does result in doubling lateral surface area, because the lateral surface area is either Ph or Ch.

Mixed Review

37. $A = \pi r^2 \approx 3.14(13^2) = 530.66$

The area of the circle is about 530.66 square inches.

38. $A = \pi r^2 \approx 3.14(50^2) = 7850$

The area of the circle is about 7850 square centimeters.

39. $r = \dfrac{d}{2} = \dfrac{36}{2} = 18 \text{ ft}$

$A = \pi r^2 \approx 3.14(18^2) = 1017.36$

The area of the circle is about 1017.36 square feet.

40. $r = \dfrac{d}{2} = \dfrac{24}{2} = 12 \text{ m}$

$A = \pi r^2 \approx 3.14(12^2) = 452.16$

The area of the circle is about 452.16 square meters.

41. $\sin 78° = 0.9781$ **42.** $\tan 23° = 0.4245$

43. $\cos 14° = 0.9703$ **44.** $\sin 66° = 0.9135$

45. C; $A = bh = 16(11) = 176$

The area of the parallelogram is 176 square feet.

Lesson 10.5

10.5 Guided Practice (pp. 549–550)

1.

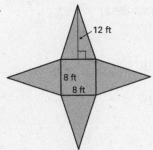

$S = B + \tfrac{1}{2}P\ell = 8^2 + \tfrac{1}{2}(4)(8)(12) = 256$

The surface area of the pyramid is 256 square feet.

2.

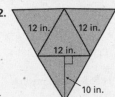

$S = B + \tfrac{1}{2}P\ell \approx 62.4 + \tfrac{1}{2}(12 + 12 + 12)(10) = 242.4$

The surface area of the pyramid is 242.4 square inches.

3.

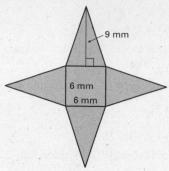

$$S = B + \frac{1}{2}P\ell = 6^2 + \frac{1}{2}(4)(6)(9) = 144$$

The surface area of the pyramid is 144 square millimeters.

4. Lateral surface area $= \frac{1}{2}P\ell = \frac{1}{2}(4)(12.5)(8.4) = 210$

The lateral surface area is 210 square centimeters.

5. $S = \pi r^2 + \pi r\ell = \pi(6)^2 + \pi(6)(12) \approx 339.3$

Lateral surface area $= \pi r\ell = \pi(6)12 \approx 226.2$

The surface area of the cone is about 339.3 square meters and the lateral surface area is about 226.2 square meters.

10.5 Exercises (pp. 550–552)

Skill Practice

1.

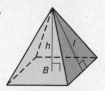

2.

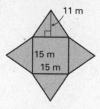

$$S = B + \frac{1}{2}P\ell = 15^2 + \frac{1}{2}(4)(15)(11) = 555$$

The surface area of the pyramid is 555 square meters.

3.

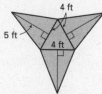

$$S = B + \frac{1}{2}P\ell \approx 6.9 + \frac{1}{2}(4 + 4 + 4)(5) = 36.9$$

The surface area of the pyramid is 36.9 square feet.

4.

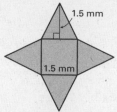

$$S = B + \frac{1}{2}P\ell = (1.5)^2 + \frac{1}{2}(4)(1.5)(1.5) = 6.75$$

The surface area of the pyramid is about 6.8 square millimeters.

5.

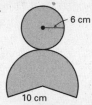

$$S = \pi r^2 + \pi r\ell = \pi(6)^2 + \pi(6)(10) \approx 301.6$$

The surface area of the cone is about 301.6 square centimeters.

6.

$$S = \pi r^2 + \pi r\ell = \pi(8)^2 + \pi(8)(14) \approx 552.9$$

The surface area of the cone is about 552.9 square inches.

7.

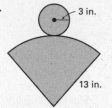

$$S = \pi r^2 + \pi r\ell = \pi(3)^2 + \pi(3)(13) \approx 150.8$$

The surface area of the cone is about 150.8 square inches.

8. C; $S = B + \frac{1}{2}P\ell = 7^2 + \frac{1}{2}(4)(7)(5) = 119$ m²

9. $S = B + \frac{1}{2}P\ell = 5^2 + \frac{1}{2}(4)(5)(4.2) = 67$

The surface area of the pyramid is 67 square centimeters.

10. $S = B + \frac{1}{2}P\ell = 15^2 + \frac{1}{2}(4)(15)(10) = 525$

The surface area of the pyramid is 525 square yards.

11. $S = \pi r^2 + \pi r\ell = \pi(12)^2 + \pi(12)(6.5) \approx 697.4$

The surface area of the cone is about 697.4 square meters.

12. $S = \pi r^2 + \pi r \ell = \pi(4)^2 + \pi(4)(5.5) \approx 119.4$

The surface area of the cone is about 119.4 square millimeters.

13. The slant height ℓ is 10 feet, not 8 feet.

$S = \pi r^2 + \pi r \ell = \pi(6)^2 + \pi(6)(10) \approx 301.59$

The surface area of the cone is about 301.59 square feet.

14. Use the Pythagorean theorem to find the hypotenuse of the right triangle formed by the height of the pyramid, 3 meters, and half of the side length of the base, 4 meters.

$a^2 + b^2 = c^2$

$3^2 + 4^2 = \ell^2$

$9 + 16 = \ell^2$

$25 = \ell^2$

$\sqrt{25} = \ell$

$5 = \ell$

$S = B + \frac{1}{2}P\ell = 8^2 + \frac{1}{2}(4)(8)(5) = 144$

The slant height is 5 meters.

The surface area of the pyramid is 144 square meters.

15. Use the Pythagorean theorem to find the hypotenuse of the right triangle formed by the height of the cone, 12 feet, and the radius of the base, 5 feet.

$a^2 + b^2 = c^2$

$12^2 + 5^2 = \ell^2$

$144 + 25 = \ell^2$

$169 = \ell^2$

$\sqrt{169} = \ell$

$13 = \ell$

$S = \pi r^2 + \pi r \ell = \pi(5)^2 + \pi(5)(13) \approx 282.7$

The slant height is 13 feet. The surface area of the cone is about 282.7 square feet.

16. Use the Pythagorean theorem to find the hypotenuse of the right triangle formed by the height of the cone, 5 yards, and the radius of the cone, 2 yards.

$a^2 + b^2 = c^2$

$5^2 + 2^2 = \ell^2$

$25 + 4 = \ell^2$

$29 = \ell^2$

$\sqrt{29} = \ell$

$5.39 \approx \ell$

$S = \pi r^2 + \pi r \ell = \pi(2)^2 + \pi(2)(\sqrt{29}) \approx 46.4$

The slant height is about 5.4 yards. The surface area of the cone is about 46.4 square yards.

17. $S = 4\pi r^2 = 4\pi(1.25)^2 \approx 19.6$

The surface area of the sphere is about 19.6 square inches.

18. $S = 4\pi r^2 = 4\pi(4.4)^2 \approx 243.3$

The surface area of the sphere is about 243.3 square inches.

19. $S = 4\pi r^2 = 4\pi(3.5)^2 \approx 153.9$

The surface area of the sphere is about 153.9 square inches.

20. $S = B + \frac{1}{2}P\ell$

$555 = 15^2 + \frac{1}{2}(4)(15)(2x + 1)$

$555 = 225 + 60x + 30$

$555 = 255 + 60x$

$300 = 60x$

$\dfrac{300}{60} = \dfrac{60x}{60}$

$5 = x$

The value of x is 5.

21. $S = B + \frac{1}{2}P\ell$

$460 = 10^2 + \frac{1}{2}(4)(10)(3x - 3)$

$460 = 100 + 60x - 60$

$460 = 40 + 60x$

$420 = 60x$

$\dfrac{420}{60} = \dfrac{60x}{60}$

$7 = x$

The value of x is 7.

22. $S = B + \frac{1}{2}P\ell$

$125.6 = 5^2 + \frac{1}{2}(4)(5)(x + 2)$

$125.6 = 25 + 10x + 20$

$125.6 = 45 + 10x$

$80.6 = 10x$

$\dfrac{80.6}{10} = \dfrac{10x}{10}$

$8.06 = x$

The value of x is 8.06.

Problem Solving

23. $S = B + \frac{1}{2}P\ell = 10^2 + \frac{1}{2}(4)(10)(15) = 400$

400 square feet of material is needed to build the pyramid.

24. A; Lateral surface area $= \pi r \ell = \pi(1)\left(4\frac{1}{4}\right) \approx 13.4$

25. *Sample answer:* The slant height of a regular pyramid is the height of any face that is not a base. The slant height of a cone is the distance from the edge of the base to the vertex. The height of a pyramid or cone is the distance from the center of the base to the vertex.

Chapter 10, *continued*

26. a. $S = \pi r \ell = \pi(4)(7) \approx 88.0$

The surface area of Pablo's cone is about 88.0 square inches.

b. $S = \pi r \ell = \pi(8)(14) \approx 351.9$

The surface area of Monica's cone is about 351.9 square inches, which is $351.9 \div 88 \approx 4$ times that of Pablo's cone.

27. $S = \pi r \ell = \pi(1)(6) = 6\pi$

The lateral surface area of the icicle is 6π square inches.

28. $S = \pi r \ell = \pi(2)(12) = 24\pi$

The lateral surface area of the icicle is 24π square inches.

29. $S = \pi r \ell = \pi(3)(18) = 54\pi$

The lateral surface area of the icicle is 54π square inches.

30. $S = \pi r \ell = \pi(4)(24) = 96\pi$

The lateral surface area of the icicle is 96π square inches.

31. When both r and ℓ are multiplied by the same number, the surface area is multiplied by the square of that number. If $r = 5$ in. and $\ell = 30$ in., they have been multiplied by 5. The surface area is $6\pi \cdot 5^2 = 150\pi$ square inches.

32. *Sample answer:* I predict the square pyramid will have the greater surface area because when comparing the bases, a square with side length of 10 units is greater than the area of a circle with diameter of 10 units.

Pyramid:

$S = B + \frac{1}{2}Ph = 10^2 + \frac{1}{2}(4)(10)(12) = 340 \text{ units}^2$

Cone:

$S = \pi r^2 + \pi r \ell = \pi(5)^2 + \pi(5)(12) \approx 267.0 \text{ units}^2$

The pyramid has a greater surface area.

33. Use the Pythagorean theorem to find the hypotenuse of the right triangle formed by the height of the pyramid, 100 feet, and the distance from the center of the base to the side, $200 \div 2 = 100$ feet.

$$a^2 + b^2 = c^2$$
$$100^2 + 100^2 = \ell^2$$
$$20{,}000 = \ell^2$$
$$\sqrt{20{,}000} = \ell$$
$$100\sqrt{2} = \ell$$

Lateral surface area $= \frac{1}{2}P\ell = \frac{1}{2}(4)(200)(100\sqrt{2}) \approx 56{,}569$

The slant height is $100\sqrt{2}$ feet and the lateral surface area is about 56,569 square feet.

34. To find the area of the base use a rule for 30°-60°-90° triangles to find the height.

longer leg = shorter leg $\cdot \sqrt{3} = 3\sqrt{3}$

Area of base:

$B = 6 \cdot \frac{1}{2}bh = 6\left(\frac{1}{2}\right)(6)(3\sqrt{3}) \approx 93.5 \text{ cm}^2$

Surface area:

$S = B + \frac{1}{2}P\ell = 93.5 + \frac{1}{2}(6)(6)(15) = 363.5$

The surface area of the hexagonal pyramid is about 363.5 square centimeters.

Mixed Review

35. $S = 2B + Ph = 2(9)^2 + 4(9)(9) = 486$

The surface area of the cube is 486 square meters.

36. $S = 2\pi r^2 + 2\pi rh = 2\pi(8)^2 + 2\pi(8)(5) \approx 653.5$

The surface area of the cylinder is about 653.5 square feet.

37. $S = 2B + Ph = 2\left(\frac{1}{2}\right)(12)(5) + (5 + 12 + 13)(22) = 720$

The surface area of the prism is 720 square millimeters.

38.

The solid is a rectangular pyramid. This is the only possible solid fitting the description with one rectangular face, its base, and four triangular faces, its lateral faces.

Lesson 10.6

Investigation (p. 553)

1.

Dimensions of the prism	Cubes to cover the bottom of the prism	Layers of cubes to make the prism	Volume of the prism
$4 \times 2 \times 3$	8	3	24
$6 \times 1 \times 2$	6	2	12
$7 \times 5 \times 3$	35	3	105
$4 \times 2 \times 8$	8	8	64

2. $B = \ell w$

$V = Bh$

10.6 Guided Practice (pp. 555–557)

1. $V = Bh = \ell wh = 6(11)(3) = 198$

The volume is 198 cubic feet.

2. $V = Bh = \frac{1}{2}(12)(8)(6) = 288$

The volume is 288 cubic millimeters.

3. $V = Bh = \pi r^2 h = \pi\left(1\frac{1}{2}\right)^2(10) \approx 70.7$

The volume is about 70.7 cubic inches.

4. Because the solids have the same heights, you need only compare the areas of the bases.

Since the area of the base of the prism, $12(10) = 120$, is greater than the area of the base of the cylinder, $\pi(6)^2 \approx 113$, the prism has the greater volume.

5. $V = Bh = [(5 \cdot 3) \cdot (3 \cdot 3)](3 \cdot 3) = 1215 \text{ m}^3$

$\dfrac{1215 \text{ m}^3}{45 \text{ m}^3} = 27$

The volume is multiplied by 27.

Chapter 10, *continued*

10.6 Exercises (pp. 557–559)

Skill Practice

1. *Sample answer:* Area is the amount of space covered by a figure. Volume is the amount of space that a solid occupies.

2. The volume of a prism or cylinder is the area of the *base* times the *height*.

3. $V = Bh = \ell wh = 6(2)(11) = 132$

   The volume is 132 cubic meters.

4. $V = Bh = \ell wh = 7(7)(7) = 343$

   The volume is 343 cubic inches.

5. $V = Bh = \ell wh = (3.8)3(1.2) = 13.68$

   The volume is 13.68 cubic centimeters.

6. $V = Bh = \ell wh = 16(3)\left(2\frac{1}{2}\right) = 120$

   The volume is 120 cubic feet.

7. $V = Bh = \pi r^2 h = \pi(4)^2(11) \approx 552.9$

   The volume is about 552.9 cubic feet.

8. $V = Bh = \pi r^2 h = \pi(3)^2(9) \approx 254.5$

   The volume is about 254.5 cubic centimeters.

9. $V = Bh = \pi r^2 h = \pi(1.2)^2(4.5) \approx 20.4$

   The volume is about 20.4 cubic meters.

10. $V = Bh = \pi r^2 h = \pi(6.4)^2(12) \approx 1544.2$

    The volume is about 1544.2 cubic inches.

11. $V = Bh = \pi r^2 h = \pi(7)^2(15) \approx 2309.1$

    The volume is about 2309.1 cubic meters.

12. $V = Bh = \pi r^2 h = \pi(8.3)^2(1.6) \approx 346.3$

    The volume is about 346.3 cubic yards.

13. $V = Bh = \ell wh = 8(4)(2) = 64$

    The volume is 64 cubic yards.

14. $V = Bh = \pi r^2 h = \pi(2)^2(12) \approx 150.8$

    The volume is about 150.8 cubic centimeters.

15. $V = Bh = \frac{1}{2}(24)(7)(15) = 1260$

    The volume is 1260 cubic meters.

16. $V = Bh = 60(8) = 480$

    The volume is 480 cubic centimeters.

17. $V = Bh = \pi r^2 h = \pi(6)^2(3) \approx 339.3$

    The volume is about 339.3 cubic centimeters.

18. $V = Bh = \frac{1}{2}(6)(5)(3) = 45$

    The volume is 45 cubic millimeters.

19. The area of the base, B, is found using the formula πr^2.

    $V = Bh = \pi r^2 h = \pi(4)^2(5) \approx 251.3$

    The volume is about 251.3 cubic meters.

20. 2 ft = 24 in.

    $V = Bh = \frac{1}{2}(24)(15)(18) = 3240$

    The volume is 3240 cubic inches.

21. 2 yd = 6 ft

    $V = Bh = \frac{1}{2}(11 + 17)(4)(6) = 336$

    The volume is 336 cubic feet.

22. 3 yd = 9 ft

    $V = Bh = \left(7(5) + \frac{1}{2}(7)(3)\right)(9) = 409.5$

    The volume is 409.5 cubic feet.

23. $\dfrac{3\,\text{m}}{9\,\text{m}} = \dfrac{5\,\text{m}}{x}$

    $3x = 45$

    $x = 15$

    The height of solid B is 15 meters.

    The length of the base of solid B is $4 \times 3 = 12$ meters.

    Solid A: $V = Bh = \frac{1}{2}(4)(3)(5) = 30 \text{ m}^3$

    Solid B: $V = Bh = \frac{1}{2}(12)(9)(15) = 810 \text{ m}^3$

    $\dfrac{810 \text{ m}^3}{30 \text{ m}^3} = 27$

    The volume of solid B is 27 times the volume of solid A.

24. $\dfrac{5\,\text{m}}{25\,\text{m}} = \dfrac{6\,\text{m}}{x}$

    $5x = 15$

    $x = 3$

    The height of solid B is 3 meters.

    Solid A: $V = Bh = \pi(5)^2(6) \approx 471.2 \text{ m}^3$

    Solid B: $V = Bh = \pi(25)^2(3) \approx 58.9 \text{ m}^3$

    $\dfrac{471.2 \text{ m}^3}{58.9 \text{ m}^3} = 8$

    The volume of solid A is 8 times the volume of solid B.

25. *Doubling the radius* would have a greater effect on the volume of a cylinder because the radius is squared. The volume would be four times greater.

    You will get the same results if you double the length or double the width of a rectangular prism that is longer than it is wide. The volume will be doubled.

26. D;

    1 yd = 3 ft

    $6 \text{ yd}^3 \cdot \dfrac{3 \text{ ft}}{1 \text{ yd}} \cdot \dfrac{3 \text{ ft}}{1 \text{ yd}} \cdot \dfrac{3 \text{ ft}}{1 \text{ yd}} = 162 \text{ ft}^3$

27. Break the solid down into 3 parts.

    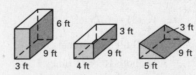

    $V = 3(9)(6) + 4(9)(3) + \frac{1}{2}(5)(3)(9) = 337.5$

    The volume is 337.5 cubic feet.

Chapter 10, *continued*

28. Use the Pythagorean theorem to find the base of the triangle.

$a^2 + b^2 = c^2$

$3^2 + b^2 = 5^2$

$\quad b^2 = 16$

$\quad b = \sqrt{16}$

$\quad b = 4$

Triangular prism: $V = Bh = \frac{1}{2}(3)(4)(6) = 36$ in.^{3}

Cylinder: $V = Bh = \pi r^2 h = \pi(0.5)^2(6) \approx 4.7$

The volume is about $36 - 4.7 = 31.3$ cubic inches.

Problem Solving

29. You need to calculate the surface area to determine the amount of wrapping paper needed to wrap a gift because it goes around the outside.

30. You need to calculate volume to determine the amount of cereal that will fit in a box because it goes inside.

31. You need to calculate volume to determine the amount of water needed to fill a watering can because it goes inside.

32. B; $V = Bh = \pi r^2 h = \pi(8)^3(19) \approx 3820$ cm^3

33. Rectangular pool:

$V = Bh = \ell w h = 40(16)(4) = 2560$

The rectangular pool holds about 2560 cubic feet of water.

Cylindrical pool:

$V = Bh = \pi r^2 h = \pi(12)^2(6) \approx 2714.3$

The cylindrical pool holds about 2714.3 cubic feet of water.

The cylindrical pool holds about $2714.3 - 2560 = 154.3$ cubic feet more water than the rectangular pool.

34. Large eraser:

$V = Bh = 10(52)(20) = 10,400$ mm^3

Pencil top eraser:

$V = Bh = \pi r^2 h = \pi(3)^2(5) \approx 141.4$ mm^3

You would go through $10,4000 \div 141.4$, or about 74 pencil-top erasers in the time it takes you to completely use the larger eraser.

35. Cylindrical container:

$V = Bh = \pi r^2 h = \pi(2)^2(6) \approx 75.4$ in.^{3}

Rectangular prism:

$V = Bh = \ell w h = \left(1\frac{1}{2}\right)\left(1\frac{1}{2}\right)(3) = 6.75$ in.^{3}

The salt in the container will fill the salt shaker.

$75.4 \div 6.75 \approx 75 \div 7$, or about 10 or 11 times.

36. Two prisms with different surface areas can have the same volume.

Sample answer: Consider two prisms. Prism A is 2 by 3 by 4 and Prism B is 1 by 4 by 6.

Prism A:

$S = 2B + Ph = 2(2)(3) + (2(3) + 2(2))(4) = 52$ units^2

$V = Bh = 2(3)(4) = 24$ units^3

Prism B:

$S = 2B + Ph = 2(1)(4) + (2(1) + 2(4))(6) = 68$ units^2

$V = Bh = 1(4)(6) = 24$ units^3

The surface area of the prisms is different but the volume is the same, 24 cubic units.

37. a. Original cylinder:

$S = 2\pi r^2 + 2\pi r h = 2\pi(4)^2 + 2\pi(4)(9) \approx 326.7$ cm^2

$V = Bh = \pi r^2 h = \pi(4)^2(9) \approx 452.4$ cm^3

Cylinder with $r = 3 \times 4 = 12$:

$S = 2\pi r^2 + 2\pi r h = 2\pi(12)^2 + 2\pi(12)(9) \approx 1583.4$ cm^2

$V = Bh = \pi r^2 h = \pi(12)^2(9) \approx 4071.5$ cm^3

Ratio of surface areas: $\dfrac{1583.4 \text{ cm}^2}{326.7 \text{ cm}^2} \approx 4.8$

Ratio of volumes: $\dfrac{4071.5 \text{ cm}^3}{452.4 \text{ cm}^3} \approx 9$

The surface area is about 4.8 times as great and the volume is about 9 times as great when the radius is tripled.

b. Cylinder with $h = 3 \times 9 = 27$

$S = 2\pi r^2 + 2\pi r h = 2\pi(4)^2 + 2\pi(4)(27) \approx 779.1$ cm^2

$V = Bh = \pi r^2 h = \pi(4)^2 27 \approx 1357.2$ cm^3

Ratio of surface areas: $\dfrac{779.1 \text{ cm}^2}{327.6 \text{ cm}^2} \approx 2.4$

Ratio of volumes: $\dfrac{1357.2 \text{ cm}^3}{452.2 \text{ cm}^3} \approx 3$

The surface area is about 2.4 times as great and the volume is about 3 times as great when the height is tripled.

c. Cylinder with $r = 12$ and $h = 27$:

$S = 2\pi r^2 + 2\pi r h$

$\quad = 2\pi(12)^2 + 2\pi(12)(27)$

$\quad \approx 2940.5$ cm^2

$V = Bh = \pi r^2 h = \pi(12)^2(27) \approx 12,214.5$ cm^3

Ratio of surface areas: $\dfrac{2940.5 \text{ cm}^2}{326.7 \text{ cm}^2} \approx 9$

Ratio of volumes: $\dfrac{12,214.5 \text{ cm}^3}{452.4 \text{ cm}^3} \approx 27$

The surface area is about 9 times as great and the volume is about 27 times as great when the radius and height are both tripled.

Chapter 10, continued

38. $S = 2B + Ph = 2(1)^2 + 4(1)(1) = 6 \text{ m}^2$

$V = Bh = 1^2(1) = 1 \text{ m}^3$

The surface area of the cube is 6 square meters and the volume is 1 cubic meter.

Sample answer: Another prism with a square base has dimensions 2 meters by 2 meters by 0.5 meter and meets the ratio criteria.

$S = 2B + Ph = 2(2)^2 + 2(4)(0.5) = 12 \text{ m}^2$

$V = Bh = 2^2(0.5) = 2 \text{ m}^3$.

Surface area: $\dfrac{12 \text{ m}^2}{6 \text{ m}^2} = 2$

Volume: $\dfrac{2 \text{ m}^3}{1 \text{ m}^3} = 2$

Mixed Review

39. $S = B + \frac{1}{2}P\ell = 8^2 + \frac{1}{2}(4)(8)(8) = 192$

The surface area is 192 square inches.

40. $S = \pi r^2 + \pi r\ell \approx \pi(3)^2 + \pi(3)(5) \approx 75.4$

The surface area is about 75.4 square feet.

41. $S = B + \frac{1}{2}P\ell = 15.6 + \frac{1}{2}(6 + 6 + 6)11 = 114.6$

The surface area is 114.6 square millimeters.

42. $a^2 + b^2 = c^2$

$15^2 + b^2 = 39^2$

$225 + b^2 = 1521$

$b^2 = 1296$

$b = 36$

The unknown length is 36 units.

43. $a^2 + b^2 = c^2$

$16^2 + 63^2 = c^2$

$256 + 3969 = c^2$

$4225 = c^2$

$\sqrt{4225} = c$

$65 = c$

The hypotenuse is 65 units.

44. A; $r = \dfrac{d}{2} = \dfrac{2}{2} = 1 \text{ cm}$

$A = \pi r^2 \approx 3.14(1)^2 = 3.14 \text{ cm}^2$

Lesson 10.7

Investigation (p. 560)

1. $V = \frac{1}{3}\ell wh = \frac{1}{3}(2)(2)(4) = 5\frac{1}{3} \text{ cm}^3$

2. $V = \frac{1}{3}\ell wh = \frac{1}{3}(6)(6)(5) = 60 \text{ cm}^3$

3. $V = \frac{1}{3}\ell wh = \frac{1}{3}(3)(3)(8) = 24 \text{ cm}^3$

4. Check student models. The heights are the same and the bases are the same.

The ratio of the volumes of the cone to the cylinder is also $1 : 3$.

10.7 Guided Practice (pp. 561–563)

1. $V = \frac{1}{3}Bh = \frac{1}{3}(4^2)(5) = 26.\overline{6}$

The pyramid has a volume of $26.\overline{6}$ cubic centimeters.

2. $V = \frac{1}{3}Bh = \frac{1}{3}(6^2)(15) = 180$

The pyramid has a volume of 180 cubic inches.

3. $V = \frac{1}{3}Bh = \frac{1}{3}(8^2)(27) = 576$

The pyramid has a volume of 576 cubic millimeters.

4. $V = \frac{1}{3}Bh = \frac{1}{3}(3^2)(3) = 9$

The pyramid has a volume of 9 cubic yards.

5. $V = \frac{1}{3}Bh = \frac{1}{3}(7^2)(9) = 147$

The pyramid has a volume of 147 cubic meters.

6. $V = \frac{1}{3}Bh = \frac{1}{3}(12^2)(21) = 1008$

The pyramid has a volume of 1008 cubic feet.

7. $V = \frac{1}{3}Bh = \frac{1}{3}(8)(4) = 10.\overline{6}$

The pyramid has a volume of $10.\overline{6}$ cubic centimeters.

8. $V = \frac{1}{3}Bh = \frac{1}{3}(81)(12) = 324$

The pyramid has a volume of 324 cubic inches.

9. $V = \frac{1}{3}Bh = \frac{1}{3}(21)(5) = 35$

The pyramid has a volume of 35 cubic yards.

10. $B = S^2 = 8^2 = 64$

$V = \frac{1}{3}Bh = \frac{1}{3}(64)(9) = 192$

The base of the pyramid is 64 square inches. The pyramid has a volume of 192 cubic inches.

11. $B = \frac{1}{2}bh = \frac{1}{2}(5)(12) = 30$

$V = \frac{1}{3}Bh = \frac{1}{3}(30)(10) = 100$

The base of the pyramid is 30 square feet. The pyramid has a volume of 100 cubic feet.

12. $B = \ell w = 20(8) = 160$

$V = \frac{1}{3}Bh = \frac{1}{3}(160)(15) = 800$

The base of the pyramid is 160 square meters. The pyramid has a volume of 800 cubic meters.

13. $V = \frac{1}{3}Bh = \frac{1}{3}\pi r^2 = \frac{1}{3}\pi(24)^2(18) \approx 10{,}857.34$

The cone has a volume of about 10,857.34 cubic meters.

14. $V = \frac{1}{3}Bh = \frac{1}{3}\pi r^2 = \frac{1}{3}\pi(4)^2 16 \approx 268.08$

The cone has a volume of about 268.08 cubic inches.

Chapter 10, continued

15. $V = \frac{1}{3}Bh = \frac{1}{3}\pi r^2 = \frac{1}{3}\pi(15)^2 28 \approx 6597.34$

The cone has a volume of about 6597.34 cubic feet.

10.7 Exercises (pp. 563–566)

Skill Practice

1. D; The formula for the volume of a prism is $V = Bh$.

2. B; The formula for the volume of a cylinder is $V = \pi r^2 h$.

3. A; The formula for the volume of a pyramid is $V = \frac{1}{3}Bh$.

4. C; The formula for the volume of a cone is $V = \frac{1}{3}\pi r^2 h$.

5. $V = \frac{1}{3}Bh = \frac{1}{3}(9)(4) = 12$

The pyramid has a volume of 12 cubic inches.

6. $V = \frac{1}{3}Bh = \frac{1}{3}(12)(15) = 60$

The pyramid has a volume of 60 cubic feet.

7. $V = \frac{1}{3}Bh = \frac{1}{3}(1.5)(0.6) = 0.3$

The pyramid has a volume of 0.3 cubic meters.

8. $V = \frac{1}{3}Bh = \frac{1}{3}(15)^2(4) = 300$

The pyramid has a volume of 300 cubic meters.

9. $V = \frac{1}{3}Bh = \frac{1}{3}(12)^2(3) = 144$

The pyramid has a volume of 144 cubic yards.

10. $V = \frac{1}{3}Bh = \frac{1}{3}(6)^2\left(\frac{1}{2}\right) = 6$

The pyramid has a volume of 6 cubic inches.

11. $V = \frac{1}{3}Bh = \frac{1}{3}(16)(24)(20) = 2560$

The pyramid has a volume of 2560 cubic meters.

12. $V = \frac{1}{3}Bh = \frac{1}{3}(25)(29)(17) \approx 4108.3$

The pyramid has a volume of about 4108.3 cubic inches.

13. $V = \frac{1}{3}Bh = \frac{1}{3}\left(\frac{1}{2} \cdot 9 \cdot 15\right)(11) = 247.5$

The pyramid has a volume of 247.5 cubic feet.

14. $V = \frac{1}{3}Bh = \frac{1}{3}\pi r^2 h = \frac{1}{3}\pi(11)^2(27) \approx 3421.2$

The cone has a volume of about 3421.2 cubic centimeters.

15. $V = \frac{1}{3}Bh = \frac{1}{3}\pi r^2 h = \frac{1}{3}\pi(45)^2(45) \approx 95,425.9$

The cone has a volume of about 95,425.9 cubic feet.

16. $V = \frac{1}{3}Bh = \frac{1}{3}\pi r^2 h = \frac{1}{3}\pi(4)^2(11) \approx 184.3$

The cone has a volume of about 184.3 cubic yards.

17. C; $V = \frac{1}{3}Bh = \frac{1}{3}\pi r^2 h = \frac{1}{3}\pi(7)^2(3) = 49\pi \text{ ft}^3$

18. $V = \frac{1}{3}Bh = \frac{1}{3}\pi r^2 h = \frac{1}{3}\pi(3)^2(7) \approx 66.0$

The cone has a volume of about 66.0 cubic inches.

19. $V = \frac{1}{3}Bh = \frac{1}{3}\pi r^2 h = \frac{1}{3}\pi(11)^2(4) \approx 506.8$

The cone has a volume of about 506.8 cubic feet.

20. $d = 1.2$ m, $r = 0.6$ m

$V = \frac{1}{3}Bh = \frac{1}{3}\pi r^2 h = \frac{1}{3}\pi(0.6)^2(4.5) \approx 1.7$

The cone has a volume of about 1.7 cubic meters.

21. $r = 2.8$ m $= 280$ cm

$V = \frac{1}{3}Bh = \frac{1}{3}\pi r^2 h = \frac{1}{3}\pi(83)^2(280) = 2,019,960.3$

The cone has a volume of about 2,019,960.3 cubic centimeters.

22. $d = 5$ m $= 500$ cm, $r = 250$ cm

$V = \frac{1}{3}Bh = \frac{1}{3}\pi r^2 h = \frac{1}{3}\pi(250)^2(492) = 32,201,324.7$

The cone has a volume of about 32,201,324.7 cubic centimeters.

23. $d = 3$ ft, $r = 1.5$ ft

$h = 10$ yd $= 30$ ft

$V = \frac{1}{3}Bh = \frac{1}{3}\pi r^2 h = \frac{1}{3}\pi(1.5)^2(30) \approx 70.7$

The cone has a volume of about 70.7 cubic feet.

24. Use the Pythagorean theorem to find the height of the base.

$$a^2 + b^2 = c^2$$
$$h^2 + 1.2^2 = 1.3^2$$
$$h^2 = 0.25$$
$$h = \sqrt{0.25}$$
$$h = 0.5$$

$B = \frac{1}{2}bh = \frac{1}{2}(1.2)(0.5) = 0.3$

$V = \frac{1}{3}Bh = \frac{1}{3}(0.3)(1.8) = 0.18$

The area of the base is 0.3 square centimeters. The volume of the pyramid is 0.18 cubic centimeters.

25. $B = 2\left(\frac{1}{2}(6 + 12)5.2\right) = 93.6$

$V = \frac{1}{3}Bh = \frac{1}{3}(93.6)(8) = 249.6$

The area of the base is 93.6 square meters. The volume of the pyramid is 249.6 cubic meters.

26. $B =$ area of triangle + area of trapezoid

$= \frac{1}{2}bh + \frac{1}{2}(b_1 + b_2)(h)$

$= \frac{1}{2}(16)(6) + \frac{1}{2}(16 + 10)(8)$

$= 48 + 104 = 152$

$V = \frac{1}{3}Bh = \frac{1}{3}(152)(18) = 912$

The area of the base is 152 square inches. The volume of the pyramid is 912 cubic inches.

27. $V = \frac{1}{3}Bh$

$156 = \frac{1}{3}(6)^2 h$

$156 = 12h$

$13 = h$

The height is 13 yards.

28. $V = \frac{1}{3}Bh$

$V = \frac{1}{3}\pi r^2 h$

$216\pi = \frac{1}{3}\pi r^2 (8)$

$216\pi = \frac{8}{3}\pi r^2$

$81 = r^2$

$\sqrt{81} = r$

$9 = r$

The radius is 9 feet.

29. $V = \frac{1}{3}Bh$

$28 = \frac{1}{3}\left(\frac{1}{2}(3)(4)\right)h$

$28 = 2h$

$14 = h$

The height is 14 inches.

30. Find the height of the pyramid by using the Pythagorean theorem.

$a^2 + b^2 = c^2$

$h^2 + 10^2 = 15^2$

$h^2 = 125$

$h = \sqrt{125}$

$h = 5\sqrt{5}$

Pyramid: $V = \frac{1}{3}Bh = \frac{1}{3}(20)^2\left(5\sqrt{5}\right) \approx 1490.7$

Cube: $V = Bh = (20)^2(20) = 8000$

The volume of the solid is about
$1490.7 + 8000 = 9490.7$ cubic feet.

31. Top cone: $V = \frac{1}{3}Bh = \frac{1}{3}\pi r^2 h = \frac{1}{3}\pi(6)^2(10) \approx 377.0$

Bottom cone: $V = \frac{1}{3}Bh = \frac{1}{3}\pi r^2 h = \frac{1}{3}\pi(6)^2(14) \approx 527.8$

The volume of the solid is about $377.0 + 527.8 = 904.8$ cubic centimeters.

32. Top cone: $V = \frac{1}{3}Bh = \frac{1}{3}\pi r^2 h = \frac{1}{3}\pi(2)^2(2) \approx 8.4$

Cylinder: $V = Bh = \pi r^2 h = \pi(2)^2(2) \approx 25.1$

Bottom cone: $V = \frac{1}{3}Bh = \frac{1}{3}\pi r^2 h = \frac{1}{3}\pi(2)^2(7) \approx 29.3$

The volume of the solid is about $8.4 + 25.1 + 29.3 = 62.8$ cubic inches.

33. Square pyramid:

$V = \frac{1}{3}Bh = \frac{1}{3}s^2 h$

Square pyramid with dimensions doubled:

$V = \frac{1}{3}(2s)(2s)(2h) = \frac{8}{3}s^2 h = 8\left(\frac{1}{3}s^2 h\right)$

When you double the dimensions, you multiply the volume by 8.

34. To find the volume of the solid, find the area of one pyramid and double it.

$V = 2\left(\frac{1}{3}Bh\right) = 2\left(\frac{1}{3}s^2 h\right) = \frac{2}{3}s^2 h$

35. To find the volume of the solid, add the volumes of the prism and the pyramid.

$V = Bh_2 + \frac{1}{3}Bh_1 = \ell wh_2 + \frac{1}{3}\ell wh_1 = \ell w\left(h_2 + \frac{1}{3}h_1\right)$

36. To find the volume of the solid, add the volumes of the cylinder and the cone.

$V = Bh + \frac{1}{3}Bh$

$V = \pi r^2 h_2 + \frac{1}{3}\pi r^2 h_1 = \pi r^2\left(h_2 + \frac{1}{3}h_1\right)$

37.

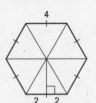

Using the diagram and a rule for 30°-60°-90° triangles, find the height of a triangle in the base.

$h_1 =$ longer leg $=$ shorter leg $\cdot \sqrt{3} = 2\sqrt{3}$

$V = \frac{1}{3}Bh = \frac{1}{3}\left[6\left(\frac{1}{2}bh_1\right)\right](h) = \frac{1}{3}\left[6\left(\frac{1}{2}\right)(4)\left(2\sqrt{3}\right)\right](6) \approx 83.1$

The volume of the hexagonal pyramid is about 83.1 cubic meters.

Problem Solving

38. $V = \frac{1}{3}Bh = \frac{1}{3}\pi r^2 h = \frac{1}{3}\pi(10)^2(24) \approx 2513.3$

The volume of the space is about 2513.3 cubic feet.

39. C;

Square pyramid: $V = \frac{1}{3}Bh = \frac{1}{3}(8)^2(6) = 128$

Rectangular pyramid: $V = \frac{1}{3}Bh = \frac{1}{3}(8)(6)(6) = 96$

Cylinder: $V = Bh = \pi r^2 h = \pi(4)^2(6) \approx 302$

Cone: $V = \frac{1}{3}Bh = \frac{1}{3}\pi r^2 h = \frac{1}{3}\pi(4)^2(6) \approx 101$

40. Doubling the radius would increase the volume more than doubling the height because the radius is squared in the volume formula, but the height is not.

41. Dirt: $V = Bh = 10(12)(8) = 960 \text{ ft}^3$

Pyramid: $V = \frac{1}{3}Bh$

$$960 = \frac{1}{3}(10^2)h$$

$$960 = \frac{100}{3}h$$

$$28.8 = h$$

Cone: $V = \frac{1}{3}Bh$

$$V = \frac{1}{3}\pi r^2 h$$

$$960 = \frac{1}{3}\pi(5)^2 h$$

$$960 = \frac{25\pi}{3}h$$

$$36.7 \approx h$$

The height of the cone, about 36.7 feet, is greater than the height of the pyramid, about 28.8 feet. The cone is the taller solid that can be formed.

42. $d = 8.3 \text{ cm}, r = 4.15 \text{ cm}$

Use the Pythagorean theorem to find the height of a brick.

$$a^2 + b^2 = c^2$$
$$h^2 + 4.15^2 = 10.1^2$$
$$h^2 = 84.7875$$
$$h = \sqrt{84.7875}$$
$$h \approx 9.208$$

$$V = \frac{1}{3}Bh = \frac{1}{3}\pi r^2 h = \frac{1}{3}\pi(4.15)^2(9.208) \approx 166.07$$

The volume of one brick is about 166.07 cubic centimeters. 27 bricks would occupy about $27 \times 166.07 = 4483.89$ cubic centimeters.

43. a. $d = 9 \text{ in.}, r = 4.5 \text{ in.}$

$$V = \frac{1}{3}Bh = \frac{1}{3}\pi r^2 h = \frac{1}{3}\pi(4.5)^2(3) \approx 63.6$$

The volume of the sand is about 63.6 cubic inches.

b. $\dfrac{63.6 \text{ in.}^3}{60 \text{ min}} = \dfrac{1.06 \text{ in.}^3}{1 \text{ min}}$

The sand falls through the opening at a rate of about 1.06 cubic inches per minute.

c. When $h = 2 \text{ in.}, r = 3 \text{ in.}$

$$V = \frac{1}{3}Bh = \frac{1}{3}\pi r^2 h = \frac{1}{3}\pi(3)^2(2) \approx 18.85 \text{ in.}^3$$

When the pile of sand is about 2 inches tall, about $18.85 \div 1.06 \approx 17.8$ minutes have passed.

44.

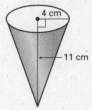

Draw similar triangles to find the radius of the water line when the cup is filled to a height of 9 cm.

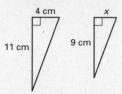

$$\frac{4}{x} = \frac{11}{9}$$

$$36 = 11x$$

$$3.27 \approx x$$

The radius of the water line that is 2 centimeters below the top of the cup is about 3.27 centimeters.

$$V = \frac{1}{3}Bh$$

$$V = \frac{1}{3}\pi r^2 h = \frac{1}{3}\pi(3.27)^2(9) \approx 100.8 \text{ cm}^3$$

There are about 100.8(0.0338), or 3.4 fluid ounces of water in the cup.

Mixed Review

45. $5x - 4^2 = 5(6) - 4^2 = 30 - 16 = 14$

46. $3x + 9^2 = 3(6) + 9^2 = 18 + 81 = 99$

47. $2x^2 + 14 = 2(6)^2 + 14 = 2(36) + 14 = 72 + 14 = 86$

48. $7x^2 - 23 = 7(6)^2 - 23 = 7(36) - 23 = 252 - 23 = 229$

49. Method 1: Sketch the solid.

Method 2: Sketch the top, front, and side views.

top   front   side

50. Method 1: Sketch the solid.

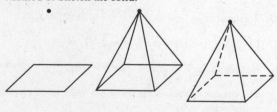

Chapter 10, *continued*

Method 2: Sketch the top, front, and side views.

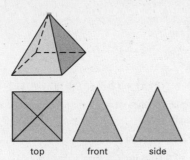

top   front   side

51.

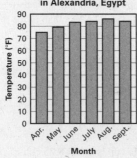

Average High Temperatures in Alexandria, Egypt

52. C;
$$V = Bh = \pi r^2 h = \pi(5)^2(14) = 350\pi$$
The volume of the cylinder is 350π cubic inches.

Quiz 10.4–10.7 (p. 566)

1. $S = 2B + Ph = 2(24)(10) + (2(24) + 2(10))6 = 888$
The surface area of the prism is 888 square meters.

2. $S = 2\pi r^2 + 2\pi rh = 2\pi(3.5)^2 + 2\pi(3.5)(14) \approx 384.8$
The surface area is about 384.8 square yards.

3. $S = \pi r^2 + \pi r\ell = \pi(5)^2 + \pi(5)(8) \approx 204.2$
The surface area of the cone is about 204.2 square centimeters.

4. $V = Bh = \pi r^2 h = \pi(32)^2(150) \approx 482{,}548.6$
The volume of the cylinder is about 482,548.6 cubic yards.

5. $V = \frac{1}{3}Bh = \frac{1}{3}\pi r^2 h = \frac{1}{3}\pi(3)^2(3) \approx 28.27$
The volume of the cone is about 28.3 cubic feet.

6. $V = \frac{1}{3}Bh = \frac{1}{3}(3)(1.5)(2) = 3$
The volume of the pyramid is 3 cubic meters.

7. $V = Bh = \frac{1}{2}(25 \cdot 2)(10) = 250$
You need 250 cubic feet of cement to make the ramp.

10.7 Extension (p. 567)

1. $V = \frac{4}{3}\pi r^3 = \frac{4}{3}\pi(2)^3 \approx 33.5$
The volume of the sphere is about 33.5 cubic feet.

2. $V = \frac{4}{3}\pi r^3 = \frac{4}{3}\pi(4)^3 \approx 268.1$

The volume of the sphere is about 268.1 cubic millimeters.

3. $d = 2$ yd, $r = 1$ yd
$$V = \frac{4}{3}\pi r^3 = \frac{4}{3}\pi(1)^3 \approx 4.2$$
The volume of the sphere is about 4.2 cubic yards.

4. $V = \frac{4}{3}\pi r^3 = \frac{4}{3}\pi(9)^3 \approx 3053.6$

The volume of the sphere is about 3053.6 cubic inches.

5. $d = 12$ m, $r = 6$ m
$$V = \frac{4}{3}\pi r^3 = \frac{4}{3}\pi(6)^3 \approx 904.8$$
The volume of the sphere is about 904.8 cubic meters.

6. $d = 16$ km, $r = 8$ km
$$V = \frac{4}{3}\pi r^3 = \frac{4}{3}\pi(8)^3 \approx 2144.7$$
The volume of the sphere is about 2144.7 cubic kilometers.

7. Sphere: $V = \frac{4}{3}\pi r^3$

Cone: $V = \frac{1}{3}Bh = \frac{1}{3}\pi r^2 h = \frac{1}{3}\pi r^2(2r) = \frac{2}{3}\pi r^3$

Cylinder: $V = Bh = \pi r^2 h = \pi r^2(2r) = 2\pi r^3$

A word equation that relates the three volumes is volume of sphere = volume of cylinder − volume of cone.

Mixed Review of Problem Solving (p. 568)

1. a. Cylinder: $d = 1$ ft, $r = 0.5$ ft
$$S = 2\pi r^2 + 2\pi rh = 2\pi(0.5)^2 + 2\pi(0.5)(1.25) \approx 5.5 \text{ ft}^2$$
Prism:
$$S = 2B + Ph = 2(0.75)^2 + 4(0.75)(1) = 4.125 \text{ ft}^2$$
The aluminum for the cylinder will cost $5.5 \times \$.02 = \$.11$.

The aluminum for the prism will cost about $4.125 \times \$.02 \approx \$.08$.

b. Cylinder:
$$V = Bh = \pi r^2 h = \pi(0.5)^2(1.25) \approx 0.98 \text{ ft}^3$$
Prism:
$$V = Bh = (0.75)^2(1) = 0.5625 \text{ ft}^3$$
The cylinder has a greater capacity.

c. Divide the cost by the capacity.

Cylinder: $0.11 \div 0.98 \approx 0.11$

Prism: $0.08 \div 0.5625 \approx 0.14$

The cylinder has the lower cost per cubic foot of capacity at about 11 cents.

Chapter 10, *continued*

2. The volume of the pool is

$V = Bh = 40(20)(4) = 3200$ ft³.

Given that 1 cubic foot of water contains 7.5 gallons, the capacity of the pool is $7.5(3200) = 24,000$ gallons. Multiply by the ratio $\frac{10}{1,000,000}$ to find that 0.24 gallon of sodium hypochlorite is needed.

3. 4; $V = Bh = \pi r^2 h = \pi(0.5)^2(1) \approx 0.785$ ft³

After the log is split it will take up $\frac{4}{3} \times 0.785 \approx 1.05$ ft³.

A cord of split firewood is made up of about $128 \div 1.05 \approx 122$ logs. The cord weighs about $122 \times 36 = 4392$ pounds.

Leon will need to take $4392 \div 1200 = 3.66$, or 4 trips to deliver the wood.

4. *Sample answer:*

Pyramid:

$V = Bh = (1)^2(1) = 1$ mm³

Cone:

$V = \frac{1}{3}Bh = \frac{1}{3}\pi r^2 h = \frac{1}{3}\pi(1)^2(1) = \frac{1}{3}\pi$ mm³

Similar pyramid:

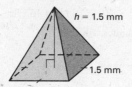

$V = Bh = (1.5)^2(1.5) = 3.375$ mm³

Similar cone:

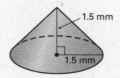

$V = \frac{1}{3}Bh = \frac{1}{3}\pi r^2 h = \frac{1}{3}\pi(1.5)^2(1.5) = 1.125\pi$ mm³

When compared:

$3.375 \div 1 = 3.375$

$1.125\pi \div \frac{1}{3}\pi = 3.375$

The volumes of the similar solids are 3.375, or 1.5³ times the volumes of the original solids.

5. a.

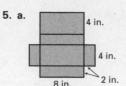

$S = 2B + Ph = 2(8)(4) + (2(8) + 2(4))(2) = 112$

At least 112 square inches of wrapping paper is needed to cover the package.

b. $8 + 2 + 8 + 2 + 10 = 30$

The ribbon is 30 inches long.

c. No; Because two faces are touching, one face of each box does not need wrapping paper. The surface area of the combined packages will be less than twice the surface area of one box.

6. a. $V = \frac{1}{3}Bh = \frac{1}{3}\pi r^2 h = \frac{1}{3}\pi(1.2)^2(3) \approx 4.52$

The capacity of the small cup is about 4.52 cubic inches.

b. $V = \frac{1}{3}Bh = \frac{1}{3}\pi r^2 h = \frac{1}{3}\pi(1.5)^2(3.5) \approx 8.25$

The capacity of the large cup is about 8.25 cubic inches.

c. You can fill $41 \div 4.52 \approx 9.07$, 9 small cups, or $41 \div 8.25 \approx 4.97$, 4 large cups.

Chapter 10 Review (pp. 569–572)

1. B; The solid has two triangular bases, so it is a prism.

2. C; The solid is a sphere.

3. D; The figure is a quadrilateral with exactly one pair of parallel sides, so it is a trapezoid.

4. A; The figure is a quadrilateral with two pairs of parallel sides, so it is a parallelogram.

5. $A = \frac{1}{2}(b_1 + b_2)h = \frac{1}{2}(6 + 9)(8) = 60$

The area of the trapezoid is 60 square yards.

6. $A = bh = 20(8) = 160$

The area of the parallelogram is 160 square feet.

7. Parallelogram: $A = bh = 36(21) = 756$ cm²

Similar parallelogram:

$A = bh = \left(\frac{1}{3} \times 36\right)\left(\frac{1}{3} \times 21\right) = 12(7) = 84$ cm²

The area of the larger parallelogram is $756 \div 84 = 9$ times the area of the smaller parallelogram.

8. $A = \pi r^2 \approx 3.14(2.5)^2 \approx 19.63$

The area of the circle is about 19.63 square millimeters.

9. $A = \pi r^2 \approx 3.14(3.7)^2 \approx 42.99$

The area of the circle is about 42.99 square miles.

10. $r = \frac{d}{2} = \frac{7}{2} = 3.5$ km

$A = \pi r^2 \approx 3.14(3.5)^2 \approx 38.47$

The area of the circle is about 38.47 square kilometers.

Chapter 10, *continued*

11.
$$A = \pi r^2$$
$$1808.64 \approx (3.14)r^2$$
$$576 \approx r^2$$
$$\sqrt{576} \approx r$$
$$24 \approx r$$

The radius of the circle is about 24 inches.

12.
$$A = \pi r^2$$
$$50.24 \approx (3.14)r^2$$
$$16 \approx r^2$$
$$\sqrt{16} \approx r$$
$$4 \approx r$$

The radius of the circle is about 4 millimeters.

13.
$$A = \pi r^2$$
$$254.34 \approx (3.14)r^2$$
$$81 \approx r^2$$
$$\sqrt{81} \approx r$$
$$9 \approx r$$

The radius of the circle is about 9 yards.

14. The solid has two triangular bases that lie in parallel planes, so it is a triangular prism. It is a polyhedron because it is enclosed by polygons.

15. The solid has two circular bases that lie in parallel planes, so the solid is a cylinder. It is not a polyhedron because circles are not polygons.

16. The solid has one pentagonal base, so it is a pentagonal pyramid. It is a polyhedron because it is enclosed by polygons.

17. The prism has 5 faces, 9 edges, and 6 vertices.

18. $S = 2B + Ph = 2\left(\frac{1}{2}\right)(10)(12) + (13 + 13 + 10)(23) = 948$

The surface area of the solid is 948 square inches. It is a triangular prism because it has two triangular bases that lie in parallel planes.

19. $S = 2B + Ph = 2(5)(2) + (2(5) + 2(2))(9) = 146$

The surface area of the prism is 146 square feet.

20. $S = 2\pi r^2 + 2\pi rh = 2\pi(5)^2 + 2\pi(5)(10) \approx 471.2$

The surface area of the cylinder is about 471.2 square meters.

21. $S = B + \frac{1}{2}P\ell = 7^2 + \frac{1}{2}(4 \cdot 7)(4) = 105$

The surface area of the pyramid is 105 square meters.

22. $r = \frac{d}{2} = \frac{20}{2} = 10$ ft

$S = \pi r^2 + \pi r\ell = \pi(10)^2 + \pi(10)(15) \approx 785.4$

The surface area of the cone is about 784.5 square feet.

23. $S = B + \frac{1}{2}P\ell = 4^2 + \frac{1}{2}(4 \cdot 4)(5) = 56$

You need 56 square inches of wrapping paper.

24. $V = Bh = \frac{1}{2}(12 \cdot 5)(8) = 240$

The volume of the prism is 240 cubic millimeters.

25. $V = Bh = (5 \cdot 9)(3) = 135$

The volume of the prism is 135 cubic inches.

26. $V = Bh = \pi r^2 h = \pi(5.4)^2(5.4) \approx 494.7$

The volume of the cylinder is about 494.7 cubic centimeters.

27. $V = \frac{1}{3}Bh = \frac{1}{3}(6 \cdot 9)(7) = 126$

The volume of the pyramid is 126 cubic centimeters.

28. $V = \frac{1}{3}Bh = \frac{1}{3}\pi r^2 h = \frac{1}{3}\pi(4)^2 8 \approx 134.0$

The volume of the cone is about 134.0 cubic inches.

29. $V = \frac{1}{3}Bh = \frac{1}{3}(3)^2(5) = 15$ in.^{3}

You do not have enough wax to make the candle; you need 3 more cubic inches of wax.

Chapter 10 Test (p. 573)

1. $A = bh = 13(7) = 91$

The parallelogram has an area of 91 square centimeters.

2. $A = \frac{1}{2}(b_1 + b_2)h = \frac{1}{2}(26 + 16)(18) = 378$

The trapezoid has an area of 378 square meters.

3. $A = \frac{1}{2}(b_1 + b_2)h = \frac{1}{2}(21 + 32)(15) = 397.5$

The trapezoid has an area of 397.5 square inches.

4. $A = \pi r^2 \approx 3.14(4)^2 = 50.24$

The area of the circle is about 50.24 square feet.

5. $r = \frac{d}{2} = \frac{14}{2} = 7$ yd

$A = \pi r^2 \approx 3.14(7)^2 = 153.86$

The area of the circle is about 153.86 square yards.

6. $A = \pi r^2 \approx 3.14(9)^2 = 254.34$

The area of the circle is about 254.34 square millimeters.

7.
$$A = \pi r^2$$
$$3.7994 \approx 3.14r^2$$
$$1.21 \approx r^2$$
$$\sqrt{1.21} \approx r$$
$$1.1 \approx r$$

The radius is about 1.1 feet.

8.
$$A = \pi r^2$$
$$0.785 \approx 3.14r^2$$
$$0.25 \approx r^2$$
$$\sqrt{0.25} \approx r$$
$$0.5 \approx r$$

The radius is about 0.5 meter.

9.
$$A = \pi r^2$$
$$94.985 \approx 3.14r^2$$
$$30.25 \approx r^2$$
$$\sqrt{30.25} \approx r$$
$$5.5 \approx r$$

The radius is about 5.5 yards.

Chapter 10, *continued*

10. The solid has two circular bases that lie in parallel planes, so the solid is a cylinder. It is not a polyhedron because circles are not polygons.

11. The solid has two hexagonal bases that lie in parallel planes, so it is a hexagonal prism. It is a polyhedron because it is enclosed by polygons.

12. The solid has one square base, so it is a square pyramid. It is a polyhedron because it is enclosed by polygons.

13. The prism has 8 faces, 18 edges, and 12 vertices.

14. $S = 2\pi r^2 + 2\pi rh = 2(\pi)(30)^2 + 2(\pi)(30)(8) \approx 7162.8$

    The surface area of the cylinder is about 7162.8 square meters.

15. $S = B + \frac{1}{2}P\ell = 15^2 + \frac{1}{2}(4)(15)(16) = 705$

    The surface area of the pyramid is 705 square inches.

16. $S = \pi r^2 + \pi r\ell = \pi(6.5)^2 + \pi(6.5)(21) \approx 561.6$

    The surface area of the cone is about 561.6 square millimeters.

17. $V = Bh = \frac{1}{2}(4)(2)(3) = 12$

    The volume of the prism is 12 cubic feet.

18. $V = \frac{1}{3}Bh = \frac{1}{3}\pi r^2 h = \frac{1}{3}(\pi)(2)^2(3) \approx 12.6$

    The volume is about 12.6 cubic millimeters.

19. $V = \frac{1}{3}Bh = \frac{1}{3}(13)(8)(9) = 312$

    The volume of the pyramid is 312 cubic inches.

20. $S = B + Ph = 15(12) + [2(15) + 2(12)](8) = 612 \text{ ft}^2$

    You will need $612 \div 400 \approx 2$ cans of paint.

21. $V = Bh = \pi r^2 h = \pi(2)^2(12) \approx 150.8 \text{ cm}^3$

    You can cut $150.8 \div 2 \approx 75$ whole slices of pepperoni from the stick.

Standardized Test Preparation (p. 575)

1. Partial credit; The student used the wrong formulas, but the calculations are correct. Instead of volume, the student calculated the surface area of each container.

   To earn full credit, use the correct volume formulas, $V = \frac{1}{3}\pi r^2 h$ for the small container and $V = \pi r^2 h$ for the large container.

Standardized Test Practice (pp. 576–577)

1.

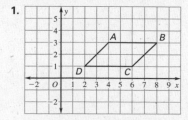

The figure is a polygon, a quadrilateral, and a parallelogram. To find the area, multiply the base, 4 units, by the height, 2 units. The area is 8 square units.

When the side lengths are doubled, $b = 8$ units and $h = 4$ units. The area is $4 \times 8 = 32$ square units. So the area is multiplied by $32 \div 8 = 4$ when the side lengths are doubled.

2. **a.** The area of the field is the sum of the areas of the two semicircles on the ends and the area of the rectangle in the middle.

   b. The radius of the semicircle is $62.8 \div 2 = 31.4$ m.

   Area of the field:

   $A = \ell w + 2\left(\frac{1}{2}\pi r^2\right)$

   $\approx 100(62.8) + 2\left(\frac{1}{2} \cdot 3.14(31.4)^2\right)$

   ≈ 9375.91

   The area of the field is about 9375.91 square meters.

   c. $9375.91 \times 1\frac{1}{4} \approx 11{,}719.89$

   You will use about 11,719.89 gallons of water.

3. **a.** $r = \frac{d}{2} = \frac{40}{2} = 20$ ft

   Lateral surface area $= 2\pi rh = 2\pi(20)(23) \approx 2888.8$

   The area of the curved wall is about 2888.8 square feet.

   b. $V = Bh = \pi r^2 h = \pi(20)^2 23 \approx 28{,}888$

   The volume is about 28,888 cubic feet.

   c. $28{,}902.7 \times 7.48 \approx 216{,}082.2$

   The capacity is about 216,082.2 gallons.

4. Volume:

   Cylinder:

   $r = \frac{d}{2} = \frac{6}{2} = 3 \text{ in.}^3$

   $V = \pi r^2 h = \pi(3)^2(8) \approx 226.1 \text{ in.}^3$

   Prism:

   $V = Bh = (12 \cdot 6)(4) = 288 \text{ in.}^3$

   The prism has the greater capacity.

   Lateral surface area:

   Cylinder:

   $2\pi rh = 2\pi(3)(8) \approx 150.7 \text{ in.}^2$

   Prism:

   $Ph = (2(6) + 2(12))(4) = 144 \text{ in.}^2$

   The cylinder requires more material for labels because it has a greater lateral surface area.

5. C;

   Area of garden = area of entire circle − area of tree trunk

   $= \pi(4)^2 - \pi(2)^2$

   $\approx 3.14(4)^2 - 3.14(2)^2$

   $= 37.68$

   The area of the flower garden is about 37.68 square feet.

Chapter 10, *continued*

6. B;

$S_A = 2B + Ph = 2(4)(2) + (2(4) + 2(2))(4) = 64$ m²

$S_B = 2B + Ph = 2(6)(4) + (2(6) + 2(4))(1) = 68$ m²

7. 175; $V = Bh = (10 \cdot 3.5)(5) = 175$

The crate has a volume of 175 cubic yards.

8. 84; $S = B + \frac{1}{2}P\ell = 6^2 + \frac{1}{2}(4)(6)(4) = 84$

The surface area of the pyramid is 84 square meters.

9. 81.6;

$S = \pi r^2 + 2\pi rh \approx 3.14(2)^2 + 2(3.14)(2)(5.5) \approx 81.6$

The surface area is about 81.6 square inches.

10. 251; $r = \frac{d}{2} = \frac{8}{2} = 4$ ft

Cone:

$V = \frac{1}{3}\pi r^2 h \approx \frac{1}{3}(3.14)(4)^2(3) \approx 50.2$ ft³

Cylinder:

$V = \pi r^2 h \approx (3.14)(4)^2(4) \approx 201.0$ ft³

The volume of the solid is about $50 + 201 = 251$ cubic feet.

11. The solid on the left is a polyhedron and a triangular prism. This solid has 5 faces, 9 edges, and 6 vertices.

The solid on the right is a polyhedron and a hexagonal pyramid. This solid has 7 faces, 12 edges, and 7 vertices.

12. Find the radius of the broadcast region.

$A = \pi r^2$

$182 \approx (3.14)r^2$

$58 \approx r^2$

$\sqrt{58} \approx r$

$7.6 \approx r$

The radius of the broadcast region is about 7.6 miles. So, a radio 8 miles away cannot receive the signal, but a radio 6 miles away can.

13. The shape of the floor is a circle, so we will use the formula for the area of a circle to find the area of the igloo's floor.

The diameter of the floor is 15 feet, and each block is 8 inches, or $\frac{8}{12}$ of a foot, so the radius is

$\frac{15}{2} - \frac{8}{12} = 6\frac{5}{6}$ feet.

$A = \pi r^2 = \pi\left(6\frac{5}{6}\right)^2 \approx 146.6$

The area of the igloo's floor is about 147 square feet. The height of the igloo is the radius of the half sphere, $\frac{15}{2} = 7.5$ feet.

Cumulative Review, Chs. 1–10 (pp. 578–579)

1–8. Expressions evaluated when $a = 3$, $b = -15$, $x = 7$, and $y = 5$.

1. $3x + 2 = 3(7) + 2 = 21 + 2 = 23$

2. $30 - 2x = 30 - 2(7) = 30 - 14 = 16$

3. $2c - y = 2(15) - 5 = 30 - 5 = 25$

4. $8a - 3c = 8(3) - 3(15) = 24 - 45 = -21$

5. $\frac{y + x}{x - y} = \frac{5 + 7}{7 - 5} = \frac{12}{2} = 6$

6. $\frac{6b}{2c} = \frac{6(-15)}{2(15)} = \frac{-90}{30} = -3$

7. $\frac{c}{-5a} = \frac{15}{-5(3)} = \frac{15}{-15} = -1$

8. $\frac{b^2}{a^2} = \frac{(-15)^2}{3^2} = \frac{225}{9} = 25$

9.

So, $54 = 2 \times 3 \times 3 \times 3 = 2 \times 3^3$.

10.
```
      70
     /  \
    2  × 35
       /  \
      5  ×  7
```
So, $70 = 2 \times 5 \times 7$.

11.
```
        150
       /  \
      2  × 75
          /  \
     2 × 3 × 25
              /  \
   2 × 3 × 5 × 5
```
So, $150 = 2 \times 3 \times 5 \times 5 = 2 \times 3 \times 5^2$.

12.
```
        184
       /  \
      2  × 92
          /  \
      2 × 2 × 46
              /  \
  2 × 2 × 2 × 23
```
So, $184 = 2 \times 2 \times 2 \times 23 = 2^3 \times 23$.

13. $\frac{a}{b} = \frac{p}{100}$

$\frac{a}{16} = \frac{500}{100}$

$\frac{a}{16} \cdot 16 = \frac{500}{100} \cdot 16$

$a = 80$

80 is 500% of 16.

14. $\frac{a}{b} = \frac{p}{100}$

$\frac{200.2}{b} = \frac{65}{100}$

$200.2 \cdot 100 = b \cdot 65$

$308 = b$

200.2 is 65% of 308.

15. $\dfrac{a}{b} = \dfrac{p}{100}$

$\dfrac{44}{80} = \dfrac{p}{100}$

$\dfrac{44}{80} \cdot 100 = \dfrac{p}{100} \cdot 100$

$55 = p$

44 is 55% of 80.

16. $\dfrac{a}{b} = \dfrac{p}{100}$

$\dfrac{1.7}{340} = \dfrac{p}{100}$

$\dfrac{1.7}{340} \cdot 100 = \dfrac{p}{100} \cdot 100$

$0.5 = p$

1.7 is 0.5% of 340.

17. The triangle has a 98° angle and two congruent sides. So, it is an obtuse, isosceles triangle.

18. The quadrilateral is a parallelogram with 4 right angles. So, it is a rectangle.

19. The triangle has all sides of equal length.

So, it is an equilateral triangle.

20. $\dfrac{d}{5} + 13 = -10$

$\dfrac{d}{5} + 13 - 13 = -10 - 13$

$\dfrac{d}{5} = -23$

$\dfrac{d}{5} \cdot 5 = -23 \cdot 5$

$d = -115$

21. $17 = \dfrac{x}{12} - 31$

$17 + 31 = \dfrac{x}{12} - 31 + 31$

$48 = \dfrac{x}{12}$

$48 \cdot 12 = \dfrac{x}{12} \cdot 12$

$576 = x$

22. $-21 - \dfrac{t}{3} = -6$

$-21 - \dfrac{t}{3} + 21 = -6 + 21$

$-\dfrac{t}{3} = 15$

$\dfrac{t}{-3} \cdot (-3) = 15 \cdot (-3)$

$t = -45$

23. $\dfrac{2}{3}h - 3 \geq 1$

$\dfrac{2}{3}h - 3 + 3 \geq 1 + 3$

$\dfrac{2}{3}h \geq 4$

$\dfrac{2}{3}h\left(\dfrac{3}{2}\right) \geq 4\left(\dfrac{3}{2}\right)$

$h \geq 6$

24. $\dfrac{1}{2}x + 4 \leq 7$

$\dfrac{1}{2}x + 4 - 4 \leq 7 - 4$

$\dfrac{1}{2}x \leq 3$

$2 \cdot \left(\dfrac{1}{2}\right)x \leq 2 \cdot 3$

$x \leq 6$

25. $-\dfrac{3}{4}x - 10 \geq 8$

$-\dfrac{3}{4}x - 10 + 10 \geq 8 + 10$

$-\dfrac{3}{4}x \geq 18$

$-\dfrac{4}{3} \cdot \left(-\dfrac{3}{4}\right)x \leq -\dfrac{4}{3} \cdot 18$

$x \leq -24$

26. $m^2 = 196$

$m = \pm\sqrt{196}$

$m = \pm 14$

27. $a^2 - 1296 = 0$

$a^2 - 1296 + 1296 = 0 + 1296$

$a^2 = 1296$

$a = \pm\sqrt{1296}$

$a = \pm 36$

28. $c^2 - 28 = 36$

$c^2 - 28 + 28 = 36 + 28$

$c^2 = 64$

$c = \pm\sqrt{64}$

$c = \pm 8$

29. $A = \dfrac{1}{2}bh = \dfrac{1}{2}(9)(6) = 27 \text{ cm}^2$

The triangle has an area of 27 square centimeters.

30. $A = bh = 13 \cdot 7 = 91 \text{ cm}^2$

The parallelogram has an area of 91 square centimeters.

31. $A = \dfrac{1}{2}bh = \dfrac{1}{2}(12)(10) = 60 \text{ yd}^2$

The triangle has an area of 60 square yards.

32. $A = \dfrac{1}{2}(b_1 + b_2)h = \dfrac{1}{2}(26 + 16)18 = 378 \text{ m}^2$

The trapezoid has an area of 378 square meters.

Chapter 10, *continued*

33. $A = \pi r^2 \approx 3.14(3)^2 \approx 28.3 \text{ cm}^2$

The circle has an area of about 28.3 square centimeters.

34. $A = \pi r^2 \approx 3.14(5)^2 \approx 78.5 \text{ ft}^2$

The circle has an area of about 78.5 square feet.

35. $V = Bh = (9 \cdot 7)4 = 252 \text{ ft}^3$

The volume is 252 cubic feet.

36. $V = \pi r^2 h = \pi(5)^2(12) \approx 942.5 \text{ m}^3$

The volume is about 942.5 cubic meters.

37. $V = \frac{1}{3}\pi r^2 h = \frac{1}{3}\pi(2)^2(6) \approx 25.1 \text{ in.}^3$

The volume is about 25.1 cubic inches.

38. *Sample answer:*

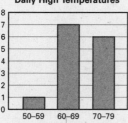

Daily High Temperatures

I chose an interval of 10 degrees to show the number of days that the high temperature was in the 50s, 60s, and 70s.

39. Classroom: $A = \ell w = 25(40) = 1000 \text{ ft}^2$

Desk/Chair: $A = 28 \cdot 9 = 252 \text{ ft}^2$

Table: $A = 20 \text{ ft}^2$

The classroom has $1000 - 252 - 20 = 728$ square feet of walking space.

40. Rice pilaf: $\frac{35 \div 5}{220 \div 5} = \frac{7}{44}$

Soup: $\frac{15 \div 5}{70 \div 5} = \frac{3}{14}$

Compare the fractions using the least common denominator to write equivalent fractions.

$\frac{7}{44} = \frac{49}{308}$ $\frac{3}{14} = \frac{66}{308}$

Since $66 > 49$, $\frac{3}{14} > \frac{7}{44}$. The soup has a greater fraction of calories from fat.

41. $\frac{15}{16} - \frac{11}{16} = \frac{15 - 11}{16} = \frac{4}{16} = \frac{1}{4}$

A quarter is $\frac{1}{4}$ inch wider than a dime.

42. $I = Prt = 300(0.035)(1) = 10.5$

$\quad I = Prt$

$10.5 = P(0.02)(1)$

$10.5 = 0.02P$

$\quad 525 = P$

You would need to invest $525.

43.

24° 156°
156° 24°

44. $a^2 + b^2 = c^2$

$\quad 12^2 + 12^2 = x^2$

$\qquad 288 = x^2$

$\qquad \sqrt{288} = x$

$\qquad 17 \approx x$

The value of x is about 17 inches.

45. $\sin 20° = \dfrac{\text{opposite}}{\text{hypotenuse}}$

$\sin 20° = \dfrac{x}{8}$

$\quad 2.7 \approx x$

$\cos 20° = \dfrac{\text{adjacent}}{\text{hypotenuse}}$

$\cos 20° = \dfrac{y}{8}$

$\quad 7.5 \approx y$

The value of x is about 2.7 feet and y is about 7.5 feet.

46. Cylinder:

$S = 2\pi r^2 + 2\pi rh = 2\pi(6)^2 + 2\pi(6)(7) \approx 490.1 \text{ cm}^2$

Prism:

$S = 2B + Ph = 2(9 \cdot 8) + (2(9) + 2(8))(11) = 518 \text{ cm}^2$

The cylinder uses about $518 - 490.1 = 27.9$ square centimeters less material than the rectangular prism.

Chapter 11

Chapter Get-Ready Games (pp. 580–581)

1. K: $-6x + 3 = -x - 17$

$17 + 3 = -x + 6x$

$20 = 5x$

$4 = x$

H: $4(x + 5) = -10x - 8$

$4x + 20 = -10x - 8$

$4x + 10x = -8 - 20$

$14x = -28$

$x = -2$

A: $7x + 15 - 4x = 18$

$3x + 15 = 18$

$3x = 18 - 15$

$3x = 3$

$x = 1$

L: $2x + 3 = 4x - 1$

$1 + 3 = 4x - 2x$

$4 = 2x$

$2 = x$

C: $-9x - 3 = -4x + 12$

$-12 - 3 = -4x + 9x$

$-15 = 5x$

$-3 = x$

2. CHALK

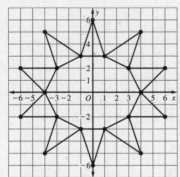

Stop and Think (p. 581)

1. The first step in solving the equation $-6x + 3 = -x - 17$ is to add the opposite of $-x$ to both sides of the equation. Because the opposite of $-x$ is x, you need to add x to both sides.

2. Check work.

Review Prerequisite Skills (p. 582)

1.

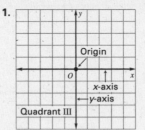

2. The symbol means greater than or equal to.

3. From the origin, move 3 units to the left and 2 units up.

4. $A(0, 3)$, $B(2, -2)$, $C(-2, 0)$, $D(2, 1)$

5–8.

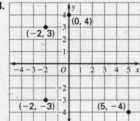

9. $3 = 9x - 24$

$27 = 9x$

$3 = x$

10. $7 - 8x = 3$

$-8x = -4$

$x = \dfrac{1}{2}$

11. $6x + 9 = -45$

$6x = -54$

$x = -9$

12. $\dfrac{x}{4} - 1 = 6$

$\dfrac{x}{4} - 1 + 1 = 6 + 1$

$\dfrac{x}{4} = 7$

$\dfrac{x}{4} \cdot 4 = 7 \cdot 4$

$x = 28$

13. $15 - x = -22$

$15 - x - 15 = -22 - 15$

$-x = -37$

$\dfrac{-x}{-1} = \dfrac{-37}{-1}$

$x = 37$

14. $-9 = \frac{x}{2} + 4$

$-9 - 4 = \frac{x}{2} + 4 - 4$

$-13 = \frac{x}{2}$

$-13 \cdot 2 = \frac{x}{2} \cdot 2$

$-26 = x$

15. $3x - 4 \le 5$

$3x \le 9$

$x \le 3$

16. $-4x - 3 \ge 12$

$-4x \ge 15$

$x \le -\frac{15}{4}$

$x \le -3\frac{3}{4}$

17. $6 + 2x < 2$

$2x < -4$

$x < -2$

Lesson 11.1

11.1 Guided Practice (pp. 583–585)

1. The relation is not a function. -2 has two outputs.

2. The relation is a function. Each input has exactly one output.

3. The relation is a function. Each input has exactly one output.

4.

Input g	Function	Output p
0	$p = 4(0) - 50$	-50
10	$p = 4(10) - 50$	-10
13	$p = 4(13) - 50$	2

The team needs to sell 13 glow sticks.

5. $y = x - 8$

11.1 Exercises (pp. 585–587)

Skill Practice

1. For a function, the set of all possible input values is its *domain* and the set of all possible output values is its *range*.

2. The relation is not a function. 4 has two outputs.

3. The relation is a function. Each input has exactly one output.

4. The relation is a function. Each input has exactly one output.

5. The relation is not a function. -8 has 2 output values.

6. The relation is a function. Each input has exactly one output.

7. The relation is not a function. 4 has two outputs.

8.

Input x	Function	Output y
-2	$y = -2 - 1$	-3
-1	$y = -1 - 1$	-2
0	$y = 0 - 1$	-1
1	$y = 1 - 1$	0
2	$y = 2 - 1$	1

The range of the function is -3, -2, -1, 0, and 1.

9.

Input x	Function	Output y
-2	$y = -\frac{1}{4}(-2)$	$\frac{1}{2}$
-1	$y = -\frac{1}{4}(-1)$	$\frac{1}{4}$
0	$y = -\frac{1}{4}(0)$	0
1	$y = -\frac{1}{4}(1)$	$-\frac{1}{4}$
2	$y = -\frac{1}{4}(2)$	$-\frac{1}{2}$

The range of the function is $\frac{1}{2}$, $\frac{1}{4}$, 0, $-\frac{1}{4}$, and $-\frac{1}{2}$.

10.

Input x	Function	Output y
-2	$y = 5(-2)$	-10
-1	$y = 5(-1)$	-5
0	$y = 5(0)$	0
1	$y = 5(1)$	5
2	$y = 5(2)$	10

The range of the function is -10, -5, 0, 5, and 10.

11.

Input x	Function	Output y
-2	$y = (-2)^2$	4
-1	$y = (-1)^2$	1
0	$y = 0^2$	0
1	$y = 1^2$	1
2	$y = 2^2$	4

The range of the function is 0, 1, and 4.

12. A; $y = \frac{1}{3}x$

$1 = \frac{1}{3}(3)$

$2 = \frac{1}{3}(6)$

$3 = \frac{1}{3}(9)$

13.

$+1 \quad +1 \quad +1$

Input x	−1	0	1	2
Output y	5	6	7	8

$+1 \quad +1 \quad +1$

$y = ax + b$

$a = \dfrac{\text{change in output}}{\text{change in input}} = \dfrac{1}{1} = 1$

$y = 1x + b$

Let $(x, y) = (0, 6)$.

$6 = 1 \cdot 0 + b$

$6 = 0 + b$

$6 = b$

$y = x + 6$

A function rule that relates x and y is $y = x + 6$.

14.

$+1 \quad +1 \quad +1$

Input x	0	1	2	3
Output y	0	−5	−10	−15

$-5 \quad -5 \quad -5$

$y = ax + b$

$a = \dfrac{\text{change in output}}{\text{change in input}} = \dfrac{-5}{1} = -5$

$y = -5x + b$

Let $(x, y) = (0, 0)$.

$0 = -5 \cdot 0 + b$

$0 = 0 + b$

$0 = b$

$y = -5x$

A function rule that relates x and y is $y = -5x$.

15.

$+1 \quad +1 \quad +1$

Input x	1	2	3	4
Output y	1	4	7	10

$+3 \quad +3 \quad +3$

$y = ax + b$

$a = \dfrac{\text{change in output}}{\text{change in input}} = \dfrac{3}{1} = 3$

$y = 3x + b$

Let $(x, y) = (1, 1)$.

$1 = 3 \cdot 1 + b$

$1 = 3 + b$

$-2 = b$

$y = 3x - 2$

A function rule that relates x and y is $y = 3x - 2$.

16.

$+1 \quad +1 \quad +1$

Input x	0	1	2	3
Output y	2	1.5	1	0.5

$-0.5 -0.5 -0.5$

$y = ax + b$

$a = \dfrac{\text{change in output}}{\text{change in input}} = \dfrac{-0.5}{1} = -0.5$

$y = -0.5x + b$

Let $(x, y) = (0, 2)$.

$2 = -0.5(0) + b$

$2 = 0 + b$

$2 = b$

$y = -0.5x + 2$

A function rule that relates x and y is $y = -0.5x + 2$.

17.

$+1 \quad +1 \quad +1$

Position	1	2	3	4	n
Value of terms	3	7	11	15	A

$+4 \quad +4 \quad +4$

$A = an + b$

$a = \dfrac{4}{1} = 4$, so $A = 4n + b$.

Let $(n, A) = (2, 7)$.

$7 = 4(2) + b$

$7 = 8 + b$

$-1 = b$

$A = 4n - 1$

A function rule that relates n and A is $A = 4n - 1$.

18.

$+1 \quad +1 \quad +1$

Position	1	2	3	4	n
Value of terms	7	10	13	16	A

$+3 \quad +3 \quad +3$

$A = an + b$

$a = \dfrac{3}{1} = 3$, so $A = 3n + b$.

Let $(n, A) = (2, 10)$.

$10 = 3(2) + b$

$10 = 6 + b$

$4 = b$

$A = 3n + 4$

A function rule that relates n and A is $A = 3n + 4$.

Chapter 11, *continued*

19. *Sample answer:*

x	−1	0	1	2	3
y	−2	0	2	4	6

$y = ax + b$

$a = \frac{2}{1} = 2$, so $y = 2x + b$.

Let $(x, y) = (1, 2)$.

$2 = 2(1) + b$

$2 = 2 + b$

$0 = b$

$y = 2x$

A function rule that relates x and y is $y = 2x$.

20.

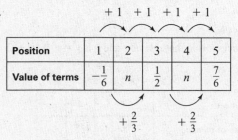

As the position increases by 2, the value increases by $\frac{2}{3}$.

So, as the position increases by 1, the value will increase by $\frac{1}{3}$.

$a = \frac{\frac{1}{3}}{1} = \frac{1}{3}$, so $A = \frac{1}{3}n + b$

Let $(n, A) = \left(3, \frac{1}{2}\right)$

$\frac{1}{2} = \frac{1}{3}(3) + b$

$\frac{1}{2} = 1 + b$

$-\frac{1}{2} = b$

$A = \frac{1}{3}n - \frac{1}{2}$

To find the missing values: $A = \frac{1}{3}(2) - \frac{1}{2} = \frac{1}{6}$

$A = \frac{1}{3}(4) - \frac{1}{2} = \frac{5}{6}$

The missing values are $\frac{1}{6}$ and $\frac{5}{6}$. The function rule that relates n and A is $A = \frac{1}{3}n - \frac{1}{2}$.

Problem Solving

21.

Input p	Function	Output E
12	$E = 0.4(12)$	4.8
13	$E = 0.4(13)$	5.2
14	$E = 0.4(14)$	5.6
15	$E = 0.4(15)$	6

Stanley needs 15 lb to earn $6.

22. Yes. The tickets are all the same price, therefore there cannot be two different prices for the same number of tickets.

23. Let f be the number of times fed and g be the total amount consumed.

$a = \frac{\text{change in output}}{\text{change in input}} = \frac{2}{1} = 2$

$g = 2f + b$

Let $(f, g) = (1, 2)$.

$2 = 2 \cdot 1 + b$

$2 = 2 + b$

$0 = b$

$g = 2f$

A function rule that relates f and g is $g = 2f$.

$g = 2(7)$

$g = 14$

The whales consume 14 gal in 7 feedings.

24. No, your friend is not correct. Your friend's mistake was the input value −9 has 2 output values.

25. *Sample answer:* If $b \neq 0$, then for each input value b, there are 2 output values for a, one positive and one negative.

26. *Sample answer:* Wages are a function of hours worked. The length of a movie is not a function of the price of the movie ticket.

27. a. Speed is miles per hour which equals x.

Distance is miles which equals y.

90 minutes = 1.5 hours

$d = rt$ or $y = tx$ (where $t = $ time)

$y = 1.5x$

A function rule that relates x and y is $y = 1.5x$.

b. Determine how many miles you traveled by using the function rule in *a*.

1st stop: $1.5(35) = 52.5$ miles

2nd stop: $1.5(40) = 60$ miles

3rd stop: $1.5(45) = 67.5$ miles

4th stop: $1.5(50) = 75$ miles

total miles: $52.5 + 60 + 67.5 + 75 = 255$ miles

distance = rate × time or $d = rt$

We know the distance and the rate, we are looking for time.

Chapter 11, *continued*

$d = 255$ miles, $r = 60$ miles per hour

$255 = 60t$

$\dfrac{255}{60} = \dfrac{60}{60}t$

$4.25 = t$

It will take 4 hours 15 minutes to complete the trip.

Mixed Review

28–31.

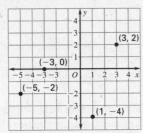

32. $\dfrac{-2x^3y}{xy} = \dfrac{-2 \cdot \cancel{x} \cdot x \cdot x \cdot \cancel{y}}{\cancel{x} \cdot \cancel{y}} = -2x^2$

33. $\dfrac{5xy^2z}{5xy} = \dfrac{\cancel{5} \cdot \cancel{x} \cdot \cancel{y} \cdot y \cdot z}{\cancel{5} \cdot \cancel{x} \cdot \cancel{y}} = yz$

34. $\dfrac{2x^3y}{-3xyz} = \dfrac{2 \cdot \cancel{x} \cdot x \cdot x \cdot \cancel{y}}{-3 \cdot \cancel{x} \cdot \cancel{y} \cdot z} = -\dfrac{2x^2}{3z}$

35. $\dfrac{-8^2z^2}{16x^2yz} = \dfrac{\cancel{2} \cdot \cancel{2} \cdot \cancel{2} \cdot \cancel{2} \cdot 2 \cdot 2 \cdot \cancel{2} \cdot z}{\cancel{2} \cdot \cancel{2} \cdot \cancel{2} \cdot \cancel{2} \cdot x \cdot x \cdot y \cdot \cancel{z}} = -\dfrac{4z}{x^2y}$

36. A; $-\left| -10 \right| = -10$

Lesson 11.2

11.2 Guided Practice (pp. 588–589)

1.

2.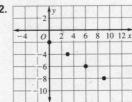

3.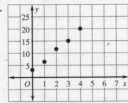

4.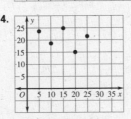

x and y have a positive relationship.

x and y have no relationship.

11.2 Exercises (pp. 590–592)

Skill Practice

1. A *scatter plot* is a graph with a collection of ordered pairs.

2. In a *positive relationship,* both coordinates increase.

3.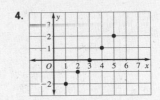

4.

5. In the scatter plot, no pattern exists between the coordinates. The quantities have no relationship.

6. In the scatter plot, the y-coordinates tend to increase as the x-coordinates increase. The quantities have a positive relationship.

7. In the scatter plot, the y-coordinates tend to decrease as the x-coordinates increase. The quantities have a negative relationship.

8. 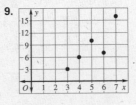 **9.**

x and y have a positive relationship.

x and y have a positive relationship.

10. 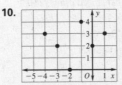 The last 3 ordered pairs were not graphed. There is no relationship.

11. You would expect no relationship because a student's test score does not depend on his or her height.

12. You would expect a positive relationship because an increase in size should determine an increase in cost.

13. You would expect a negative relationship because an increase in the amount of money you pay should determine a decrease in the amount you owe.

14. C; n increases as m increases.

15.

x	0	1	2	3	4	5	6
y	1	−1	1	−1	1	−1	1

 The value of y will be 1 when $x = 500$.

Sample answer: $y = 1$ when x is even and $y = -1$ when x is odd.

16. 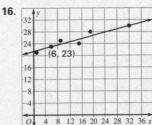 *Sample answer:* When the input is 6 the output is about 23.

Chapter 11, continued

17.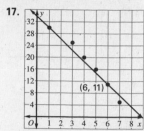

Sample answer: When the input is 6 the output is about 11.

Problem Solving

18. a.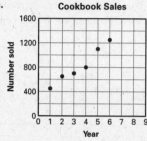

b. The *y*-coordinates tend to increase as the *x*-coordinates increase. *x* and *y* have a positive relationship.

c. *Sample answer:* In the ninth year, more than 1250 cookbooks will be sold.

19. *Sample answer:* If *x* is the day of the year and *y* is the length of time between sunrise and sunset.

20.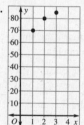

There is a positive relationship. As study time increases, test scores will increase.

21. B; As the months go by, less water is sold.

22. The vehicle is traveling toward point A. As the time increases the distance decreases, so the vehicle is moving toward point A.

23. *Sample answer:* The newspaper means that when the weather is nicer, more people will vote. It is not reasonable for the newspaper to use a scatter plot because it would be hard to find a single measure that would accurately indicate how "nice" weather is.

24.

ℓ	4	5	6	7
w	4	3	2	1

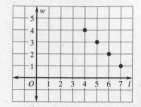

Sample answer: The estimated width of the rectangle is 2.5 inches. Using a vertical line through $\ell = 5.5$, I observed that $\ell = 5.5$ corresponds with $w = 2.5$ on the scatter plot.

25. *Sample answer:* For the positive relationship, as the average margin of victory increased, the number of wins increased because "better" teams won more games and won by more points. The number of points scored had no relationship with the number of wins because the difference between the two teams' scores is the important factor, not just the number of points scored by one team.

Mixed Review

26.
$$2y - 3 = 7$$
$$2y - 3 + 3 = 7 + 3$$
$$2y = 10$$
$$\frac{2y}{2} = \frac{10}{2}$$
$$y = 5$$
Check: $2(5) - 3 \stackrel{?}{=} 7$
$$10 - 3 \stackrel{?}{=} 7$$
$$7 = 7 ✓$$

27.
$$9 - 3x = 6$$
$$9 - 3x - 9 = 6 - 9$$
$$-3x = -3$$
$$\frac{-3x}{-3} = \frac{-3}{-3}$$
$$x = 1$$
Check: $9 - 3(1) \stackrel{?}{=} 6$
$$9 - 3 \stackrel{?}{=} 6$$
$$6 = 6 ✓$$

28.
$$5 = 12 + \frac{z}{4}$$
$$5 - 12 = 12 + \frac{z}{4} - 12$$
$$-7 = \frac{z}{4}$$
$$-7 \cdot 4 = \frac{z}{4} \cdot 4$$
$$-28 = z$$
Check: $5 \stackrel{?}{=} 12 + \frac{-28}{4}$
$$5 \stackrel{?}{=} 12 + (-7)$$
$$5 = 5 ✓$$

29.
$$-5w + 11 = -34$$
$$-5w + 11 - 11 = -34 - 11$$
$$-5w = -45$$
$$\frac{-5w}{-5} = \frac{-45}{-5}$$
$$w = 9$$

Check: $-5(9) + 11 \overset{?}{=} -34$
$$-45 + 11 \overset{?}{=} -34$$
$$-34 = -34 \checkmark$$

30.

Input x	Function	Output y
−2	$y = 0.7(-2)$	−1.4
−1	$y = 0.7(-1)$	−0.7
0	$y = 0.7(0)$	0
1	$y = 0.7(1)$	0.7
2	$y = 0.7(2)$	1.4

The range of the function is −1.4, −0.7, 0, 0.7, and 1.4.

31.

Input x	Function	Output y
−2	$y = 3(-2) + 4$	−2
−1	$y = 3(-1) + 4$	1
0	$y = 3(0) + 4$	4
1	$y = 3(1) + 4$	7
2	$y = 3(2) + 4$	10

The range of the function is −2, 1, 4, 7, and 10.

32.

Input x	Function	Output y
−2	$y = 0.4(-2) - 1$	−1.8
−1	$y = 0.4(-1) - 1$	−1.4
0	$y = 0.4(0) - 1$	−1
1	$y = 0.4(1) - 1$	−0.6
2	$y = 0.4(2) - 1$	−0.2

The range of the function is −1.8, −1.4, −1, −0.6, and −0.2.

33.

Input x	Function	Output y
−2	$y = -2(-2) + 1$	5
−1	$y = -2(-1) + 1$	3
0	$y = -2(0) + 1$	1
1	$y = -2(1) + 1$	−1
2	$y = -2(2) + 1$	−3

The range of the function is 5, 3, 1, −1, and −3.

34. B; $A = \frac{1}{2}(b_1 + b_2)h$
$$A = \frac{1}{2}(14 + 16)6$$
$$A = \frac{1}{2}(30)6$$
$$A = 90 \text{ m}^2$$

Lesson 11.3

11.3 Guided Practice (pp. 593–594)

1.
$$C = 10 + 7h$$
$$35 = 10 + 7h$$
$$35 - 10 = 10 + 7h - 10$$
$$25 = 7h$$
$$\frac{25}{7} = \frac{7h}{7}$$
$$3.57 = h$$

You can skate 3.5 hours or less.

2. $y = 3x - 7$
$$5 \overset{?}{=} 3(6) - 7$$
$$5 \overset{?}{=} 18 - 7$$
$$5 \neq 11$$

The ordered pair (6, 5) is not a solution of $y = 3x - 7$.

3.
$$-2x - 4y = 12$$
$$-2(-4) - 4(-1) \overset{?}{=} 12$$
$$8 + 4 \overset{?}{=} 12$$
$$12 = 12$$

The ordered pair (−4, −1) is a solution of $-2x - 4y = 12$.

4. *Sample answer:*

x-value	Substitute for x.	Solve for y.
−1	$y = -2(-1) + 6$	8
0	$y = -2(0) + 6$	6
1	$y = -2(1) + 6$	4
2	$y = -2(2) + 6$	2

Four solutions are (−1, 8), (0, 6), (1, 4), and (2, 2).

5. *Sample answer:* $3x + y = 4$
$$y = -3x + 4$$

x-value	Substitute for x.	Solve for y.
−1	$y = -3(-1) + 4$	7
0	$y = -3(0) + 4$	4
1	$y = -3(1) + 4$	1
2	$y = -3(2) + 4$	−2

Four solutions are (−1, 7), (0, 4), (1, 1), (2, −2).

Chapter 11, *continued*

Skill Practice

1. A *solution* of an equation in two variables is an ordered pair.

2. When an equation is solved for *y*, the equation is in *function* form.

3.

x-value	Substitute for *x*.	Solve for *y*.
−5	$y = -5 + 8$	3
0	$y = 0 + 8$	8
5	$y = 5 + 8$	13
10	$y = 10 + 8$	18

4.

x-value	Substitute for *x*.	Solve for *y*.
−5	$y = 4 - 3(-5)$	19
0	$y = 4 - 3(0)$	4
5	$y = 4 - 3(5)$	−11
10	$y = 4 - 3(10)$	−26

5.

x-value	Substitute for *x*.	Solve for *y*.
−5	$y = -20 + (-5)$	−25
0	$y = -20 + 0$	−20
5	$y = -20 + 5$	−15
10	$y = -20 + 10$	−10

6. $y = 4x + 2$
$10 \stackrel{?}{=} 4(2) + 2$
$10 \stackrel{?}{=} 8 + 2$
$10 = 10 \checkmark$
The ordered pair (2, 10) is a solution of $y = 4x + 2$.

7. $y = -2x + 5$
$5 \stackrel{?}{=} -2(7) + 5$
$5 \stackrel{?}{=} -14 + 5$
$5 \neq -9$
The ordered pair (7, 5) is not a solution of $y = -2x + 5$.

8. $y = 6 - x$
$3 \stackrel{?}{=} 6 - (-3)$
$3 \stackrel{?}{=} 6 + 3$
$3 \neq 9$
The ordered pair (−3, 3) is not a solution of $y = 6 - x$.

9. $x + 8y = 2$
$10 + 8(-1) \stackrel{?}{=} 2$
$10 + (-8) \stackrel{?}{=} 2$
$2 = 2$
The ordered pair (10, −1) is a solution of $x + 8y = 2$.

10. $y = 6x + 7$
$21 \stackrel{?}{=} 6(2) + 7$
$21 \stackrel{?}{=} 12 + 7$
$21 \neq 19$
The ordered pair (2, 21) is not a solution of $y = 6x + 7$.

11. $y = 3x - 26$
$-8 \stackrel{?}{=} 3(6) - 26$
$-8 \stackrel{?}{=} 18 - 26$
$-8 = -8 \checkmark$
The ordered pair (6, −8) is a solution of $y = 3x - 26$.

12. The student switched the *x* and *y* values.
$2x + 3y = -7$
$2(-5) + 3(4) \stackrel{?}{=} -7$
$-10 + 12 \stackrel{?}{=} -7$
$2 \neq -7$
The ordered pair (−5, 4) is not a solution of $2x + 3y = -7$.

13. A; $-3(-2) + 11 \stackrel{?}{=} 17$
$6 + 11 \stackrel{?}{=} 17$
$17 = 17 \checkmark$

14. *Sample answer:*

Input *x*	Substitute for *x*.	Output *y*
−1	$y = -2(-1) + 5$	7
0	$y = -2(0) + 5$	5
1	$y = -2(1) + 5$	3
2	$y = -2(2) + 5$	1

Four solutions are (−1, 7), (0, 5), (1, 3), (2, 1).

15. *Sample answer:*

x-value	Substitute for *x*.	Solve for *y*.
−1	$y = -51 - 6(-1)$	−45
0	$y = -51 - 6(0)$	−51
1	$y = -51 - 6(1)$	−57
2	$y = -51 - 6(2)$	−63

Four solutions are (−1, −45), (0, −51), (1, −57), (2, −63).

16. *Sample answer:*

x-value	Substitute for *x*.	Solve for *y*
−1	$y = 16(-1) + 24$	8
0	$y = 16(0) + 24$	24
1	$y = 16(1) + 24$	40
2	$y = 16(2) + 24$	56

Four solutions are (−1, 8), (0, 24), (1, 40), and (2, 56).

Chapter 11, *continued*

17. *Sample answer:*

x-value	Substitute for x.	Solve for y.
−1	$y = -5(-1) + 3$	8
0	$y = -5(0) + 3$	3
1	$y = -5(1) + 3$	−2
2	$y = -5(2) + 3$	−7

Four solutions are $(-1, 8)$, $(0, 3)$, $(1, -2)$, and $(2, -7)$.

18. *Sample answer:*

x-value	Substitute for x.	Solve for y.
−1	$y = \frac{1}{2}(-1) - 1$	$-1\frac{1}{2}$
0	$y = \frac{1}{2}(0) - 1$	−1
1	$y = \frac{1}{2}(1) - 1$	$-\frac{1}{2}$
2	$y = \frac{1}{2}(2) - 1$	0

Four solutions are $\left(-1, -1\frac{1}{2}\right)$, $(0, -1)$, $\left(1, -\frac{1}{2}\right)$, and $(2, 0)$.

19. *Sample answer:*

x-value	Substitute for x.	Solve for y.
−3	$y = \frac{1}{3}(-3) - 5$	−6
0	$y = \frac{1}{3}(0) - 5$	−5
3	$y = \frac{1}{3}(3) - 5$	−4
6	$y = \frac{1}{3}(6) - 5$	−3

Four solutions are $(-3, -6)$, $(0, -5)$, $(3, -4)$, and $(6, -3)$.

20. $x + y = 8$

$y = -x + 8$

Sample answer:

x-value	Substitute for x.	Solve for y.
−1	$y = -(-1) + 8$	9
0	$y = -0 + 8$	8
1	$y = -1 + 8$	7
2	$y = -2 + 8$	6

Four solutions are $(-1, 9)$, $(0, 8)$, $(1, 7)$, and $(2, 6)$.

21. $42 = 4x + y$

$-4x + 42 = y$

Sample answer:

x-value	Substitute for x.	Solve for y.
−1	$y = -4(-1) + 42$	46
0	$y = -4(0) + 42$	42
1	$y = -4(1) + 42$	38
2	$y = -4(2) + 42$	34

Four solutions are $(-1, 46)$, $(0, 42)$, $(1, 38)$, and $(2, 34)$.

22. $33 = -3x + y$

$3x + 33 = y$

Sample answer:

x-value	Substitute for x.	Solve for y.
−1	$y = 3(-1) + 33$	30
0	$y = 3(0) + 33$	33
1	$y = 3(1) + 33$	36
2	$y = 3(2) + 33$	39

Four solutions are $(-1, 30)$, $(0, 33)$, $(1, 36)$, and $(2, 39)$.

23. $5x + y = 10$

$y = -5x + 10$

Sample answer:

x-value	Substitute for x.	Solve for y.
−1	$y = -5(-1) + 10$	15
0	$y = -5(0) + 10$	10
1	$y = -5(1) + 10$	5
2	$y = -5(2) + 10$	0

Four solutions are $(-1, 15)$, $(0, 10)$, $(1, 5)$, and $(2, 0)$.

24. $12 = 3x + y$

$-3x + 12 = y$

Sample answer:

x-value	Substitute for x.	Solve for y.
−1	$-3(-1) + 12 = y$	15
0	$-3(0) + 12 = y$	12
1	$-3(1) + 12 = y$	9
2	$-3(2) + 12 = y$	6

Four solutions are $(-1, 15)$, $(0, 12)$, $(1, 9)$ and $(2, 6)$.

25. $19 = -2x + y$

$2x + 19 = y$

Sample answer:

x-value	Substitute for x.	Solve for y.
−1	$2(-1) + 19 = y$	17
0	$2(0) + 19 = y$	19
1	$2(1) + 19 = y$	21
2	$2(2) + 19 = y$	23

Four solutions are $(-1, 17)$, $(0, 19)$, $(1, 21)$, and $(2, 23)$.

26. $4y = 8x + 12$

$y = 2x + 3$

Sample answer:

x-value	Substitute for x.	Solve for y.
−1	$y = 2(-1) + 3$	1
0	$y = 2(0) + 3$	3
1	$y = 2(1) + 3$	5
2	$y = 2(2) + 3$	7

Four solutions are $(-1, 1)$, $(0, 3)$, $(1, 5)$, and $(2, 7)$.

27. $5y + 15x = 10$

$5y = -15x + 10$

$y = -3x + 2$

Sample answer:

x-value	Substitute for x.	Solve for y.
−1	$y = -3(-1) + 2$	5
0	$y = -3(0) + 2$	2
1	$y = -3(1) + 2$	−1
2	$y = -3(2) + 2$	−4

Four solutions are $(-1, 5)$, $(0, 2)$, $(1, -1)$, and $(2, -4)$.

28. $-32 = 4x - 12y$

$-4x - 32 = -12y$

$\frac{1}{3}x + \frac{8}{3} = y$

Sample answer:

x-value	Substitute for x.	Solve for y.
−2	$y = \frac{1}{3}(-2) + \frac{8}{3}$	2
1	$y = \frac{1}{3}(1) + \frac{8}{3}$	3
4	$y = \frac{1}{3}(4) + \frac{8}{3}$	4
7	$y = \frac{1}{3}(7) + \frac{8}{3}$	5

Four solutions are $(-2, 2)$, $(1, 3)$, $(4, 4)$, and $(7, 5)$.

29. $8y = 16x - 10$

$y = 2x - \frac{5}{4}$

Sample answer:

x-value	Substitute for x.	Solve for y.
−1	$y = 2(-1) - \frac{5}{4}$	$-3\frac{1}{4}$
0	$y = 2(0) - \frac{5}{4}$	$-1\frac{1}{4}$
1	$y = 2(1) - \frac{5}{4}$	$\frac{3}{4}$
2	$y = 2(2) - \frac{5}{4}$	$2\frac{3}{4}$

Four solutions are $\left(-1, -3\frac{1}{4}\right)$, $\left(0, -1\frac{1}{4}\right)$, $\left(1, \frac{3}{4}\right)$, and $\left(2, 2\frac{3}{4}\right)$.

30. $-6y + 3x = 9$

$-6y = -3x + 9$

$y = \frac{1}{2}x - \frac{3}{2}$

Sample answer:

x-value	Substitute for x.	Solve for y.
−1	$y = \frac{1}{2}(-1) - \frac{3}{2}$	−2
0	$y = \frac{1}{2}(0) - \frac{3}{2}$	$-1\frac{1}{2}$
1	$y = \frac{1}{2}(1) - \frac{3}{2}$	−1
2	$y = \frac{1}{2}(2) - \frac{3}{2}$	$-\frac{1}{2}$

Four solutions are $(-1, -2)$, $\left(0, -1\frac{1}{2}\right)$, $(1, -1)$, and $\left(2, -\frac{1}{2}\right)$.

31. $42 - 7y = 15x$

$-7y = 15x - 42$

$y = -\frac{15}{7}x + 6$

Sample answer:

x-value	Substitute for x.	Solve for y.
−1	$y = -\frac{15}{7}(-1) + 6$	$8\frac{1}{7}$
0	$y = -\frac{15}{7}(0) + 6$	6
1	$y = -\frac{15}{7}(1) + 6$	$3\frac{6}{7}$
2	$y = -\frac{15}{7}(2) + 6$	$1\frac{5}{7}$

Four solutions are $\left(-1, 8\frac{1}{7}\right)$, $(0, 6)$, $\left(1, 3\frac{6}{7}\right)$, and $\left(2, 1\frac{5}{7}\right)$.

Chapter 11, *continued*

32. *Sample answers:*

Solutions: $(0, 24)$, $(1, 30)$

$-24 \stackrel{?}{=} 6(0) - 24$ $-24 \stackrel{?}{=} 6(1) - 30$

$-24 = -24$ $-24 = -24$

Not solutions: $(0, 0)$, $(1, 1)$

$-24 \stackrel{?}{=} 6(0) - 0$ $-24 \stackrel{?}{=} 6(1) - 1$

$-24 \neq 0$ $-24 \neq 5$

33. *Sample answers:*

$9x = 9\left(\dfrac{7}{3}\right) = 21$

$8y = 8\left(\dfrac{5}{8}\right) = 5$

$9x + 8y = 21 + 5 = 26$

This is not equal to 16.

34.

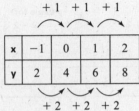

$y = ax + b$

$a = \dfrac{\text{change in output}}{\text{change in input}} = \dfrac{2}{1} = 2$

$y = 2x + b$

Let $(x, y) = (0, 4)$.

$4 = 2(0) + b$

$4 = b$

$y = 2x + 4$

The equation in x and y is $y = 2x + 4$.

Sample answers:

$y = 2(101) + 4 = 202 + 4 = 206$

$y = 2(102) + 4 = 204 + 4 = 208$

$y = 2(103) + 4 = 206 + 4 = 210$

$y = 2(104) + 4 = 208 + 4 = 212$

Four solutions are $(104, 206)$, $(102, 208)$, $(103, 210)$, and $(104, 212)$.

35.

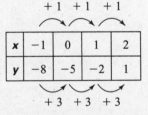

$y = ax + b$

$a = \dfrac{\text{change in output}}{\text{change in input}} = \dfrac{1}{2}$

$y = \dfrac{1}{2}x + b$

Let $(x, y) = (0, 2)$.

$2 = \dfrac{1}{2}(0) + b$

$2 = b$

$y = \dfrac{1}{2}x + 2$

The equation in x and y is $y = \dfrac{1}{2}x + 2$.

Sample answer:

$y = \dfrac{1}{2}(102) + 2 = 51 + 2 = 53$

$y = \dfrac{1}{2}(104) + 2 = 52 + 2 = 54$

$y = \dfrac{1}{2}(106) + 2 = 53 + 2 = 55$

$y = \dfrac{1}{2}(108) + 2 = 54 + 2 = 56$

Four solutions are $(102, 53)$, $(104, 54)$, $(106, 55)$, and $(108, 56)$.

36.

<table>
<tr><td></td><td>+1</td><td>+1</td><td>+1</td></tr>
</table>

x	−1	0	1	2
y	−8	−5	−2	1

$+3 \quad +3 \quad +3$

$y = ax + b$

$a = \dfrac{\text{change in output}}{\text{change in input}} = \dfrac{3}{1}$

$y = 3x + b$

Let $(x, y) = (-1, -8)$.

$-8 = 3(-1) + b$

$-8 = -3 + b$

$-5 = b$

$y = 3x - 5$

The equation in x and y is $y = 3x - 5$.

Chapter 11, *continued*

Sample answer:

$y = 3(101) - 5 = 303 - 5 = 298$

$y = 3(102) - 5 = 306 - 5 = 301$

$y = 3(103) - 5 = 309 - 5 = 304$

$y = 3(104) - 5 = 312 - 5 = 307$

Four solutions are (101, 298), (102, 301), (103, 304), and (104, 307).

37.

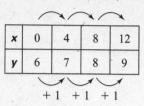

$y = ax + b$

$a = \dfrac{\text{change in output}}{\text{change in input}} = \dfrac{1}{4}$

$y = \dfrac{1}{4}x + b$

Let $(x, y) = (0, 6)$.

$6 = \dfrac{1}{4}(0) + b$

$6 = 0 + b$

$6 = b$

$y = \dfrac{1}{4}x + 6$

The equation in x and y is $y = \dfrac{1}{4}x + 6$.

Sample answer:

$y = \dfrac{1}{4}(104) + 6 = 26 + 6 = 32$

$y = \dfrac{1}{4}(108) + 6 = 27 + 6 = 33$

$y = \dfrac{1}{4}(112) + 6 = 28 + 6 = 34$

$y = \dfrac{1}{4}(116) + 6 = 29 + 6 = 35$

Four solutions are (104, 32), (108, 33), (112, 34), and (116, 35).

38.

x-value	y-value for $y = -2x + 3$	y-value for $y = 0.5x - 2$
-2	$-2(-2) + 3 = 7$	$0.5(-2) - 2 = -3$
-1	$-2(-1) + 3 = 5$	$0.5(-1) - 2 = -2.5$
0	$-2(0) + 3 = 3$	$0.5(0) - 2 = -2$
1	$-2(1) + 3 = 1$	$0.5(1) - 2 = -1.5$
2	$-2(2) + 3 = -1$	$0.5(2) - 2 = -1$

The ordered pair $(2, -1)$ is a solution of both the equations $y = -2x + 3$ and $y = 0.5x - 2$.

39.

x-value	y-value for $y = 6x - 10$	y-value for $y = -3x + 26$
1	$y = 6(1) - 10 = -4$	$y = -3(1) + 26 = 23$
2	$y = 6(2) - 10 = 2$	$y = -3(2) + 26 = 20$
3	$y = 6(3) - 10 = 8$	$y = -3(3) + 26 = 17$
4	$y = 6(4) - 10 = 14$	$y = -3(4) + 26 = 14$

The ordered pair $(4, 14)$ is a solution of both the equations $y = 6x - 10$ and $y = -3x + 26$.

40. $x + 2y = 4 \qquad\qquad x + y = -2$

$ 2y = -x + 4 \qquad\qquad y = -x - 2$

$ y = -\dfrac{1}{2}x + 2$

x-value	y-value for $y = -\dfrac{1}{2}x + 2$	y-value for $y = -x - 2$
-5	$y = -\dfrac{1}{2}(-5) + 2 = 4\dfrac{1}{2}$	$y = -(-5) - 2 = 3$
-6	$y = -\dfrac{1}{2}(-6) + 2 = 5$	$y = -(-6) - 2 = 4$
-7	$y = -\dfrac{1}{2}(-7) + 2 = 5\dfrac{1}{2}$	$y = -(-7) - 2 = 5$
-8	$y = -\dfrac{1}{2}(-8) + 2 = 6$	$y = -(-8) - 2 = 6$

The ordered pair $(-8, 6)$ is a solution of both the equations $x + 2y = 4$ and $x + y = -2$.

41. $-x - 4y = 4 \qquad\qquad x - 2y = 14$

$ -4y = x + 4 \qquad\qquad -2y = -x + 14$

$ y = -\dfrac{1}{4}x - 1 \qquad\qquad y = \dfrac{1}{2}x - 7$

x-value	y-value for $y = -\dfrac{1}{4}x - 1$	y-value for $y = \dfrac{1}{2}x - 7$
0	$y = -\dfrac{1}{4}(0) - 1 = -1$	$y = \dfrac{1}{2}(0) - 7 = -7$
2	$y = -\dfrac{1}{4}(2) - 1 = -1\dfrac{1}{2}$	$y = \dfrac{1}{2}(2) - 7 = -6$
4	$y = -\dfrac{1}{4}(4) - 1 = -2$	$y = \dfrac{1}{2}(4) - 7 = -5$
8	$y = -\dfrac{1}{4}(8) - 1 = -3$	$y = \dfrac{1}{2}(8) - 7 = -3$

The ordered pair $(8, -3)$ is a solution of both the equations $-x - 4y = 4$ and $x - 2y = 14$.

42. $P = 15 - 2.5n$

n-value	Substitute for n.	Solve for P.
2	$P = 15 - 2.5(2)$	10
4	$P = 15 - 2.5(4)$	5
6	$P = 15 - 2.5(6)$	0

It will take you 6 weeks to pay back your friend.

43. a. $C = 24n + 14$

$C = 24(4) + 14$

$C = 96 + 14$

$C = 110$

4 sets of wheels cost \$110.

b. $C = 24n + 14$

$182 = 24n + 14$

$182 - 14 = 24n + 14 - 14$

$168 = 24n$

$\dfrac{168}{24} = \dfrac{24n}{24}$

$7 = n$

You can buy 7 sets of wheels for \$182.

c. No, the total cost will be \$350.

$C = 24(14) + 14 = 336 + 14 = 350$

The total cost includes \$14, which is only charged once. The shipping and handling does not double when the number of orders double.

44. B;

Movies seen m	Total cost C
1	$C = 25 + 3(1) = 28$
5	$C = 25 + 3(5) = 40$
10	$C = 25 + 3(10) = 55$
25	$C = 25 + 3(25) = 100$

When $C = 60$:

$C = 25 + 3m$

$60 = 25 + 3m$

$35 = 3m$

$11\frac{2}{3} = m$

You can see 11 movies for \$60.

45. *Sample answer:* When an equation is in function form. You can select any value for x and quickly calculate the corresponding y value.

46. a. $h = 1200 - 1000m$

$h = 1200 - 1000(1)$

$h = 200$

The height of the elevator after 1 minute is 200 feet.

b. $h = 1200 - 1000m$

$0 = 1200 - 1000m$

$0 - 1200 = 1200 - 1000m - 1200$

$-1200 = -1000m$

$\dfrac{-1200}{-1000} = \dfrac{-1000m}{-1000}$

$1.2 = m$

1.2 min

$0.2 \cdot 60 = 12$ sec

It will take the elevator 1 minutes 12 seconds.

47. $1x + 2y = 9$ or $x + 2y = 9$

Substitute 4 for x and 3 for y.

$4 + 2(3) \overset{?}{\leq} 9$

$4 + 6 \overset{?}{\leq} 9$

$10 \nleq 9$

No, you can't buy 4 bottles of water and 3 bottles of sports drink.

48. Yes. The original equation and the equation solved for y are equivalent.

Sample answer:

If $x = -1$, then $y = 19$ when $4(-1) + y = 15$ is solved for y.

If $x = 0$, then $y = 15$ when $4(0) + y = 15$ is solved for y.

If $x = 1$, then $y = 11$ when $4(1) + y = 15$ is solved for y.

If $x = 2$, then $y = 7$ when $4(2) + y = 15$ is solved for y.

49. Let $x =$ number of rides and let $y =$ number of minutes spent playing games.

2 hours equals 120 minutes.

Then $10x + y = 120$ models the situation described.

When $x = 8$:

$10x + y = 120$

$10(8) + y = 120$

$80 + y = 120$

$y = 40$

You can play games for 40 minutes.

50. $ax + by = c$

$ax + by - ax = c - ax$

$by = c - ax$

$\dfrac{by}{b} = \dfrac{c - ax}{b}$

$y = \dfrac{c - ax}{b}$ or $y = -\dfrac{ax}{b} + \dfrac{c}{b}$

51. Let $x =$ the number of walks.

Let $y =$ the number of meals.

Week 1: $2x + 4y = 38$

Week 2: $4x + 2y = 40$

Week 3: $4x + 4y = 52$

Sample answer:

x-value	$2x + 4y = 38$ or $y = -\frac{1}{2}x + \frac{19}{2}$	$4x + 2y = 40$ or $y = -2x + 20$
5	$y = -\frac{1}{2}(5) + \frac{19}{2} = 7$	$y = -2(5) + 20 = 10$
6	$y = -\frac{1}{2}(6) + \frac{19}{2} = 6\frac{1}{2}$	$y = -2(6) + 20 = 8$
7	$y = -\frac{1}{2}(7) + \frac{19}{2} = 6$	$y = -2(7) + 20 = 6$

x-value	4x + 4y = 52 or y = −x + 13
5	y = −(5) + 13 = 8
6	y = −(6) + 13 = 7
7	y = −(7) + 13 = 6

There were 7 walks, and 6 meals each week.

Mixed Review

52. Quadrant II

53. *y*-axis

54. Quadrant IV

55. *x*-axis

56.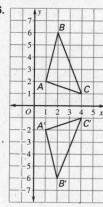

57.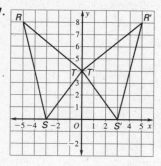

58. D; $r = \dfrac{d}{2} = \dfrac{25}{2} = 12.5$

$A = \pi r^2 \approx 3.14(12.5)^2 = 490.625$

The area of the circle is about 490.6 square inches.

Lesson 11.4

Activity (p. 598)

x	−4	−2	0	2	4
y	−10	−4	2	8	14

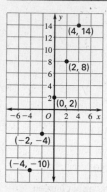

The points fall on a straight line.

Sample answer:

x	−3	−1	1	3
y	−7	−1	5	11

The points are on the line as well.

The graph of all solutions of $y = 3x + 2$ is a straight line.

11.4 Guided Practice (pp. 599–600)

1.

x	−4	−3	−2	−1	0
y	0	1	2	3	4

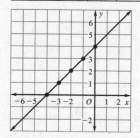

The line is the graph of $y = x + 4$.

2.

x	−6	−4	−2	0
y	0	2	4	6

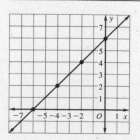

The line is the graph of $y = x + 6$.

3.

x	0	2	4	6	8	10
y	−7	−6	−5	−4	−3	−2

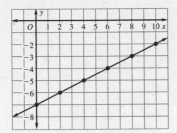

The line is the graph of $y = \frac{1}{2}x - 7$.

4.

x	−2	−1	0	1
y	1	−1	−3	−5

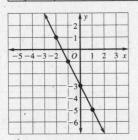

The line is the graph of $y = -2x - 3$.

5.

m	0	1	2	3
ℓ	4	$4\frac{1}{2}$	5	$5\frac{1}{2}$

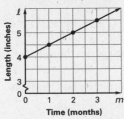

Growth of Sue's Hair

Sue's hair will take 3 months to grow to $5\frac{1}{2}$ inches.

6.
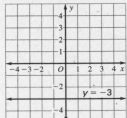

7.
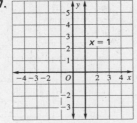

11.4 Exercises (pp. 600–603)

Skill Practice

1. The graph of the solutions of a linear equation is a *line*.

2. The equation $3x + y = 8$ is a linear equation.

3. The equation $2y - 5x = 10$ is a linear equation.

4. The equation $9x^2 = y + 4$ is not a linear equation.

5. The equation $y = -4$ is a linear equation.

6. C;

   $y = \frac{1}{2}x$

   $0 \overset{?}{=} \frac{1}{2}(0)$

   $0 = 0$

7.

x	−8	−6	−4	−2	0
y	1	3	5	7	9

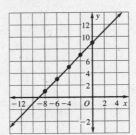

8.

x	0	2	4	6	8	10	12	14
y	−14	−12	−10	−8	−6	−4	−2	0

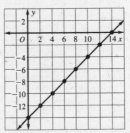

9.

x	0	5	10	15	20
y	−17	−12	−7	−2	3

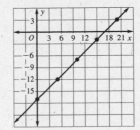

10.

x	−1	0	1	2
y	3	1	−1	−3

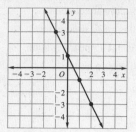

11.

x	1	2	3
y	4	0	−4

12.

x	−1	0	1
y	−8	0	8

13.

x	−1	0	1
y	3	0	−3

14.

x	−4	−2	0	2	4
y	3	4	5	6	7

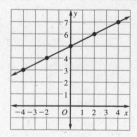

15.

x	−8	−4	0	4	8
y	14	13	12	11	10

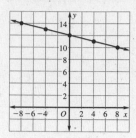

16.

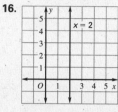

17.

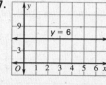

18.

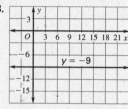

19.

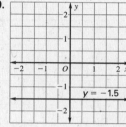

20.

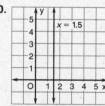

21.

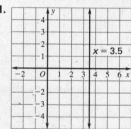

22. Because the line is vertical and passes through (5, 0), the equation of the line is $x = 5$.

The graph shows a vertical line, not a horizontal line.

23. $16x − 4y = 8$

$$-4y = -16x + 8$$

$$y = 4x - 2$$

x	0	1
y	−2	2

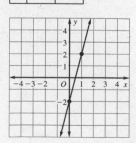

24. $9x + 3y = 18$

$$3y = -9x + 18$$
$$y = -3x + 6$$

x	0	1	2
y	6	3	0

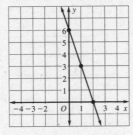

25. $10x = -2y \longrightarrow y = -5x$

x	-1	0	1
y	5	0	-5

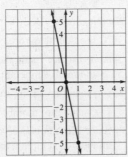

26. Since the line is horizontal and crosses the *y*-axis at -2, the equation of the line is $y = -2$.

27. Since the line is vertical and crosses the *x*-axis at 3, the equation of the line is $x = 3$.

28. Since the line is vertical and crosses the *x*-axis at -2.5, the equation of the line is $x = -2.5$.

29–32. *Sample answer:*

$y = x$

x	0	1	2
y	0	1	2

$y = x + 7$

x	-9	-7	0	2
y	-2	0	7	9

$y = x - 5$

x	0	2	4	5
y	-5	-3	-1	0

$y = x - 9$

x	0	3	9	10
y	-9	-6	0	1

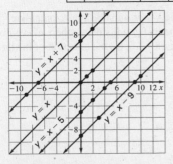

All four lines are parallel. They cross the *y*-axis at different points.

33–36. *Sample answer:*

$y = x$

x	-1	0	1
y	-1	0	1

$y = 3x$

x	-1	0	1
y	-3	0	3

$y = -x$

x	-1	0	1
y	1	0	-1

$y = -4x$

x	-1	0	1
y	4	0	-4

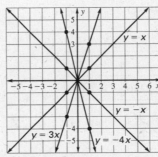

Alike: All four lines contain the origin $(0, 0)$.

Different: They have different "tilts."

37.

$$+1 \quad +1 \quad +1$$

x	0	1	2	3
y	-3	-2	-1	0

$$+1 \quad +1 \quad +1$$

$a = \dfrac{1}{1}$

$y = 1x + b$

$-3 = 1(0) + b$

$-3 = b$

$y = x - 3$

The equation of the line is $y = x - 3$.

38.

$$-1 \quad -1$$

x	1	0	-1
y	-2	0	2

$$+2 \quad +2$$

$a = \dfrac{2}{-1} = -2$

$y = -2x + b$

$-2 = -2(1) + b$

$-2 = -2 + b$

$0 = b$

$y = -2x$

The equation of the line is $y = -2x$.

Chapter 11, *continued*

39.

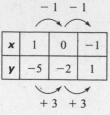

$-1 \quad -1$

x	1	0	−1
y	−5	−2	1

$+3 \quad +3$

$a = -\dfrac{3}{1} = -3$

$y = -3x + b$

$-5 = -3(1) + b$

$-5 = -3 + b$

$-2 = b$

$y = -3x - 2$

The equation of the line is $y = -3x - 2$.

Problem Solving

40.

m	0	2	4	6	8	10
C	50	70	90	110	130	150

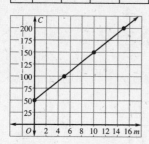

You pay about $170 in 12 months.

41.

x	0	6	12
y	80	173	266

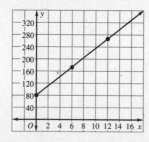

In about 11 months, Janet will have $250.

42. a.

Time (minutes)	4	8	12	16
Depth (feet)	−140	−120	−100	−80

$-160 + 20 = -140,\ -140 + 20 = -120,$

$-120 + 20 = -100,\ -100 + 20 = -80$

b. Yes; the relationship between time and depth is linear because they lie on a line (time, depth).

43. A; $C = 40$

44.

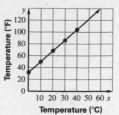

C (°C)	0	10	20	30	40
F (°F)	32	50	68	86	104

$F = \dfrac{9}{5}C + 32$

45. *Sample answer:* Body temperature is about 37°C.

46. 10°C is colder than room temperature.

Sample answer: Using the graph or the table, 10°C is 50°F and room temperature is around 70°F.

47. a. $y = $ total time spent treading

$x = $ number of months

Since Max starts everyone at 1 minute and adds 2 minutes each month, the total equals 2 minutes times the number of months plus the beginning 1 minute.

$y = 2x + 1$

b.

x	0	6
y	1	13

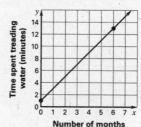

It will take 6 months.

c. $\quad 2x + 1 = 13$

$2x + 1 - 1 = 13 - 1$

$\qquad\quad 2x = 12$

$\qquad\quad \dfrac{2x}{2} = \dfrac{12}{2}$

$\qquad\qquad x = 6$

48. A line parallel to the x-axis must be a horizontal line. A horizontal line that is 8.6 units below the x-axis will have a y-coordinate of −8.6. So the equation of the line must be $y = -8.6$.

49. The two situations can be represented by $j = k + 7$ and $j = 2k$. Graph the 2 lines. The lines intersect at $(7, 14)$, which indicates Karen is 7 years old when Jared is 14 years old.

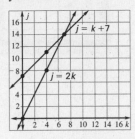

$j = k + 7$

k	0	4	7
j	7	11	14

$j = 2k$

k	0	4	7
j	0	8	14

Mixed Review

50. *Sample answer:*

x-value	Substitute for x.	y-value
-1	$y = 3(-1) + 2$	-1
0	$y = 3(0) + 2$	2
1	$y = 3(1) + 2$	5

Three solutions for the equation $y = 3x + 2$ are $(-1, -1)$, $(0, 2)$, and $(1, 5)$.

51. *Sample answer:*

x-value	Substitute for x	y-value
-1	$y = -6(-1) - 5$	1
0	$y = -6(0) - 5$	-5
1	$y = -6(1) - 5$	-11

Three solutions for the equation $y = -6x - 5$ are $(-1, 1)$, $(0, -5)$, and $(1, -11)$.

52. *Sample answer:*

x-value	Substitute for x.	y-value
-1	$y = -2(-1) + 4$	6
0	$y = -2(0) + 4$	4
1	$y = -2(1) + 4$	2

Three solutions for the equation $y = -2x + 4$ are $(-1, 6)$, $(0, 4)$, and $(1, 2)$.

53. $A = bh = (10)(14) = 140$

The area of the parallelogram is 140 square units.

54. $A = bh = (17)(23) = 391$

The area of the parallelogram is 391 square units.

55. $A = bh = (32)(33) = 1056$

The area of the parallelogram is 1056 square units.

56. C; A relation is a function if for each input there is exactly one output. Since 1, 2, and 4 have an output, x must equal 3.

Quiz 11.1–11.4 (p. 603)

1.

Input x	Function	Output y
0	$y = -\frac{1}{3}(0)$	0
1	$y = -\frac{1}{3}(1)$	$-\frac{1}{3}$
2	$y = -\frac{1}{3}(2)$	$-\frac{2}{3}$
3	$y = -\frac{1}{3}(3)$	-1

The range of the function is 0, $-\frac{1}{3}$, $-\frac{2}{3}$, and -1.

2. $7y + x = 21$

$7y = -x + 21$

$y = -\frac{1}{7}x + 3$

Sample answer:

x	0	7	21
y	3	2	0

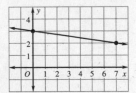

3. $-5x - 2y = -20$

$-2y = 5x - 20$

$y = -\frac{5}{2}x + 10$

Sample answer:

x	0	2	4
y	10	5	0

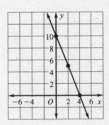

4. $-3x + 9y = -18$

$9y = 3x - 18$

$y = \frac{1}{3}x - 2$

Sample answer:

x	-3	0	3
y	-3	-2	-1

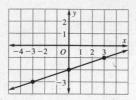

5. $y = ax + b$

$a = \dfrac{\text{change in output}}{\text{change in input}} = \dfrac{1}{1} = 1$

$y = x + b$

Let $(x, y) = (0, 2)$.

$2 = 0 + b$

$2 = b$

$y = x + 2$

A function rule that relates x and y is $y = x + 2$.

6. $y = ax + b$

$a = \dfrac{\text{change in output}}{\text{change in input}} = \dfrac{6}{3} = 2$

$y = 2x + b$

Let $(x, y) = (0, 1)$.

$1 = 2(0) + b$

$1 = b$

$y = 2x + 1$

A function rule that relates x and y is $y = 2x + 1$.

7. $4x + 2y = 120$

$2y = -4x + 120$

$y = -2x + 60$

x	0	10	20	30
y	60	40	20	0

Pottery Sales

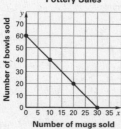

There is a negative relationship because as the number of mugs increases, the number of bowls decreases.

Technology Activity 11.4 (p. 604)

1. 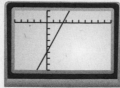 **2.**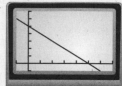

3. $x - y = 11$

$-y = -x + 11$

$y = x - 11$

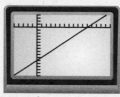

4. $x + y = 6$

$y = -x + 6$

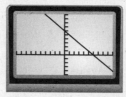

5. The viewing window is appropriate for the graph of the equation.

6. The viewing window is not appropriate.

Sample answer: Xmin = -10, Xmax = 5,

Ymin = -5, Ymax = 15

Mixed Review of Problem Solving (p. 605)

1. a.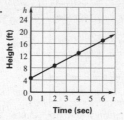

t	0	2	4	6
h	5	9	13	17

b. It will take 1.5 seconds for the balloon to get 8 feet off the ground.

c. No, the balloon will not be 16 feet off the ground after 3 seconds.

$2(1.5) = 3$

$h = 5 + 2(3)$

$h = 5 + 6$

$h = 11$

The balloon will be 11 feet off the ground after 3 seconds.

Chapter 11, continued

2. 1 year = 12 months

$C = 45 + 8(12)$

$C = 45 + 96$

$C = 141$

The total cost to buy and operate the model airplane for 1 year is $141. With the gift money, $141 - 25 = 116$, you will need $116 more to operate the plane in the first year.

3.

a.

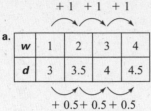

w	1	2	3	4
d	3	3.5	4	4.5

$d = aw + b$

$a = \dfrac{0.5}{1} = 0.5$

Let $(w, d) = (1, 3)$.

$3 = 0.5(1) + b$

$3 = 0.5 + b$

$2.5 = b$

$d = 0.5w + 2.5$

b. $d = 0.5w + 2.5$

$d = 0.5(9) + 2.5$

$d = 4.5 + 2.5$

$d = 7$

You run 7 miles.

c.

$d = 0.5w + 2.5$

$10 = 0.5w + 2.5$

$10 - 2.5 = 0.5w + 2.5 - 2.5$

$7.5 = 0.5w$

$\dfrac{7.5}{0.5} = \dfrac{0.5w}{0.5}$

$15 = w$

You will run 10 miles in week 15.

4. Answers may vary.

5. a. $C = 300 + 0.43h$

b. It will be less expensive at home.

Sample answer: 200 loads means $h = 200$.

Home: $C = 300 + 0.43(200)$

$C = 300 + 86$

$C = 386$

Laundromat: $C = 2.50(200)$

$C = 500$

c. *Sample answer:* Set the equations equal to each other.

$2.5\ell = 300 + 0.43\ell$

$2.5\ell - 0.43\ell = 300 + 0.43\ell - 0.43\ell$

$2.07\ell = 300$

$\dfrac{2.07\ell}{2.07} = \dfrac{300}{2.07}$

$\ell \approx 144.9$, or about 145

The cost would be the same for about 145 loads.

6. a. $S = 8 + 4t$

b. First convert miles per hour to feet per second.

$\dfrac{60\text{ miles}}{\text{hour}} \cdot \dfrac{1\text{ hour}}{3600\text{ seconds}} \cdot \dfrac{5280\text{ feet}}{1\text{ mile}} = 88$ ft per sec

$S = 8 + 4t$

$88 = 8 + 4t$

$88 - 8 = 8 + 4t - 8$

$80 = 4t$

$\dfrac{80}{4} = \dfrac{4t}{4}$

$20 = t$

It will take the car 20 sec.

7. a. Casey: $m = 36 + 2w$

Krystal: $m = 5w$

b. Krystal because $m = 5w$. If $2w$ is substituted for w in the equation $m = 5w$, it will result in $m = 10w$, which doubles the money.

c. Casey: $m = 36 + 2w$

$110 = 36 + 2w$

$110 - 36 = 36 + 2w - 36$

$74 = 2w$

$\dfrac{74}{2} = \dfrac{2w}{2}$

$37 = w$

Krystal: $m = 5w$

$110 = 5w$

$\dfrac{110}{5} = \dfrac{5w}{5}$

$22 = w$

Krystal will have enough money to purchase the DVD player in 22 weeks, while Casey will have enough money in 37 weeks. So Krystal will be able to purchase the DVD player first.

Chapter 11, *continued*

Lesson 11.5

11.5 Guided Practice (p. 607)

1. x-intercept:

$y = 2x - 10$

$0 = 2x - 10$

$10 = 2x$

$5 = x$

y-intercept:

$y = 2x - 10$

$y = 2(0) - 10$

$y = -10$

The x-intercept is 5 and the y-intercept is -10. The graph of the equation contains the points (5, 0) and (0, -10).

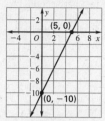

2. x-intercept:

$3x + y = -1$

$3x + 0 = -1$

$3x = -1$

$x = -\frac{1}{3}$

y-intercept:

$3x + y = -1$

$3(0) + y = -1$

$0 + y = -1$

$y = -1$

The x-intercept is $-\frac{1}{3}$ and the y-intercept is -1.

The graph of the equation contains the points $\left(-\frac{1}{3}, 0\right)$ and (0, -1).

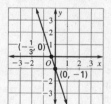

3. x-intercept:

$5x + 3y = 18$

$5x + 3(0) = 18$

$5x + 0 = 18$

$5x = 18$

$x = \frac{18}{5}$

y-intercept:

$5x + 3y = 18$

$5(0) + 3y = 18$

$0 + 3y = 18$

$3y = 18$

$y = 6$

The x-intercept is $3\frac{3}{5}$ and the y-intercept is 6. The graph

of the equation contains the points $\left(3\frac{3}{5}, 0\right)$ and (0, 6).

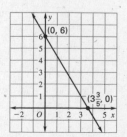

4. Both intercepts are increased.

x-intercept:

$4x + 2y = 12$

$4x + 2(0) = 12$

$4x = 12$

$x = 3$

y-intercept:

$4x + 2y = 12$

$4(0) + 2y = 12$

$2y = 12$

$y = 6$

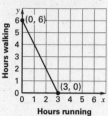

11.5 Exercises (pp. 608–609)

Skill Practice

1. x-intercept: 6

y-intercept: 1

2. x-intercept: 3

y-intercept: -1

3. x-intercept:

$y = 6x - 3$

$0 = 6x - 3$

$3 = 6x$

$\frac{1}{2} = x$

y-intercept:

$y = 6x - 3$

$y = 6(0) - 3$

$y = -3$

The x-intercept is $\frac{1}{2}$ and the y-intercept is -3. The graph

of the equation contains the points $\left(\frac{1}{2}, 0\right)$ and (0, -3).

4. x-intercept:

$x + 4y = 12$

$x + 4(0) = 12$

$x = 12$

y-intercept:

$x + 4y = 12$

$0 + 4y = 12$

$4y = 12$

$y = 3$

The x-intercept is 12 and the y-intercept is 3. The graph of the equation contains the points (12, 0) and (0, 3).

5. x-intercept:

$5x - 2y = 10$

$5x - 2(0) = 10$

$5x = 10$

$x = 2$

y-intercept:

$5x - 2y = 10$

$5(0) - 2y = 10$

$-2y = 10$

$y = -5$

The x-intercept is 2 and the y-intercept is -5. The graph of the equation contains the points (2, 0) and (0, -5).

6. x-intercept:

$x + 9y = 18$

$x + 9(0) = 18$

$x = 18$

y-intercept:

$x + 9y = 18$

$0 + 9y = 18$

$9y = 18$

$y = 2$

The x-intercept is 18 and the y-intercept is 2. The graph of the equation contains the points (18, 0) and (0, 2).

7. x-intercept:

$$4x + 5y = 20$$
$$4x + 5(0) = 20$$
$$4x = 20$$
$$x = 5$$

y-intercept:

$$4x + 5y = 20$$
$$4(0) + 5y = 20$$
$$5y = 20$$
$$y = 4$$

The x-intercept is 5 and the y-intercept is 4. The graph of the equation contains the points (5, 0) and (0, 4).

8. x-intercept:

$$7x - 9y = -63$$
$$7x - 9(0) = -63$$
$$7x = -63$$
$$x = -9$$

y-intercept:

$$7x - 9y = -63$$
$$7(0) - 9y = -63$$
$$-9y = -63$$
$$y = 7$$

The x-intercept is -9 and the y-intercept is 7. The graph of the equation contains the points $(-9, 0)$ and $(0, 7)$.

9. A; $2x - y = 4$

$$2(0) - y = 4$$
$$-y = 4$$
$$y = -4$$

10. Substitute $x = 0$ and $y = 0$ one at a time, and solve for the other variable.

x-intercept:

$$4x - 3y = 12$$
$$4x - 3(0) = 12$$
$$4x = 12$$
$$x = 3$$

y-intercept:

$$4x - 3y = 12$$
$$4(0) - 3y = 12$$
$$-3y = 12$$
$$y = -4$$

The x-intercept is 3 and the y-intercept is -4.

11.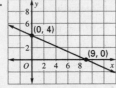

12.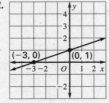

13.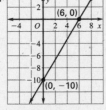

14. x-intercept:

$$y = 5x - 15$$
$$0 = 5x - 15$$
$$15 = 5x$$
$$3 = x$$

y-intercept:

$$y = 5x - 15$$
$$y = 5(0) - 15$$
$$y = -15$$

The x-intercept is 3 and the y-intercept is -15. The graph of the equation contains the points (3, 0) and $(0, -15)$.

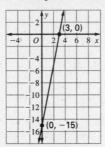

15. x-intercept:

$$y = -2x + 7$$
$$0 = -2x + 7$$
$$-7 = -2x$$
$$3.5 = x$$

y-intercept:

$$y = -2x + 7$$
$$y = -2(0) + 7$$
$$y = 7$$

The x-intercept is 3.5 and the y-intercept is 7. The graph of the equation contains the points (3.5, 0) and (0, 7).

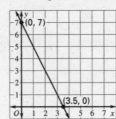

16. x-intercept:

$$8x + 10y = 30$$
$$8x + 10(0) = 30$$
$$8x = 30$$
$$x = 3.75$$

y-intercept:

$$8x + 10y = 30$$
$$8(0) + 10y = 30$$
$$10y = 30$$
$$y = 3$$

The x-intercept is 3.75 and the y-intercept is 3. The graph of the equation contains the points (3.75, 0) and (0, 3).

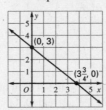

Chapter 11, *continued*

17. *x*-intercept:

$$7.5x + 3y = 19.5$$
$$7.5x + 3(0) = 19.5$$
$$7.5x = 19.5$$
$$x = 2.6$$

y-intercept:

$$7.5x + 3y = 19.5$$
$$7.5(0) + 3y = 19.5$$
$$3y = 19.5$$
$$y = 6.5$$

The *x*-intercept is 2.6 and the *y*-intercept is 6.5. The graph of the equation contains the points (2.6, 0) and (0, 6.5).

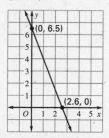

18. *x*-intercept:

$$-\frac{3}{4}x + y = -\frac{1}{2}$$
$$-\frac{3}{4}x + 0 = -\frac{1}{2}$$
$$-\frac{3}{4}x = -\frac{1}{2}$$
$$x = \frac{2}{3}$$

y-intercept:

$$-\frac{3}{4}x + y = -\frac{1}{2}$$
$$-\frac{3}{4}(0) + y = -\frac{1}{2}$$
$$y = -\frac{1}{2}$$

The *x*-intercept is $\frac{2}{3}$ and the *y*-intercept is $-\frac{1}{2}$. The graph of the equation contains the points $\left(\frac{2}{3}, 0\right)$ and $\left(0, -\frac{1}{2}\right)$.

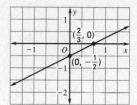

19. *x*-intercept:

$$-\frac{1}{6}x + \frac{1}{3}y = \frac{1}{3}$$
$$-\frac{1}{6}x + \frac{1}{3}(0) = \frac{1}{3}$$
$$-\frac{1}{6}x = \frac{1}{3}$$
$$x = -2$$

y-intercept:

$$-\frac{1}{6}x + \frac{1}{3}y = \frac{1}{3}$$
$$-\frac{1}{6}(0) + \frac{1}{3}y = \frac{1}{3}$$
$$\frac{1}{3}y = \frac{1}{3}$$
$$y = 1$$

The *x*-intercept is -2 and the *y*-intercept is 1. The graph of the equation contains the points $(-2, 0)$ and $(0, 1)$.

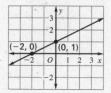

20. *x*-intercept

$$x + 2y = 5$$
$$x + 2(0) = 5$$
$$x = 5$$

$$x - 2y = 5$$
$$x - 2(0) = 5$$
$$x = 5$$

21. *y*-intercept

$$3x - 2y = 6$$
$$3(0) - 2y = 6$$
$$-2y = 6$$
$$y = -3$$

$$-3x - 2y = 6$$
$$-3(0) - 2y = 6$$
$$-2y = 6$$
$$y = -3$$

22. neither

$$7x + 5y = 35$$
$$7x + 5(0) = 35$$
$$7x = 35$$
$$x = 5$$
$$7(0) + 5y = 35$$
$$5y = 35$$
$$y = 7$$

$$7x + 5y = -35$$
$$7x + 5(0) = -35$$
$$7x = -35$$
$$x = -5$$
$$7(0) + 5y = -35$$
$$5y = -35$$
$$y = -7$$

23. Because the graph of $y = 9$ is a horizontal line passing through (0, 9), there is no *x*-intercept and the *y*-intercept is 9.

24. Because the graph of $y = 14$ is a horizontal line passing through (0, 14), there is no *x*-intercept and the *y*-intercept is 14.

25. Because the graph of $x = 21$ is a vertical line passing through (21, 0), there is no *y*-intercept and the *x*-intercept is 21.

26. $-3x + y = 12$

x-intercept:

$$-3x + 0 = 12$$
$$-3x = 12$$
$$x = -4$$

y-intercept:

$$-3(0) + y = 12$$
$$y = 12$$

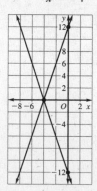

The *x*-intercept does not change, but the new *y*-intercept is the opposite of the original.

27. x-intercept:

$$-4x + 6y = 20$$
$$-4x + 6(0) = 20$$
$$-4x = 20$$
$$x = -5$$

y-intercept:

$$-4x + 6y = 20$$
$$-4(0) + 6y = 20$$
$$6y = 20$$
$$y = 3\frac{1}{3}$$

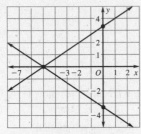

The x-intercept does not change, but the new y-intercept is the opposite of the original.

28. x-intercept:

$$3x - 8y = 32$$
$$3x - 8(0) = 32$$
$$3x = 32$$
$$x = 10\frac{2}{3}$$

y-intercept:

$$3x - 8y = 32$$
$$3(0) - 8y = 32$$
$$-8y = 32$$
$$y = -4$$

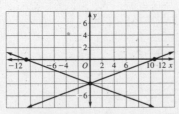

The y-intercept does not change, but the new x-intercept is the opposite of the original.

Problem Solving

29. a. The variable x represents the number of CDs you can buy and the variable y represents the number of videos you can buy.

b. x-intercept:

$$12x + 10y = 60$$
$$12x + 10(0) = 60$$
$$12x = 60$$
$$x = 5$$

y-intercept:

$$12x + 10y = 60$$
$$12(0) + 10y = 60$$
$$10y = 60$$
$$y = 6$$

The x-intercept is 5 and the y-intercept is 6. The graph of the equation contains the points (5, 0) and (0, 6).

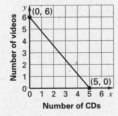

c. The x-intercept represents the number of CDs you can buy if you don't buy any videos and the y-intercept represents the number of videos you can buy if you don't buy any CDs.

30.
$$4x + 2y = 12$$
$$4x + 2(0) = 12$$
$$4x = 12$$
$$x = 3$$

The x-intercept tells you that you can buy 3 packs of T-shirts and 0 packs of DVD gift certificates.

31. x-intercept:

$$2x + 3y = 18$$
$$2x + 3(0) = 18$$
$$2x = 18$$
$$x = 9$$

y-intercept:

$$2x + 3y = 18$$
$$2(0) + 3y = 18$$
$$3y = 18$$
$$y = 6$$

The x-intercept is 9 and the y-intercept is 6. The graph of the equation contains the points (9, 0) and (0, 6).

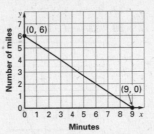

The x-intercept represents the length, in minutes, of the bus ride and the y-intercept represents the distance between the school and home. The points along the graph represent the distance from home at any given number of minutes.

32. No, not all graphs of linear equations have a y-intercept.

Sample answer: A vertical line, such as $x = -1$ or $x = 5$, is parallel to the y-axis and has no y-intercept.

33. The line slants up from left to right because the y-intercept is down and to the left of the x-intercept. The x-intercept is positive, so the line passes through Quadrants I and IV on either side of the intercept. The y-intercept is negative, so the line passes through Quadrants III and IV on either side of the intercept. The line passes through Quadrants I, III, and IV.

34. The s-intercept shows how much money to invest to earn $100 interest using only a savings account, and the c-intercept shows how much money to invest to earn $100 interest using only a certificate of deposit.

Sample answer: Graph the line through the intercepts (5000, 0) and (0, 2000). Also graph the line $s + c = 3500$. The intersection of the lines is (2500, 1000). So you can earn $100 by investing $2500 in the savings account and $1000 in the CD.

35. *x*-intercept:

$y = 0.5x$
$0 = 0.5x$
$0 = x$

$y = 3x$
$0 = 3x$
$0 = x$

$y = 5x$
$0 = 5x$
$0 = x$

y-intercept:

$y = 0.5x$
$y = 0.5(0)$
$y = 0$

$y = 3x$
$y = 3(0)$
$y = 0$

$y = 5x$
$y = 5(0)$
$y = 0$

All the *x*-intercepts are 0 and all the *y*-intercepts are 0.

Sample answer: The graph of $y = kx$ has an *x*-intercept of 0 and a *y*-intercept of 0. So, the graph passes through the origin.

Mixed Review

36. $7 - 16 = -9$

37. $8 - (-15) = 23$

38. $-4 - 31 = -35$

39. $-24 - (-18) = -6$

40.

x	−1	0	1
y	4	5	6

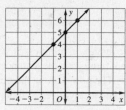

41.

x	0	1	2
y	−6	−4	−2

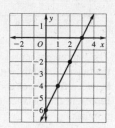

42.

x	0	$\frac{4}{7}$	1
y	4	0	−3

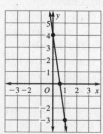

43. B; $\dfrac{2ab^2}{6a^2} = \dfrac{2 \cdot 4 \cdot (6)^2}{6 \cdot (4)^2} = \dfrac{2 \cdot \cancel{4} \cdot \cancel{6} \cdot 6}{\cancel{6} \cdot \cancel{4} \cdot 4} = \dfrac{12}{4} = 3$

Lesson 11.6

Investigation (pp. 610–611)

1.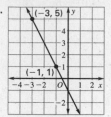

Slope $= \dfrac{\text{rise}}{\text{run}} = \dfrac{-4}{2} = -2$

The slope of the line passing through the points $(-1, 1)$ and $(-3, 5)$ is -2.

2. The operation you use on the rise is subtraction.

The operation you use on the run is subtraction.

3. $(5, 6)$ and $(-2, 3)$

rise: $6 - 3 = 3$

run: $5 - (-2) = 7$

The slope of the line passing through the points $(5, 6)$ and $(-2, 3)$ is $\dfrac{3}{7}$.

4.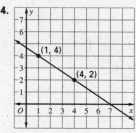

Slope $= \dfrac{\text{rise}}{\text{run}} = \dfrac{-2}{3} = -\dfrac{2}{3}$

The slope of the line passing through the points $(1, 4)$ and $(4, 2)$ is $-\dfrac{2}{3}$.

5.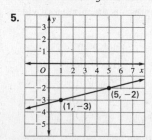

Slope $= \dfrac{\text{rise}}{\text{run}} = \dfrac{1}{4}$

The slope of the line passing through the points $(1, -3)$ and $(5, -2)$ is $\dfrac{1}{4}$.

6.

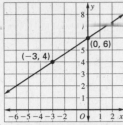

$$\text{Slope} = \frac{\text{rise}}{\text{run}} = \frac{2}{3}$$

The slope of the line passing through the points $(-3, 4)$ and $(0, 6)$ is $\frac{2}{3}$.

7.

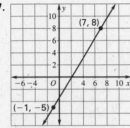

$$\text{Slope} = \frac{\text{rise}}{\text{run}} = \frac{13}{8}$$

The slope of the line passing through the points $(7, 8)$ and $(-1, -5)$ is $\frac{13}{8}$.

8.

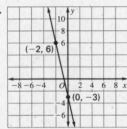

$$\text{Slope} = \frac{\text{rise}}{\text{run}} = \frac{-9}{2} = -\frac{9}{2}$$

The slope of the line passing through the points $(-2, 6)$ and $(0, -3)$ is $-\frac{9}{2}$.

9.

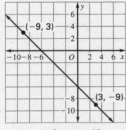

$$\text{Slope} = \frac{\text{rise}}{\text{run}} = \frac{-12}{12} = -1$$

The slope of the line passing through the points $(-9, 3)$ and $(3, -9)$ is -1.

10. One of them is negative, and one is positive.

11. They are both positive or both negative.

12. A line with a slope greater than 1 is steeper than a line with a slope between 0 and 1.

13. $\text{Slope} = \dfrac{\text{rise}}{\text{run}} = \dfrac{2}{3}$

14. $\text{Slope} = \dfrac{\text{rise}}{\text{run}} = \dfrac{-1}{4} = -\dfrac{1}{4}$

15. $\text{Slope} = \dfrac{\text{rise}}{\text{run}} = \dfrac{-6}{2} = -3$

16. $\text{Slope} = \dfrac{d - b}{c - a}$ or slope $= \dfrac{b - d}{a - c}$

11.6 Guided Practice (pp. 612–613)

1. $m = \dfrac{\text{rise}}{\text{run}} = \dfrac{6}{18} = \dfrac{1}{3}$

2. $m = \dfrac{\text{rise}}{\text{run}} = \dfrac{y_2 - y_1}{x_2 - x_1} = \dfrac{4 - 1}{6 - 2} = \dfrac{3}{4}$

The slope is $\dfrac{3}{4}$.

3. $m = \dfrac{\text{rise}}{\text{run}} = \dfrac{y_2 - y_1}{x_2 - x_1} = \dfrac{0 - 6}{10 - 0} = \dfrac{-6}{10} = -\dfrac{3}{5}$

The slope is $-\dfrac{3}{5}$.

4. $m = \dfrac{\text{rise}}{\text{run}} = \dfrac{y_2 - y_1}{x_2 - x_1} = \dfrac{2 - (-4)}{5 - (-3)} = \dfrac{2 + 4}{5 + 3} = \dfrac{6}{8} = \dfrac{3}{4}$

The slope is $\dfrac{3}{4}$.

5. $m = \dfrac{\text{rise}}{\text{run}} = \dfrac{y_2 - y_1}{x_2 - x_1} = \dfrac{5 - 5}{-3 - 1} = \dfrac{0}{-4} = 0$

The slope is 0.

6. $m = \dfrac{\text{rise}}{\text{run}} = \dfrac{y_2 - y_1}{x_2 - x_1} = \dfrac{2 - 6}{1 - 1} = \dfrac{-4}{0}$

The slope is undefined.

7. $m = \dfrac{\text{rise}}{\text{run}} = \dfrac{y_2 - y_1}{x_2 - x_1} = \dfrac{3 - 3}{8 - (-8)} = \dfrac{0}{16} = 0$

The slope is 0.

11.6 Exercises (pp. 614–617)

Skill Practice

1. Between two points, the change in the y-coordinates is called the *rise*.

2. Between two points, the change in the x-coordinates is called the *run*.

3. The ratio of vertical change to horizontal change between any two points on a line is the *slope* of the line.

4. Points: $(-3, -3)$ and $(1, 2)$

$m = \dfrac{\text{rise}}{\text{run}} = \dfrac{y_2 - y_1}{x_2 - x_1} = \dfrac{2 - (-3)}{1 - (-3)} = \dfrac{5}{4}$

The slope is $\dfrac{5}{4}$.

5. Points: $(-2, 6)$ and $(1, 0)$

$m = \dfrac{\text{rise}}{\text{run}} = \dfrac{y_2 - y_1}{x_2 - x_1} = \dfrac{0 - 6}{1 - (-2)} = \dfrac{-6}{3} = -2$

The slope is -2.

Chapter 11, *continued*

6. Points: (3, 4) and (3, 0)

$$m = \frac{\text{rise}}{\text{run}} = \frac{y_2 - y_1}{x_2 - x_1} = \frac{0 - 4}{3 - 3} = \frac{-4}{0}$$

The slope is undefined.

7. $m = \frac{\text{rise}}{\text{run}} = \frac{y_2 - y_1}{x_2 - x_1} = \frac{6 - 8}{6 - (-4)} = \frac{-2}{10} = -\frac{1}{5}$

The slope is $-\frac{1}{5}$.

8. $m = \frac{\text{rise}}{\text{run}} = \frac{y_2 - y_1}{x_2 - x_1} = \frac{-7 - 4}{1 - 1} = \frac{-11}{0}$

The slope is undefined.

9. $m = \frac{\text{rise}}{\text{run}} = \frac{y_2 - y_1}{x_2 - x_1} = \frac{4 - 4}{3 - (-5)} = \frac{0}{8} = 0$

The slope is 0.

10. $m = \frac{\text{rise}}{\text{run}} = \frac{y_2 - y_1}{x_2 - x_1} = \frac{2 - (-4)}{4 - (-2)} = \frac{6}{6} = 1$

The slope is 1.

11. $m = \frac{\text{rise}}{\text{run}} = \frac{y_2 - y_1}{x_2 - x_1} = \frac{-2 - 1}{-3 - (-3)} = \frac{-3}{0}$

The slope is undefined.

12. $m = \frac{\text{rise}}{\text{run}} = \frac{y_2 - y_1}{x_2 - x_1} = \frac{5 - 8}{0 - 5} = \frac{-3}{-5} = \frac{3}{5}$

The slope is $\frac{3}{5}$.

13. $m = \frac{\text{rise}}{\text{run}} = \frac{y_2 - y_1}{x_2 - x_1} = \frac{-7 - (-2)}{6 - (-6)} = \frac{-5}{12}$

The slope is $-\frac{5}{12}$.

14. $m = \frac{\text{rise}}{\text{run}} = \frac{y_2 - y_1}{x_2 - x_1} = \frac{-8 - (-8)}{15 - 9} = \frac{0}{6} = 0$

The slope is 0.

15. $m = \frac{\text{rise}}{\text{run}} = \frac{y_2 - y_1}{x_2 - x_1} = \frac{19 - 22}{-20 - 12} = \frac{-3}{-32} = \frac{3}{32}$

The slope is $\frac{3}{32}$.

16. The x- and y-coordinates are switched.

$$\text{Slope} = \frac{\text{rise}}{\text{run}} = \frac{y_2 - y_1}{x_2 - x_1} = \frac{-3 - 0}{0 - 4} = \frac{3}{4}$$

17. *Sample answer:*

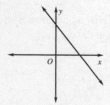

18. *Sample answer:*

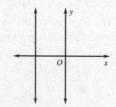

19. *Sample answer:*

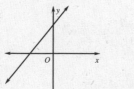

20. *Sample answer:*

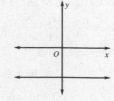

21.

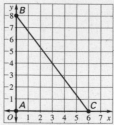

Slope of $\overline{AB}$:

$$m = \frac{\text{rise}}{\text{run}} = \frac{y_2 - y_1}{x_2 - x_1} = \frac{8 - 0}{0 - 0} = \frac{8}{0}$$

The slope of $\overline{AB}$ is undefined.

Slope of $\overline{BC}$:

$$m = \frac{\text{rise}}{\text{run}} = \frac{y_2 - y_1}{x_2 - x_1} = \frac{0 - 8}{6 - 0} = -\frac{8}{6} = -\frac{4}{3}$$

The slope of $\overline{BC}$ is $-\frac{4}{3}$.

Slope of $\overline{AC}$:

$$m = \frac{\text{rise}}{\text{run}} = \frac{y_2 - y_1}{x_2 - x_1} = \frac{0 - 0}{6 - 0} = \frac{0}{6} = 0$$

The slope of $\overline{AC}$ is 0.

22.

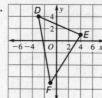

Slope of $\overline{DE}$:

$$m = \frac{\text{rise}}{\text{run}} = \frac{y_2 - y_1}{x_2 - x_1} = \frac{1 - 4}{4 - (-3)} = \frac{-3}{7} = -\frac{3}{7}$$

The slope of $\overline{DE}$ is $-\frac{3}{7}$.

Slope of $\overline{EF}$:

$$m = \frac{\text{rise}}{\text{run}} = \frac{y_2 - y_1}{x_2 - x_1} = \frac{-7 - 1}{-1 - 4} = \frac{-8}{-5} = \frac{8}{5}$$

The slope of $\overline{EF}$ is $\frac{8}{5}$.

Slope of $\overline{DF}$:

$$m = \frac{\text{rise}}{\text{run}} = \frac{y_2 - y_1}{x_2 - x_1} = \frac{-7 - 4}{-1 - (-3)} = \frac{-11}{2} = -\frac{11}{2}$$

The slope of $\overline{DF}$ is $-\frac{11}{2}$.

Chapter 11, *continued*

23.

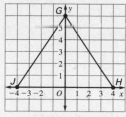

Slope of $\overline{GH}$:

$$m = \frac{\text{rise}}{\text{run}} = \frac{y_2 - y_1}{x_2 - x_1} = \frac{0 - 6}{4 - 0} = \frac{-6}{4} = -\frac{3}{2}$$

The slope of $\overline{GH}$ is $-\frac{3}{2}$.

Slope of $\overline{HJ}$:

$$m = \frac{\text{rise}}{\text{run}} = \frac{y_2 - y_1}{x_2 - x_1} = \frac{0 - 0}{-4 - 4} = \frac{0}{-8} = 0$$

The slope of $\overline{HJ}$ is 0.

Slope of $\overline{GJ}$:

$$m = \frac{\text{rise}}{\text{run}} = \frac{y_2 - y_1}{x_2 - x_1} = \frac{0 - 6}{-4 - 0} = \frac{-6}{-4} = \frac{3}{2}$$

The slope of $\overline{GJ}$ is $\frac{3}{2}$.

24.

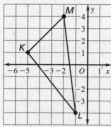

Slope of $\overline{KL}$:

$$m = \frac{\text{rise}}{\text{run}} = \frac{y_2 - y_1}{x_2 - x_1} = \frac{-4 - 1}{-1 - (-5)} = \frac{-5}{4} = -\frac{5}{4}$$

The slope of $\overline{KL}$ is $-\frac{5}{4}$.

Slope of $\overline{LM}$:

$$m = \frac{\text{rise}}{\text{run}} = \frac{y_2 - y_1}{x_2 - x_1} = \frac{4 - (-4)}{-2 - (-1)} = \frac{8}{-1} = -8$$

The slope of $\overline{LM}$ is -8.

Slope of $\overline{KM}$:

$$m = \frac{\text{rise}}{\text{run}} = \frac{y_2 - y_1}{x_2 - x_1} = \frac{4 - 1}{-2 - (-5)} = \frac{3}{3} = 1$$

The slope of $\overline{KM}$ is 1.

25. line a: $m = \dfrac{\text{rise}}{\text{run}} = \dfrac{y_2 - y_1}{x_2 - x_1} = \dfrac{0 - \left(-\frac{3}{2}\right)}{\frac{2}{1} - \frac{1}{2}} = \dfrac{1\frac{1}{2}}{\frac{1}{2}} = 3$

line b: $m = \dfrac{\text{rise}}{\text{run}} = \dfrac{y_2 - y_1}{x_2 - x_1} = \dfrac{1 - 10}{-\frac{1}{2} - 4} = \dfrac{-9}{-4\frac{1}{2}} = 2$

Line a is steeper than line b.

26. line a: $m = \dfrac{\text{rise}}{\text{run}} = \dfrac{y_2 - y_1}{x_2 - x_1} = \dfrac{3 - (-9)}{-11 - 2} = \dfrac{12}{-13} = -\dfrac{12}{13}$

line b: $m = \dfrac{\text{rise}}{\text{run}} = \dfrac{y_2 - y_1}{x_2 - x_1} = \dfrac{6 - \left(-\frac{1}{4}\right)}{-\frac{5}{8} - \frac{5}{8}} = \dfrac{6\frac{1}{4}}{-1\frac{1}{4}} = -5$

Line b is steeper than line a.

27. A; $m = \dfrac{\text{rise}}{\text{run}} = \dfrac{y_2 - y_1}{x_2 - x_1} = \dfrac{3 - (-3)}{-3 - (-7)} = \dfrac{6}{4} = \dfrac{3}{2}$

28.
$$m = \frac{y_2 - y_1}{x_2 - x_1}$$
$$\frac{7}{4} = \frac{0 - (-7)}{16 - x}$$
$$\frac{7}{4} = \frac{7}{16 - x}$$
$$7(16 - x) = 4(7)$$
$$16 - x = 4$$
$$-x = -12$$
$$x = 12$$

29. $m = \dfrac{y_2 - y_1}{x_2 - x_1}$
$$0 = \frac{y - 7}{3 - 0}$$
$$0 = \frac{y - 7}{3}$$
$$0 = y - 7$$
$$7 = y$$

30. $m = \dfrac{\text{rise}}{\text{run}} = \dfrac{y_2 - y_1}{x_2 - x_1} = \dfrac{q + 2 - q}{p + 2 - p} = \dfrac{2}{2} = 1$

The slope is 1.

31. The triangle is a right triangle.

The slope of $\overline{RT}$ is $\dfrac{b - d}{a - c}$.

The slope of $\overline{ST}$ is $\dfrac{b - d}{c - c}$, which is undefined.

The slope of $\overline{RS}$ is $\dfrac{b - b}{a - c}$, which is 0.

32.

$$m = \frac{y_2 - y_1}{x_2 - x_1} \qquad\qquad m = \frac{y_2 - y_1}{x_2 - x_1}$$

$$\frac{1}{2} = \frac{2 - 4}{x - (-8)} \qquad\qquad \frac{1}{2} = \frac{y - 2}{6 - (-12)}$$

$$\frac{1}{2} = \frac{-2}{x + 8} \qquad\qquad \frac{1}{2} = \frac{y - 2}{18}$$

$$x + 8 = 2(-2) \qquad\qquad 2(y - 2) = 18$$

$$x + 8 = -4 \qquad\qquad y - 2 = 9$$

$$x = -12 \qquad\qquad y = 11$$

33.
$$m = \frac{y_2 - y_1}{x_2 - x_1}$$

$$-4 = \frac{1 - y}{-1 - 2}$$

$$-4 = \frac{1 - y}{-3}$$

$$12 = 1 - y$$

$$11 = -y$$

$$-11 = y$$

$$-4 = \frac{-19 - 1}{x - (-1)}$$

$$-4 = \frac{-20}{x + 1}$$

$$-4x - 4 = -20$$

$$-4x = -16$$

$$x = 4$$

Problem Solving

34. The rise of the roof is 3 units.

35. The run of the roof is 3 units.

36. Slope $= \dfrac{\text{rise}}{\text{run}} = \dfrac{3}{3} = 1$

The slope of the roof is 1.

37. B; $m = \dfrac{\text{rise}}{\text{run}} = \dfrac{6}{14} = \dfrac{3}{7}$

38. Slope at low tide: $m = \dfrac{\text{rise}}{\text{run}} = \dfrac{-3.6}{7.7} \approx -0.47$

Slope at high tide: $m = \dfrac{\text{rise}}{\text{run}} = \dfrac{-1.3}{8.4} \approx -0.15$

The ramp is steeper at low tide.

39. Slope of $\overleftrightarrow{MN}$:

$$m = \frac{\text{rise}}{\text{run}} = \frac{y_2 - y_1}{x_2 - x_1} = \frac{4 - 1}{3 - 1} = \frac{3}{2}$$

The slope of $\overline{MN}$ is $\dfrac{3}{2}$.

Slope of $\overline{PQ}$:

$$m = \frac{\text{rise}}{\text{run}} = \frac{y_2 - y_1}{x_2 - x_1} = \frac{8 - 5}{5 - 2} = \frac{3}{3} = 1$$

The slope of $\overline{PQ}$ is 1.

The line through M and N has the greater slope. You can tell which line has a greater slope from their graphs because the line with the greater slope will be steeper. You can tell which line has a greater slope by calculating their slopes because the line with the greater slope has the larger number as its slope.

40. *Sample answer:* (0, 0) and (7, 5)

$$m = \frac{\text{rise}}{\text{run}}$$

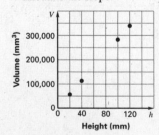

41. No, because $\dfrac{y_2 - y_1}{x_2 - x_1} = \dfrac{-(y_2 - y_1)}{-(x_2 - x_1)} = \dfrac{y_1 - y_2}{x_1 - x_2}$.

Consider the slope of the line that contains (1, 1) and (2, 4). Then $m = \dfrac{y_2 - y_1}{x_2 - x_1} = \dfrac{4 - 1}{2 - 1} = \dfrac{3}{1} = 3$

and $m = \dfrac{y_1 - y_2}{x_1 - x_2} = \dfrac{1 - 4}{1 - 2} = \dfrac{-3}{-1} = 3$.

Now consider the slope of the line that contains $(-2, 3)$ and $(1, -1)$. Then $m = \dfrac{y_2 - y_1}{x_2 - x_1} = \dfrac{-1 - 3}{1 - (-2)} = \dfrac{-4}{3} = -\dfrac{4}{3}$

and $m = \dfrac{y_1 - y_2}{x_1 - x_2} = \dfrac{3 - (-1)}{-2 - 1} = \dfrac{4}{-3} = -\dfrac{4}{3}$.

42. slope $= \dfrac{\text{rise}}{\text{run}} = \dfrac{1886 - 2800}{3299} = \dfrac{-914}{3299} \approx -0.28$

The slope of the ski slope is about -0.28.

43. (height, volume)

$$V = \pi r^2 h$$

20 mm:

$$V = \pi(30)^2(20)$$

$$V \approx 56{,}549 \text{ mm}^3$$

40 mm:

$$V = \pi(30)^2(40)$$

$$V \approx 113{,}097 \text{ mm}^3$$

100 mm:

$$V = \pi(30)^2(100)$$

$$V \approx 282{,}743 \text{ mm}^3$$

120 mm:

$$V = \pi(30)^2(120)$$

$$V \approx 339{,}292 \text{ mm}^3$$

Find the slope: (100, 282,743) and (120, 339,292)

$$m = \frac{\text{rise}}{\text{run}} = \frac{339{,}292 - 282{,}743}{120 - 100} = \frac{56{,}549}{20} \approx 2827$$

This is the area of the base of the cylinder. The four points lie on a line, so any pair of points can be used to calculate the slope.

44. a. Yes this ramp meets the standard.

Sample answer:

Standard: $\dfrac{1}{12}$ or $0.8\overline{3}$

Ramp: $\dfrac{2}{45}$ or $0.0\overline{4}$

$0.0\overline{4} < 0.8\overline{3}$

Chapter 11, *continued*

b. The minimum horizontal length is 24 feet.

Sample answer: A ramp 2 feet high with a 24 foot

horizontal length has a slope of $\frac{2}{24} = \frac{1}{12}$, which is the

maximum slope allowed by standards.

c. *Sample answer:* If a 2 foot high ramp has a slope

of $\frac{1}{20}$, then the horizontal length is 40 feet, $\frac{2}{40} = \frac{1}{20}$.

So for 2 foot high ramps, if the horizontal distance is
less than 40 feet a handrail is needed; if the horizontal
distance is greater than or equal to 40 feet, no handrail
is needed.

45. *Sample answer:*

$$a^2 + b^2 = c^2$$
$$100^2 + b^2 = 1613^2$$
$$10,000 + b^2 = 2,601,769$$
$$b^2 = 2,591,769$$
$$b \approx 1609.9 \text{ ft}$$

$$\frac{100}{1609.9} \approx 6.21\%$$

So the road grade is the same as the slope.

46. $C = 2\pi r$

$$C = \frac{3}{4}(2)\pi(200)$$

$$C \approx 942.5 \text{ ft}$$

$$m = \frac{\text{rise}}{\text{run}} = \frac{-16}{942.5} \approx -0.017$$

The slope of the ramp is -0.017.

Mixed Review

47. $y - 5x = 12$

$\qquad y = 5x + 12$

48. $\qquad -6 = 12y + 3x$

$\quad -3x - 6 = 12y$

$\quad -\frac{1}{4}x - \frac{1}{2} = y$

49. $9x - y = 15$

$\qquad -y = -9x + 15$

$\qquad y = 9x - 15$

50. $4y = 2x - 2$

$\quad y = \frac{1}{2}x - \frac{1}{2}$

51. $6x - y = -1$

$\qquad -y = -6x - 1$

$\qquad y = 6x + 1$

52. $3x + 10y = 20$

$\qquad 10y = -3x + 20$

$\qquad y = -\frac{3}{10}x + 2$

53.

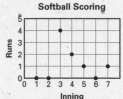

Softball Scoring

The quantities have no relationship.

54. D; $\quad 42 = \frac{t}{3} + 21$

$$42 - 21 = \frac{t}{3} + 21 - 21$$

$$21 = \frac{t}{3}$$

$$63 = t$$

11.6 Extension (pp. 618–619)

1. Neither; The data can be represented by $y = x + 1$,
which is neither a direct variation nor inverse variation.

2. Direct variation; The data can be represented by $y = 3x$.

3. Inverse variation; The data can be represented by $xy = 2$.

4. Inverse variation; The equation is of the form $xy = k$.

5. Direct variation; The equation can be written as
$11x = 2.2y$ or $\frac{y}{x} = 5$.

6. Neither; The equation can be written as $y = -5x - 3$,
which is neither direct variation nor inverse variation.

7. Direct variation; The equation can be written as
$y = -\frac{1}{3}x$.

8. Inverse variation; The equation can be written as
$xy = -3$.

9. Neither; The equation can be written as $xy = -3 + x$,
which is neither direct nor inverse variation.

10. $m = 4t$; Yes; m and t are directly proportional because the
variables m and t show direct variation. The ratio of m to
t is constant $\left(\frac{m}{t} = 4\right)$ and the equation is in the form
$y = kx$, where $k = 4$.

11. No; The equation would be $m = 4t + 20$. The variables
m and t do not show direct variation because the ratio of
m to t is not constant, due to the initial 20 dollars. The
equation cannot be written in the form $y = kx$.

Lesson 11.7

Investigation (p. 620–621)

1.

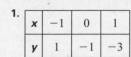

x	-1	0	1
y	1	-1	-3

Chapter 11, *continued*

2.

3. Slope $= \dfrac{\text{rise}}{\text{run}} = \dfrac{-2}{1} = -2$

 y-intercept: -1

4.

Equation	Slope	y-Intercept
$y = 4x + 3$	4	3
$y = -2x - 1$	-2	-1

5.

x	0	1	2
y	-7	-2	3

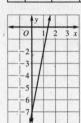

Slope $= \dfrac{\text{rise}}{\text{run}} = \dfrac{5}{1} = 5$

y-intercept $= -7$

6.

x	-1	0	1
y	5	2	-1

Slope $= \dfrac{\text{rise}}{\text{run}} = \dfrac{-3}{1} = -3$

y-intercept $= 2$

7.

x	-3	0	3
y	-4	-6	-8

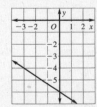

Slope $= \dfrac{\text{rise}}{\text{run}} = \dfrac{-2}{3} = -\dfrac{2}{3}$

y-intercept $= -6$

8.

x	-4	0	4
y	-4	1	6

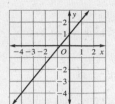

Slope $= \dfrac{\text{rise}}{\text{run}} = \dfrac{5}{4}$

y-intercept $=, 1$

9. $y + 2 = \dfrac{1}{2}x$

$y = \dfrac{1}{2}x - 2$

x	-2	-1	0	1	2
y	-3	-2.5	-2	-1.5	-1

$m = \dfrac{y_2 - y_1}{x_2 - x_1} = \dfrac{-2 - (-3)}{0 - (-2)} = \dfrac{1}{2}$

y-intercept: $y = \dfrac{1}{2}x - 2$

$\qquad\qquad y = \dfrac{1}{2}(0) - 2$

$\qquad\qquad y = -2$

The slope is $\dfrac{1}{2}$ and the y-intercept is -2.

10. $3y = -2x + 9$

$y = -\dfrac{2}{3}x + 3$

x	-2	-1	0	1	2
y	$4\dfrac{1}{3}$	$3\dfrac{2}{3}$	3	$2\dfrac{1}{3}$	$1\dfrac{2}{3}$

$m = \dfrac{y_2 - y_1}{x_2 - x_1} = \dfrac{4\frac{1}{3} - 2\frac{1}{3}}{-2 - 1} = \dfrac{2}{-3} = -\dfrac{2}{3}$

y-intercept: $y = -\dfrac{2}{3}x + 3$

$\qquad\qquad y = -\dfrac{2}{3}(0) + 3$

$\qquad\qquad y = 3$

The slope is $-\dfrac{2}{3}$ and the y-intercept is 3.

11. $y + 4x = -5$

$\qquad y = -4x - 5$

x	-2	-1	0	1	2
y	3	-1	-5	-9	-13

$m = \dfrac{y_2 - y_1}{x_2 - x_1} = \dfrac{-5 - 3}{0 - (-2)} = \dfrac{-8}{2} = -4$

y-intercept: $y = -4x - 5$

$\qquad\qquad y = -4(0) - 5$

$\qquad\qquad y = -5$

The slope is -4 and the y-intercept is -5.

12. $6x - 2y = 10$

$$-2y = -6x + 10$$
$$y = 3x - 5$$

x	-2	-1	0	1	2
y	-11	-8	-5	-2	1

$$m = \frac{y_2 - y_1}{x_2 - x_1} = \frac{-5 - (-8)}{0 - (-1)} = \frac{3}{1} = 3$$

y-intercept: $y = 3x - 5$

$$y = 3(0) - 5$$
$$y = -5$$

The slope is 3 and the y-intercept is -5.

13. a.

Equation	Slope	y-intercept
$y = 3x + 5$	3	5

b. *Sample answer:* When a linear equation is solved for y, the slope is the coefficient of x, and the y-intercept is the constant term.

c. Yes, the conjecture is true.

14. m is the slope, and b is the y-intercept.

11.7 Guided Practice (pp. 622–623)

1. $y = 6x + 1$

The line has a slope of 6 and a y-intercept of 1.

2. $y = \frac{1}{4}x$

The line has a slope of $\frac{1}{4}$ and a y-intercept of 0.

3. $-2x + 3y = 6$

$$3y = 2x + 6$$
$$y = \frac{2}{3}x + 2$$

The line has a slope of $\frac{2}{3}$ and a y-intercept of 2.

4. $y = 2x + 5$

The line has a slope of 2 and a y-intercept of 5.

5. $y = 7x$

The line has a slope of 7 and y-intercept of 0.

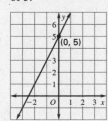

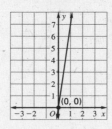

6. $-x + y = 6$

$$y = x + 6$$

The line has a slope of 1 and a y-intercept of 6.

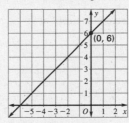

7. $y = -0.005x + 55.2$

Find y when $x = 2500$.

$$y = -0.005(2500) + 55.2$$
$$y = -12.5 + 55.2$$
$$y = 42.7$$

The temperature 2500 feet above the base is 42.7°F.

11.7 Exercises (pp. 624–626)

Skill Practice

1. For the graph of the linear equation $y = -5x + 7$, -5 is the *slope*.

2. The linear equation $y = mx + b$ is in *slope-intercept* form.

3. $2x = y + 5$

$$2x - 5 = y$$
$$y = 2x - 5$$

4. $8x - 4y = 32$

$$-4y = -8x + 32$$
$$y = 2x - 8$$

5. $x - y = -2$

$$-y = -x - 2$$
$$y = x + 2$$

6. C; It is not in slope-intercept form.

7. $y = x + 3$

The line has a slope of 1 and a y-intercept of 3.

8. $y = 6 - x$

$$y = -x + 6$$

The line has a slope of -1 and a y-intercept of 6.

9. $1 = 2x - y$

$$y + 1 = 2x$$
$$y = 2x - 1$$

The line has a slope of 2 and a y-intercept of -1.

10. $6x = 10 - y$

$$y = 10 - 6x$$
$$y = -6x + 10$$

The line has a slope of -6 and a y-intercept of 10.

11. $y - 9 = -\frac{3}{4}x$

$y = -\frac{3}{4}x + 9$

The line has a slope of $-\frac{3}{4}$ and a y-intercept of 9.

12. $\frac{2}{3}x - y = 3$

$-y = -\frac{2}{3}x + 3$

$y = \frac{2}{3}x - 3$

The line has a slope of $\frac{2}{3}$ and a y-intercept of -3.

13. $2y - 6 = 0$

$2y = 6$

$y = 3$

The line has a slope of 0 and a y-intercept of 3.

14. $y + 12x = 0$

$y = -12x$

The line has a slope of -12 and a y-intercept of 0.

15. $13x - 11y = 143$

$-11y = -13x + 143$

$y = \frac{13}{11}x - 13$

The line has a slope of $\frac{13}{11}$ and a y-intercept of -13.

16. B; $3x + y = 4$

$y = -3x + 4$

The slope is -3.

17. $y = x - 8$

$y = 1x + (-8)$

The line has a slope of 1 and a y-intercept of -8.

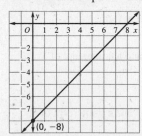

18. $y = -x + 7$

$y = -1x + 7$

The line has a slope of -1 and a y-intercept of 7.

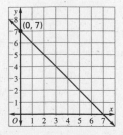

19. $y = 3$

$y = 0x + 3$

The line has a slope of 0 and a y-intercept of 3.

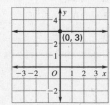

20. $2x - 2y = 1$

$-2y = -2x + 1$

$y = x - \frac{1}{2}$

The line has a slope of 1 and a y-intercept of $-\frac{1}{2}$.

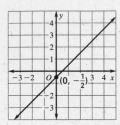

21. $-2x + 3y = -12$

$3y = 2x - 12$

$y = \frac{2}{3}x - 4$

The line has a slope of $\frac{2}{3}$ and a y-intercept of -4.

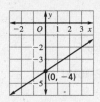

22. $y = \frac{1}{5}x$

$y = \frac{1}{5}x + 0$

The line has a slope of $\frac{1}{5}$ and a y-intercept of 0.

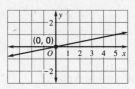

23. The student graphed the y-intercept incorrectly.

Slope $= -2$

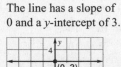

24. $m = \dfrac{\text{rise}}{\text{run}} = \dfrac{2}{1} = 2$

$b = -2$

$y = mx + b$

$y = 2x + (-2) = 2x - 2$

25. $m = \dfrac{\text{rise}}{\text{run}} = \dfrac{-3}{2} = -\dfrac{3}{2}$

$b = -3$

$y = mx + b$

$y = -\dfrac{3}{2}x + (-3) = -\dfrac{3}{2}x - 3$

26. $m = \dfrac{\text{rise}}{\text{run}} = \dfrac{1}{2}$

$b = 1$

$y = mx + b$

$y = \dfrac{1}{2}x + 1$

27. $y = 3x - 1$

Slope: 3

$y = 2x - 1$

Slope: 2

$y = 3x - 1$ is steeper because its slope is larger.

28. $(1, 4)$; $m = 4$

$y = mx + b$

$4 = 4(1) + b$

$4 = 4 + b$

$0 = b$

The y-intercept is 0.
The equation of the line is $y = 4x$.

29. $(3, -4)$; $m = 0$

$y = mx + b$

$-4 = 0(3) + b$

$-4 = b$

The y-intercept is -4.
The equation of the line is $y = -4$.

30. $(9, 0)$; $m = \dfrac{1}{3}$

$y = mx + b$

$0 = \dfrac{1}{3}(9) + b$

$0 = 3 + b$

$-3 = b$

The y-intercept is -3.
The equation of the line is $y = \dfrac{1}{3}x - 3$.

31. $(-2, 2)$; $m = -\dfrac{1}{2}$

$y = mx + b$

$2 = -\dfrac{1}{2}(-2) + b$

$2 = 1 + b$

$1 = b$

The y-intercept is 1.
The equation of the line is $y = -\dfrac{1}{2}x + 1$.

32. $(-5, 6)$; $m = 0$

$y = mx + b$

$6 = 0(-5) + b$

$6 = b$

The y-intercept is 6. The equation of the line is $y = 6$.

33. $\left(\dfrac{1}{2}, 6\right)$; $m = 2$

$y = mx + b$

$6 = 2\left(\dfrac{1}{2}\right) + b$

$6 = 1 + b$

$5 = b$

The y-intercept is 5. The equation of the line is $y = 2x + 5$.

34. $m = \dfrac{\text{rise}}{\text{run}} = \dfrac{y_2 - y_1}{x_2 - x_1} = \dfrac{-1 - 9}{-4 - (-2)} = \dfrac{-10}{-2} = 5$

$y = mx + b$

$9 = 5(-2) + b$

$9 = -10 + b$

$19 = b$

The equation of the line is $y = 5x + 19$.

35. $m = \dfrac{\text{rise}}{\text{run}} = \dfrac{y_2 - y_1}{x_2 - x_1} = \dfrac{12 - 10}{3 - 6} = \dfrac{2}{-3} = -\dfrac{2}{3}$

$y = mx + b$

$10 = -\dfrac{2}{3}(6) + b$

$10 = -4 + b$

$14 = b$

The equation of the line is $y = -\dfrac{2}{3}x + 14$.

36. $m = \dfrac{\text{rise}}{\text{run}} = \dfrac{y_2 - y_1}{x_2 - x_1} = \dfrac{7 - 4}{6 - (-4)} = \dfrac{3}{10}$

$y = mx + b$

$4 = \dfrac{3}{10}(-4) + b$

$4 = -1\dfrac{1}{5} + b$

$5\dfrac{1}{5} = b$

The equation of the line is $y = \dfrac{3}{10}x + 5\dfrac{1}{5}$.

37. $ax + by + c = 0$

$by = -ax - c$

$y = -\dfrac{a}{b}x - \dfrac{c}{b}$

The slope is $-\dfrac{a}{b}$. The y-intercept is $-\dfrac{c}{b}$.

Problem Solving

38. y-intercept: 1500

Slope: $\dfrac{-1500}{75} = -20$

Equation of the line: $y = -20x + 1500$

The slope represents the change in altitude each second.
The y-intercept represents the altitude at the time $t = 0$.

39. B; The rental costs $9 per hour.

40. a.

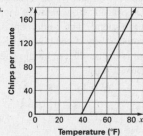

b. The *x*-intercept, (39, 0), indicates that at 39°F, the cricket does not chirp.

c. The *y*-intercept would be the number of chirps per minute when the temperature is 0°F. That would be a negative number, which does not make sense in this situation.

41. Both students' graphs are correct. Up 2 units and right 3 units represents the slope $\frac{2}{3}$. Down 2 units and left 3 units represents the slope $\frac{-2}{-3}$, and $\frac{2}{3} = \frac{-2}{-3}$.

42. a. $P = 3.5b - 28$

b.
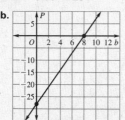

c. $P = 3.5b - 28$

Set *P* equal to 0 to determine how many bracelets you need to make to cover your expenses.

$0 = 3.5b - 28$

$28 = 3.5b$

$8 = b$

You need to make 8 bracelets to cover your expenses.

You will need to make 9 or more to make a profit.

43. Slope of the line perpendicular to $y = 2x + 8$:

$2(m) = -1$

$m = -\frac{1}{2}$

$b = 8$

The line perpendicular to $y = 2x + 8$ with the same *y*-intercept is $y = -\frac{1}{2}x + 8$.

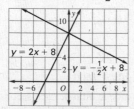

44. Answers will vary.

Sample answer: A boxed set of blank DVDs costs $6, and a single blank DVD costs $1. How many of each can you buy if you have $90 to spend? The *x*-intercept is the number of boxed sets you can buy if you buy no single ones, and the *y*-intercept is the number of single ones you can buy if you buy no boxed sets.

45. a. $4x - 6y = -18$ $\qquad$ $-2x + 3y = 15$

$-6y = -4x - 18$ $\qquad$ $3y = 2x + 15$

$y = \frac{2}{3}x + 3$ $\qquad$ $y = \frac{2}{3}x + 5$

Both equations have a slope equal to $\frac{2}{3}$.

b.
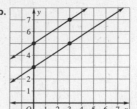
The two lines are parallel.

c. If two lines have the same slope, the lines will be parallel.

46. $y = -2x + 6$

$A = \frac{1}{2}bh$

$A = \frac{1}{2}(3)(6)$

$A = 9$

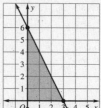

The area of the triangle is 9 units².

47. $y = 3x + 1$ (or any equation $y = 3x + b_1$, where $b_1 \neq -3$) forms another side of the rectangle.

$y = -\frac{1}{3}x + 1$ and $y = -\frac{1}{3}x + 2$ (or any equation of the form $y = -\frac{1}{3}x + b_2$, for any 2 values of b_2) will form the remaining 2 sides.

Mixed Review

48. $\qquad 2y + 3 \leq 11$

$2y + 3 - 3 \leq 11 - 3$

$\qquad\qquad 2y \leq 8$

$\qquad\qquad \frac{2y}{2} \leq \frac{8}{2}$

$\qquad\qquad\quad y \leq 4$

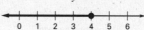

49. $\qquad -4x + 6 > 18$

$-4x + 6 - 6 > 18 - 6$

$\qquad\qquad -4x > 12$

$\qquad\qquad \frac{-4x}{-4} < \frac{12}{-4}$

$\qquad\qquad\quad x < -3$

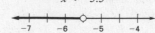

50. $\qquad 7x + 2 < 5x - 9$

$7x + 2 - 2 < 5x - 9 - 2$

$\qquad\qquad 7x < 5x - 11$

$7x - 5x < 5x - 11 - 5x$

$\qquad\qquad 2x < -11$

$\qquad\qquad \frac{2x}{2} < -\frac{11}{2}$

$\qquad\qquad\quad x < -5.5$

Chapter 11, *continued*

51. $V = \pi r^2 h \approx 3.14(3^2)(7) = 3.14(9)(7) = 197.82$

The volume of the cylinder is about 197.82 cubic inches.

52. $V = \frac{1}{3}Bh = \frac{1}{3}(25)(9) = 75$

The volume of the pyramid is 75 cubic feet.

53. B; $a^2 + b^2 = c^2$

$$68^2 + b^2 = 85^2$$
$$4624 + b^2 = 7225$$
$$b^2 = 2601$$
$$b = 51$$

11.7 Extension (p. 627–628)

1. Equation 1   Equation 2

  $y = -x + 3$ $y = x + 1$

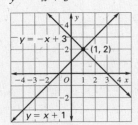

It appears that the point of intersection is $(1, 2)$.

Check whether $(1, 2)$ is the solution by substituting 1 for x and 2 for y in each of the equations.

Equation 1	Equation 2
$y = -x + 3$	$y = x + 1$
$2 \stackrel{?}{=} -1 + 3$	$2 \stackrel{?}{=} 1 + 1$
$2 = 2 ✓$	$2 = 2 ✓$

The solution is $(1, 2)$.

2. Equation 1   Equation 2

  $x - y = 1$ $5x - 4y = 0$

    $-y = 1 - x$ $-4y = -5x$

     $y = x - 1$ $y = \frac{5}{4}x$

It appears that the point of intersection is $(-4, -5)$.

Check whether $(-4, -5)$ is the solution by substituting -4 for x and -5 for y in each of the equations.

Equation 1	Equation 2
$x - y = 1$	$5x - 4y = 0$
$-4 - (-5) \stackrel{?}{=} 1$	$5(-4) - 4(-5) \stackrel{?}{=} 0$
$1 = 1 ✓$	$0 = 0 ✓$

The solution is $(-4, -5)$.

3. Equation 1   Equation 2

  $y = 2x - 15$ $x = -2y$

                     $2y = -x$

                        $y = -\frac{1}{2}x$

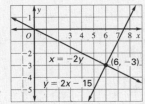

It appears that the point of intersection is $(6, -3)$.

Check whether $(6, -3)$ is the solution by substituting 6 for x and -3 for y in each of the equations.

Equation 1	Equation 2
$y = 2x - 15$	$x = -2y$
$-3 \stackrel{?}{=} 2(6) - 15$	$6 \stackrel{?}{=} -2(-3)$
$-3 = -3 ✓$	$6 = 6 ✓$

The solution is $(6, -3)$.

4. $x = 4$

  $x + y = 2$

Substitute 4 for x in $x + y = 2$.

$$x + y = 2$$
$$4 + y = 2$$
$$y = -2$$

The solution is $(4, -2)$.

5. $x + y = 4$

    $y = 4 - x$

Substitute $4 - x$ for y in $4x + y = 1$.

$$4x + y = 1$$
$$4x + (4 - x) = 1$$
$$3x + 4 = 1$$
$$3x = -3$$
$$x = -1$$

Substitute -1 for x in $x + y = 4$.

$$x + y = 4$$
$$-1 + y = 4$$
$$y = 5$$

The solution is $(-1, 5)$.

Chapter 11, continued

6. $2x - y = -2$

$-y = -2x - 2$

$y = 2x + 2$

Substitute $2x + 2$ for y in $4x + y = 20$.

$4x + y = 20$

$4x + (2x + 2) = 20$

$6x + 2 = 20$

$6x = 18$

$x = 3$

Substitute 3 for x in $2x - y = -2$.

$2x - y = -2$

$2(3) - y = -2$

$6 - y = -2$

$-y = -8$

$y = 8$

The solution is $(3, 8)$.

7. $x + y = 8$ $3x + 3y = 6$

$y = -x + 8$ $3y = -3x + 6$

$y = -x + 2$

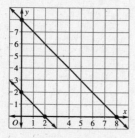

There is no solution because the lines are parallel.

8.

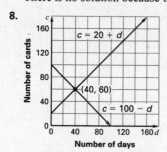

It appears that the point of intersection is $(40, 60)$.

You both have the same number of cards on the 40th day.

Lesson 11.8

Activity (p. 629)

Steps 1–3.

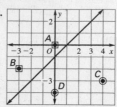

Step 3. $y < x - 1$:

When $(x, y) = (0, 0)$:

$y < x - 1$

$0 \overset{?}{<} 0 - 1$

$0 \not< -1$

When $(x, y) = (-3, -2)$:

$y < x - 1$

$-2 \overset{?}{<} -3 - 1$

$-2 \not< -4$

When $(x, y) = (4, -3)$:

$y < x - 1$

$-3 \overset{?}{<} 4 - 1$

$-3 < 3$

When $(x, y) = (0, -4)$:

$y < x - 1$

$-4 \overset{?}{<} 0 - 1$

$-4 < -1$

So points C and D make the inequality true.

$y > x - 1$:

When $(x, y) = (0, 0)$:

$y > x - 1$

$0 \overset{?}{>} 0 - 1$

$0 > -1$

When $(x, y) = (-3, -2)$:

$y > x - 1$

$-2 \overset{?}{>} -3 - 1$

$-2 > -4$

When $(x, y) = (4, -3)$:

$y > x - 1$

$-3 \overset{?}{>} 4 - 1$

$-3 \not> 3$

When $(x, y) = (0, -4)$:

$y > x - 1$

$-4 \overset{?}{>} 0 - 1$

$-4 \not> -1$

So points A and B make the inequality true.

Step 4. The solutions of $y \leq x - 1$ lie below the line $y = x - 1$ and the solutions of $y \geq x - 1$ lie above the line $y = x - 1$.

11.8 Guided Practice (pp. 629–631)

1. When $(x, y) = (0, 0)$:

$$2x + 3y < 5$$
$$2(0) + 3(0) \overset{?}{<} 5$$
$$0 + 0 \overset{?}{<} 5$$
$$0 < 5$$

$(0, 0)$ is a solution.

2. When $(x, y) = (-4, 2)$:

$$2x + 3y < 5$$
$$2(-4) + 3(2) \overset{?}{<} 5$$
$$-8 + 6 \overset{?}{<} 5$$
$$-2 < 5$$

$(-4, 2)$ is a solution.

3. When $(x, y) = (5, -1)$:

$$2x + 3y < 5$$
$$2(5) + 3(-1) \overset{?}{<} 5$$
$$10 - 3 \overset{?}{<} 5$$
$$7 \not< 5$$

$(5, -1)$ is not a solution.

4. When $(x, y) = (1, 1)$:

$$2x + 3y < 5$$
$$2(1) + 3(1) \overset{?}{<} 5$$
$$2 + 3 \overset{?}{<} 5$$
$$5 \not< 5$$

$(1, 1)$ is not a solution.

5. $y = x + 1$

$y = 1x + 1$

Use $(0, 0)$ as a test point.

$$y < x + 1$$
$$0 \overset{?}{<} 0 + 1$$
$$0 < 1$$

$(0, 0)$ is a solution.

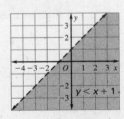

6. $3x + y = 3$

$y = -3x + 3$

Use $(0, 0)$ as a test point.

$$y \geq -3x + 3$$
$$0 \overset{?}{\geq} -3(0) + 3$$
$$0 \not> 3$$

$(0, 0)$ is not a solution.

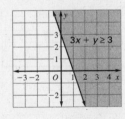

7. $x - 2y = -1$

$$-2y = -x - 1$$
$$y = \frac{1}{2}x + \frac{1}{2}$$

Use $(0, 0)$ as a test point.

$$y \leq \frac{1}{2}x + \frac{1}{2}$$
$$0 \overset{?}{\leq} \frac{1}{2}(0) + \frac{1}{2}$$
$$0 < \frac{1}{2}$$

$(0, 0)$ is a solution.

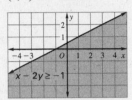

8. $y = -2$

Use $(0, 0)$ as a test point.

$$y \geq -2$$
$$0 \geq -2$$

$(0, 0)$ is a solution.

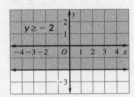

9. $6x + 4y = 36$

$$4y = -6x + 36$$
$$y = -\frac{3}{2}x + 9$$

Use $(0, 0)$ as a test point.

$$y \leq -\frac{3}{2}x + 9$$
$$0 \overset{?}{\leq} -\frac{3}{2}(0) + 9$$
$$0 < 9$$

$(0, 0)$ is a solution.

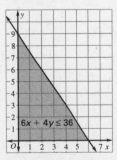

Sample answer:

You could buy 6 tubes of paint and 0 brushes, or 0 tubes of paint and 9 brushes.

Chapter 11, *continued*

11.8 Exercises (pp. 631–634)

Skill Practice

1. When graphing $y < 2x + 1$, the dashed line on the graph divides the coordinate plane into two *half-planes*.

2. All the points in the shaded region of the graph of an inequality are *solutions* of the inequality.

3. When $(x, y) = (1, 2)$:
$$5x + y \leq 17$$
$$5(1) + 2 \overset{?}{\leq} 17$$
$$7 \leq 17$$
$(1, 2)$ is a solution.

4. When $(x, y) = (-11, 2)$:
$$3x + 7y < 20$$
$$3(-11) + 7(2) \overset{?}{<} 20$$
$$-33 + 14 \overset{?}{<} 20$$
$$-19 < 20$$
$(-11, 2)$ is a solution.

5. When $(x, y) = (3, -4)$:
$$9x + 12y > 26$$
$$9(3) + 12(-4) \overset{?}{>} 26$$
$$27 - 48 \overset{?}{>} 26$$
$$-21 \not> 26$$
$(3, -4)$ is not a solution.

6. When $(x, y) = (-6, -7)$:
$$11x + 18y \geq 31$$
$$11(-6) + 18(-7) \overset{?}{\geq} 31$$
$$-66 - 126 \overset{?}{\geq} 31$$
$$-192 \not\geq 31$$
$(-6, -7)$ is not a solution.

7. $y = 14 - 4x$
$$y = -4x + 14$$
Use $(0, 0)$ as a test point.
$$y > 14 - 4x$$
$$0 \overset{?}{>} 14 - 4(0)$$
$$0 \not> 14$$
$(0, 0)$ is not a solution.

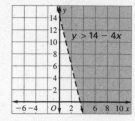

8. $y = x + 5$
Use $(0, 0)$ as a test point.
$$y < x + 5$$
$$0 \overset{?}{<} 0 + 5$$
$$0 < 5$$
$(0, 0)$ is a solution.

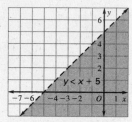

9. $3x - 4 = y$
$$y = 3x - 4$$
Use $(0, 0)$ as a test point.
$$3x - 4 \geq y$$
$$3(0) - 4 \overset{?}{\geq} 0$$
$$-4 \not\geq 0$$
$(0, 0)$ is not a solution.

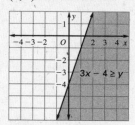

10. $y + 3 = 4x$
$$y = 4x - 3$$
Use $(0, 0)$ as a test point.
$$y + 3 \geq 4x$$
$$0 + 3 \overset{?}{\geq} 4(0)$$
$$3 \geq 0$$
$(0, 0)$ is a solution.

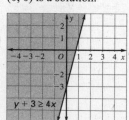

Chapter 11, *continued*

11. $-96 = -3x$

$32 = x$

Use $(0, 0)$ as a test point.

$-96 \le -3x$

$-96 \overset{?}{\le} -3(0)$

$-96 \le 0$

$(0, 0)$ is a solution.

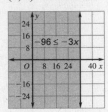

12. $6y = 36$

$y = 6$

Use $(0, 0)$ as a test point.

$6y > 36$

$6(0) \overset{?}{>} 36$

$0 \not> 36$

$(0, 0)$ is not a solution.

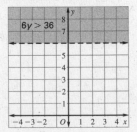

13. $y = 3x - 7$

Use $(0, 0)$ as a test point.

$y \ge 3x - 7$

$0 \overset{?}{\ge} 3(0) - 7$

$0 \ge -7$

$(0, 0)$ is a solution.

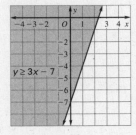

14. $y = 4x - 12$

Use $(0, 0)$ as a test point.

$y \le 4x - 12$

$0 \overset{?}{\le} 4(0) - 12$

$0 \not\le -12$

$(0, 0)$ is not a solution.

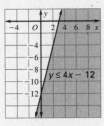

15. $y = 7x + 19$

Use $(0, 0)$ as a test point.

$y < 7x + 19$

$0 \overset{?}{<} 7(0) + 19$

$0 < 19$

$(0, 0)$ is a solution.

16. $4x - 13 = y$

$y = 4x - 13$

Use $(0, 0)$ as a test point.

$4x - 13 > y$

$4(0) - 13 \overset{?}{>} 0$

$-13 \not> 0$

$(0, 0)$ is not a solution.

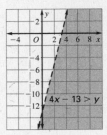

Chapter 11, *continued*

17. $y = 9 - 2x$

$y = -2x + 9$

Use $(0, 0)$ as a test point.

$y > 9 - 2x$

$0 \overset{?}{>} 9 - 2(0)$

$0 \not> 9$

$(0, 0)$ is not a solution.

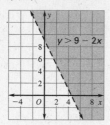

18. $22 = 2x$

$11 = x$

Use $(0, 0)$ as a test point.

$22 < 2x$

$22 \overset{?}{<} 2(0)$

$22 \not< 0$

$(0, 0)$ is not a solution.

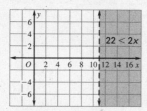

19. $-2y = 74$

$y = -37$

Use $(0, 0)$ as a test point.

$-2y \geq 74$

$-2(0) \overset{?}{\geq} 74$

$0 \not\geq 74$

$(0, 0)$ is not a solution.

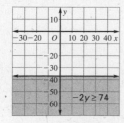

20. $4x - 3y = 12$

$-3y = -4x + 12$

$y = \frac{4}{3}x - 4$

Use $(0, 0)$ as a test point.

$4x - 3y \geq 12$

$4(0) - 3(0) \overset{?}{\geq} 12$

$0 \not\geq 12$

$(0, 0)$ is not a solution.

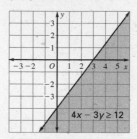

21. $-2x - 4y = 8$

$-4y = 2x + 8$

$y = -\frac{1}{2}x - 2$

Use $(0, 0)$ as a test point.

$-2x - 4y > 8$

$-2(0) - 4(0) \overset{?}{>} 8$

$0 \not> 8$

$(0, 0)$ is not a solution.

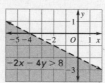

22. $6x + 3y = -12$

$3y = -6x - 12$

$y = -2x - 4$

Use $(0, 0)$ as a test point.

$6x + 3y \leq -12$

$6(0) + 3(0) \overset{?}{\leq} -12$

$0 \not\leq -12$

$(0, 0)$ is not a solution.

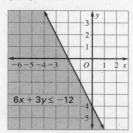

Chapter 11, *continued*

23. The symbol $\leq$ requires the graph have a solid line not a doted line.

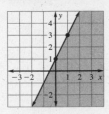

24. D; $y = -2x + 200$

Use $(0, 0)$ as a test point.

$y \geq -2x + 200$

$0 \overset{?}{\geq} -2(0) + 200$

$0 \not\geq 200$

$(0, 0)$ is not a solution.

25. $x + y > 10$

$x + y = 10$

$\quad y = -x + 10$

Use $(0, 0)$ as a test point.

$x + y > 10$

$0 + 0 \overset{?}{>} 10$

$0 \not> 10$

$(0, 0)$ is not a solution.

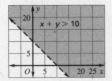

26. $y \leq 15$

$y = 15$

Use $(0, 0)$ as a test point.

$y \leq 15$

$0 \leq 15$

$(0, 0)$ is a solution.

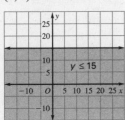

27. $x \geq 20$

$x = 20$

Use $(0, 0)$ as a test point.

$x \geq 20$

$0 \not\geq 20$

$(0, 0)$ is not a solution.

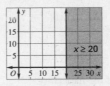

28. $x - y \leq 15$

$x - y = 15$

$\quad -y = -x + 15$

$\quad\quad y = x - 15$

Use $(0, 0)$ as a test point.

$x - y \leq 15$

$0 - 0 \overset{?}{\leq} 15$

$\quad 0 \leq 15$

$(0, 0)$ is a solution.

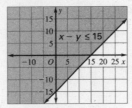

29. $y > 2x$

$y = 2x$

Use $(-1, 0)$ as a test point.

$y > 2x$

$0 \overset{?}{>} 2(-1)$

$0 > -2$

$(-1, 0)$ is a solution.

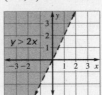

30. $x \leq 3y$

$3y = x$

$\quad y = \frac{1}{3}x$

Use $(-3, 0)$ as a test point.

$\quad x \leq 3y$

$-3 \overset{?}{\leq} 3(0)$

$-3 \leq 0$

$(-3, 0)$ is a solution.

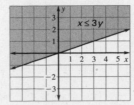

31. $y \leq 5x - a;\ (a, 2a)$

$2a \overset{?}{\leq} 5(a) - a$

$2a \overset{?}{\leq} 4a$

$a \leq 2a$

The point is always a solution of the inequality.

32. $3y > x + a;\ (a, a + 1)$

$3(a + 1) \overset{?}{>} a + a$

$3a + 3 \overset{?}{>} 2a$

$3 > -a$

The point is always a solution of the inequality.

33. $10x > a - 2y;\ (-a, 5a)$

$10(-a) \overset{?}{>} a - 2(5a)$

$-10a \overset{?}{>} a - 10a$

$-10a \not> -9a$

The point is never a solution of the inequality.

34.

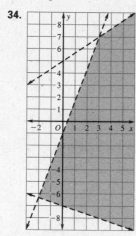

Sample answer: (6, 0) and (3, 0) satisfy all 3 inequalities.

1st: $0 < \left(\frac{2}{3}\right)6 + 5;$ $0 < \left(\frac{2}{3}\right)3 + 5$

     $0 < 9$ $0 < 7$

2nd: $0 > \left(-\frac{1}{3}\right)6 - 7$ $0 > \left(-\frac{1}{3}\right)3 - 7$

     $0 > -9$ $0 > -8$

3rd: $0 < \left(\frac{8}{3}\right)6 - 1$ $0 < \left(\frac{8}{3}\right)3 - 1$

     $0 < 15$ $0 < 7$

Problem Solving

35. $2x + 1.50y = 6$

$1.50y = 6 - 2x$

$y = 4 - \frac{4}{3}x$

$y = -\frac{4}{3}x + 4$

Use (0, 0) as a test point.

$2x + 1.50y \leq 6$

$2(0) + 1.50(0) \overset{?}{\leq} 6$

$0 + 0 \overset{?}{\leq} 6$

$0 \leq 6$

(0, 0) is a solution.

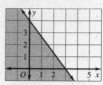

Sample answer: You could use 1 pound of peanuts and 2 pounds of raisins, or 2 pounds of peanuts and 1 pound of raisins.

36. Yes; The points which lie on the line having equation $y = x + 3$ are not included.

37. D; When $(x, y) = (25, 12)$:

$4x + 2y \leq 125$

$4(25) + 2(12) \overset{?}{\leq} 125$

$100 + 24 \overset{?}{\leq} 125$

$124 \leq 125$

38. *Sample answers:* $y > x;\ y \leq x$

39. $5x + y < 2$; The graph of $5x + y \geq 2$ includes points on the line $5x + y = 2$ and all the points above that line. The rest of the points in the plane are below the line $5x + y = 2$, and these points are solutions of $5x + y < 2$.

40. a. $16x + 10y \leq 160$

   b. $16x + 10y = 160$

$10y = -16x + 160$

$y = -\frac{8}{5}x + 16$

Use (0, 0) as a test point.

$16(0) + 10(0) \leq 160$

$0 \leq 160$

(0, 0) is a solution.

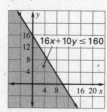

She can pack 7 water bottles.

If $y = 4$, then $16x + 40 \leq 160$

$16x \leq 120$

$x \leq 7.5$

The number of water bottles must be a whole number.

   c. Yes she can take 5 water bottles and 6 meals because the point (5, 6) falls in the shaded area.

41. Lee: $6x + 3y \le 12$ Vivian: $4x + 2y \ge 10$

$$6x + 3y = 12 \qquad\qquad 4x + 2y = 10$$
$$3y = -6x + 12 \qquad\quad 2y = -4x + 10$$
$$y = -2x + 4 \qquad\qquad y = -2x + 5$$

Use $(0, 0)$ as a test point.   Use $(0, 0)$ as a test point.

$$6(0) + 3(0) \stackrel{?}{\le} 12 \qquad 4(0) + 2(0) \stackrel{?}{\ge} 10$$
$$0 \le 12 \qquad\qquad\qquad 0 \not\ge 10$$

$(0, 0)$ is a solution. $(0, 0)$ is not a solution.

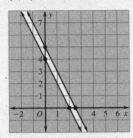

No, it is not possible that Lee and Vivian charge the same price because the graphs do not overlap.

Mixed Review

42.

```
      x
      x   x
      x   x   x
  x   x   x   x   x
  +---+---+---+---+---
  7   8   9   10  11
```

43.

```
  x   x   x   x
  x   x   x   x
  x   x   x   x
  +---+---+---+---
  1   2   3   4
```

44. $1.34 = 1\frac{34}{100} = 1\frac{17}{50}$ **45.** $3.75 = 3\frac{75}{100} = 3\frac{3}{4}$

46. $8.125 = 8\frac{125}{1000} = 8\frac{1}{8}$ **47.** $7.164 = 7\frac{164}{1000} = 7\frac{41}{250}$

48. D; $m = \dfrac{\text{rise}}{\text{run}} = \dfrac{y_2 - y_1}{x_2 - x_1} = \dfrac{8 - (-4)}{7 - (-3)} = \dfrac{12}{10} = \dfrac{6}{5}$

The slope is $\dfrac{6}{5}$.

Quiz 11.5–11.8 (p. 634)

1. x-intercept: y-intercept:

$$y = 2x + 3 \qquad\qquad y = 2x + 3$$
$$0 = 2x + 3 \qquad\qquad y = 2(0) + 3$$
$$-3 = 2x \qquad\qquad\quad y = 3$$
$$-\frac{3}{2} = x$$

The x-intercept is $-\dfrac{3}{2}$ and the y-intercept is 3. The graph

of the equation contains the points $\left(-\dfrac{3}{2}, 0\right)$ and $(0, 3)$.

2. x-intercept: y-intercept:

$$2y + x = 6 \qquad\qquad 2y + x = 6$$
$$2(0) + x = 6 \qquad\quad 2y + 0 = 6$$
$$x = 6 \qquad\qquad\qquad 2y = 6$$
$$\qquad\qquad\qquad\qquad y = 3$$

The x-intercept is 6 and the y-intercept is 3. The graph of the equation contains the points $(6, 0)$ and $(0, 3)$.

3. Because the line is vertical and passes through $(3, 0)$, there is no y-intercept and the x-intercept is 3.

4. $m = \dfrac{y_2 - y_1}{x_2 - x_1} = \dfrac{7 - 4}{5 - 3} = \dfrac{3}{2}$

The slope is $\dfrac{3}{2}$.

5. $m = \dfrac{y_2 - y_1}{x_2 - x_1} = \dfrac{0 - (-3)}{0 - (-1)} = \dfrac{3}{1} = 3$

The slope is 3.

6. $m = \dfrac{y_2 - y_1}{x_2 - x_1} = \dfrac{3 - 3}{4 - (-5)} = \dfrac{0}{9} = 0$

The slope is 0.

7. $y = \dfrac{6}{5}x - 2$

$$y = \frac{6}{5}x + (-2)$$

The slope is $\dfrac{6}{5}$ and the y-intercept is -2.

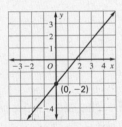

8. $-5x - 5y = -20$

$$-5y = 5x - 20$$
$$y = -x + 4$$

The slope is -1 and the y-intercept is 4.

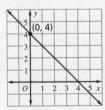

9. $y = -x$

The slope is -1 and the y-intercept is 0.

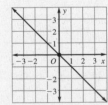

10. $y = x - 3$

Use $(0, 0)$ as a test point.

$y > x - 3$

$0 \overset{?}{>} 0 - 3$

$0 > -3$

$(0, 0)$ is a solution.

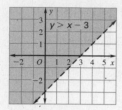

Sample answer: Three solutions of the inequality are $(0, 0)$, $(1, 4)$, and $(-2, 3)$.

11. $x - 3y = -9$

$-3y = -x - 9$

$y = \frac{1}{3}x + 3$

Use $(0, 0)$ as a test point.

$x - 3y \le -9$

$0 - 3(0) \overset{?}{\le} -9$

$0 \not\le -9$

$(0, 0)$ is not a solution.

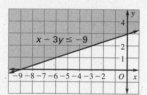

Sample answer: Three solutions of the inequality are $(0, 4)$, $(1, 5)$, and $(2, 6)$.

12. $6x + 7y = -21$

$7y = -6x - 21$

$y = -\frac{6}{7}x - 3$

Use $(0, 0)$ as a test point.

$6x + 7y < -21$

$6(0) + 7(0) < -21$

$0 \not< -21$

$(0, 0)$ is not a solution.

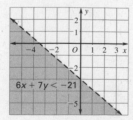

Sample answer: Three solutions of the inequality are $(-6, 0)$, $(-8, 1)$, and $(1, -4)$.

13. *x*-intercept:

$10x + 15y = 180$

$10x + 15(0) = 180$

$10x = 180$

$x = 18$

y-intercept:

$10x + 15y = 180$

$10(0) + 15y = 180$

$15y = 180$

$y = 12$

The *x*-intercept is 18 and represents the number of small vehicles that were washed if no large vehicles were washed. The *y*-intercept is 12 and represents the number of large vehicles that were washed if no small vehicles were washed.

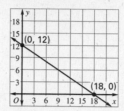

14. $0.5x + y \ge 20$

$0.5x + y = 20$

$y = -0.5x + 20$

Use $(0, 0)$ as a test point.

$0.5(0) + 0 \overset{?}{\ge} 20$

$0 \not\ge 20$

$(0, 0)$ is not a solution.

Lemonade Sales

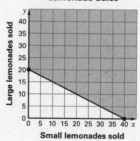

Sample answer: 20 small and 21 large lemonades

35 small and 4 large lemonades

Brain Game (p. 634)

E. $y = 2x + 1$

$m = 2, b = 1$

L. $2x - y = 6$

$-y = -2x + 6$

$y = 2x - 6$

$m = 2, b = -6$

P. $4y = 6x - 20$

$y = \frac{3}{2}x - 5$

$m = \frac{3}{2}, b = -5$

S. $2x + 4y = 12$

$4y = -2x + 12$

$y = -\frac{1}{2}x + 3$

$m = -\frac{1}{2}, \ b = 3$

U. $y = \frac{1}{3}x + 2$

$m = \frac{1}{3}, b = 2$

N. $2y = 6x - 14$

$y = 3x - 7$

$m = 3, b = -7$

A. $2x + 2y = 20$

$2y = -2x + 20$

$y = -x + 10$

$m = -1, b = 10$

O. $y = 5x + 9$

$m = 5, b = 9$

T. $4x + y = 20$

$y = -4x + 20$

$m = -4, b = 20$

I. $6x - y = 18$

$-y = -6x + 18$

$y = 6x - 18$

$m = 6, b = -18$

R. $5x - 5y = 40$

$-5y = -5x + 40$

$y = x - 8$

$m = 1, b = -8$

M. $x + 3y = 18$

$3y = -x + 18$

$y = -\frac{1}{3}x + 6$

$m = -\frac{1}{3}, b = 6$

PLANETARIUM

Mixed Review of Problem Solving (p. 635)

1. x represents the number of hours of each individual lesson.

y represents the number of hours of each partner lesson.

$12x + 8y = 24$

$8y = -12x + 24$

$y = -\frac{3}{2}x + 3$

x-intercept: $0 = -\frac{3}{2}x + 3$

$-3 = -\frac{3}{2}x$

$2 = x$

y-intercept: $y = 3$

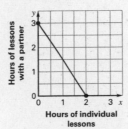

The intercepts mean that she can have 2 hour individual lessons and 0 hour partner lessons, or she can have 0 hour individual lessons and 3 hour partner lessons.

2. *Sample answer:* Peanuts cost $4/lb and raisins cost $3/lb. How many of each can you buy for $9?

3. a. $2.5x + 2y \le 10$

b. $2.5x + 2y = 10$

$2y = -2.5x + 10$

$y = -\frac{5}{4}x + 5$

Use $(0, 0)$ as a test point.

$2.5(0) + 2(0) \overset{?}{\le} 10$

$0 \le 10$

$(0, 0)$ is a solution.

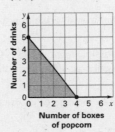

c. The maximum number of boxes of popcorn he can buy is 2.

d. No, he cannot. The point $(2, 3)$ is not in the shaded half-plane.

4. $(5, -1), (x, 3)$

For the line to be undefined, the x-value must be 0. $5 - x = 0$ or $x = 5$.

Chapter 11, *continued*

5. Yes, you can buy 14 pounds of fruit.

$(1, 13)$: $3.75(1) + 2(13) \le 30$

$3.75 + 26 \le 30$

$29.75 \le 30$

$(0, 14)$: $3.75(0) + 2(14) \le 30$

$28 \le 30$

6. All four lines in the graph are dashed, so the inequality symbols are $<$ or $>$, not $\le$ or $\ge$. The graph is shaded below $y = -\frac{1}{3}x + 5$ and $y = -\frac{2}{3}x + 6$, so 2 inequalities are $y < -\frac{1}{3}x + 5$ and $y < -\frac{2}{3}x + 6$. The graph is shaded above $y = \frac{1}{3}x - 5$ and $y = \frac{2}{3}x - 6$, so the other 2 inequalities are $y > \frac{1}{3}x - 5$ and $y > \frac{2}{3}x - 6$.

7. a. $y = 1.1x + 1.3(10 - x)$

b. $y = 1.1x + 13 - 1.3x$

$y = -0.2x + 13$

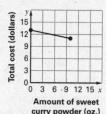

Amount of sweet curry powder (oz.)

The scale is 0 through 10 because the total number of ounces of curry powder is 10.

c. The slope -0.2 indicates that the total cost goes down by $.20 each time the amount of sweet curry powder increases by 1 ounce. The y-intercept is the cost for buying 0 ounces of sweet curry powder (and 10 ounces of hot curry powder). The point at $x = 10$ represents the cost of 10 ounces of sweet curry powder (and 0 ounces of hot curry powder).

Chapter 11 Review (pp. 636–640)

1. A relation that has exactly one output for each input is a *function*.

2. The graph of a linear inequality in two variables is a *half-plane*.

3. For a function, the set of all possible *input* values is the domain, and the set of all possible *output* values is the range.

4. The slope of a nonvertical line is the ratio of its *rise* to its *run*.

5. To find the x-intercept of a graph of an equation, set $y = 0$ and solve for x. To find the y-intercept of the graph of an equation, set $x = 0$ and solve for y.

6. *Sample answer:* Let y be the amount of money made from selling x units of a particular product. The slope tells you how the amount of money increases as the number of units sold increases.

7. Step 1: Change the inequality symbol to "$=$" and graph the equation. Use a dashed line for $<$ or $>$ and use a solid line for $\le$ or $\ge$.

Step 2: Test a point in one of the half-planes to check whether it is a solution of the inequality.

Step 3: If the test point is a solution, shade its half-plane. If the test point is not a solution, shade the other half-plane.

8. The relation is not a function because the input 0 and 2 have 2 outputs.

9. The relation is a function

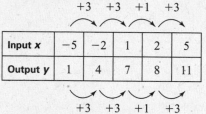

Input x	-5	-2	1	2	5
Output y	1	4	7	8	11

$a = \dfrac{\text{change in output}}{\text{change in input}}$

$a = \dfrac{3}{3} = 1$, so $y = 1x + b$.

Let $(x, y) = (-5, 1)$.

$1 = 1(-5) + b$

$1 = -5 + b$

$6 = b$

A function rule that relates x and y is $y = x + 6$.

10. The relation is a function. Each input has exactly one output.

| | $+6$ | $+6$ | $+6$ | |

Input x	-8	-2	4	10
Output y	4	1	-2	-5

$-3 \quad -3 \quad -3$

$a = \dfrac{\text{change of } y}{\text{change of } x} = \dfrac{-3}{6} = -\dfrac{1}{2}$, so $y = -\dfrac{1}{2}x + b$

Let $(x, y) = (-8, 4)$.

$4 = -\dfrac{1}{2}(-8) + b$

$4 = 4 + b$

$0 = b$

A function rule that relates x and y is $y = -\dfrac{1}{2}x$.

11. The relation is a function. Each input has exactly one output.

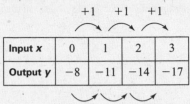

Input x	0	1	2	3
Output y	-8	-11	-14	-17

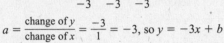

$a = \dfrac{\text{change of } y}{\text{change of } x} = \dfrac{-3}{1} = -3$, so $y = -3x + b$

Let $(x, y) = (0, -8)$

$-8 = -3(0) + b$

$-8 = 0 + b$

$-8 = b$

A function rule that relates x and y is $y = -3x - 8$.

12.

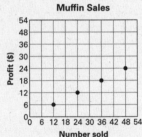

The profit increases as the number of muffins sold increases. The quantities have a positive relationship.

13.

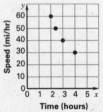

As the speed increases, time decreases. The relationship is negative.

14.

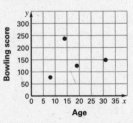

There is no relationship.

15. $x + 4y = 16$

$4y = -x + 16$

$y = -\dfrac{1}{4}x + 4$

Sample answer:

x-value	Substitute for x.	y-value
-4	$y = -\dfrac{1}{4}(-4) + 4$	5
0	$y = -\dfrac{1}{4}(0) + 4$	4
4	$y = -\dfrac{1}{4}(4) + 4$	3

Three solutions are $(-4, 5)$, $(0, 4)$, and $(4, 3)$.

16. $t = 81 - 0.005a$

800 ft/h $\times$ 4 h = 3200 ft

$t = 81 - 0.005(3200)$

$t = 81 - 16$

$t = 65$

The temperature will be 65°F.

17.

x	-2	-1	0
y	0	1	2

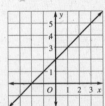

18.

x	-2	-1	0
y	2	$\frac{1}{2}$	-1

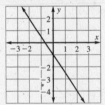

19.

x	-2	0	2
y	8	8	8

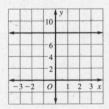

20. $-6x + 2y = 9$

x-intercept:	*y*-intercept:
$-6x + 2(0) = 9$	$-6(0) + 2y = 9$
$-6x + 0 = 9$	$2y = 9$
$-6x = 9$	$y = 4.5$
$x = -1.5$	

The *x*-intercept is -1.5. The *y*-intercept is 4.5.

21. *y*-intercept:

$y = 57.1x + 488$

$y = 57.1(0) + 488$

$y = 488$

The *y*-intercept is 488.

It represents the billions of dollars of taxes collected by the IRS in 1980.

22. *Sample answer:* $(0, 0), (1, -1)$

$m = \dfrac{y_2 - y_1}{x_2 - x_1} = \dfrac{-1 - 0}{1 - 0} = \dfrac{-1}{1} = -1$

The slope is -1.

23. *Sample answer:* $(0, 3), (1, 3)$

$m = \dfrac{y_2 - y_1}{x_2 - x_1} = \dfrac{3 - 3}{1 - 0} = \dfrac{0}{1} = 0$

The slope is 0.

24. $y = 6x - 1$

The slope is 6. The *y*-intercept is -1.

25. $y = -\dfrac{2}{3}x + 4$

The slope is $-\dfrac{2}{3}$. The *y*-intercept is 4.

26. $y = 8$

The slope is 0. The *y*-intercept is 8.

27. $y - 4x = 10$

$y = 4x + 10$

The slope is 4 and the *y*-intercept is 10.

28. $2y + 6 = x$

$2y = x - 6$

$y = \dfrac{1}{2}x - 3$

The slope is $\dfrac{1}{2}$ and the *y*-intercept is -3.

29. $-3x - 7y = 21$

$-7y = 3x + 21$

$y = -\dfrac{3}{7}x - 3$

The slope is $-\dfrac{3}{7}$ and the *y*-intercept is -3.

30. $y = -\dfrac{3}{5}x - 3$

Use $(0, 0)$ as a test point.

$y < -\dfrac{3}{5}x - 3$

$0 \overset{?}{<} -\dfrac{3}{5}(0) - 3$

$0 \not< -3$

$(0, 0)$ is not a solution.

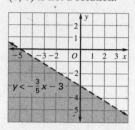

31. $3x - 7y = 21$

$-7y = -3x + 21$

$y = \dfrac{3}{7}x - 3$

Use $(0, 0)$ as a test point.

$3x - 7y \geq 21$

$3(0) - 7(0) \overset{?}{\geq} 21$

$0 \not> 21$

$(0, 0)$ is not a solution.

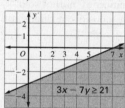

32. $4x + 8y = 32$

$8y = -4x + 32$

$y = -\dfrac{1}{2}x + 4$

Use $(0, 0)$ as a test point.

$4x + 8y \leq 32$

$4(0) + 8(0) \overset{?}{\leq} 32$

$0 \leq 32$

$(0, 0)$ is a solution.

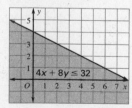

Chapter 11, *continued*

Chapter 11 Test (p. 641)

1.

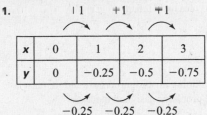

x	0	1	2	3
y	0	−0.25	−0.5	−0.75

$$y = ax + b$$

$$a = \frac{\text{change in output}}{\text{change in input}} = \frac{-0.25}{1} = -0.25$$

$$y = -0.25x + b$$

Let $(x, y) = (0, 0)$.

$$y = -0.25x + b$$

$$0 = -0.25(0) + b$$

$$0 = b$$

$$y = -0.25x + 0$$

$$y = -0.25x$$

A function rule that relates x and y is $y = -0.25x$.

2.

x	−2	−1	0	1
y	−9	−3	3	9

+6 +6 +6

$$y = ax + b$$

$$a = \frac{\text{change in output}}{\text{change in input}} = \frac{6}{1} = 6$$

$$y = 6x + b$$

Let $(x, y) = (0, 3)$.

$$y = 6x + b$$

$$3 = 6(0) + b$$

$$3 = b$$

$$y = 6x + 3$$

A function rule that relates x and y is $y = 6x + 3$.

3.
$$12x + 3y = 21$$
$$12(-1) + 3(11) \overset{?}{=} 21$$
$$-12 + 33 \overset{?}{=} 21$$
$$21 = 21$$

The ordered pair $(-1, 11)$ is a solution of $12x + 3y = 21$.

4.
$$12x + 3y = 21$$
$$12(-4) + 3(-9) \overset{?}{=} 21$$
$$-48 - 27 \overset{?}{=} 21$$
$$-75 \neq 21$$

The ordered pair $(-4, -9)$ is not a solution of $12x + 3y = 21$.

5.
$$12x + 3y = 21$$
$$12(2) + 3(-15) \overset{?}{=} 21$$
$$24 - 45 \overset{?}{=} 21$$
$$-21 \neq 21$$

The ordered pair $(2, -15)$ is not a solution of $12x + 3y = 21$.

6.
$$12x + 3y = 21$$
$$12(6) + 3(-17) \overset{?}{=} 21$$
$$72 - 51 \overset{?}{=} 21$$
$$21 = 21$$

The ordered pair $(6, -17)$ is a solution of $12x + 3y = 21$.

7. $y = 6x - 3$

$$y = 6x + (-3)$$

The line has a slope of 6 and a y-intercept of -3.

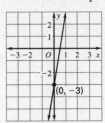

8. $-5x + y = 1$

$$y = 5x + 1$$

The line has a slope of 5 and a y-intercept of 1.

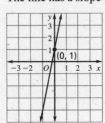

9. $y = -\frac{1}{4}x$

$$y = -\frac{1}{4}x + 0$$

The line has a slope of $-\frac{1}{4}$ and a y-intercept of 0.

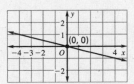

Chapter 11, *continued*

10. $3x + 6y = 12$

$$6y = -3x + 12$$

$$y = -\frac{1}{2}x + 2$$

Use $(0, 0)$ as a test point.

$$3x + 6y \geq 12$$

$$3(0) + 6(0) \overset{?}{\geq} 12$$

$$0 \not\geq 12$$

$(0, 0)$ is not a solution.

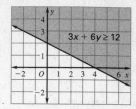

11. $7x - y = 49$

$$-y = -7x + 49$$

$$y = 7x - 49$$

Use $(0, 0)$ as a test point.

$$7x - y \leq 49$$

$$7(0) - 0 \overset{?}{\leq} 49$$

$$0 \leq 49$$

$(0, 0)$ is a solution.

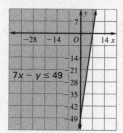

12. $8x - 15y = 30$

$$-15y = -8x + 30$$

$$y = \frac{8}{15}x - 2$$

Use $(0, 0)$ as a test point.

$$8x - 15y > 30$$

$$8(0) - 15(0) \overset{?}{>} 30$$

$$0 \not> 30$$

$(0, 0)$ is not a solution.

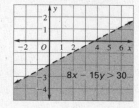

13. The run of the seesaw is 12 feet.

14. The rise of the seesaw is 5 feet.

15. $m = \dfrac{\text{rise}}{\text{run}} = \dfrac{5}{12}$

The slope of the seesaw is $\dfrac{5}{12}$.

16. The time spent doing an assignment should increase as the number of problems assigned increases.

There is a positive relationship.

17. $y = 0.50x + 10$

$$16 \overset{?}{=} 0.50(8) + 10$$

$$16 \overset{?}{=} 4 + 10$$

$$16 \neq 14$$

No, your friend is wrong. You would make $14 if you filled 8 bags.

18.

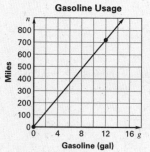

$n = 60g$

$n = 60(12)$

$n = 720$ miles

You will travel 720 miles on 12 gallons of gasoline.

19. $4x + 8y = 25$

$$8y = -4x + 25$$

$$y = -\frac{1}{2}x + \frac{25}{8}$$

Use $(0, 0)$ as a test point.

$$4(0) + 8(0) \leq 25$$

$$0 \leq 25$$

$(0, 0)$ is a solution.

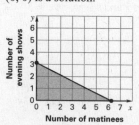

The greatest number of evening shows Ken can see is 1 if he sees 3 matinees.

Standardized Test Preparation (p. 643)

1. *Sample answer:* The slope is positive, so $(x, 8)$ has to be up and to the right or down and to the left of $(-3, 5)$, but $(-9, 8)$ is up and to the left.

2. *Sample answer:* If y is negative, then 7(3) plus a positive number will be greater than 5.

Standardized Test Practice (pp. 644–645)

1. D; There is no relationship.

2. C; $m = \dfrac{\text{rise}}{\text{run}} = \dfrac{1}{1} = 1$

3. B; $(1, 2), (2, y)$; $m = 0$

$$m = \frac{y_2 - y_1}{x_2 - x_1}$$

$$0 = \frac{y - 2}{2 - 1}$$

$$0 = y - 2$$

$$2 = y$$

4. B; $a^2 + b^2 = c^2$

$$24 \text{ in.} = 2 \text{ ft}$$

$$2^2 + b^2 = 4^2$$

$$4 + b^2 = 16$$

$$b^2 = 12$$

$$b \approx 3.5$$

Slope: $\dfrac{2}{3.5} \approx 0.6$

The slope of the board is about 0.6.

5. C; This equation is not linear because the x-value is cubed.

6. B; Slope $= \dfrac{\text{rise}}{\text{run}} = \dfrac{-1}{4} = -\dfrac{1}{4}$

y-intercept $= 3.5$

$$y = -\frac{1}{4}x + 3.5$$

7. D; $9x - 3y = 12$

$$-3y = -9x + 12$$

$$y = 3x - 4$$

8. B; The relation is not a function because the input 2 has 2 outputs.

9. C; $C = 10h + 15$

$$50 = 10h + 15$$

$$35 = 10h$$

$$3.5 = h$$

The greatest total number of hours is 4.

10. When $x = 7$:

$$y = x - 7$$

$$y = 7 - 7$$

$$y = 0$$

11. $(-4, 29)$; $m = 0$

$$y = mx + b$$

$$29 = 0(-4) + b$$

$$29 = b$$

The y-intercept is 29.

12.

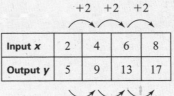

Input x	2	4	6	8
Output y	5	9	13	17

$$m = \frac{\text{change of } y}{\text{change of } x} = \frac{4}{2} = 2$$

The slope is 2.

13. $6x + 5y = 120$

$$5y = -6x + 120$$

$$y = -\frac{6}{5}x + 24$$

x-intercept:

$$y = -\frac{6}{5}x + 24$$

$$0 = -\frac{6}{5}x + 24$$

$$-24 = -\frac{6}{5}x$$

$$20 = x$$

y-intercept:

$$y = -\frac{6}{5}x + 24$$

$$y = -\frac{6}{5}(0) + 24$$

$$y = 24$$

The intercepts indicate that two ways to raise \$120 are to sell 20 hats and 0 T-shirts or to sell 0 hats and 24 T-shirts.

14. $x + y = 5$

$$y = -x + 5$$

Use $(0, 0)$ as a test point.

$$0 + 0 \overset{?}{\le} 5$$

$$0 \le 5$$

$(0, 0)$ is a solution.

$$x \ge 0$$

$$y \ge 0$$

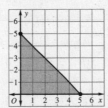

Sample answer: The region is a triangle with base 5 and height 5.

$$A = \frac{1}{2}bh$$

$$A = \frac{1}{2}(5)(5)$$

$$A = 12.5$$

The area is 12.5 units^2.

15. $y = 6x + 50$

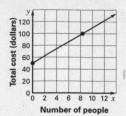

Sample answer: $6x + 50 = 100$

$$6x = 50$$

$$x = 8\frac{1}{3}$$

Since the number must be a whole number, you can invite no more than 8 people.

16. a.

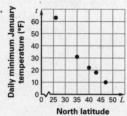

b. There is a negative relationship.

c. *Sample answer:* I drew a line to approximate the data values. Then I started at 30°N latitude and went up vertically to find the corresponding temperature value. The temperature will be about 49°F.

17. a.

Number of toppings	1	2	3	4	5	6
Cost	$7.00	$7.75	$8.50	$9.25	$10.00	$10.75

b.

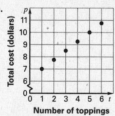

c. The 24 inch pizza would have the greatest slope because the cost per topping is the slope of each graph, and the 24 inch pizza has the greatest cost per topping.

Chapter 12

Chapter Get-Ready Games (p. 646)

1. A, E, II, $\frac{23}{89} = 0.258 \approx 26\%$

2. 152 years old; A = 1, E = 5, H = 2

Stop and Think (p. 647)

1. *Sample answer:* The number of sections in the graph would change.

2. Yes; *Sample answer:* The area of Isabela is about 1775 square miles. The total area of the next four largest islands is about $380 + 250 + 215 + 205 = 1275$ square miles, and $1775 > 1275$.

Review Prerequisite Skills (p. 648)

1. When you flip a coin, heads and tails are the two possible *outcomes*.

2. Find the sum of the values of a set of data and then divide by the number of data values to find the *mean* of the data.

3. The *probability of an event* is a measure of how likely it is that the event will occur.

4. 12, 13, 19, 21, 23, 24, 25, 25, 27

   Mean $= \frac{189}{9} = 21$

   Median $= 23$

5. 0.05, 0.2, 0.35, 0.5, 1.32, 1.33

   Mean $= \frac{3.75}{6} = 0.625$

   Median $= \frac{0.35 + 0.5}{2} = 0.425$

6. $P(>4) = \frac{2}{6} = \frac{1}{3}$

   The probability of rolling a number greater than 4 is $\frac{1}{3}$, $0.\overline{3}$, or $33\frac{1}{3}\%$.

7. $P(A) = \frac{3}{8}$

   The probability of drawing an A is $\frac{3}{8}$, 0.375, or 37.5%.

Lesson 12.1

12.1 Guided Practice (pp. 649–650)

1. | 1 | 0 2 5 5 9
    | 2 | 0 4 4 5 7 9 9
    | 3 | 0 5 6 9
    | 4 | 0 3 7
    | 5 | 0 1

    Key: 1|0 = 10

2.
Kenyon's Calls		Jason's Calls
8 8 5	0	5 5 6 7
7 6 6 4 2	1	1 1 2 3 4 6 9
9 8 8 3 1	2	4 4 8
4 1	3	1

    Key: 5|0|5 represents 5 and 5

    In general, Kenyon made longer calls because Kenyon made more calls in the twenties and thirties.

12.1 Exercises (pp. 651–653)

Skill Practice

1. The key for a stem-and-leaf plot says 7|4 = 74. In the plot, 7 is the *stem* and 4 is the *leaf*.

2. *Sample answer:* It is important to include a key in a stem-and-leaf plot because the key tells you how to interpret the numbers in the stem-and-leaf plot.

3. The number 80 would appear in a stem-and-leaf plot as 8|0, where 8 is the stem, and 0 is the leaf.

4. The number 117 would appear in a stem-and-leaf plot as 11|7, where 11 is the stem, and 7 is the leaf.

5. The number 12.9 would appear in a stem-and-leaf plot as 12|9, where 12 is the stem, and 9 is the leaf.

6. The number 4.6 would appear in a stem-and-leaf plot as 4|6, where 4 is the stem, and 6 is the leaf.

7. | 4 | 0 5 8
    | 5 | 0 2
    | 6 | 1 3 5 6 7
    | 7 | 4
    | 8 | 2 4

    Key: 4|0 = 40

    The 60–69 interval has the most data values.

8. | 0 | 4 6 8 8 9
    | 1 | 2 4 5
    | 2 | 0 6 9
    | 3 | 2 3 5 7

    Key: 0|4 = 4

    The 0–9 interval has the most data values.

9. | 8 | 9
    | 9 | 2 4 5
    | 10 | 3 5 8 9
    | 11 | 2 5

    Key: 8|9 = 89

    The 100–109 interval has the most data values.

10. | 43 | 9
     | 44 |
     | 45 | 1
     | 46 | 1 1 7 8
     | 47 | 5
     | 48 | 5
     | 49 | 2 4
     | 50 | 1
     | 51 | 0

    Key: 43|9 = 439

    The 460–469 interval has the most data values.

Chapter 12, *continued*

11.

18	1 3 4 6 7
19	
20	2
21	9
22	5 6 8

Key: $18 \mid 1 = 18.1$

The 18.0–18.9 interval has the most data values.

12.

3	2
4	0 6 7 9
5	1 2 3 3 5 7
6	7 9

Key: $3 \mid 2 = 3.2$

The 5.0–5.9 interval has the most data values.

13. The bottom row on the stem-and-leaf plot should be two rows with stems 10 and 11. The key is also incorrect, it should be $11 \mid 5 = 115$.

8	3
9	1 5
10	8
11	1 5

Key: $11 \mid 5 = 115$

14. D; Range $= 138 - 101 = 37$

15. B; The interval $110 - 119$ has the most data values.

16.

Set A		Set B
8 5	0	8 9
9 8 6	1	2 5 6
2 0	2	5
2	3	1
	4	2

Key: $5 \mid 0 \mid 8$ represents 5 and 8

17.

Set C		Set D
	6	5
7 0	7	
	8	7 8
8 2	9	3 5
2	10	2
8 1	11	5

Key: $2 \mid 9 \mid 3$ represents 92 and 93

18.

Set A		Set B
8 7 5 4	2	1 2 2 9
2 2 2	3	1 6
	4	3
8	5	5

Key: $4 \mid 2 \mid 1$ represents 24 and 21

19.

Set C		Set D
7	4	
	5	5
8 3	6	8
7	7	8
8 0	8	
8	9	1 3 5
	10	0

Key: $3 \mid 6 \mid 8$ represents 6.3 and 6.8

20. Mean

$$= \frac{(50+50+51+56+65+69+69+71+71+72+74+74+74+78)}{14}$$

$$= \frac{924}{14}$$

$$= 66$$

The mean is 66.

Median: 50, 50, 51, 56, 65, 69, **69**, **71**, 71, 72, 74, 74, 74, 78

$$\text{Median} = \frac{69+71}{2} = \frac{140}{2} = 70$$

The median is 70.

Mode: The number that occurs most often is 74.

21. Mean

$$= \frac{(0.1+0.1+1.4+1.5+1.9+2.0+2.0+2.5+2.8+2.8+3.0+3.9)}{12}$$

$$= \frac{24}{12}$$

$$= 2.0$$

The mean is 2.0.

Median: 0.1, 0.1, 1.4, 1.5, 1.9, **2.0**, **2.0**, 2.5, 2.8, 2.8, 3.0, 3.9

$$\text{Median} = \frac{2.0+2.0}{2} = \frac{4.0}{2} = 2.0$$

The median is 2.0.

Mode: The numbers that occur most often are 0.1, 2.0, and 2.8.

22. *Sample answer:*

3	0 0 1
4	9
5	1 4
6	5
7	
8	1 2

Key: $4 \mid 9 = 49$

Range $= 82 - 30 = 52$

Mode: The number that occurs most often is 30.

23. *Sample answer:*

$$
\begin{array}{c|cccc}
0 & 2 & 3 & 3 & 3 \\
1 & 5 & 6 & 6 & 6 & 6
\end{array}
$$

Key: $1\,|\,5 = 15$

$$\text{Mean} = \frac{2 + 3 + 3 + 3 + 15 + 16 + 16 + 16 + 16}{9}$$

$$= \frac{90}{9}$$

$$= 10$$

The mean is 10.

Median: 2, 3, 3, 3, **15,** 16, 16, 16, 16

The median is 15.

Problem Solving

24 a. The highest data value is 40 and the lowest data value is 10.

b.
$$
\begin{array}{c|cccccc}
1 & 0 & 2 & 5 & 7 & 8 \\
2 & 0 & 2 & 5 & 5 & 8 & 8 \\
3 & 0 & 2 & 5 \\
4 & 0
\end{array}
$$

Key: $4\,|\,0 = 40$

c. Most of the times fall in the 20–29 minute interval.

25. The shortest waiting time is 5 minutes, while the longest is 45 minutes. The 30–39 minute interval has the fewest number of waiting times.

26. C; Median: 13, 17, 19, 20, 21, 24, **25, 37,** 39, 40, 41, 42, 42, 42

$$\text{Median} = \frac{25 + 37}{2} = \frac{62}{2} = 31$$

The median is 31.

27.
$$
\begin{array}{c|cc}
4 & 3 & 7 \\
5 & 5 & 9 \\
6 & 2 & 2 \\
7 & 2 & 8 \\
8 & 4 & 4 \\
9 & 6
\end{array}
$$

Key: $8\,|\,4 = 84$

Median: 43, 47, 55, 59, 62, **62,** 72, 78, 84, 84, 96

The median is $62.

Range = 96 − 43 = 53

The range is $53.

28. *Sample answer:* The stem-and-leaf plot is more useful for finding both the median and the range. With an ordered stem-and-leaf plot, you can quickly find the median and the highest and lowest data values to calculate the range.

29. You cannot make a stem-and-leaf plot from a frequency table because a frequency table shows a tally mark if a number occurred in the interval, not the number itself.

30.

Wins				Losses				
			0	6	7	7		
		8	1	0	2	4	5	6
7 4 4 3	0	2	1					
			3					
		1	4					

Key: $8\,|\,1\,|\,0$ represents 18 and 10

Sample answer: When the Browns scored less than 20 points, they usually lost. When they scored 20 or more points, they usually won.

31. a.
$$
\begin{array}{c|cc}
56 & 8 & 9 \\
57 & 6 \\
58 & 0 \\
59 & \\
60 & 1 \\
61 & 6 \\
62 & 7 \\
63 & \\
64 & \\
65 & 7 \\
66 & 8 \\
67 & \\
68 & \\
69 & 1 & 9 \\
70 & 5
\end{array}
$$

Key: $56\,|\,8 = 56.8$

The range of temperatures is 70.5 − 56.8, or 13.7°F.

b. $56.8°F = \frac{5}{9}(56.8 - 32) \approx 13.8°C$

$56.9°F = \frac{5}{9}(56.9 - 32) \approx 13.8°C$

$57.6°F = \frac{5}{9}(57.6 - 32) \approx 14.2°C$

$58.0°F = \frac{5}{9}(58.0 - 32) \approx 14.4°C$

$60.1°F = \frac{5}{9}(60.1 - 32) \approx 15.6°C$

$61.6°F = \frac{5}{9}(61.6 - 32) \approx 16.4°C$

$62.7°F = \frac{5}{9}(62.7 - 32) \approx 17.1°C$

$65.7°F = \frac{5}{9}(65.7 - 32) \approx 18.7°C$

$66.8°F = \frac{5}{9}(66.8 - 32) \approx 19.3°C$

$69.1°F = \frac{5}{9}(69.1 - 32) \approx 20.6°C$

$69.9°F = \frac{5}{9}(69.9 - 32) \approx 21.1°C$

$70.5°F = \frac{5}{9}(70.5 - 32) \approx 21.4°C$

Chapter 12, continued

c.
```
13 | 8  8
14 | 2  4
15 | 6
16 | 4
17 | 1
18 | 7
19 | 3
20 | 6
21 | 1  4
```
Key: 13 | 8 = 13.8

Sample answer: The temperatures in degrees Celsius are lower than the temperatures in degrees Fahrenheit, and temperatures in degrees Celsius are distributed over a smaller range. This is because as temperatures change by 1 degree Celsius, they change by 1.8 degrees Fahrenheit.

32. Convert the times to seconds to make a stem-and-leaf plot.

2 min 30 sec = $(2 \times 60 + 30)$ sec = 150 sec

2 min 29 sec = $(2 \times 60 + 29)$ sec = 149 sec

2 min 14 sec = $(2 \times 60 + 14)$ sec = 134 sec

2 min 19 sec = $(2 \times 60 + 19)$ sec = 139 sec

1 min 49 sec = $(1 \times 60 + 49)$ sec = 109 sec

2 min 30 sec = $(2 \times 60 + 30)$ sec = 150 sec

2 min 57 sec = $(2 \times 60 + 57)$ sec = 177 sec

2 min 30 sec = $(2 \times 60 + 30)$ sec = 150 sec

2 min 1 sec = $(2 \times 60 + 1)$ sec = 121 sec

2 min 21 sec = $(2 \times 60 + 21)$ sec = 141 sec

1 min 53 sec = $(1 \times 60 + 53)$ sec = 113 sec

```
10 | 9
11 | 3
12 | 1
13 | 4  9
14 | 1  9
15 | 0  0  0
16 |
17 | 7
```
Key: 14 | 1 = 141 seconds

The data ranges from 109 seconds to 177 seconds, so the stems represent the digits in the hundreds' and tens' places, and the leaves are the ones' digits.

Because 15 minutes is equal to $15 \times 60 = 900$ seconds, the sum of the times of the segments used may not be more than 900. If you fill the time using the shortest segments, you can fit at most 6 segments on the video because $109 + 113 + 121 + 134 + 139 + 141 = 757$ seconds, and you will have $900 - 757 = 143$ seconds left over. If you fill the time using the longest segments, you can fit at most 5 segments on the video because $149 + 150 + 150 + 150 + 177 = 776$ seconds, and you will have $900 - 776 = 124$ seconds left over which is enough time for 1 more segment, either the 109, 113, or 121 second segment.

33. 78, 78, 83, 84, 85, 89, 93, 95, 95, 100

Mean = $\frac{880}{10}$ = 88

Median = $\frac{85 + 89}{2} = \frac{174}{2} = 87$

Modes: 78 and 95

Range = $100 - 78 = 22$

34. $-22, -10, -7, -5, -2, 6, 6, 12, 14, 14, 16, 20$

Mean = $\frac{42}{12}$ = 3.5

Median = 6

Modes: 6 and 14

Range = $20 - (-20) = 42$

35. $-17 + (-5) = -22$ **36.** $-28 + 19 = -9$

37. $59 + (-34) = 25$

38. $18 - (-11) = 18 + 11 = 29$

39. $-48 - 7 = -48 + (-7) = -55$

40. $-74 - (-52) = -74 + 52 = -22$

41. A; $7x + 4y = 24$

$$4y = -7x + 24$$

$$y = -\frac{7}{4}x + 6$$

The slope of the graph is $-\frac{7}{4}$.

Lesson 12.2

12.2 Guided Practice (p. 655)

1. Ming: 15, 21, 23, 24, 24, 26, 27, 30, 34, 35

Median = $\frac{24 + 26}{2}$ = 25

Lower quartile = 23

Upper quartile = 30

Lower extreme = 15

Upper extreme = 35

Chantelle: 21, 25, 26, 29, 33, 34, 35, 36, 36, 41

Median = $\frac{33 + 34}{2}$ = 33.5

Lower quartile = 26

Upper quartile = 36

Lower extreme = 21

Upper extreme = 41

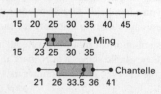

Chapter 12, *continued*

2. Chantelle usually works out longer because $\frac{3}{4}$ of her times are higher than about $\frac{1}{2}$ of Ming's times.

3. Both girls work out about half of the time for 25–35 minutes.

12.2 Exercises (pp. 656–658)

Skill Practice

1. The median of the lower half of a data set is the *lower quartile*.

2. The upper and lower *extremes* of a data set are the greatest and least data values.

3. 28, 33, 41, 44, 48, 52, 53, 54, 56, 59, 62, 65, 67, 70, 72

Median = 54

Lower quartile = 44

Upper quartile = 65

Lower extreme = 28

Upper extreme = 72

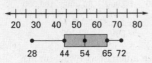

4. 0, 9, 111, 126, 192, 254, 284, 299, 327, 419

Median $= \frac{192 + 254}{2} = \frac{446}{2} = 223$

Lower quartile = 111

Upper quartile = 299

Lower extreme = 0

Upper extreme = 419

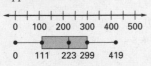

5. 26, 144, 357, 389, 404, 421, 423, 515, 593, 878

Median $= \frac{404 + 421}{2} = \frac{825}{2} = 412.5$

Lower quartile = 357

Upper quartile = 515

Lower extreme = 26

Upper extreme = 878

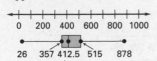

6. 12, 84, 92, 106, 120, 256, 297, 396, 1024

Median = 120

Lower quartile $= \frac{84 + 92}{2} = \frac{176}{2} = 88$

Upper quartile $= \frac{297 + 396}{2} = \frac{693}{2} = 346.5$

Lower extreme = 12

Upper extreme = 1024

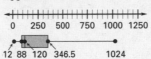

7. The greatest data value is the upper extreme, so 35 is the upper extreme, not the upper quartile. The upper quartile is 33.

8. The median is about 15 inches.

9. The lower quartile is about 11 inches.

10. The range is 28 − 4, or 24 inches.

11. The upper extreme is 28 inches.

12. About $\frac{1}{4}$ of the data values are in the interval from 40 to 50.

13. The median and about half of the data are located between 25 and 50.

14. C; About 75% of the data values are not in the range from 15 to 25.

15. D; Because 75 is the upper extreme, 75 must be a data value from which the box-and-whisker plot was made.

16. True; A box-and-whisker plot divides the data into 4 portions that each represent about one quarter of the data. The interquartile range represents the two middle portions, which is about half the data.

17. False; Both of these intervals include about one quarter of the data.

18. False; A box-and-whisker plot divides the data into 4 equal portions in terms of the number of data values in each portion, but the range of each portion may be different.

19. *Sample answer:* Change 5 to 14. Because the desired median and lower quartile are above the actual values, change a data value from the first quartile to a greater value. To keep the upper quartile the same, choose a value that lies between the new median and new upper quartile. The new data set is 3, 4, 7, 9, 11, 13, 14, 15, 17, 18, and 21.

Problem Solving

20. D;

731, 785, 789, 810, 811.5, 822.5, 826.5, 838, 853, 1020

The upper quartile is 838.

21. 141, 159, 197, 211, 227, 235, 267, 280, 296, 306, 324, 351

    a. Range = 351 − 141 = 210

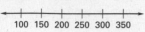

    100 150 200 250 300 350

    b. Median = $\dfrac{235 + 267}{2} = \dfrac{502}{2} = 251$

    Lower quartile = $\dfrac{197 + 211}{2} = \dfrac{408}{2} = 204$

    Upper quartile = $\dfrac{296 + 306}{2} = \dfrac{602}{2} = 301$

    Lower extreme = 141

    Upper extreme = 351

    c.

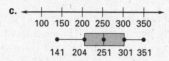

    100 150 200 250 300 350

    141 204 251 301 351

22. *Sample answer:* A line plot and a stem-and-leaf plot can help you make a box-and-whisker plot because the data is in order. This makes it easier to find the extremes, the quartiles, and the median.

    A line plot is useful only for small data sets over a small range.

23. *Sample answer:* Khalila has a higher median score than Tasha, 11 points versus 9 points, but her overall performance is much more variable. For Khalila, it took an interval of 7, from 7 to 14, to contain half of her total points, but for Tasha, it took only an interval of 4, from 8 to 12, to contain half of her total points. So, Tasha's scoring is more consistent. This is also shown by the fact that the extremes for Tasha are between the extremes for Khalila. Also, the range for Tasha is only 8 points, and the range for Khalila is 15 points.

24. $179.99, $229.99, $259.99, $259.99, $284.99, $299.99, $329.99, $379.99, $399.99

    Median = 284.99

    Lower quartile = $\dfrac{229.99 + 259.99}{2} = 244.99$

    Upper quartile = $\dfrac{329.99 + 379.99}{2} = 354.99$

    Lower extreme = 179.99

    Upper extreme = 399.99

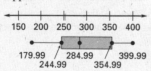

    150 200 250 300 350 400

    179.99   284.99   399.99

    244.99   354.99

    Sample answer: Half of the prices fall between $244.99 and $354.99, with a median price of $284.99.

25. 28,900, 31,300, 31,500, 32,900, 57,800, 59,600, 64,500, 69,500, 82,100, 371,000

    Median = $\dfrac{57,800 + 59,600}{2} = \dfrac{117,400}{2} = 58,700$

    Lower quartile = 31,500

    Upper quartile = 69,500

Lower extreme = 28,900

Upper extreme = 371,000

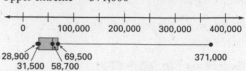

0   100,000   200,000   300,000   400,000

28,900   69,500   371,000

31,500 58,700

The data value 371,000 square kilometers is an outlier.

26. 28,900, 31,300, 31,500, 32,900, 57,800, 59,600, 64,500, 69,500, 82,100

    Median = 57,800

    Lower quartile = $\dfrac{31,300 + 31,500}{2} = \dfrac{62,800}{2} = 31,400$

    Upper quartile = $\dfrac{64,500 + 69,500}{2} = \dfrac{134,000}{2} = 67,000$

    Lower extreme = 28,900

    Upper extreme = 82,100

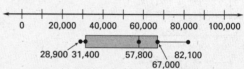

0   20,000   40,000   60,000   80,000   100,000

28,900 31,400   57,800   82,100

              67,000

An outlier does not have much of an effect on the quartiles or median, but it makes the box-and-whisker plot very long and thus greatly increases the range.

27. Check work.

28. **a.** Factory A: 198.5, 198.5, 199, 200, 200.5, 200.8, 200.9, 201, 201, 202

    Median = $\dfrac{200.5 + 200.8}{2} = 200.65$

    Lower quartile = 199

    Upper quartile = 201

    Lower extreme = 198.5

    Upper extreme = 202

    Factory B:

    200.4, 200.6, 200.8, 200.9, 201, 201, 201, 203, 203.1, 203.4

    Median = 201

    Lower quartile = 200.8

    Upper quartile = 203

    Lower extreme = 200.4

    Upper extreme = 203.4

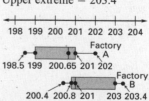

198 199 200 201 202 203 204

                     Factory A

198.5 199   200.65 201 202

                         Factory B

200.4 200.8 201   203 203.4

    b. Factory A does a better job of making the bolts within the desired mass range. All of their bolts fell in the range. Factory B had more than $\frac{1}{4}$ of their bolts fall outside the desired mass range.

29. Check work.

Chapter 12, *continued*

30. The upper quartile of the first data set, must be the mean of 19 and some other age that is at least 16. So, the other age could be 16, 17, 18, or 19. The minimum upper quartile is $\frac{16 + 19}{2} = 17.5$ and the maximum upper quartile is $\frac{19 + 19}{2} = 19$.

The upper quartile of the second data set must be the mean of 18 and some other age that is greater than 40 and less than or equal to 47. So, the other age could be 41, 42, 43, 44, 45, 46, or 47. The minimum upper quartile is $\frac{18 + 41}{2} = 29.5$ and the maximum upper quartile is $\frac{18 + 47}{2} = 32.5$.

Mixed Review

31. $\frac{x}{9} = \frac{5}{36}$

$36x = 45$

$x = 1.25$

32. $\frac{21}{9} = \frac{7}{a}$

$21a = 63$

$a = 3$

33. $\frac{10}{40} = \frac{b}{4}$

$40 = 40b$

$1 = b$

34. $\frac{2}{c} = \frac{8}{20}$

$40 = 8c$

$5 = c$

35. $3x - 5y = 30$

$-5y = -3x + 30$

$y = \frac{3}{5}x - 6$

x-intercept: $0 = \frac{3}{5}x - 6$

$6 = \frac{3}{5}x$

$10 = x$

y-intercept: $y = \frac{3}{5}(0) - 6$

$y = -6$

Slope $= \frac{3}{5}$

The x-intercept is 10, the y-intercept is -6, and the slope is $\frac{3}{5}$.

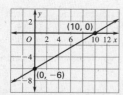

36. B; A leaf is usually a single digit, so if 2 is a leaf, then 4 must be a stem.

Lesson 12.3

12.3 Guided Practice (pp. 660–661)

1. Ben: $\frac{55}{100} = \frac{x}{360°}$

$x \approx 198°$

Alice: $\frac{45}{100} = \frac{y}{360°}$

$y \approx 162°$

Who Will You Vote For?

Alice 45%

Ben 55%

2.

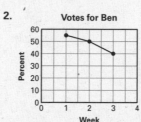

The graph shows a decrease over time.

3. The percents total 100%, so a circle graph is appropriate.

12.3 Exercises (pp. 661–664)

Skill Practice

1. Use a *circle graph* to display data as parts of a whole and a *line graph* to display changes in a quantity over time.

2. 31%: $\frac{31}{100} = \frac{x}{360°}$

$x = 111.6°$

3. $\frac{3}{8}$: $\frac{3}{8} = \frac{x}{360°}$

$x = 135°$

4. 14%: $\frac{14}{100} = \frac{x}{360°}$

$x = 50.4°$

5. 27 out of 60: $\frac{27}{60} = \frac{x}{360°}$

$x = 162°$

6. Never: $\frac{20}{200} = \frac{a}{360°}$

$a = 36°$

Rarely: $\frac{90}{200} = \frac{b}{360°}$

$b = 162°$

Sometimes: $\frac{70}{200} = \frac{c}{360°}$

$c = 126°$

Often: $\frac{20}{200} = \frac{d}{360°}$

$d = 36°$

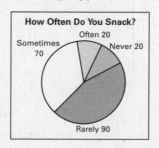

How Often Do You Snack?

Often 20

Sometimes 70

Never 20

Rarely 90

Chapter 12, *continued*

7. Never: $\dfrac{0}{200} = \dfrac{a}{360°}$

$a = 0°$

Rarely: $\dfrac{50}{200} = \dfrac{b}{360°}$

$b = 90°$

Sometimes: $\dfrac{120}{200} = \dfrac{c}{360°}$

$c = 216°$

Often: $\dfrac{30}{200} = \dfrac{d}{360°}$

$d = 54°$

How Often Do You Snack?
Never 0
Often 30   Rarely 50
Sometimes 120

8. Never: $\dfrac{40}{200} = \dfrac{a}{360°}$

$a = 72°$

Rarely: $\dfrac{20}{200} = \dfrac{b}{360°}$

$b = 36°$

Sometimes: $\dfrac{85}{200} = \dfrac{c}{360°}$

$c = 153°$

Often: $\dfrac{55}{200} = \dfrac{d}{360°}$

$d = 99°$

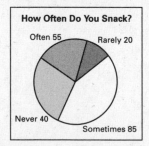

How Often Do You Snack?
Often 55   Rarely 20
Never 40
Sometimes 85

9.

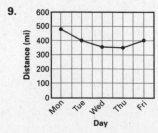

10.

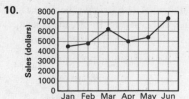

11.

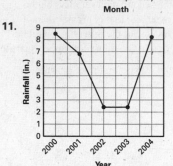

12. The student used the number of responses as the percent.

Yes: $\dfrac{50}{75} = 66\dfrac{2}{3}\%$

$\dfrac{50}{75} = \dfrac{a}{360°}$

$a = 240°$

No: $\dfrac{10}{75} = 13\dfrac{1}{3}\%$

$\dfrac{10}{75} = \dfrac{b}{360°}$

$b = 48°$

Undecided: $\dfrac{15}{75} = 20\%$

$\dfrac{15}{75} = \dfrac{c}{360°}$

$c = 72°$

13. *Sample answer:* The data represent parts of a whole, so a circle graph is appropriate.

14. *Sample answer:* The data change over time, so a line graph is appropriate.

15. A; $\dfrac{\text{Number that pay more than \$25}}{\text{Total number surveyed}} = \dfrac{x}{360}$

$\dfrac{12}{30} = \dfrac{x}{360}$

16. a. *Sample answer:* How much television do you watch each day? The students will be given choices such as "None," "Not much," "Some," and "A lot." The data will represent parts of a whole, so a circle graph should be used.

b. *Sample answer:* What are the company's sales in each of the past 5 years? The data will not represent parts of a whole, so a circle graph should not be used.

17. You should use a line graph because it shows a trend over time.

18. You should use a bar graph because it shows distinct categories, or locations.

19. You should use a histogram because it shows the frequencies of data that are grouped in equal intervals.

20. *Sample answer:* The data set can be the heights of 25 mountain peaks. You can order the data set using a stem-and-leaf plot. You can summarize the data using a box-and-whisker plot. You can also organize the data in a histogram.

For the stem-and-leaf plot, order the data and group it into the plot. For the box-and-whisker plot, find the median, quartiles, and extremes, and then draw the plot. For the histogram, choose intervals of equal size for the data, tally the data in each interval, determine the frequency of each interval, and draw the histogram.

Problem Solving

21. Friday: $\frac{130}{837} = \frac{x}{360°}$

$x \approx 55.9° \approx 56°$

Saturday (2 P.M.): $\frac{231}{837} = \frac{y}{360°}$

$y \approx 99.4° \approx 99°$

Saturday (8 P.M.): $\frac{291}{837} = \frac{z}{360°}$

$z \approx 125.2° \approx 125°$

Sunday: $\frac{185}{837} = \frac{w}{360°}$

$w \approx 79.6° \approx 80°$

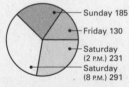

Play Attendance
- Sunday 185
- Friday 130
- Saturday (2 P.M.) 231
- Saturday (8 P.M.) 291

22. Friday: $7(130) = \$910$

Saturday (2 P.M.): $7(231) = \$1617$

Saturday (8 P.M.): $7(291) = \$2037$

Sunday: $7(185) = \$1295$

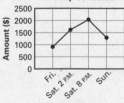

Money Collected

23. Queens: $\frac{110}{303} = \frac{x}{100}$

$x \approx 36.3\% \approx 36\%$

Manhattan: $\frac{23}{303} = \frac{y}{100}$

$y \approx 7.6\% \approx 8\%$

Staten Island: $\frac{56}{303} = \frac{z}{100}$

$z \approx 18.48\% \approx 18\%$

Bronx: $\frac{41}{303} = \frac{a}{100}$

$a \approx 13.5\% \approx 14\%$

Brooklyn: $\frac{73}{303} = \frac{b}{100}$

$b \approx 24.1\% \approx 24\%$

24. Queens: $\frac{36.3}{100} = \frac{x}{360°}$

$x \approx 131°$

Manhattan: $\frac{7.6}{100} = \frac{y}{360°}$

$y \approx 27°$

Staten Island: $\frac{18.5}{100} = \frac{z}{360°}$

$z \approx 67°$

Bronx: $\frac{13.5}{100} = \frac{a}{360°}$

$a \approx 49°$

Brooklyn: $\frac{24.1}{100} = \frac{b}{360°}$

$b \approx 87°$

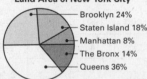

Land Area of New York City
- Brooklyn 24%
- Staten Island 18%
- Manhattan 8%
- The Bronx 14%
- Queens 36%

Queens is the largest borough and Manhattan is the smallest. The Bronx and Staten Island are very similar in size.

25. *Sample answer:* A circle graph would be appropriate because it shows parts of a whole. A bar graph would be appropriate because there are distinct categories.

26. B; $a = p\% \cdot b$

$= 13\% \cdot 500$

$= 0.13 \cdot 500$

$= 65$

About 65 people out of 500 will be unable to whistle.

27.

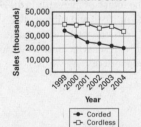

Telephone Sales

The vertical axis is marked off by 10,000s because all of the data are between 20,000 and 40,000.

28. The two consecutive years in which the number of cordless telephones sold increased the most between 2002 and 2003. This is easier to tell from the graph because the line segment between 2002 and 2003 is the steepest.

29. 1999 to 2000: 34,486 − 29,670 = 4816

2000 to 2001: 29,670 − 24,957 = 4713

2001 to 2002: 24,957 − 23,813 = 1144

2002 to 2003: 23,813 − 21,918 = 1895

2003 to 2004: 21,918 − 20,051 = 1867

$$\text{Mean} = \frac{4816 + 4713 + 1144 + 1895 + 1867}{5}$$

$$= \frac{14,435}{5}$$

$$= 2887$$

The mean of the annual decreases in sales of corded telephones from 1999 to 2004 is 2887 thousand, or 2,887,000 telephones per year.

30. *Sample answer:* As you can see from the graph, sales of corded telephones decreased each year, while the sales of cordless telephones decreased, then increased, then decreased, and so on.

31.

Season	1989	1990	1991	1992	1993
Attempts	280	255	342	312	243
Average yards	5.25	5.10	4.53	4.33	4.59
Total yards	1470	2771	4320	5671	6786

Season	1994	1995	1996	1997	1998
Attempts	331	314	307	335	343
Average yards	5.69	4.78	5.06	6.13	4.35
Total yards	8669	10,170	11,723	13,777	15,269

32. *Sample answer:* Because the table shows data over time, a line graph is appropriate.

33. *Sample answer:* Subtract the total rushing yards in 1989 from the total rushing yards in 1993, and subtract the total rushing yards in 1994 from the total rushing yards in 1998. The larger number represents the interval during which Sanders accumulated more rushing yards.

34. Answers will vary.

Mixed Review

35. Total number of marbles = 12 + 15 + 5 = 32

$$P(\text{red}) = \frac{15}{32}$$

The probability of drawing a red marble is $\frac{15}{32}$.

36. $P(\text{blue}) = \frac{12}{32} = \frac{3}{8}$

The probability of drawing a blue marble is $\frac{3}{8}$.

37. $P(\text{yellow}) = \frac{0}{32} = 0$

The probability of drawing a yellow marble is 0.

38.

```
1 | 0  1  5  6  7  7  8
2 | 0  1  4  6  8  9
3 | 1  4  6  7  9
```

Key: 3 | 1 = 31

Because there are 18 numbers, count to the ninth and tenth numbers in the plot. Then find the mean of these two numbers. This value is the median.

Quiz 12.1–12.3 (p. 664)

1. April: 990, 995, 997, 1001, 1025, 1030, 1058, 1099, 1116, 1122

June: 1042, 1048, 1056, 1097, 1123, 1125, 1125, 1131, 1151, 1164

```
  April         June
7 5 0 | 99  |
    1 | 100 |
      | 101 |
    5 | 102 |
    0 | 103 |
      | 104 | 2  8
    8 | 105 | 6
      | 106 |
      | 107 |
      | 108 |
    9 | 109 | 7
      | 110 |
    6 | 111 |
    2 | 112 | 3  5  5
      | 113 | 1
      | 114 |
      | 115 | 1
      | 116 | 4
```

Key: 2 | 112 | 3 represents 1122 and 1123

April:

$$\text{Median} = \frac{1025 + 1030}{2} = 1027.5$$

Lower quartile = 997

Upper quartile = 1099

Lower extreme = 990

Upper extreme = 1122

June:

Median $= \dfrac{1123 + 1125}{2} = 1124$

Lower quartile $= 1056$

Upper quartile $= 1131$

Lower extreme $= 1042$

Upper extreme $= 1164$

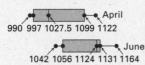

Both displays clearly show that more people attended games in June than in April.

2. A line graph is more appropriate than a circle graph because the data change over time.

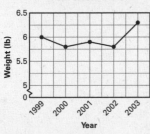

Technology Activity 12.3 (pp. 665–666)

1.

2.

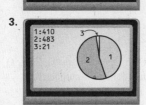

3.

12.3 Extension (p. 668)

1. No; *Sample answer:* There is a break in the vertical scale, so the relative change is smaller than it appears.

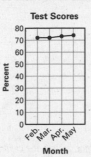

2. No; *Sample answer:* The range of values on the vertical axis is greater than needed. It appears that the price rises are slight, but prices have nearly doubled during the period shown.

3. Positive performance: Negative performance:

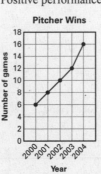
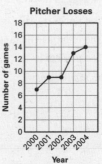

Mixed Review of Problem Solving (p. 669)

1. **a.** Range $= 25 - 4 = 21$

   b. The interval 10–19 includes the most home runs.

   c. 4, 5, 7, 8, 12, 14, 15, 16, 16, 18, 21, 24, 25,

   Median $= 15$

   Lower quartile $= \dfrac{7 + 8}{2} = \dfrac{15}{2} = 7.5$

   Upper quartile $= \dfrac{18 + 21}{2} = \dfrac{39}{2} = 19.5$

   Lower extreme $= 4$

   Upper extreme $= 25$

Chapter 12, continued

2. a.

```
2 | 3  7  9
3 | 0  2  3  8
4 | 2
```

Key: 2 | 7 = 27

b.

	Cars		Trucks				
		1	6	9			
9 7 3		2	0	1	3	4	5	8
8 3 2 0		3					
		4					

Key: 3 | 2 | 0 represents 23 and 20

c. In general, the number of miles per gallon for cars is greater than the number of miles per gallon for trucks.

3. A circle graph would not be a good display for the data because the percents total more than 100%.

4. *Sample answer:* The range of gasoline prices in city A is greater than the range in city B. The prices in city A are also more spread out than the prices in city B.

5. No; If two sets of data have identical box-and-whisker plots, the data must have the same extremes, median and quartiles, but the data values are not necessarily identical.

6. *Sample answer:* 32, 33, 33, 35, 35, 37, 38, 39, 41, 42, 42, 44, 45, 45, 52, 55, 55

The data set has 17 values.

The lower extreme is 32.

The range is $55 - 32 = 23$.

The upper quartile is 45.

The interquartile range is $45 - 35 = 10$.

The median is 41.

7. a. *Sample answer:*

	You	Your Friend		
		0	5	8	8
9 8 7 6 5 4		1	0	2	8
6 5 3 2 2 2 0		2	0		

Key: 4 | 1 | 0 represents 14 and 10

b. *Sample answer:* A double stem-and-leaf plot is a good choice for comparing each person's times.

c. *Sample answer:* A line graph would not be a good choice to display the data because the data do not represent changes over time.

8. 135; Total students = $18 + 30 = 48$

$$\frac{18}{48} = \frac{a}{360°}$$

$$a = 135°$$

You should use an angle of 135° to represent the portion of your class that is male.

Lesson 12.4

Activity (p. 670)

1. Possible outfits: TJ, BJ, SJ, TK, BK, SK

2. There are 3 more possible outfits: TD, BD, SD. There are now 9 possible outfits.

12.4 Guided Practice (pp. 671–672)

1.

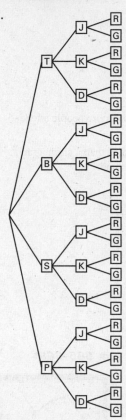

There are 24 different possible outfits.

2.

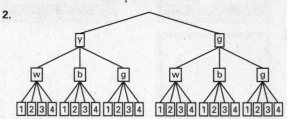

There are 24 different uniforms possible.

3. $24 \cdot 25 \cdot 25 \cdot 10 \cdot 10 = 1,500,000$

If the passwords cannot start with an A or use the letter Q, there are 24 choices for the first letter, 25 choices for each of the next two letters, and 10 choices for each of the digits. So, there are 1,500,000 different possible passwords.

4. $\dfrac{\text{Number of favorable outcomes}}{\text{Number of possible outcomes}} = \dfrac{1 \cdot 1 \cdot 1 \cdot 1 \cdot 1 \cdot 1}{2 \cdot 2 \cdot 2 \cdot 2 \cdot 2 \cdot 2} = \dfrac{1}{64}$

The probability of getting six heads is $\dfrac{1}{64}$.

Chapter 12, *continued*

Skill Practice

1. If one event can occur in *m* ways and for each of those a second event can occur in *n* ways, then the two events can occur together in *m* · *n* ways.

2. The probability of an event when all outcomes are equally likely is the number of *favorable* outcomes divided by the number of *possible* outcomes.

3. There are 4(2), or 8 choices.

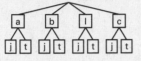

4. There are 3(3), or 9 choices.

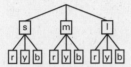

5. There are 2(3), or 6 choices.

6. There are 5(2), or 10 choices.

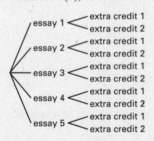

7. C; 26 · 26 · 26 · 10 · 10 · 10 · 10 = 175,760,000

   There are 175,760,000 different possible license plates.

8. The number of choices is the product of 2 and 3, not the sum.

   There are 2(3) = 6 drink choices available.

9. $\dfrac{\text{Number of favorable outcomes}}{\text{Number of possible outcomes}} = \dfrac{21 \cdot 26 \cdot 26 \cdot 26}{26 \cdot 26 \cdot 26 \cdot 26}$

   $= \dfrac{369,096}{456,976}$

   $= \dfrac{21}{26}$

   The probability that the code starts with a consonant is $\dfrac{21}{26}$.

10. $\dfrac{\text{Number of favorable outcomes}}{\text{Number of possible outcomes}} = \dfrac{5 \cdot 5 \cdot 5 \cdot 5}{26 \cdot 26 \cdot 26 \cdot 26}$

    $= \dfrac{625}{456,976}$

    The probability that the code contains only vowels is $\dfrac{625}{456,976}$.

11. $\dfrac{\text{Number of favorable outcomes}}{\text{Number of possible outcomes}} = \dfrac{1 \cdot 1 \cdot 1 \cdot 1}{26 \cdot 26 \cdot 26 \cdot 26}$

    $= \dfrac{1}{456,976}$

    The probability that the code is MNYR is $\dfrac{1}{456,976}$.

12. $\dfrac{\text{Number of favorable outcomes}}{\text{Number of possible outcomes}} = \dfrac{26 \cdot 1 \cdot 1 \cdot 1}{26 \cdot 26 \cdot 26 \cdot 26}$

    $= \dfrac{26}{456,976}$

    $= \dfrac{1}{17,576}$

    The probability that the code uses the same letter in each spot is $\dfrac{1}{17,576}$.

13. Ways to choose 2 U.S. coins:

    Coin 1, Coin 2

    Coin 1, Coin 3

    Coin 1, Coin 4

    Coin 2, Coin 3

    Coin 2, Coin 4

    Coin 3, Coin 4

    Ways to choose 2 U.S. bills:

    Bill 1, Bill 2

    Bill 1, Bill 3

    Bill 2, Bill 3

    Outcomes = 6 · 3 = 18

    There are 18 different outcomes.

14. Ways to choose 2 U.S. coins:

    Coin 1, Coin 2

    Coin 1, Coin 3

    Coin 1, Coin 4

    Coin 2, Coin 3

    Coin 2, Coin 4

    Coin 3, Coin 4

    Ways to choose 3 foreign coins:

    Coin 1, Coin 2, Coin 3; Coin 1, Coin 2, Coin 4

    Coin 1, Coin 2, Coin 5; Coin 1, Coin 2, Coin 6

    Coin 1, Coin 2, Coin 7; Coin 1, Coin 2, Coin 8

    Coin 2, Coin 3, Coin 4; Coin 2, Coin 3, Coin 5

    Coin 2, Coin 3, Coin 6; Coin 2, Coin 3, Coin 7

    Coin 2, Coin 3, Coin 8; Coin 3, Coin 4, Coin 5

    Coin 3, Coin 4, Coin 6; Coin 3, Coin 4, Coin 7

    Coin 3, Coin 4, Coin 8; Coin 4, Coin 5, Coin 6

    Coin 4, Coin 5, Coin 7; Coin 4, Coin 5, Coin 8

    Coin 5, Coin 6, Coin 7; Coin 5, Coin 6, Coin 8

    Coin 6, Coin 7, Coin 8; Coin 1, Coin 3, Coin 4

    Coin 1, Coin 3, Coin 5; Coin 1, Coin 3, Coin 6

    Coin 1, Coin 3, Coin 7; Coin 1, Coin 3, Coin 8

Coin 1, Coin 4, Coin 5; Coin 1, Coin 4, Coin 6
Coin 1, Coin 4, Coin 7; Coin 1, Coin 4, Coin 8
Coin 1, Coin 5, Coin 6; Coin 1, Coin 5, Coin 7
Coin 1, Coin 5, Coin 8; Coin 1, Coin 6, Coin 7
Coin 1, Coin 6, Coin 8; Coin 1, Coin 7, Coin 8
Coin 2, Coin 4, Coin 5; Coin 2, Coin 4, Coin 6
Coin 2, Coin 4, Coin 7; Coin 2, Coin 4, Coin 8
Coin 2, Coin 5, Coin 6; Coin 2, Coin 5, Coin 7
Coin 2, Coin 5, Coin 8; Coin 3, Coin 5, Coin 6
Coin 3, Coin 5, Coin 7; Coin 3, Coin 5, Coin 8
Coin 3, Coin 6, Coin 7; Coin 3, Coin 6, Coin 8
Coin 3, Coin 7, Coin 8; Coin 4, Coin 6, Coin 7
Coin 4, Coin 6, Coin 8; Coin 4, Coin 7, Coin 8
Coin 5, Coin 7, Coin 8; Coin 2, Coin 6, Coin 7
Coin 2, Coin 6, Coin 8; Coin 2, Coin 7, Coin 8
Outcomes = 6 • 56 = 336

There are 336 different outcomes.

15. If no password with 5 numbers may use a digit more than once, then there are 10 choices for the first digit, 9 choices for the second digit, 8 choices for the third digit, 7 choices for the fourth digit, and 6 choices for the fifth digit. So, there are 10 • 9 • 8 • 7 • 6 = 30,240 possible choices for a password.

Problem Solving

16.

There are 3(2)(2), or 12 possibilities.

17. *Sample answer:* You can find the number of different pairs of 1 CD and 1 book that you can buy by drawing a tree diagram to list and then count all the possibilities. Or you can use the counting principle.

18.

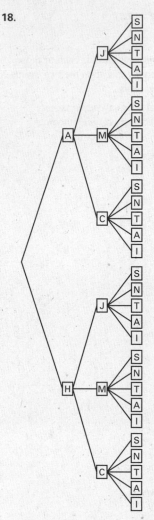

There are 2(3)(5), or 30 different ways the president, treasurer, and secretary can be chosen.

19. D; $\dfrac{\text{Number of favorable outcomes}}{\text{Number of possible outcomes}} = \dfrac{1 \cdot 1 \cdot 1 \cdot 1}{4 \cdot 4 \cdot 4 \cdot 4} = \dfrac{1}{256}$

The probability that you all pick the same movie is $\dfrac{1}{256}$.

20. $\dfrac{\text{Number of favorable outcomes}}{\text{Number of possible outcomes}} = \dfrac{2 \cdot 2}{50 \cdot 50}$

$= \dfrac{4}{2500}$

$= \dfrac{1}{625}$

The probability that you both choose a state that starts with a T is $\dfrac{1}{625}$.

Chapter 12, *continued*

21. *Sample answer:* Let S represent a sandwich, let O represent a side order, and let D represent a drink.

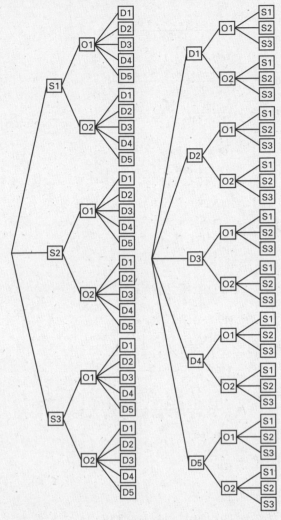

Both tree diagrams show there are 30 different possible lunches. The outcomes will be the same no matter how you draw the tree diagram.

22. (Main course)(Salad)(Dessert) = 36

$$6(2)d = 36$$
$$12d = 36$$
$$d = 3$$

Using the counting principle you can see that there are 3 different desserts.

23. Each dot can be raised or not raised. Each symbol has 6 dots. So, there are $2 \cdot 2 \cdot 2 \cdot 2 \cdot 2 \cdot 2 = 64$ possible symbols. There is one symbol possible with 6 raised dots, and one symbol possible with no raised dots.

24. Yes; There are 6 symbols possible with one raised dot because that one dot could be in any of the 6 locations. Similarly, there are 6 symbols possible with 5 raised dots because the one non-raised dot could be in any of the 6 locations.

25. a.

```
        ┌ 0.5-liter
lime  ──┼ 1 liter
        └ 2-liter
        ┌ 0.5-liter
lemon ──┼ 1-liter
        └ 2-liter
        ┌ 0.5-liter
cherry──┼ 1-liter
        └ 2-liter
        ┌ 0.5-liter
orange──┼ 1-liter
        └ 2-liter
```

There are 12 different bottles of flavored water that you can choose.

b. If 5 new flavors become available, you now have 4 + 5, or 9 flavors from which to choose.

There are 9(3) or 27 total different bottles.

c. 0.5 L + 1 L + 2 L = \$.59 + \$.69 + \$.99 = \$2.27

0.5 L + 0.5 L + 0.5 L = \$.59 + \$.59 + \$.59 = \$1.77

0.5 L + 0.5 L + 1 L = \$.59 + \$.59 + \$.69 = \$1.87

0.5 L + 1 L + 1 L = \$.59 + \$.69 + \$.69 = \$1.97

0.5 L + 0.5 L + 2 L = \$.59 + \$.59 + \$.99 = \$2.17

0.5 L + 2 L + 2 L = \$.59 + \$.99 + \$.99 = \$2.57

1 L + 1 L + 1 L = \$.69 + \$.69 + \$.69 = \$2.07

1 L + 1 L + 2 L = \$.69 + \$.69 + \$.99 = \$2.37

1 L + 2 L + 2 L = \$.69 + \$.99 + \$.99 = \$2.67

2 L + 2 L + 2 L = \$.99 + \$.99 + \$.99 = \$2.97

If you only have \$2.60, the largest quantity of water you can buy is 0.5 + 2 + 2, or 4.5 liters for \$2.57.

Mixed Review

26. There are 8 numbers greater than 4 in the bag, 5, 6, 7, 8, 9, 10, 11, and 12.

$$P(\text{drawing a number greater than 4}) = \frac{8}{12} = \frac{2}{3}$$

The probability of drawing a number greater than 4 is $\frac{2}{3}$.

27. There are 2 numbers in the bag that are divisible by 5, 5 and 10.

$$P(\text{drawing a number divisible by 5}) = \frac{2}{12} = \frac{1}{6}$$

The probability of drawing a number that is divisible by 5 is $\frac{1}{6}$.

28. 8, 8, 9, 10, 11, 12, 12, 13, 16, 17

$$\text{Median} = \frac{11 + 12}{2} = 11.5$$

Lower quartile = 9

Upper quartile = 13

Lower extreme = 8

Upper extreme = 17

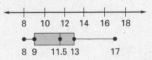

Chapter 12, *continued*

29. C; $m = \dfrac{y_2 - y_1}{x_2 - x_1} = \dfrac{3 - 6}{-2 - 4} = \dfrac{-3}{-6} = \dfrac{1}{2}$

The slope of the line is $\dfrac{1}{2}$.

Lesson 12.5

12.5 Guided Practice (pp. 676–677)

1. $3! = 3 \cdot 2 \cdot 1 = 6$

2. $6! = 6 \cdot 5 \cdot 4 \cdot 3 \cdot 2 \cdot 1 = 720$

3. $1! = 1$

4. $4! = 4 \cdot 3 \cdot 2 \cdot 1 = 24$

Chris can watch the movies in 24 different orders.

5. $7 \cdot 6 \cdot 5 = 210$

There are 210 ways that 7 runners can finish in first, second, and third place.

6. $_5P_3 = \dfrac{5!}{(5-3)!} = \dfrac{5!}{2!} = \dfrac{5 \cdot 4 \cdot 3 \cdot 2 \cdot 1}{2 \cdot 1} = 60$

7. $_6P_6 = \dfrac{6!}{(6-6)!} = \dfrac{6!}{0!} = \dfrac{6 \cdot 5 \cdot 4 \cdot 3 \cdot 2 \cdot 1}{1} = 720$

8. $_8P_7 = \dfrac{8!}{(8-7)!} = \dfrac{8!}{1!} = \dfrac{8 \cdot 7 \cdot 6 \cdot 5 \cdot 4 \cdot 3 \cdot 2 \cdot 1}{1} = 40{,}320$

9. $_{100}P_2 = \dfrac{100!}{(100-2)!}$

$= \dfrac{100!}{98!}$

$= \dfrac{100 \cdot 99 \cdot 98 \cdot \ldots \cdot 3 \cdot 2 \cdot 1}{98 \cdot 97 \cdot 96 \cdot \ldots \cdot 3 \cdot 2 \cdot 1}$

$= 9900$

10. $_8P_3 = \dfrac{8!}{(8-3)!} = \dfrac{8!}{5!} = \dfrac{8 \cdot 7 \cdot 6 \cdot 5 \cdot 4 \cdot 3 \cdot 2 \cdot 1}{5 \cdot 4 \cdot 3 \cdot 2 \cdot 1} = 336$

The students can be chosen in 336 ways.

12.5 Exercises (pp. 677–679)

Skill Practice

1. The number of permutations of 15 objects taken 7 at a time is written $_{15}P_7$.

2. The product of all integers from 1 to a number n is written $n!$.

3. $2! = 2 \cdot 1 = 2$ **4.** $0! = 1$

5. $7! = 7 \cdot 6 \cdot 5 \cdot 4 \cdot 3 \cdot 2 \cdot 1 = 5040$

6. $9! = 9 \cdot 8 \cdot 7 \cdot 6 \cdot 5 \cdot 4 \cdot 3 \cdot 2 \cdot 1 = 362{,}880$

7. $_4P_2 = \dfrac{4!}{(4-2)!} = \dfrac{4!}{2!} = \dfrac{4 \cdot 3 \cdot 2 \cdot 1}{2 \cdot 1} = 12$

8. $_9P_6 = \dfrac{9!}{(9-6)!}$

$= \dfrac{9!}{3!}$

$= \dfrac{9 \cdot 8 \cdot 7 \cdot 6 \cdot 5 \cdot 4 \cdot 3 \cdot 2 \cdot 1}{3 \cdot 2 \cdot 1}$

$= 60{,}480$

9. $_{10}P_7 = \dfrac{10!}{(10-7)!}$

$= \dfrac{10!}{3!}$

$= \dfrac{10 \cdot 9 \cdot 8 \cdot \ldots \cdot 3 \cdot 2 \cdot 1}{3 \cdot 2 \cdot 1}$

$= 604{,}800$

10. $_5P_5 = \dfrac{5!}{(5-5)!} = \dfrac{5!}{0!} = \dfrac{5 \cdot 4 \cdot 3 \cdot 2 \cdot 1}{1} = 120$

11. $_{12}P_6 = \dfrac{12!}{(12-6)!}$

$= \dfrac{12!}{6!}$

$= \dfrac{12 \cdot 11 \cdot 10 \cdot \ldots \cdot 3 \cdot 2 \cdot 1}{6 \cdot 5 \cdot 4 \cdot 3 \cdot 2 \cdot 1}$

$= 665{,}280$

12. $_7P_4 = \dfrac{7!}{(7-4)!}$

$= \dfrac{7!}{3!}$

$= \dfrac{7 \cdot 6 \cdot 5 \cdot 4 \cdot 3 \cdot 2 \cdot 1}{3 \cdot 2 \cdot 1}$

$= 840$

13. $_{15}P_5 = \dfrac{15!}{(15-5)!}$

$= \dfrac{15!}{10!}$

$= \dfrac{15 \cdot 14 \cdot 13 \cdot \ldots \cdot 3 \cdot 2 \cdot 1}{10 \cdot 9 \cdot 8 \cdot 7 \cdot 6 \cdot 5 \cdot 4 \cdot 3 \cdot 2 \cdot 1}$

$= 360{,}360$

14. $_{20}P_3 = \dfrac{20!}{(20-3)!}$

$= \dfrac{20!}{17!}$

$= \dfrac{20 \cdot 19 \cdot 18 \cdot 17 \cdot \ldots \cdot 3 \cdot 2 \cdot 1}{17 \cdot \ldots \cdot 3 \cdot 2 \cdot 1}$

$= 6840$

15. The denominator should be $(5-3)!$

$_5P_3 = \dfrac{5!}{(5-3)!} = \dfrac{5!}{2!} = \dfrac{5 \cdot 4 \cdot 3 \cdot \cancel{2} \cdot \cancel{1}}{\cancel{2} \cdot \cancel{1}} = 5 \cdot 4 \cdot 3 = 60$

16. D

17. $_7P_7 = \dfrac{7!}{(7-7)!} = \dfrac{7!}{0!} = \dfrac{7 \cdot 6 \cdot 5 \cdot 4 \cdot 3 \cdot 2 \cdot 1}{1} = 5040$

There are 5040 different ways to arrange the letters in the word HOLIDAY.

18. $_8P_6 = \dfrac{8!}{(8-6)!} = \dfrac{8!}{2!} = \dfrac{8 \cdot 7 \cdot 6 \cdot 5 \cdot 4 \cdot 3 \cdot 2 \cdot 1}{2 \cdot 1} = 20{,}160$

There are 20,160 different ways to arrange 6 of the cast members in a row.

Chapter 12, *continued*

19. $_{52}P_5 = \dfrac{52!}{(52-5)!}$

$= \dfrac{52!}{47!}$

$= \dfrac{52 \cdot 51 \cdot 50 \cdot \cdots \cdot 3 \cdot 2 \cdot 1}{47 \cdot 46 \cdot 45 \cdot \cdots \cdot 3 \cdot 2 \cdot 1}$

$= 311,875,200$

There are 311,875,200 different arrangements of 5 cards that can be made from the deck.

20. $_5P_5 = \dfrac{5!}{(5-5)!} = \dfrac{5!}{0!} = \dfrac{5 \cdot 4 \cdot 3 \cdot 2 \cdot 1}{1} = 120$

You can read the books in 120 different orders.

21. $_{24}P_4 = \dfrac{24!}{(24-4)!}$

$= \dfrac{24!}{20!}$

$= \dfrac{24 \cdot 23 \cdot 22 \cdot \cdots \cdot 3 \cdot 2 \cdot 1}{20 \cdot 19 \cdot 18 \cdot \cdots \cdot 3 \cdot 2 \cdot 1}$

$= 255,024$

There are 255,024 ways the club can select a president, vice president, secretary, and treasurer.

22. $_8P_5 = \dfrac{8!}{(8-5)!} = \dfrac{8!}{3!} = \dfrac{8 \cdot 7 \cdot 6 \cdot 5 \cdot 4 \cdot 3 \cdot 2 \cdot 1}{3 \cdot 2 \cdot 1} = 6720$

$_8P_1 = \dfrac{8!}{(8-1)!} = \dfrac{8!}{7!} = \dfrac{8 \cdot 7 \cdot 6 \cdot 5 \cdot 4 \cdot 3 \cdot 2 \cdot 1}{7 \cdot 6 \cdot 5 \cdot 4 \cdot 3 \cdot 2 \cdot 1} = 8$

$_8P_5 > {_8P_1}$

23. $_6P_2 = \dfrac{6!}{(6-2)!} = \dfrac{6!}{4!} = \dfrac{6 \cdot 5 \cdot 4 \cdot 3 \cdot 2 \cdot 1}{4 \cdot 3 \cdot 2 \cdot 1} = 30$

$_6P_4 = \dfrac{6!}{(6-4)!} = \dfrac{6!}{2!} = \dfrac{6 \cdot 5 \cdot 4 \cdot 3 \cdot 2 \cdot 1}{2 \cdot 1} = 360$

$_6P_2 < {_6P_4}$

24. $_{10}P_{10} = \dfrac{10!}{(10-10)!}$

$= \dfrac{10!}{0!}$

$= \dfrac{10 \cdot 9 \cdot 8 \cdot 7 \cdot 6 \cdot 5 \cdot 4 \cdot 3 \cdot 2 \cdot 1}{1}$

$= 3,628,800$

$_9P_9 = \dfrac{9!}{(9-9)!}$

$= \dfrac{9!}{0!}$

$= \dfrac{9 \cdot 8 \cdot 7 \cdot 6 \cdot 5 \cdot 4 \cdot 3 \cdot 2 \cdot 1}{1}$

$= 362,880$

$_{10}P_{10} > {_9P_9}$

25. $_5P_1 = \dfrac{5!}{(5-1)!} = \dfrac{5!}{4!} = \dfrac{5 \cdot 4 \cdot 3 \cdot 2 \cdot 1}{4 \cdot 3 \cdot 2 \cdot 1} = 5$

$_8P_1 = \dfrac{8!}{(8-1)!} = \dfrac{8!}{7!} = \dfrac{8 \cdot 7 \cdot 6 \cdot 5 \cdot 4 \cdot 3 \cdot 2 \cdot 1}{7 \cdot 6 \cdot 5 \cdot 4 \cdot 3 \cdot 2 \cdot 1} = 8$

$_5P_1 < {_8P_1}$

26. $_7P_7 = \dfrac{7!}{(7-7)!} = \dfrac{7!}{0!} = \dfrac{7 \cdot 6 \cdot 5 \cdot 4 \cdot 3 \cdot 2 \cdot 1}{1} = 5040$

$7! = 7 \cdot 6 \cdot 5 \cdot 4 \cdot 3 \cdot 2 \cdot 1 = 5040$

$_7P_7 = 7!$

27. $_4P_3 = \dfrac{4!}{(4-3)!} = \dfrac{4!}{1!} = \dfrac{4 \cdot 3 \cdot 2 \cdot 1}{1} = 24$

$_6P_2 = \dfrac{6!}{(6-2)!} = \dfrac{6!}{4!} = \dfrac{6 \cdot 5 \cdot 4 \cdot 3 \cdot 2 \cdot 1}{4 \cdot 3 \cdot 2 \cdot 1} = 30$

$_4P_3 < {_6P_2}$

28. Consider the number of permutations of x objects taken x at a time. This is equal to $x!$ as shown in Example 1 on page 675 in the text. When you calculate $_xP_x$ using the permutation formula, the numerator is $x!$, while the denominator is $(x - x)! = 0!$. Because you already know that the number of permutations of x objects taken x at a time is equal to $x!$, $0!$ must equal 1.

Problem Solving

29. $10 \cdot 9 \cdot 8 \cdot 7 = 5040$

There are 5040 different permutations possible.

30. $15 \cdot 14 \cdot 13 \cdot 12 \cdot 11 = 360,360$

The batters can be chosen in 360,360 different ways.

31. Your friend is correct in saying $11! = 11 \cdot 10!$

$11! = 11 \cdot (10 \cdot 9 \cdot 8 \cdot 7 \cdot 6 \cdot 5 \cdot 4 \cdot 3 \cdot 2 \cdot 1) = 11 \cdot 10!$

32. C; $_6P_4 = \dfrac{6!}{(6-4)!} = \dfrac{6!}{2!} = \dfrac{6 \cdot 5 \cdot 4 \cdot 3 \cdot 2 \cdot 1}{2 \cdot 1} = 360$

You can knit 360 different hats.

33. $_7P_3 = \dfrac{7!}{(7-3)!} = \dfrac{7!}{4!} = \dfrac{7 \cdot 6 \cdot 5 \cdot 4 \cdot 3 \cdot 2 \cdot 1}{4 \cdot 3 \cdot 2 \cdot 1} = 210$

There are 210 permutations.

34. In Example 1, you found the number of permutations of 5 CDs taken 5 at a time, or $_5P_5$, which is

$_5P_5 = \dfrac{5!}{(5-5)!} = 5! = 120.$

35. $_4P_2 = \dfrac{4!}{(4-2)!} = \dfrac{4!}{2!} = \dfrac{4 \cdot 3 \cdot 2 \cdot 1}{2 \cdot 1} = 12$

There are 12 different ways you can call two friends.

Ed	Sue
Ed	Ty
Ed	Nestor
Sue	Ed
Sue	Ty
Sue	Nestor
Ty	Ed
Ty	Sue
Ty	Nestor
Nestor	Ed
Nestor	Sue
Nestor	Ty

Chapter 12, *continued*

36. a. $_{50}P_3 = \dfrac{50!}{(50-3)!}$

$= \dfrac{50!}{47!}$

$= \dfrac{50 \cdot 49 \cdot 48 \cdot \ldots \cdot 3 \cdot 2 \cdot 1}{47 \cdot 46 \cdot 45 \cdot \ldots \cdot 3 \cdot 2 \cdot 1}$

$= 117,600$

The winners can be chosen in 117,600 different ways.

b. $_{50}P_4 = \dfrac{50!}{(50-4)!}$

$= \dfrac{50!}{46!}$

$= \dfrac{50 \cdot 49 \cdot 48 \cdot \ldots \cdot 3 \cdot 2 \cdot 1}{46 \cdot 45 \cdot 44 \cdot \ldots \cdot 3 \cdot 2 \cdot 1}$

$= 5,527,200$

The winners can be chosen in 5,527,200 different ways.

c. The number in part (b) is 47 times the number in part (a). This is because there are 47 people left to win the fourth prize.

37. a. $15 \cdot 14 \cdot 13 \cdot 12 = 32,760$

There are 32,760 ways the trophies can be awarded.

b. There would be fewer ways to give the awards. If order does not matter, then there will be fewer ways to give the awards.

38.

r	$_6P_r$	$_7P_r$	$_8P_r$
1	6	7	8
2	30	42	56
3	120	210	336
4	360	840	1680
5	720	2520	6720
6	720	5040	20,160
7		5040	40,320
8			40,320

The last two values in each column are the same.

39. The expression $_{23}P_{23}$ has the greatest value. For a given value of n, the permutation $_nP_r$ is greatest when $r = n$ (or $r = n - 1$).

40. Make an input-output table for $_{20}P_r$.

r	$_{20}P_r$
1	20
2	380
3	6840
4	116,280
5	1,860,480
6	27,907,200

Note in the table that $20 \cdot 19 = 380$, $380 \cdot 18 = 6840$, $6840 \cdot 17 = 116,280$, $116,280 \cdot 16 = 1,860,480$, and $1,860,480 \cdot 15 = 27,907,200$. So, each time r is increased by 1, $_{20}P_r$ increases by a factor of $20 - r$.

So, $_{20}P_{r+1} = (_{20}P_r)(20 - r)$.

Mixed Review

41.

There are 2(2), or 4 choices possible.

42.

red — black, silver
green — black, silver
blue — black, silver
gray — black, silver

There are 4(2), or 8 choices possible.

43.

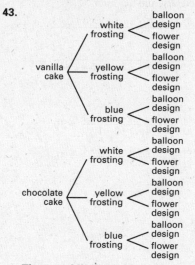

There are 2(3)(2), or 12 possible cakes that you can make.

44. (1) Read and Understand

(2) Make a Plan: Draw a Diagram

(3) Solve the Problem:

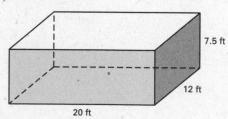

Chapter 12, *continued*

We need to find the total area of the 4 walls. There are 2 walls each of:

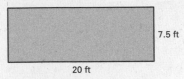

7.5 ft

20 ft

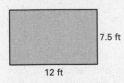

7.5 ft

12 ft

$A = 2(20)(7.5) + 2(12)(7.5) = 300 + 180 = 480 \text{ ft}^2$

The cost for paint is 480($.40), or $192. The cost for wallpaper is 480($.70), or $336.

(4) Look Back

Sample answer: I used Draw a Diagram to draw the walls so I could easily find the area and compute the costs.

45. A; $S = \pi r^2 + \pi r \ell = \pi(5)^2 + \pi(5)(24) = 145\pi$

The surface area of the cone is 145π square inches.

Lesson 12.6

12.6 Guided Practice (pp. 680–682)

1. AB ~~BA~~
AC ~~CA~~
AD ~~DA~~
BC ~~CB~~
BD ~~DB~~
CD ~~DC~~

You have 6 choices of groups to take to the fair.

2. $_8C_8 = \dfrac{_8P_8}{8!} = \dfrac{8 \cdot 7 \cdot 6 \cdot 5 \cdot 4 \cdot 3 \cdot 2 \cdot 1}{8 \cdot 7 \cdot 6 \cdot 5 \cdot 4 \cdot 3 \cdot 2 \cdot 1} = 1$

3. $_8C_7 = \dfrac{_8P_7}{7!} = \dfrac{8 \cdot 7 \cdot 6 \cdot 5 \cdot 4 \cdot 3 \cdot 2}{7 \cdot 6 \cdot 5 \cdot 4 \cdot 3 \cdot 2 \cdot 1} = 8$

4. $_7C_2 = \dfrac{_7P_2}{2!} = \dfrac{7 \cdot 6}{2 \cdot 1} = 21$

5. $_6C_1 = \dfrac{_6P_1}{1!} = \dfrac{6}{1} = 6$

6. $_7C_4 = \dfrac{_7P_4}{4!} = \dfrac{7 \cdot 6 \cdot 5 \cdot 4}{4 \cdot 3 \cdot 2 \cdot 1} = 35$

There are 35 combinations of books that can be purchased.

7. Order is not important in choosing the toppings, so, the possibilities can be counted by evaluating $_{12}C_3$.

8. Because the members can be president or vice president, order is important. So, the possibilities can be counted by evaluating $_{15}P_2$.

12.6 Exercises (pp. 682–684)

Skill Practice

1. The expression $_9C_5$ represents the number of combinations of 9 objects taken 5 at a time.

2. To find the number of combinations of n objects taken r at a time, divide the number of *permutations* of n objects taken r at a time by $r!$.

3. 12 13 14 15
~~21~~ 23 24 25
~~31~~ ~~32~~ 34 35
~~41~~ ~~42~~ ~~43~~ 45
~~51~~ ~~52~~ ~~53~~ ~~54~~

There are 10 different pairs of essay questions.

4. D; $_6C_3 = \dfrac{_6P_3}{3!} = \dfrac{6 \cdot 5 \cdot 4}{3!}$

5. $_4C_1 = \dfrac{_4P_1}{1!} = \dfrac{4}{1} = 4$

6. $_4C_4 = \dfrac{_4P_4}{4!} = \dfrac{4 \cdot 3 \cdot 2 \cdot 1}{4 \cdot 3 \cdot 2 \cdot 1} = 1$

7. $_7C_6 = \dfrac{_7P_6}{6!} = \dfrac{7 \cdot 6 \cdot 5 \cdot 4 \cdot 3 \cdot 2}{6 \cdot 5 \cdot 4 \cdot 3 \cdot 2 \cdot 1} = 7$

8. $_5C_2 = \dfrac{_5P_2}{2!} = \dfrac{5 \cdot 4}{2 \cdot 1} = 10$

9. $_8C_6 = \dfrac{_8P_6}{6!} = \dfrac{8 \cdot 7 \cdot 6 \cdot 5 \cdot 4 \cdot 3}{6 \cdot 5 \cdot 4 \cdot 3 \cdot 2 \cdot 1} = 28$

10. $_8C_1 = \dfrac{_8P_1}{1!} = \dfrac{8}{1} = 8$

11. $_{10}C_8 = \dfrac{_{10}P_8}{8!} = \dfrac{10 \cdot 9 \cdot 8 \cdot 7 \cdot 6 \cdot 5 \cdot 4 \cdot 3}{8 \cdot 7 \cdot 6 \cdot 5 \cdot 4 \cdot 3 \cdot 2 \cdot 1} = 45$

12. $_9C_5 = \dfrac{_9P_5}{5!} = \dfrac{9 \cdot 8 \cdot 7 \cdot 6 \cdot 5}{5 \cdot 4 \cdot 3 \cdot 2 \cdot 1} = 126$

13. $_{11}C_3 = \dfrac{_{11}P_3}{3!} = \dfrac{11 \cdot 10 \cdot 9}{3 \cdot 2 \cdot 1} = 165$

14. $_{13}C_{11} = \dfrac{_{13}P_{11}}{11!}$

$= \dfrac{13 \cdot 12 \cdot 11 \cdot 10 \cdot 9 \cdot 8 \cdot 7 \cdot 6 \cdot 5 \cdot 4 \cdot 3}{11 \cdot 10 \cdot 9 \cdot 8 \cdot 7 \cdot 6 \cdot 5 \cdot 4 \cdot 3 \cdot 2 \cdot 1}$

$= 78$

15. $_9C_2 = \dfrac{_9P_2}{2!} = \dfrac{9 \cdot 8}{2 \cdot 1} = 36$

16. $_{100}C_{99} = \dfrac{_{100}P_{99}}{99!} = \dfrac{100 \cdot 99 \cdot 98 \cdot \,\cdots\, \cdot 3 \cdot 2}{99 \cdot 98 \cdot \,\cdots\, \cdot 3 \cdot 2 \cdot 1} = 100$

17. Order of the colors is not important, so the possibilities can be counted by evaluating $_8C_2$, not $_8P_2$.

$_8C_2 = \dfrac{_8P_2}{2!} = \dfrac{8 \cdot 7}{2 \cdot 1} = 28$ color pairs

18. Order is not important in choosing balloon colors, so the possibilities can be counted by evaluating $_4C_2$.

$_4C_2 = \dfrac{_4P_2}{2!} = \dfrac{4 \cdot 3}{2 \cdot 1} = 6$

You can choose from 6 groups of balloons.

Chapter 12, *continued*

19. Order is important in choosing how to do your homework, so the possibilities can be counted by evaluating a permutation.

$$4! = 4 \cdot 3 \cdot 2 \cdot 1 = 24$$

You can do your homework in 24 different orders.

20. Order is important in choosing how to play the songs, so the possibilities can be counted by evaluating a permutation.

$$5! = 5 \cdot 4 \cdot 3 \cdot 2 \cdot 1 = 120$$

You can play the songs in 120 ways.

21. Order is not important in choosing the vegetables for the soup, so the possibilities can be counted by evaluating $_5C_3$.

$$_5C_3 = \frac{_5P_3}{3!} = \frac{5 \cdot 4 \cdot 3}{3 \cdot 2 \cdot 1} = 10$$

You can choose from 10 groups of vegetables.

22.

$_7C_0$	$_7C_1$	$_7C_2$	$_7C_3$	$_7C_4$	$_7C_5$	$_7C_6$	$_7C_7$
1	7	21	35	35	21	7	1

$$_7C_0 = \frac{_7P_0}{0!} = \frac{1}{1} = 1$$

$$_7C_1 = \frac{_7P_1}{1!} = \frac{7}{1} = 7$$

$$_7C_2 = \frac{_7P_2}{2!} = \frac{7 \cdot 6}{2 \cdot 1} = 21$$

$$_7C_3 = \frac{_7P_3}{3!} = \frac{7 \cdot 6 \cdot 5}{3 \cdot 2 \cdot 1} = 35$$

$$_7C_4 = \frac{_7P_4}{4!} = \frac{7 \cdot 6 \cdot 5 \cdot 4}{4 \cdot 3 \cdot 2 \cdot 1} = 35$$

$$_7C_5 = \frac{_7P_5}{5!} = \frac{7 \cdot 6 \cdot 5 \cdot 4 \cdot 3}{5 \cdot 4 \cdot 3 \cdot 2 \cdot 1} = 21$$

$$_7C_6 = \frac{_7P_6}{6!} = \frac{7 \cdot 6 \cdot 5 \cdot 4 \cdot 3 \cdot 2}{6 \cdot 5 \cdot 4 \cdot 3 \cdot 2 \cdot 1} = 7$$

$$_7C_7 = \frac{_7P_7}{7!} = \frac{7 \cdot 6 \cdot 5 \cdot 4 \cdot 3 \cdot 2 \cdot 1}{7 \cdot 6 \cdot 5 \cdot 4 \cdot 3 \cdot 2 \cdot 1} = 1$$

Sample answer: The numbers form a symmetrical pattern increasing from 1 to 35, then decreasing from 35 to 1. If two values of r in $_7C_r$ have a sum of 7, then the corresponding values of $_7C_r$ are the same.

23.
$$_nC_3 \geq 20$$

$$\frac{_nP_3}{3!} \geq 20$$

$$_nP_3 \geq 3!(20)$$
$$_nP_3 \geq 6 \cdot 20$$
$$_nP_3 \geq 120$$

$$\frac{n!}{(n-3)!} \geq 120$$

$$n! \geq 120(n-3)!$$

Because $5! = 120$, n is any whole number greater than or equal to 6, i.e., 6, 7, 8, ...

24.
$$_nC_2 < 21$$

$$\frac{_nP_2}{2!} < 21$$

$$_nP_2 < 2!(21)$$
$$_nP_2 < 2 \cdot 21$$
$$_nP_2 < 42$$

$$\frac{n!}{(n-2)!} < 42$$

$$n! < 42(n-2)!$$

You can't evaluate the factorial of a negative integer, so $n \geq 2$. Because 3! and 4! are both less than 42, $n = 3$ and $n = 4$ are also solutions to the inequality.

Check $n = 5$:　　　Check $n = 6$:　　　Check $n = 7$:

$5! \overset{?}{<} 42(5-2)!$　　$6! \overset{?}{<} 42(6-2)!$　　$7! < 42(7-2)!$

$120 \overset{?}{<} 42(3!)$　　$720 \overset{?}{<} 42(4!)$　　$5040 < 42(5!)$

$120 < 252$ ✓　　$720 < 1008$ ✓　　$5040 \not< 5040$

So, $n = 2, 3, 4, 5,$ or 6.

25. $_6C_r \leq 15$

$$_6C_0 = \frac{_6P_0}{0!} = \frac{1}{1} = 1$$

$$_6C_1 = \frac{_6P_1}{1!} = \frac{6}{1} = 6$$

$$_6C_2 = \frac{_6P_2}{2!} = \frac{6 \cdot 5}{2 \cdot 1} = 15$$

$$_6C_3 = \frac{_6P_3}{3!} = \frac{6 \cdot 5 \cdot 4}{3 \cdot 2 \cdot 1} = 20$$

$$_6C_4 = \frac{_6P_4}{4!} = \frac{6 \cdot 5 \cdot 4 \cdot 3}{4 \cdot 3 \cdot 2 \cdot 1} = 15$$

$$_6C_5 = \frac{_6P_5}{5!} = \frac{6 \cdot 5 \cdot 4 \cdot 3 \cdot 2}{5 \cdot 4 \cdot 3 \cdot 2 \cdot 1} = 6$$

$$_6C_6 = \frac{_6P_6}{6!} = \frac{6 \cdot 5 \cdot 4 \cdot 3 \cdot 2 \cdot 1}{6 \cdot 5 \cdot 4 \cdot 3 \cdot 2 \cdot 1} = 1$$

So, $r = 0, 1, 2, 4, 5,$ or 6.

26. $_8C_r > 28$

$$_8C_0 = \frac{_8P_0}{0!} = \frac{1}{1} = 1$$

$$_8C_1 = \frac{_8P_1}{1!} = \frac{8}{1} = 8$$

$$_8C_2 = \frac{_8P_2}{2!} = \frac{8 \cdot 7}{2 \cdot 1} = 28$$

$$_8C_3 = \frac{_8P_3}{3!} = \frac{8 \cdot 7 \cdot 6}{3 \cdot 2 \cdot 1} = 56$$

$$_8C_4 = \frac{_8P_4}{4!} = \frac{8 \cdot 7 \cdot 6 \cdot 5}{4 \cdot 3 \cdot 2 \cdot 1} = 70$$

$$_8C_5 = \frac{_8P_5}{5!} = \frac{8 \cdot 7 \cdot 6 \cdot 5 \cdot 4}{5 \cdot 4 \cdot 3 \cdot 2 \cdot 1} = 56$$

$$_8C_6 = \frac{_8P_6}{6!} = \frac{8 \cdot 7 \cdot 6 \cdot 5 \cdot 4 \cdot 3}{6 \cdot 5 \cdot 4 \cdot 3 \cdot 2 \cdot 1} = 28$$

$$_8C_7 = \frac{_8P_7}{7!} = \frac{8 \cdot 7 \cdot 6 \cdot 5 \cdot 4 \cdot 3 \cdot 2}{7 \cdot 6 \cdot 5 \cdot 4 \cdot 3 \cdot 2} = 8$$

$$_8C_8 = \frac{_8P_8}{8!} = \frac{8 \cdot 7 \cdot 6 \cdot 5 \cdot 4 \cdot 3 \cdot 2 \cdot 1}{8 \cdot 7 \cdot 6 \cdot 5 \cdot 4 \cdot 3 \cdot 2 \cdot 1} = 1$$

So, $r = 3, 4,$ or 5.

Chapter 12, *continued*

Problem Solving

27. $_6C_2 = \frac{_6P_2}{2!} = \frac{6 \cdot 5}{2 \cdot 1} = 15$

There are 15 combinations of 2 projects possible.

28. $_{18}C_2 = \frac{_{18}P_2}{2!} = \frac{18 \cdot 17}{2 \cdot 1} = 153$

There are 153 combinations possible.

29. $_{12}C_5 = \frac{_{12}P_5}{5!} = \frac{12 \cdot 11 \cdot 10 \cdot 9 \cdot 8}{5 \cdot 4 \cdot 3 \cdot 2 \cdot 1} = 792$

You can choose from 792 different teams.

30. $_9C_4 = \frac{_9P_4}{4!} = \frac{9 \cdot 8 \cdot 7 \cdot 6}{4 \cdot 3 \cdot 2 \cdot 1} = 126$

There are 126 groups of vegetables.

31. C; $_5C_3 = \frac{_5P_3}{3!} = \frac{5 \cdot 4 \cdot 3}{3 \cdot 2 \cdot 1} = 10$

You and your friends can make 10 different groups of 3 people.

32. No; $_nC_r$ is the number of combinations of n objects taken r at a time. You cannot take more objects at a time than total objects. For example, you cannot take 4 objects at a time from a group of 3 objects.

33. *Sample answer:* When order is not important, use combinations. For example, you want to find the number of groups of 4 movies you can take from a collection of 30 movies. When order is important, use permutations. For example, you want to find the number of orders in which you can watch the 4 movies.

34. If $r = 1$, then $_nP_1 = \frac{n!}{(n-1)!}$ and $_nC_1 = \frac{_nP_1}{1!} = \frac{n!}{(n-1)!}$.

So, $_nP_r = {}_nC_r$. Because $_nC_r = \frac{_nP_r}{r!}$, for $r > 1$ and $r \le n$, $_nP_r > {}_nC_r$. So, the value of $_nP_r$ is sometimes greater than the value of $_nC_r$.

35. a. When finding the number of ways to color 8 states using 8 colors, find 8!.

$8! = 8 \cdot 7 \cdot 6 \cdot 5 \cdot 4 \cdot 3 \cdot 2 \cdot 1 = 40{,}320$

You can color the map in 40,320 ways if you have 8 colors.

b. Order is not important when finding the number of ways to choose 8 colors from 10 colors. So, find $_{10}C_8$.

$_{10}C_8 = \frac{10 \cdot 9 \cdot 8 \cdot 7 \cdot 6 \cdot 5 \cdot 4 \cdot 3}{8 \cdot 7 \cdot 6 \cdot 5 \cdot 4 \cdot 3 \cdot 2 \cdot 1} = 45$

There are 45 groups of eight colors.

c. When finding the number of ways to color the map, order is important. So, find $_{10}P_8$.

$_{10}P_8 = \frac{10!}{(10-8)!}$

$= \frac{10!}{2!}$

$= \frac{10 \cdot 9 \cdot 8 \cdot 7 \cdot 6 \cdot 5 \cdot 4 \cdot 3 \cdot 2 \cdot 1}{2 \cdot 1}$

$= 1{,}814{,}400$

There are 1,814,400 ways to color the map.

36. Order is not important when finding the groups of games you borrow. So, find $_{20}C_4$.

$_{20}C_4 = \frac{_{20}P_4}{4!} = \frac{20 \cdot 19 \cdot 18 \cdot 17}{4 \cdot 3 \cdot 2 \cdot 1} = 4845$

There are 4845 groups of 4 games.

If you already know 2 of the games, then you need to choose 2 more from 18 video games.

$_{18}C_2 = \frac{_{18}P_2}{2!} = \frac{18 \cdot 17}{2 \cdot 1} = 153$

There are 153 groups of 4 games when you know 2 of your choices.

37. $_nC_r$ when $r = n$:

$_nC_r = {}_nC_n = \frac{_nP_n}{n!} = \frac{n!}{n!} = 1$

So when $r = n$, $_nC_r = 1$.

$_nC_r$ when $n - r = 1$:

$_nC_r = \frac{_nP_r}{r!} = \frac{\frac{n!}{(n-r)!}}{r!} = \frac{\frac{n!}{1}}{r!} = \frac{n!}{r!} = n$

When $n - r = 1$, $_nC_r = n$.

Mixed Review

38. $P(\text{blue}) = \frac{2}{6} = \frac{1}{3}$

The probability of landing on blue is $\frac{1}{3}$.

39. $P(\text{red}) = \frac{1}{6}$

The probability of landing on red is $\frac{1}{6}$.

40. $P(\text{green}) = \frac{3}{6} = \frac{1}{2}$

The probability of landing on green is $\frac{1}{2}$.

41. $P(\text{white}) = \frac{0}{6} = 0$

The probability of landing on white is 0.

42. $_{10}P_5 = \frac{10!}{(10-5)!}$

$= \frac{10!}{5!}$

$= \frac{10 \cdot 9 \cdot 8 \cdot 7 \cdot 6 \cdot 5 \cdot 4 \cdot 3 \cdot 2 \cdot 1}{5 \cdot 4 \cdot 3 \cdot 2 \cdot 1}$

$= 30{,}240$

43. $_{11}P_4 = \frac{11!}{(11-4)!}$

$= \frac{11!}{7!}$

$= \frac{11 \cdot 10 \cdot 9 \cdot 8 \cdot 7 \cdot 6 \cdot 5 \cdot 4 \cdot 3 \cdot 2 \cdot 1}{7 \cdot 6 \cdot 5 \cdot 4 \cdot 3 \cdot 2 \cdot 1}$

$= 7920$

Chapter 12, continued

44. $_{18}P_3 = \dfrac{18!}{(18-3)!}$

$= \dfrac{18!}{15!}$

$= \dfrac{18 \cdot 17 \cdot 16 \cdot 15 \cdot \ldots \cdot 3 \cdot 2 \cdot 1}{15 \cdot \ldots \cdot 3 \cdot 2 \cdot 1}$

$= 4896$

45. $_{21}P_2 = \dfrac{21!}{(21-2)!}$

$= \dfrac{21!}{19!}$

$= \dfrac{21 \cdot 20 \cdot 19 \cdot \ldots \cdot 3 \cdot 2 \cdot 1}{19 \cdot \ldots \cdot 3 \cdot 2 \cdot 1}$

$= 420$

46.

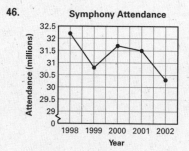

Symphony Attendance

Sample answer: Overall, the attendance appears to be decreasing over time.

Lesson 12.7

Activity (p. 685)

1. It is more likely for the spinner to land on red because there are more red sections.

2. a. $\dfrac{\text{Number of red sections}}{\text{Number of blue sections}} = \dfrac{3}{1}$

It is 3 times more likely that the spinner will land on red than blue.

b. $\dfrac{\text{Number of blue sections}}{\text{Number of red sections}} = \dfrac{1}{3}$

It is $\dfrac{1}{3}$ as likely the spinner will land on blue as on red.

3. To find the probability of the spinner not landing on red, find the probability of the spinner landing on blue.

12.7 Guided Practice (pp. 686–687)

1. $P(\text{not A}) = 1 - P(\text{A}) = 1 - \dfrac{3}{4} = \dfrac{1}{4}$

2. $P(\text{not A}) = 1 - P(\text{A}) = 1 - 0.45 = 0.55$

3. $P(\text{not A}) = 1 - P(\text{A}) = 100\% - 32\% = 68\%$

4. $P(\text{not A}) = 1 - P(\text{A}) = 1 - \dfrac{7}{10} = \dfrac{3}{10}$

5. $P(\text{S}) = \dfrac{4}{11}$

$P(\text{not S}) = 1 - P(\text{S}) = 1 - \dfrac{4}{11} = \dfrac{7}{11}$

The probability of drawing as S from the bag is $\dfrac{4}{11}$ and the probability of not drawing an S is $\dfrac{7}{11}$.

6. Odds in favor $= \dfrac{1}{23}$

The odds in favor of choosing a 10 is 1 to 23.

7. Odds in favor $= \dfrac{12}{12} = 1$

The odds in favor of choosing an add number is 1 to 1.

8. Odds in favor $= \dfrac{8}{16} = \dfrac{1}{2}$

The odds in favor of choosing an even number greater than 8 is 1 to 2.

9. Odds $= \dfrac{0.85}{1-0.85} = \dfrac{0.85}{0.15} = \dfrac{85}{15} = \dfrac{17}{3}$

Sean's odds in favor of making a free throw are 17 to 3.

12.7 Exercises (pp. 687–689)

Skill Practice

1. Find the ratio of the numbers of favorable outcomes to the number of unfavorable outcomes to find the *odds in favor* of an event.

2. Two events are *complementary* when one event or the other (but not both) must occur.

3. $P(\text{not A}) = 1 - P(\text{A}) = 100\% - 84\% = 16\%$

4. $P(\text{not A}) = 1 - P(\text{A}) = 1 - \dfrac{2}{5} = \dfrac{3}{5}$

5. $P(\text{not A}) = 1 - P(\text{A}) = 1 - 0.37 = 0.63$

6. $P(\text{not A}) = 1 - P(\text{A}) = 1 - \dfrac{9}{10} = \dfrac{1}{10}$

7. $P(\text{red}) = \dfrac{3}{10}$

$P(\text{not red}) = 1 - P(\text{red}) = 1 - \dfrac{3}{10} = \dfrac{7}{10}$

Odds of blue $= \dfrac{7}{3}$

The probability of choosing a red marble is $\dfrac{3}{10}$ and the probability of not choosing red is $\dfrac{7}{10}$. The odds of choosing a blue marble are 7 to 3.

8. $P(\text{red}) = \dfrac{4}{13}$

$P(\text{not red}) = 1 - P(\text{red}) = 1 - \dfrac{4}{13} = \dfrac{9}{13}$

Odds of blue $= \dfrac{9}{4}$

The probability of choosing a red marble is $\dfrac{4}{13}$ and the probability of not choosing red is $\dfrac{9}{13}$. The odds of choosing a blue marble are 9 to 4.

9. $P(\text{red}) = \dfrac{6}{11}$

$P(\text{not red}) = 1 - P(\text{red}) = 1 - \dfrac{6}{11} = \dfrac{5}{11}$

Odds of blue $= \dfrac{5}{6}$

The probability of choosing a red marble is $\dfrac{6}{11}$ and the probability of not choosing red is $\dfrac{5}{11}$. The odds of choosing a blue marble are 5 to 6.

10. $P(\text{red}) = \frac{6}{14} = \frac{3}{7}$

$P(\text{not red}) = 1 - P(\text{red}) = 1 - \frac{3}{7} = \frac{4}{7}$

Odds of blue $= \frac{5}{9}$

The probability of choosing a red marble is $\frac{3}{7}$ and the probability of not choosing red is $\frac{4}{7}$. The odds of choosing a blue marble are 5 to 9.

11. The odds of rolling a 3 are 1 to 5.

12. The odds of rolling a number less than 6 are 5 to 1.

13. The odds of rolling a number greater than 2 are 4 to 2, or 2 to 1.

14. The odds of rolling an odd number less than 5 are 2 to 4, or 1 to 2.

15. The numerator and denominator are switched.

Odds $= \frac{2}{4} = \frac{1}{2}$

The odds in favor are 1 to 2.

16. Odds $= \frac{0.05}{1 - 0.05} = \frac{0.05}{0.95} = \frac{5}{95} = \frac{1}{19}$

The odds in favor of selecting the letter I are 1 to 19.

17. Odds $= \frac{0.05}{1 - 0.55} = \frac{0.55}{0.45} = \frac{55}{45} = \frac{11}{9}$

The odds in favor of selecting the letter E are 11 to 9.

18. Odds $= \frac{0.12}{1 - 0.12} = \frac{0.12}{0.88} = \frac{12}{88} = \frac{3}{22}$

The odds in favor of selecting the letter S are 3 to 22.

19. Odds $= \frac{0.08}{1 - 0.08} = \frac{0.08}{0.92} = \frac{8}{92} = \frac{2}{23}$

The odds in favor of selecting the letter R are 2 to 23.

20. D; odds $= \frac{0.60}{1 - 0.60} = \frac{0.60}{0.40} = \frac{60}{40} = \frac{3}{2}$

The odds in favor are 3 to 2.

21. $\frac{P}{1 - P} = \frac{1}{3}$

$3P = 1 - P$

$4P = 1$

$P = \frac{1}{4}$

The probability of the event is $\frac{1}{4}$.

22. $\frac{P}{1 - P} = \frac{1}{1}$

$P = 1 - P$

$2P = 1$

$P = \frac{1}{2}$

The probability of the event is $\frac{1}{2}$.

23. $\frac{P}{1 - P} = \frac{27}{23}$

$23P = 27 - 27P$

$50P = 27$

$P = \frac{27}{50}$

The probability of the event is $\frac{27}{50}$.

24. $\frac{P}{1 - P} = \frac{7}{13}$

$13P = 7 - 7P$

$20P = 7$

$P = \frac{7}{20}$

The probability of the events is $\frac{7}{20}$.

25. Let P represent the probability of the event.

$\frac{P}{1 - P} = \frac{a}{b}$

$bP = a - aP$

$aP + bP = a$

$(a + b)P = a$

$P = \frac{a}{a + b}$

26. If $n = 12$, then there are 3 numbers on the spinner greater than 9. So, $\frac{3}{12}$ or 25% of the numbers are greater than 9.

Odds $= \frac{4}{8} = \frac{1}{2}$

The odds in favor of getting a number less than 5 are 1 to 2.

Problem Solving

27. $P(\text{gym sock}) = \frac{8}{20} = \frac{2}{5}$

$P(\text{not gym sock}) = 1 - P(\text{gym sock}) = 1 - \frac{2}{5} = \frac{3}{5}$

The probability that you do not choose a gym sock is $\frac{3}{5}$.

28. $P(\text{thin crust}) = \frac{28}{100} = \frac{7}{25}$

$P(\text{not thin crust}) = 1 - P(\text{thin crust}) = 1 - \frac{7}{25} = 1 - \frac{18}{25}$

The probability that a randomly chosen pizza order is not for thin crust is $\frac{18}{25}$.

29. The odds in favor of a randomly chosen person ordering a regular crust are 52 to 48, or 13 to 12.

30. The odds in favor of a randomly chosen person not ordering a stuffed crust are 80 to 20, or 4 to 1.

31. Odds $= \frac{0.93}{1 - 0.93} = \frac{0.93}{0.07} = \frac{93}{7}$

The goalie's odds in favor of making a save are 93 to 7.

Chapter 12, *continued*

32. A; Odds of rain $= \dfrac{0.30}{1-0.30} = \dfrac{0.30}{0.70} = \dfrac{30}{70}$

The odds in favor of rain are 3 to 7.

33. Sam and Jan are both right. *Sample answer:* A probability of 0.2, or $\frac{1}{5}$, describes a situation where there is one favorable outcome for every four unfavorable outcomes, which also describes an event where the odds in favor are 1 to 4.

34. The odds in favor of choosing a green chip are 5 to 9. The odds against choosing a green chip are 9 to 5.

35. Your friend is talking about the odds *against* getting hit by lightning because you have 1,000,000 unfavorable outcomes to the one favorable outcome of getting hit by lightning.

36. a. Area of the bull's-eye:

$A = \pi r^2 = \pi(3)^2 = 9\pi$ in.^{2}

Total area of target:

$A = \pi r^2 = \pi(15)^2 = 225\pi$ in.^{2}

b. The probability that an arrow lands within the bull's-eye is $\dfrac{9\pi}{225\pi} = \dfrac{9}{225} = \dfrac{1}{25} = 0.04$.

c. The area of the blue region is

$A = \pi(9)^2 - \pi(3)^2 = 81\pi - 9\pi = 72\pi$

The odds that the arrow hits the blue region are

$\dfrac{72\pi}{225\pi - 72\pi} = \dfrac{72\pi}{153\pi} = \dfrac{8}{17}$.

37. Let P be the probability of winning by drinking a bottle of Beverage A.

$\dfrac{P}{1-P} = \dfrac{1}{11}$

$11P = 1 - P$

$12P = 1$

$P = \dfrac{1}{12}$

The probability of winning with Beverage A is $\dfrac{1}{12}$

Number of times you can expect to win with A:

$\dfrac{1}{12} \cdot 132 = 11$ times

Number of times you can expect to win with B:

$1 + 11 = 12$ times

$132 \cdot x\% = 12$

$\left(\dfrac{100}{132}\right) \cdot \dfrac{132}{100}x = \dfrac{100}{132} \cdot 12$

$x = 9\dfrac{1}{11}$

You have a $9\dfrac{1}{11}\%$ chance of winning with Beverage B.

Mixed Review

38. $\dfrac{1}{5} \cdot \dfrac{1}{5} = \dfrac{1 \cdot 1}{5 \cdot 5} = \dfrac{1}{25}$

39. $\dfrac{3}{4} \cdot \dfrac{3}{4} = \dfrac{3 \cdot 3}{4 \cdot 4} = \dfrac{9}{16}$

40. $\dfrac{5}{6} \cdot \dfrac{4}{5} = \dfrac{\overset{1}{\cancel{5}} \cdot \overset{2}{\cancel{4}}}{\underset{3}{\cancel{6}} \cdot \underset{1}{\cancel{5}}} = \dfrac{2}{3}$

41. $\dfrac{4}{9} \cdot \dfrac{3}{8} = \dfrac{\overset{1}{\cancel{4}} \cdot \overset{1}{\cancel{3}}}{\underset{3}{\cancel{9}} \cdot \underset{2}{\cancel{8}}} = \dfrac{1}{6}$

42. $m = \dfrac{y_2 - y_1}{x_2 - x_1} = \dfrac{12 - 2}{-8 - 9} = \dfrac{10}{-17} = -\dfrac{10}{17}$

The slope of the line is $-\dfrac{10}{17}$.

43. $m = \dfrac{y_2 - y_1}{x_2 - x_1} = \dfrac{5 - 6}{7 - (-3)} = \dfrac{-1}{10} = -\dfrac{1}{10}$

The slope of the line is $-\dfrac{1}{10}$.

44. $m = \dfrac{y_2 - y_1}{x_2 - x_1} = \dfrac{-5 - (-10)}{-1 - (-4)} = \dfrac{5}{3}$

The slope of the line is $\dfrac{5}{3}$.

45. C; $a^2 + b^2 = c^2$

$24^2 + 45^2 = c^2$

$576 + 2025 = c^2$

$2601 = c^2$

$\sqrt{2601} = c$

$51 = c$

The hypotenuse is 51 inches.

12.7 Extension (p. 691)

1. $\sim A = \{-7, -5, -4, -2, -1, 1, 2, 4, 5, 7\}$

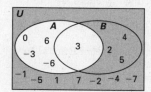

2. $\sim B = \{-7, -6, -5, -4, -3, -2, -1, 0, 1, 6, 7\}$

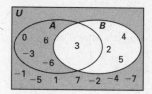

3. $\sim(A \cup B) = \{-7, -5, -4, -2, -1, 1, 7\}$

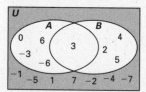

4. $\sim(A \cap B) = \{-7, -6, -5, -4, -3, -2, -1, 0, 1, 2, 4, 5, 6, 7\}$

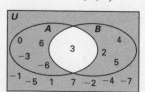

Chapter 12, *continued*

5. $\sim A \cup B = \{-7, -5, -4, -2, -1, 1, 2, 3, 4, 5, 6, 7\}$

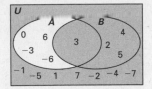

6. $A \cap \sim B = \{-6, -3, 0, 6\}$

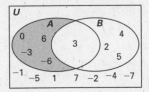

7. $\sim A \cap \sim B = \{-7, -5, -4, -2, -1, 1, 7\}$

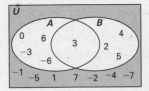

8. $\sim A \cup \sim B = \{-7, -6, -5, -4, -3, -2, -1, 0, 1, 2, 4, 5, 6, 7\}$

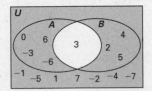

9. $P(\sim A \cup B) = \dfrac{\text{Number of elements in } \sim A \cup B}{\text{Number of elements in } U} = \dfrac{11}{15}$

10. $P(A \cap \sim B) = \dfrac{\text{Number of elements in } A \cap \sim B}{\text{Number of elements in } U} = \dfrac{4}{15}$

11. $P(\sim A \cap \sim B) = \dfrac{\text{Number of elements in } \sim A \cap \sim B}{\text{Number of elements in } U} = \dfrac{7}{15}$

12. $P(\sim A \cup \sim B) = \dfrac{\text{Number of elements in } \sim A \cup \sim B}{\text{Number of elements in } U} = \dfrac{14}{15}$

13. The intersection of a set A and its complement is the empty set. There are no elements that are both in A and not in A.

The union of a set A and its complement is the universal set. The set of all elements in A or not in A is all the elements in U.

14. $\sim A \cup \sim B = \sim(A \cap B)$

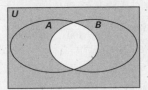

15. $\sim A \cap \sim B = \sim(A \cup B)$

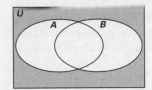

16. $A \cap \sim B = \sim(\sim A \cup B)$

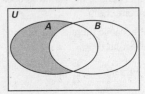

17. $A \cup \sim B = \sim(\sim A \cap B)$

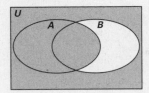

Lesson 12.8

Investigation (pp. 692–693)

Steps 1–3. A good answer will include an accurate recording of the results for drawing 10 pairs of cards and correct experimental probability computed.

1. Answers will vary. Check class results.

2. *Sample answer:* You can roll the die twice and record your results. Each pair n, n must be disregarded because you need to choose two different students. Keep repeating until 10 pairs are recorded.

Explore 2

Step 4. Answers will vary.

3. *Sample answer:* Assign random numbers 1, 2, and 3 to the choices, and simulate the situation by using a calculator to generate a random integer of 1, 2, or 3.

4. *Sample answer:* Write the numbers 1 through 10 on index cards. Simulate choosing co-captains by drawing two index cards. Do not replace the first card before drawing the second.

5. The class results are more likely to be close to the theoretical probability.

Sample answer: There were more trials.

Chapter 12, *continued*

6. *Sample answer:* In the simulation, (1, 1), (2, 2), (3, 3), (4, 4), (5, 5), (6, 6), (7, 7) and (8, 8) are all favorable outcomes. The probability that you are the person chosen twice in a row is lower than the probability that any student is chosen twice in a row, so consider only (1, 1) a favorable outcome.

12.8 Guided Practice (pp. 695–696)

1. The events are independent because the coin toss does not affect rolling the number cube.

2. The events are dependent because there is one fewer marble in the bag for the second draw.

3. $P(2 \text{ heads}) = P(\text{heads}) \cdot P(\text{heads}) = \frac{1}{2} \cdot \frac{1}{2} = \frac{1}{4}$

The probability is $\frac{1}{4}$, or 25%.

4. $P(\text{B7 or N44}) = \frac{2}{36} = \frac{1}{18}$

$P(\text{remaining number}) = \frac{1}{35}$

$P(\text{both numbers}) = \frac{1}{18} \cdot \frac{1}{35} = \frac{1}{630}$

The probability that you will get bingo when the next two numbers are called is $\frac{1}{630}$, or about 0.2%.

5. $P(\text{dry cleaners or hair salon}) = \frac{2}{40} = \frac{1}{20}$

$P(\text{remaining card}) = \frac{1}{39}$

$P(\text{both dry cleaners and hair salon}) = \frac{1}{20} \cdot \frac{1}{39} = \frac{1}{780}$

The probability that you choose the cards for the dry cleaners and the hair salon is $\frac{1}{780}$, or about 0.1%.

12.8 Exercises (pp. 697–700)

Skill Practice

1. When the occurrence of an event does not affect the probability of the next event, the events are *independent*.

2. Two events are *dependent* events if the occurrence of one event affects the probability that the other event will occur.

3. Because you replace the marble, the events are independent.

4. The events are dependent because once you have been chosen, there is one less student from which to choose.

5. The events are dependent because there is one fewer password in the list when your friend chooses a password.

6. Because you replace the card, the events are independent.

7. $P(\text{A and B}) = P(\text{A}) \cdot P(\text{B}) = 0.4(0.6) = 0.24$

8. $P(\text{A and B}) = P(\text{A}) \cdot P(\text{B})$

$0.09 = 0.9 \cdot P(\text{B})$

$0.1 = P(\text{B})$

9. $P(\text{A and B}) = P(\text{A}) \cdot P(\text{B})$

$0.12 = P(\text{A}) \cdot 0.6$

$0.2 = P(\text{A})$

10. $P(\text{C and D}) = P(\text{C}) \cdot P(\text{D given C}) = 0.75(0.5) = 0.375$

11. $P(\text{C and D}) = P(\text{C}) \cdot P(\text{D given C})$

$0.32 = 0.8 \cdot P(\text{D given C})$

$0.4 = P(\text{D given C})$

12. $P(\text{C and D}) = P(\text{C}) \cdot P(\text{D given C})$

$0.39 = P(\text{C})(0.3)$

$0.13 = P(\text{C})$

13. C; $P(\text{both blue}) = P(\text{blue}) \cdot P(\text{blue}) = \frac{2}{4} \cdot \frac{2}{4} = \frac{1}{4}$

14. The probability is the product, not the sum.

$P(\text{A and B}) = P(\text{A}) \cdot P(\text{B given A}) = 0.2(0.25) = 0.05$

15. *Sample answer:*

Independent events:

You toss a coin and roll a number cube. What is the probability of getting a head and rolling a 4.

$P(\text{head}) = \frac{1}{2}$

$P(\text{rolling a 4}) = \frac{1}{6}$

$P(\text{head and rolling a 4}) = \frac{1}{2} \cdot \frac{1}{6} = \frac{1}{12}$

Dependent events:

You draw a card from a deck of cards. Then your friend draws another card. What is the probability of drawing a king and then drawing a queen?

$P(\text{king or queen}) = \frac{4}{52}$

$P(\text{queen given king}) = \frac{4}{51}$

$P(\text{king and queen}) = \frac{4}{52} \cdot \frac{4}{51} = \frac{16}{2652} = \frac{4}{663}$

16. Yes; The blue region is about $\frac{1}{2}$, or 0.5, of the spinner, and the red region is about $\frac{1}{4}$, or 0.25, of the spinner. So, the probability of the spinner landing on the blue region and then the red region is about $0.5 \cdot 0.25$, or 0.125.

17. $P(\text{A then A}) = P(\text{A}) \cdot P(\text{A}) = \frac{9}{100} \cdot \frac{9}{100} = \frac{81}{10,000}$

18. $P(\text{A then A}) = P(\text{A}) \cdot P(\text{A given A})$

$= \frac{9}{100} \cdot \frac{8}{99}$

$= \frac{72}{9900}$

$= \frac{2}{275}$

19. $P(\text{T then H}) = P(\text{T}) \cdot P(\text{H})$

$$= \frac{6}{100} \cdot \frac{2}{100}$$

$$= \frac{12}{10,000}$$

$$= \frac{3}{2500}$$

20. $P(\text{T then H}) = P(\text{T}) \cdot P(\text{H given T})$

$$= \frac{6}{100} \cdot \frac{2}{99}$$

$$= \frac{12}{9900}$$

$$= \frac{1}{825}$$

21. $P(\text{D then A}) = P(\text{D}) \cdot P(\text{A given D})$

$$\frac{1}{275} = \frac{x}{100} \cdot \frac{9}{99}$$

$$\frac{1}{275} = \frac{x}{100} \cdot \frac{1}{11}$$

$$\frac{1}{275} = \frac{x}{1100}$$

$$1100 = 275x$$

$$4 = x$$

There are 4 D's in the bag.

22. $P(\text{E then T}) = P(\text{E}) \cdot P(\text{T})$

$$\frac{9}{1250} = \frac{x}{100} \cdot \frac{6}{100}$$

$$\frac{9}{1250} = \frac{6x}{10,000}$$

$$90,000 = 7500x$$

$$12 = x$$

There are 12 E's in the bag.

Problem Solving

23. The events are dependent because you do not replace the button you drew.

$P(\text{red then yellow}) = P(\text{red}) \cdot P(\text{yellow given red})$

$$= \frac{10}{20} \cdot \frac{2}{19}$$

$$= \frac{1}{19}$$

The probability of drawing a red button and then a yellow button is $\frac{1}{19}$.

$P(\text{yellow then blue}) = P(\text{yellow}) \cdot P(\text{blue given yellow})$

$$= \frac{2}{20} \cdot \frac{4}{19}$$

$$= \frac{8}{380}$$

$$= \frac{2}{95}$$

The probability of drawing a yellow button and then a blue button is $\frac{2}{95}$.

24. The events are independent because an order of a main course does not affect the drink order.

There are 4(5), or 20 choices.

The probability of ordering a chef's salad and juice is $\frac{1}{20}$.

25. The events are dependent because there is one less roll after the first pick. There are $5 + 6 + 8 + 9$, or 28 rolls.

The probability of choosing a sesame, then a cheese roll is $\frac{8}{28} \cdot \frac{9}{27}$, or $\frac{2}{21}$.

26. $P(\text{win both days})$

$= P(\text{win on Wednesday}) \cdot P(\text{win on Thursday})$

$$= \frac{1}{127} \cdot \frac{1}{134}$$

$$= \frac{1}{17,018}$$

The probability that you win on both days is $\frac{1}{17,018}$.

27. The probability of B given A is $\frac{3}{9}$ because the first card drawn was not replaced.

$P(\text{A and B}) = P(\text{A}) \cdot P(\text{B given A}) = \frac{4}{10} \cdot \frac{3}{9} = \frac{12}{90} = \frac{2}{15}$

28. The probability that your name will be chosen first is $\frac{1}{25}$.

Yes; *Sample answer:* After one name is drawn, there are only 24 left, so the first drawing affects the second drawing.

29. a.

There are 6 possible outfits.

The probability of choosing one outfit is $\frac{1}{6}$. The denominator of the probability fraction is the total number of outfits.

b. $P(\text{red shirt}) = \frac{2}{6} = \frac{1}{3}$

$P(\text{jeans}) = \frac{3}{6} = \frac{1}{2}$

$P(\text{red shirt and jeans}) = \frac{1}{3} \cdot \frac{1}{2} = \frac{1}{6}$

c. $P(\text{red shirt and jeans}) = P(\text{red shirt}) \cdot P(\text{jeans})$

$$\frac{1}{10} = x \cdot \frac{1}{2}$$

$$\frac{1}{10} = \frac{x}{2}$$

$$\frac{2}{10} = x$$

$$\frac{1}{5} = x$$

If the probability of choosing jeans is $\frac{1}{2}$ and the probability of choosing a red shirt and jeans is $\frac{1}{10}$, then the probability of choosing a red shirt is $\frac{1}{5}$. So, you must have 5 shirts.

Chapter 12, *continued*

30. $P(A \text{ and } B) = P(A) \cdot P(B)$

$$0.40 = 0.8x$$
$$0.5 = x$$

Her opponent served first in the second match because the probability that she won the second match is 50%.

31. $P(7 \text{ heads}) = \frac{1}{2} \cdot \frac{1}{2} \cdot \frac{1}{2} \cdot \frac{1}{2} \cdot \frac{1}{2} \cdot \frac{1}{2} \cdot \frac{1}{2} = \frac{1}{128}$

The probability of getting 7 heads in a row is $\frac{1}{128}$.

The probability of each toss is independent, so the probability that you will get heads is always $\frac{1}{2}$.

32. The last statement leads you to think that investing money today is independent of past investments. The first statement suggests the opposite. *Sample answer:* The last statement says that what happens in the future does not depend on what happened in the past. The first statement indicates that what has happened in the past 5 years has depended on what happened in the previous years.

33. There were 0.75(800), or 600 voters.

$$\frac{600}{800} \cdot \frac{599}{799} = \frac{\overset{3}{\cancel{600}}}{\underset{4}{\cancel{800}}} \cdot \frac{599}{799} = \frac{1797}{3196} \approx 0.5623$$

The probability that two different randomly selected people both voted is about 0.5623, or 56.23%.

Mixed Review

34. $a + 3a + 7a = (1 + 3 + 7)a = 11a$

35. $11x + 2y + 6y + 2x = 11x + 2x + 2y + 6y$
$$= (11 + 2)x + (2 + 6)y$$
$$= 13x + 8y$$

36. $4b - a + 5c - 3c = -a + 4b + (5 - 3)c$
$$= -a + 4b + 2c$$

37. $2m + 5k + m + 2m - 3 = 5k + 2m + m + 2m - 3$
$$= 5k + (2 + 1 + 2)m - 3$$
$$= 5k + 5m - 3$$

38.

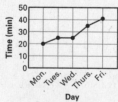

Cindy's Treadmill Time

Sample answer: Cindy will run about 46 minutes on Saturday. If you extend the graph, it passes through 46 on Saturday.

39. D; The relation is not a function because the input 4 has two outputs.

Quiz 12.4–12.8 (p. 700)

1.

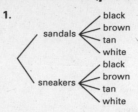

There are 8 choices for shoes.

2. $_4P_4 = \frac{4!}{(4-4)!} = \frac{4!}{0!} = \frac{4 \cdot 3 \cdot 2 \cdot 1}{1} = 24$

There are 24 different schedules.

3. $_{20}C_2 = \frac{_{20}P_2}{2!} = \frac{20 \cdot 19}{2 \cdot 1} = 190$

There are 190 ways to choose two players.

4. $P(\text{rain}) = \frac{0.4}{1 - 0.4} = \frac{0.4}{0.6} = \frac{4}{6} = \frac{2}{3}$

The odds in favor of rain are 2 to 3.

The probability that it will not rain is $1 - 0.4$, or 0.6.

5. $P(5 \text{ and } 5) = P(5) \cdot P(5) = \frac{1}{6} \cdot \frac{1}{6} = \frac{1}{36}$

The probability is $\frac{1}{36}$.

6. $P(\text{red, then blue}) = P(\text{red}) \cdot P(\text{blue given red})$
$$= \frac{3}{8} \cdot \frac{5}{7}$$
$$= \frac{15}{56}$$

The probability is $\frac{15}{56}$.

Brain Game (p. 700)

For each player, the events are dependent.

Bo: $P(\text{blue, then 3 or 4}) = P(\text{blue}) \cdot P(3 \text{ or } 4 \text{ given blue})$
$$= \frac{7}{13} \cdot \frac{2}{12}$$
$$= \frac{7}{13} \cdot \frac{1}{6}$$
$$= \frac{7}{78}$$
$$\approx 0.0897$$

Sherry: $P(\text{even, then green}) = P(\text{even}) \cdot P(\text{green given even})$
$$= \frac{6}{13} \cdot \frac{2}{12}$$
$$= \frac{6}{13} \cdot \frac{1}{6}$$
$$= \frac{1}{13}$$
$$\approx 0.0769$$

Chapter 12, *continued*

Eva: P(red, then red) $= P$(red) $\cdot P$(red given red)

$$= \frac{4}{13} \cdot \frac{3}{12}$$

$$= \frac{4}{13} \cdot \frac{1}{4}$$

$$= \frac{1}{13}$$

$$\approx 0.0769$$

Bo has the best chance of winning.

12.8 Extension (p. 702)

1. People that call into a sports radio talk show will likely favor a new baseball stadium, so the method could lead to biased results.

2. Asking every tenth person in the phone book will reflect a wide range of people. So, the method is not likely to lead to biased results.

3. People that enter the sporting goods store likely favor a new baseball stadium. So, the method could lead to biased results.

4. *Sample answer:* Ask every tenth person listed in the phone book.

5. The question could produce biased results because it implies the mall will be noisy and crowded, instead of relaxing.

6. The question could produce biased results because it implies that all dogs are messy and dangerous, and should not be allowed in the park.

7. The question is fairly written and is not likely to produce biased results.

8. The question assumes that the respondents know what the store's policy is. This could lead to biased results unless a description of the policy is also given.

Mixed Review of Problem Solving (p. 703)

1. a.

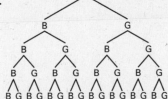

There are 16 outcomes for the 4 cousins.

b. P(4 boys) $= \frac{1}{2} \cdot \frac{1}{2} \cdot \frac{1}{2} \cdot \frac{1}{2} = \frac{1}{16}$

The outcomes are independent events, so the probability of each event is $\frac{1}{2}$. So, the probability that all 4 cousins are boys is $\frac{1}{16}$, or 6.25%.

c. From the tree diagram, there is only one outcome where all 4 cousins are girls. So, the probability that all 4 cousins are not girls is $\frac{5}{16}$.

2. Order is not important when finding the ways to group the people, so evaluate $_{10}C_5$.

$$_{10}C_5 = \frac{_{10}P_5}{5!} = \frac{10 \cdot 9 \cdot 8 \cdot 7 \cdot 6}{5 \cdot 4 \cdot 3 \cdot 2 \cdot 1} = 252$$

There are 252 different groups that can go in one car. If you choose a group for one car, the other car's group is whomever is left over.

3. 10; $_5C_3 = \frac{_5P_3}{3!} = \frac{5 \cdot 4 \cdot 3}{3 \cdot 2 \cdot 1} = 10$

A team can win 3 out of 5 games in 10 ways.

4. P(rain) $= 0.40$

P(not rain) $= 1 - P$(rain) $= 1 - 0.40 = 0.60$

The probability that it will not rain is 60%.

The odds in favor of it not raining is the ratio of the probability of not raining to the probability of raining. So, the odds in favor of it not raining is $\frac{0.60}{0.40} = \frac{60}{40} = \frac{3}{2}$, or 3 to 2.

5. P(5 threes) $= \frac{1}{6} \cdot \frac{1}{6} \cdot \frac{1}{6} \cdot \frac{1}{6} \cdot \frac{1}{6} = \frac{1}{7776}$

The probability that you roll a three 5 times in a row is $\frac{1}{7776}$.

If you have already rolled a three 4 times in a row, the probability that you will roll a three on the next roll is $\frac{1}{6}$. Because they are independent events, the previous rolls do not affect the next roll.

6. 4060; $_{30}C_3 = \frac{_{30}P_3}{3!} = \frac{30 \cdot 29 \cdot 28}{3 \cdot 2 \cdot 1} = 4060$

You can randomly select 4060 groups of 3 CDs from the case.

7. Because the first digit cannot be 0 or 1, there are 4 choices for the first digit. Because each digit can only be used once, there are 5 choices for the second digit and 4 choices for the third digit. So, there are 4(5)(4), or 80 possible prefixes.

8. a. $3 \cdot 4 \cdot 4 = 48$

   There are 48 different kinds of sandwiches possible.

   b. $4 \cdot 4 \cdot 4 = 64$

   There are 64 different kinds of sandwiches possible if salami is added as a meat.

   c. $3 \cdot 4 \cdot 5 = 60$

   There are 60 different kinds of sandwiches possible if mustard is added to the dressing choices instead of adding salami as a meat choice.

   d. The results of parts (b) and (c) do not produce the same number of possible sandwiches. There are 64 kinds if you add a meat, but 60 kinds if you add a dressing.

9. 364; $_{14}C_3 = \frac{_{14}P_3}{3!} = \frac{14 \cdot 13 \cdot 12}{3 \cdot 2 \cdot 1} = 364$

You can get 364 different groups of 3 DVDs with the coupon.

Chapter 12, *continued*

Chapter 12 Review (pp. 704–708)

1. A permutation is an arrangement in which order is important.

2. A combination is an arrangement in which order is not important.

3. A circle graph displays data in distinct categories.

4. A line graph is a graph used to display changes in a quantity over time.

5. A stem-and-leaf plot is a plot used to order a data set.

6. A box-and-whisker plot is a plot that divides a data set into 4 quarters.

7.
1	5 6 9
2	0 1 2 5 7 8 9
3	1 2 6 7
4	2

Key: $3 \mid 1 = 31$

The 20–29 interval has the most data values.

8.
6	7
7	3 5
8	4
9	2
10	6
11	2 3 9
12	
13	
14	
15	0 1 6 7 8

Key: $6 \mid 7 = 6.7$

The interval 15.0–15.9 has the most data values.

9.
8	1 4 6
9	4 6 7 7 9
10	0 0

Key: $10 \mid 0 = 100$

The 90–99 interval has the most data values.

10.
0	2 7 7 8 9
1	1 1 2 4 5 5 8 9
2	1 4

Key: $2 \mid 1 = 21$

11. 3, 5, 9, 11, 13, 14, 16, 18, 21, 22, 23, 25, 25, 31, 32

Median = 18

Lower quartile = 11

Upper quartile = 25

Lower extreme = 3

Upper extreme = 32

12. 41, 42, 61, 62, 65, 68, 68, 70, 74, 76, 79, 80, 81, 83, 85

Median = 70

Lower quartile = 62

Upper quartile = 80

Lower extreme = 41

Upper extreme = 85

13. 15, 20, 35, 38, 40, 45, 50, 60, 95

Median = 40

Lower quartile = $\dfrac{20 + 35}{2} = 27.5$

Upper quartile = $\dfrac{50 + 60}{2} = 55$

Lower extreme = 15

Upper extreme = 95

Sample answer: The cheapest chess set is $15, while the most expensive is $95. Half of the chess sets cost between $27.50 and $55. The $95 set lies well beyond the third quartile and appears to be an outlier.

14. Iced tea: $\dfrac{50}{100} = \dfrac{a}{360°}$

$a = 180°$

Lemonade: $\dfrac{25}{100} = \dfrac{b}{360°}$

$b = 90°$

Limeade: $\dfrac{10}{100} = \dfrac{c}{360°}$

$c = 36°$

Other: $\dfrac{15}{100} = \dfrac{d}{360°}$

$d = 54°$

Favorite Summer Treat

- Iced tea 50%
- Lemonade 25%
- Other 15%
- Limeade 10%

Chapter 12, continued

15. Let H represent a hat and let S represent a shirt.

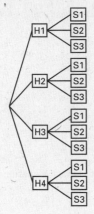

There are 4(3), or 12 hat-shirt pairs.

16. $_8P_4 = \dfrac{8!}{(8-4)!}$

$= \dfrac{8!}{4!}$

$= \dfrac{8 \cdot 7 \cdot 6 \cdot 5 \cdot 4 \cdot 3 \cdot 2 \cdot 1}{4 \cdot 3 \cdot 2 \cdot 1}$

$= 1680$

17. $_{10}P_3 = \dfrac{10!}{(10-3)!}$

$= \dfrac{10!}{7!}$

$= \dfrac{10 \cdot 9 \cdot 8 \cdot 7 \cdot 6 \cdot 5 \cdot 4 \cdot 3 \cdot 2 \cdot 1}{7 \cdot 6 \cdot 5 \cdot 4 \cdot 3 \cdot 2 \cdot 1}$

$= 720$

18. $_{12}P_1 = \dfrac{12!}{(12-1)!}$

$= \dfrac{12!}{11!}$

$= \dfrac{12 \cdot 11 \cdot 10 \cdot \cdots \cdot 3 \cdot 2 \cdot 1}{11 \cdot 10 \cdot 9 \cdot \cdots \cdot 3 \cdot 2 \cdot 1}$

$= 12$

19. $_{13}P_5 = \dfrac{13!}{(13-5)!}$

$= \dfrac{13!}{8!}$

$= \dfrac{13 \cdot 12 \cdot 11 \cdot \cdots \cdot 3 \cdot 2 \cdot 1}{8 \cdot 7 \cdot 6 \cdot 5 \cdot 4 \cdot 3 \cdot 2 \cdot 1}$

$= 154{,}440$

20. $6! = 6 \cdot 5 \cdot 4 \cdot 3 \cdot 2 \cdot 1 = 720$

The Griffiths can line up their children for a picture in 720 ways.

21. $_9C_2 = \dfrac{_9P_2}{2!} = \dfrac{9 \cdot 8}{2 \cdot 1} = 36$

22. $_6C_1 = \dfrac{_6P_1}{1!} = \dfrac{6}{1} = 6$

23. $_9C_9 = \dfrac{_9P_9}{9!} = \dfrac{9 \cdot 8 \cdot 7 \cdot 6 \cdot 5 \cdot 4 \cdot 3 \cdot 2 \cdot 1}{9 \cdot 8 \cdot 7 \cdot 6 \cdot 5 \cdot 4 \cdot 3 \cdot 2 \cdot 1} = 1$

24. $_{12}C_8 = \dfrac{_{12}P_8}{8!} = \dfrac{12 \cdot 11 \cdot 10 \cdot 9 \cdot 8 \cdot 7 \cdot 6 \cdot 5}{8 \cdot 7 \cdot 6 \cdot 5 \cdot 4 \cdot 3 \cdot 2 \cdot 1} = 495$

25. Order is not important in counting the number of possible groups, so evaluate $_{30}C_{15}$.

$_{30}C_{15} = \dfrac{_{30}P_{15}}{15!}$

$= \dfrac{30 \cdot 29 \cdot 28 \cdot \cdots \cdot 18 \cdot 17 \cdot 16}{15 \cdot 14 \cdot 13 \cdot \cdots \cdot 3 \cdot 2 \cdot 1}$

$= 155{,}117{,}520$

There are 155,117,520 groups possible.

26. The probability of not winning the contest is 100% − 76%, or 24%.

The odds that you will lose the contest are 24 to 76, or 6 to 19.

27. $P(\text{B then L}) = P(\text{B}) \cdot P(\text{L}) = \dfrac{2}{11} \cdot \dfrac{1}{11} = \dfrac{2}{121}$

The probability that the first tile is B and the second is L is $\dfrac{2}{121}$.

28. $P(\text{snow Wednesday and Thursday})$

$= P(\text{snow Wednesday}) \cdot P(\text{snow Thursday})$

$= 0.60(0.25)$

$= 0.15$

There is a probability of 15% that it will snow both Wednesday and Thursday.

Chapter 12 Test (p. 709)

1. 21, 43, 46, 52, 55, 56, 59, 60, 70, 72, 88, 96, 104, 136

2	1
3	
4	3 6
5	2 5 6 9
6	0
7	0 2
8	8
9	6
10	4
11	
12	
13	6

Key: $2 \mid 1 = 21$

The interval 50–59 has the most data values.

Median $= \dfrac{59 + 60}{2} = \dfrac{119}{2} = 59.5$

Lower quartile $= 52$

Upper quartile $= 88$

Lower extreme $= 21$

Upper extreme $= 136$

2. 7, 8.2, 10, 10.1, 11.1, 11.2, 11.7, 12, 12.1, 12.5, 12.8, 12.9, 13.3, 13.5, 13.7

7	0
8	2
9	
10	0 1
11	1 2 7
12	0 1 5 8 9
13	3 5 7

Key: 7 | 0 = 7.0

The interval 12.0–12.9 has the most data values.

Median = 12

Lower quartile = 10.1

Upper quartile = 12.9

Lower extreme = 7

Upper extreme = 13.7

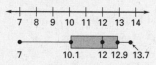

3. The probability that a randomly chosen student replied *rodeo star* is 13%.

4. 100% − 35% = 65%

The probability that a randomly chosen student did not reply *veterinarian* is 65%.

5. Odds = $\dfrac{0.21}{1 - 0.21} = \dfrac{0.21}{0.79} = \dfrac{21}{79}$

The odds in favor of a randomly chosen student replying *zookeeper* are 21 to 79.

6. The events are independent because the outcome of the first roll has no effect on the second roll.

$P(6 \text{ and } 2) = P(6) \cdot P(2) = \dfrac{1}{6} \cdot \dfrac{1}{6} = \dfrac{1}{36}$

The probability is $\dfrac{1}{36}$.

7. The events are dependent because there is one less marble to pick from after the first drawing.

$P(\text{blue then blue}) = P(\text{blue}) \cdot P(\text{blue given blue})$

$= \dfrac{8}{20} \cdot \dfrac{7}{19}$

$= \dfrac{2}{5} \cdot \dfrac{7}{19}$

$= \dfrac{14}{95}$

The probability is $\dfrac{14}{95}$.

8. 99, 118, 122, 131, 142, 160, 177, 183, 194, 197

Median = $\dfrac{142 + 160}{2} = 151$

Lower quartile = 122

Upper quartile = 183

Lower extreme = 99

Upper extreme = 197

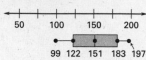

The data seem to be evenly distributed in each quarter.

9.

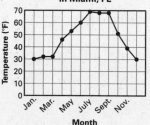

The table shows data over time. So, a line graph is appropriate.

10.

1	2	3	4
1	2	4	3
1	3	2	4
1	3	4	2
1	4	2	3
1	4	3	2
2	1	3	4
2	1	4	3
2	3	1	4
2	3	4	1
2	4	1	3
2	4	3	1
3	1	2	4
3	1	4	2
3	2	1	4
3	2	4	1
3	4	1	2
3	4	2	1
4	1	2	3
4	1	3	2
4	2	1	3
4	2	3	1
4	3	1	2
4	3	2	1

There are 24 orders in which you can pick up your friends.

11. $_8C_4 = \dfrac{_8P_4}{4!} = \dfrac{8 \cdot 7 \cdot 6 \cdot 5}{4 \cdot 3 \cdot 2 \cdot 1} = 70$

Chapter 12, *continued*

Standardized Test Preparation (p. 711)

1. C, 74, 75, 82, 88, 90, 95

Median $= \dfrac{82 + 88}{2} = \dfrac{170}{2} = 85$

The median of the temperatures is 85°F.

2. A; $P(\text{green then red}) = P(\text{green}) \cdot P(\text{red})$

$= \dfrac{6}{24} \cdot \dfrac{10}{24}$

$= \dfrac{1}{4} \cdot \dfrac{5}{12}$

$= \dfrac{5}{48}$

The probability of choosing a green mint and then a red mint is $\dfrac{5}{48}$.

Standardized Test Practice (p. 712–713)

1. B; 56 represents the median.

2. A; A bar graph would be appropriate because there are distinct categories. A circle graph is not appropriate because the percents do not add up to 100%.

3. C; $_{16}P_3 = \dfrac{16!}{(16 - 3)!}$

$= \dfrac{16!}{13!}$

$= \dfrac{16 \cdot 15 \cdot 14 \cdot \ldots \cdot 3 \cdot 2 \cdot 1}{13 \cdot 12 \cdot 11 \cdot \ldots \cdot 3 \cdot 2 \cdot 1}$

$= 3360$

There are 3360 different codes possible.

4. C; $3 \cdot 6 \cdot 4 \cdot 3 = 216$

You can make 216 combinations.

5. B; Odds $= \dfrac{\text{Number of favorable outcomes}}{\text{Number of unfavorable outcomes}} = \dfrac{1}{5}$

The odds in favor of rolling a four are 1 to 5.

6. D; Range $\approx 100 - 15 = 85$

The range of the data is about 85.

7. D; $P(\text{red then white}) = P(\text{red}) \cdot P(\text{white})$

$= \dfrac{16}{40} \cdot \dfrac{24}{40}$

$= \dfrac{2}{5} \cdot \dfrac{3}{5}$

$= \dfrac{6}{25}$

The probability of drawing a red ball and then a white ball is $\dfrac{6}{25}$.

8. B; The lower extreme is $50, so the least price for a stereo system is $50.

9. C; The vertical line in the box represents the median. So, the median price of the stereo systems is $125.

10. 12

The trophies can be awarded in 4(3), or 12 different ways.

11. $\dfrac{7}{13}$; $P(\text{cheese}) = \dfrac{12}{26} = \dfrac{6}{13}$

$P(\text{not cheese}) = 1 - P(\text{cheese}) = 1 - \dfrac{6}{13} = \dfrac{7}{13}$

The probability that Joey will not choose a cheese pizza is $\dfrac{7}{13}$.

12. $\dfrac{6}{55}$;

$P(\text{I then I}) = P(\text{I}) \cdot P(\text{I given I}) = \dfrac{4}{11} \cdot \dfrac{3}{10} = \dfrac{12}{110} = \dfrac{6}{55}$

The probability of drawing the letter I twice is $\dfrac{6}{55}$.

13. 56; $_8C_3 = \dfrac{_8P_3}{3!} = \dfrac{8 \cdot 7 \cdot 6}{3 \cdot 2 \cdot 1} = 56$

You can choose 56 different dishes.

14. a. *Sample answer:* Draw a grid with the numbers 1 to 6 at the top and left sides. Find the sum of each combination.

	1	2	3	4	5	6
1	2	3	4	5	6	7
2	3	4	5	6	7	8
3	4	5	6	7	8	9
4	5	6	7	8	9	10
5	6	7	8	9	10	11
6	7	8	9	10	11	12

There are 10 favorable outcomes out of 36 possible rolls. So, the probability that the sum of the numbers is less than or equal to 5 is $\dfrac{10}{36}$, or $\dfrac{5}{18}$.

b. Rolling a sum less than or equal to 5 and rolling a sum greater than 5 are complementary events. So, the probability that the sum is greater than 5 is

$1 - \dfrac{5}{18} = \dfrac{13}{18}$.

15. a. 4, 5, 6, 6, 9, 11, 12, 12, 14, 14, 17, 18, 21, 24, 25

Median $= 12$

Lower quartile $= 6$

Upper quartile $= 18$

Lower extreme $= 4$

Upper extreme $= 25$

b. *Sample answer:* The median number of home runs is 12, with half of the home run totals between 6 and 18. The range of the data is 21.

Chapter 12, *continued*

16. **a.** The height of the tallest football player is 88 inches, or 7 feet 4 inches.

b. There are 6 basketball players over 82 inches tall.

c. The median height of the football players is 73 inches. The median height of the basketball players is 78 inches.

d. In general, the basketball players are taller. Although there are comparable numbers of players in each range of values, the basketball players are taller than the football players within the 70–79 inch interval.

Chapter 13

Chapter Get-Ready Games (pp. 714–715)

1. $(5 - 11)^3 \cdot 2 \cdot (-6)^{-2} = (-6)^3 \cdot 2 \cdot (-6)^{-2}$

$$= -216 \cdot 2 \cdot \frac{1}{36}$$

$$= \frac{-432}{36}$$

$$= -12$$

$\dfrac{4^7}{(9-5)^3} = \dfrac{4^7}{4^3} = 4^{7-3} = 4^4 = 256$

$3^{-3} \cdot 3^8 + 5 = 3^{-3+8} + 5 = 3^5 + 5 = 243 + 5 = 248$

$2^5 \cdot 7 \cdot 2^{-1} = 32 \cdot 7 \cdot \dfrac{1}{2} = \dfrac{224}{2} = 112$

$\dfrac{(7+1)^6}{8^4} = \dfrac{8^6}{8^4} = 8^{6-4} = 8^2 = 64$

The stick above the expression $2^5 \cdot 7 \cdot 2^{-1}$ breaks the piñata. You should hit the spot labeled 112.

2. Mask 1: $x - 4x + 3 + 9x = 6x + 3$ = John

   Mask 2: $-7x + 8 - 2(3x + 4) = -7x + 8 - 6x - 8$
   $$= -13x = \text{Sam}$$

   Mask 3: $5(x - 6) + 10x - 3 = 5x - 30 + 10x - 3$
   $$= 15x - 33 = \text{Sophie}$$

   Mask 4: $8x - 3 - 4(2x + 3) = 8x - 3 - 8x - 12$
   $$= -15 = \text{Carol}$$

   Mask 5: $4 - (3x - 1) + x = 4 - 3x + 1 + x$
   $$= -2x + 5 = \text{Vincent}$$

   Mask 6: $17 - 4x - 13 + 2x = -2x + 4 = \text{Maria}$

Stop and Think (p. 715)

1. *Sample answer:* The first step is to use the distributive property to simplify $-2(3x + 4)$. Then add and subtract from left to right to combine like terms.

2. $2^5 \cdot 7 \cdot 2^{-1} = 2^5 \cdot 2^{-1} \cdot 7 = 2^{5 + (-1)} \cdot 7 = 2^4 \cdot 7$

Review Prerequisite Skills (p. 716)

1. In the monomial $2x^3$, the 2 is the *coefficient* and the 3 is the *exponent*.

2. A relation that assigns exactly one output value to each input value is a *function*.

3. A number, a variable, or a product of a number and one or more variables is a *monomial*.

4. $6x - 4 + 4x - 3 = 10x - 7$

5. $-5(2x + 3) - 4x = -10x - 15 - 4x = -14x - 15$

6. $7(3x - 5) - (-x) = 21x - 35 + x = 22x - 35$

7. $-2x - (-5x) = -2x + 5x = 3x$

8. $-2(-4x - 8) = 8x + 16$

9. $-3(3x) + 18x = -9x + 18x = 9x$

10. $\dfrac{y^4}{y^6} = y^{4-6} = y^{-2} = \dfrac{1}{y^2}$

11. $\dfrac{5^{37}}{5^{35}} = 5^{37-35} = 5^2 = 25$

12. $x^4 \cdot x^5 = x^{4+5} = x^9$

---

13. $y = 3x - 5$

x	y
0	−5
1	−2
2	1
3	4

Four solutions are $(0, -5)$, $(1, -2)$, $(2, 1)$, and $(3, 4)$.

14. $y = -2x + 1$

x	y
0	1
1	−1
2	−3
3	−5

Four solutions are $(0, 1)$, $(1, -1)$, $(2, -3)$, and $(3, -5)$.

15. $y = \dfrac{1}{2}x$

x	y
0	0
2	1
4	2
6	3

Four solutions are $(0, 0)$, $(2, 1)$, $(4, 2)$, and $(6, 3)$.

Lesson 13.1

13.1 Guided Practice (pp. 717–718)

1. The polynomial $b^2 - 8b + 4$ has 3 terms, so it is a trinomial.

2. The polynomial $2n^4 + 5n^2 - 7n + 11$ has 4 terms, so it is simply called a polynomial.

3. The polynomial $3x^2 - 5$ has 2 terms, so it is a binomial.

4. $7p + 5p^2 - 2 - 3p^2 = (5p^2 - 3p^2) + 7p - 2$
   $$= 2p^2 + 7p - 2$$

5. $10s^4 - 3s + s^4 - 1 = (10s^4 + s^4) - 3s - 1$
   $$= 11s^4 - 3s - 1$$

6. $2(a^2 + 3a - 1) + 2a^2 = 2a^2 + 6a - 2 + 2a^2$
   $$= (2a^2 + 2a^2) + 6a - 2$$
   $$= 4a^2 + 6a - 2$$

7. $8x + 3(2x^2 - x + 1) = 8x + 6x^2 - 3x + 3$
   $$= 6x^2 + (8x - 3x) + 3$$
   $$= 6x^2 + 5x + 3$$

8. $6d^3 - 4d - 4d^3 - 6d = (6d^3 - 4d^3) - 4d - 6d$
   $$= 2d^3 - 10d$$

Chapter 13, *continued*

9. $-5x^2 + 7 + 2(-6 + 7x^2) = -5x^2 + 7 - 12 + 14x^2$
$$= (-5x^2 + 14x^2) + 7 - 12$$
$$= 9x^2 - 5$$

10. $-16t^2 + 150 = -16(0.5)^2 + 150$
$$= -16(0.25) + 150$$
$$= -4 + 150$$
$$= 146$$

The pinecone's height after 0.5 second is 146 feet.

11. $-16t^2 + 150 = -16(1)^2 + 150$
$$= -16(1) + 150$$
$$= -16 + 150$$
$$= 134$$

The pinecone's height after 1 second is 134 feet.

12. $-16t^2 + 150 = -16(1.5)^2 + 150$
$$= -16(2.25) + 150$$
$$= -36 + 150$$
$$= 114$$

The pinecone's height after 1.5 seconds is 114 feet.

13. $-16t^2 + 150 = -16(3)^2 + 150$
$$= -16(9) + 150$$
$$= -144 + 150$$
$$= 6$$

The pinecone's height after 3 seconds is 6 feet.

13.1 Exercises (pp. 719–720)

Skill Practice

1. The polynomial $x^2 + 3x - 7$ has 3 terms, so it is a trinomial.

2. The polynomial $y - 5$ has 2 terms, so it is a binomial.

3. The polynomial $8s^2t$ has one term, so it is a monomial.

4. The polynomial $2a^2 + 9a^3 + a$, or $9a^3 + 2a^2 + a$, has 3 terms, so it is a trinomial.

5. $7 + 3m = 3m + 7$

The polynomial $3m + 7$ has two terms, so it is a binomial.

6. $8 - n + 2n^2 = 2n^2 - n + 8$

The polynomial $2n^2 - n + 8$ has three terms, so it is a trinomial.

7. $5n - 1 - n^2 = -n^2 + 5n - 1$

The polynomial $-n^2 + 5n - 1$ has 3 terms, so it is a trinomial.

8. $4b - 4 + 6b^3 = 6b^3 + 4b - 4$

The polynomial $6b^3 + 4b - 4$ has 3 terms, so it is a trinomial.

9. $2 - 5y + y^2 = y^2 - 5y + 2$

The polynomial $y^2 - 5y + 2$ has 3 terms, so it is a trinomial.

10. $z^3 + 4z^2 + 7z^7 = 7z^7 + z^3 + 4z^2$

The polynomial $7z^7 + z^3 + 4z^2$ has 3 terms, so it is a trinomial.

11. $-13x^3 + 4x^{10} = 4x^{10} - 13x^3$

The polynomial $4x^{10} - 13x^3$ has 2 terms, so it is a binomial.

12. $3 - r^4 + r + 2r^3 = -r^4 + 2r^3 + r + 3$

The polynomial $-r^4 + 2r^3 + r + 3$ has 4 terms, so it is simply called a polynomial.

13. $2c^2 - c^2 + 5c = (2c^2 - c^2) + 5c = c^2 + 5c$

14. $4q^3 - 7q^5 + 3q - q^3 = -7q^5 + (4q^3 - q^3) + 3q$
$$= -7q^5 + 3q^3 + 3q$$

15. $g^3 - 10 + 2g^2 - 5g^3 = (g^3 - 5g^3) + 2g^2 - 10$
$$= -4g^3 + 2g^2 - 10$$

16. $1 + 12m^2 - 5m + 6m - 7$
$$= 12m^2 + (-5m + 6m) + (1 - 7)$$
$$= 12m^2 + m - 6$$

17. $3x^2 + 5(x^2 - 3x + 6) = 3x^2 + 5x^2 - 15x + 30$
$$= (3x^2 + 5x^2) - 15x + 30$$
$$= 8x^2 - 15x + 30$$

18. $-6(2y^3 - 4y^2 + 1) + 10y^2 = -12y^3 + 24y^2 - 6 + 10y^2$
$$= -12y^3 + (24y^2 + 10y^2) - 6$$
$$= -12y^3 + 34y^2 - 6$$

19. $-4(t - 3t^2 + 8 - 4t) + 6t^2 - 5$
$$= -4t + 12t^2 - 32 + 16t + 6t^2 - 5$$
$$= (12t^2 + 6t^2) + (-4t + 16t) + (-32 - 5)$$
$$= 18t^2 + 12t - 37$$

20. $-3(-s^4 + 2s - 6 - s) - 8s + s^4$
$$= 3s^4 - 6s + 18 + 3s - 8s + s^4$$
$$= (3s^4 + s^4) + (-6s + 3s - 8s) + 18$$
$$= 4s^4 - 11s + 18$$

21. Like terms have the same variable and the same exponent, so $-3x^2$ and $-20x$ cannot be combined.
$$-3x^2 - 4(5x + 1) = -3x^2 - 20x - 4$$

22. D; $5(x^2 - 2x - 3) - 9x^2 = 5x^2 - 10x - 15 - 9x^2$
$$= (5x^2 - 9x^2) - 10x - 15$$
$$= -4x^2 - 10x - 15$$

23. $5a - 4(3b + 6) + 4b = 5a - 12b - 24 + 4b$
$$= 5a + (-12b + 4b) - 24$$
$$= 5a - 8b - 24$$

24. $-z^2 + 3z - 2(4y - 5z) = -z^2 + 3z - 8y + 10z$
$$= -z^2 - 8y + (3z + 10z)$$
$$= -z^2 - 8y + 13z$$

25. $-3ab^2 + 2ab + 5a^2b^2 - 3ab^2 + 4ab$
$$= 5a^2b^2 + (-3ab^2 - 3ab^2) + (2ab + 4ab)$$
$$= 5a^2b^2 - 6ab^2 + 6ab$$

26. $3xy + 2xy^2 - 5x^2y^2 + 3x^2y - 4xy - 7xy^2$
$$= -5x^2y^2 + 3x^2y + (2xy^2 - 7xy^2) + (3xy - 4xy)$$
$$= -5x^2y^2 + 3x^2y - 5xy^2 - xy$$

27. *Sample answer:*

Examples: $3x^2 - 4x + 7$, $x + 2$, $9x + 7$

Non-examples: $-4x + 3x^2 + 7$, $2 + x$, $7 + 9x$

28. $P = 2(2x + 3) + 4x$

$= 4x + 6 + 4x$

$= (4x + 4x) + 6$

$= 8x + 6$

29. $P = 2[2(x + 1)] + 2x$

$= 2(2x + 2) + 2x$

$= 4x + 4 + 2x$

$= (4x + 2x) + 4$

$= 6x + 4$

30. $3xy + 6y - 2x^2 + 4 + \underline{\ ?\ } = 3x^2 - 5y - 7xy - 4x$

Move all the terms to the right side of the equation to find the missing expression.

$\underline{\ ?\ } = 3x^2 - 5y - 7xy - 4x - 3xy - 6y + 2x^2 - 4$

Combine like terms.

$\underline{\ ?\ } = (3x^2 + 2x^2) + (-5y - 6y) + (-7xy - 3xy) - 4x - 4$

$= 5x^2 - 4x - 11y - 10xy - 4$

The missing part of the expression is
$5x^2 - 4x - 11y - 10xy - 4$.

31. $4y^2 + 2x^2 + 9 + \underline{\ ?\ } = 3y^2 + x^2 + 5xy + 6$

Move all the terms to the right side of the equation to find the missing expression.

$\underline{\ ?\ } = 3y^2 + x^2 + 5xy + 6 - 4y^2 - 2x^2 - 9$

Combine like terms.

$\underline{\ ?\ } = (3y^2 - 4y^2) + (x^2 - 2x^2) + 5xy + (6 - 9)$

$= -y^2 - x^2 + 5xy - 3$

$= -x^2 - y^2 + 5xy - 3$

The missing part of the expression is
$-x^2 - y^2 + 5xy - 3$.

Problem Solving

32. $-16t^2 + 88t + 2 = -16(1.5)^2 + 88(1.5) + 2$

$= -16(2.25) + 132 + 2$

$= -36 + 132 + 2$

$= 98$

The ball's height after 1.5 seconds is 98 feet.

33. $-16t^2 + 88t + 2 = -16(2)^2 + 88(2) + 2$

$= -16(4) + 176 + 2$

$= -64 + 176 + 2$

$= 114$

The ball's height after 2 seconds is 114 feet.

34. $-16t^2 + 88t + 2 = -16(2.5)^2 + 88(2.5) + 2$

$= -16(6.25) + 220 + 2$

$= -100 + 220 + 2$

$= 122$

The ball's height after 2.5 seconds is 122 feet.

35. $-16t^2 + 88t + 2 = -16(3)^2 + 88(3) + 2$

$= -16(9) + 264 + 2$

$= -144 + 264 + 2$

$= 122$

The ball's height after 3 seconds is 122 feet.

36. *Sample answer:* The prefix *poly-* means much or many. A polygon has many sides and a polynomial (except for a monomial) has many terms.

37. A; $-16t^2 + 45 = -16(1.5)^2 + 45 = -36 + 45 = 9$

The pebble's height after 1.5 seconds is 9 feet.

38. always true; Every term in a polynomial is a monomial.

39. sometimes true; The monomial 1 has one factor, but the monomial $5x$ has two factors.

40. never true; A binomial is a polynomial with 2 terms.

41. short leg: x

long leg: $2x + 4$

hypotenuse: $3x - 4$

$x + (2x + 4) + 3x - 4 = 6x$

The expression for the perimeter of the triangle is $6x$.

When $x = 10$ in.: $6(10) = 60$

The perimeter is 60 inches.

42. The value of the greatest exponent is $n - 1$. For example, if $n = 3$ the polynomial can be $x^2 + x + 1$.

43. The equation $4g^2 + 3g = 7g^3$ is sometimes true.

Sample answer: If $g = 0$ or $g = 1$, then $4g^2 + 3g = 7g^3$, but if $g = -1$ then $4g^2 + 3g = 4 - 3 = 1$ and $7g^3 = -7$.

Mixed Review

44. $8(3 + 9x) = 24 + 72x$

45. $-3(11x - 4) = -33x + 12$

46. $-5x(7 + 2) = -5x(9) = -45x$

47. $12(6 - 1x) = 72 - 12x$

48. $P(N) = \frac{2}{8} = \frac{1}{4}$

49. B; $V = \pi r^2 h = \pi(4)^2 (5) = 80\pi$

The volume of the cylinder is 80π m^3.

Lesson 13.2

Activity (p. 721)

1. $(2x^2 + 3x + 5) + (x^2 + 4x + 1)$

2.

$3x^2 + 7x + 6$

Chapter 13, continued

3. a. (1) $(3x^2 + 6x + 1) + (x^2 + x)$

(2)

(3)
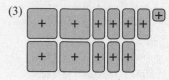

$4x^2 + 7x + 1$

b. (1) $(2x^2 + 3x + 1) + (4x^2 + x)$

(2)
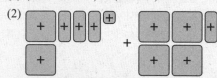

(3)
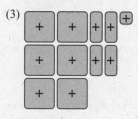

$6x^2 + 4x + 1$

13.2 Guided Practice (pp. 722–723)

1. $(6x^2 - 3x + 1) + (3x^3 + 4x^2 - 5x)$
$= 3x^3 + 6x^2 + 4x^2 - 3x - 5x + 1$
$= 3x^3 + 10x^2 - 8x + 1$

2. $(5n^2 + 2n - 9) + (3n^2 - 4) = 5n^2 + 3n^2 + 2n - 9 - 4$
$= 8n^2 + 2n - 13$

3. $(y^2 - y + 1) + (-2y^2 + 2y - 1)$
$= y^2 - 2y^2 - y + 2y + 1 - 1$
$= -y^2 + y$

4. $(3p^2 - p - 1) + (p^2 + p - 4)$
$= 3p^2 + p^2 - p + p - 1 - 4$
$= 4p^2 - 5$

5. $(4r^2 - r + 8) - (r^2 + 6r - 1)$
$= (4r^2 - r + 8) + (-r^2 - 6r + 1)$
$= 4r^2 - r^2 - r - 6r + 8 + 1$
$= 3r^2 - 7r + 9$

6. $(6m^2 + 2m - 3) - (7m^2 + 4)$
$= (6m^2 + 2m - 3) + (-7m^2 - 4)$
$= 6m^2 - 7m^2 + 2m - 3 - 4$
$= -m^2 + 2m - 7$

7. Area of large rectangle $= 10x \cdot 6x = 60x^2$
Area of small rectangle $= 4x^2 - 2x$
Area of floor $= 60x^2 - (4x^2 - 2x)$
$= 60x^2 - 4x^2 + 2x$
$= 56x^2 + 2x$

13.2 Exercises (pp. 723–725)

Skill Practice

1. To add polynomials, you should combine *like terms*.

2. To find the *opposite* of a polynomial, multiply each of its terms by -1.

3. $(8y + 5) + (4y - 3) = 8y + 4y + 5 - 3 = 12y + 2$

4. $(x - 6) + (2x + 9) = x + 2x - 6 + 9 = 3x + 3$

5. $(4x + 7) + (x - 3) = 4x + x + 7 - 3 = 5x + 4$

6. $(-2a - 9) + (a + 4) = -2a + a - 9 + 4 = -a - 5$

7. $(-g^2 + g + 9) + (7g^2 - 6) = -g^2 + 7g^2 + g + 9 - 6$
$= 6g^2 + g + 3$

8. $(3z^2 - 2z + 1) + (4z^3 + 3z) = 4z^3 + 3z^2 - 2z + 3z + 1$
$= 4z^3 + 3z^2 + z + 1$

9. $(2k^2 + 5k) + (4k^2 - 5k) = 2k^2 + 4k^2 + 5k - 5k = 6k^2$

10. $(6x^3 - 12x + 1) + (8x^2 - 4) = 6x^3 + 8x^2 - 12x + 1 - 4$
$= 6x^3 + 8x^2 - 12x - 3$

11. The terms $5x^2$ and $-6x$, as well as $-7x$ and 10, are not like terms, so they cannot be combined.

$$
\begin{array}{r}
-4x^3 + 5x^2 - 7x + 2 \\
+\ \underline{\ 2x^3 \ - 6x + 10} \\
-2x^3 + 5x^2 - 13x + 12
\end{array}
$$

12. A; $(-7x^3 + 4x^2 - 1) + (x^3 - 9x + 3)$
$= -7x^3 + x^3 + 4x^2 - 9x - 1 + 3$
$= -6x^3 + 4x^2 - 9x + 2$

13. $(7x + 10) - (x - 2) = (7x + 10) + (-x + 2)$
$= 7x - x + 10 + 2$
$= 6x + 12$

14. $(4p + 1) - (p - 7) = (4p + 1) + (-p + 7)$
$= 4p - p + 1 + 7$
$= 3p + 8$

15. $(-5d - 1) - (5d + 6) = (-5d - 1) + (-5d - 6)$
$= -5d - 5d - 1 - 6$
$= -10d - 7$

16. $(7y + 1) - (3y - 2) = (7y + 1) + (-3y + 2)$
$= 7y - 3y + 1 + 2$
$= 4y + 3$

17. $(6r^2 + 2r - 5) - (3r^2 - 9)$
$= (6r^2 + 2r - 5) + (-3r^2 + 9)$
$= 6r^2 - 3r^2 + 2r - 5 + 9$
$= 3r^2 + 2r + 4$

18. $(-4b^3 - 9b + 2) - (b^3 - b + 3)$
$= (-4b^3 - 9b + 2) + (-b^3 + b - 3)$
$= -4b^3 - b^3 - 9b + b + 2 - 3$
$= -5b^3 - 8b - 1$

19. $(5a^2 + 3a + 8) - (2a^2 - 2a - 9)$
$= (5a^2 + 3a + 8) + (-2a^2 + 2a + 9)$
$= 5a^2 - 2a^2 + 3a + 2a + 8 + 9$
$= 3a^2 + 5a + 17$

Chapter 13, *continued*

20. $(4p^3 + p^2 - 8) - (7p^3 + 2p + 5)$
$= (4p^3 + p^2 - 8) + (-7p^3 - 2p - 5)$
$= 4p^3 - 7p^3 + p^2 - 2p - 8 - 5$
$= -3p^3 + p^2 - 2p - 13$

21. $(4n - 3) + (9n + 5) - (n - 1)$
$= (4n - 3) + (9n + 5) - n + 1$
$= 4n + 9n - n - 3 + 5 + 1$
$= 12n + 3$

22. $(-8m + 1) - (2m - 6) + 5m$
$= (-8m + 1) + (-2m + 6) + 5m$
$= -8m - 2m + 5m + 1 + 6$
$= -5m + 7$

23. $-2(5y + 3) - 9(y + 1) = (-10y - 6) + (-9y - 9)$
$= -10y - 9y - 6 - 9$
$= -19y - 15$

24. $4(-3s^2 + s - 4) + (5s^2 + s + 7)$
$= (-12s^2 + 4s - 16) + (5s^2 + s + 7)$
$= -12s^2 + 5s^2 + 4s + s - 16 + 7$
$= -7s^2 + 5s - 9$

25. $3(q^2 - q) + 2(7q^2 - 2q) = (3q^2 - 3q) + (14q^2 - 4q)$
$= 3q^2 + 14q^2 - 3q - 4q$
$= 17q^2 - 7q$

26. $6(t^3 - t^2 + 3t) - 4(5t^3 + t^2 - t)$
$= (6t^3 - 6t^2 + 18t) + (-20t^3 - 4t^2 + 4t)$
$= 6t^3 - 20t^3 - 6t^2 - 4t^2 + 18t + 4t$
$= -14t^3 - 10t^2 + 22t$

27. $5(4x^3 - 2x^2 + 1) + 3(7x^2 - 5x)$
$= (20x^3 - 10x^2 + 5) + (21x^2 - 15x)$
$= 20x^3 - 10x^2 + 21x^2 - 15x + 5$
$= 20x^3 + 11x^2 - 15x + 5$

28. $-7(2v^4 + 3v^2 - 1) - 5(-3v^3 - 6)$
$= (-14v^4 - 21v^2 + 7) + (15v^3 + 30)$
$= -14v^4 + 15v^3 - 21v^2 + 7 + 30$
$= -14v^4 + 15v^3 - 21v^2 + 37$

29. $(2x^2 - 3x + 4) - (x^2 - 3x + 13) = 0$
$(2x^2 - 3x + 4) + (-x^2 + 3x - 13) = 0$
$2x^2 - x^2 - 3x + 3x + 4 - 13 = 0$
$x^2 - 9 = 0$
$x^2 = 9$
$x = \pm 3$

30. $(-6x^2 + 7x - 5) - (-6x^2 - 5x + 7) = 0$
$(-6x^2 + 7x - 5) + (6x^2 + 5x - 7) = 0$
$-6x^2 + 6x^2 + 7x + 5x - 5 - 7 = 0$
$12x - 12 = 0$
$12x - 12 + 12 = 12$
$12x = 12$
$\dfrac{12x}{12} = \dfrac{12}{12}$
$x = 1$

31. *Sample answer:* $(A + B) + (A - B) = 2A$
$(5z - 4) + (3z + 10) = 8z + 6$
So, $2A = 8z + 6$
$A = 4z + 3$
$(A + B) - A = B$
$(5z - 4) - (4z + 3) = z - 7$
$A = 4z + 3$ and $B = z - 7$.

Problem Solving

32. $(-x^2 + 11x + 8) + (x^2 + 3x - 4) + (2x^2 - x + 10)$
$= -x^2 + x^2 + 2x^2 + 11x + 3x - x + 8 - 4 + 10$
$= 2x^2 + 13x + 14$

33. $2(-x^2 + 10x + 1) + 2(2x^2 - 2x + 3)$
$= -2x^2 + 20x + 2 + 4x^2 - 4x + 6$
$= -2x^2 + 4x^2 + 20x - 4x + 2 + 6$
$= 2x^2 + 16x + 8$

34. A; $118 = 2(3x + 4) + 2(2x + 5)$
$118 = 6x + 8 + 4x + 10$
$118 = 10x + 18$
$118 - 18 = 10x + 18 - 18$
$100 = 10x$
$\dfrac{100}{10} = \dfrac{10x}{10}$
$10 = x$

The value of x is 10.

35. *Sample answer:* Subtract the area of the window from the area of the wall.
$(7x)(3x) - (4x^2 + 2x) = 21x^2 - 4x^2 - 2x = 17x^2 - 2x$
The area is $17x^2 - 2x$.

36. *Sample answer:*
1. $(x^2 + x + 1) + (x^2 + x - 1) = 2x^2 + 2x$
2. $(x^2 - x + 1) + (x^2 + x + 1) = 2x^2 + 2$
3. $(x^2 + x + 1) + (-x^2 + x + 1) = 2x + 2$

37. a. Area of square piece: $A = s^2 = (4r)^2 = 4r(4r) = 16r^2$
Area of one coaster: $A = \pi r^2$
Four coasters have an area of $4\pi r^2$.
$16r^2 - 4\pi r^2$ or $(16 - 4\pi)r^2$

b. The area of the clay that remains after you remove the circles is $16r^2 - 12.56r^2 = 3.44r^2$.

c. Because the area of one coaster is $3.14r^2$, you will have enough clay left over to make another coaster.

38. $S = \left(b \cdot b + \dfrac{1}{2} \cdot 4b \cdot 3\right) + \left(b \cdot b + \dfrac{1}{2} \cdot 4b \cdot 2\right)$
$= (b^2 + 6b) + (b^2 + 4b)$
$= b^2 + b^2 + 6b + 4b$
$= 2b^2 + 10b$

39. *Sample answer:* A similarity is that to subtract, you add the opposite. A difference is that polynomials may have many terms to subtract, while an integer is a single term.

40. *Sample answer:* Consecutive angles are supplementary, so $(x + 3y) + x = 180$ and $(x + 3y) + (y + 15) = 180$. I solved the system $2x + 3y = 180$ and $x + 4y = 165$. Solve for x ($x = 165 - 4y$) and substitute it in the other equation.

$$2(165 - 4y) + 3y = 180$$
$$330 - 8y + 3y = 180$$
$$330 - 5y = 180$$
$$-5y = -150$$
$$y = 30$$

Then I used the property that opposite angles are congruent to get $x = y + 15$

$$x = 30 + 15$$
$$x = 45$$

The value for x is 45 and the value for y is 30.

Mixed Review

41. $b^3 \cdot b^7 = b^{3+7} = b^{10}$

42. $x^{12} \cdot x^2 = x^{12+2} = x^{14}$

43. $m^4 \cdot m^5 = m^{4+5} = m^9$

44. $a^3 \cdot a^6 = a^{3+6} = a^9$

45. $10 \times 9 \times 8 \times 7 = 5040$

There are 5040 password possibilities.

46. B; $\dfrac{2}{6} = \dfrac{1}{3}$

Lesson 13.3

Activity (p. 726)

1.

Expression	Expand	Regroup	Simplify
$(3x)(4x^2)$	$3 \cdot x \cdot 4 \cdot x \cdot x$	$3 \cdot 4 \cdot x \cdot x \cdot x$	$12x^3$
$(-2x)(5x^4)$	$-2 \cdot x \cdot 5 \cdot x$ $\cdot x \cdot x \cdot x$	$-2 \cdot 5 \cdot x \cdot x$ $\cdot x \cdot x \cdot x$	$-10x^5$
$(xy)^3$	$xy \cdot xy \cdot xy$	$x \cdot x \cdot x$ $\cdot y \cdot y \cdot y$	x^3y^3
$(4x)^2$	$4x \cdot 4x$	$4 \cdot 4 \cdot x \cdot x$	$16x^2$
$(-3x)^3$	$-3x \cdot (-3x)$ $\cdot (-3x)$	$-3 \cdot (-3)(-3)$ $\cdot x \cdot x \cdot x$	$-27x^3$

In the table, the coefficients are multiplied, and the exponents of each variable are added.

2. $(5x)(2x^3) = 5 \cdot 2 \cdot x \cdot x^3 = 10x^4$

$(3pq)^2 = 3pq \cdot 3pq = 3 \cdot 3 \cdot p \cdot p \cdot q \cdot q = 9p^2q^2$

13.3 Guided Practice (pp. 726–728)

1. $4a(a^2) = 4 \cdot a \cdot a \cdot a = 4a^3$

2. $(-2m)(7m^2) = -2 \cdot 7 \cdot m \cdot m \cdot m = -14m^3$

3. $(-x)(8x^2) = -1 \cdot x \cdot 8 \cdot x \cdot x = -1 \cdot 8 \cdot x \cdot x \cdot x = -8x^3$

4. $(y^5)(5y^3) = 5 \cdot y \cdot y \cdot y \cdot y \cdot y \cdot y \cdot y \cdot y = 5y^8$

5. $p(2p + 3) = p(2p) + p(3) = 2p^2 + 3p$

6. $-t^2(-2t + 8) = -t^2(-2t) - t^2(8) = 2t^3 - 8t^2$

7. $(5yz)^3 = 5^3 \cdot y^3 \cdot z^3 = 125y^3z^3$

8. $(-xy)^2 = (-x)^2 \cdot y^2 = x^2y^2$

9. $V = \pi r^2 h$
$V = \pi(3h)^2 h$
$V = \pi(3^2 \cdot h^2)h$
$V = \pi \cdot 9 \cdot h^2 \cdot h$
$V = 9\pi h^3$

An expression for the volume of the container is $9\pi h^3$.

10. $(2^4)^2 = 2^{4 \cdot 2} = 2^8 = 256$

11. $(x^6)^2 = x^{6 \cdot 2} = x^{12}$

12. $(5m^3)^2 = 5^2 \cdot m^{3 \cdot 2} = 25m^6$

13. $(a^2b)^2 = a^{2 \cdot 2} \cdot b^2 = a^4b^2$

13.3 Exercises (pp. 728–731)

Skill Practice

1. B   **2.** A   **3.** C

4. $(-4x)(5x^3) = -4 \cdot 5 \cdot x \cdot x^3 = -20x^4$

5. $(-16t)(-3t^9) = -16(-3) \cdot t \cdot t^9 = 48t^{10}$

6. $(-x^2)(-3x) = -1(-3) \cdot x^2 \cdot x = 3x^3$

7. $3s(-2s^3) = 3(-2) \cdot s \cdot s^3 = -6s^4$

8. $(-b^3)(-b^8) = -1(-1) \cdot b^3 \cdot b^8 = b^{11}$

9. $(-y^2)(y^3) = -1 \cdot y^2 \cdot y^3 = -y^5$

10. $2w(3w + 1) = 2w(3w) + 2w(1) = 6w^2 + 2w$

11. $-t(t^2 - 4) = -t(t^2) - t(-4) = -t^3 + 4t$

12. $-8x(x^5 + x) = -8x(x^5) - 8x(x) = -8x^6 - 8x^2$

13. $3k^2(12 - k^5) = 3k^2(12) + 3k^2(-k^5)$
$$= 36k^2 - 3k^7$$
$$= -3k^7 + 36k^2$$

14. $4q^3(3q + 6) = 4q^3(3q) + 4q^3(6) = 12q^4 + 24q^3$

15. $-7a^2(5a^3 - 9a) = -7a^2(5a^3) - (-7a^2)(9a)$
$$= -35a^5 + 63a^3$$

16. $(5z)^3 = 5^3 \cdot z^3 = 125z^3$

17. $(xyz)^5 = x^5y^5z^5$

18. $(2ab)^4 = 2^4 \cdot a^4 \cdot b^4 = 16a^4b^4$

19. $(-6z)^3 = (-6)^3 \cdot z^3 = -216z^3$

20. $(-dt)^4 = (-1)^4 \cdot d^4 \cdot t^4 = d^4t^4$

21. $(3rs)^2 = 3^2 \cdot r^2 \cdot s^2 = 9r^2s^2$

22. $(-3xy)^3 = (-3)^3 \cdot x^3 \cdot y^3 = -27x^3y^3$

23. $(10bh)^5 = 10^5 \cdot b^5 \cdot h^5 = 100{,}000b^5h^5$

24. $(t^4)^2 = t^{4 \cdot 2} = t^8$

25. $(y^2)^2 = y^{2 \cdot 2} = y^4$

26. $(c^2)^9 = c^{2 \cdot 9} = c^{18}$

27. $(-x^2)^{10} = (-1)^{10}x^{2 \cdot 10} = x^{20}$

28. $(ab^3)^2 = a^2 \cdot b^{3 \cdot 2} = a^2b^6$

29. $(x^2y^2)^3 = x^{2 \cdot 3} \cdot y^{2 \cdot 3} = x^6y^6$

30. $(3a^2)^2 = 3^2 \cdot a^{2 \cdot 2} = 9a^4$

01. $(2r^3)^3 = 2^3 \cdot r^{3 \cdot 3} = 8r^9$

32. Both factors, 3 and x^3, should be squared.

$(3x^3)^2 = (3x^3)(3x^3) = 9x^6$

33. A; $(-2b^4)^3 = (-2)^3 b^{4 \cdot 3} = -8b^{12}$

34. $(3 \times 10^4)^3 = 3^3 \times 10^{4 \cdot 3} = 27 \times 10^{12} = 2.7 \times 10^{13}$

35. $(9 \times 10^{10})^3 = 9^3 \times 10^{10 \cdot 3} = 729 \times 10^{30} = 7.29 \times 10^{32}$

36. $(5 \times 10^7)^4 = 5^4 \times 10^{7 \cdot 4} = 625 \times 10^{28} = 6.25 \times 10^{30}$

37. $2(5mn^4)^3 = 2(5^3 m^3 \cdot n^{4 \cdot 3}) = 2(125m^3 n^{12}) = 250m^3 n^{12}$

38. $-3a^{10}(a^4 b^2 c)^4 = -3a^{10}(a^{4 \cdot 4} \cdot b^{2 \cdot 4} \cdot c^4)$

$= -3a^{10}(a^{16} b^8 c^4)$

$= -3a^{10 + 16} b^8 c^4$

$= -3a^{26} b^8 c^4$

39. $(-2x^4)^3(x^4 yz^8) = [(-2^3)x^{4 \cdot 3}](x^4 yz^8)$

$= (-8x^{12})(x^4 yz^8)$

$= -8x^{12+4} yz^8$

$= -8x^{16} yz^8$

40. $3[(r^4 s^3)^4 \cdot r^8 s]^3 = 3[(r^{4 \cdot 4} s^{3 \cdot 4}) \cdot r^8 s]^3$

$= 3[r^{16} s^{12} \cdot r^8 s]^3$

$= 3[r^{16 + 8} s^{12 + 1}]^3$

$= 3[r^{24} s^{13}]^3$

$= 3[r^{24 \cdot 3} s^{13 \cdot 3}]$

$= 3r^{72} s^{39}$

41. $2[(c^2 d)^3 \cdot (c^3 d^4)^4]^2 = 2[(c^{2 \cdot 3} d^3) \cdot (c^{3 \cdot 4} d^{4 \cdot 4})]^2$

$= 2[c^6 d^3 c^{12} d^{16}]^2$

$= 2[c^{6 + 12} d^{3 + 16}]^2$

$= 2[c^{18} d^{19}]^2$

$= 2[c^{18 \cdot 2} d^{19 \cdot 2}]$

$= 2c^{36} d^{38}$

42. $\left(\dfrac{2x^2}{x}\right)^3 = \dfrac{2^3 x^{2 \cdot 3}}{x^3} = \dfrac{8x^6}{x^3} = 8x^3$

43. $\left(\dfrac{9h^5}{h^7}\right)^2 = \dfrac{9^2 h^{5 \cdot 2}}{h^{7 \cdot 2}} = \dfrac{81 h^{10}}{h^{14}} = \dfrac{81}{h^4}$

44. $\dfrac{(4x^2)^3}{(2x)^4} = \dfrac{4^3 x^{2 \cdot 3}}{2^4 x^4} = \dfrac{64 x^6}{16 x^4} = 4x^2$

45. $\dfrac{(-3mn)^2}{(n^2)^3} = \dfrac{(-3)^2 m^2 n^2}{n^{2 \cdot 3}} = \dfrac{9m^2 n^2}{n^6} = \dfrac{9m^2}{n^4}$

46. $8a^6 + 64a^3 = 8a^3(a^3 + 8)$

47. $12b^2 - 9b^2 c^4 = 3b^2(4 - 3c^4)$

48. $18x^2 y - 9xy^2 = 9xy(2x - y)$

49. $12x^3 y^6 + 20x^5 y^2 = 4x^3 y^2(3y^4 + 5x^2)$

Problem Solving

50. The length of the page is $2w$ and the width is w. The area of the page before the margin is $A = \ell w = 2w \cdot w = 2w^2$. The area of the binding is $2 \cdot 2w$, or $4w$, so the total area is $2w^2 + 4w$ square inches.

51. $V = s^3$

$V = (5x)^3$

$V = 5^3 x^3$

$V = 125 x^3$

52. a. $\left(\dfrac{x}{y}\right)^4 = \left(\dfrac{x}{y}\right) \cdot \left(\dfrac{x}{y}\right) \cdot \left(\dfrac{x}{y}\right) \cdot \left(\dfrac{x}{y}\right)$

b. $\dfrac{x^4}{y^4}$

c. To simplify a quotient raised to a power, rewrite so that the numerator is raised to the power and the denominator is raised to the power.

53. $A = \dfrac{1}{2}(b_1 + b_2)h$

$= \dfrac{1}{2}(3b + b)(b - 6)$

$= \dfrac{1}{2}(4b)(b - 6)$

$= 2b(b - 6)$

$= 2b^2 - 12b$

54. $(4y)^2 = 4^2 \cdot y^2 = 16y^2$

$(4y)^2$ is different from $4y^2$ because the 4 is also squared to give $16y^2$.

55. $V = \dfrac{1}{3}\pi r^2 h$

$V = \dfrac{1}{3}\pi (2r)^2 h$

$V = \dfrac{1}{3}\pi (2^2 r^2)h$

$V = \dfrac{4}{3}\pi r^2 h$

It is 4 times the original expression.

56. $\dfrac{\text{Area of circle}}{\text{Area of square}} = \dfrac{\pi r^2}{s^2} = \dfrac{\pi r^2}{(2r)^2} = \dfrac{\pi r^2}{2^2 r^2} = \dfrac{\pi r^2}{4r^2} = \dfrac{\pi}{4}$

57. B; $S = 2\pi r^2 + 2\pi rh$

$S = 2\pi\left(\dfrac{d}{2}\right)^2 + \pi dh$

$S = 2\pi\left(\dfrac{4h}{2}\right)^2 + \pi(4h)h$

$S = 8\pi h^2 + \pi 4h^2$

$S = 12\pi h^2$

58. $V = \dfrac{1}{3}\ell wh$

$= \dfrac{1}{3}(3x)(3x)(x)$

$= \dfrac{1}{3}(3 \cdot 3 \cdot x \cdot x \cdot x)$

$= \dfrac{1}{3}(9x^3)$

$= 3x^3$

Chapter 13, *continued*

59. a. $V = \frac{4}{3}\pi r^3$

$= \frac{4}{3}(\pi)(6.0 \times 10^4)^3$

$= \frac{4}{3}(\pi)(6.0^3 \times 10^{4 \cdot 3})$

$= \frac{4}{3}(\pi)(216 \times 10^{12})$

$\approx \frac{4}{3}(\pi)(2.16 \times 10^{14})$

$= 9.05 \times 10^{14}$

The volume of Saturn is about 9.05×10^{14} cubic kilometers.

b. $V = \frac{4}{3}\pi r^3 \approx \frac{4}{3}\pi(560)^3 \approx 736,000,000$

The volume of Saturn's moon Dione is about 7.36×10^8 cubic kilometers.

c. $\dfrac{\text{Volume of Saturn}}{\text{Volume of Dione}} \approx \dfrac{\frac{4}{3}\pi(6.0 \times 10^4)^3}{\frac{4}{3}\pi(5.6 \times 10^2)^3}$

$= \dfrac{6.0^3 \times 10^{4 \cdot 3}}{5.6^3 \times 10^{2 \cdot 3}}$

$\approx \dfrac{2.16 \times 10^{14}}{1.76 \times 10^8}$

$\approx 1.23 \times 10^{14 - 8}$

$\approx 1.23 \times 10^6$

Saturn is about 1,230,000 times larger than Dione.

60. *Sample answer:* The difference in decibel levels is $110 - 60 = 50$dB. Each 10dB represents 10 times the intensity so 50dB represents 10^5 or 100,000 times the intensity.

61. *Sample answer:* $\frac{a}{b} = a \cdot b^{-1}$ since $b^{-1} = \frac{1}{b}$. So $\left(\frac{a}{b}\right)^m = (a \cdot b^{-1})^m = (a^m \cdot b^{-1})^m$ (by the power of a product property) $= a^m \cdot b^{-m}$ (by the power of a power property) $= \frac{a^m}{b^m}$ (by the definition of a negative exponent).

Mixed Review

62. $3(5x + 1) = 15x + 3$

63. $-5(2x - 7) = -10x + 35$

64. $-4(8 - x) = -32 + 4x$

65. $3(6x + 7y) = 18x + 21y$

66. $55\% = \frac{55}{100} = \frac{11}{20}$

67. $71\% = \frac{71}{100}$

68. $29\% = \frac{29}{100}$

69. $18\% = \frac{18}{100} = \frac{9}{50}$

70. *Sample answer:* You have four pockets in your coat. Your friend is going to put your movie ticket in one of the pockets. The odds in favor of it being in any one pocket are $1:3$.

Quiz 13.1–13.3 (p. 731)

1. $5x^2 + 4x - 3x^2 - 11x = (5x^2 - 3x^2) + (4x - 11x)$

$= 2x^2 - 7x$

2. $-5k^3 - 2(3k^3 + k - 4) = -5k^3 - 6k^3 - 2k + 8$

$= -11k^3 - 2k + 8$

3. $(6n^3 - 2n^2) + (n^3 + 7n^2 - 4n)$

$= 6n^3 + n^3 - 2n^2 + 7n^2 - 4n$

$= 7n^3 + 5n^2 - 4n$

4. $(4b^2 - 3b + 8) - (2b^2 - 6)$

$= (4b^2 - 3b + 8) + (-2b^2 + 6)$

$= 4b^2 - 2b^2 - 3b + 8 + 6$

$= 2b^2 - 3b + 14$

5. $(x^2 + 6x + 1) - (2x^2 - 8x + 4)$

$= (x^2 + 6x + 1) + (-2x^2 + 8x - 4)$

$= x^2 - 2x^2 + 6x + 8x + 1 - 4$

$= -x^2 + 14x - 3$

6. $(3m^2 + m - 9) + (7m^2 + 2) = 3m^2 + 7m^2 + m - 9 + 2$

$= 10m^2 + m - 7$

7. Area surrounding rug = Area of floor − Area of rug

$A = 2x \cdot 3x - x(x - 3) = 6x^2 - x^2 + 3x = 5x^2 + 3x$

8. $(3t^4)(4t^2) = 3 \cdot 4 \cdot t^4 \cdot t^2 = 12t^6$

9. $(2c^3)^4 = 2^4 c^{3 \cdot 4} = 16c^{12}$

10. $(-2y)^4 = (-2)^4 \cdot y^4 = 16y^4$

11. $-5d(3d^2 + 2) = -5d(3d^2) - 5d(2) = -15d^3 - 10d$

Brain Game (p. 731)

Fragrances E and F:

$(3x^2 + 5x - 4) + (-2x^2 + x - 3)$

$= (3x^2 - 2x^2) + (5x + x) + (-4 - 3)$

$= x^2 + 6x - 7$

Fragrances E and D:

$(3x^2 + 5x - 4) + (-3x^2 + 2x - 1)$

$= (3x^2 - 3x^2) + (5x + 2x) + (-4 - 1)$

$= 7x - 5$

Fragrances C and F:

$(2x^2 - 3x + 1) + (-2x^2 + x - 3)$

$= (2x^2 - 2x^2) + (-3x + x) + (1 - 3)$

$= -2x - 2$

Fragrances A and B:

$(x^2 - 2x + 2) + (-x^2 - 6x - 2)$

$= (x^2 - x^2) + (-2x - 6x) + (2 - 2)$

$= -8x$

Fragrances C and E:

$(2x^2 - 3x + 1) + (3x^2 + 5x - 4)$

$= (2x^2 + 3x^2) + (-3x + 5x) + (1 - 4)$

$= 5x^2 + 2x - 3$

Fragrances B and C:

$(-x^2 - 6x - 2) + (2x^2 - 3x + 1)$

$= (-x^2 + 2x^2) + (-6x - 3x) + (-2 + 1)$

$= x^2 - 9x - 1$

Chapter 13, continued

1. a. Making T-shirts: $3000 + 3x$

Revenue: $12x$

b. Profit = $12x - (3000 + 3x) = 9x - 3000$

c. $9x - 3000 = 9(680) - 3000 = 6120 - 3000 = 3120$

The company made $3120.

2. a.
$$(2x - 11) + x + (2x + 1) = 180$$
$$(2x + x + 2x) + (-11 + 1) = 180$$
$$5x - 10 = 180$$
$$5x - 10 + 10 = 180 + 10$$
$$5x = 190$$
$$\frac{5x}{5} = \frac{190}{5}$$
$$x = 38$$

b. $x = 38°$

$2x - 11 = 2(38) - 11 = 65°$

$2x + 1 = 2(38) + 1 = 77°$

c.
$$y^2 + 34 + 65 = 180$$
$$y^2 + 99 = 180$$
$$y^2 = 81$$
$$y = \pm 9$$

3. a. Making the sandwiches: $1.5x + 3y$

Revenue: $3x + 5y$

b. Profit − Cost of sandwiches:
$$3x + 5y - (1.5x + 3y) = 3x + 5y - 1.5x - 3y$$
$$= 3x - 1.5x + 5y - 3y$$
$$= 1.5x + 2y$$

c. *Sample answer:*
$$1.5x + 2y \geq 500$$
$$1.5(200) + 2y \geq 500$$
$$300 + 2y \geq 500$$
$$2y \geq 200$$
$$\frac{2y}{2} \geq \frac{200}{2}$$
$$y \geq 100$$

The restaurant needs to sell 100 whole submarine sandwiches.

4. a. $S = 4\pi r^2$

Double radius: $4\pi(2r)^2 = 4\pi(4)r^2 = 16\pi r^2$

Triple radius: $4\pi(3r)^2 = 4\pi(9)r^2 = 36\pi r^2$

b. $V = \frac{4}{3}\pi r^3$

Double radius: $\frac{4}{3}\pi(2r)^3 = \frac{4}{3}\pi(8)r^3 = \frac{32}{3}\pi r^3$

Triple radius: $\frac{4}{3}\pi(3r)^3 = \frac{4}{3}\pi(27)r^3 = 36\pi r^3$

c. Ratio: $\dfrac{\text{Volume}}{\text{Surface area}} = \dfrac{\frac{4}{3}\pi r^3}{4\pi r^2} = \dfrac{r}{3}$

When $r = 9$: $\dfrac{9}{3} = \dfrac{3}{1}$

The ratio is 3 to 1.

5. After 1 sec the height is:
$$-16t^2 + 75$$
$$= -16(1)^2 + 75$$
$$= -16 + 75$$
$$= 59 \text{ ft}$$

After 2 sec the height is:
$$-16(2)^2 + 75$$
$$= -16(4) + 75$$
$$= -64 + 75$$
$$= 11 \text{ ft}$$

The walnut hits the ground at just before 2.2 sec because its height at 2.1 sec is $-16(2.1)^2 + 75 = -70.56 + 75 = 4.44$ feet and after 2.2 sec the height would be $-16(2.2)^2 + 75 = -77.44 + 75 = -2.44$ feet, so it hit the ground before falling for 2.2 sec.

6. *Sample answer:* For a triangle "distribute" the perimeter $7x + 5$ among the three sides. One possibility is $2x + 1$, $2x + 2$, and $3x + 2$. For a quadrilateral, "distribute" $7x + 5$ among the four sides. One possibility is $2x + 1$, $2x + 2$, $2x$, and $x + 2$.

7.
$$4(2x + 1) = 36$$
$$8x + 4 = 36$$
$$8x + 4 - 4 = 36 - 4$$
$$8x = 32$$
$$\frac{8x}{8} = \frac{32}{8}$$
$$x = 4$$

The sink is 4 feet long.

Lesson 13.4

Investigation (p. 733)

1. $(x + 1)(x + 2)$

$(x + 1)(x + 2) = x^2 + 3x + 2$

2. $(x + 4)(x + 4)$

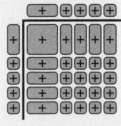

$(x + 4)(x + 4) = x^2 + 8x + 16$

3. $(x + 2)(2x + 2)$

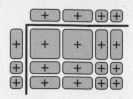

$$(x + 2)(2x + 2) = 2x^2 + 6x + 4$$

4. $x^2 + 5x + 6$

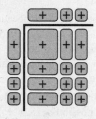

$$x^2 + 5x + 6 = (x + 2)(x + 3)$$

5. $x^2 + 2x + 1$

$$x^2 + 2x + 1 = (x + 1)(x + 1)$$

6.

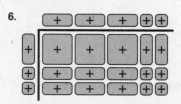

$$3x^2 + 8x + 4 = (3x + 2)(x + 2)$$

7. *Sample answer:* To find the product, each part of one dimension is distributed across the two parts of the other dimension.

13.4 Guided Practice (p. 735)

1. $(x + 1)(x + 3) = x(x + 3) + 1(x + 3)$
$= x^2 + 3x + x + 3$
$= x^2 + 4x + 3$

2. $(b - 4)(b - 3) = b(b - 3) - 4(b - 3)$
$= b^2 - 3b - 4b + 12$
$= b^2 - 7b + 12$

3. $(3t - 4)(t + 2) = 3t(t + 2) - 4(t + 2)$
$= 3t^2 + 6t - 4t - 8$
$= 3t^2 + 2t - 8$

4. $(d + 6)(d + 5) = d^2 + 5d + 6d + 30 = d^2 + 11d + 30$

5. $(x - 3)(x - 1) = x^2 - x - 3x + 3 = x^2 - 4x + 3$

6. $(5s + 3)(2s - 4) = 10s^2 - 20s + 6s - 12$
$= 10s^2 - 14s - 12$

13.4 Exercises (pp. 736–738)

Skill Practice

1. A polynomial with two terms is called a *binomial*.

2. *Sample answer:* Find the product of the First terms, the Outer terms, the Inner terms, and the Last terms. Then simplify.

3. $(y - 4)(y + 1) = y^2 + y - 4y - 4 = y^2 - 3y - 4$

4. $(g + 3)(g + 7) = g^2 + 7g + 3g + 21 = g^2 + 10g + 21$

5. $(x - 4)(x + 4) = x^2 + 4x - 4x - 16 = x^2 - 16$

6. $(2m + 3)(m - 7) = 2m^2 - 14m + 3m - 21$
$= 2m^2 - 11m - 21$

7. $(3q - 1)(5q - 1) = 15q^2 - 3q - 5q + 1$
$= 15q^2 - 8q + 1$

8. $(7b - 3)(9b + 4) = 63b^2 + 28b - 27b - 12$
$= 63b^2 + b - 12$

9. $(x + 9)(x - 2) = x^2 - 2x + 9x - 18 = x^2 + 7x - 18$

10. $(x + 3)(x - 3) = x^2 - 3x + 3x - 9 = x^2 - 9$

11. $(a + 10)(a - 4) = a^2 - 4a + 10a - 40 = a^2 + 6a - 40$

12. $(6r + 7)(r - 1) = 6r^2 - 6r + 7r - 7 = 6r^2 + r - 7$

13. $(t - 1)(-3t - 4) = -3t^2 - 4t + 3t + 4 = -3t^2 - t + 4$

14. $(-2x - 5)(11x - 12) = -22x^2 + 24x - 55x + 60$
$= -22x^2 - 31x + 60$

15. $(3x + 1)(3x - 1) = 9x^2 - 3x + 3x - 1 = 9x^2 - 1$

16. $(3x - 1)(5x - 4) = 15x^2 - 12x - 5x + 4$
$= 15x^2 - 17x + 4$

17. $(2m + 7)(3m + 1) = 6m^2 + 2m + 21m + 7$
$= 6m^2 + 23m + 7$

18. $(7b - 3)(-2b + 5) = -14b^2 + 35b + 6b - 15$
$= -14b^2 + 41b - 15$

19. $(6z + 5)(6z + 5) = 36z^2 + 30z + 30z + 25$
$= 36z^2 + 60z + 25$

20. $(2g + 9)(2g - 9) = 4g^2 - 18g + 18g - 81 = 4g^2 - 81$

21. $\left(\frac{1}{2}x + 2\right)(4x - 6) = 2x^2 - 3x + 8x - 12$
$= 2x^2 + 5x - 12$

22. $(9b - 12)\left(\frac{1}{3}b - 6\right) = 3b^2 - 54b - 4b + 72$
$= 3b^2 - 58b + 72$

23. $(n^2 - 2)(n^2 + 1) = n^4 + n^2 - 2n^2 - 2 = n^4 - n^2 - 2$

24. The error occurred when the negative sign was forgotten on -4.
$(x + 2)(x - 4) = x \cdot x + x(-4) + 2 \cdot x + 2 \cdot (-4)$
$= x^2 - 4x + 2x - 8$
$= x^2 - 2x - 8$

25. D; $(x + 6)(x - 2) = x^2 - 2x + 6x - 12 = x^2 + 4x - 12$

26. $(x + 5)(2x^2 + 5x + 7)$
$= 2x^3 + 5x^2 + 7x + 10x^2 + 25x + 35$
$= 2x^3 + (5x^2 + 10x^2) + (7x + 25x) + 35$
$= 2x^3 + 15x^2 + 32x + 35$

27. $(x - 4)(x^2 + 3x + 9)$

$= x^3 + 3x^2 + 9x - 4x^2 - 12x - 36$

$= x^3 + (3x^2 - 4x^2) + (9x - 12x) - 36$

$= x^3 - x^2 - 3x - 36$

28. $(x + 6)(3x^2 - 4x + 1)$

$= 3x^3 - 4x^2 + x + 18x^2 - 24x + 6$

$= 3x^3 + (-4x^2 + 18x^2) + (x - 24x) + 6$

$= 3x^3 + 14x^2 - 23x + 6$

29. $(2x + 1)(4x^2 - x + 5)$

$= 8x^3 - 2x^2 + 10x + 4x^2 - x + 5$

$= 8x^3 + (-2x^2 + 4x^2) + (10x - x) + 5$

$= 8x^3 + 2x^2 + 9x + 5$

30. $(3x + 2)(2x^2 + 6x - 4)$

$= 6x^3 + 18x^2 - 12x + 4x^2 + 12x - 8$

$= 6x^3 + (18x^2 + 4x^2) + (-12x + 12x) - 8$

$= 6x^3 + 22x^2 - 8$

31. $(4x - 3)(-x^2 - 5x - 6)$

$= -4x^3 - 20x^2 - 24x + 3x^2 + 15x + 18$

$= -4x^3 + (-20x^2 + 3x^2) + (-24x + 15x) + 18$

$= -4x^3 - 17x^2 - 9x + 18$

32. $A = \frac{1}{2}bh$

$A = \frac{1}{2}(4x + 4)(2x + 1)$

$A = \frac{1}{2}(8x^2 + 4x + 8x + 4)$

$A = 4x^2 + 6x + 2$

33. $A = bh$

$A = (3x - 5)(x + 7)$

$A = 3x^2 + 21x - 5x - 35$

$A = 3x^2 + 16x - 35$

34. $A = \frac{1}{2}(b_1 + b_2)h$

$A = \frac{1}{2}[(x + 2) + (3x + 1)](2x + 6)$

$A = \frac{1}{2}[4x + 3](2x + 6)$

$A = \frac{1}{2}(8x^2 + 24x + 6x + 18)$

$A = 4x^2 + 15x + 9$

35. $x^2 + 8x + 7 = (?)(x + 7)$

$x^2 + 8x + 7 = x^2 + 7x + x + 7$

$= x(x + 7) + 1(x + 7)$

$= (x + 1)(x + 7)$

36. $x^2 + 6x + 8 = (x + 2)(?)$

$x^2 + 6x + 8 = x^2 + 2x + 4x + 8$

$= x(x + 2) + 4(x + 2)$

$= (x + 2)(x + 4)$

37. $x^2 - 9x + 14 = (?)(x - 2)$

$x^2 - 9x + 14 = x^2 - 2x - 7x + 14$

$= x(x - 2) - 7(x - 2)$

$= (x - 7)(x - 2)$

38. $x^2 - 7x - 18 = (x - 9)(?)$

$x^2 - 7x - 18 = x^2 - 9x + 2x - 18$

$= x(x - 9) + 2(x - 9)$

$= (x - 9)(x + 2)$

Problem Solving

39. $50(1 + r)^2 = 50(1 + r)(1 + r)$

$= 50(1 + r + r + r^2)$

$= 50(1 + 2r + r^2)$

$= 50 + 100r + 50r^2$

When $r = 0.03$:

$50 + 100(0.03) + 50(0.03)^2 = 50 + 3 + 0.045$

≈ 53.05

The account balance is $53.05.

40. C; $(2x + 18)(2x + 8)$

41. *Sample answer:* The products of the inner terms and of the outer terms cancel out, leaving just the products of the first terms and of the last terms.

42. $(x + 3)^2 = (x + 3)(x + 3)$

$= x^2 + 3x + 3x + 9$

$= x^2 + 6x + 9$

$(x + 3)^2$ does not equal $x^2 + 9$ because $(x + 3)^2 = x^2 + 6x + 9$.

43. *Sample answer:*

Same: You distribute factors to terms of other factors.

Different: For two binomials you distribute two times, while for a monomial and a polynomial you distribute just one time.

44. $(2x + 25)(2x + 50) = 4x^2 + 100x + 50x + 1250$

$= 4x^2 + 150x + 1250$

45. *Sample answer:*

$(2x + 1)(2x^2 + 2) = 4x^3 + 4x + 2x^2 + 2$

$= 4x^3 + 2x^2 + 4x + 2$

46. $4\pi(0.6875 + x)^2 = 4\pi(0.6875 + x)(0.6875 + x)$

$= 4\pi(0.4727 + 1.375x + x^2)$

$\approx 5.940 + 17.28x + 12.57x^2$

47. $20(1 + r)^3 = 20(1 + r)(1 + r)(1 + r)$
$$= 20(1 + r)(1 + r + r + r^2)$$
$$= 20(1 + r)(1 + 2r + r^2)$$
$$= 20[1(1 + 2r + r^2) + r(1 + 2r + r^2)]$$
$$= 20(1 + 2r + r^2 + r + 2r^2 + r^3)$$
$$= 20(r^3 + 3r^2 + 3r + 1)$$
$$= 20r^3 + 60r^2 + 60r + 20$$

When $r = 0.05$:

$20(0.05)^3 + 60(0.05)^2 + 60(0.05) + 20$
$= 20(0.000125) + 60(0.0025) + 3 + 20$
$= 0.0025 + 0.15 + 23$
$= 23.1525$

The account balance is about $23.15.

48. $\ell = 30 - 2x$

$w = 20 - x$

$A = \ell w$
$\quad = (30 - 2x)(20 - x)$
$\quad = 600 - 30x - 40x + 2x^2$
$\quad = 2x^2 - 70x + 600$

When $x = 5$:

$A = 2(5)^2 - 70(5) + 600$
$\quad = 2(25) - 350 + 600$
$\quad = 50 - 350 + 600$
$\quad = 300$

The area of the platform when $x = 5$ is 300 square feet.

49. a. $A = \frac{1}{2}bh$; $b = 2n - 6$; $h = 6n + 6$

$A = \frac{1}{2}(2n - 6)(6n + 6)$

$A = \frac{1}{2}(12n^2 + 12n - 36n - 36)$

$A = \frac{1}{2}(12n^2 - 24n - 36)$

$A = 6n^2 - 12n - 18$

b. Mean: 20

$n = \frac{1}{4}(20) = 5$

$6(5)^2 - 12(5) - 18 = 150 - 60 - 18 = 72$

Check: $A = \frac{1}{2}bh$

$72 \stackrel{?}{=} \frac{1}{2}[2(5) - 6][6(5) + 6]$

$72 \stackrel{?}{=} \frac{1}{2}(4)(36)$

$72 = 72$ ✓

When the mean is 20 inches, the area is 72 square inches.

50. a. Length: $17 - 2x$

Width: $11 - 2x$

Height: x

b. $(17 - 2x)(11 - 2x)(x) = (187 - 34x - 22x + 4x^2)(x)$
$$= (187 - 56x + 4x^2)(x)$$
$$= 187x - 56x^2 + 4x^3$$
$$= 4x^3 - 56x^2 + 187x$$

c. When $x = 1$:

$4x^3 - 56x^2 + 187x = 4(1)^3 - 56(1)^2 + 187(1)$
$$= 4 - 56 + 187$$
$$= 135 \text{ in.}^3$$

When $x = 2$:

$4x^3 - 56x^2 + 187x = 4(2)^3 - 56(2)^2 + 187(2)$
$$= 32 - 224 + 374$$
$$= 182 \text{ in.}^3$$

When $x = 3$:

$4x^3 - 56x^2 + 187x = 4(3)^3 - 56(3)^2 + 187(3)$
$$= 108 - 504 + 561$$
$$= 165 \text{ in.}^3$$

When $x = 4$:

$4x^3 - 56x^2 + 187x = 4(4)^3 - 56(4)^2 + 187(4)$
$$= 256 - 896 + 748$$
$$= 108 \text{ in.}^3$$

$x = 2$ gives the greatest volume.

d. No because the width is only 11 in., which is less than two 6 in. side widths.

51. a. Total area of the house and yard:

$(2x + 30)(x + 30) = 2x^2 + 60x + 30x + 900$
$$= 2x^2 + 90x + 900$$

Area of the lawn:

$(2x^2 + 90x + 900) - (2x)(x) - 3(15)$
$= 2x^2 + 90x + 900 - 2x^2 - 45$
$= 90x + 855$

b. Total area: Since the house is twice as long as wide, divide 60 by 2 to find the value of x, which is 30 ft.

$2(30)^2 + 90(30) + 900 = 2(900) + 2700 + 900$
$$= 5400 \text{ ft}^2$$

Area of lawn: $90(30) + 855 = 2700 + 855 = 3555 \text{ ft}^2$

The total area of the house and lawn is 5400 ft². The area of the lawn is 3555 ft².

Mixed Review

52. $y = 6x - 4$

53. $y = x - 3$

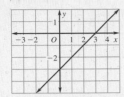

54. $y = -2x + 7$

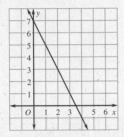

55. $-4r(r + 6) = -4r \cdot r - 4r \cdot 6 = -4r^2 - 24r$

56. $3c(4c^2 + 2c) = 3c \cdot 4c^2 + 3c \cdot 2c = 12c^3 + 6c^2$

57. $-5x(-3x + 2) = -5x(-3x) - 5x(2) = 15x^2 - 10x$

58. D; Odds in favor $= \dfrac{14}{21-14} = \dfrac{14}{7} = \dfrac{2}{1}$

Lesson 13.5

13.5 Guided Practice (pp. 739–741)

1. $y = x^2$

$f(x) = x^2$

$f(3) = (3)^2$

$f(3) = 9$

2. $y = 3x^2 + 4$

$f(x) = 3x^2 + 4$

$f(3) = 3(3)^2 + 4 = 3(9) + 4 = 27 + 4 = 31$

3. $y = -\dfrac{1}{2}x^2$

$f(x) = -\dfrac{1}{2}x^2$

$f(3) = -\dfrac{1}{2}(3)^2 = -\dfrac{1}{2}(9) = -4.5$

4. $f(x) = -x^2 + 4$

x	−2	−1	0	1	2
f(x)	0	3	4	3	0

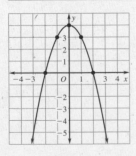

5. $f(x) = x^2 + 1$

x	−2	−1	0	1	2
f(x)	5	2	1	2	5

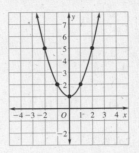

6. $f(x) = 2x^2$

x	−2	−1	0	1	2
f(x)	8	2	0	2	8

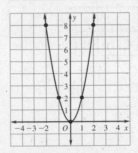

7. No vertical line intersects the graph at more than one point. So, the graph represents a function.

8. A vertical line intersects the graph at more than one point. So, the graph does not represent a function.

13.5 Exercises (pp. 741–745)

Skill Practice

1. The left side should be $f(x)$, not just f.

2. You can use the *vertical line test* to determine whether a graph represents a function.

3. $f(x) = x^2$

$f(-2) = (-2)^2 = 4$

$f(0) = (0)^2 = 0$

$f(2) = (2)^2 = 4$

4. $f(x) = 4x^2$

$f(-2) = 4(-2)^2 = 4(4) = 16$

$f(0) = 4(0)^2 = 4(0) = 0$

$f(2) = 4(2)^2 = 4(4) = 16$

5. $f(x) = -3x^2$

$f(-2) = -3(-2)^2 = -3(4) = -12$

$f(0) = -3(0)^2 = -3(0) = 0$

$f(2) = -3(2)^2 = -3(4) = -12$

6. $f(x) = -x^2 + 10$

$f(-2) = -(-2)^2 + 10 = -4 + 10 = 6$

$f(0) = -(0)^2 + 10 = 0 + 10 = 10$

$f(2) = -(2)^2 + 10 = -4 + 10 = 6$

7. $f(x) = x^2 - 5$

$f(-2) = (-2)^2 - 5 = 4 - 5 = -1$

$f(0) = 0^2 - 5 = 0 - 5 = -5$

$f(2) = 2^2 - 5 = 4 - 5 = -1$

8. $f(x) = 2x^2 - x$

$f(-2) = 2(-2)^2 - (-2) = 2(4) - (-2) = 10$

$f(0) = 2(0)^2 - (0) = 0$

$f(2) = 2(2)^2 - 2 = 2(4) - 2 = 6$

9. The square of -5 should be 25, not -25.

$f(-5) = (-5)^2 - 3 = 25 - 3 = 22$

10. B; $f(x) = x^2 + 7$ **11.** C

12. $f(x) = 4x^2$

x	-3	-2	-1	0	1	2	3
f(x)	36	16	4	0	4	16	36

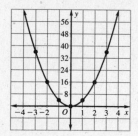

13. $f(x) = x^2 + 8$

x	-3	-2	-1	0	1	2	3
f(x)	17	12	9	8	9	12	17

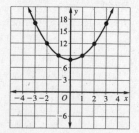

14. $f(x) = -x^2 + 5$

x	-3	-2	-1	0	1	2	3
f(x)	-4	1	4	5	4	1	-4

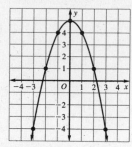

15. $f(x) = -2x^2$

x	-3	-2	-1	0	1	2	3
f(x)	-18	-8	-2	0	-2	-8	-18

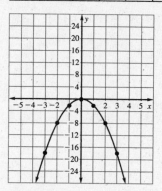

16. $f(x) = 3x^2 - 4$

x	-3	-2	-1	0	1	2	3
f(x)	23	8	-1	-4	-1	8	23

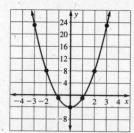

17. $f(x) = -\frac{1}{2}x^2$

x	−3	−2	−1	0	1	2	3
f(x)	$-4\frac{1}{2}$	−2	$-\frac{1}{2}$	0	$-\frac{1}{2}$	−2	$-4\frac{1}{2}$

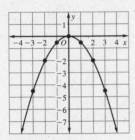

18. $f(x) = 5 - 5x^2$

x	−3	−2	−1	0	1	2	3
f(x)	−40	−15	0	5	0	−15	−40

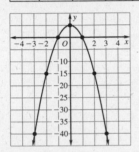

19. $f(x) = 4x^2 + x$

x	−3	−2	−1	0	1	2	3
f(x)	33	14	3	0	5	18	39

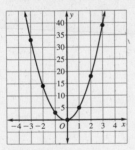

20. $f(x) = x^2 - 3x$

x	−3	−2	−1	0	1	2	3
f(x)	18	10	4	0	−2	−2	0

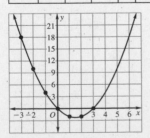

21. No vertical line intersects the graph at more than one point. So, the graph is a function.

The graph is nonlinear.

22. A vertical line intersects the graph at more than one point. So, the graph does *not* represent a function.

The graph is nonlinear.

23. A vertical line intersects the graph at more than one point. So, the graph does not represent a function.

The graph is not nonlinear.

24. C; It does not represent a function like the rest of the graphs.

25. $f(x) = (x - 1)^2$
$$= (x - 1)(x - 1)$$
$$= x^2 - x - x + 1$$
$$= x^2 - 2x + 1$$

x	−2	−1	0	1	2
f(x)	9	4	1	0	1

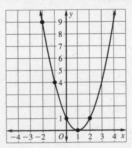

26. $f(x) = (x + 2)^2$
$$= (x + 2)(x + 2)$$
$$= x^2 + 2x + 2x + 4$$
$$= x^2 + 4x + 4$$

x	−2	−1	0	1	2
f(x)	0	1	4	9	16

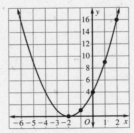

27. $f(x) = x^3 - 2$

x	−2	−1	0	1	2
f(x)	−10	−3	−2	−1	6

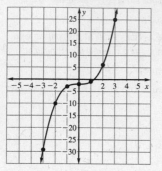

28. $f(x) = 2x^3 - 3x$

x	−2	−1	0	1	2
f(x)	−10	1	0	−1	10

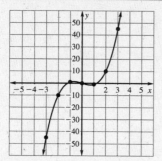

29. $f(x) = -x^4$

x	−2	−1	0	1	2
f(x)	−16	−1	0	−1	−16

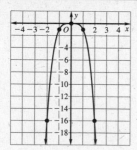

30. $f(x) = 1 - \frac{1}{5}x^5$

x	−2	−1	0	1	2
f(x)	$7\frac{2}{5}$	$1\frac{1}{5}$	1	$\frac{4}{5}$	$-5\frac{2}{5}$

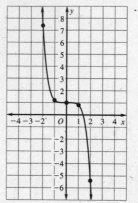

31. $f(x) = x^2$

$4 = x^2$

$2, -2 = x$

32. $f(x) = 5x^2 - 6$

$4 = 5x^2 - 6$

$4 + 6 = 5x^2 - 6 + 6$

$10 = 5x^2$

$\dfrac{10}{5} = \dfrac{5x^2}{5}$

$2 = x^2$

$\sqrt{2}, -\sqrt{2} = x$

33. $f(x) = 8 - 4x^2$

$4 = 8 - 4x^2$

$4 - 8 = 8 - 4x^2 - 8$

$-4 = -4x^2$

$\dfrac{-4}{-4} = \dfrac{-4x^2}{-4}$

$1 = x^2$

$1, -1 = x$

34. $f(x) = (x + 7)^2$

$4 = (x + 7)^2$

$\sqrt{4} = \sqrt{(x + 7)^2}$

$\pm 2 = x + 7$

$2 - 7 = x$ or $-2 - 7 = x$

$-5 = x$ or $-9 = x$

35. $f(x) = (1 - x)^2$

$4 = (1 - x)^2$

$\sqrt{4} = \sqrt{(1 - x)^2}$

$\pm 2 = 1 - x$

$2 = 1 - x$ or $-2 = 1 - x$

$2 - 1 = 1 - x - 1$ $-2 - 1 = 1 - x - 1$

$1 = -x$ $-3 = -x$

$\dfrac{1}{-1} = \dfrac{-x}{-1}$ $\dfrac{-3}{-1} = \dfrac{-x}{-1}$

$-1 = x$ $3 = x$

36. $f(x) = x^3 + 4$

$4 = x^3 + 4$

$4 - 4 = x^3 + 4 - 4$

$0 = x^3$

$0 = x$

37. $f(x) = x^3$ **38.** $f(x) = |x|$

39. The graph of $y = c$ is a function because it is a horizontal line. If it is rotated 90°, it is a vertical line, so it would not represent a function.

40. $f(x) = x^2 - 6$

Problem Solving

41. Because $V = \ell wd = 50 \cdot 30d = 1500d$, you can write $f(d) = 1500d$.

The function is linear.

42. $f(t) = -16t^2 + 4$

Sample answer: $f(3) = -16(3)^2 + 4$

$= -16(9) + 4$

$= -144 + 4$

$= -140$

$f(0) = -16(0)^2 + 4$

$f(0) = 4$

So $f(0) - f(3) = 4 - (-140) = 144$ ft

43. $f(t) = 20(1.002)^t$

$f(1) = 20(1.002)^1 = \$20.04$

$f(2) = 20(1.002)^2 = \$20.08$

$f(3) = 20(1.002)^3 = \$20.12$

The balance after 1 month is $20.04, after 2 months is $20.08, and after 3 months is $20.12.

44. $A = \frac{1}{2}hh = \frac{1}{2}x \cdot x = \frac{1}{2}x^2$

$f(x) = \frac{1}{2}x^2$

x	0	2	4	6
f(x)	0	2	8	18

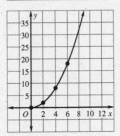

A reasonable estimate of x if the area of the triangle is 30 square inches is about 8 inches.

45. $A = \pi r^2 = \pi \left(\frac{x}{2}\right)^2 = \frac{\pi x^2}{4}$

$f(x) = \frac{\pi x^2}{4}$

$f(8) = \frac{\pi(8)^2}{4} = 50.3$ in.^{2}

x	0	2	4	6	8
f(x)	0	3.14	12.57	28.27	50.27

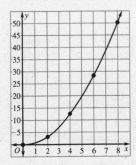

46. *Sample answer:* If any vertical line can intersect the graph in more than one point, then the graph does not represent a function. The test works because for a function, each input value (a location for a vertical line) has no more than one output value.

47. *Sample answer:* $y = x^2$; If the graph of this function is rotated 90° clockwise, the resulting graph does not represent a function. It does not pass the vertical line test.

x	−2	0	2
y	4	0	4

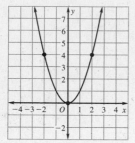

48. $f(x) = x^3$

x	−2	−1	0	1	2
f(x)	−8	−1	0	1	8

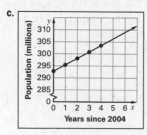

Sample answer: The graph of $f(x) = x^3$ does not have line symmetry while the graph $f(x) = x^2$ does have line symmetry.

49. B; $f(d) = 2^d$

50. a. $y = (292,800,000)(1.009)^t$

$f(t) = (292,800,000)(1.009)^t$

b.

t	0	1	2	3	4
f(t) (in millions)	292.8	295.4	298.1	300.8	303.5

c.

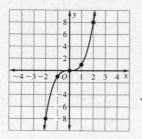

The population of the United States in 2010 will be about 309.0 million people.

51. $f(x) = x^2$

x	−2	0	2
f(x)	4	0	4

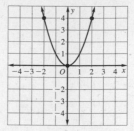

$f(x) = -x^2$

x	−2	0	2
f(x)	−4	0	−4

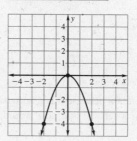

$f(x) = \frac{1}{2}x$

x	−2	0	2
f(x)	−1	0	1

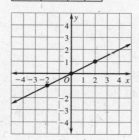

$f(x) = -\frac{1}{2}x$

x	−2	0	2
f(x)	1	0	−1

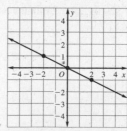

Sample answer: The graphs of $f(x) = x^2$ and $f(x) = -x^2$ are reflections of each other in the x-axis, as are the graphs of $f(x) = \frac{1}{2}x$ and $f(x) = -\frac{1}{2}x$. If the right side of function is multiplied by -1, the graph is reflected in the x-axis.

Chapter 13, *continued*

52. $f(x) = 90x$

53. *Sample answer:*

$f(x) = 90x$ describes the horizontal distance in terms of time.

$315 = 90x$

$\dfrac{315}{90} = \dfrac{90}{90}x$

$3.5 = x$

$f(x) = -16x^2 + 63x + 2.5$

$f(3.5) = -16(3.5)^2 + 63(3.5) + 2.5$

$\qquad = -196 + 220.5 + 2.5$

$\qquad = 27$

The height of the wall is 21 ft and 27 > 21, so the ball is high enough to be a home run.

54. *Sample answer:* The domain for *t* is all positive numbers for which $f(t)$ is greater than or equal to zero. The player would not have hit a home run over the left-center field wall.

$362 = 90x$

$4.0\overline{2} = x$

$f(4.0\overline{2}) = -16(4.0\overline{2})^2 + 63(4.0\overline{2}) + 2.5$

$\qquad = -258.9 + 253.4 + 2.5$

$\qquad = -3$

This means the ball would hit the ground before reaching the left-center field wall.

55. $A = \ell w = (10 - x)x = 10x - x^2$

$f(x) = 10x - x^2$

x	0	1	2	3	4	5	6	7	8	9	10
f(x)	0	9	16	21	24	25	24	21	16	9	0

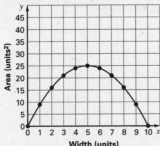

Rectangle Area

The maximum area is 25 units, where the width is 5 units, and the length is $w - 5$, or 5 units.

56. $f(x) = (x - 7)(x + 4)$

x	−4	1	2	7
f(x)	0	−30	−30	0

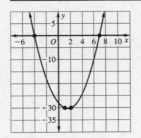

$g(x) = (x - 5)(x + 1)$

x	−1	0	3	4	5
g(x)	0	−5	−8	−5	0

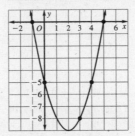

$h(x) = (x - 2)(x + 3)$

x	−3	−1	0	2
h(x)	0	−6	−6	0

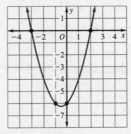

The *x*-intercepts of $k(x) = (x - a)(x + b)$ are $(-b, 0)$ and $(a, 0)$.

Mixed Review

57. $\quad 3x + 1 = 7$

$\quad 3x + 1 - 1 = 7 - 1$

$\qquad\quad 3x = 6$

$\qquad\quad \dfrac{3x}{3} = \dfrac{6}{3}$

$\qquad\qquad x = 2$

Chapter 13, *continued*

58.
$$2x + 5 = -17$$
$$2x + 5 - 5 = -17 - 5$$
$$2x = -22$$
$$\frac{2x}{2} = \frac{-22}{2}$$
$$x = -11$$

59.
$$-x + 1 = 2$$
$$-x + 1 - 1 = 2 - 1$$
$$-x = 1$$
$$\frac{-x}{-1} = \frac{1}{-1}$$
$$x = -1$$

60.
$$-3x - 4 = 11$$
$$-3x - 4 + 4 = 11 + 4$$
$$-3x = 15$$
$$\frac{-3x}{-3} = \frac{15}{-3}$$
$$x = -5$$

61. (1) Read and Understand

(2) Make a Plan: Break into Parts

(3) Solve the Problem:

If you put one penny in on the first day, 2 on the second day, 3 on the third day, and so on, you will have $1 + 2 + 3 + \ldots + 97 + 98 + 100$ pennies on day 100.

Instead of adding these numbers, we can make pairs that add to 100.

$(1 + 99) + (2 + 98) + (3 + 97) + \ldots$

There are 49 of these pairs, with 50 and 100 left over.

$49(100) + 50 + 100 = 4900 + 50 + 100 = 5050$

You will have \$50.50 on day 100.

(4) Look Back

62. $(x + 2)(x + 2) = x^2 + 2x + 2x + 4 = x^2 + 4x + 4$

63. $(3z - 2)(2z - 1) = 6z^2 - 3z - 4z + 2 = 6z^2 - 7z + 2$

64. $(5a - 1)(a + 3) = 5a^2 + 15a - a - 3 = 5a^2 + 14a - 3$

65. A; $2x + 4y = -12$
$$2(-2) + 4(-2) \stackrel{?}{=} -12$$
$$-4 + (-8) \stackrel{?}{=} -12$$
$$-12 = -12$$

Quiz 13.4–13.5 (p. 745)

1. $(x - 1)(x + 9) = x^2 + 9x - x - 9 = x^2 + 8x - 9$

2. $(a + 4)(a + 9) = a^2 + 9a + 4a + 36 = a^2 + 13a + 36$

3. $(m - 2)(m - 8) = m^2 - 8m - 2m + 16 = m^2 - 10m + 16$

4. $(4y + 5)(y - 2) = 4y^2 - 8y + 5y - 10 = 4y^2 - 3y - 10$

5. $(b + 3)(4b - 3) = 4b^2 - 3b + 12b - 9 = 4b^2 + 9b - 9$

6. $(3z - 2)(2z - 7) = 6z^2 - 21z - 4z + 14$
$$= 6z^2 - 25z + 14$$

7. $y = 3x + 9$
$f(x) = 3x + 9$

8. $y = -2x^2 - 4$
$f(x) = -2x^2 - 4$

9. $y = 19 - x + x^2$
$f(x) = 19 - x + x^2$

10. $f(x) = 2 - x^2$
$$f(-2) = 2 - (-2)^2 = 2 - 4 = -2$$
$$f(-1) = 2 - (-1)^2 = 2 - 1 = 1$$
$$f(0) = 2 - 0^2 = 2 - 0 = 2$$
$$f(1) = 2 - 1^2 = 2 - 1 = 1$$
$$f(2) = 2 - 2^2 = 2 - 4 = -2$$

11. $f(x) = \frac{1}{2}x^2 - 6$
$$f(-2) = \frac{1}{2}(-2)^2 - 6 = \frac{1}{2} \cdot 4 - 6 = 2 - 6 = -4$$
$$f(-1) = \frac{1}{2}(-1)^2 - 6 = \frac{1}{2} \cdot 1 - 6 = \frac{1}{2} - 6 = -5\frac{1}{2}$$
$$f(0) = \frac{1}{2}(0)^2 - 6 = \frac{1}{2} \cdot 0 - 6 = 0 - 6 = -6$$
$$f(1) = \frac{1}{2}(1)^2 - 6 = \frac{1}{2} \cdot 1 - 6 = \frac{1}{2} - 6 = -5\frac{1}{2}$$
$$f(2) = \frac{1}{2}(2)^2 - 6 = \frac{1}{2}(4) - 6 = 2 - 6 = -4$$

12. $f(x) = x^2 + x$
$$f(-2) = (-2)^2 + (-2) = 4 - 2 = 2$$
$$f(-1) = (-1)^2 + (-1) = 1 - 1 = 0$$
$$f(0) = 0^2 + 0 = 0 + 0 = 0$$
$$f(1) = 1^2 + 1 = 1 + 1 = 2$$
$$f(2) = 2^2 + 2 = 4 + 2 = 6$$

13. $f(x) = -x^2 + 1$

x	-2	-1	0	1	2
$f(x)$	-3	0	1	0	-3

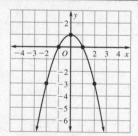

14. $f(x) = \frac{1}{4}x^2$

x	-4	-2	0	2	4
$f(x)$	4	1	0	1	4

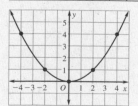

15. $f(x) = -3x^2 - 4$

x	−2	−1	0	1	2
f(x)	−16	−7	−4	−7	−16

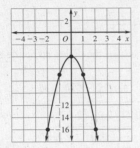

Technology Activity 13.5 (p. 746)

1–4.

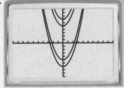

Sample answer: The graphs are all parabolas with the same shape and with vertices on the *y*-axis, but the graph moves up or down compared to the graph of $y = x^2$ by the number of units that are added to or subtracted from x^2. The graph moves up if this number is positive and down if this number is negative.

5–8.

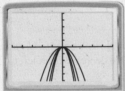

Sample answer: The graphs are the same as the graphs in the example, except they are reflected about the *x*-axis.

9.

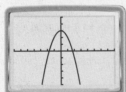

Sample answer: The graph is the same shape as the first gaph in the example, reflected about the *x*-axis and shifted vertically 3 units.

10.

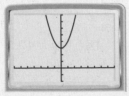

Sample answer: The graph is the same shape as the first graph in the example, shifted vertically 3 units.

11.

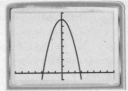

Sample answer: The graph is the same shape as the first graph in the example, reflected about the *x*-axis and shifted vertically 8 units.

12.

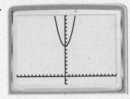

Sample answer: The graph is the same shape as the first graph in the example, shifted vertically 8 units.

Mixed Review of Problem Solving (p. 747)

1. a. $V = s^3$

$V = (x + 1)^3$

$V = (x + 1)(x + 1)(x + 1)$

$V = (x^2 + x + x + 1)(x + 1)$

$V = (x^2 + 2x + 1)(x + 1)$

$V = x^3 + 2x^2 + x + x^2 + 2x + 1$

$V = x^3 + 2x^2 + x^2 + x + 2x + 1$

$V = x^3 + 3x^2 + 3x + 1$

b. $V = s^3$

$V = x^3$

c. $x^3 + 3x^2 + 3x + 1 - x^3 = 3x^2 + 3x + 1$

2. $2400(0.5)^t < 0.05(2400)$

$2400(0.5)^t < 120$

$(0.5)^t < 0.05$

When $t = 4$: $2400(0.5)^4 = 0.0625 \not< 0.05$

When $t = 5$: $2400(0.5)^5 = 0.03125 < 0.05$

$2005 + 5 = 2010$

2010 will be the first year that the value of the computer will be less than 5% of the original value.

3. *Sample answer:* All the graphs have the same shape and all open upward. All contain $(0, 0)$. The graphs all have different lowest points and the second x-intercepts are different. The graph of $f(x) = x^2 - 25x$ will go through $(0, 0)$ and $(25, 0)$; it will open upward, and its lowest point will be below the other graphs.

$c = 1$

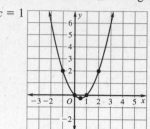

$c = 2$

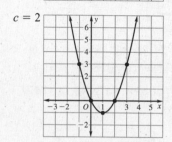

$c = 3$

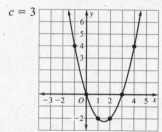

4. *Sample answer:* A soccer ball is kicked. Its initial speed is 5 ft/sec, its initial height is 1.5 ft.

$f(x) = -16x^2 + 5x + 1.5$

5. The difference is

$(5t - 3)^2 - 50 - (16t^2 - 12t - 41)$
$= (25t^2 - 30t + 9 - 50) - (16t^2 - 12t - 41)$
$= 25t^2 - 30t - 41 - 16t^2 + 12t + 41$
$= (25t^2 - 16t^2) + (-30t + 12t) + (-41 + 41)$
$= 9t^2 - 18t$

When $t = 4$: $9(4)^2 - 18(4) = 144 - 72 = 72$

The business owner's profit prediction is $72,000 more than the accountant's profit prediction.

6. a.

x	0	2	8	18	32	50
f(x)	0	6	12	18	24	30

b. *Sample answer:*

I chose values close to those in the table.

$f(7) = 11, f(20) = 19, f(30) = 23$.

c.

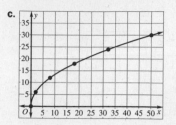

The graph is not linear because the points do not lie on a line.

d. *Sample answer:* $f(11) = 14, f(22) = 20, f(35) = 25$

7. a.

x	0	0.5	1.0	1.5	2.0	2.5
f(x)	90	86	74	54	26	-10

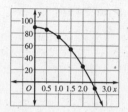

b. The nut hits the ground when $f(x) = 0$, which is at about $x = 2.4$ seconds.

c. The nut was dropped from a height of 90 ft, because that is the value of $f(x)$ when $x = 0$.

Chapter 13 Review (pp. 748–750)

1. The sum of two or more monomials is called a *polynomial*.

2. The polynomial $x^3 - 2x + 1$ is a *trinomial*.

3. A polynomial in one variable is written in *standard form* if the exponents of the variable decrease from left to right.

4. You can use the *vertical line test* to tell whether a graph represents a function.

5. The polynomial $5x^3 + 2x + 3$ has 3 terms, so it is called a trinomial.

6. The polynomial $5a^3$ has one term, so it is called a monomial.

7. The polynomial $5y + 3$ has two terms, so it is called a binomial.

8. The polynomial $-r + 3$ has 2 terms, so it is called a binomial.

9. $8k + 1 + 3k + k^2 - 4 = k^2 + 8k + 3k + 1 - 4$
$= k^2 + 11k - 3$

10. $5w - 2w + 2w^2 - 8 = 2w^2 + 5w - 2w - 8$
$= 2w^2 + 3w - 8$

11. $6p^2 + 9(2p^3 + 3 + p^2) = 6p^2 + 18p^3 + 27 + 9p^2$
$= 18p^3 + 6p^2 + 9p^2 + 27$
$= 18p^3 + 15p^2 + 27$

12. $3x^2 + 4(7 - x^2 + 4x) = 3x^2 + 28 - 4x^2 + 16x$

$\qquad = 3x^2 - 4x^2 + 16x + 28$

$\qquad = -x^2 + 16x + 28$

13. $-8(2s - 3s^2 + 7) + 4s^3 = -16s + 24s^2 - 56 + 4s^3$

$\qquad = 4s^3 + 24s^2 - 16s - 56$

14. $4(5y - 2y^2 + 11) - 2y^2 = 20y - 8y^2 + 44 - 2y^2$

$\qquad = -8y^2 - 2y^2 + 20y + 44$

$\qquad = -10y^2 + 20y + 44$

15. $-16t^2 + 70 = -16(2)^2 + 70 = -16(4) + 70 = 6$

The acorn's height is 6 feet.

16. $(10q^2 - 6) - (q^2 + 1) = 10q^2 - 6 - q^2 - 1$

$\qquad = (10q^2 - q^2) + (-6 - 1)$

$\qquad = 9q^2 - 7$

17. $(7y^2 + y - 4) + (y^2 - y - 1)$

$\qquad = 7y^2 + y^2 + y - y - 4 - 1$

$\qquad = 8y^2 - 5$

18. $4(m^2 - 3m) + 5(2m^2 - m) = 4m^2 - 12m + 10m^2 - 5m$

$\qquad = 4m^2 + 10m^2 - 12m - 5m$

$\qquad = 14m^2 - 17m$

19. $-2(v^3 - v^2 + v) - 3(v^3 + 4v^2)$

$\qquad = -2v^3 + 2v^2 - 2v - 3v^3 - 12v^2$

$\qquad = -2v^3 - 3v^3 + 2v^2 - 12v^2 - 2v$

$\qquad = -5v^3 - 10v^2 - 2v$

20. $(x + 4) + x + (x^2 + 2) + x^2$

$\qquad = (x^2 + x^2) + x + x + 4 + 2$

$\qquad = 2x^2 + 2x + 6$

21. $(-6a^2b^4)^3 = (-6)^3a^{2 \cdot 3}b^{4 \cdot 3} = -216a^6b^{12}$

22. $x^2(5x - 7) = x^2(5x) - x^2 \cdot 7 = 5x^3 - 7x^2$

23. $-3a(a^2 - 2a) = -3a(a^2) - 3a(-2a) = -3a^3 + 6a^2$

24. $A = \ell w = (x + 4)(2x) = 2x(x) + 2x(4) = 2x^2 + 8x$

25. $A = \frac{1}{2}bh$

$\qquad = \frac{1}{2}(3x + 9)6x$

$\qquad = 3x(3x + 9)$

$\qquad = 3x(3x) + 3x(9)$

$\qquad = 9x^2 + 27x$

26. $A = bh = 4x(x - 5) = 4x(x) + 4x(-5) = 4x^2 - 20x$

27. $V = \frac{4}{3}\pi r^3$

$\qquad = \frac{4}{3}\pi(3x)^3$

$\qquad = \frac{4}{3}\pi(27x^3)$

$\qquad = 36\pi x^3$

28. $(t + 3)(t - 4) = t^2 - 4t + 3t - 12 = t^2 - t - 12$

29. $(q - 7)(q - 9) = q^2 - 9q - 7q + 63 = q^2 - 16q + 63$

30. $(2k - 9)(-4k - 1) = -8k^2 - 2k + 36k + 9$

$\qquad = -8k^2 + 34k + 9$

31. $f(x) = x^2 + 3$

x	-2	-1	0	1	2
$f(x)$	7	4	3	4	7

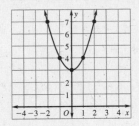

32. $f(x) = 7 - x^2$

x	-2	-1	0	1	2
$f(x)$	3	6	7	6	3

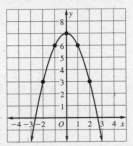

33. $f(x) = x^2 - 4$

x	-2	-1	0	1	2
$f(x)$	0	-3	-4	-3	0

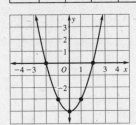

34. $f(x) = 3x^2 + 1$

x	-2	-1	0	1	2
$f(x)$	13	4	1	4	13

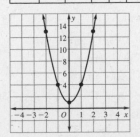

Chapter 13, *continued*

35. No vertical line intersects the graph at more than one point. So, the graph represents a function.

36. No vertical line intersects the graph at more than one point. So, the graph represents a function.

37. A vertical line intersects the graph at more than one point. So, the graphs does not represent a function.

Chapter 13 Test (p. 751)

1. $10x - 7x + 4 + x^2 - 3x + 4$
$= x^2 + 10x - 7x - 3x + 4 + 4$
$= x^2 + 8$

2. $-y + 6(y^2 - y^3 + 1) = -y + 6y^2 - 6y^3 + 6$
$= -6y^3 + 6y^2 - y + 6$

3. $(3r^2 + 4r - 7) + (-r^2 - r + 11)$
$= 3r^2 - r^2 + 4r - r - 7 + 11$
$= 2r^2 + 3r + 4$

4. $(4s^2 - 11s) - (s^2 - 6s + 21)$
$= (4s^2 - 11s) + (-s^2 + 6s - 21)$
$= 4s^2 - s^2 - 11s + 6s - 21$
$= 3s^2 - 5s - 21$

5. $(4a^5 - a) + (-3a^5 + 1) = 4a^5 - 3a^5 - a + 1$
$= a^5 - a + 1$

6. $(-y^2 + 12) + (8y^2 - 10) = -y^2 + 8y^2 + 12 - 10$
$= 7y^2 + 2$

7. $(5x^6 - 3x^2 + x) - (4x^2 + 2x)$
$= (5x^6 - 3x^2 + x) + (-4x^2 - 2x)$
$= 5x^6 - 3x^2 - 4x^2 + x - 2x$
$= 5x^6 - 7x^2 - x$

8. $(-7z^3 + z^2 - 5) - (z^3 - 3z^2 + 1)$
$= (-7z^3 + z^2 - 5) + (-z^3 + 3z^2 - 1)$
$= -7z^3 - z^3 + z^2 + 3z^2 - 5 - 1$
$= -8z^3 + 4z^2 - 6$

9. $(3a^2)(5a^2b) = 15a^{2+2}b = 15a^4b$

10. $(9z^2) = 9^2z^2 = 81z^2$

11. $(3d^2)^4 = 3^4d^{2 \cdot 4} = 81d^8$

12. $(-2w^4)^3 = (-2)^3w^{4 \cdot 3} = -8w^{12}$

13. $(-2p^2)^4 = (-2)^4p^{2 \cdot 4} = 16p^8$

14. $(x^4y)^8 = x^{4 \cdot 8}y^8 = x^{32}y^8$

15. $(4n^2)(-3n) = 4(-3)n^{2+1} = -12n^3$

16. $(3r)^3(3r) = (3^3r^3)(3r) = (27r^3)(3r) = 27 \cdot 3r^{3+1} = 81r^4$

17. $m(3m + 8) = 3m^2 + 8m$

18. $7n(n^2 - 2) = 7n^3 - 14n$

19. $3p(2p^2 + 3p) = 3p(2p^2) + 3p(3p) = 6p^3 + 9p^2$

20. $(2x + 7)(3x + 2) = 6x^2 + 4x + 21x + 14$
$= 6x^2 + 25x + 14$

21. $(4y + 12)(y - 3) = 4y^2 - 12y + 12y - 36 = 4y^2 - 36$

22. $(z - 9)(5z + 8) = 5z^2 + 8z - 45z - 72$
$= 5z^2 - 37z - 72$

23. $(4k + 5)(2k + 8) = 8k^2 + 32k + 10k + 40$
$= 8k^2 + 42k + 40$

24. $(7b + 9)(b - 4) = 7b^2 - 28b + 9b - 36$
$= 7b^2 - 19b - 36$

25. $(t - 6)(3t + 12) = 3t^2 + 12t - 18t - 72 = 3t^2 - 6t - 72$

26. $f(x) = -5x^2$

x	-2	-1	0	1	2
$f(x)$	-20	-5	0	-5	-20

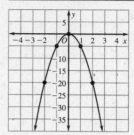

27. $f(x) = x^2 + 3$

x	-2	-1	0	1	2
$f(x)$	7	4	3	4	7

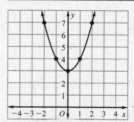

28. $f(x) = x^2 - 1$

x	-2	-1	0	1	2
$f(x)$	3	0	-1	0	3

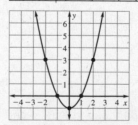

29. No vertical line passes through more than one point. So, the graph represents a function.

30. A vertical line intersects the graph at more than one point. So, the graph does *not* represent a function.

31. No vertical line passes through more than one point. So, the graph represents a function.

32. $-16t^2 + 28 = -16(0.5)^2 + 28$

$\qquad = -16(0.25) + 28$

$\qquad = -4 + 28$

$\qquad = 24$

The apple's height after 0.5 second is 24 feet.

33. $P = a + b + c$

$\qquad = (10x - 7) + (x + 2) + (9x - 5)$

$\qquad = 10x + x + 9x - 7 + 2 - 5$

$\qquad = 20x - 10$

34. $f(t) = \frac{1}{2}at^2 = \frac{1}{2}15t^2 = 7.5t^2$

t	0	1
f(t)	0	$7\frac{1}{2}$

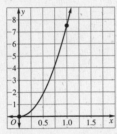

Standardized Test Preparation (pp. 752–753)

1. This problem would receive no credit. Two of the three points of the answer are incorrect (the height after 1 sec is correct) and none are justified.

2. This problem would receive full credit. The steps are clearly stated and reflect correct mathematical reasoning.

Standardized Test Practice (pp. 754–755)

1. $S = 4\pi r^2$

$f(r) = 4\pi r^2$

r	0	1	2	3
f(r)	0	12.56	50.24	113.04

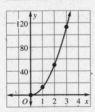

The graph shows $y = 12.56x^2$ where y is the surface area and x is the radius. To find the radius of the sphere with a surface area of 50 square centimeters, look for 50 on the y-axis and find the corresponding x-coordinate to find the radius, which is about 2 centimeters.

2. The area of the polygon is the area of the large square minus the area of the small square.

$(6x)^2 - (3x)^2 = 36x^2 - 9x^2 = 27x^2$

Both unlabeled sides of the figure are

$6x - 3x = 3x.$

The perimeter of the figure is

$6x + 6x + 3x + 3x + 3x + 3x = 24x.$

When $x = 4$:

$A = 27(4)^2 = 432 \text{ m}^2$

$P = 24(4) = 96 \text{ m}$

The area of the figure is 432 square meters and the perimeter is 96 meters.

3. $f(x) = -16x^2 + 110x + 3$

x	0	1	2	3.5	5	6	7
f(x)	0	97	159	192	153	87	−11

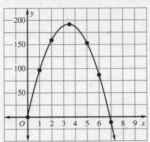

The graph shows that $f(x) = 0$ when x is about 7, so the ball will hit the ground in about 7 seconds.

4. Blue: $A = (x + x)(2x) = 2x(2x) = 4x^2$

Green: $A = 5(2x) = 10x$

Red: $A = 1(x + x) = 1(2x) = 2x$

Yellow: $A = (1 + 1 + 1 + 1 + 1)(1) = (5)(1) = 5$

A polynomial expression for the sum is

$4x^2 + 10x + 2x + 5$, or $4x^2 + 12x + 5$.

An expression for the area of the entire figure as a product of two binomials is $(2x + 1)(2x + 5)$.

The length of the rectangle is $2x + 5$ and the width is $2x + 1$, so its area is $(2x + 1)(2x + 5)$.

5. One side of the corral is ℓ units. The side against the barn uses no fencing, and two sides each use ℓ ft, so the other side is $(400 - 2\ell)$ ft.

Therefore $A = \ell(400 - 2\ell) = 400\ell - 2\ell^2$.

6. $-16t^2 + 100$

After 1 s: $-16(1)2 + 100 = 84$ ft

After 2 s: $-16(2)^2 + 100 = 36$ ft

When it hits the ground, the height is 0.

$0 = -16t^2 + 100$

$t^2 = \frac{100}{16}$

$t = \frac{10}{4}$ or 2.5 seconds

7. $S = 2\pi r^2 + 2\pi rh$

$\quad = 2\pi r^2 + 2\pi r\left(\dfrac{r}{3}\right)$

$\quad = 2\pi r^2 + \dfrac{2}{3}\pi r^2$

$\quad = \dfrac{8}{3}\pi r^2$

$S = 2\pi r^2 + 2\pi rh$

$\quad = 2\pi(3h)^2 + 2\pi(3h)h$

$\quad = 18\pi h^2 + 6\pi h^2$

$\quad = 24\pi h^2$

8. Perimeter $= (7x - 2) + (x + 3) + 3x + (x + 3)$

$\quad\quad\quad\quad = 7x + x + 3x + x + (-2 + 3 + 3)$

$\quad\quad\quad\quad = 12x + 4$

Area $= \dfrac{1}{2}(7x - 2 + 3x)(3x + 1)$

$\quad\quad = \dfrac{1}{2}(10x - 2)(x + 1)$

$\quad\quad = (5x - 1)(x + 1)$

$\quad\quad = 5x^2 + 5x - x - 1$

$\quad\quad = 5x^2 + 4x - 1$

$P(x) = 12x + 4$ is linear because it is of the form $y = mx + b$.

$A(x) = 5x^2 + 4x - 1$ is not linear because the variable has an exponent of 2.

9. $f(x) = 3x^2 - 1$

x	−1	0	1
f(x)	2	−1	2

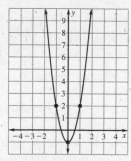

$f(x) = 3x^2 - 3$

x	−1	0	1
f(x)	0	−3	0

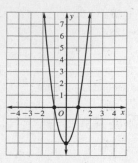

$f(x) = 3x^2 - 5$

x	−1	0	1
f(x)	−2	−5	−2

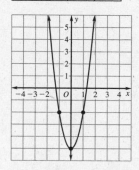

Alike: All 3 graphs have the same shape. They all open upward, and the y-axis is a line of symmetry.

Different: The lowest points are at different heights.

The graph of $f(x) = 3x^2 - 100$ will have the same shape. The y-axis will be a line of symmetry, and the lowest point will be $(0, -100)$

10. C; $(3a^2)(4a + 1) = (3a^2)(4a) + (3a^2)(1)$

$\quad\quad\quad\quad\quad\quad\quad = 12a^{2 + 1} + 3a^2$

$\quad\quad\quad\quad\quad\quad\quad = 12a^3 + 3a^2$

11. B; $(3x + 3)(2x - 2) = 6x^2 + (-6x) + 6x + (-6)$

$\quad\quad\quad\quad\quad\quad\quad\quad = 6x^2 - 6$

12. B; $V = \pi r^2 h$

$\quad V = \pi\left(\dfrac{6}{2}h\right)^2 h = \pi\dfrac{36}{4}h^2 h = 9\pi h^3$

13. $\quad\quad P = 4s$

$\quad\quad\quad 52 = 4(4x + 1)$

$\quad\quad\quad 52 = 16x + 4$

$\quad 52 - 4 = 16x + 4 - 4$

$\quad\quad\quad 48 = 16x$

$\quad\quad\dfrac{48}{16} = \dfrac{16x}{16}$

$\quad\quad\quad 3 = x$

14. $\quad f(x) = 3x^2 + 14$

$\quad f(-2) = 3(-2)^2 + 14 = 12 + 14 = 26$

Chapter 13, continued

15. $A = \frac{1}{2}bh$

$A = \frac{1}{2}(4)(3(4) + 5) = \frac{1}{2}(4)(17) = 34 \text{ in.}^2$

16. $f(x) = 40(1.0025)^t$

$f(0) = 40(1.0025)^0$

$f(0) = 40(1)$

$f(0) = 40$

17. a. $f(t) = -16t^2 + 65$

t	0	0.5	1	1.5	2	2.5
$f(t)$	65	61	49	29	1	−35

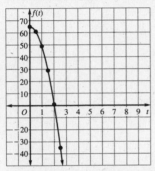

b. It will hit the ground after about 2 seconds.

c. When $t = 0$ the value of $f(t)$ is 65, so its initial height is 65 feet. The domain is values of t from 0 to about $\sqrt{\frac{65}{16}}$ because those are the values of t for which the object is in the air.

18. a. Cost of making: $3x + 3.5y$

Revenue: $6x + 8y$

b. Profit = Revenue − Cost

$= 6x + 8y - (3x + 3.5y)$

$= 6x + 8y - 3x - 3.5y$

$= 3x + 4.5y$

c. If the profit is at least $1200 then

$3x + 4.5y \geq 1200$

$3(100) + 4.5y \geq 1200$

$300 + 4.5y \geq 1200$

$300 + 4.5y - 300 \geq 1200 - 300$

$4.5y \geq 900$

$\frac{4.5y}{4.5} \geq \frac{900}{4.5}$

$y \geq 200$

The store needs to sell at least 200 long-sleeved shirts.

Cumulative Review, Chs. 1–13 (pp. 756–757)

1. −45, −43.5, −43, 43, 45

2. −25, −$|20|$, $|-16|$, −(−25), $|35|$

3. $\frac{11}{5}$, 2.25, $2\frac{3}{10}$, 2.32, $\frac{5}{2}$ **4.** $\frac{3}{8}$, 0.4, $\frac{5}{12}$, 0.45, 0.46

5. $0.1\overline{81}$, $0.\overline{18}$, 0.188, $0.1\overline{88}$ **6.** 2.72, $2.\overline{72}$, $2.\overline{727}$, $2.\overline{7}$

7. $(-3, 2)$ **8.** $(0, 1)$

9. $(-2, -2)$ **10.** $(1, -2)$

11. $(-3, -1)$ **12.** $(2, 0)$

13. $\sqrt{x^2 - y^2} = \sqrt{(5)^2 - (3)^2} = \sqrt{25 - 9} = \sqrt{16} = 4$

14. $\sqrt{x^2 - y^2} = \sqrt{(10)^2 - (8)^2} = \sqrt{100 - 64} = \sqrt{36} = 6$

15. $\sqrt{x^2 - y^2} = \sqrt{(15)^2 - (12)^2} = \sqrt{225 - 144} = \sqrt{81} = 9$

16. $a^2 + b^2 = c^2$

$(9)^2 + (40)^2 = c^2$

$81 + 1600 = c^2$

$1681 = c^2$

$\sqrt{1681} = \sqrt{c^2}$

$41 = c$

$P = 9 + 40 + 41 = 90$

The perimeter is 90 inches.

17. $a^2 + b^2 = c^2$

$(24)^2 + (32)^2 = c^2$

$576 + 1024 = c^2$

$1600 = c^2$

$\sqrt{1600} = \sqrt{c^2}$

$40 = c$

$P = 24 + 32 + 40 = 96$

The perimeter is 96 feet.

18. $a^2 + b^2 = c^2$

$(60)^2 + b^2 = (61)^2$

$3600 + b^2 = 3721$

$3600 + b^2 - 3600 = 3721 - 3600$

$b^2 = 121$

$\sqrt{b^2} = \sqrt{121}$

$b = 11$

$P = 60 + 61 + 11 = 132$

The perimeter is 132 centimeters.

19. $y = 4 + \frac{2}{3}x$

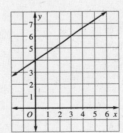

20. $x + y = 6$

$x + y - x = -x + 6$

$y = -x + 6$

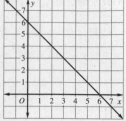

21. $2y + 6x = 10$

$2y + 6x - 6x = -6x + 10$

$2y = -6x + 10$

$\dfrac{2y}{2} = \dfrac{-6x}{2} + \dfrac{10}{2}$

$y = -3x + 5$

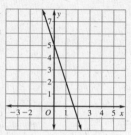

22. $y < x - 4$

$y = x - 4$

Use $(0, 0)$ as a test point.

$0 \overset{?}{<} 0 - 4$

$0 \not< -4$

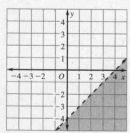

23. $y \geq 2x - 3$

$y = 2x - 3$

Use $(0, 0)$ as a test point.

$0 \overset{?}{\geq} 2(0) - 3$

$0 \geq -3$

$(0, 0)$ is a solution.

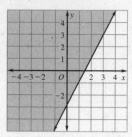

24. $x + y > 6$

$x + y = 6$

$y = -x + 6$

Use $(0, 0)$ as a test point.

$0 + 0 \overset{?}{>} 6$

$0 \not> 6$

$(0, 0)$ is not a solution.

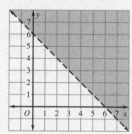

25.

2	1
4	6
5	2 5
6	0
7	0 2
10	4
13	6

Key: $5 \mid 5 = 55$

Stems 5 and 7 have the most values.

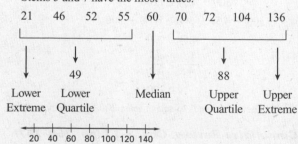

Chapter 13, continued

26.

7	0
10	0
11	1 2
12	0 1 8 9
13	5 7

Key: 11 | 1 = 11.1

Stem 12 has the most values.

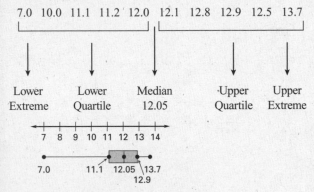

7.0   10.0   11.1   11.2   12.0   12.1   12.8   12.9   12.5   13.7

Lower Extreme — Lower Quartile — Median 12.05 — Upper Quartile — Upper Extreme

7.0   11.1   12.05   13.7
12.9

27. $_{11}P_5 = 11 \cdot 10 \cdot 9 \cdot 8 \cdot 7 = 55{,}440$

28. $_{13}P_4 = 13 \cdot 12 \cdot 11 \cdot 10 = 17{,}160$

29. $_{10}C_3 = \dfrac{_{10}P_3}{3!} = \dfrac{10 \cdot 9 \cdot 8}{3 \cdot 2 \cdot 1} = 120$

30. $_{12}C_7 = \dfrac{_{12}P_7}{7!} = \dfrac{12 \cdot 11 \cdot 10 \cdot 9 \cdot 8 \cdot 7 \cdot 6}{7 \cdot 6 \cdot 5 \cdot 4 \cdot 3 \cdot 2 \cdot 1} = 792$

31. $(10q^2 - 6) + (q^2 + 1) = (10q^2 + q^2) + (-6 + 1)$
$$= 11q^2 - 5$$

32. $(7y^2 + y - 4) + (y^2 - y - 1)$
$$= (7y^2 + y^2) + (y - y) + (-4 - 1)$$
$$= 8y^2 - 5$$

33. $(3x^3 + 4x - 1) + (x^3 - x^2 - 8)$
$$= (3x^3 + x^3) + (-x^2) + (4x) + (-1 - 8)$$
$$= 4x^3 - x^2 + 4x - 9$$

34. $(4x^2 - 2x + 5) - (x^2 - 6x + 8)$
$$= (4x^2 - 2x + 5) + (-x^2 + 6x - 8)$$
$$= (4x^2 - x^2) + (-2x + 6x) + (5 - 8)$$
$$= 3x^2 + 4x - 3$$

35. $(2xy)^3 = 2^3 x^3 y^3 = 8x^3 y^3$

36. $(7z)(-4z)^2 = (7z)(-4^2 z^2) = (7z)(16z^2) = 112z^3$

37. $(-c^3)(2c^4) = -2c^7$

38. $-y^3(-y^2 + 11y) = y^5 - 11y^4$

39. Use x for the number of logs.

$$15x \le 300$$
$$\frac{15x}{15} \le \frac{300}{15}$$
$$x \le 20$$

You can haul no more than 20 logs in the cart on each trip.

40. $5 - 3\frac{3}{4} = 4\frac{4}{4} - 3\frac{3}{4} = (4 - 3) + \left(\frac{4}{1} - \frac{3}{1}\right) = 1\frac{1}{4}$

There are $1\frac{1}{4}$ miles left of the trail.

$$1\frac{1}{4} \cdot \frac{1}{2} = \frac{5}{4} \cdot \frac{1}{2} = \frac{5 \cdot 1}{4 \cdot 2} = \frac{5}{8}$$

You ran $\frac{5}{8}$ of a mile.

41. $a = p\% \cdot b$
$$87 = 58\% \cdot b$$
$$87 = 0.58b$$
$$\frac{87}{0.58} = \frac{0.58}{0.58}b$$
$$150 = b$$

The total amount the science club made is $150.

Cookies: $150 \cdot 27\% = 150 \cdot 0.27 = 40.50$

Apples: $150 \cdot 15\% = 150 \cdot 0.15 = 22.50$

The club made $40.50 selling cookies and $22.50 selling apples.

42. $A = 3721 \text{ ft}^2$
$$A = s^2$$
$$3721 = s^2$$
$$\sqrt{3721} = \sqrt{s^2}$$
$$61 = s$$

Each side is 61 feet.

$$P = 4s$$
$$P = 4(61)$$
$$P = 244 \text{ ft}$$
$$a^2 + b^2 = c^2$$
$$61^2 + 61^2 = c^2$$
$$3721 + 3721 = c^2$$
$$7442 = c^2$$
$$\sqrt{7442} = \sqrt{c^2}$$
$$86 \approx c$$

The perimeter of the base of the building is 244 feet.
The diagonal of the base is 86 feet.

43.

There are 9 faces.
There are 16 edges.
There are 9 vertices.

44. $6x + 3y = 60$

$\quad\quad\quad 3y = -6x + 60$

$\quad\quad\quad\ y = -2x + 20$

x	10	0
y	0	20

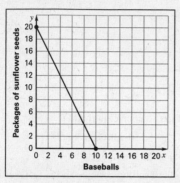

The x-intercept 10 means you can buy 10 baseballs and 0 packages of sunflower seeds. The y-intercept 20 means you can buy 0 baseballs and 20 packages of sunflower seeds.

45. $3x + 4y = 20$

$\quad\quad\quad 4y = -3x + 20$

$\quad\quad\quad\ y = -\dfrac{3}{4}x + 5$

Use $(0, 0)$ as a test point.

$\quad 3(0) + 4(0) \le 20$

$\quad\quad\quad\quad\quad 0 \le 20$

$(0, 0)$ is a solution.

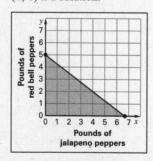

46. $7! = 7 \cdot 6 \cdot 5 \cdot 4 \cdot 3 \cdot 2 \cdot 1 = 5040$

You can line up 5040 ways.

47. Odds $= \dfrac{0.35}{1 - 0.35} = \dfrac{0.35}{0.65} = \dfrac{7}{13}$

48. $-16t^2 + 64t + 5$

When $t = 1$:

$-16(1)^2 + 64(1) + 5 = -16 + 64 + 5 = 53$ ft

When $t = 3$:

$-16(3)^2 + 64(3) + 5 = -144 + 192 + 5 = 53$ ft

At $t = 1$ the projectile is rising and at $t = 3$ the projectile is falling.

49. $25(r + 1)^2 = 25(r + 1)(r + 1) = 25(r^2 + 2r + 1)$

$\quad\quad\quad\quad\quad\quad\quad\quad\quad = 25r^2 + 50r + 25$

Skills Review Handbook

Place Value (p. 759)

1. $56,809 = 50,000 + 6000 + 800 + 9$
   $= 5 \times 10,000 + 6 \times 1000 + 8 \times 100 + 9 \times 1$

2. $3.075 = 3 + 0.07 + 0.005$
   $= 3 \times 1 + 7 \times 0.01 + 5 \times 0.001$

3. $1002.003 = 1000 + 2 + 0.003$
   $= 1 \times 1000 + 2 \times 1 + 3 \times 0.001$

4. $306.405 = 300 + 6 + 0.4 + 0.005$
   $= 3 \times 100 + 6 \times 1 + 4 \times 0.1 + 5 \times 0.001$

5. $5 \times 100,000 + 6 \times 10 + 9 \times 1 + 7 \times 0.001$
   $= 500,000 + 60 + 9 + 0.007$
   $= 500,069.007$

6. Write 5 in the millions' place, 1 in the tens' place, 3 in the hundredths' places, and 6 in the thousandths' place. The answer is 5,000,010.036.

Rounding (p. 760)

1. The digit to the right of the 2 in the hundreds' place is the 5 in the tens' place. Because $5 = 5$, round up.
   1253 rounded to the nearest hundred is 1300.

2. The digit to the right of the 0 in the tens' place is the 9 in the ones' place. Because $9 > 5$, round up.
   57,309 rounded to the nearest ten is 57,310.

3. The digit to the right of the 1 in the tenths' place is the 8 in the hundredths' place. Because $8 > 5$, round up.
   8.183 rounded to the nearest tenth is 8.2.

4. The digit to the right of the 2 in the ones' place is the 7 in the tenths' place. Because $7 > 5$, round up.
   32.76 rounded to the nearest one is 33.

5. The digit to the right of the 4 in the ten thousands' place is the 4 in the thousands' place. Because $4 < 5$, round down.
   44,380 rounded to the nearest ten thousand is 40,000.

6. The digit to the right of the 3 in the hundredths' place is the 5 in the thousandths' place. Because $5 = 5$, round up.
   12.535 rounded to the nearest hundredth is 12.54.

7. The digit to the right of the 5 in the tens' place is the 2 in the ones' place. Because $2 < 5$, round down.
   452.84 rounded to the nearest ten is 450.

8. The digit to the right of the 9 in the ten thousands' place is the 8 in the thousands' place. Because $8 > 5$, round up.
   998,543 rounded to the nearest ten thousand is 1,000,000.

9. The digit to the right of the 8 in the tenths' place is the 4 in the hundredths' place. Because $4 < 5$, round down.
   62.847 rounded to the nearest tenth is 62.8.

10. The digit to the right of the 6 in the hundred thousands' place is the 4 in the ten thousands' place. Because $4 < 5$, round down.
    640,796 rounded to the nearest hundred thousand is 600,000.

11. The digit to the right of the 4 in the tenths' place is the 7 in the hundredths' place. Because $7 > 5$, round up.
    164.479 rounded to the nearest tenth is 164.5.

12. The digit to the right of the 9 in the ones' place is the 4 in the tenths' place. Because $4 < 5$, round down.
    1209.4 rounded to the nearest one is 1209.

13. The digit to the right of the 6 in the hundredths' place is the 1 in the thousandths' place. Because $1 < 5$, round down.
    52.961 rounded to the nearest hundredth is 52.96.

14. The digit to the right of the 4 in the tens' place is the 2 in the ones' place. Because $2 < 5$, round down.
    12,742.5 rounded to the nearest ten is 12,740.

15. The digit to the right of the 6 in the hundreds' place is the 5 in the tens' place. Because $5 = 5$, round up.
    3,501,652 rounded to the nearest hundred is 3,501,700.

Divisibility Tests (p. 761)

1. The last digit of 34 is 4, so it is divisible by 2, but not by 5 or by 10. The sum of the digits is $3 + 4 = 7$, so it is not divisible by 3 or 9. 34 is not divisible by 4 or 8. Because 34 is divisible by 2 but not by 3, it is not divisible by 6.
   34 is divisible by 2.

2. The last digit of 84 is 4, so it is divisible by 2, but not by 5 or 10. The sum of the digits is $8 + 4 = 12$, so it is divisible by 3 but not by 9. 84 is divisible by 4 but not by 8. Because 84 is divisible by 2 and by 3, it is divisible by 6.
   84 is divisible by 2, 3, 4, and 6.

3. The last digit of 285 is 5, so it is divisible by 5, but not by 2 or 10. The sum of the digits is $2 + 8 + 5 = 15$, so it is divisible by 3 but not by 9. The last two digits, 85, are not divisible by 4, so 285 is not divisible by 4. Because 285 is divisible by 3 but not by 2, it is not divisible by 6. 285 is not divisible by 8.
   285 is divisible by 3 and 5.

4. The last digit of 560 is 0, so it is divisible by 2, 5, and 10. The sum of the digits is $5 + 6 + 0 = 11$, so it is not divisible by 3 or 9. The last two digits, 60, are divisible by 4, so 560 is divisible by 4. Because 560 is divisible by 2 but not by 3, it is not divisible by 6. 560 is divisible by 8.
   560 is divisible by 2, 4, 5, 8, and 10.

5. The last digit of 972 is 2, so it is divisible by 2, but not by 5 or 10. The sum of the digits is $9 + 7 + 2 = 18$, so it is divisible by 3 and by 9. The last two digits, 72, are divisible by 4, so 972 is divisible by 4. Because 972 is divisible by 2 and by 3, it is divisible by 6. 972 is not divisible by 8.
   972 is divisible by 2, 3, 4, 6, and 9.

6. The last digit of 4210 is 0, so it is divisible by 2, 5, and 10. The sum of the digits is $4 + 2 + 1 + 0 = 7$, so it is not divisible by 3 or 9. The last two digits, 10, are not divisible by 4, so 4210 is not divisible by 4. Because 4210 is divisible by 2, but not by 3, it is not divisible by 6. The last three digits, 210, are not divisible by 8, so 4210 is not divisible by 8.
   4210 is divisible by 2, 5, and 10.

7. The last digit of 2815 is 5, so it is divisible by 5, but not by 2 or 10. The sum of the digits is $2 + 8 + 1 + 5 = 16$, so it is not divisible by 3 or 9. The last two digits, 15, are not divisible by 4, so 2815 is not divisible by 4. Because 2815 is not divisible by 2 or 3, it is not divisible by 6. The last three digits, 815, are not divisible by 8, so 2815 is not divisible by 8.

2815 is divisible by 5.

8. The last digit of 6390 is 0, so it is divisible by 2, 5, and 10. The sum of the digits is $6 + 3 + 9 + 0 = 18$, so it is divisible by 3 and 9. The last two digits, 90, are not divisible by 4, so 6390 is not divisible by 4. Because 6390 is divisible by 2 and 3, it is divisible by 6. The last three digits, 390, are not divisible by 8, so 6390 is not divisible by 8.

6390 is divisible by 2, 3, 5, 6, 9, and 10.

9. The last digit of 88,004 is 4, so it is divisible by 2, but not 5 or 10. The sum of the digits is $8 + 8 + 0 + 0 + 4 = 20$, so it is not divisible by 3 or 9. The last two digits, 04, are divisible by 4, so 88,004 is divisible by 4. Because 88,004 is divisible by 2 but not by 3, it is not divisible by 6. The last three digits, 004, are not divisible by 8, so 88,004 is not divisible by 8.

88,004 is divisible by 2 and 4.

10. The last digit of 75,432 is 2, so it is divisible by 2, but not by 5 or 10. The sum of the digits is $7 + 5 + 4 + 3 + 2 = 21$, so it is divisible by 3 but not by 9. The last two digits, 32, are divisible by 4, so 75,432 is divisible by 4. Because 75,432 is divisible by 2 and 3, it is divisible by 6. The last three digits, 432, are divisible by 8, so 75,432 is divisible by 8.

75,432 is divisible by 2, 3, 4, 6, and 8.

Mixed Numbers and Improper Fractions (p. 762)

1. $7\frac{3}{5} = \frac{35 + 3}{5} = \frac{38}{5}$

2. $3\frac{1}{6} = \frac{18 + 1}{6} = \frac{19}{6}$

3.
$$\begin{array}{r} 5\ R3 \\ 4\overline{)23} \\ \underline{20} \\ 3 \end{array}$$
$\frac{23}{4} = 5 + \frac{3}{4} = 5\frac{3}{4}$

4.
$$\begin{array}{r} 2\ R3 \\ 7\overline{)17} \\ \underline{14} \\ 3 \end{array}$$
$\frac{17}{7} = 2 + \frac{3}{7} = 2\frac{3}{7}$

5. $3\frac{1}{2} = \frac{6 + 1}{2} = \frac{7}{2}$

6. $1\frac{5}{6} = \frac{6 + 5}{6} = \frac{11}{6}$

7. $4\frac{3}{8} = \frac{32 + 3}{8} = \frac{35}{8}$

8. $8\frac{5}{7} = \frac{56 + 5}{7} = \frac{61}{7}$

9. $10\frac{3}{4} = \frac{40 + 3}{4} = \frac{43}{4}$

10.
$$\begin{array}{r} 2\ R3 \\ 4\overline{)11} \\ \underline{8} \\ 3 \end{array}$$
$\frac{11}{4} = 2 + \frac{3}{4} = 2\frac{3}{4}$

11.
$$\begin{array}{r} 7\ R1 \\ 2\overline{)15} \\ \underline{14} \\ 1 \end{array}$$
$\frac{15}{2} = 7 + \frac{1}{2} = 7\frac{1}{2}$

12.
$$\begin{array}{r} 4\ R1 \\ 6\overline{)25} \\ \underline{24} \\ 1 \end{array}$$
$\frac{25}{6} = 4 + \frac{1}{6} = 4\frac{1}{6}$

13.
$$\begin{array}{r} 5\ R2 \\ 3\overline{)17} \\ \underline{15} \\ 2 \end{array}$$
$\frac{17}{3} = 5 + \frac{2}{3} = 5\frac{2}{3}$

14.
$$\begin{array}{r} 4\ R1 \\ 8\overline{)33} \\ \underline{32} \\ 1 \end{array}$$
$\frac{33}{8} = 4 + \frac{1}{8} = 4\frac{1}{8}$

Ratio and Rate (p. 763)

1. $\dfrac{\text{Number of boys in Mr. Smith's class}}{\text{Number of girls in Mr. Smith's class}} = \dfrac{13}{12}$

$ = 13 \text{ to } 12$

$ = 13 : 12$

2. $\dfrac{\text{Number of boys in Mr. Smith's class}}{\text{Number of boys in Ms. Jung's class}} = \dfrac{13}{17}$

$ = 13 \text{ to } 17$

$ = 13 : 17$

3. Total number of girls $= 12 + 11 = 23$

$\dfrac{\text{Number of girls in Ms. Jung's class}}{\text{Total number of girls}} = \dfrac{11}{23}$

$ = 11 \text{ to } 23$

$ = 11 : 23$

4. $8 \div 2$

$$\frac{8 \text{ feet}}{2 \text{ seconds}} = \frac{4 \text{ feet}}{1 \text{ second}}$$

$2 \div 2$

5. $24 \div 8$

$$\frac{\$24}{8 \text{ pens}} = \frac{\$3}{1 \text{ pen}}$$

$8 \div 8$

6. $333 \div 6$

$$\frac{333 \text{ miles}}{6 \text{ hours}} = \frac{55.5 \text{ miles}}{1 \text{ hour}}$$

$6 \div 6$

7. $280 \div 5$

$$\frac{280 \text{ words}}{5 \text{ minutes}} = \frac{56 \text{ words}}{1 \text{ minute}}$$

$5 \div 5$

8. $3 \div 2.50$

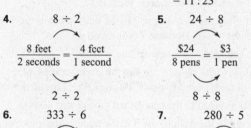

$$\frac{3 \text{ qt}}{\$2.50} = \frac{1.2 \text{ qt}}{\$1}$$

$2.50 \div 2.50$

9. $8 \div 6$

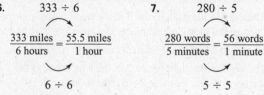

$$\frac{8 \text{ inches}}{6 \text{ days}} = \frac{1\frac{1}{3} \text{ inches}}{1 \text{ day}}$$

$6 \div 6$

Skills Review Handbook, *continued*

Adding and Subtracting Decimals (p. 764)

1. $\overset{1}{3.56}$
$+\ 2.74$
6.30

2. $\overset{1}{12.7}$
$+\ 93.8$
106.5

3. $\overset{1\ 1}{27.5}$
$+\ 3.6$
31.1

4. $\overset{1\ 1\ 1}{0.923}$
$+\ 0.179$
1.102

5. $\overset{1}{4.217}$
$+\ 6.739$
10.956

6. $\overset{8\ 13}{9\cancel{3}}$
$-\ 2.8$
6.5

7. $\overset{3\ 15}{4\cancel{.}\cancel{5}6}$
$-\ 1.65$
2.91

8. $\overset{12\ 15\ 14}{13.\cancel{6}\cancel{4}}$
$-\ 5.85$
7.79

9. $\overset{2\ 17\ 13\ 15}{\cancel{3}8.\cancel{4}\cancel{5}}$
$-\ 19.57$
18.88

10. $\overset{6\ 13\ 10\ 14\ 12}{7\cancel{4}\cancel{1}.\cancel{5}\cancel{2}}$
$-\ 48.66$
692.86

11. $\overset{1\ 1}{56.98}$
$+\ 0.82$
57.80

12. $\overset{9\ 9\ 13\ 16\ 16}{10\cancel{0}.\cancel{4}\cancel{7}\cancel{6}}$
$-\ 4.989$
95.487

13. $\overset{2\ 15\ 15\ 4\ 17}{3\cancel{6}\cancel{5}.\cancel{5}7}$
$-\ 79.38$
286.19

14. $\overset{1\ 1\ 1}{49.86}$
$+\ 2.65$
52.51

15. $\overset{8\ 17\ 0\ 15}{9\cancel{7}.\cancel{1}\cancel{5}6}$
$-\ 9.092$
88.064

16. $\overset{2\ 11\ 14\ 14}{2\cancel{3}2.\cancel{5}\cancel{4}3}$
$-\ 209.692$
22.851

Adding and Subtracting Fractions (p. 765)

1. $\frac{1}{3} + \frac{1}{3} = \frac{1+1}{3} = \frac{2}{3}$

2. $\frac{8}{9} + \frac{5}{9} = \frac{8+5}{9} = \frac{13}{9} = 1\frac{4}{9}$

3. $\frac{6}{7} - \frac{3}{7} = \frac{6-3}{7} = \frac{3}{7}$

4. $\frac{11}{12} - \frac{4}{12} = \frac{11-4}{12} = \frac{7}{12}$

5. $\frac{1}{8} + \frac{7}{8} = \frac{1+7}{8} = \frac{8}{8} = 1$

6. $\frac{8}{11} + \frac{7}{11} = \frac{8+7}{11} = \frac{15}{11} = 1\frac{4}{11}$

7. $\frac{13}{15} - \frac{2}{15} = \frac{13-2}{15} = \frac{11}{15}$

8. $\frac{5}{6} - \frac{4}{6} = \frac{5-4}{6} = \frac{1}{6}$

9. $\frac{1}{9} + \frac{1}{9} = \frac{1+1}{9} = \frac{2}{9}$

10. $\frac{10}{11} - \frac{2}{11} = \frac{10-2}{11} = \frac{8}{11}$

11. $\frac{11}{12} + \frac{8}{12} = \frac{11+8}{12} = \frac{19}{12} = 1\frac{7}{12}$

12. $\frac{9}{10} - \frac{6}{10} = \frac{9-6}{10} = \frac{3}{10}$

13. $\frac{5}{9} - \frac{4}{9} = \frac{5-4}{9} = \frac{1}{9}$

14. $\frac{9}{16} + \frac{12}{16} = \frac{9+12}{16} = \frac{21}{16} = 1\frac{5}{16}$

15. $\frac{11}{14} - \frac{2}{14} = \frac{11-2}{14} = \frac{9}{14}$

16. $\frac{8}{15} - \frac{8}{15} = \frac{8-8}{15} = \frac{0}{15} = 0$

17. $\frac{5}{12} + \frac{2}{12} = \frac{5+2}{12} = \frac{7}{12}$

18. $\frac{8}{10} + \frac{1}{10} = \frac{8+1}{10} = \frac{9}{10}$

19. $\frac{6}{7} + \frac{5}{7} = \frac{6+5}{7} = \frac{11}{7} = 1\frac{4}{7}$

20. $\frac{5}{8} - \frac{2}{8} = \frac{5-2}{8} = \frac{3}{8}$

Estimation in Addition and Subtraction (p. 766)

1. $935 + 887 + 912 \approx 900 + 900 + 900 = 2700$

2. $4967 + 4802 + 5218 \approx 5000 + 5000 + 5000 = 15,000$

3. $5971 + 6032 + 7865 \approx 6000 + 6000 + 8000 = 20,000$

4. (1) 8000
$-\ 4000$
4000

(2) 900
$-\ 900$
0

$8891 - 4932 \approx 4000$

5. (1) 4000
$-\ 2000$
2000

(2) 400
$-\ 200$
200

$4373 - 2158 \approx 2000 + 200 = 2200$

6. (1) 400,000
$-\ 200,000$
200,000

(2) 90,000
$-\ 50,000$
40,000

$449,739 - 285,921 \approx 200,000 - 40,000 = 160,000$

Solving Problems Using Addition and Subtraction (p. 767)

1. Total amount spent $= 48 + 45 = 93$

You spent $93 in all.

2. Number of pencils you have left $= 96 - 28 = 68$

You have 68 pencils left.

3. Amount of money you have left $= 18 - 15.99 = 2.01$

You have $2.01 left.

4. Total number of CDs $= 24 + 18 = 42$

You have 42 country and pop CDs in all.

5. Number of minutes you have left $= 900 - 652 = 248$

You have 248 minutes left.

6. Amount of money you have $= 149 + 24 = 173$

You have $173.

Multiplying Fractions (p. 768)

1. $6 \times \frac{2}{15} = \frac{6 \times 2}{15} = \frac{12}{15} = \frac{4}{5}$

2. $2 \times \frac{6}{11} = \frac{2 \times 6}{11} = \frac{12}{11} = 1\frac{1}{11}$

3. $4 \times \frac{5}{9} = \frac{4 \times 5}{9} = \frac{20}{9} = 2\frac{2}{9}$

4. $8 \times \frac{5}{9} = \frac{8 \times 5}{9} = \frac{40}{9} = 4\frac{4}{9}$

5. $\frac{3}{4} \times 7 = \frac{3 \times 7}{4} = \frac{21}{4} = 5\frac{1}{4}$

6. $\frac{4}{7} \times 5 = \frac{4 \times 5}{7} = \frac{20}{7} = 2\frac{6}{7}$

7. $\frac{6}{7} \times 3 = \frac{6 \times 3}{7} = \frac{18}{7} = 2\frac{4}{7}$

8. $\frac{3}{7} \times \frac{6}{11} = \frac{3 \times 6}{7 \times 11} = \frac{18}{77}$

9. $\frac{2}{3} \times \frac{4}{5} = \frac{2 \times 4}{3 \times 5} = \frac{8}{15}$

10. $\frac{3}{4} \times \frac{1}{7} = \frac{3 \times 1}{4 \times 7} = \frac{3}{28}$

11. $\frac{1}{8} \times \frac{3}{5} = \frac{1 \times 3}{8 \times 5} = \frac{3}{40}$

12. $\frac{7}{9} \times \frac{5}{8} = \frac{7 \times 5}{9 \times 8} = \frac{35}{72}$

13. $\frac{5}{9} \times \frac{2}{3} = \frac{5 \times 2}{9 \times 3} = \frac{10}{27}$

14. $\frac{3}{8} \times \frac{4}{5} = \frac{3 \times \overset{1}{\cancel{4}}}{\underset{2}{\cancel{8}} \times 5} = \frac{3}{10}$

15. $\frac{5}{12} \times \frac{5}{6} = \frac{5 \times 5}{12 \times 6} = \frac{25}{72}$

Skills Review Handbook, *continued*

Multiplication of a Decimal by a Whole Number (p. 769)

1.
```
    2.3
  ×  9 8
   18 4
  207
  225.4
```

2.
```
   0.62
  ×  46
   3 72
  24 8
  28.52
```

3.
```
    85
  × 7.9
   76 5
  595
  671.5
```

4.
```
   0.56
  ×  63
   1 68
  33 6
  35.28
```

5.
```
   2.08
  ×  14
   8 32
  20 8
  29.12
```

6.
```
   6.52
  ×  36
  39 12
  195 6
  234.72
```

7.
```
   7.24
  ×  89
  65 16
  579 2
  644.36
```

8.
```
   8.35
  ×  16
  50 10
  83 5
  133.60
```

9.
```
   77.6
  ×  22
  155 2
  1552
  1707.2
```

10.
```
    3.45
  ×  105
   17 25
  345
  362.25
```

11.
```
      453
  ×  41.2
    90 6
    453
   18 12
  18,663.6
```

12.
```
      614
  ×  6.71
     6 14
   429 8
  3684
  4119.94
```

13.
```
     32.6
  ×   463
    97 8
   1 956
  13 04
  15,093.8
```

14.
```
     71.8
  ×  93 4
   287 2
   2 154
  64 62
  67,061.2
```

15.
```
     90.5
  ×   407
   633 5
  36 20
  36,833.5
```

16.
```
    15.36
  ×   123
   46 08
   307 2
  1536
  1889.28
```

17.
```
    3.442
  ×   276
   20 652
  240 94
  688 4
  949.992
```

18.
```
    93.08
  ×   306
   558 48
  27 924
  28,482.48
```

19.
```
     5.436
  ×    682
   10 872
   434 88
  3261 6
  3707.352
```

20.
```
     60.97
  ×    708
   487 76
  42 679
  43,166.76
```

21.
```
    142.82
  ×     35
   714 10
  4284 6
  4998.70
```

22.
```
   25.987
  ×    76
  155 922
  1819 09
  1975.012
```

23.
```
   32.903
  ×     55
  164 515
  1645 15
  1809.665
```

24.
```
   243.72
  ×     38
  1949 76
  7311 6
  9261.36
```

25.
```
   75.032
  ×     73
  225 096
  5252 24
  5477.336
```

26.
```
    380.77
  ×     114
   1 523 08
   3 807 7
  38 077
  43,407.78
```

27.
```
     508.25
  ×      237
    3 557 75
   15 247 5
  101 650
  120,455.25
```

28.
```
    15.456
  ×    591
   15 456
  1391 04
  7728 0
  9134.496
```

29.
```
   36.902
  ×    205
  184 510
  7380 4
  7564.910
```

30.
```
      8257.6
  ×      459
    74 318 4
   412 880
  3 303 04
  3,790,238.4
```

Dividing Decimals (p. 770)

1.
```
     0.45
  6)2.70
    2 4
     30
     30
      0
```

2.
```
     0.95
  4)3.80
    3 6
     20
     20
      0
```

3.
```
     0.85
  8)6.80
    6 4
     40
     40
      0
```

4.
```
     6.7
  7)46.9
    42
     4 9
     4 9
       0
```

5.
```
      4.57
  3)13.71
    12
     1 7
     1 5
       21
       21
        0
```

6.
```
        6
  2.5)15.0
      15 0
         0
```

7.
```
        6 R2
  1.3)8.0
      7 8
         2
```

8.
$$\begin{array}{r} 5\ \text{R470} \\ 5.46\overline{)32.00} \\ \underline{27\ 30} \\ 4\ 70 \end{array}$$

9.
$$\begin{array}{r} 8\ \text{R604} \\ 7.12\overline{)63.00} \\ \underline{56\ 96} \\ 6\ 04 \end{array}$$

10.
$$\begin{array}{r} 11\ \text{R5073} \\ 6.357\overline{)75.000} \\ \underline{63\ 57} \\ 11\ 430 \\ \underline{6\ 357} \\ 5\ 073 \end{array}$$

Estimation in Multiplication and Division (p. 771)

1. Low estimate: $43 \times 16 \approx 40 \times 10 = 400$
High estimate: $43 \times 16 \approx 50 \times 20 = 1000$

2. Low estimate: $359 \times 28 \approx 300 \times 20 = 6000$
High estimate: $359 \times 28 \approx 400 \times 30 = 12,000$

3. Low estimate: $852 \times 53 \approx 800 \times 50 = 40,000$
High estimate: $852 \times 53 \approx 900 \times 60 = 54,000$

4. Low estimate: $734 \times 76 \approx 700 \times 70 = 49,000$
High estimate: $734 \times 76 \approx 800 \times 80 = 64,000$

5. Low estimate:
$225 \div 6 \approx 30$
$$\begin{array}{r} 30 \\ 6\overline{)180} \\ \underline{180} \\ 0 \end{array}$$

High estimate:
$225 \div 6 \approx 40$
$$\begin{array}{r} 40 \\ 6\overline{)240} \\ \underline{240} \\ 0 \end{array}$$

6. Low estimate:
$2795 \div 7 \approx 300$
$$\begin{array}{r} 300 \\ 7\overline{)2100} \\ \underline{2100} \\ 0 \end{array}$$

High estimate:
$2795 \div 7 \approx 400$
$$\begin{array}{r} 400 \\ 7\overline{)2800} \\ \underline{2800} \\ 0 \end{array}$$

7. Low estimate:
$17,934 \div 77 \approx 200$
$$\begin{array}{r} 200 \\ 80\overline{)16,000} \\ \underline{16\ 000} \\ 0 \end{array}$$

High estimate:
$17,934 \div 77 \approx 300$
$$\begin{array}{r} 300 \\ 70\overline{)21,000} \\ \underline{21\ 000} \\ 0 \end{array}$$

8. Low estimate:
$41,042 \div 92 \approx 410$
$$\begin{array}{r} 410 \\ 100\overline{)41,000} \\ \underline{41\ 000} \\ 0 \end{array}$$

High estimate:
$41,042 \div 92 \approx 500$
$$\begin{array}{r} 500 \\ 90\overline{)45,000} \\ \underline{45\ 000} \\ 0 \end{array}$$

9. Low estimate: $326 \times 48 \approx 300 \times 40 = 12,000$
High estimate: $326 \times 48 \approx 400 \times 50 = 20,000$

10. Low estimate: $612 \times 273 \approx 600 \times 200 = 120,000$
High estimate: $612 \times 273 \approx 700 \times 300 = 210,000$

11. Low estimate: $745 \times 158 \approx 700 \times 100 = 70,000$
High estimate: $745 \times 158 \approx 800 \times 200 = 160,000$

12. Low estimate: $905 \times 657 \approx 900 \times 600 = 540,000$
High estimate: $905 \times 657 \approx 1000 \times 700 = 700,000$

13. Low estimate: $625 \times 28 \approx 600 \times 20 = 12,000$
High estimate: $625 \times 28 \approx 700 \times 30 = 21,000$

14. Low estimate: $809 \times 97 \approx 800 \times 90 = 72,000$
High estimate: $809 \times 97 \approx 900 \times 100 = 90,000$

15. Low estimate:
$742 \div 8 \approx 90$
$$\begin{array}{r} 90 \\ 8\overline{)720} \\ \underline{720} \\ 0 \end{array}$$

High estimate:
$742 \div 8 \approx 100$
$$\begin{array}{r} 100 \\ 8\overline{)800} \\ \underline{800} \\ 0 \end{array}$$

16. Low estimate:
$231 \div 38 \approx 5$
$$\begin{array}{r} 5 \\ 40\overline{)200} \\ \underline{200} \\ 0 \end{array}$$

High estimate:
$231 \div 38 \approx 8$
$$\begin{array}{r} 8 \\ 30\overline{)240} \\ \underline{240} \\ 0 \end{array}$$

17. Low estimate:
$5421 \div 7 \approx 700$
$$\begin{array}{r} 700 \\ 7\overline{)4900} \\ \underline{4900} \\ 0 \end{array}$$

High estimate:
$5421 \div 7 \approx 800$
$$\begin{array}{r} 800 \\ 7\overline{)5600} \\ \underline{5600} \\ 0 \end{array}$$

18. Low estimate:
$4972 \div 18 \approx 240$
$$\begin{array}{r} 240 \\ 20\overline{)4800} \\ \underline{40} \\ 80 \\ \underline{80} \\ 0 \end{array}$$

High estimate:
$4972 \div 18 \approx 500$
$$\begin{array}{r} 500 \\ 10\overline{)5000} \\ \underline{5000} \\ 0 \end{array}$$

19. Low estimate:
$1583 \div 82 \approx 10$
$$\begin{array}{r} 10 \\ 90\overline{)900} \\ \underline{900} \\ 0 \end{array}$$

High estimate:
$1583 \div 82 \approx 20$
$$\begin{array}{r} 20 \\ 80\overline{)1600} \\ \underline{1600} \\ 0 \end{array}$$

20. Low estimate:
$43,789 \div 64 \approx 600$
$$\begin{array}{r} 600 \\ 70\overline{)42,000} \\ \underline{42\ 000} \\ 0 \end{array}$$

High estimate:
$43,789 \div 64 \approx 800$
$$\begin{array}{r} 800 \\ 60\overline{)48,000} \\ \underline{48\ 000} \\ 0 \end{array}$$

Solving Problems Using Multiplication and Division (p. 772)

1. Total cost of the notebooks $= 6 \times 1.58 = 9.48$

You paid $9.48 for the notebooks.

2. Number of cards you gave to friend $= \frac{1}{4} \cdot 92 = 23$

You gave your friend 23 cards.

Skills Review Handbook, *continued*

3. Total number of flowers = 12 • 48 = 576

You have 576 flowers.

4. Amount paid for each package = 22.95 ÷ 9 = 2.55

You paid $2.55 for each package.

Points, Lines, and Planes (p. 773)

1. B **2.** C **3.** A

4. *Sample answer: U, R, V*

5. *Sample answer: $\overrightarrow{SR}$ and $\overrightarrow{ST}$*

6. *Sample answer: $\overleftrightarrow{UV}$ and $\overleftrightarrow{RT}$*

7. *Sample answer: $\overrightarrow{SR}$*

Angles (p. 774)

1. C **2.** A **3.** B

4. ∠DEF, ∠E, ∠FED **5.** ∠HJK, ∠J, ∠KJH

6. ∠WXY, ∠X, ∠YXW **7.** ∠TUV, ∠U, ∠VUT

8. ∠LMN, ∠M, ∠NML **9.** ∠FGH, ∠G, ∠HGF

10.

∠PQR, ∠Q, ∠RQP;
∠QRP, ∠R, ∠PRQ;
∠RPQ, ∠P, ∠QPR

Using a Ruler (p. 775)

1. $\frac{7}{16}$ in. **2.** Check drawings.

3. 4.3 cm

4. 2.7 cm

5. $2\frac{5}{16}$ in.

6. 6.5 cm

7. 2.9 cm

8. $1\frac{1}{4}$ in.

Using a Protractor (p. 776)

1. 110° **2.** 32° **3.** 88°

4.

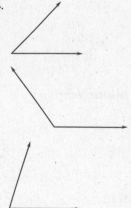

Using a Compass (p. 777)

1. Check student drawings. The circle should have a diameter of 8 centimeters.

2. Check student drawings. The line should be $3\frac{3}{4}$ inches long.

3. Check student drawings. The line should be $\frac{3}{4}$ inches long.

Solving Problems Involving Time (p. 778)

1.
$$\begin{array}{r} 9:24 \\ -\ 7:13 \\ \hline 2:11 \end{array}$$

The concert lasted 2 hours 11 minutes.

2.
$$\begin{array}{r} 3:15 \\ +\ 12:00 \\ \hline 15:15 \end{array} \qquad \begin{array}{r} 15:15 \\ -\ 8:10 \\ \hline 7:05 \end{array}$$

The school day lasted 7 hours 5 minutes.

3.
$$\begin{array}{r} 0:10 \\ +\ 0:40 \\ \hline 0:50 \end{array} \qquad \begin{array}{r} 2:45 \\ +\ 0:50 \\ \hline 2:95 = 3:35 \end{array}$$

Practice ended at 3:35 P.M.

4.
$$\begin{array}{r} 1:39 \\ +\ 0:25 \\ \hline 1:64 = 2:04 \end{array} \qquad \begin{array}{r} 7:25 \\ +\ 2:04 \\ \hline 9:29 \end{array}$$

Jeff finished watching the DVD at 9:29 P.M.

Converting Customary Units (p. 779)

1. $23 \text{ yd} \times \dfrac{3 \text{ ft}}{1 \text{ yd}} = \dfrac{23 \text{ yd} \times 3 \text{ ft}}{1 \text{ yd}} = 69 \text{ ft}$

23 yd = 69 ft

2. $4 \text{ lb} \times \dfrac{16 \text{ oz}}{1 \text{ lb}} = \dfrac{4 \text{ lb} \times 16 \text{ oz}}{1 \text{ lb}} = 64 \text{ oz}$

4 lb = 64 oz

3. $42 \text{ qt} \times \dfrac{1 \text{ gal}}{4 \text{ qt}} = \dfrac{\overset{21}{42 \text{ qt}} \times 1 \text{ gal}}{\underset{2}{4 \text{ qt}}} = \dfrac{21}{2} \text{ gal} = 10\frac{1}{2} \text{ gal}$

$42 \text{ qt} = 10\frac{1}{2} \text{ gal}$

4. $18 \text{ in.} \times \dfrac{1 \text{ yd}}{36 \text{ in.}} = \dfrac{\overset{1}{18 \text{ in.}} \times 1 \text{ yd}}{\underset{2}{36 \text{ in.}}} = \dfrac{1}{2} \text{ yd}$

$18 \text{ in.} = \dfrac{1}{2} \text{ yd}$

5. $3 \text{ gal} \times \dfrac{4 \text{ qt}}{1 \text{ gal}} \times \dfrac{2 \text{ pt}}{1 \text{ qt}} = \dfrac{3 \text{ gal} \times 4 \text{ qt} \times 2 \text{ pt}}{1 \text{ gal} \times 1 \text{ qt}} = 24 \text{ pt}$

3 gal = 24 pt

6. $32 \text{ oz} \times \dfrac{1 \text{ lb}}{16 \text{ oz}} = \dfrac{\overset{2}{32 \text{ oz}} \times 1 \text{ lb}}{\underset{1}{16 \text{ oz}}} = 2 \text{ lb}$

32 oz = 2 lb

7. $26 \text{ fl oz} \times \dfrac{1 \text{ c}}{8 \text{ fl oz}} = \dfrac{\overset{13}{26 \text{ fl oz}} \times 1 \text{ c}}{\underset{4}{8 \text{ fl oz}}} = \dfrac{13}{4} \text{ c} = 3\frac{1}{4} \text{ c}$

$\dfrac{1 \text{ c}}{4} \times \dfrac{8 \text{ fl oz}}{1 \text{ c}} = \dfrac{\overset{}{1 \text{ c}} \times \overset{2}{8} \text{ fl oz}}{\underset{1}{4} \times 1 \text{ c}} = 2 \text{ fl oz}$

26 fl oz = 3 c 2 fl oz

Skills Review Handbook, *continued*

8. $165 \text{ min} \times \dfrac{1 \text{ h}}{60 \text{ min}} = \dfrac{165 \overset{11}{\cancel{\text{min}}} \times 1 \text{ h}}{\underset{4}{\cancel{60 \text{ min}}}} = \dfrac{11}{4} \text{ h} = 2\dfrac{3}{4} \text{ h}$

$165 \text{ min} = 2\dfrac{3}{4} \text{ h}$

9. $75 \text{ in.} \times \dfrac{1 \text{ ft}}{12 \text{ in.}} = \dfrac{\overset{25}{\cancel{75 \text{ in.}}} \times 1 \text{ ft}}{\underset{4}{\cancel{12 \text{ in.}}}} = \dfrac{25}{4} \text{ ft} = 6\dfrac{1}{4} \text{ ft}$

$\dfrac{1 \text{ ft}}{4} \times \dfrac{12 \text{ in.}}{1 \text{ ft}} = \dfrac{\cancel{1 \text{ ft}} \times \overset{3}{\cancel{12 \text{ in.}}}}{\underset{1}{\cancel{4} \times \cancel{1 \text{ ft}}}} = 3 \text{ in.}$

$75 \text{ in.} = 6 \text{ ft } 3 \text{ in.}$

Converting Metric Units (p. 780)

1. $6.42 \times 1000 = 6420$

$6.42 \text{ kL} = 6420 \text{ L}$

2. $4 \div 100 = 0.04$

$4 \text{ cm} = 0.04 \text{ m}$

3. $5.5 \times 1000 = 5500$

$5.5 \text{ g} = 5500 \text{ mg}$

4. $8 \text{ km} \underline{\ \ ?\ \ } 8000 \text{ m}$

$8 \text{ km} \underline{\ \ ?\ \ } (8000 \div 1000) \text{ km}$

$8 \text{ km} = 8 \text{ km}$

$8 \text{ km} = 8000 \text{ m}$

5. $1200 \text{ mg} \underline{\ \ ?\ \ } 12 \text{ g}$

$1200 \text{ mg} \underline{\ \ ?\ \ } (12 \times 1000) \text{ mg}$

$1200 \text{ mg} < 12{,}000 \text{ mg}$

$1200 \text{ mg} < 12 \text{ g}$

6. $\quad 9.2 \text{ L} \underline{\ \ ?\ \ } 0.0092 \text{ mL}$

$(9.2 \times 1000) \text{ mL} \underline{\ \ ?\ \ } 0.0092 \text{ mL}$

$9200 \text{ mL} > 0.0092 \text{ mL}$

$9.2 \text{ L} > 0.0092 \text{ mL}$

Converting Between Metric and Customary Units (p. 781)

1. $80 \text{ kg} \times \dfrac{2.2 \text{ lb}}{1 \text{ kg}} = \dfrac{80 \cancel{\text{ kg}} \times 2.2 \text{ lb}}{1 \cancel{\text{ kg}}} = 176 \text{ lb}$

$80 \text{ kg} \approx 176 \text{ lb}$

2. $56 \text{ mi} \times \dfrac{1 \text{ km}}{0.621 \text{ mi}} = \dfrac{56 \cancel{\text{ mi}} \times 1 \text{ km}}{0.621 \cancel{\text{ mi}}} \approx 90.177 \text{ km}$

$56 \text{ mi} \approx 90 \text{ km}$

3. $24 \text{ qt} \times \dfrac{1 \text{ L}}{1.06 \text{ qt}} = \dfrac{24 \cancel{\text{ qt}} \times 1 \text{ L}}{1.06 \cancel{\text{ qt}}} \approx 22.64 \text{ L}$

$24 \text{ qt} \approx 23 \text{ L}$

4. $\quad 808 \text{ mm} \underline{\ \ ?\ \ } 33 \text{ in.}$

$(808 \times 0.0394) \text{ in.} \underline{\ \ ?\ \ } 33 \text{ in.}$

$31.8352 \text{ in.} < 33 \text{ in.}$

$808 \text{ mm} < 33 \text{ in.}$

5. $\quad 40 \text{ gal} \underline{\ \ ?\ \ } 0.5 \text{ kL}$

$(40 \div 264) \text{ kL} \underline{\ \ ?\ \ } 0.5 \text{ kL}$

$0.\overline{15} \text{ kL} < 0.5 \text{ kL}$

$40 \text{ gal} < 0.5 \text{ kL}$

---

6. $1 \text{ oz} \underline{\ \ ?\ \ } 20 \text{ g}$

$1 \text{ oz} \underline{\ \ ?\ \ } (20 \times 0.0353) \text{ oz}$

$1 \text{ oz} > 0.706 \text{ oz}$

$1 \text{ oz} > 20 \text{ g}$

Reading and Making Line Plots (p. 782)

1.
```
 ×
 ×  ×
 ×
 ×  ×
 ×  ×  ×  ×
 ×  ×  ×  ×  ×
+--+--+--+--+--+
 1  2  3  4  5
```

2.
```
             ×
 ×  ×  ×  ×
 ×  ×  ×  ×
 ×  ×  ×  ×  ×  ×  ×  ×
+--+--+--+--+--+--+--+--+
 1  2  3  4  5  6  7  8
```

3. $2 + 3 + 2 + 5 + 2 + 3 + 1 + 1 = 19$

Nineteen people completed the questionnaire.

4. $5 - 3 = 2$

Two more people exercise 4 hours each week than 6 hours each week.

5. $2 + 3 = 5$

Five people exercise less than 3 hours each week.

Reading and Making Bar Graphs (p. 783)

1. Nine students chose butter pecan as a favorite ice cream flavor.

2. Eight students chose vanilla as a favorite ice cream flavor.

3. Vanilla and rocky road were chosen by the same number of students.

4.

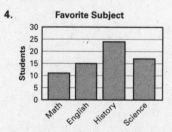

Reading and Making Line Graphs (p. 784)

1. The growth was 1 inch between Thursday and Friday.

2. The height remained the same between Saturday and Sunday.

3.

Puppy's Weight Gain

Skills Review Handbook, *continued*

Venn Diagrams and Logical Reasoning (p. 785)

1.

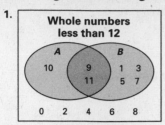

Whole numbers less than 12

A: 10, 9, 11 | B: 1, 3, 5, 7

(9, 11 in overlap)

0 2 4 6 8

2.

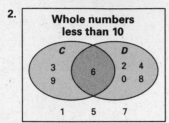

Whole numbers less than 10

C: 3, 9, 6 | D: 2, 4, 0, 8

(6 in overlap)

1 5 7

3. False; Both 9 and 11 are odd and greater than 8 and less than 12.

4. Sometimes; Six is a number less than 10, a multiple of 3, and even. Three is a number less than 10, a multiple of 3, but not even.

Problem Solving Handbook

Problem Solving Strategy Review

Make a Model: Practice the Strategy (p. 786)

The circular pizza; Make a model of the two pizzas by drawing and then cutting the exact shapes of the pizzas out of the paper. Place the rectangle over the circle. Cut off the largest piece of the rectangle that will fit inside the circle. Then cut the remaining pieces of the rectangle and place them on the remaining parts of the circle. You can see that the circle has the greater area because the pieces of the rectangle do not completely cover the circle.

Draw a Diagram: Practice the Strategy (p. 787)

$\frac{5}{8}$ mile south; Draw a diagram of the situation.

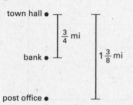

You can see from the diagram that the distance between the bank and the post office is $1\frac{3}{8} - \frac{3}{4} = \frac{5}{8}$ mile. Because the post office is south of the bank, you would have to drive $\frac{5}{8}$ mile south to get from the bank to the post office.

Guess, Check, and Revise: Practice the Strategy (p. 788)

20; Guess, check, and revise values of the numbers until they meet the given conditions. Guess 16 for one number. The product of the two numbers is 64, so the second number would be 4, because 16(4) = 64. The difference of the two numbers is 16 − 4 = 12. The sum of the two numbers is 16 + 4 = 20.

Work Backward: Practice the Strategy (p. 789)

9; Work backward from the 4 stickers that Mrs. O'Neil gave out on Monday. She gave out three times as many stickers on Tuesday as she did on Monday, so the number of stickers she gave out on Tuesday is 4(3) = 12. She gave out 3 fewer stickers on Wednesday than on Tuesday, so on Wednesday she gave out 12 − 3 = 9 stickers.

Make a List or Table: Practice the Strategy (p. 790)

5; Make a table that looks like a calendar to keep track of the days that Sam does his laundry. Mark an X on each day he does his laundry.

Sun	Mon	Tue	Wed	Thu	Fri	Sat
		x				
x					x	
			x			
	x					x
				x		
		x				

You can see from the table that the next time Sam will do his laundry on a Tuesday will be in 5 weeks.

Look for a Pattern: Practice the Strategy (p. 791)

12:45 P.M.; Look for a pattern in the starting times of the lessons. Each lesson starts 35 minutes after the previous lesson. This means that the fifth lesson starts at 11:35 A.M., the sixth lesson starts at 12:10 P.M., and the seventh lesson starts at 12:45 P.M.

Break into Parts: Practice the Strategy (p. 792)

$1175; Break the problem into parts by finding each type of cost. The cost of the rink rental is $125 • 3 = $375. The cost of the DJ is $80 • 3 = $240. The cost of the skate rental is $2 • 280 = $560. The total cost is $375 + $240 + $560 = $1175.

Solve a Simpler Problem: Practice the Strategy (p. 793)

14; Solve the simpler problem of how many tables the caterer would need to seat 10 people.

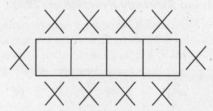

As shown in the diagram, 10 people can be seated at 4 tables. Notice that at one long table there are always 2 people sitting at the left and right ends of the table, plus 2 people per table sitting at the sides of the table. To find the number of tables needed for 10 people, subtract 2 from 10 to account for the people sitting on the left and right ends. This leaves 8 people sitting on the sides. Because each table seats 2 people on the sides, divide 8 by 2 to find the number of tables: 8 ÷ 2 = 4 tables. Use this same method to find the number of tables needed for 30 people. Subtract 2 from 30 to account for the people sitting on the left and right ends. This leaves 28 people sitting on the sides. Divide 28 by 2 to find the number of tables: 28 ÷ 2 = 14 tables.

Problem Solving Handbook, *continued*

Use a Venn Diagram: Practice the Strategy (p. 794)

27; Use a Venn diagram to organize the given information.

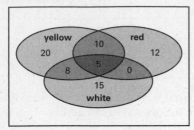

You can see from the Venn diagram that the number of tulips with some red in them is $12 + 10 + 5 + 0 = 27$.

Act It Out: Practice the Strategy (p. 795)

$2.20; Act out the problem. Place 8 quarters, 10 dimes, and 7 nickels on your desk. If these coins are not available, use objects that are available, such as colored beads, to represent the coins. Use a different color to represent each type of coin.

You give half of your dimes, which is $10 \div 2 = 5$ dimes, and 2 nickels, to a friend. Act this out by removing 5 dimes and 2 nickels from your desk, leaving 8 quarters, 5 dimes, and 5 nickels. You then spend one fourth of your quarters, which is $8 \div 4 = 2$ quarters, and 1 nickel. Act this out by removing 2 quarters and 1 nickel form your desk, leaving 6 quarters. 5 dimes, and 4 nickels. Because a quarter is worth $.25, a dime is worth $.10, and a nickel is worth $.05, the amount of money you have left is $6 \times \$.25 + 5 \times \$.10 + 4 \times \$.05 = \$1.50 + \$.50 + \$.20 = \$2.20$.

Problem Solving Strategy Practice (p. 796)

1. Yes; Yes; Yes; Make models out of graph paper by cutting out 1 rectangle that is 8 units by 12 units and 4 rectangles that are each 4 units by 6 units. Examples of the 3 layouts:

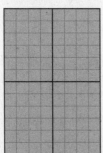
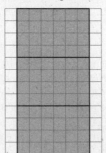

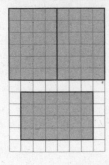

2. 45; Make a model out of paper. Cut out a rectangle that is 9 inches by 10 inches. Then see how many 3 inch by 2 inch rectangles you can cut out of it. You can cut out a maximum of 15 rectangles. So, with 3 sheets of cellophane, Joe can make $3 \cdot 15 = 45$ wrappers.

3. Make models to find the order and orientation of the page numbers. Diagrams of the front and back of the paper are shown.

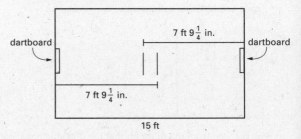

4. $6\frac{1}{2}$ in.; Draw a diagram of the basement to see what calculations need to be done.

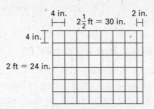

Add the toe line distances:

7 feet $9\frac{1}{4}$ inches + 7 feet $9\frac{1}{4}$ inches = 14 feet $18\frac{1}{2}$ inches

$= 15$ feet $6\frac{1}{2}$ inches.

Subtract the distance between the walls to find the distance between the toe lines:

15 feet $6\frac{1}{2}$ inches − 15 feet $= 6\frac{1}{2}$ inches.

5. 45; Draw a diagram of the wall area.

From the diagram, you can see that Thomas will need 42 whole tiles and 6 half tiles, so he needs $42 + 3 = 45$ tiles.

6. $\frac{7}{16}$ in.; Draw a diagram of the bracelet

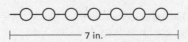

You can see from the diagram that there are 8 equal spaces. To find the distance between beads, subtract the length of the beads from the length of the bracelet and divide by 8. 7 in. $- 7\left(\frac{1}{2}\right)$ in. $= 7$ in. $- 3\frac{1}{2}$ in.

$= 3\frac{1}{2}$ in. $3\frac{1}{2}$ in. $\div 8 = \frac{7}{2}$ in. $\cdot \frac{1}{8} = \frac{7}{16}$ in.

The beads should be $\frac{7}{16}$ inches apart.

Problem Solving Handbook, *continued*

7. 3; Draw a diagram on graph paper. Each grid square represents one block.

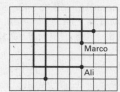

From the diagram, you can see that their routes cross 3 times.

8. 213 and 321; Guess, check, and revise values for the two numbers until they meet the given conditions. Guess 213 for one number. The other number would then be $534 - 213 = 321$. Both numbers contain each of the digits 1, 2, and 3. The numbers are 213 and 321.

9. 4 on bicycles, 3 on tricycles; Guess, check, and revise the number on bicycles and the number on tricycles until they meet the given conditions. Guess 4 children are on bicycles. That would mean that $7 - 4 = 3$ children are on tricycles. The total number of wheels would then be $4 \cdot 2 + 3 \cdot 3 = 8 + 9 = 17$. There are 4 children on bicycles and 3 children on tricycles.

10. $7.50; Guess, check, and revise the prices of the plants until they meet the given conditions. Guess $7.50 for the small plant. The medium plant would then cost $7.50 + $5.00 = $12.50, and the large plant would cost $12.50 + $5.00 = $17.50. The total cost of the plants is $7.50 + $12.50 + $17.50 = $37.50. The small plant cost $7.50.

11. 21, 22, and 23; Guess, check, and revise the values for the three numbers until they meet the given conditions. Guess 21 for the first number. The other two numbers would then be 22 and 23, giving three consecutive numbers. The sum of these numbers is $21 + 22 + 23 = 66$. The numbers are 21, 22, and 23.

12. 17 blue, 3 green; Guess, check, and revise the number of blue chips and the number of green chips that you have until they meet the given conditions. Guess 17 blue chips. Because you have a total of 20 chips, you have $20 - 17 = 3$ green chips. Because you get one point for every blue chip and lose one point for every green chip, you have a total of $17 + (-3) = 14$ points. You have 17 blue chips and 3 green chips.

13. 69 mi; Work backward from the 12 miles that Mr. Sanchez drove on the third day of vacation. He drove 7 more miles on the second day than on the third day, so he drove $12 + 7 = 19$ miles on the second day. He drove twice as many miles on the first day as on the second day, so he drove $2(19) = 38$ miles on the first day. Mr. Sanchez drove a total of $38 + 19 + 12 = 69$ miles during his vacation.

14. Wednesday; Aisha runs every 3 days so working backward from Tuesday, she also ran on Saturday and Wednesday. Aisha does sit-ups every other day, so working backward from Tuesday, she also did sit-ups on Sunday, Friday, and Wednesday. Wednesday is the day that Aisha last did both activities.

15. 60; Work backward from the 5 dancers who made it to the third round of auditions. Because $\frac{1}{4}$ of the remaining dancers after the second round were asked back for the third round, there were $5 \div \frac{1}{4} = 5 \cdot 4 = 20$ dancers in the second round. Because $\frac{2}{3}$ of the dancers were cut after the first round, $\frac{1}{3}$ of the dancers were not cut. So, $\frac{1}{3}$ were asked back for the second round. There were $20 \div \frac{1}{3} = 20 \cdot 3 = 60$ dancers in the first round.

16. 5:35 P.M.; Work backward from 7:15 P.M. So, 35 minutes before 7:15 P.M. is 6:40 P.M., 50 minutes before 6:40 P.M. is 5:50 P.M., and 15 minutes before 5:50 P.M. is 5:35 P.M. Andrew starts his workouts at 5:35 P.M.

17. 21; Work backward from 4 students. Before 2 students left your group, there were $4 + 2 = 6$ students in your group. Before your group joined an equal group, there were $6 \div 2 = 3$ students in your group. Because your class was divided into 7 equal groups, there were $7 \cdot 3 = 21$ students in your class at the beginning of the year.

18. 6; Make a list of all the possible orders that the initials ABC could have: ABC, ACB, BAC, BCA, CAB, and CBA. There are 6 possible orders, so the employee would have to make 6 bags.

19. Two keychains; Make a table of all the possible combinations of 2 souvenirs and their total cost.

Pen	Keychain	Hat	Total cost
0	0	2	$2(\$6.25) = \$12.50$
0	2	0	$2(\$4.75) = \$9.50$
2	0	0	$2(\$2.50) = \$5.00$
0	1	1	$\$4.75 + \$6.25 = \$11.00$
1	0	1	$\$2.50 + \$6.25 = \$8.75$
1	1	0	$\$2.50 + \$4.75 = \$7.25$

If Ben has $5.50 left, that means his purchase cost $15.00 - $5.50 = $9.50. The cost of two keychains is $9.50, so Ben bought two keychains.

20. 12; Make a list of the possible arrangements using the first letter of each name and listing the cheerleaders from the top row to the bottom row and from left to right in each row: SDAMOT, SDAMTO, SDAOMT, SDAOTM, SDATMO, SDATOM, SADMOT, SADMTO, SADOMT, SADOTM, SADTMO, and SADTOM. There are 12 different ways the six cheerleaders can form a pyramid.

21. $265; Look for a pattern. Every 6 weeks, Veronica saves $10 + $0 + $5 + $10 + $5 + $0 = $30. So, in the first 48 weeks of the year, she saves $8 \cdot $30 = $240. In the remaining 4 weeks of the year, she saves $10 + $0 + $5 + $10 = $25. So, Veronica will save $240 + $25 = $265 with the coupons that year.

22. 6; Look for a pattern in the distances at which Mara and Dan sprint, Mara sprints every 6 quarter-laps, so she will sprint after 6, 12, 18, and 24 quarter-laps. Dan sprints every 8 quarter-laps, so he will sprint after 8, 16, and 24 quarter laps. Mara and Dan will both start sprinting at the same time after 24 quarter-laps, which is 6 laps.

23. $18; The individual fares; Look for a pattern in how the family fares compare to the individual fares. The family fare is always 4 times the individual fare, so the family fare for traveling 6 zones is 4 • $4.50 = $18. For a family of 3 people, paying the individual fare is cheaper than paying the family fare.

24. 45; Look for a pattern in the total number of crates used as the height of the staircase increases. For a staircase with a height of 3 feet, the total number of crates used is $1 + 2 + 3 = 6$.

For a staircase with a height of 4 feet, the total number of crates used is $1 + 2 + 3 + 4 = 10$.

So, for a staircase with a height of 9 feet, the total number of crates used is $10 + 5 + 6 + 7 + 8 + 9 = 45$.

25. 3 hr 11 min; Break the problem into parts by finding the time needed for all the acting auditions and the time needed for all the chorus auditions. There are 25 students auditioning for an acting part. So, the time needed for the acting auditions is $25(5) = 125$ minutes. There are 22 students auditioning for a chorus part. So, the time needed for the chorus auditions is $22(3) = 66$ minutes. The total amount of time needed is $125 + 66 = 191$ minutes, or 3 hours and 11 minutes.

26. 18; The figure is composed of 6 small rectangles. Break the problem into parts by finding the number of rectangles that are composed of 1 small rectangle, then finding the number of rectangles that are composed of 2 small rectangles, and so on. Then find the total number of rectangles.

Number of rectangles that are composed of 1 small rectangle: 6

Number of rectangles that are composed of 2 small rectangles: 7

Number of rectangles that are composed of 3 small rectangles: 2

Number of rectangles that are composed of 4 small rectangles: 2

Number of rectangles that are composed of 5 small rectangles: 0

Number of rectangles that are composed of 6 small rectangles: 1

The number of different rectangles in the figure is $6 + 7 + 2 + 2 + 0 + 1 = 18$.

27. $1054.50; Break the problem into parts by finding the individual costs associated with the party if 150 people are expected. The cost of the decorations will be $42. The total cost of the appetizers will be $150(\$5) = \$750$. The total cost of the drinks will be $150(\$1.75) = \$262.50$. So, the total cost of the party will be $\$42 + \$750 + \$262.50 = \$1054.50$.

28. 2550; If Bridget continues increasing reading using the pattern shown, she will read 100 pages on the 50th day. The total number of pages she will read is $2 + 4 + 6 + \cdots + 96 + 98 + 100$. To find this sum, solve the simpler problem of grouping the numbers in the sum into pairs of numbers whose sum is 102:

$$2 + 100 = 102$$
$$2 + 4 + 6 + \cdots + 96 + 98 + 100$$
$$4 + 98 = 102$$

There are 25 pairs of numbers whose sum is 102, so $2 + 4 + 6 + \cdots + 96 + 98 + 100 = 25(102) = 2550$. Bridget will read 2550 pages in all.

29. 1496; Solve the simpler problem of finding how many columns and rows of holes that are $\frac{1}{4}$ inch in diameter can be punched out of one sheet of $8\frac{1}{2}$ inch by 11 inch paper. Because $8\frac{1}{2} \div \frac{1}{4} = \frac{17}{2} \cdot \frac{4}{1} = 34$, about 34 columns of holes can be punched out of the paper. Because $11 \div \frac{1}{4} = 11 \cdot \frac{4}{1} = 44$, about 44 rows of holes can be punched out of the paper. So, about $34 \times 44 = 1496$ holes can be punched out of the paper.

30. 50; Solve the simpler problem of finding the number of photos of sixth graders in the first group of 4 photos. There is one photo of sixth graders in the first group of 4 photos. For a total of 200 photos, this grouping pattern of 4 photos repeats 50 times. So, 50 of the 200 photos in the slide show will be of sixth graders.

31. 220; Solve the simpler problem of finding how many times a 2 or a 5 appears in the numbers from 1 to 99. The 20 numbers 2, 5, 12, 15, . . . 92, 95 each have a 2 or a 5 in the ones' place. The 20 numbers 20, 21, 22, . . . , 29 and 50, 51, 52, . . ., 59 each have a 2 or a 5 in the tens' place. So, there are $20 + 20 = 40$ times that a 2 or a 5 appears in the numbers from 1 to 99. Likewise, for the numbers from 100 to 199, there are 40 times that a 2 or 5 appears in these numbers. For the numbers from 200 to 300, there are $100 + 40 = 140$ times that a 2 or a 5 appears, which includes the 100 times a 2 appears in the hundreds' place. So, there are $40 + 40 + 140 = 220$ times that a 2 or a 5 appears in the numbers form 1 to 300. The manager will need to use the number 5 stencil 220 times.

Problem Solving Handbook, *continued*

32. 172; Use a Venn diagram to organize the given information.

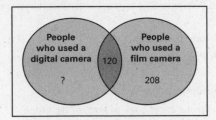

A total of $120 + 208 = 328$ people used a film camera at the high school graduation. Because there were 500 people with cameras, $500 - 328 = 172$ people used only a digital camera.

33. 20; Use a Venn diagram to organize the given information.

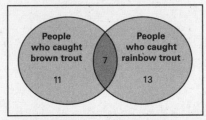

You can see from the Venn diagram that the number of people who caught rainbow trout that day is $7 + 13 = 20$.

34. 7; Use a Venn diagram to organize the given information. Because 8 students have a cat and 2 students have both a cat and a dog, $8 - 2 = 6$ students have a cat only. Because 5 students have a dog and 2 students have both a cat and a dog, $5 - 2 = 3$ students have a dog only.

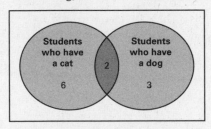

You can see from the Venn diagram that $6 + 2 + 3 = 11$ students have a cat or a dog. Because there are 18 students in your class, the number of students who have neither a cat nor a dog is $18 - 11 = 7$.

35. 7; Use a Venn diagram to organize the given information.

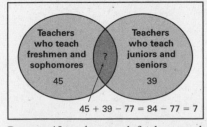

$$45 + 39 - 77 = 84 - 77 = 7$$

Because 45 teachers teach freshmen and sophomores, 39 teachers teach juniors and seniors, and there are 77 teachers at the high school, the number of teachers who teach students in all four grade levels is
$$45 + 39 - 77 = 84 - 77 = 7.$$

36. 11; Use a Venn diagram to organize the given information.

Because 10 cats are black and 3 cats are black and have short tails, $10 - 3 = 7$ cats are black only. Because 6 cats have short tails and 3 cats are black and have short tails, $6 - 3 = 3$ cats have short tails only.

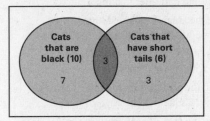

You can see from the Venn diagram that $7 + 3 + 3 = 13$ cats are black or have short tails. Because there are 24 cats in the shelter, the number of cats that are not black and do not have short tails is $24 - 13 = 11$

37. Bob, Kelly, Justin, Rebecca, Michelle; Act out the problem. You need five students to play the roles of Justin, Bob, Kelly, Michelle, and Rebecca. The relationships between the heights of the students should be the same as those given in the problem. Have the students stand in line from tallest to shortest. Because Bob is the tallest of the five, he is first in line. Because Rebecca is shorter than Justin and taller than Michelle, the order of these three students, from tallest to shortest, is Justin, Rebecca, and Michelle. Because Kelly is taller than Michelle and Justin, she is also taller than Rebecca, so she is second in line. Justin, Rebecca, and Michelle would take the remaining three places in line. So, in order from tallest to shortest, the students are Bob, Kelly, Justin, Rebecca, and Michelle.

38. 24; Act out the problem. You need 8 students to play the roles of the 4 sets of twins. Say their names are Ann and Jan, Bo and Flo, Cat and Pat, and Ed and Ted. Each person shakes hands one time with every other person except his or her twin. Write down the names of the people shaking hands. Make sure not to write duplicates. For example, Ann shaking hands with Bo is the same as Bo shaking hands with Ann, so it is not necessary to write both of these. The handshakes that take place are:

Ann, Bo	Jan, Bo	Bo, Cat	Flo, Cat	Cat, Ed	Pat, Ed
Ann, Flo	Jan, Flo	Bo, Pat	Flo, Pat	Cat, Ted	Pat, Ted
Ann, Cat	Jan, Cat	Bo, Ed	Flo, Ed		
Ann, Pat	Jan, Pat	Bo, Ted	Flo, Ted		
Ann, Ed	Jan, Ed				
Ann, Ted	Jan, Ted				

So there are 24 handshakes that take place.

39. 10; Act out the problem by using a piece of graph paper that has 1000 squares to represent a poster board with an area of 1000 square inches. For example, a rectangular piece of graph paper that is 50 units long and 20 units wide has 1000 squares. Cut the paper in half repeatedly, setting aside one half each time, and write down the area of each resulting half after making a cut.

After 1 cut, the area of each resulting half is $1000 \div 2 = 500$ square inches.

After 2 cuts, the area of each resulting half is $500 \div 2 = 250$ square inches.

After 3 cuts, the area of each resulting half is $250 \div 2 = 125$ square inches.

After 4 cuts, the area of each resulting half is $125 \div 2 = 62.5$ square inches.

After 5 cuts, the area of each resulting half is $62.5 \div 2 = 31.25$ square inches.

After 6 cuts, the area of each resulting half is $31.25 \div 2 = 15.625$ square inches.

After 7 cuts, the area of each resulting half is $15.625 \div 2 = 7.8125$ square inches.

After 8 cuts, the area of each resulting half is $7.8125 \div 2 = 3.90625$ square inches.

After 9 cuts, the area of each resulting half is $3.90625 \div 2 = 1.953125$ square inches.

After 10 cuts, the area of each resulting half is $1.953125 \div 2 = 0.9765625$ square inch.

So, you will make 10 cuts before the area of the remaining piece is less than 1 square inch.

40. 27; 81; Act out the problem. Fold a piece of paper into thirds. Unfold it and count 3 rectangles. Refold the paper, and then fold it into thirds again. Unfold it and this time, count 9 rectangles. Repeat the process a third and a fourth time. Each time, the number of rectangles that are formed increases by a factor of 3. So, folding the paper into thirds 3 times gives $9 \times 3 = 27$ rectangles and folding the paper into thirds 4 times gives $27 \times 3 = 81$ rectangles.

41. Act out the problem. You need 3 boxes of different sizes that you can stack on top of each other and you need 3 tables. Call the boxes, in order from largest to smallest, box A, box B, and box C. Call the tables table 1, table 2, and table 3. Stack the boxes on top of table 1, with box A on the bottom, box B in the middle, and box C on the top. Move box C to table 3, move box B to table 2, stack box C on top of box B on table 2, move box A to table 3, move box C to table 1, stack box B on top of box A on table 3, and stack box C on top of boxes B and A on table 3.

42. 6; Act out the problem. You need 4 slips of paper. Write a 4 on two of the slips, a 2 on another slip, and a 6 on the last slip. Arrange the slips to form all possible arrangements of 4 digit numbers that could be your PIN. Because you know that the first digit is a 4, the possible arrangements are 4426, 4462, 4246, 4264, 4642, and 4624. So, there are 6 possibilities for your PIN.

43. Darryl, Carlene, Tyrone, Penelope; Act out the problem. You need 4 students to play the roles of Darryl, Carlene, Tyrone, and Penelope. The original order that they are in line is:

Darryl, Carlene, Tyrone, Penelope

Carlene lets Penelope cut in front of her, so the order becomes:

Darryl, Penelope, Carlene, Tyrone

Darryl lets Tyrone cut in back of him, so the order becomes:

Darryl, Tyrone, Penelope, Carlene

Tyrone then lets Carlene cut in front of him, so now they are in line in the following order:

Darryl, Carlene, Tyrone, Penelope

Extra Practice

1. **Student Heights**

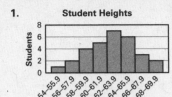

2. The interval 62–63.9 has the greatest number of students.

3. Yes. To determine the number of students who are between 60 and 69.9 inches tall, add the frequencies for the intervals 60–61.9, 62–63.9, 64–65.9, 66–67.9, and 68–69.9.

4. $15 - 3 \cdot 2 + 4 = 15 - 6 + 4 = 9 + 4 = 13$

5. $42 \div [(5 - 2) \cdot (1 + 1)] = 42 \div (3 \cdot 2) = 42 \div 6 = 7$

6. $2 + \dfrac{100 - 36}{7 + 9} = 2 + \dfrac{64}{16} = 2 + 4 = 6$

7. $4 \cdot 7 - 8 \cdot 3 = 28 - 24 = 4$

8. $3 + 10 \cdot 5 \div 2 = 3 + 50 \div 2 = 3 + 25 = 28$

9. $(11 - 56 \div 8) \cdot 9 = (11 - 7) \cdot 9 = 4 \cdot 9 = 36$

10. When $r = 1.5$ and $s = 2.4$:
   $10r + s = 10(1.5) + 2.4 = 15 + 2.4 = 17.4$

11. When $r = 1.5$ and $s = 2.4$:
   $\dfrac{7s}{r + 0.5} = \dfrac{7(2.4)}{1.5 + 0.5} = \dfrac{16.8}{2} = 8.4$

12. When $r = 1.5$ and $s = 2.4$:
   $8rs = 8(1.5)(2.4) = 12(2.4) = 28.8$

13. When $r = 1.5$ and $s = 2.4$:
   $3(r + s) = 3(1.5 + 2.4) = 3(3.9) = 11.7$

14. $24 - (2^3 + 1) \cdot 2 = 24 - (8 + 1) \cdot 2$
   $= 24 - 9 \cdot 2$
   $= 24 - 18$
   $= 6$

15. $6^3 \div (2 + 1)^2 + 3 = 216 \div 3^2 + 3$
   $= 216 \div 9 + 3$
   $= 24 + 3$
   $= 27$

16. $(8 - 5)^4 + 7 \cdot 5^2 = 3^4 + 7 \cdot 5^2$
   $= 81 + 7 \cdot 25$
   $= 81 + 175$
   $= 256$

17. $5n = 35$
   $n = 7$

18. $\dfrac{60}{t} = 4$
   $t = 15$

19. $12 + w = 75$
   $w = 63$

20. $41 - a = 23$
   $a = 18$

21. $9 + b = 17$
   $b = 8$

22. $63 - c = 10$
   $c = 53$

23. $6x = 54$
   $x = 9$

24. $\dfrac{m}{12} = 9$
   $m = 108$

25. Perimeter $= 2\ell + 2w = 2(13) + 2(8) = 26 + 16 = 42$
   Area $= \ell w = (13)(8) = 104$
   The perimeter of the garden is 42 feet and the area of the garden is 104 square feet.

26. $d = rt$
   $d = 5(1.5)$
   $d = 7.5$
   Ramon jogs 7.5 miles in 1.5 hours.

27. Perimeter $= 4s$
   $32 = 4s$
   $8 = s$
   The side length of the square is 8 centimeters.

28. (1) Read and Understand
   (2) Make a Plan: Write a Verbal Model

   $\text{Amount of money you have left} = \text{Amount earned} - \text{Amount spent}$

   (3) Solve the Problem:

   $\text{Amount of money you have left} = \text{Amount earned} - \text{Amount spent}$
   $= 5(4)(6) - 2(12)$
   $= 20(6) - 2(12)$
   $= 120 - 24$
   $= 96$

   You have $96 left.

   (4) Look Back

Chapter 2 Extra Practice (p. 802)

1.
   $-43 \quad -24 \quad -2 \quad 7 \quad 19 \quad 33$

   The integers from least to greatest are -43, -24, -2, 7, 19, and 33.

2.
   $-230 \quad -146 \quad -68 \quad 5 \quad 94 \quad 157$

   The integers from least to greatest are -230, -146, -68, 5, 94, and 157.

3. The opposite of -25 is 25.
   $|-25| = 25$

4. The opposite of 467 is -467.
   $|467| = 467$

5. The opposite of 0 is 0.
   $|0| = 0$

6. Because $|-2| = 2$, the opposite of $|-2|$ is -2.
   $||-2|| = |2| = 2$

7. $342 + (-751) = -409$

8. $-147 + 71 = -76$

9. $-89 + 268 = 179$

10. $-29 + (-51) + 36 = -80 + 36 = -44$

11. $-78 + 65 + 13 = -13 + 13 = 0$

12. $93 + (-57) + (-102) = 36 + (-102) = -66$

13. $-12 - 4 = -12 + (-4) = -16$

14. $10 - 13 = 10 + (-13) = -3$

15. $34 - (-17) = 34 + 17 = 51$

16. $-18 - (-17) = -18 + 17 = -1$

17. $23 - 38 = 23 + (-38) = -15$

18. $81 - (-16) = 81 + 16 = 97$

19. $-9 - (-77) = -9 + 77 = 68$

20. $-63 - 19 = -63 + (-19) = -82$

21. $(-7)(-50) = 350$

22. $25(-7) = -175$

23. $-4(16) = -64$

24. $(-12)(-21) = 252$

25. $-95(0)(-58) = 0(-58) = 0$

26. $54(-1)(5) = -54(5) = -270$

27. $8(-2)(-3)(5) = -16(-3)(5) = 48(5) = 240$

28. $(-14)(4)(6)(9) = -56(6)(9) = -336(9) = -3024$

29. $\frac{96}{-8} = -12$

30. $\frac{-48}{-12} = 4$

31. $\frac{0}{4} = 0$

32. $\frac{-80}{5} = -16$

33. Sum of data $= -8 + 6 + 3 + (-20) + (-9) + 4 = -24$

    Mean $= \frac{-24}{6} = -4$

34. $-28 + (74 - 32)$

    $= -28 + [74 + (-32)]$ Write subtraction as addition.

    $= -28 + [(-32) + 74]$ Commutative property of addition

    $= [-28 + (-32)] + 74$ Associative property of addition

    $= -60 + 74$ Add.

    $= 14$ Add.

35. $7\left(2 \cdot \frac{3}{7}\right) = 7\left(\frac{3}{7} \cdot 2\right)$ Commutative property of multiplication

    $= \left(7 \cdot \frac{3}{7}\right) \cdot 2$ Associative property of multiplication

    $= 3 \cdot 2$ Multiply.

    $= 6$ Multiply.

36. $(-7.2 + 3.5) + (-3.5)$

    $= -7.2 + [3.5 + (-3.5)]$ Associative property of addition

    $= -7.2 + 0$ Inverse property of addition

    $= -7.2$ Identity property of addition

37. $-5(-3 + 8) = (-5)(-3) + (-5)(8) = 15 + (-40) = -25$

38. $3(m - 4) = 3m - 12$

39. $-1(4 + 9r) = -4 - 9r$

40. $8(-4j - 3) = -32j - 24$

41. $-x + 3y - 5y + 6x = -x + 6x + 3y - 5y = 5x - 2y$

42. $2(3k - 6) + 4 + 5k = 6k - 12 + 4 + 5k$

    $= 6k + 5k - 12 + 4$

    $= 11k - 8$

43. $5a - 3(2a + b) - 7b = 5a - 6a - 3b - 7b = -a - 10b$

44. Begin at the origin, move 3 units to the right, then 2 units down. Point A is in Quadrant IV.

45. Begin at the origin, move 5 units to the right, then 1 unit up. Point B is in Quadrant I.

46. Begin at the origin, move 4 units down. Point C is on the y-axis.

47. Begin at the origin, move 1 unit to the left, then 3 units down. Point D is in Quadrant III.

Chapter 3 Extra Practice (p. 803)

1. $n - 3 = 5$

    $n - 3 + 3 = 5 + 3$

    $n = 8$

    Check: $8 - 3 \overset{?}{=} 5$

           $5 = 5$ ✓

2. $36 = p + 20$

    $36 - 20 = p + 20 - 20$

    $16 = p$

    Check: $36 \overset{?}{=} 16 + 20$

           $36 = 36$ ✓

3. $-4 = h - 9$

    $-4 + 9 = h - 9 + 9$

    $5 = h$

    Check: $-4 \overset{?}{=} 5 - 9$

           $-4 = -4$ ✓

4. $27 + z = 51$

    $27 + z - 27 = 51 - 27$

    $z = 24$

    Check: $27 + 24 \overset{?}{=} 51$

           $51 = 51$ ✓

5. $32 = \frac{x}{2}$

    $2 \cdot 32 = \frac{2x}{2}$

    $64 = x$

    Check: $32 \overset{?}{=} \frac{64}{2}$

           $32 = 32$ ✓

6. $11k = -55$

    $\frac{11k}{11} = \frac{-55}{11}$

    $k = -5$

    Check: $11(-5) \overset{?}{=} -55$

           $-55 = -55$ ✓

7. $76 = 19r$

$\dfrac{76}{19} = \dfrac{19r}{19}$

$4 = r$

Check: $76 \stackrel{?}{=} 19(4)$

$76 = 76$ ✓

8. $\dfrac{y}{-1.4} = -5$

$-1.4 \cdot \dfrac{y}{-1.4} = -1.4(-5)$

$y = 7$

Check: $\dfrac{7}{-1.4} \stackrel{?}{=} -5$

$-5 = -5$ ✓

9. $5a - 2 = 33$

$5a - 2 + 2 = 33 + 2$

$5a = 35$

$\dfrac{5a}{5} = \dfrac{35}{5}$

$a = 7$

Check: $5(7) - 2 \stackrel{?}{=} 33$

$35 - 2 \stackrel{?}{=} 33$

$33 = 33$ ✓

10. $\dfrac{d}{3} + 8 = -6$

$\dfrac{d}{3} + 8 - 8 = -6 - 8$

$\dfrac{d}{3} = -14$

$3 \cdot \dfrac{d}{3} = 3(-14)$

$d = -42$

Check: $\dfrac{-42}{3} + 8 \stackrel{?}{=} -6$

$-14 + 8 \stackrel{?}{=} -6$

$-6 = -6$ ✓

11. $-1 = 14 - 2h$

$-1 - 14 = 14 - 2h - 14$

$-15 = -2h$

$\dfrac{-15}{-2} = \dfrac{-2h}{-2}$

$7.5 = h$

Check: $-1 \stackrel{?}{=} 14 - 2(7.5)$

$-1 \stackrel{?}{=} 14 - 15$

$-1 = -1$ ✓

12. $84 - z = 96$

$84 - z - 84 = 96 - 84$

$-z = 12$

$\dfrac{-z}{-1} = \dfrac{12}{-1}$

$z = -12$

Check: $84 - (-12) \stackrel{?}{=} 96$

$84 + 12 \stackrel{?}{=} 96$

$96 = 96$ ✓

13. $\dfrac{c}{4} + 7 = 12$

$\dfrac{c}{4} + 7 - 7 = 12 - 7$

$\dfrac{c}{4} = 5$

$4 \cdot \dfrac{c}{4} = 4(5)$

$c = 20$

Check: $\dfrac{20}{4} + 7 \stackrel{?}{=} 12$

$5 + 7 \stackrel{?}{=} 12$

$12 = 12$ ✓

14. $47 = -6y + 5$

$47 - 5 = -6y + 5 - 5$

$42 = -6y$

$\dfrac{42}{-6} = \dfrac{-6y}{-6}$

$-7 = y$

Check: $47 \stackrel{?}{=} -6(-7) + 5$

$47 \stackrel{?}{=} 42 + 5$

$47 = 47$ ✓

15. $73 = 15 - b$

$73 - 15 = 15 - b - 15$

$58 = -b$

$\dfrac{58}{-1} = \dfrac{-b}{-1}$

$-58 = b$

Check: $73 \stackrel{?}{=} 15 - (-58)$

$73 \stackrel{?}{=} 15 + 58$

$73 = 73$ ✓

16. $55 = 7t - 8$

$55 + 8 = 7t - 8 + 8$

$63 = 7t$

$\dfrac{63}{7} = \dfrac{7t}{7}$

$9 = t$

Check: $55 \stackrel{?}{=} 7(9) - 8$

$55 \stackrel{?}{=} 63 - 8$

$55 = 55$ ✓

Extra Practice, continued

17.
$$6n - 5 = 13$$
$$6n - 5 + 5 = 13 + 5$$
$$6n = 18$$
$$\frac{6n}{6} = \frac{18}{6}$$
$$n = 3$$

18.
$$5 + \frac{n}{3} = -1$$
$$5 + \frac{n}{3} - 5 = -1 - 5$$
$$\frac{n}{3} = -6$$
$$3 \cdot \frac{n}{3} = 3(-6)$$
$$n = -18$$

19. Let t = time required to repair the car.

$$\begin{array}{ccccc} \text{Total} \\ \text{cost} \end{array} = \begin{array}{c} \text{Cost for} \\ \text{labor} \end{array} \cdot \begin{array}{c} \text{Time required} \\ \text{to repair car} \end{array} + \begin{array}{c} \text{Cost for} \\ \text{parts} \end{array}$$

$$201 = 48t + 129$$
$$201 - 129 = 48t + 129 - 129$$
$$72 = 48t$$
$$\frac{72}{48} = \frac{48t}{48}$$
$$1.5 = t$$

One and a half hours are required to repair the car.

20. Area $= \frac{1}{2}bh = \frac{1}{2}(21)(20) = 210$

Perimeter $= 20 + 21 + 29 = 41 + 29 = 70$

The area is 210 square centimeters and the perimeter is 70 centimeters.

21. Area $= \frac{1}{2}bh = \frac{1}{2}(10)(12) = 5(12) = 60$

Perimeter $= 10 + 13 + 13 = 23 + 13 = 36$

The area is 60 square inches and the perimeter is 36 inches.

22. Area $= \frac{1}{2}bh = \frac{1}{2}(12)(15) = 6(15) = 90$

Perimeter $= 12 + 17 + 25 = 29 + 25 = 54$

The area is 90 square feet and the perimeter is 54 feet.

23. Area $= \ell w$
$$60 = 12w$$
$$5 = w$$

Perimeter $= 2\ell + 2w = 2(12) + 2(5) = 24 + 10 = 34$

The width is 5 meters and the perimeter is 34 meters.

24. Area $= s^2$
$$81 = s^2$$
$$\sqrt{81} = s$$
$$9 = s$$

The side length is 9 feet.

25.
$$4 + j \geq -1$$
$$4 + j - 4 \geq -1 - 4$$
$$j \geq -5$$

26.
$$0 < m - 6$$
$$0 + 6 < m - 6 + 6$$
$$6 < m$$

27.
$$z + 4.5 \leq 2$$
$$z + 4.5 - 4.5 \leq 2 - 4.5$$
$$z \leq -2.5$$

28.
$$-38 > t - 46$$
$$-38 + 46 > t - 46 + 46$$
$$8 > t$$

29. $5x < -25$
$$\frac{5x}{5} < \frac{-25}{5}$$
$$x < -5$$

30.
$$3 \leq -\frac{1}{3}y$$
$$-3(3) \geq -3\left(-\frac{1}{3}y\right)$$
$$-9 \geq y$$

31.
$$2 \geq \frac{s}{4}$$
$$4(2) \geq 4\left(\frac{s}{4}\right)$$
$$8 \geq s$$

32. $-13k > -65$
$$\frac{-13k}{-13} < \frac{-65}{-13}$$
$$k < 5$$

Chapter 4 Extra Practice (p. 804)

1. $72 = 2 \cdot 2 \cdot 2 \cdot 3 \cdot 3 = 2^3 \cdot 3^2$

2. $65 = 5 \cdot 13$

3. $153 = 3 \cdot 3 \cdot 17 = 3^2 \cdot 17$

4. $196 = 2 \cdot 2 \cdot 7 \cdot 7 = 2^2 \cdot 7^2$

5. $25pq = 5 \cdot 5 \cdot p \cdot q = 5^2 \cdot p \cdot q$

6. $7a^3 = 7 \cdot a \cdot a \cdot a$

7. $22xy^2 = 2 \cdot 11 \cdot x \cdot y \cdot y$

8. $54s^2t = 2 \cdot 3 \cdot 3 \cdot 3 \cdot s \cdot s \cdot t = 2 \cdot 3^3 \cdot s \cdot s \cdot t$

9. $45 = 3^2 \cdot 5$

$75 = 3 \cdot 5^2$

$GCF = 3 \cdot 5 = 15$

10. $108 = 2^2 \cdot 3^3$

$162 = 2 \cdot 3^4$

$GCF = 2 \cdot 3^3 = 2 \cdot 27 = 54$

11. $6bc = 2 \cdot 3 \cdot b \cdot c$

$35abc^2 = 5 \cdot 7 \cdot a \cdot b \cdot c^2$

$GCF = b \cdot c = bc$

12. $4p^2 = 2^2 \cdot p^2$

$18qr = 2 \cdot 3^2 \cdot q \cdot r$

$GCF = 2$

13. $21mn = 3 \cdot 7 \cdot m \cdot n$

$9km^2 = 3^2 \cdot k \cdot m^2$

$GCF = 3 \cdot m = 3m$

14. $14x^2y^3 = 2 \cdot 7 \cdot x^2 \cdot y^3$

$28xy^2 = 2^2 \cdot 7 \cdot x \cdot y^2$

$GCF = 2 \cdot 7 \cdot x \cdot y^2 = 14xy^2$

15. $34w^2z^2 = 2 \cdot 17 \cdot w^2 \cdot z^2$

$51w^5z^4 = 3 \cdot 17 \cdot w^5 \cdot z^4$

$GCF = 17 \cdot w^2 \cdot z^2 = 17w^2z^2$

16. $abcdf = a \cdot b \cdot c \cdot d \cdot f$

$a^2d^3gh = a^2 \cdot d^3 \cdot g \cdot h$

$GCF = a \cdot d = ad$

17. $\dfrac{32}{64} = \dfrac{1 \cdot \cancel{32}}{2 \cdot \cancel{32}} = \dfrac{1}{2}$

18. $\dfrac{-15}{39} = \dfrac{\cancel{3} \cdot (-5)}{\cancel{3} \cdot 13} = -\dfrac{5}{13}$

19. $\dfrac{-22}{77} = \dfrac{-2 \cdot \cancel{11}}{7 \cdot \cancel{11}} = -\dfrac{2}{7}$

20. $\dfrac{17}{51} = \dfrac{1 \cdot \cancel{17}}{3 \cdot \cancel{17}} = \dfrac{1}{3}$

21. $\dfrac{10x}{45xy} = \dfrac{2 \cdot \cancel{5x}}{9 \cdot \cancel{5x} \cdot y} = \dfrac{2}{9y}$

22. $\dfrac{-16mn}{40mn} = \dfrac{-2 \cdot \cancel{8mn}}{5 \cdot \cancel{8mn}} = -\dfrac{2}{5}$

23. $\dfrac{-6ab}{4bc} = \dfrac{-3 \cdot \cancel{2} \cdot a \cdot \cancel{b}}{2 \cdot \cancel{2} \cdot \cancel{b} \cdot c} = -\dfrac{3a}{2c}$

24. $\dfrac{28rs}{7rst} = \dfrac{4 \cdot \cancel{7} \cdot \cancel{r} \cdot \cancel{s}}{\cancel{7} \cdot \cancel{r} \cdot \cancel{s} \cdot t} = \dfrac{4}{t}$

25. $30 = 2 \cdot 3 \cdot 5$

$60 = 2^2 \cdot 3 \cdot 5$

$LCM = 2^2 \cdot 3 \cdot 5 = 60$

26. $4x = 2^2 \cdot x$

$18xy^2 = 2 \cdot 3^2 \cdot x \cdot y^2$

$LCM = 2^2 \cdot 3^2 \cdot x \cdot y^2 = 36xy^2$

27. $5ab^2 = 5 \cdot a \cdot b^2$

$3bc^2 = 3 \cdot b \cdot c^2$

$LCM = 3 \cdot 5 \cdot a \cdot b^2 \cdot c^2 = 15ab^2c^2$

28. $12x^3y = 2^2 \cdot 3 \cdot x^3 \cdot y$

$8x^2y^4 = 2^3 \cdot x^2 \cdot y^4$

$LCM = 2^3 \cdot 3 \cdot x^3 \cdot y^4 = 24x^3y^4$

29. $\dfrac{7}{8} = \dfrac{7 \cdot 11}{8 \cdot 11} = \dfrac{77}{88}$

$\dfrac{9}{11} = \dfrac{9 \cdot 8}{11 \cdot 8} = \dfrac{72}{88}$

Because $\dfrac{77}{88} > \dfrac{72}{88}, \dfrac{7}{8} > \dfrac{9}{11}$.

30. $3\dfrac{3}{5} = \dfrac{18}{5} = \dfrac{18 \cdot 3}{5 \cdot 3} = \dfrac{54}{15}$

$\dfrac{11}{3} = \dfrac{11 \cdot 5}{3 \cdot 5} = \dfrac{55}{15}$

Because $\dfrac{54}{15} < \dfrac{55}{15}, 3\dfrac{3}{5} < \dfrac{11}{3}$.

31. $\dfrac{17}{6} = \dfrac{17 \cdot 3}{6 \cdot 3} = \dfrac{51}{18}$

$2\dfrac{13}{18} = \dfrac{49}{18}$

Because $\dfrac{51}{18} > \dfrac{49}{18}, \dfrac{17}{6} > 2\dfrac{13}{18}$.

32. $1\dfrac{10}{15} = \dfrac{25}{15} = \dfrac{\cancel{5} \cdot 5}{\cancel{5} \cdot 3} = \dfrac{5}{3}$

$\dfrac{35}{21} = \dfrac{\cancel{7} \cdot 5}{\cancel{7} \cdot 3} = \dfrac{5}{3}$

Because $\dfrac{5}{3} = \dfrac{5}{3}, 1\dfrac{10}{15} = \dfrac{35}{21}$.

33. $\dfrac{11}{10} = \dfrac{11 \cdot 4}{10 \cdot 4} = \dfrac{44}{40}$

$1\dfrac{1}{8} = \dfrac{9}{8} = \dfrac{9 \cdot 5}{8 \cdot 5} = \dfrac{45}{40}$

Because $\dfrac{44}{40} < \dfrac{45}{40}, \dfrac{11}{10} < 1\dfrac{1}{8}$.

34. $\dfrac{4}{5} = \dfrac{4 \cdot 11}{5 \cdot 11} = \dfrac{44}{55}$

$\dfrac{6}{11} = \dfrac{6 \cdot 5}{11 \cdot 5} = \dfrac{30}{55}$

Because $\dfrac{44}{55} > \dfrac{30}{55}, \dfrac{4}{5} > \dfrac{6}{11}$.

35. $\dfrac{50}{9} = \dfrac{50 \cdot 7}{9 \cdot 7} = \dfrac{350}{63}$

$5\dfrac{2}{7} = \dfrac{37}{7} = \dfrac{37 \cdot 9}{7 \cdot 9} = \dfrac{333}{63}$

Because $\dfrac{350}{63} > \dfrac{333}{63}, \dfrac{50}{9} > 5\dfrac{2}{7}$.

36. $\dfrac{63}{15} = \dfrac{63 \cdot 4}{15 \cdot 4} = \dfrac{252}{60}$

$4\dfrac{5}{12} = \dfrac{53}{12} = \dfrac{53 \cdot 5}{12 \cdot 5} = \dfrac{265}{60}$

Because $\dfrac{252}{60} < \dfrac{265}{60}, \dfrac{63}{15} < 4\dfrac{5}{12}$.

37. $z^5 \cdot z = z^5 \cdot z^1 = z^{5+1} = z^6$

38. $5^8 \cdot 5^4 = 5^{8+4} = 5^{12}$

39. $(-7)^6 \cdot (-7)^3 = (-7)^{6+3} = (-7)^9$

40. $a^2 \cdot a^4 = a^{2+4} = a^6$

41. $\dfrac{6^9}{6^5} = 6^{9-5} = 6^4$

42. $\dfrac{(-8)^{12}}{(-8)^2} = (-8)^{12-2} = (-8)^{10}$

43. $\dfrac{(-v)^7}{(-v)^4} = (-v)^{7-4} = (-v)^3$

44. $\dfrac{c^9}{c} = c^{9-1} = c^8$

45. $6k^{-1} = 6 \cdot \dfrac{1}{k} = \dfrac{6}{k}$

46. $a^3 \cdot a^{-3} = a^3 \cdot \dfrac{1}{a^3} = \dfrac{a^3}{a^3} = 1$

47. $\dfrac{s^{-3}}{s^4} = \dfrac{\frac{1}{s^3}}{s^4} = \dfrac{1}{s^3 \cdot s^4} = \dfrac{1}{s^7}$

48. $n^{-4} \cdot n^{-2} = \dfrac{1}{n^4} \cdot \dfrac{1}{n^2} = \dfrac{1}{n^4 \cdot n^2} = \dfrac{1}{n^6}$

49. $124{,}000{,}000 = 1.24 \times 10^8$

50. $0.0000005 = 5 \times 10^{-7}$

51. $0.0000791 = 7.91 \times 10^{-5}$

52. $32{,}100 = 3.21 \times 10^4$

53. $2.7 \times 10^{-3} = 0.0027$

54. $9.09 \times 10^2 = 909$

55. $5.88 \times 10^{11} = 588{,}000{,}000{,}000$

56. $6.2 \times 10^{-8} = 0.000000062$

Chapter 5 Extra Practice (p. 805)

1. $\dfrac{7}{8} + \dfrac{5}{8} = \dfrac{7+5}{8} = \dfrac{12}{8} = 1\dfrac{1}{2}$

2. $5\dfrac{1}{5} - 3\dfrac{4}{5} = 4\dfrac{6}{5} - 3\dfrac{4}{5} = 1\dfrac{2}{5}$

3. $-\dfrac{11m}{15} + \dfrac{m}{15} = \dfrac{-11m+m}{15} = -\dfrac{10m}{15} = -\dfrac{2m}{3}$

4. $\dfrac{5a}{9b} - \dfrac{4a}{9b} = \dfrac{-5a-4a}{9b} = -\dfrac{9a}{9b} = -\dfrac{a}{b}$

5. $\dfrac{9}{10} - \dfrac{5}{6} = \dfrac{27}{30} - \dfrac{25}{30} = \dfrac{27-25}{30} = \dfrac{2}{30} = \dfrac{1}{15}$

6. $\dfrac{2}{5} - \dfrac{3}{7} = \dfrac{14}{35} - \dfrac{15}{35} = \dfrac{14-15}{35} = -\dfrac{1}{35}$

7. $4\dfrac{1}{4} + 3\dfrac{7}{8} = 4\dfrac{2}{8} + 3\dfrac{7}{8} = 7\dfrac{9}{8} = 8\dfrac{1}{8}$

8. $-\dfrac{5}{12} + \dfrac{11}{16} = -\dfrac{20}{48} + \dfrac{33}{48} = \dfrac{-20+33}{48} = \dfrac{13}{48}$

9. $\dfrac{7}{8} \cdot \dfrac{3}{14} = \dfrac{\overset{1}{\cancel{7}} \cdot 3}{8 \cdot \underset{2}{\cancel{14}}} = \dfrac{3}{16}$

10. $5 \cdot \left(-3\dfrac{1}{4}\right) = 5 \cdot \left(-\dfrac{13}{4}\right) = \dfrac{5 \cdot (-13)}{4} = -\dfrac{65}{4} = -16\dfrac{1}{4}$

11. $-\dfrac{5}{18} \cdot 1\dfrac{1}{3} = -\dfrac{5}{18} \cdot \dfrac{4}{3} = \dfrac{-5 \cdot \overset{2}{\cancel{4}}}{\underset{9}{\cancel{18}} \cdot 3} = -\dfrac{10}{27}$

12. $-1\dfrac{3}{5} \cdot \left(-2\dfrac{1}{4}\right) = -\dfrac{8}{5} \cdot \left(-\dfrac{9}{4}\right)$

$$= \dfrac{\overset{-2}{\cancel{-8}} \cdot (-9)}{5 \cdot \underset{1}{\cancel{4}}}$$

$$= \dfrac{18}{5}$$

$$= 3\dfrac{3}{5}$$

13. $\dfrac{5}{9} \div 2 = \dfrac{5}{9} \div \dfrac{2}{1} = \dfrac{5}{9} \cdot \dfrac{1}{2} = \dfrac{5 \cdot 1}{9 \cdot 2} = \dfrac{5}{18}$

14. $-\dfrac{7}{12} \div \dfrac{2}{3} = -\dfrac{7}{12} \cdot \dfrac{3}{2} = \dfrac{-7 \cdot \overset{1}{\cancel{3}}}{\underset{4}{\cancel{12}} \cdot 2} = -\dfrac{7}{8}$

15. $4\dfrac{1}{8} \div \left(-1\dfrac{1}{3}\right) = \dfrac{33}{8} \div \left(-\dfrac{4}{3}\right)$

$$= \dfrac{33}{8} \cdot \left(-\dfrac{3}{4}\right)$$

$$= \dfrac{33 \cdot (-3)}{8 \cdot 4}$$

$$= -\dfrac{99}{32}$$

$$= -3\dfrac{3}{32}$$

16. $-2\dfrac{1}{2} \div (-10) = -\dfrac{5}{2} \div \left(-\dfrac{10}{1}\right)$

$$= -\dfrac{5}{2} \cdot \left(-\dfrac{1}{10}\right)$$

$$= \dfrac{\overset{1}{\cancel{5}} \cdot 1}{2 \cdot (\underset{2}{\cancel{-10}})}$$

$$= \dfrac{1}{4}$$

17.
$$\begin{array}{r} 0.384 \\ 125\overline{)48.000} \\ \underline{37\ 5} \\ 10\ 50 \\ \underline{10\ 00} \\ 500 \\ \underline{500} \\ 0 \end{array}$$

$-\dfrac{48}{125} = -0.384$

18.
$$\begin{array}{r} 0.91\overline{6} \\ 12\overline{)11.000} \\ \underline{10\ 8} \\ 20 \\ \underline{12} \\ 80 \\ \underline{72} \\ 8 \end{array}$$

$4\dfrac{11}{12} = 4.91\overline{6}$

19. $-0.28 = -\dfrac{28}{100} = -\dfrac{7}{25}$

20. Let $x = 0.7272\ldots$. Then

$$\begin{array}{r} 100x = 72.72\ldots \\ -\quad\ \ x = \ \ 0.72\ldots \end{array}$$

$99x = 72 \longrightarrow x = \dfrac{72}{99} = \dfrac{8}{11}$

So, $0.\overline{72} = \dfrac{8}{11}$.

21. $0.006 = \dfrac{6}{1000} = \dfrac{3}{500}$

22. $-8.34 = -8\dfrac{34}{100} = -8\dfrac{17}{50}$

Extra Practice, *continued*

23.
```
   0.875
8)7.000
  6 4
   60
   56
   40
   40
    0
```

$3\frac{7}{8} = 3.875$

24.
```
     0.064
250)16.000
    15 00
     1 000
     1 000
         0
```

$-\frac{16}{250} = -0.064$

25. $-\frac{7}{3} = -2.\overline{3}$

$-2\frac{5}{12} = -2.41\overline{6}$

$-2\frac{2}{5} = -2.4$

The numbers from least to greatest are -2.5, -2.43, $-2\frac{5}{12}$, $-2\frac{2}{5}$, and $-\frac{7}{3}$.

26. $\frac{18}{5} = 3.6$

$3\frac{1}{3} = 3.\overline{3}$

$3\frac{7}{12} = 3.58\overline{3}$

The numbers from least to greatest are $3\frac{1}{3}$, 3.55, $3\frac{7}{12}$, $\frac{18}{5}$, and 3.8.

27. $\frac{26}{5} = 5.2$

$5\frac{2}{9} = 5.\overline{2}$

$5\frac{3}{8} = 5.375$

The numbers from least to greatest are $\frac{26}{5}$, 5.21, $5\frac{2}{9}$, 5.3, and $5\frac{3}{8}$.

28. $-4\frac{1}{6} = -4.1\overline{6}$

$-\frac{59}{14} \approx -4.214$

$-4\frac{3}{7} \approx -4.429$

The numbers from least to greatest are $-4\frac{3}{7}$, $-\frac{59}{14}$, -4.2, $-4\frac{1}{6}$, and -4.04.

29. $7.21 + (-3.4) = 3.81$

30. $-9.8 + (-3.7) = -13.5$

31. $0.8 - (-12.3) = 0.8 + 12.3 = 13.1$

32. $8.217 - 9.68 = 8.217 + (-9.68) = -1.463$

33. $-10.2 + (-6.35) = -16.55$

34. $-8.78 + 3.9 = -4.88$

35. $3.28 - 11.395 = 3.28 + (-11.395) = -8.115$

36. $-0.04 - 5.789 = -0.04 + (-5.789) = -5.829$

37.
```
   8.32
× 0.47
  5824
3 328
3.9104
```

$-8.32 \cdot (-0.47) = 3.9104$

38.
```
    20.51
×   3.14
   8204
  2 051
 61 53
64.4014
```

$-20.51 \cdot 3.14 = -64.4014$

39.
```
          1.5
0.29)0.43 5
      29
      14 5
      14 5
         0
```

$0.435 \div 0.29 = 1.5$

40.
```
          2.8
0.74)2.07 2
      1 48
       59 2
       59 2
          0
```

$2.072 \div (-0.74) = -2.8$

41.
```
   6.78
×  4.7
 4 746
27 12
31.866
```

$4.7 \cdot (-6.78) = -31.866$

42.
```
   9.43
× 0.14
 3772
  943
1.3202
```

$-0.14 \cdot (-9.43) = 1.3202$

43.
```
            8.2
2.35)19.27 0
      18 80
        47 0
        47 0
           0
```

$-19.27 \div 2.35 = -8.2$

44.
```
         0.04
5.6)0.2 24
     2 24
        0
```

$0.224 \div 5.6 = 0.04$

Extra Practice, *continued*

45. Sum of times

$= 24 + 37 + 57 + 81 + 31 + 25 + 43 + 39 + 33 + 40 + 34 + 65 + 50$

$= 559$

Mean $= \dfrac{559}{13} = 43$

Times from least to greatest: 24, 25, 31, 33, 34, 37, 39, 40, 43, 50, 57, 65, 81

Median $= 39$

Mode $=$ none

Range $= 81 - 24 = 57$

46. Sum of temperatures

$= -6 + (-7) + (-6) + 5 + 3 + 0 + (-3)$

$= -14$

Mean $= \dfrac{-14}{7} = -2$

Temperatures from least to greatest: $-7, -6, -6, -3, 0, 3, 5$

Median $= -3$

Mode $= -6$

Range $= 5 - (-7) = 5 + 7 = 12$

47. Sum of grades

$= 93 + 84 + 100 + 95 + 89 + 78 + 78 + 85 + 83 + 95$

$= 880$

Mean $= \dfrac{880}{10} = 88$

Grades from least to greatest: 78, 78, 83, 84, 85, 89, 93, 95, 95, 100

Median $= \dfrac{85 + 89}{2} = \dfrac{174}{2} = 87$

Modes $= 78$ and 95

Range $= 100 - 78 = 22$

Chapter 6 Extra Practice (p. 806)

1. $6k - 8 - 4k = 6$

$2k - 8 = 6$

$2k = 14$

$k = 7$

Check: $6(7) - 8 - 4(7) \stackrel{?}{=} 6$

$42 - 8 - 28 \stackrel{?}{=} 6$

$34 - 28 \stackrel{?}{=} 6$

$6 = 6 \checkmark$

2. $16 = 2(s + 9) - 4$

$16 = 2s + 18 - 4$

$16 = 2s + 14$

$2 = 2s$

$1 = s$

Check: $16 \stackrel{?}{=} 2(1 + 9) - 4$

$16 \stackrel{?}{=} 2(10) - 4$

$16 \stackrel{?}{=} 20 - 4$

$16 = 16 \checkmark$

3. $5(n + 7) + 1 = -9$

$5n + 35 + 1 = -9$

$5n + 36 = -9$

$5n = -45$

$n = -9$

Check: $5(-9 + 7) + 1 \stackrel{?}{=} -9$

$5(-2) + 1 \stackrel{?}{=} -9$

$-10 + 1 \stackrel{?}{=} -9$

$-9 = -9 \checkmark$

4. $-8 = -3m + 2 + 5m$

$-8 = 2m + 2$

$-10 = 2m$

$-5 = m$

Check: $-8 \stackrel{?}{=} -3(-5) + 2 + 5(-5)$

$-8 \stackrel{?}{=} 15 + 2 + (-25)$

$-8 \stackrel{?}{=} 17 + (-25)$

$-8 = -8 \checkmark$

5. $\dfrac{7a - 2}{3} = 4$

$7a - 2 = 12$

$7a = 14$

$a = 2$

Check: $\dfrac{7(2) - 2}{3} \stackrel{?}{=} 4$

$\dfrac{14 - 2}{3} \stackrel{?}{=} 4$

$\dfrac{12}{3} \stackrel{?}{=} 4$

$4 = 4 \checkmark$

6. $2 = \dfrac{3 - 4t}{5}$

$10 = 3 - 4t$

$7 = -4t$

$-\dfrac{7}{4} = t$

$-1\dfrac{3}{4} = t$

Check: $2 \stackrel{?}{=} \dfrac{3 - 4\left(-\frac{7}{4}\right)}{5}$

$2 \stackrel{?}{=} \dfrac{3 - (-7)}{5}$

$2 \stackrel{?}{=} \dfrac{3 + 7}{5}$

$2 \stackrel{?}{=} \dfrac{10}{5}$

$2 = 2 \checkmark$

Extra Practice, *continued*

7. $3a + 2 = 7a + 10$

$\qquad 2 = 4a + 10$

$\qquad -8 = 4a$

$\qquad -2 = a$

Check: $3(-2) + 2 \overset{?}{=} 7(-2) + 10$

$\qquad -6 + 2 \overset{?}{=} -14 + 10$

$\qquad\qquad -4 = -4\ ✓$

8. $9y - 8 = 6y + 7$

$\qquad 3y - 8 = 7$

$\qquad\ \ 3y = 15$

$\qquad\ \ y = 5$

Check: $9(5) - 8 \overset{?}{=} 6(5) + 7$

$\qquad 45 - 8 \overset{?}{=} 30 + 7$

$\qquad\quad 37 = 37\ ✓$

9. $5x + 7 = 8(x - 1)$

$\quad 5x + 7 = 8x - 8$

$\qquad\ \ 7 = 3x - 8$

$\qquad 15 = 3x$

$\qquad\ \ 5 = x$

Check: $5(5) + 7 \overset{?}{=} 8(5 - 1)$

$\qquad 25 + 7 \overset{?}{=} 8(4)$

$\qquad\quad 32 = 32\ ✓$

10. $13v = 7(9 - v)$

$\quad 13v = 63 - 7v$

$\quad 20v = 63$

$\qquad v = 3.15$

Check: $13(3.15) \overset{?}{=} 7(9 - 3.15)$

$\qquad 40.95 \overset{?}{=} 7(5.85)$

$\qquad 40.95 = 40.95\ ✓$

11. $5(w + 3) = -10w$

$\quad 5w + 15 = -10w$

$\qquad\ \ 15 = -15w$

$\qquad\ -1 = w$

Check: $5(-1 + 3) \overset{?}{=} -10(-1)$

$\qquad\quad 5(2) \overset{?}{=} 10$

$\qquad\quad\ 10 = 10\ ✓$

12. $2(z + 5) = 3z + 14$

$\quad 2z + 10 = 3z + 14$

$\qquad\ \ -4 = z$

Check: $2(-4 + 5) \overset{?}{=} 3(-4) + 14$

$\qquad\quad 2(1) \overset{?}{=} -12 + 14$

$\qquad\qquad 2 = 2\ ✓$

13. $2.8y + 8.6 = 9.12 - 1.2y$

$\qquad 4y + 8.6 = 9.12$

$\qquad\quad 4y = 0.52$

$\qquad\quad y = 0.13$

Check: $2.8(0.13) + 8.6 \overset{?}{=} 9.12 - 1.2(0.13)$

$\qquad 0.364 + 8.6 \overset{?}{=} 9.12 - 0.156$

$\qquad\qquad 8.964 = 8.964\ ✓$

14. $7.25p - 3 + p = 14.325$

$\qquad 8.25p - 3 = 14.325$

$\qquad\quad 8.25p = 17.325$

$\qquad\qquad p = 2.1$

Check: $7.25(2.1) - 3 + 2.1 \overset{?}{=} 14.325$

$\qquad 15.225 - 3 + 2.1 \overset{?}{=} 14.325$

$\qquad 12.225 + 2.1 \overset{?}{=} 14.325$

$\qquad\qquad 14.325 = 14.325\ ✓$

15. $7 - 2.65z = -4.4z$

$\qquad 7 = -1.75z$

$\qquad -4 = z$

Check: $7 - 2.65(-4) \overset{?}{=} -4.4(-4)$

$\qquad 7 + 10.6 \overset{?}{=} 17.6$

$\qquad\quad 17.6 = 17.6\ ✓$

16. $x - \dfrac{2}{3}x = \dfrac{3}{4}$

$\qquad \dfrac{1}{3}x = \dfrac{3}{4}$

$\qquad\ \ x = \dfrac{9}{4} = 2\dfrac{1}{4}$

Check: $\dfrac{9}{4} - \dfrac{2}{3}\left(\dfrac{9}{4}\right) \overset{?}{=} \dfrac{3}{4}$

$\qquad \dfrac{9}{4} - \dfrac{6}{4} \overset{?}{=} \dfrac{3}{4}$

$\qquad\quad \dfrac{3}{4} = \dfrac{3}{4}\ ✓$

17. $\dfrac{9}{10}n + \dfrac{1}{5} = \dfrac{7}{10}n - \dfrac{3}{5}$

$\qquad \dfrac{2}{10}n + \dfrac{1}{5} = -\dfrac{3}{5}$

$\qquad\quad \dfrac{2}{10}n = -\dfrac{4}{5}$

$\qquad\quad\ \dfrac{1}{5}n = -\dfrac{4}{5}$

$\qquad\qquad n = -4$

Check: $\dfrac{9}{10}(-4) + \dfrac{1}{5} \overset{?}{=} \dfrac{7}{10}(-4) - \dfrac{3}{5}$

$\qquad -\dfrac{36}{10} + \dfrac{1}{5} \overset{?}{=} -\dfrac{28}{10} - \dfrac{3}{5}$

$\qquad -\dfrac{18}{5} + \dfrac{1}{5} \overset{?}{=} -\dfrac{14}{5} - \dfrac{3}{5}$

$\qquad\qquad -\dfrac{17}{5} = -\dfrac{17}{5}\ ✓$

Extra Practice, continued

18. $\frac{6}{4}r - \frac{21}{8} = \frac{3}{4}r$

$-\frac{21}{8} = -\frac{3}{4}r$

$-\frac{4}{3}\left(-\frac{21}{8}\right) = r$

$\frac{7}{2} = r$

$3\frac{1}{2} = r$

Check: $\frac{6}{4}\left(\frac{7}{2}\right) - \frac{21}{8} \stackrel{?}{=} \frac{3}{4}\left(\frac{7}{2}\right)$

$\frac{42}{8} - \frac{21}{8} \stackrel{?}{=} \frac{21}{8}$

$\frac{21}{8} = \frac{21}{8}$ ✓

19. $r = \frac{d}{2}$

$r = \frac{9}{2}$

$r = 4.5$ cm

20. $C = 2\pi r = 2\pi \cdot 14 \approx 2\left(\frac{22}{7}\right)(14) = 2(22)(2) = 88$ ft

Because the radius is a multiple of 7, $\frac{22}{7}$ was used for π.

21. $C = 2\pi r$

$44 = 2\pi r$

$\frac{44}{2\pi} = r$

$\frac{22}{\pi} = r$

$22 \div \frac{22}{7} \approx r$

$22 \cdot \frac{7}{22} = r$

7 yd $= r$

Because the circumference is a multiple of 22, $\frac{22}{7}$ was used for π.

22. $C = \pi d$

$15.7 = \pi d$

$\frac{15.7}{\pi} = d$

$\frac{15.7}{3.14} \approx d$

5 in. $= d$

Because the circumference is a multiple of 3.14, 3.14 was used for π.

23. $19 - 8c > 3$

$-8c > -16$

$c < 2$

24. $2(7 + n) \le -10$

$14 + 2n \le -10$

$2n \le -24$

$n \le -12$

25. $5s + 3 \ge -7 - 5s$

$10s + 3 \ge -7$

$10s \ge -10$

$s \ge -1$

26. $20 - 11x \ge -2$

$-11x \ge -22$

$x \le 2$

27. $4(b - 3) > 20$

$4b - 12 > 20$

$4b > 32$

$b > 8$

28. $-6y - 13 < 11 + 2y$

$-13 < 11 + 8y$

$-24 < 8y$

$-3 < y$

29. $\frac{1}{2}n + 12 \le 8$

$\frac{1}{2}n \le -4$

$n \le -8$

30. $3n - 2 > 7$

$3n > 9$

$n > 3$

31. $4n \ge 16$

$n \ge 4$

32. $\frac{18}{6n} < 3$

$18 < 18n$

$\frac{18}{18} < \frac{18n}{18}$

$1 < n$

33. Let $t =$ amount of time spent biking.

Distance traveled so far + Speed • Time ≥ 28

$10 + 12t \ge 28$

$12t \ge 18$

$t \ge 1.5$

You must bike for at least 1.5 hours.

Extra Practice, *continued*

34. Let t = number of tickets Nathan can buy.

$$\text{Amount spent on entrance fee} + \text{Cost of ticket} \cdot \text{Number of tickets} \le 20$$

$$10 + 0.75t \le 20$$
$$0.75t \le 10$$
$$t \le 13.\overline{3}$$

Nathan can buy 13 tickets.

Chapter 7 Extra Practice (p. 807)

1. $\dfrac{\text{Wins}}{\text{Losses}} = \dfrac{12}{4} = \dfrac{3}{1}$

Two other ways to write the ratio $\dfrac{3}{1}$ are $3:1$ and 3 to 1.

2. Games played $= 12 + 4 + 2 = 18$

$\dfrac{\text{Losses}}{\text{Games played}} = \dfrac{4}{18} = \dfrac{2}{9}$

Two other ways to write the ratio $\dfrac{2}{9}$ are $2:9$ and 2 to 9.

3. $\dfrac{\text{Wins}}{\text{Games played}} = \dfrac{12}{18} = \dfrac{2}{3}$

Two other ways to write the ratio $\dfrac{2}{3}$ are $2:3$ and 2 to 3.

4. $\dfrac{9000 \text{ tickets}}{6 \text{ hours}} = \dfrac{(9000 \div 6) \text{ tickets}}{(6 \div 6) \text{ hours}} = \dfrac{1500 \text{ tickets}}{\text{hour}}$

5. $\dfrac{240 \text{ tickets}}{\text{hour}} = \dfrac{\overset{4}{\cancel{240}} \text{ tickets}}{\cancel{\text{hour}}} \cdot \dfrac{1 \text{ hour}}{\underset{1}{\cancel{60}} \text{ minutes}} = \dfrac{4 \text{ tickets}}{\text{minute}}$

6. $\dfrac{7 \text{ meters}}{\text{second}} = \dfrac{7 \text{ meters}}{\cancel{\text{second}}} \cdot \dfrac{60 \cancel{\text{ seconds}}}{1 \text{ minute}} = \dfrac{420 \text{ meters}}{\text{minute}}$

7. $\dfrac{x}{18} = \dfrac{25}{2}$

$18 \cdot \dfrac{x}{18} = 18 \cdot \dfrac{25}{2}$

$x = \dfrac{\overset{9}{\cancel{18}} \cdot 25}{\underset{1}{\cancel{2}}}$

$x = 225$

Check: $\dfrac{225}{18} \overset{?}{=} \dfrac{25}{2}$

$225 \cdot 2 \overset{?}{=} 18 \cdot 25$

$450 = 450$ ✓

8. $\dfrac{4}{9} = \dfrac{5}{y}$

$4y = 9(5)$

$4y = 45$

$y = 11.25$

Check: $\dfrac{4}{9} \overset{?}{=} \dfrac{5}{11.25}$

$4(11.25) \overset{?}{=} 9(5)$

$45 = 45$ ✓

9. $\dfrac{3.6}{n} = \dfrac{4.8}{12.4}$

$12.4 \cdot 3.6 = 4.8n$

$44.64 = 4.8n$

$9.3 = n$

Check: $\dfrac{3.6}{9.3} \overset{?}{=} \dfrac{4.8}{12.4}$

$3.6(12.4) \overset{?}{=} 4.8(9.3)$

$44.64 = 44.64$ ✓

10. $\dfrac{m}{6} = \dfrac{35}{42}$

$6 \cdot \dfrac{m}{6} = 6 \cdot \dfrac{35}{42}$

$m = \dfrac{\overset{1}{\cancel{6}} \cdot \overset{5}{\cancel{35}}}{\underset{7}{\cancel{42}}}$

$m = 5$

Check: $\dfrac{5}{6} \overset{?}{=} \dfrac{35}{42}$

$5(42) \overset{?}{=} 6(35)$

$210 = 210$ ✓

11. $\dfrac{a}{b} = \dfrac{p}{100}$

$\dfrac{9}{75} = \dfrac{p}{100}$

$100 \cdot \dfrac{9}{75} = 100 \cdot \dfrac{p}{100}$

$12 = p$

9 is 12% of 75.

12. $\dfrac{a}{b} = \dfrac{p}{100}$

$\dfrac{42}{b} = \dfrac{25}{100}$

$4200 = 25b$

$168 = b$

42 is 25% of 168.

13. $\dfrac{a}{b} = \dfrac{p}{100}$

$\dfrac{a}{128} = \dfrac{7}{100}$

$128 \cdot \dfrac{a}{128} = 128 \cdot \dfrac{7}{100}$

$a = 8.96$

8.96 is 7% of 128.

Extra Practice, *continued*

14. $\dfrac{a}{b} = \dfrac{p}{100}$

$\dfrac{7}{56} = \dfrac{p}{100}$

$100 \cdot \dfrac{7}{56} = 100 \cdot \dfrac{p}{100}$

$12.5 = p$

7 is 12.5% of 56.

15. $0.125 = \dfrac{125}{1000} = \dfrac{12.5}{100} = 12.5\%$

16. $1.42 = \dfrac{142}{100} = 142\%$

17. $\dfrac{18}{25} = \dfrac{18 \cdot 4}{25 \cdot 4} = \dfrac{72}{100} = 72\%$

18. $\dfrac{197}{200} = \dfrac{197 \div 2}{200 \div 2} = \dfrac{98.5}{100} = 98.5\%$

19. $31\% = 0.31$

$31\% = \dfrac{31}{100}$

20. $55\% = 0.55$

$55\% = \dfrac{55}{100} = \dfrac{11}{20}$

21. $175\% = 1.75$

$175\% = \dfrac{175}{100} = \dfrac{7}{4}$

22. $1.28\% = 0.0128$

$1.28\% = \dfrac{1.28}{100} = \dfrac{128}{10,000} = \dfrac{8}{625}$

23. The change is an increase.

$p = \dfrac{28 - 25}{25} = \dfrac{3}{25} = 0.12$

The percent of change is 12%.

24. The change is a decrease.

$p = \dfrac{144 - 126}{144} = \dfrac{18}{144} = 0.125$

The percent of change is 12.5%.

25. The change is a decrease.

$p = \dfrac{5000 - 4950}{5000} = \dfrac{50}{5000} = 0.01$

The percent of change is 1%.

26. Markup = 110% of $28 = 1.1(28) = 30.8$

Retail price $= 28 + 30.8 = 58.8$

The retail price is $58.80.

27. Tip = 15% of $18.40 = 0.15(18.4) = 2.76$

Sales tax = 5% of $18.40 = 0.05(18.4) = 0.92$

Total cost $= 18.4 + 2.76 + 0.92 = 22.08$

The total cost of the meal is $22.08.

28. $a = p\% \cdot b$

$a = 121\% \cdot 412$

$a = 1.21 \cdot 412$

$a = 498.52$

498.52 is 121% of 412.

29. $a = p\% \cdot b$

$13 = 15.6\% \cdot b$

$13 = 0.156 \cdot b$

$83.\overline{3} = b$

13 is 15.6% of $83.\overline{3}$.

30. $a = p\% \cdot b$

$57 = p \cdot 76$

$\dfrac{57}{76} = p$

$0.75 = p$

57 is 75% of 76.

31. $a = p\% \cdot b$

$a = 0.3\% \cdot 28$

$a = 0.003 \cdot 28$

$a = 0.084$

0.084 is 0.3% of 28%.

32. Number of slips greater than 4 = 8

Probability $= \dfrac{\text{Number of slips greater than 4}}{\text{Total number of slips}} = \dfrac{8}{12} = \dfrac{2}{3}$

The probability of drawing a number greater than 4 is $\dfrac{2}{3}$.

33. Number of slips divisible by 5 = 2

Probability $= \dfrac{\text{Number of slips divisible by 5}}{\text{Total number of slips}} = \dfrac{2}{12} = \dfrac{1}{6}$

The probability of drawing a number that is divisible by 5 is $\dfrac{1}{6}$.

Chapter 8 Extra Practice (p. 808)

1. $m\angle 1 = 90° - 40° = 50°$

2. $m\angle 2 = 180° - 38° = 142°$

$m\angle 3 = 38°$

$m\angle 4 = m\angle 2 = 142°$

3. $m\angle 5 = 50°$

$m\angle 6 = 50°$

$m\angle 7 = 180° - 50° = 130°$

4. $x° + 60° + 60° = 180°$

$x + 120 = 180$

$x = 60$

The triangle is acute.

5. $x° + 55° + 35° = 180°$

$x + 90 = 180$

$x = 90$

The triangle is right.

6. $x° + 42° + 42° = 180°$

$x + 84 = 180$

$x = 96$

The triangle is obtuse.

7. The quadrilateral is a rhombus.

Extra Practice, *continued*

8. The quadrilateral is a rectangle.

9. The quadrilateral is a trapezoid.

10. Sum of angle measures in an 11-gon = 180(11 − 2)

$$= 180(9)$$
$$= 1620$$

The sum of the angle measures in an 11-gon is 1620°.

11. Sum of angle measures in an 18-gon = 180(18 − 2)

$$= 180(16)$$
$$= 2880$$

Measure of one angle in a regular 18-gon = 2880 ÷ 18

$$= 160$$

The measure of one angle in a regular 18-gon is 160°.

12. $\overline{AB} \cong \overline{PQ}$; $\overline{BC} \cong \overline{QR}$; $\overline{AC} \cong \overline{PR}$

13. $\angle A \cong \angle P$; $\angle B \cong \angle Q$; $\angle C \cong \angle R$

14. By Angle-Side-Angle, $\triangle ABC \cong \triangle PQR$.

15.

(x, y)	$\longrightarrow$	$(x, -y)$
$A(-2, 4)$	$\longrightarrow$	$A'(-2, -4)$
$B(0, 2)$	$\longrightarrow$	$B'(0, -2)$
$C(-2, -6)$	$\longrightarrow$	$C'(-2, 6)$

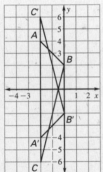

16.

(x, y)	$\longrightarrow$	$(-x, y)$
$A(-2, 4)$	$\longrightarrow$	$A'(2, 4)$
$B(0, 2)$	$\longrightarrow$	$B'(0, 2)$
$C(-2, -6)$	$\longrightarrow$	$C'(2, -6)$

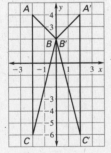

17.

(x, y)	$\longrightarrow$	$(x - 1, y + 4)$
$A(-2, 4)$	$\longrightarrow$	$A'(-3, 8)$
$B(0, 2)$	$\longrightarrow$	$B'(-1, 6)$
$C(-2, -6)$	$\longrightarrow$	$C'(-3, -2)$

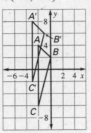

18.

(x, y)	$\longrightarrow$	$(x + 2, y - 3)$
$A(-2, 4)$	$\longrightarrow$	$A'(0, 1)$
$B(0, 2)$	$\longrightarrow$	$B'(2, -1)$
$C(-2, -6)$	$\longrightarrow$	$C'(0, -9)$

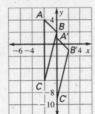

19. $(x, y) \rightarrow (y, -x)$

$A(-2, 4)$	$\longrightarrow$	$A'(4, 2)$
$B(0, 2)$	$\longrightarrow$	$B'(2, 0)$
$C(-2, -6)$	$\longrightarrow$	$C'(-6, 2)$

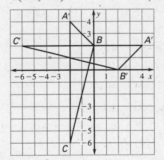

20.

(x, y)	$\longrightarrow$	$(2x, 2y)$
$A(-2, 4)$	$\longrightarrow$	$A'(-4, 8)$
$B(0, 2)$	$\longrightarrow$	$B'(0, 4)$
$C(-2, -6)$	$\longrightarrow$	$C'(-4, -12)$

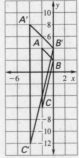

Extra Practice, continued

21.

$$(x, y) \longrightarrow \left(\tfrac{1}{2}x, \tfrac{1}{2}y\right)$$

$$A(-2, 4) \longrightarrow A'(-1, 2)$$
$$B(0, 2) \longrightarrow B'(0, 1)$$
$$C(-2, -6) \longrightarrow C'(-1, -3)$$

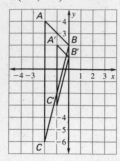

Chapter 9 Extra Practice (p. 809)

1. $\sqrt{52} \approx 7.2$

2. $\sqrt{9.6} \approx 3.1$

3. $-\sqrt{738} \approx -27.2$

4. $-\sqrt{2037} \approx -45.1$

5. $k^2 = 900$

$k = \pm\sqrt{900}$

$k = \pm 30$

Check: $k = -30$: $(-30)^2 \stackrel{?}{=} 900$

$900 = 900 ✓$

$k = 30$: $30^2 \stackrel{?}{=} 900$

$900 = 900 ✓$

6. $h^2 - 5 = 44$

$h^2 = 49$

$h = \pm\sqrt{49}$

$h = \pm 7$

Check: $h = -7$: $(-7)^2 - 5 \stackrel{?}{=} 44$

$49 - 5 \stackrel{?}{=} 44$

$44 = 44 ✓$

$h = 7$: $7^2 - 5 \stackrel{?}{=} 44$

$49 - 5 \stackrel{?}{=} 44$

$44 = 44 ✓$

7. $153 + z^2 = 378$

$z^2 = 225$

$z = \pm\sqrt{225}$

$z = \pm 15$

Check: $z = -15$: $153 + (-15)^2 \stackrel{?}{=} 378$

$153 + 225 \stackrel{?}{=} 378$

$378 = 378 ✓$

$z = 15$: $153 + (15)^2 \stackrel{?}{=} 378$

$153 + 225 \stackrel{?}{=} 378$

$378 = 378 ✓$

8. $168 = v^2 - 1$

$169 = v^2$

$\pm\sqrt{169} = v$

$\pm 13 = v$

Check: $v = -13$: $168 \stackrel{?}{=} (-13)^2 - 1$

$168 \stackrel{?}{=} 169 - 1$

$168 = 168 ✓$

$v = 13$: $168 \stackrel{?}{=} 13^2 - 1$

$168 \stackrel{?}{=} 169 - 1$

$168 = 168 ✓$

9. $a^2 + 7 = 88$

$a^2 = 81$

$a = \pm\sqrt{81}$

$a = \pm 9$

Check: $a = -9$: $(-9)^2 + 7 \stackrel{?}{=} 88$

$81 + 7 \stackrel{?}{=} 88$

$88 = 88 ✓$

$a = 9$: $9^2 + 7 \stackrel{?}{=} 88$

$81 + 7 \stackrel{?}{=} 88$

$88 = 88 ✓$

10. $m^2 = 3600$

$m = \pm\sqrt{3600}$

$m = \pm 60$

Check: $m = -60$: $(-60)^2 \stackrel{?}{=} 3600$

$3600 = 3600 ✓$

$m = 60$: $60^2 \stackrel{?}{=} 3600$

$3600 = 3600 ✓$

11. $x^2 - 11 = 53$

$x^2 = 64$

$x = \pm\sqrt{64}$

$x = \pm 8$

Check: $x = -8$: $(-8)^2 - 11 \stackrel{?}{=} 53$

$64 - 11 \stackrel{?}{=} 53$

$53 = 53 ✓$

$x = 8$: $8^2 - 11 \stackrel{?}{=} 53$

$64 - 11 \stackrel{?}{=} 53$

$53 = 53 ✓$

12. $w^2 + 78 = 478$

$w^2 = 400$

$w = \pm\sqrt{400}$

$w = \pm 20$

Check: $w = -20$: $(-20)^2 + 78 \stackrel{?}{=} 478$

$400 + 78 \stackrel{?}{=} 478$

$478 = 478 ✓$

$w = 20$: $20^2 + 78 \stackrel{?}{=} 478$

$400 + 78 \stackrel{?}{=} 478$

$478 = 478 ✓$

13.

$\sqrt{18} \approx 4.24$

3.8 3.9 4.0 4.1 4.2 4.3 4.4

4    $\sqrt{18} \approx 4.24$

$\sqrt{18} > 4$

14.

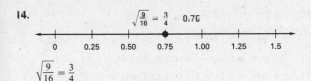

$$\sqrt{\frac{9}{16}} = \frac{3}{4}$$

15.

$$-8 > -\sqrt{70}$$

16.

$$\frac{2}{3} > \sqrt{\frac{1}{9}}$$

17. The decimals from least to greatest are $0.\overline{1}$, 0.12, $0.\overline{12}$, 0.123, and $0.\overline{123}$.

18. The decimals from least to greatest are $0.\overline{3}$, 0.334, 0.34, and $0.\overline{34}$.

19.
$$a^2 + b^2 = c^2$$
$$21^2 + 28^2 = c^2$$
$$441 + 784 = c^2$$
$$1225 = c^2$$
$$\sqrt{1225} = c$$
$$35 = c$$

20.
$$a^2 + b^2 = c^2$$
$$a^2 + 63^2 = 65^2$$
$$a^2 + 3969 = 4225$$
$$a^2 = 256$$
$$a = \sqrt{256}$$
$$a = 16$$

21.
$$a^2 + b^2 = c^2$$
$$56^2 + b^2 = 65^2$$
$$3136 + b^2 = 4225$$
$$b^2 = 1089$$
$$b = \sqrt{1089}$$
$$b = 33$$

22.
$$a^2 + b^2 = c^2$$
$$1.5^2 + 3.6^2 = c^2$$
$$2.25 + 12.96 = c^2$$
$$15.21 = c^2$$
$$\sqrt{15.21} = c$$
$$3.9 = c$$

23.
$$a^2 + b^2 = c^2$$
$$a^2 + 100^2 = 125^2$$
$$a^2 + 10{,}000 = 15{,}625$$
$$a^2 = 5625$$
$$a = \sqrt{5625}$$
$$a = 75$$

24.
$$a^2 + b^2 = c^2$$
$$32^2 + b^2 = 68^2$$
$$1024 + b^2 = 4624$$
$$b^2 = 3600$$
$$b = \sqrt{3600}$$
$$b = 60$$

25.
$$a^2 + b^2 = c^2$$
$$40^2 + 42^2 \stackrel{?}{=} 58^2$$
$$1600 + 1764 \stackrel{?}{=} 3364$$
$$3364 = 3364$$
The numbers form a Pythagorean triple.

26.
$$a^2 + b^2 = c^2$$
$$37^2 + 39^2 \stackrel{?}{=} 54^2$$
$$1369 + 1521 \stackrel{?}{=} 2916$$
$$2890 \neq 2916$$
The numbers do not form a Pythagorean triple.

27.
$$a^2 + b^2 = c^2$$
$$15^2 + 112^2 \stackrel{?}{=} 113^2$$
$$225 + 12{,}544 \stackrel{?}{=} 12{,}769$$
$$12{,}769 = 12{,}769$$
The numbers form a Pythagorean triple.

28.
$$a^2 + b^2 = c^2$$
$$12^2 + 35^2 \stackrel{?}{=} 38^2$$
$$144 + 1225 \stackrel{?}{=} 1444$$
$$1369 \neq 1444$$
The numbers do not form a Pythagorean triple.

29. hypotenuse $= \text{leg} \cdot \sqrt{2} = 7\sqrt{2}$
$$x = 7\sqrt{2}$$
$$y = 7$$

30. hypotenuse $= 2 \cdot \text{shorter leg}$
$$18 = 2x$$
$$9 = x$$
longer leg $= \text{shorter leg} \cdot \sqrt{3}$
$$y = 9\sqrt{3}$$

31. hypotenuse $= 2 \cdot \text{shorter leg}$
$$y = 2 \cdot 19$$
$$y = 38$$
longer leg $= \text{shorter leg} \cdot \sqrt{3}$
$$x = 19\sqrt{3}$$

32. $\sin\angle A = \dfrac{\text{opposite}}{\text{hypotenuse}} = \dfrac{30}{34} = \dfrac{15}{17}$

$\cos\angle A = \dfrac{\text{adjacent}}{\text{hypotenuse}} = \dfrac{16}{34} = \dfrac{8}{17}$

$\tan\angle A = \dfrac{\text{opposite}}{\text{adjacent}} = \dfrac{30}{16} = \dfrac{15}{8}$

$\sin\angle B = \dfrac{\text{opposite}}{\text{hypotenuse}} = \dfrac{16}{34} = \dfrac{8}{17}$

$\cos\angle B = \dfrac{\text{adjacent}}{\text{hypotenuse}} = \dfrac{30}{34} = \dfrac{15}{17}$

$\tan\angle B = \dfrac{\text{opposite}}{\text{adjacent}} = \dfrac{16}{30} = \dfrac{8}{15}$

33. $\sin\angle A = \dfrac{\text{opposite}}{\text{hypotenuse}} = \dfrac{36}{85}$

$\cos\angle A = \dfrac{\text{adjacent}}{\text{hypotenuse}} = \dfrac{77}{85}$

$\tan\angle A = \dfrac{\text{opposite}}{\text{adjacent}} = \dfrac{36}{77}$

$\sin\angle B = \dfrac{\text{opposite}}{\text{hypotenuse}} = \dfrac{77}{85}$

$\cos\angle B = \dfrac{\text{adjacent}}{\text{hypotenuse}} = \dfrac{36}{85}$

$\tan\angle B = \dfrac{\text{opposite}}{\text{adjacent}} = \dfrac{77}{36}$

34. $\sin\angle A = \dfrac{\text{opposite}}{\text{hypotenuse}} = \dfrac{36}{39} = \dfrac{12}{13}$

$\cos\angle A = \dfrac{\text{adjacent}}{\text{hypotenuse}} = \dfrac{15}{39} = \dfrac{5}{13}$

$\tan\angle A = \dfrac{\text{opposite}}{\text{adjacent}} = \dfrac{36}{15} = \dfrac{12}{5}$

$\sin\angle B = \dfrac{\text{opposite}}{\text{hypotenuse}} = \dfrac{15}{39} = \dfrac{5}{13}$

$\cos\angle B = \dfrac{\text{adjacent}}{\text{hypotenuse}} = \dfrac{36}{39} = \dfrac{12}{13}$

$\tan\angle B = \dfrac{\text{opposite}}{\text{adjacent}} = \dfrac{15}{36} = \dfrac{5}{12}$

35. $\sin 62° \approx 0.8829$
$\cos 62° \approx 0.4695$
$\tan 62° \approx 1.8807$

Extra Practice, *continued*

1.
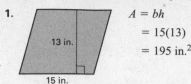

$A = bh$
$= 15(13)$
$= 195$ in.^{2}

The area is 195 square inches.

2.

$A = bh$
$= (9.4)(4.8)$
$= 45.12$ ft^2

The area is 45.12 square feet.

3.

$1\frac{1}{5}$ cm

$8\frac{1}{3}$ cm

$A = bh$

$= \left(8\frac{1}{3}\right)\left(1\frac{1}{5}\right)$

$= \left(\frac{25}{3}\right)\left(\frac{6}{5}\right)$

$= \dfrac{\overset{5}{\cancel{25}} \cdot \overset{2}{\cancel{6}}}{\underset{1}{\cancel{3}} \cdot \underset{1}{\cancel{5}}}$

$= 10$ cm^2

The area is 10 square centimeters.

4.

9 m

18 m

16 m

$A = \frac{1}{2}(b_1 + b_2)h$

$= \frac{1}{2}(9 + 16)(18)$

$= \frac{1}{2}(25)(18)$

$= 225$ m^2

The area is 225 square meters.

5.

40 yd

10.5 yd

28 yd

$A = \frac{1}{2}(b_1 + b_2)h$

$= \frac{1}{2}(40 + 28)10.5$

$= \frac{1}{2}(68)(10.5)$

$= 357$ yd^2

The area is 357 square yards.

6. $A = \pi r^2 \approx 3.14(18^2) = 3.14(324) = 1017.36$ mi^2

The area is about 1020 square miles.

7. $r = \frac{d}{2} = \frac{80}{2} = 40$

$A = \pi r^2 \approx 3.14(40^2) = 3.14(1600) = 5024$ in.^{2}

The area is about 5020 square inches.

8. $r = \frac{d}{2} = \frac{11}{2} = 5.5$

$A = \pi r^2 \approx 3.14(5.5^2) = 3.14(30.25) = 94.985$ mm^2

The area is about 95.0 square millimeters.

9. $A = \pi r^2 \approx 3.14(2.9^2) = 3.14(8.41) = 26.4074$ ft^2

The area is about 26.4 square feet.

10. $r = \frac{d}{2} = \frac{7.8}{2} = 3.9$

$A = \pi r^2 \approx 3.14(3.9^2) = 3.14(15.21) = 47.7594$ in.^{2}

The area is about 47.8 square inches.

11. $A = \pi r^2 \approx 3.14(0.3^2) = 3.14(0.09) = 0.2826$ cm^2

The area is about 0.283 square centimeters.

12. $A = \pi r^2 \approx 3.14(11^2) = 3.14(121) = 379.94$ ft^2

The area is about 380 square feet.

13. $r = \frac{d}{2} = \frac{16}{2} = 8$

$A = \pi r^2 \approx 3.14(8^2) = 3.14(64) = 200.96$ mi^2

The area is about 201 square miles.

14. A hexagonal pyramid has 7 faces, 12 edges, and 7 vertices.

15.
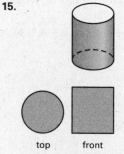

top   front

A cylinder is not a polyhedron.

16.
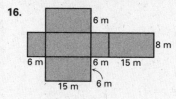

6 m

8 m

6 m   6 m   15 m

15 m   6 m

$S = 2B + Ph$

$= 2(15 \cdot 8) + (2 \cdot 15 + 2 \cdot 8)6$

$= 240 + 46(6)$

$= 240 + 276$

$= 516$ m^2

The surface area is 516 square meters.

17.
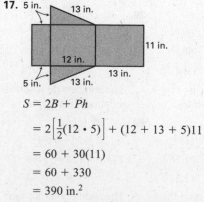

5 in.   13 in.

11 in.

12 in.

13 in.

5 in.   13 in.

$S = 2B + Ph$

$= 2\left[\frac{1}{2}(12 \cdot 5)\right] + (12 + 13 + 5)11$

$= 60 + 30(11)$

$= 60 + 330$

$= 390$ in.^{2}

The surface area is 390 square inches.

Extra Practice, *continued*

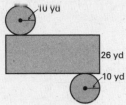

$$r = \frac{d}{2} = \frac{20}{2} = 10$$

$$S = 2\pi r^2 + 2\pi rh$$
$$= 2\pi(10^2) + 2\pi(10)(26)$$
$$= 200\pi + 520\pi$$
$$= 720\pi$$
$$\approx 2261.9 \text{ yd}^2$$

The surface area is about 2261.9 square yards.

19. $S = B + \frac{1}{2}P\ell$

$$= 12^2 + \frac{1}{2}(4 \cdot 12)9$$

$$= 144 + \frac{1}{2}(48)(9)$$

$$= 144 + 216$$

$$= 360 \text{ m}^2$$

The surface area is 360 square meters.

20. $S = \pi r^2 + \pi r\ell$
$$= \pi(8^2) + \pi(8)(9)$$
$$= 64\pi + 72\pi$$
$$= 136\pi$$
$$\approx 427.3 \text{ cm}^2$$

The surface area is about 427.3 square centimeters.

21. $r = \frac{d}{2} = \frac{15}{2} = 7.5$

$$S = \pi r^2 + \pi r\ell$$

$$= \pi(7.5^2) + \pi(7.5)(8.2)$$

$$= 56.25\pi + 61.5\pi$$

$$= 117.75\pi$$

$$\approx 369.9 \text{ m}^2$$

The surface area is about 369.9 square meters.

22. $V = \ell wh = 15(8)(6) = 720 \text{ m}^3$

The volume is 720 cubic meters.

23. $V = Bh = \left(\frac{1}{2} \cdot 12 \cdot 5\right)11 = 330 \text{ in.}^3$

The volume is 330 cubic inches.

24. $V = \pi r^2 h = \pi(10^2)26 = 2600\pi \approx 8168.1 \text{ yd}^3$

The volume is 8168.1 cubic yards.

25. $V = \frac{1}{3}Bh = \frac{1}{3}(10^2)8 = 266\frac{2}{3} \text{ ft}^3$

The volume is 266.7 cubic feet.

26. $V = \frac{1}{3}\pi r^2 h = \frac{1}{3}\pi(18^2)6 = 648\pi \approx 2035.8 \text{ m}^3$

The volume is 2035.8 cubic meters.

27. $V = \frac{1}{3}Bh = \frac{1}{3}\left(\frac{1}{2} \cdot 9 \cdot 12\right)14 = 252 \text{ cm}^3$

The volume is 252 cubic centimeters.

Chapter 11 Extra Practice (p. 811)

1. The relation is a function because each input has exactly one output.

2.

Input x	Function	Output y
-4	$y = 0.5(-4) = -2$	-2
-2	$y = 0.5(-2) = -1$	-1
0	$y = 0.5(0) = 0$	0
2	$y = 0.5(2) = 1$	1
4	$y = 0.5(4) = 2$	2

The range is $-2, -1, 0, 1,$ and 2.

3.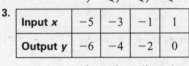

$$y = ax + b$$

$$a = \frac{2}{2} = 1 \quad \longrightarrow \quad y = x + b$$

Let $(x, y) = (1, 0)$. $\quad \longrightarrow \quad$
$$0 = 1 + b$$
$$-1 = b$$

$$y = x - 1$$

4.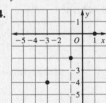

There is a positive relationship. The y-values tend to increase as the x-values increase.

5. $(1, 4): y = 3x - 7$

$$4 \stackrel{?}{=} 3(1) - 7$$
$$4 \stackrel{?}{=} 3 - 7$$
$$4 \ne -4$$

The ordered pair $(1, 4)$ is not a solution of $y = 3x - 7$.

6. $(2, -1):$
$$4x + y = 5$$
$$4(2) + (-1) \stackrel{?}{=} 5$$
$$8 + (-1) \stackrel{?}{=} 5$$
$$7 \ne 5$$

The ordered pair $(2, -1)$ is not a solution of $4x + y = 5$.

Extra Practice, continued

7. $(-3, -1)$: $y = \frac{1}{2}x + \frac{1}{2}$

$$-1 \stackrel{?}{=} \frac{1}{2}(-3) + \frac{1}{2}$$

$$-1 \stackrel{?}{=} -\frac{3}{2} + \frac{1}{2}$$

$$-1 = -1 \checkmark$$

The ordered pair $(-3, -1)$ is a solution of $y = \frac{1}{2}x + \frac{1}{2}$.

8. *Sample answer:*

x-value	Substitute for *x*.	Solve for *y*.
-1	$y = -(-1) - 3$	-2
0	$y = -0 - 3$	-3
1	$y = -1 - 3$	-4
2	$y = -2 - 3$	-5

Four solutions are $(-1, -2)$, $(0, -3)$, $(1, -4)$, and $(2, -5)$.

9. *Sample answer:*

x-value	Substitute for *x*.	Solve for *y*.
-1	$y = 7 + 2(-1)$	5
0	$y = 7 + 2(0)$	7
1	$y = 7 + 2(1)$	9
2	$y = 7 + 2(2)$	11

Four solutions are $(-1, 5)$, $(0, 7)$, $(1, 9)$, and $(2, 11)$.

10. *Sample answer:*

x-value	Substitute for *x*.	Solve for *y*.
-1	$y = -\frac{2}{3}(-1)$	$\frac{2}{3}$
0	$y = -\frac{2}{3}(0)$	0
1	$y = -\frac{2}{3}(1)$	$-\frac{2}{3}$
2	$y = -\frac{2}{3}(2)$	$-\frac{4}{3}$

Four solutions are $\left(-1, \frac{2}{3}\right)$, $(0, 0)$, $\left(1, -\frac{2}{3}\right)$, and $\left(2, -\frac{4}{3}\right)$.

11. *Sample answer:*

x-value	Substitute for *x*.	Solve for *y*.
-1	$y = -(-1)$	1
0	$y = -0$	0
1	$y = -1$	-1
2	$y = -2$	-2

Four solutions are $(-1, 1)$, $(0, 0)$, $(1, -1)$, and $(2, -2)$.

12. $-x + y = 1$

      $y = x + 1$

Sample answer:

x-value	Substitute for *x*.	Solve for *y*.
-1	$y = -1 + 1$	0
0	$y = 0 + 1$	1
1	$y = 1 + 1$	2
2	$y = 2 + 1$	3

Four solutions are $(-1, 0)$, $(0, 1)$, $(1, 2)$, and $(2, 3)$.

13. $3x + y = -2$

      $y = -3x - 2$

Sample answer:

x-value	Substitute for *x*.	Solve for *y*.
-1	$y = -3(-1) - 2$	1
0	$y = -3(0) - 2$	-2
1	$y = -3(1) - 2$	-5
2	$y = -3(2) - 2$	-8

Four solutions are $(-1, 1)$, $(0, -2)$, $(1, -5)$, and $(2, -8)$.

14. $x + 2y = 8$

      $2y = -x + 8$

        $y = -\frac{1}{2}x + 4$

Sample answer:

x-value	Substitute for *x*.	Solve for *y*.
-1	$y = -\frac{1}{2}(-1) + 4$	$\frac{9}{2}$
0	$y = -\frac{1}{2}(0) + 4$	4
1	$y = -\frac{1}{2}(1) + 4$	$\frac{7}{2}$
2	$y = -\frac{1}{2}(2) + 4$	3

Four solutions are $\left(-1, \frac{9}{2}\right)$, $(0, 4)$, $\left(1, \frac{7}{2}\right)$, and $(2, 3)$.

Extra Practice, continued

15. $-3y + 4x = 7$

$-3y = -4x + 7$

$y = \frac{4}{3}x - \frac{7}{3}$

x-value	Substitute for x.	Solve for y.
-1	$y = \frac{4}{3}(-1) - \frac{7}{3}$	$-\frac{11}{3}$
0	$y = \frac{4}{3}(0) - \frac{7}{3}$	$-\frac{7}{3}$
1	$y = \frac{4}{3}(1) - \frac{7}{3}$	-1
2	$y = \frac{4}{3}(2) - \frac{7}{3}$	$\frac{1}{3}$

Four solutions are $\left(-1, -\frac{11}{3}\right)$, $\left(0, -\frac{7}{3}\right)$, $(1, -1)$, and $\left(2, \frac{1}{3}\right)$.

16. $y = -3$

17. $y = \frac{1}{4}x - 2$

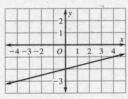

18. $x = 4$

19. $3x + y = 4$

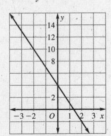

20. x-intercept:

$0 = -2x + 4$

$-4 = -2x$

$2 = x$

y-intercept:

$y = -2(0) + 4$

$y = 0 + 4$

$y = 4$

The x-intercept is 2 and the y-intercept is 4.

21. x-intercept:

$0 = 5x - 1$

$1 = 5x$

$\frac{1}{5} = x$

y-intercept:

$y = 5(0) - 1$

$y = -1$

The x-intercept is $\frac{1}{5}$ and the y-intercept is -1.

22. x-intercept:

$x + 5(0) = -5$

$x = -5$

y-intercept:

$0 + 5y = -5$

$5y = -5$

$y = -1$

The x-intercept is -5 and the y-intercept is -1.

23. x-intercept:

$2x - 3(0) = 12$

$2x = 12$

$x = 6$

y-intercept:

$2(0) - 3y - 12$

$-3y = 12$

$y = -4$

The x-intercept is 6 and the y-intercept is -4.

24.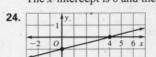

25.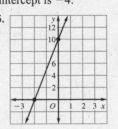

26. $m = \frac{y_2 - y_1}{x_2 - x_1} = \frac{1 - 3}{6 - (-2)} = \frac{-2}{8} = -\frac{1}{4}$

The slope is $-\frac{1}{4}$.

27. $m = \frac{y_2 - y_1}{x_2 - x_1} = \frac{-9 - 0}{5 - 5} = \frac{-9}{0}$

The slope is undefined.

28. $m = \frac{y_2 - y_1}{x_2 - x_1} = \frac{-4 - (-4)}{2 - 6} = \frac{0}{-4} = 0$

The slope is 0.

29. $m = \frac{y_2 - y_1}{x_2 - x_1} = \frac{-14 - (-5)}{-2 - 7} = \frac{-9}{-9} = 1$

The slope is 1.

30. $m = \frac{y_2 - y_1}{x_2 - x_1} = \frac{5 - 8}{-9 - (-7)} = \frac{-3}{-2} = \frac{3}{2}$

The slope is $\frac{3}{2}$.

31. $m = \frac{y_2 - y_1}{x_2 - x_1} = \frac{2 - (-2)}{-7 - (-3)} = \frac{4}{-4} = -1$

The slope is -1.

32. $m = \frac{y_2 - y_1}{x_2 - x_1} = \frac{13 - 9}{3 - 4} = \frac{4}{-1} = -4$

The slope is -4.

33. $m = \frac{y_2 - y_1}{x_2 - x_1} = \frac{-10 - 7}{-3 - 0} = \frac{-17}{-3} = \frac{17}{3}$

The slope is $\frac{17}{3}$.

34. $y = 3x - 5$

$y = 3x + (-5)$

The slope is 3 and the y-intercept is -5.

35. $y = 2$

$y = 0x + 2$

The slope is 0 and the y-intercept is 2.

36. $y = -\frac{1}{3}x + 1$

The slope is $-\frac{1}{3}$ and the y-intercept is 1.

Extra Practice, *continued*

37. $2x - y = 8$

$2x = y + 8$

$2x + (-8) = y$

The slope is 2 and the *y*-intercept is -8.

38. $y > -x - 3$

39. $6 \leq 3y$

$2 \leq y$

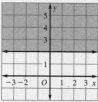

40. $5 + 2x > y$

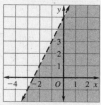

41. $4x + 3y \leq -12$

$3y \leq -4x - 12$

$y \leq -\frac{4}{3}x - 4$

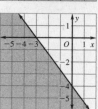

Chapter 12 Extra Practice (p. 812)

1.

9	9			
10	0	1	3	5
11	6	7	8	
12	7	9		
13	0			
14	0	0	3	

Key: $12 \mid 7 = 127$

The interval 100−109 contains the most data values.

2. Median $= \dfrac{117 + 118}{2} = \dfrac{235}{2} = 117.5$

Range $= 143 - 99 = 44$

3.

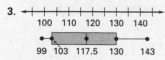

About 50% of the lengths were between 103 inches and 130 inches.

4.

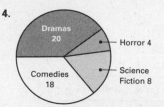

5. You should use a line graph because a line graph is used to represent data that change over time.

6.

```
              ┌ morning
      class 1 ┤
              └ afternoon
              ┌ morning
◄──── class 2 ┤
              └ afternoon
              ┌ morning
      class 3 ┤
              └ afternoon
```

There are 6 choices possible.

7. Number of license plates possible $= 10 \times 10 \times 10 \times 26 \times 26 \times 26$

$= 17,576,000$

8. $_7P_2 = \dfrac{7!}{(7-2)!} = \dfrac{7!}{5!} = \dfrac{\not{1} \cdot \not{2} \cdot \not{3} \cdot \not{4} \cdot \not{5} \cdot 6 \cdot 7}{\not{1} \cdot \not{2} \cdot \not{3} \cdot \not{4} \cdot \not{5}} = 42$

9. $_{11}P_1 = \dfrac{11!}{(11-1)!}$

$= \dfrac{11!}{10!}$

$= \dfrac{\not{1} \cdot \not{2} \cdot \not{3} \cdot \not{4} \cdot \not{5} \cdot \not{6} \cdot \not{7} \cdot \not{8} \cdot \not{9} \cdot \not{10} \cdot 11}{\not{1} \cdot \not{2} \cdot \not{3} \cdot \not{4} \cdot \not{5} \cdot \not{6} \cdot \not{7} \cdot \not{8} \cdot \not{9} \cdot \not{10}}$

$= 11$

10. $_8P_5 = \dfrac{8!}{(8-5)!}$

$= \dfrac{8!}{3!}$

$= \dfrac{\not{1} \cdot \not{2} \cdot \not{3} \cdot 4 \cdot 5 \cdot 6 \cdot 7 \cdot 8}{\not{1} \cdot \not{2} \cdot \not{3}}$

$= 6720$

11. $_{10}P_3 = \dfrac{10!}{(10-3)!}$

$= \dfrac{10!}{7!}$

$= \dfrac{\not{1} \cdot \not{2} \cdot \not{3} \cdot \not{4} \cdot \not{5} \cdot \not{6} \cdot \not{7} \cdot 8 \cdot 9 \cdot 10}{\not{1} \cdot \not{2} \cdot \not{3} \cdot \not{4} \cdot \not{5} \cdot \not{6} \cdot \not{7}}$

$= 720$

12. Number of ways $= 8 \cdot 7 \cdot 6 \cdot 5 \cdot 4 \cdot 3 \cdot 2 \cdot 1 = 40,320$

The cast can be arranged in a row 40,320 different ways.

13. $_5C_4 = \dfrac{_5P_4}{4!} = \dfrac{5 \cdot 4 \cdot 3 \cdot 2}{4!} = \dfrac{5 \cdot \not{4} \cdot \not{3} \cdot \not{2}}{1 \cdot \not{2} \cdot \not{3} \cdot \not{4}} = 5$

14. $_{20}C_2 = \dfrac{_{20}P_2}{2!} = \dfrac{\overset{10}{\not{20}} \cdot 19}{1 \cdot \not{2}} = 190$

15. $_6C_3 = \dfrac{_6P_3}{3!} = \dfrac{\overset{2}{\not{6}} \cdot 5 \cdot \overset{2}{\not{4}}}{1 \cdot \not{2} \cdot \not{3}} = 20$

Extra Practice, *continued*

16. $_{12}C_9 = \dfrac{_{12}P_9}{9!}$

$= \dfrac{12 \cdot 11 \cdot 10 \cdot 9 \cdot 8 \cdot 7 \cdot 6 \cdot 5 \cdot 4}{9!}$

$= \dfrac{\overset{2}{\cancel{12}} \cdot 11 \cdot 10 \cdot \cancel{9} \cdot \cancel{8} \cdot \cancel{7} \cdot \cancel{6} \cdot \cancel{5} \cdot \cancel{4}}{1 \cdot \cancel{2} \cdot \cancel{3} \cdot \cancel{4} \cdot \cancel{5} \cdot \cancel{6} \cdot \cancel{7} \cdot \cancel{8} \cdot \cancel{9}}$

$= 220$

17. Number of ways to choose CDs $= {_{30}C_3}$

$= \dfrac{_{30}P_3}{3!}$

$= \dfrac{\overset{5}{\cancel{30}} \cdot 29 \cdot 28}{1 \cdot \cancel{2} \cdot \cancel{3}}$

$= 4060$

You can select 3 CDs from the case in 4060 different ways.

18. Favorable outcomes: 4, 5, 6, 7, 8, 9

Unfavorable outcomes: 0, 1, 2, 3

Odds $= \dfrac{\text{Number of favorable outcomes}}{\text{Number of unfavorable outcomes}} = \dfrac{6}{4} = \dfrac{3}{2}$

The odds are 3 to 2.

19. Possible outcomes:

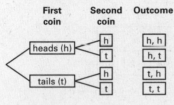

$P(\text{you do not get two heads}) = \dfrac{3}{4}$

The probability that you do not get two heads is $\dfrac{3}{4}$.

20. $P(\text{rolling a 3}) = \dfrac{1}{6}$

$P(\text{all 3 of you roll a 3}) = \dfrac{1}{6} \cdot \dfrac{1}{6} \cdot \dfrac{1}{6} = \dfrac{1}{216}$

The probability that you all roll a 3 is $\dfrac{1}{216}$.

21. Odd numbers: 1, 3, 5, 7, 9

$P(\text{both numbers are odd}) = \dfrac{5}{10} \cdot \dfrac{4}{9} = \dfrac{20}{90} = \dfrac{2}{9}$

The probability that both numbers are odd is $\dfrac{2}{9}$.

Chapter 13 Extra Practice (p. 813)

1. $3 + 5x - x^2 - 7x + 4 = -x^2 + (5x - 7x) + (3 + 4)$

$= -x^2 - 2x + 7$

2. $2t^4 + t^3 - 6 - 3t^3 + t^2 = 2t^4 + (t^3 - 3t^3) + t^2 - 6$

$= 2t^4 - 2t^3 + t^2 - 6$

3. $4(5 - k) + 4k - k^2 + 1 = 20 - 4k + 4k - k^2 + 1$

$= -k^2 + (-4k + 4k) + 20 + 1$

$= -k^2 + 21$

4. When $t = 1.5$:

$-16t^2 + 45 = -16(1.5^2) + 45 = -36 + 45 = 9$

The height is 9 feet.

5. $(3x^2 + 5x - 4) + (-2x^3 + x^2 + 9x)$

$= -2x^3 + 3x^2 + x^2 + 5x + 9x - 4$

$= -2x^3 + 4x^2 + 14x - 4$

6. $(-8x^2 - x + 1) - (7x^2 - 5x + 1)$

$= -8x^2 - 7x^2 - x + 5x + 1 - 1$

$= -15x^2 + 4x$

7. $(4x^3 - 8x^2 + 2) - (x^3 + x^2 - 6x + 5)$

$= 4x^3 - x^3 - 8x^2 - x^2 + 6x + 2 - 5$

$= 3x^3 - 9x^2 + 6x - 3$

8. $(-x^2 - 3x + 7) + (x^2 + 4x - 9)$

$= -x^2 + x^2 - 3x + 4x + 7 - 9$

$= x - 2$

9. $(2x^3 - 2x^2 + 1) + (-x^3 + 9x + 5)$

$= 2x^3 - x^3 - 2x^2 + 9x + 1 + 5$

$= x^3 - 2x^2 + 9x + 6$

10. $(3x^2 - 5x - 10) - (5x^3 + x - 2)$

$= -5x^3 + 3x^2 - 5x - x - 10 + 2$

$= -5x^3 + 3x^2 - 6x - 8$

11. $(4z)(-7z^5) = 4 \cdot (-7) \cdot z \cdot z^5 = -28z^6$

12. $(-r^2)(-3r^2) = -1 \cdot (-3) \cdot r^2 \cdot r^2 = 3r^4$

13. $-3n(2n - 5) = (-3n)(2n) - (-3n)(5) = -6n^2 + 15n$

14. $q^3(-q + 2) = q^3(-q) + q^3(2) = -q^4 + 2q^3$

15. $(5ab)^3 = 5^3a^3b^3 = 125a^3b^3$

16. $(-rst)^4 = (-1)^4 r^4 s^4 t^4 = r^4 s^4 t^4$

17. $(p^6)^4 = p^{6 \cdot 4} = p^{24}$

18. $(3y^5)^2 = 3^2(y^5)^2 = 9y^{10}$

19. $(2x + 1)(x - 5) = 2x^2 - 10x + x - 5 = 2x^2 - 9x - 5$

20. $(m - 3)(-m + 4) = -m^2 + 4m + 3m - 12$

$= -m^2 + 7m - 12$

21. $(d + 6)(d + 4) = d^2 + 4d + 6d + 24 = d^2 + 10d + 24$

22. $(4y - 3)(4y + 3) = 16y^2 + 12y - 12y - 9 = 16y^2 - 9$

23. $(a - 8)(a - 7) = a^2 - 7a - 8a + 56 = a^2 - 15a + 56$

24. $(5x + 2)(2x - 1) = 10x^2 - 5x + 4x - 2 = 10x^2 - x - 2$

25. $y = 2x - 5$

$f(x) = 2x - 5$

26. $y = 3x^2$

$f(x) = 3x^2$

27. $y = 5x^2 + 1$

$f(x) = 5x^2 + 1$

28.

x-value	Substitute for x.	Value of $f(x)$
-2	$f(-2) = 2(-2)^2 + (-2)$	6
-1	$f(-1) = 2(-1)^2 + (-1)$	1
0	$f(0) = 2(0)^2 + 0$	0
1	$f(1) = 2(1)^2 + 1$	3
2	$f(2) = 2(2)^2 + 2$	10

29.

x-value	Substitute for x.	Value of f(x)
−2	$f(-2) = \frac{1}{4}(-2)^2$	1
−1	$f(-1) = \frac{1}{4}(-1)^2$	$\frac{1}{4}$
0	$f(0) = \frac{1}{4}(0)^2$	0
1	$f(1) = \frac{1}{4}(1)^2$	$\frac{1}{4}$
2	$f(2) = \frac{1}{4}(2)^2$	1

30.

x-value	Substitute for x.	Value of f(x)
−2	$f(-2) = \frac{1}{2}(-2)^2 - (-2)$	4
−1	$f(-1) = \frac{1}{2}(-1)^2 - (-1)$	$\frac{3}{2}$
0	$f(0) = \frac{1}{2}(0)^2 - 0$	0
1	$f(1) = \frac{1}{2}(1)^2 - 1$	$-\frac{1}{2}$
2	$f(2) = \frac{1}{2}(2)^2 - 2$	0

31.

x-value	Substitute for x.	Value of f(x)
−2	$f(-2) = -3(-2)^2 + 2(-2)$	−16
−1	$f(-1) = -3(-1)^2 + 2(-1)$	−5
0	$f(0) = -3(0)^2 + 2(0)$	0
1	$f(1) = -3(1)^2 + 2(1)$	−1
2	$f(2) = -3(2)^2 + 2(2)$	−8

32.

x-value	Substitute for x.	Value of f(x)
−2	$f(-2) = (-2)^2 + 4(-2)$	−4
−1	$f(-1) = (-1)^2 + 4(-1)$	−3
0	$f(0) = (0)^2 + 4(0)$	0
1	$f(1) = (1)^2 + 4(1)$	5
2	$f(2) = (2)^2 + 4(2)$	12

33.

x-value	Substitute for x.	Value of f(x)
−2	$f(-2) = -(-2)^2 - 3$	−7
−1	$f(-1) = -(-1)^2 - 3$	−4
0	$f(0) = -(0)^2 - 3$	−3
1	$f(1) = -(1)^2 - 3$	−4
2	$f(2) = -(2)^2 - 3$	−7

34.

x	−2	−1	0	1	2
f(x)	12	3	0	3	12

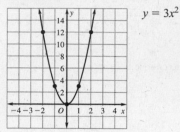

$y = 3x^2$

35.

x	−2	−1	0	1	2
f(x)	−2	1	2	1	−2

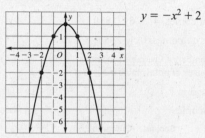

$y = -x^2 + 2$

36.

x	−2	−1	0	1	2
f(x)	4	−2	−4	−2	4

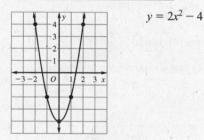

$y = 2x^2 - 4$

37. The graph does not represent a function.

38. The graph does not represent a function.

39. The graph represents a function.